METHODS OF ENZYMATIC ANALYSIS

Edited by

Hans Ulrich Bergmeyer

in collaboration with Karlfried Gawehn

Second English Edition

Translated from the Third German Edition

Volume 2

Verlag Chemie Weinheim
Academic Press, Inc.,   New York   San Francisco   London
A Subsidiary of Harcourt Brace Jovanovich, Publishers

Translated by Dermot H. Williamson, with the editorial assistance of Patricia Lund
Medical Research Council External Staff
Metabolic Research Laboratory
Nuffield Department of Clinical Medicine
The Radcliffe Infirmary Oxford, England

10/1975
Chem.

Editor's note

The methods published in this book have not been checked experimentally by the editor. Sole responsibility for the accuracy of the contents of the contributions and the literature quoted therein rests with the authors. Readers are therefore requested to direct all enquiries to the appropriate authors (author's addresses are listed on pp. XVII–XXXII).

Editions of the book to date:

a) German editions with the title "Methoden der enzymatischen Analyse"

1. Auflage 1962, one volume
2. neubearbeitete und erweiterte Auflage 1970, two volumes
3. neubearbeitete und erweiterte Auflage 1974, two volumes

b) English editions:

1st Edition 1963, one volume
2nd printing, revised, 1965
3rd printing, 1968
4th printing, 1971

2nd Edition (translated from the Third German Edition), 1974, four volumes

Science Center QH 3249 E5 B47213 1974 V. 2

With 263 figures and 546 tables.

ISBN: 3-527-25370-X (Set Verlag Chemie)
3-527-25596-6 (Vol. 2 Verlag Chemie)
0-12-091302-X (Vol. 2 Academic Press)

Library of Congress Catalog Card Number: 73-75657

Composition: Helmut Becker, 6232 Bad Soden, Germany
Printed in the United States of America

Preface

The first German edition of this book appeared in 1962, and the first English edition in 1963. In the mean time the English edition has been twice reprinted in a revised form. The development of enzymatic analysis has been so overwhelming that a completely new edition of "Methods of Enzymatic Analysis" was necessary. So in 1970 a second completely revised and enlarged German edition appeared. The translation was started soon, but it was interrupted by the work on a further 3rd German edition. So it was possible to edit two identical versions: the 3rd German and the 2nd English edition. Both include the latest developments in analytical biochemistry.

The numerous new enzymatic methods of analysis, the advances made in the various assay techniques, the methods based on completely new principles, the mechanization of the laboratory and many other topics made the need for a new edition of this book more pressing. Although many of the developments are still in progress and the new techniques are just beginning to be accepted so that a complete picture cannot be given, it was decided to bring out a new edition.

Like its predecessor, this edition is directed to the worker in the analytical laboratory. Once again authors with considerable practical experience have made available their methods. The individual contributions therefore contain the important details from a practical standpoint. The division of the work into four parts has been maintained, because this has proved successful. The composition of the individual chapters is essentially the same. The principles on which the measurements are based can be easily seen in the equations given in each chapter. A prominent feature of each method is the pipetting protocol, which is printed as a Table with data on the "Concentration in assay mixture". The accepted abbreviations for enzymes and metabolites now require no further explanations (a list of abbreviations is to be found on p. XXXV). In addition, every cited enzyme is defined by its system name and number of the *Enzyme Commission* of the *International Union of Biochemistry,* Recommendations 1972. With a few necessary exceptions only *International Units* are used (abbreviation U; for the *"Inhibitor Unit",* the symbol is IU).

Methods which have in the mean time become obsolete or out of date have been omitted; new methods have taken their place.

An innovation is the information on the assays for enzyme activity in Section B "Biochemical Reagents". The inclusion of these is at the request of many biochemists, who have previously looked in vain for these methods in Section C.

In spite of strict editing of the individual chapters the whole book is far more than twice the size of the first edition. In particular the Section on "Experimental Techniques" had to be extended considerably. New but essential sections have been included in the individual chapters, though this has not been without risk, as for example, the information on the "Accuracy and Precision of Method". None of the authors were aware of the content of the large chapter reviewing the "Statistical Analysis, Control and Assessment of Experimental Results". That is why the presentation of the data in the individual methods is not uniform. The values presented mostly concern "Precision in the Series". The presentation of the data on the reliability of enzymatic analytical methods in a standard way only recently has become accepted as a routine.

The book had to be divided into four volumes and therefore the order of sections A to D had to be changed. To make it easier for the reader each volume contains the complete index, the

list of authors and abbreviations and the complete list of contents. It is hoped that these
volumes will continue to be true laboratory books.

I wish to particularly thank all the contributors for their understanding and willing co-operation
in complying with the strict layout of the text. I thank the reviewers of the first edition for the
well-meaning and constructive criticisms, which I have taken note of in this edition. Thanks
are also due to my colleagues for numerous discussions, to Dr. D. H. Williamson for the
excellent translation and for many suggestions during this work, to my co-workers for their
help and to Verlag Chemie for the fruitful collaboration. I am especially obliged to Mr. K.
Gawehn. Without his help it would have been impossible to produce this English edition in
a form identical to the 3rd German edition.

Tutzing/Oberbayern (Germany), March 1974   Hans Ulrich Bergmeyer.

From the Preface to the 1st Edition

Today enzymes are much more widely used as analytical tools than in the past. New methods
have been worked out for the use of those enzymes which are now available in a high state of
purity, and existing techniques have been improved.

This laboratory manual contains the working directions for carefully tested procedures.
The analytical methods have been contributed by authors who have had many years of experience in their particular field of study. Consequently, the reader is certain to have reliable
experimental directions which represent the latest advances in this branch of science.

Any type of laboratory can make good use of this book, since it is designed on strictly practical
lines. The individual chapters are arranged according to the substances to be determined (not
according to the enzymes used). Grouping by substrates is employed since today the reagents
are commercially available (with the exception of a few special enzymes). For these exceptions
a short résumé of isolation techniques is included. The possibility of attempting the preparation
of these enzymes is then easily judged by the reader, bearing in mind the facilities available to
him

Tutzing/Oberbayern (Germany), March 1963   Hans Ulrich Bergmeyer

Contents

Preface V

From the Preface to the 1st Edition VI

Volume I

Contents... VII

Contributors XVII

Abbreviations XXXV

Section A: General Introduction

I. The Importance of Enzymatic Analysis

1. in Biochemistry............... 3

2. in Medicine 6

3. in Foodstuff Chemistry 71

4. in Botany and Agricultural Chemistry 82

5. in Microbiology 87

II. Principles of Enzymatic Analysis

1. Introduction 94

2. Reaction Kinetics

2.1 Basis of Reaction Kinetics 95
2.2 Kinetics of Enzyme-catalysed Reactions 99

3. Determination of Concentration of Metabolites (End-point Methods)

3.1 Simple End-point Methods 103
3.2 Measurements with Aid of Coupled Reactions 109
3.3 New Measuring Techniques 117

4. Determination of Enzyme Activities

4.1 Simple Reactions 121
4.2 Coupled Reactions 123
4.3 Factors that influence Enzyme Activity 127

5. Determination of Concentrations by Kinetic Methods

5.1 General Information 131
5.2 Catalytic Assays............... 132
5.3 "Enzymatic Cycling" 133
5.4 Determination of Concentrations by Measurement of Activation or Inhibition of Enzymes.......... 134

6. Kinetics of "Enzymatic Cycling" 135

7. Visualization of NAD(P)-dependent Reactions 136

7.1 Tetrazolium Salts and their Reduction 137
7.2 Application to Enzymatic Reactions 139
7.3 Examples..................... 140

8. Determination of Michaelis Constants and Inhibitor Constants

8.1 Michaelis Constants 144
8.2 Inhibitor Constants 151

III. Experimental Techniques

1. Handling of Biochemical Reagents
   and Samples
   1.1 Storage, Stability and Control of
       Substances and Solutions 158
   1.2 Stability of Metabolites and
       Enzymes in Samples 164
   1.3 Procedures related to Enzymatic
       Analysis 171

2. Methods of Measurement and
   Instruments Used
   2.1 Absorption Photometry 180
   2.2 Automation of Analysis 202
   2.3 Microtechniques 228
   2.4 Biological Manometry 248
   2.5 Methods with Glass Electrodes . . 254
   2.6 Measurement of Enzyme Activities
       after Electrophoresis 261
   2.7 Enzymatic Analysis with Radio-
       biochemicals 283

3. Evaluation of Experimental Results
   3.1 Experimental Data 308
   3.2 Experimental Results and Units
       of Reference 310

IV. Statistical Analysis, Control and
    Assessment of Experimental
    Results

1. Introduction 319

2. Statistical Concepts and Methods
   2.1 Describing the Data 319
   2.2 Theoretical Treatment of Data 332

3. Quality Control
   3.1 General Considerations 362
   3.2 Errors in Quantitative Biochemical
       and Clinical Chemical Analysis . . . 363
   3.3 Continuous Control of Quantitative
       Chemical Analysis 370
   3.4 Use of Quality Control Data for
       Development and Standardization
       of Analytical Methods 379

4. Assessment of Results
   4.1 General Considerations 381
   4.2 Longitudinal Assessment 383
   4.3 Definition and Determination of the
       Normal Range 385
   4.4 Transverse Assessment 391
   4.5 Clinically Atypical Findings 393

V. Cell and Tissue Disintegration

1. General 396

2. Methods for Animal Tissue and
   Micro-organisms
   2.1 Surviving Tissue 399
   2.2 Tissue Fixation 400
   2.3 Homogenates 400
   2.4 Tissue and Cell Fractionation 407

3. Methods for Plant Tissues
   3.1 Tissue Slices 410
   3.2 Tissue Fixation 410
   3.3 Wet Homogenates and Press Juices 410
   3.4 Isolation of Subcellular Particles . . 411

Section B: Biochemical Reagents

 I. Reagents for Enzymatic Analysis   417

 1. Nomenclature and Standardization 417

 2. Quality Requirements 418

 3. Suppliers of Biochemical
    Reagents 423

 II. Enzymes as Biochemical Reagents 425

III. Coenzymes, Metabolites and other
     Biochemical Reagents 523

IV. Complete Reagent Kits 557
  1. For Determination of Metabolites 557
  2. For Determination of Enzyme
     Activities 558
  3. Main Manufacturers and Suppliers 559

Index XLI

Volume II

Contents.. VII

Contributors XVII

Abbreviations XXXV

Section C: Methods for Determination of Enzyme Activity

I. Oxidoreductases

1. Sorbitol Dehydrogenase 569
2. Lactate Dehydrogenases
   2.1 Lactate Dehydrogenase
   UV-Assay with Pyruvate and
   NADH 574
   Colorimetric Assay with L-Laetate,
   NAD, Phenazine Methosulphate
   and INT 579
   Methods for Automatic Analysers 582
   2.2 Lactate Dehydrogenase, Iso-
   enzymes
   UV-Assay after Separation on
   DEAE-Sephadex 590
   Measurements after Electrophoretic
   Separation................... 593
   2.3 LDH$_1$ ("2-Hydroxybutyrate
   Dehydrogenase")
   UV-Assay 603
   Colorimetric Assay 607
   UV-Assay, Automated Method... 611
3. Malate Dehydrogenase
   UV-Assay 613
   Assay after Electrophoretic Separation 618
4. Isocitrate Dehydrogenase
   UV-Assay 624
   Colorimetric Assay 627
5. 6-Phosphogluconate Dehydro-
   genase...................... 632
6. Glucose-6-phosphate Dehydro-
   genase...................... 636
7. Xanthine Oxidase 644
8. Glutamate Dehydrogenase
   UV-Assay 650
   Colorimetric Assay 656

9. Diamine Oxidase 660
10. Dihydrofolate Reductase (Tetra-
    hydrofolate Dehydrogenase)..... 666
11. Catalase 673
12. Peroxidases 685

II. Transferases

1. Ornithine Carbamoyltransferase
   Manual Method................. 691
   Determination with Automatic
   Analysers...................... 695
2. Transamidinase 699
3. Transketolase................. 703
4. Transaldolase................. 710
5. γ-Glutamyltranspeptidase 715
6. UDP-Glucuronyltransferase 721
7. Aminotransferases and Related
   Enzymes.
   7.1 Glutamate-Oxaloacetate Trans-
   aminase
   UV-Assay, Manual Method...... 727
   UV-Assay, Automated Method... 733
   Colorimetric Assay of Reitman and
   Frankel 735
   Colorimetric Assay of Tonhazy ... 739
   Colorimetric Assay with BMTD .. 742
   Determination after Electrophoretic
   Separation.................... 745
   7.2 Glutamate-Pyruvate Transaminase
   UV-Assay, Manual Method...... 752
   UV-Assay, Automated Method... 758
   Colorimetric Assay of Reitman and
   Frankel 760
   Colorimetric Assay of Tonhazy ... 764

7.3 GOT and GPT, Assay with Auto-
matic Analysers
Fluorimetric Method for GOT and
GPT 768
Colorimetric Assay for GOT 771
8. Phosphotransferases
8.1 Pyruvate Kinase
Assay in Serum and Erythrocytes 774
Pyruvate Kinase from Yeast 778
8.2 Creatine Kinase 784
Determination with Creatine as
Substrate 785
Determination with Creatine
Phosphate as Substrate 789
Determination with
Automatic Analysers 793
8.3 Phosphoglucomutase 798
8.4 Uridyl Transferase 802
III. Hydrolases
1. Esterases
1.1 Arylesterases 806
Measurements with Phenylacetate
as Substrate 807
Measurements with β-Naphthyl-
propionate as Substrate 810
1.2 Lipase
Titrimetric Assay 814
Photometric Measurements 819
1.3 Postheparin Lipase 824
1.4 Cholinesterases
General Information 831
Manometric Method 835
Electrometric Method 838
Photometric Methods 840
Determination of Dibucaine
Number and Fluoride Number
in Serum 846
Determination in Blood with
Automated Analysers 851
1.5 Phosphomonoesterases
1.5.1 Phosphatases
Acid and Alkaline Phosphatase
in Serum, Two-point Method ... 856
Alkaline Phosphatase in Serum,
Continuous Assay 860
Alkaline Phosphatase in Serum,
Determination with Automatic
Analysers 864
Alkaline Phosphatase in Milk ... 868

1.5.2 5'-Nucleotidase 871
1.5.3 Glucose-6-phosphatase 876
1.6 Alkaline C_1-Fructose-1,6-diphos-
phatase 881
2. Glycoside Hydrolases
2.1 Amylase
Measurement of Reducing Groups 885
Determination of the Degradation
Products, Maltose and Glucose .. 890
Determination with Coloured
Insoluble Substrates 894
Measurement of the Starch-Iodine
Complex 898
Measurement by End-point
Determination on Paper 903
Measurement after Electrophoretic
Separation 909
2.2 Disaccharidases 916
2.3 Invertase 923
2.4 β-Glucuronidase 929
2.5 Hyaluronidase 944
3. Peptidases and Proteinases
3.1 Peptidases
3.1.1 Review 949
3.1.2 Aminopeptidases and Amino
Acid Arylamidases
General Information 950
Leucine Aminopeptidase 954
Amino Acid Arylamidases
("Leucine-nitroanilidase") 958
Angiotensinase 964
Oxytocinase
Determination with L-Cystine-
di-β-naphthylamide 967
Determination with S-Benzyl-L-
cysteine-p-nitroanilide 971
3.1.3 Di- and Polypeptidases
General Information 978
Glycyl-glycine Dipeptidase 982
3.1.4 Carboxypeptidases
General Information 986
Carboxypeptidase A (Determin-
ation with N-Carbobenzoxy-
glycyl-L-phenylalanine) 989
Carboxypeptidase A (Determin-
ation with N-(Carbo-naphtho-
xy)-DL-phenylalanine) 993
Carboxypeptidase B 996

3.2 Proteinases
3.2.1 Proteinases, Method for Auto-
    matic Analysers. 1000
3.2.2 Chymotrypsin 1006
3.2.3 Trypsin 1013
3.2.4 Thromboplastin Time 1025
    Original Quick Method 1027
    Quick Method using Citrated
    Blood 1029
3.2.5 Kallikrein. 1031
    Manual Method (UV-Assay) . . 1032
    Determination of Kallikrein and
    Prekallikrein with Automatic
    Analysers 1034
    Fluorimetric Method 1037
3.2.6 Elastase 1041
3.2.7 Pepsin. 1046
3.2.8 Collagenases 1058
3.2.9 Protease Inhibitors
    General Information 1064

Trypsin and Plasmin Inhibitors. 1066
Chymotrypsin Inhibitors 1074
Inhibitors for Kallikrein, Plasmin
and Thrombin 1077

4. Other C-N splitting Hydrolases
    4.1 Urease 1081
    4.2 Guanase 1086
    4.3 Adenosine Deaminase. 1092

IV. Lyases, Isomerases, Ligases

1. Fructose-1,6-diphosphate
    Aldolase
    UV-Assay, Manual Method 1100
    UV-Assay, Automated Method. 1106

2. 1-Phosphofructoaldolase 1109

3. Glucosephosphate Isomerase . . . 1113

4. Tetrahydrofolate Formylase 1118

Index. XLI

Volume III

Contents. VII

Contributors XVII

Abbreviations XXXV

Section D: Methods for Determination of Metabolites

I. Carbohydrate Metabolites

1. Poly-, Oligo- and Disaccharides
    1.1 Glycogen
        Determination with Amylo-
        glucosidase 1127
    1.2 Cellulose 1132
    1.3 Hemicelluloses 1143
    1.4 Inulin. 1149
    1.5 Heparin. 1151
    1.6 Hyaluronic Acid
        Spectrophotometric Method . . . 1157
        Colorimetric Method 1162

    1.7 Chondroitin-4-sulphate,
        Chondroitin-6-sulphate and
        Dermatan Sulphate 1165
    1.8 Raffinose. 1172
    1.9 Sucrose 1176
    1.10 Lactose and other β-D-
         Galactosides 1180
    1.11 Maltose. 1185

2. Monosaccharides and Derivatives
    2.1 D-Sedoheptulose-7-phosphate . . 1189
    2.2 D-Sedoheptulose-1,7-diphosphate 1193

2.3 D-Glucose
      Determination with HK and
      G6P-DH 1196
      Fluorimetric Determination in
      Blood with Automatic Analysers 1201
      Determination with GOD and
      POD 1205
      Determination in Blood, Serum,
      or Plasma with Automatic
      Analysers (GOD-PERID®
      Method) 1215
      Determination with AGT 1222
      D-Glucose and D-Glucosamine,
      Submicro-method with ATP-γ-
      [^{32}P] 1228
2.4 D-Glucose-1-phosphate 1233
2.5 D-Glucose-6-phosphate and
      D-Fructose-6-phosphate 1238
2.6 D-Gluconate 1243
2.7 D-Gluconate-6-phosphate 1248
2.8 D-Glucosamine 1251
2.9 D-Glucosamine-6-phosphate ... 1257
2.10 D-Mannose and D-Mannose-6-
      phosphate 1263
2.11 D-Mannose-1-phosphate 1268
2.12 D-Mannitol 1271
2.13 D-Mannitol-1-phosphate 1275
2.14 D-Galactose
      UV-Assay with Gal-DH 1279
      Determination with Gal-OD ... 1282
2.15 D-Galactose-1-phosphate
      Determination with Uridyl
      Transferase 1288
      Determination as Galactose.... 1291
2.16 D-Galactose-6-phosphate 1296
2.17 D-Galacturonate and
      D-Tagaturonate 1299
2.18 D-Fructose 1304
2.19 D-Fructose-1-phosphate 1308
2.20 D-Fructose-1,6-diphosphate,
      Dihydroxyacetone Phosphate,
      and D-Glyceraldehyde-3-
      phosphate 1314
2.21 L-Sorbose-6-phosphate 1320
2.22 D-Sorbitol
      Standard Method 1323
      Determination in Wine 1326

2.23 D-Sorbitol-6-phosphate 1331
2.24 myo-Inositol 1333
2.25 myo-Inositol-1-phosphate 1337
2.26 D-Ribose-5-phosphate 1342
2.27 5-Phospho-α-D-ribose-1-
      diphosphate 1346
2.28 L-Ribulose and L-Arabinose.... 1350
2.29 D-Ribulose 1354
2.30 D-Ribulose-5-phosphate 1359
2.31 D-Ribulose-1,5-diphosphate,
      UV-Method 1362
2.32 L-Xylulose 1365
2.33 D-Xylulose,
      Determination with NAD-Xylitol
      Dehydrogenase 1368
2.34 D-Xylulose and D-Xylose,
      Determination with D-Xylose
      Isomerase 1371
2.35 D-Xylulose-5-phosphate 1377
2.36 Xylitol 1381
2.37 D-Ribulose-1,5-diphosphate and
      Pentose Monophosphates
      (Ru-5-P, R-5-P, Xu-5-P),
      Radiochemical Assay 1385
2.38 D-Erythrose-4-phosphate 1391
2.39 L-Erythrulose 1394
2.40 L-(+)-Tartrate and meso-
      Tartrate
      L-(+)-Tartrate (Dehydrase
      Method) 1397
      meso-Tartrate (Dehydrogenase
      Method) 1400

3.   Three Carbon compounds

3.1 Glycerol
      UV-Method 1404
      Radiochemical Assay 1409
3.2 L-(−)-Glycerol-3-phosphate.... 1415
3.3 D-Glycerate 1419
3.4 D-Glycerate-3-phosphate 1424
3.5 D-Glycerate-1,3-diphosphate ... 1429
3.6 D-Glycerate-2,3-diphosphate ... 1433
3.7 L-Glyceraldehyde-3-phosphate.. 1439
3.8 Dihydroxyacetone 1442
3.9 Pyruvate, Phosphoenolpyruvate
      and D-Glycerate-2-phosphate... 1446
3.10 Pyruvate, Fluorimetric Assay... 1452
3.11 Hydroxypyruvate 1457
3.12 3-Mercaptopyruvate 1460

3.13 L-(+)-Lactate
Determination with LDH and
NAD 1464
Fluorimetric Method......... 1468
Determination with LDH and
APAD 1472
Determination with LDH, GPT
and NAD 1475
Determination with Automatic
Analysers 1479
Determination with Yeast LDH 1483
3.14 D-(—)-Lactate 1492
3.15 Methylglyoxal 1496

4. Two and One Carbon Compounds
4.1 Ethanol
Determination with ADH and
NAD 1499
Determination with ADH and
APAD 1502
4.2 Acetaldehyde
Determination with ADH 1506
Determination with Aldehyde
Dehydrogenase............... 1509
4.3 Glycolaldehyde 1514
4.4 Glyoxylate 1517
4.5 Acetate
Determination with Preceding
Indicator Reaction............ 1520
Determination with AK and
Hydroxylamine 1528
Determination with Acetyl-CoA
Synthetase and Sulphanilamide .. 1532
4.6 Acetyl Phosphate............. 1538
4.7 Oxalate 1542

4.8 Formate
Determination with Formyltetra-
hydrofolate Synthetase 1546
Determination with Formate
Dehydrogenase............... 1551
4.9 Formiminoglutamate 1556

II. Citric Acid Cycle Metabolites
1. Citrate
UV Spectrophotometric
Determination 1562
Fluorimetric Determination 1565
2. Isocitrate
UV Spectrophotometric
Determination 1570
Fluorimetric Determination 1573
3. 2-Oxoglutarate
UV Spectrophotometric
Determination 1577
Fluorimetric Determination 1580
4. L-(—)-Malate
Determination with MDH and NAD 1585
Determination with MDH and GOT 1589
Determination with MDH and APAD 1593
Determination with MDH, Citrate
Synthase and Phosphotransacetylase 1596
5. L-Malate and Fumarate
Fluorimetric Determination 1600
6. Oxaloacetate
UV-Spectrophotometric
Determination 1604
Fluorimetric Determination 1608
Determination with [14C]-Acetyl-CoA 1611
7. Succinate..................... 1616
8. Maleate 1622

Index... XLI

Volume IV

Contents... VII
Contributors XVII
Abbreviations XXXV

III. Proteins, Peptides and Amino
Acids
1. Proteins and Peptides
1.1 Characterization of Peptides and
Proteins with Enzymes 1625

1.2 Determination of Acetyl Groups
in Proteins.................... 1640
1.3 Glutathione 1643
2. Amino Acids, Amines and Amides
2.1 D-Amino Acids.............. 1648

2.2 L-Amino Acids
Determination in t RNA-Loading
Test 1656
Manometric Method 1662
Colorimetric Method with FDNB 1669
2.3 L-Alanine
Determination with Alanine
Dehydrogenase.............. 1679
Determination with GPT and
LDH 1682
2.4 D-Alanine 1686
2.5 γ-Aminobutyric Acid.......... 1690
2.6 L-Aspartate and L-Asparagine .. 1696
2.7 L-Lysine, Determination with
Automated Analysers 1701
2.8 L-Glutamate
UV-Assay with GlDH and
NAD 1704
Determination with GlDH, Diaphorase and Tetrazolium Salts.. 1708
Determination with GlDH and
APAD 1713
2.9 L-Glutamine
Determination with Glutamine
Synthetase.................. 1716
Determination with Glutaminase
and GlDH.................. 1719
2.10 L-Hydroxyproline 1723
2.11 DL-Serine and DL-Threonine.... 1727
2.12 3-Hydroxykynurenine 1731
2.13 3-Hydroxyanthranilic Acid..... 1736
2.14 Spermidine 1740
2.15 Spermine and Spermidine...... 1744
2.16 Carbamoylphosphate 1749
2.17 Carnitine and Acylcarnitines ... 1758
2.18 Creatine.................... 1772
2.19 Creatine Phosphate 1777
2.20 Creatinine 1786
2.21 Urea
Determination of urea according
to Berthelot 1791
Determination of urea with
GlDH 1794
Determination with Automatic
Analysers 1798
2.22 Ammonia.................. 1802

IV. Fatty Acid Metabolites, Lipids and
Steroids
1. Polyunsaturated Fatty Acids.... 1807

2. Lecithin 1813
3. Acetylcholine and Choline...... 1819
4. Triglycerides and Glycerol
Determination after Alkaline
Hydrolysis 1825
5. Triglycerides, Determination after
Enzymatic Hydrolysis 1831
6. D-(−)-3-Hydroxybutyrate 1836
7. Acetoacetate 1840
8. Triacetate and Fumarylacetoacetate 1844
9. Hydrolysis of Steroid Conjugates 1848
10. 20-Ketosteroids
Photometric Method.............. 1858
Fluorimetric Method............. 1864
11. Steroid Alcohols in Urine 1868
12. Prostaglandins............... 1877
13. Bile Acids.................. 1886
14. Cholesterol and Esterified
Cholesterol................. 1890

V. Nucleic Acids, Purines, Pyrimidines, Nucleosides, Coenzymes and
Related Compounds
1. Nucleic Acids and Polyribonucleotides
1.1 Transfer Ribonucleic Acids:
Determination of the Acceptor
Activity for Amino Acids 1894
1.2 Polyribonucleotides (Messenger-
RNA): Determination of the
Activity in the Peptide-
Synthesizing System 1901
2. Purines, Pyrimidines and
Nucleosides
2.1 Adenine and Guanine 1909
2.2 Cytosine 1916
2.3 Adenosine.................. 1919
2.4 Cytidine and Deoxycytidine.... 1923
2.5 Guanosine.................. 1928
2.6 Inosine.................... 1932

2.7   Deoxythymidine and Deoxy-
      uridine   1935
2.8   Hypoxanthine and Xanthine
      UV-Assay   1941
      Colorimetric Assay   1945
2.9   Uric Acid
      UV-Assay with Uricase   1951
      Colorimetric Assay with Uricase
      and Catalase   1954
2.10 Orotate
      Determination with O-5-MP-
      Pyrophosphorylase   1959
      Determination with Dihydro-
      orotate Dehydrogenase   1963

3.   Nucleotides, Coenzymes and
     Related Compounds
3.1 Coenzyme A   1967
     Determination of CoA-SH and
     CoA-S-S-CoA with HOADH . . .   1968
     Determination of CoA-SH with
     PTA
     End-point Method   1972
     Fluorimetric Assay   1981
3.2 Acyl-CoA Derivatives
3.2.1 Acetyl-CoA
       UV-Spectrophotometric Assay   1988
       Fluorimetric Assay   1993
       Radiochemical Assay   1994
3.2.2 Acetoacetyl-CoA   2001
3.2.3 Acrylyl-CoA   2005
3.2.4 Benzoyl-CoA and other CoA
       Derivatives   2008
3.2.5 Butyryl-CoA and CoA
       Derivatives of Higher Saturated
       Fatty Acids
       Colorimetric Determination . .   2010
       Fluorimetric Determination
       with Oxoglutarate Dehydro-
       genase   2015
3.2.6 Crotonyl-CoA   2017
3.2.7 L-(+)-3-Hydroxybutyryl-CoA   2022
3.2.8 3-Hydroxy-3-methylglutaryl-
       CoA   2026
3.2.9 3-Hydroxypropionyl-CoA   2031
3.2.10 Malonyl-CoA   2034
3.2.11 Malonylsemialdehyde-CoA . . .   2038
3.2.12 Succinyl-CoA   2041
3.3 Nicotinamide-Adenine
     Dinucleotides

3.3.1 Spectrophotometric and
       Fluorimetric Methods   2045
3.3.2 Measurement by Enzymatic
       Cycling   2059
3.4 Nicotinamide Mononucleotide .   2073
3.5 Analytical Differentiation of
     Purine and Pyrimidine
     Nucleotides   2078
3.6 Determination of 5'-Nucleotides
     as Nucleoside-5'-monophos-
     phates   2088
3.7 Adenosine-5'-triphosphate
     Determination with PGK   2097
     Determination with HK and
     G6P-DH   2101
     Determination with Formyltetra-
     hydrofolate Synthetase   2110
3.8 ATP and Creatine Phosphate,
     Determination with Luciferase .   2112
3.9 Adenosine-5'-diphosphate and
     Adenosine-5'-monophosphate . .   2127
3.10 Adenosine Phosphates   2132
3.11 Adenosine-3':5'-monophosphate,
     cyclic   2136
3.12 Cytidine-5'-triphosphate   2145
3.13 Cytidine-, Guanosine- and
     Uridine-5'-diphosphate . . . . ,   2149
3.14 Cytidine-5'-monophosphate and
     Uridine-5'-monophosphate   2153
3.15 Guanosine-5'-triphosphate and
     Inosine-5'-triphosphate   2158
3.16 Guanosine-5'-monophosphate . .   2162
3.17 Guanosine-3',5'-monophosphate,
     cyclic   2166
3.18 Inosine-5'-monophosphate   2168
3.19 Uridine-5'-triphosphate,
     -diphosphate and -mono-
     phosphate   2172
3.20 Flavin Mononucleotide   2179
3.21 Flavin-adenine Dinucleotide . . .   2182
3.22 Thiamine Pyrophosphate   2186
3.23 Pyridoxal-5-phosphate and
     Pyridoxamine-5-phosphate   2194
3.24 Coenzyme-B_{12}   2200

4.   Nucleoside Diphosphate Sugars
     and Derivatives
4.1 ADP-glucose   2204
4.2 CDP-glucose   2209
4.3 GDP-mannose   2213

4.4 dTDP-glucose.................. 2217
4.5 UDP-galactose................ 2221
4.6 UDP-glucose 2225

VI. Other Substrates and Effectors
   1. Inorganic Phosphate
      Fluorimetric Method.............. 2229
      UV-Spectrophotometric Method.... 2234

2. Inorganic Pyrophosphate....... 2239

3. Inorganic Peroxides 2246

4. Organophosphorus and Carbamate Insecticides.............. 2249

5. Nitrate 2260

Concentrations of Metabolites in
   Animal Tissues 2266
   1. Glycogen, Glucose and Glycolytic
      Intermediates................. 2267
   2. Tricarboxylic Acid Cycle Inter-
      mediates 2280
   3. Amino Acids and Ammonia.... 2284
   4. Pentose Phosphate Pathway Inter-
      mediates 2286

5. Coenzyme A and Intermediates of
   Lipid Metabolism 2287

6. Adenosine and other Nucleotides 2293

7. Nicotinamide-Adenine
   Dinucleotides................ 2298

8. Creatine Phosphate, Creatine, Inorganic Pyrophosphate and
   Phosphate 2299

Index.. XLI

Contributors

Abeles, Robert H.
Graduate Department of Biochemistry
Brandeis University
Waltham, Massachusetts 02154, USA
p. 2200

Aebi, Hugo
Medizinisch-Chemisches Institut der
Universität Bern
Bühlstrasse 28
CH-3000 Bern Switzerland   *p. 673*

Änggard, Erik
Department of Pharmacology
Karolinska Institute
S-10401 Stockholm 60, Sweden   *p. 1877*

Anderson, Norman G.
Molecular Anatomy Program
Oakridge National Laboratory
Oakridge, Tennessee 37830, USA
and the Molecular Anatomy Institut,
P.O. Box 17
Oakridge, Tennessee 37830, USA   *p. 213*

Appel, Walter
Zentrallaboratorium der
St.-Vincentius-Krankenhäuser
Südendstrasse 32
D-7500 Karlsruhe 1, Germany   *p. 949,
950, 954, 958, 964, 967, 978, 986, 1041, 1058*

Aprison, M. H.
Section of Neurobiology
The Institute of Psychiatric Research
Indiana University Medical Center
Indianapolis, Indiana 46202, USA   *p. 1690*

Ashwell, Gilbert
National Institutes of Health
Department of Health, Education and
Welfare
Bethesda, Maryland 20014, USA
p. 1365, 1368

Aw, Swee E.
Department of Biochemistry
Faculty of Medicine
Singapore 3, Republic of Singapore   *p. 909*

Bachrach, Uriel
Department of Bacteriology
The Hebrew University-Hadassah
Medical School
Jerusalem, Israel   *p. 1740, 1744*

Bässler, Karl-Heinz
Physiologisch-Chemisches Institut der
Johannes Gutenberg-Universität
D-6500 Mainz, Germany   *p. 1381*

Baginski, Eugene S.
St. Joseph Mercy Hospital
Pontiac, Michigan 48053, USA   *p. 876*

Beaucamp, Klaus
Boehringer Mannheim GmbH
Biochemica Werk Tutzing
D-8132 Tutzing/Obb., Germany
p. 523, 1656

Bechtler, Günter
Eppendorf Gerätebau
Netheler & Hinz GmbH
Barkhausenweg 1
D-2000 Hamburg 63, Germany
p. 611, 733, 758, 1106

Bergmeyer, Hans Ulrich

　　Boehringer Mannheim GmbH
　　Biochemica Werk Tutzing
　　D-8132 Tutzing/Obb., Germany   *p. 94, 95,*
　　103, 121, 131, 158, 221, 308, 417, 425, 523,
　　557, 574, 579, 590, 613, 624, 727, 735, 739,
　　742, 752, 760, 764, 784, 864, 1100, 1149,
　　1172, 1176, 1196, 1205, 1222, 1233, 1243,
　　1304, 1323, 1492, 1496, 1506, 1517, 1520,
　　1528, 1538, 1577, 1643, 1696, 1704, 1772,
　　1786, 1791, 1813, 1919, 1951, 1967, 2008,
　　2078, 2097, 2127, 2132, 2246

Bernt, Erich

　　Boehringer Mannheim GmbH
　　Biochemica Werk Tutzing
　　D-8132 Tutzing/Obb., Germany   *p. 158,*
　　308, 557, 574, 579, 590, 613, 624, 727, 735,
　　739, 742, 752, 760, 764, 774, 784, 864, 868,
　　1100, 1172, 1176, 1196, 1201, 1205, 1215,
　　1304, 1499, 1506, 1577, 1643, 1696, 1704,
　　1772, 1890, 1951, 2246

Beutler, Hans-Otto

　　Boehringer Mannheim GmbH
　　Biochemica Werk Tutzing
　　D-8132 Tutzing/Obb., Germany   *p. 523*
　　　　　　　　　　　　　　　　　　1314, 1708

Bevill, Rardon D.

　　Department of Molecular Biology
　　Albert Einstein College of Medicine
　　1300 Morris Park Avenue
　　Bronx, New York 10461, USA
　　　　　　　　　　　　　　　p. 2209, 2217

Birchmeier, Heidi

　　Laboratoire Central
　　Hôpital Cantonal
　　CH-1011 Lausanne, Switzerland   *p. 721*

Bodansky, Oscar

　　Sloan Kettering Institute
　　for Cancer Research
　　New York, N.Y. 10021, USA   *p. 768*

Boulanger, Paul

　　Laboratoire de Chimie Biologique
　　Faculté de Médicine et Pharmacie
　　Lille, France   *p. 1648*

Brand, Karl

　　Max-Planck-Institut
　　für Ernährungsphysiologie
　　Rheinlanddamm 201
　　D-4600 Dortmund, Germany   *p. 396,*
　　　　　　　　　　　　　　　　　　399, 710

Brin, Myron

　　Department of Biochemical Nutrition
　　Hoffmann-La Roche Inc.
　　Nutley, New Jersey 07110, USA   *p. 703*

Brock, David J. H.

　　Department of Human Genetics
　　Western General Hospital
　　Edinburgh 4, Scotland   *p. 1844*

Brosnan, John T.

　　Department of Biochemistry
　　Memorial University of
　　Newfoundland,
　　St. Johns,
　　Newfoundland, Canada   *p. 2266*

Brown, David H.

　　Department of Biological Chemistry
　　School of Medicine
　　Washington University
　　St. Louis, Missouri 63110, USA
　　　　　　　　　　　　　　　p. 1251, 1257

Brown, Joseph G.

　　Department of Pharmacology
　　School of Medicine
　　Washington University
　　St. Louis, Missouri 63110, USA   *p. 1565*

Bücher, Theodor

　　Institut für Physiologische Chemie und
　　Physikalische Biochemie der
　　Universität München
　　Goethestrasse 33
　　D-8000 Munich, Germany   *p. 254*

Büttner, Hannes

    Medizinische Hochschule Hannover
    Institut für Klinische Chemie
    Roderbruchstrasse 101
    D-3000 Hannover-Kleefeld, Germany
                            p. 318

Ceriotti, Giovanni

    Laboratorio Centrale di Analisi
    Ospedale Civile di Padova
    I-35100 Padova, Italia   *p. 691*

Chase, James F. A.*

    Department of Biochemistry
    University of Cambridge
    Tennis Court Road
    Cambridge, England   *p. 1758*

Coddington, Alan

    School of Biological Sciences
    University of East Anglia
    Norwich, NOR 88 C, England
                      p. 1928, 1932

Cohen, Patricia S.

    Medical Laboratory Assoc.
    Birmingham, Alabama 35233, USA
                      p. 793

Cooperman, Jack M.

    Department of Pediatrics
    Hematology and Nutrition Laboratories
    New York Medical College
    New York, N. Y. 10029, USA   *p. 1556*

Czok, Rudolf

    Sandoz Forschungsinstitut GmbH
    Brunnerstrasse 59
    A-1235 Wien-Liesing, Austria
                      p. 1424, 1446

Dagley, Stanley

    Department of Biochemistry
    University of Minnesota
    St. Paul, Minnesota 55101, USA
                      p. 1562

---

* deceased

Dahl, Katharina von

    Boehringer Mannheim GmbH
    Abt. Stoffwechsel
    Sandhofer Strasse
    D-6800 Mannheim 31, Germany   *p. 819*

Dahlqvist, Arne

    Department of Nutrition,
    Chemical Center
    University of Lund
    S-22007 Lund 7, Sweden   *p. 916*

Decker, Karl

    Albert Ludwigs-Universität Freiburg
    Medizinische Fakultät
    Biochemisches Institut
    Hermann-Herder-Strasse 7
    D-7800 Freiburg i. Br., Germany *p. 1127,*
    1228, 1988, 2001, 2017, 2022, 2172, 2221,
    2225

Dubach, Ulrich C.

    Medizinische Universitätspoliklinik
    Abt. für Innere Medizin
    Hebelstrasse 1
    CH-4056 Basel, Switzerland   *p. 699*

Eberhard, Arnold

    Klinisch-Chemisches Institut der
    Rhein.-Westf. Techn. Hochschule
    D-5100 Aachen, Germany   *p. 1165*

Egami, Fujio

    Mitsubishi-Kasei Institute
    of Life Sciences
    11, Minamiooya
    Machida-shi,
    Tokyo, Japan   *p. 2260*

Eggleston, Leonard V.*

    Metabolic Research Laboratory
    Nuffield Department of Clinical Medicine
    The Radcliffe Infirmary
    Oxford, England   *p. 1308*

Eggstein, Manfred

  Medizinische Universitätsklinik (IV)
  Otfried-Müller-Strasse
  D-7400 Tübingen, Germany   *p. 1825*

Eisenberg, jr., Frank

  The National Institutes of Health
  Public Health Service
  United States Department of Health,
  Education and Welfare
  Bethesda, Maryland 20014, USA
                       p. 1337

Fasold, Hugo

  Institut für Biochemie der
  J. W. Goethe-Universität Frankfurt
  Sandhofstrasse
  D-6000 Frankfurt/M.-Niederrad, Germany
                 p. 1625, 1640

Fishman, William H.

  School of Medicine
  Tufts University
  Boston, Massachusetts 02111, USA
                       p. 929

Foà, Piero P.

  Department of Research
  Sinai Hospital
  Detroit, Michigan 48235, USA   *p. 876*

Förster, Edith

  II. Med. Universitätsklinik der
  Johannes-Gutenberg-Universität
  Langenbeckstrasse 1
  D-6500 Mainz, Germany   *p. 1923*

Forster, Georg

  Schweizerische Pflegerinnenschule
  Samariterstrasse 5
  CH-8032 Zürich, Switzerland   *p. 784*

Frei, Jörg

  Laboratoire Central
  Hôpital Cantonal
  CH-1011 Lausanne, Switzerland   *p. 721*

Friebe, Ursula

  Biochemisches Institut der
  Universität Freiburg
  Hermann-Herder-Strasse 7
  D-7800 Freiburg i. Br., Germany
                       p. 1935

Fried, Lygia W.

  Department of Biochemistry
  Creighton University
  School of Medicine
  Omaha, Nebraska 68131, USA
                   p. 644, 1945

Fried, Rainer

  Department of Biochemistry
  Creighton University
  School of Medicine
  Omaha, Nebraska 68131, USA
                   p. 644, 1945

Friedmann, Herbert C.

  The University of Chicago
  Department of Biochemistry
  Chicago, Illinois 60637, USA   *p. 824,*
  1963, 2179, 2182

Fritsch, Wolf-Peter

  I. Medizinische Klinik der Universität
  Moorenstrasse 5
  D-4000 Düsseldorf 1, Germany   *p. 1046*

Fritz, Hans

  Institut für Klinische Chemie und
  Klinische Biochemie der Universität
  Nussbaumstrasse 20
  D-8000 Munich, Germany   *p. 1064*

Fromm, Herbert J.

  Iowa State University of Science
  and Technology
  Department of Biochemistry and
  Biophysics
  Ames, Iowa 50010, USA   *p. 1354*

Gale, Ernest F.

  University of Cambridge
  Department of Biochemistry
  Sub.-Dept. of Chemical Microbiology
  Cambridge, CB 2 1 QW, England
                       p. 1662

Garland, Peter Bryan

    Department of Biochemistry
    University of Dundee,
    Dundee, Scotland   *p. 1981, 1993, 2015*

Gawehn, Karlfried

    Boehringer Mannheim GmbH
    Biochemica Werk Tutzing
    D-8132 Tutzing/Obb., Germany   *p. 158,*
    425, 1263, 1492, 1496, 2172, 2234, 2239

Gerlach, Ulrich

    Medizinische Klinik und Poliklinik der
    Westfälischen Wilhelms-Universität
    D-4400 Münster/Westf., Germany
                                p. 31, 569, 871

Giang, Paul A.

    Analytical Chemistry Laboratory
    Agr. Environmental Quality Institute
    Beltsville, Maryland 20705, USA
                                        p. 2249

Gibbs, Martin

    Department of Biology
    Brandeis University
    Waltham, Massachusetts 02154, USA
                                p. 409, 881, 1385

Gitzelmann, Richard

    Labor für Stoffwechselforschung der
    Universitäts-Kinderklinik
    Steinwiesstrasse 75
    CH-8032 Zürich, Switzerland   *p. 1291*

Giusti, Guiseppe

    Clinica Delle Malattie Infetive
    dell'Università
    I'Facoltá di Medicina e Chirurgia
    Via D. Cotugno, 1 (Osp. Gesu e Maria)
    I-80135 Napoli, Italia   *p. 1086, 1092*

Goedde, Heinz W.

    Institut für Humangenetik der
    Universität
    Butenfeld 32
    D-2000 Hamburg 54, Germany
                                p. 1394, 1514

Goldberg, Nelson D.

    Department of Pharmacology
    University of Minnesota
    Medical School
    Minneapolis, Minnesota 55455, USA
                                p. 1573, 1600, 1608

Graham, Jr., L. T.

    Institute of Psychiatric Research
    Indiana University Medical Center
    Indianapolis, Indiana 46207, USA
                                        p. 1690

Grassl, Marianne

    Boehringer Mannheim GmbH
    Biochemica Werk Tutzing
    D-8132 Tutzing/Obb., Germany   *p. 308,*
    425, 1268, 1296, 1331, 1682, 1686, 2073,
    2145, 2149, 2153, 2158, 2162, 2166, 2168

Greenberg, Elaine

    University of California
    Department of Biochemistry
    and Biophysics
    Davis, California 95616, USA   *p. 2204*

Greiling, Helmut

    Klinisch-Chemisches Institut der
    Rhein.-Westf. Techn. Hochschule
    D-5100 Aachen, Germany   *p. 1157, 1165*

Gruber, Wolfgang

    Boehringer Mannheim GmbH
    Biochemica Werk Tutzing
    D-8132 Tutzing, Obb., Germany   *p. 1323,*
    1890, 2078, 2097, 2127

Gundlach, Gerd

    Universitätsklinik, Urologie
    Landeskrankenhaus
    D-6650 Homburg/Saar, Germany
                                        p. 1625

Gutmann, Ingeborg

    Boehringer Mannheim GmbH
    Biochemica Werk Tutzing
    D-8132 Tutzing/Obb., Germany   *p. 774,*
    1149, 1172, 1185, 1323, 1464, 1499, 1517,
    1585, 1791

Hagen, Alexander

    Boehringer Mannheim GmbH
    Biochemica Werk Tutzing
    D-8132 Tutzing/Obb., Germany   *p. 283*

Haid, Erich

    Boehringer Mannheim GmbH
    Biochemica Werk Tutzing
    D-8132 Tutzing/Obb., Germany   *p. 1248*

Haindl, Hans

    Institut für Klinische Biochemie
    und Physiologische Chemie
    der Medizinischen Hochschule
    Osterfeldstrasse 5
    D-3000 Hannover, Germany   *p. 1886*

Halliwell, Geoffrey

    Sub-Department of Microbiology
    Department of Botany
    University College of Swansea
    Swansea, Wales, England   *p. 1132, 1143*

Hansert, Erwin

    Abteilung für Biostatistik
    Max-Planck-Institut für Psychiatrie
    Kraepelinstrasse 10
    D-8000 Munich 40, Germany   *p. 318*

Hasegawa, Shin

    Fruit & Vegetable Chemistry
    Laboratory
    US Department of Agriculture
    263 South Chester Avenue
    Pasadena, California 91106, USA
    p. 1299

Hazen, George G.

    Merck, Sharp & Dohme
    Research Laboratories
    Division of Merck & Co., Inc.
    Rahway, New Jersey 07065, USA
    p. 1000

Heinz, Fritz

    Medizinische Hochschule Hannover
    Institut für Klinische Biochemie
    und Physiologische Chemie
    Roderbruchstrasse 101
    D-3000 Hannover, Germany   *p. 1777*

Hess, Benno

    Max-Planck-Institut für
    Ernährungsphysiologie
    Rheinlanddamm 201
    D-4600 Dortmund, Germany
    p. 3, 396, 399, 778

Heuckenkamp, Peter-Uwe

    Medizinische Poliklinik der
    Universität München
    Pettenkoferstrasse 8 a
    D-8000 Munich 2, Germany   *p. 1288*

Hiby, Walter

    Medizinische Klinik und Poliklinik der
    Westfälischen Wilhelms-Universität
    Westring 3
    D-4400 Münster/Westf., Germany
    p. 569, 871

Hildebrand, John G.

    Department of Neurobiology
    Harvard Medical School
    25 Shattuck Street
    Boston, Massachusetts 02115, USA
    p. 1819

Hillmann, Günther

    Chemisches Institut der
    Städtischen Krankenanstalten
    D-8500 Nürnberg, Germany   *p. 903*

Hjelm, Magnus

    Dept. of Clinical Chemistry University
    Hospital
    S-75014 Uppsala 14, Sweden   *p. 1282*

Hobbs, John R.

Department of Chemical Pathology
Westminster Medical School,
17, Page Street,
London, S. W. 1, England   *p. 909*

Hochella, Norman Joseph

The University of North Carolina
The School of Medicine
Department of Medicine
Chapel Hill, North Carolina 27514, USA
                                  p. 1479

Höpner, Thomas

Universität Oldenburg
Fachbereich Naturwissenschaften
Postfach 243
D-2900 Oldenburg, Germany   *p. 1551*

Hofner, Helmut

Institut für Physiologische Chemie
und Physikalische Biochemie der
Universität München
Goethestrasse 33
D-8000 Munich 2, Germany   *p. 254*

Holldorf, August W.

Institut für Physiologische Chemie
Ruhr-Universität Bochum
D-4630 Bochum, Germany   *p. 1419*
1457, 1916, 1923, 1935

Holz, Günter

Boehringer Mannheim GmbH
Biochemica Werk Tutzing
D-8132 Tutzing/Obb., Germany
                          p. 87, 1528, 1786

Holzer, Helmut

Biochemisches Institut der
Universität Freiburg
Hermann-Herder-Strasse 7
D-7800 Freiburg i. Br., Germany   *p. 1419*

Horecker, Bernhard L.

Roche Institute of Molecular Biology
Nutley, New Jersey 07110, USA
                          p. 1193, 1350, 1371

Horikoshi, Koki

The Institute of Physical and
Chemical Research
Department of Microbiology
Wako-shi, Saitama Pref., Japan   *p. 1271*

Hurlbert, Ronald E.

Department of Bacteriology and
Public Health
Washington State University
Pullman, Washington 99163, USA
                                  p. 1397

Hutzler, Joel

Department of Pediatrics
New York University School of Medicine
550 First Avenue
New York, N. Y. 10016, USA   *p. 1669*

Isselbacher, Kurt J.

Massachusetts General Hospital
Boston, Massachusetts 02114, USA
                                  p. 802

Jagow-Westermann, Barbara von

Gotthelfstrasse 97
D-8000 Munich 27, Germany   *p. 1483*

Jakoby, William B.

Section on Enzymes
National Institute of Arthritis
and Metabolic Diseases
National Institutes of Health
Bethesda, Maryland 20014, USA
p. 1346, 1397, 1542, 1622

Jaworek, Dieter

Boehringer Mannheim GmbH
Biochemica Werk Tutzing
D-8132 Tutzing/Obb., Germany
p. 2097, 2127

Jones, Mary Ellen

Department of Biochemistry
School of Medicine
The University of Southern California
2025 Zonal Avenue
Los Angeles, California 90033, USA
p. 1749

Jørgensen, Søren

Anaestesiologisk afdeling
Odense Amts og Bys Sygehus
Odense, Denmark   *p. 1941*

Kaiser, Wolfram

Medizinische Poliklinik
der Universität München
Pettenkoferstrasse 8 a
D-8000 Munich 12, Germany   *p. 1151*

Kaltwasser, Heinrich

Mikrobiologie
Universität Saarbrücken
D-6600 Saarbrücken, Germany   *p. 1081*

Kattermann, Reinhard

Abteilung Klinische Chemie
Medizinische Klinik und Poliklinik der
Universität Göttingen
D-3400 Göttingen, Germany   *p. 1419*

Kearney, Edna B.

University of California
San Francisco Medical Centre
School of Medicine
Department of Pharmacology
San Francisco, California 94122, USA
p. 1802

Keppler, Dietrich

Biochemisches Institut der
Universität Freiburg
Hermann-Herder-Strasse 7
D-7800 Freiburg i. Br., Germany   *p. 1127,*
1228, 2088, 2172, 2221, 2225

King, John

Royal Infirmary
Department of Biochemistry
Glasgow C 4, Scotland   *p. 607,*
627, 632, 656, 798, 1113

Klein, Bernard

Department of Diagnostic Research
Hoffmann-La Roche Inc.
Nutley, New Jersey 07110, USA   *p. 582*

Klingenberg, Martin

Institut für Physiologische Chemie der
Universität München
Goethestrasse 33
D-8000 Munich 15, Germany   *p. 2045*

Klose, Siegmar

Boehringer Mannheim GmbH
Biochemica Werk Tutzing
D-8132 Tutzing/Obb., Germany   *p. 221*

Klotzsch, Helmut R.

Boehringer Mannheim Corp.
219 East 44th Street
New York, N. Y. 10017, USA   *p. 557*

Klungsøyr, Leiv

Department of Physiology
University of Bergen
Aarstadveien 19
N-5000 Bergen, Norway   *p. 1275*

Knappe, Joachim

Universität Heidelberg
Institut für Biologische Chemie
Berliner Strasse 23,
D-6900 Heidelberg, Germany
                                    p. 1551, 2026

Kohn, Leonard D.

Laboratory of Biochemical Pharmacology
National Institute of Arthritis,
Metabolism und Digestive Diseases
National Institutes of Health
Bethesda, Maryland 20014, USA
                                    p. 1397

Koss, Friedrich-Wilhelm

Institut für Klinische Biochemie und
Physiologische Chemie der
Medizinischen Hochschule
Roderbruchstrasse 101
D-3000 Hannover, Germany   *p. 1886*

Krakow, Gladys

St. Joseph's Hospital
Milwaukee, Wisconsin 53210, USA
                                    p. 1963

Kuhlmann, Elisabeth

Medizinische Universitätsklinik
Olfried-Müller-Strasse
D-7400 Tübingen, Germany   *p. 1825*

Kun, Ernest

University of California
San Francisco Medical Center
School of Medicine
Dept. of Pharmacology
and Biochemistry
San Francisco, California 94122, USA
                                    p. 1460, 1802

Kurz, Gerhart

Lehrstuhl Biochemie
Chemisches Laboratorium der
Universität
D-7800 Freiburg i. Br., Germany
                                    p. 1180, 1279

Kusche, Jürgen

Institut für Klinische Chemie und
Klinische Biochemie der
Universität München
Nußbaumstrasse 20
D-8000 Munich 2, Germany   *p. 660*

Lachenicht, Rudolf

Boehringer Mannheim GmbH
Abt. Ausbildung und Training
Sandhofer Strasse,
D-6800 Mannheim 31, Germany
                                    p. 864, 1201, 1215

Lamprecht, Walther

Medizinische Hochschule Hannover
Institut für Klinische Biochemie und
Physiologische Chemie
Karl-Wiechert-Allee 9
D-3000 Hannover-Kleefeld, Germany
                                    p. 1446, 1777, 2101

Lang, Gunter

Boehringer Mannheim GmbH
Biochemica Werk Tutzing
D-8132 Tutzing/Obb., Germany
                                    p. 1238, 1415

Langenbeck, Ulrich

Institut für Humangenetik der
Universität
Nikolausberger Weg 5a
D-3400 Göttingen, Germany
                                    p. 1394, 1514

Latzko, Erwin

Chemisches Institut
Technische Universität München
D-8050 Freising-Weihenstephan, Germany
                                    p. 82, 409, 881, 1385

Laudahn, Gerhard

Schering AG
Müllerstrasse 170–172
D-1000 Berlin 65, Germany   *p. 37*

Leuthardt, Franz
  Biochemisches Institut der
  Universität
  Zürichbergstrasse 4
  CH-8032 Zürich, Switzerland   *p. 1109*

Levine, Jacob B.
  Biochemistry
  Technicon Corporation
  511 Benedict Avenue
  Tarrytown, New York 10591, USA
                                     p. 851

Linker, Alfred
  Department of Biological Chemistry
  University of Utah
  College of Medicine
  Salt Lake City, Utah 84112, USA
                                     p. 944

Löffler, Georg
  Institut für Diabetesforschung
  Städt. Krankenhaus Schwabing
  Kölner Platz
  D-8000 Munich 23, Germany
                                p. 228, 1611

Löhr, Georg Wilhelm
  Medizinische Universitätsklinik
  Hugstetter Strasse 55
  D-7800 Freiburg i. Br., Germany   *p. 636*

Löschenkohl, Karin
  Institut für Klinische Chemie und
  Klinische Biochemie der
  Universität München
  Nußbaumstrasse 20
  D-8000 Munich 2, Germany
                                p. 1731, 1736

Lorenz, Wilfried
  Institut für Klinische Chemie und
  Klinische Biochemie der
  Universität München
  Nußbaumstrasse 20
  D-8000 Munich 2, Germany   *p. 660*

Lowry, Oliver H.
  Washington University
  School of Medicine
  Department of Pharmacology
  St. Louis, Missouri 63110, USA
                            p. 135, 1452, 2059

Luhby, A. Leonard
  Department of Pediatrics
  Hematology and Nutrition Laboratories
  New York Medical College
  New York, N. Y. 10029, USA   *p. 1556*

Lund, Patricia
  Metabolic Research Laboratory
  Nuffield Dept. of Clinical Medicine
  The Radcliffe Infirmary
  Oxford, England   *p. 1719*

Lundquist, Frank
  Department of Biochemistry
  University of Copenhagen
  2100 Copenhagen, Denmark
                                p. 1509, 1532

Lynen, Feodor
  Max-Planck-Institut für Biochemie
  D-8033 Martinsried near Munich, Germany
                                     p. 2034

Mattenheimer, Hermann
  Department of Biochemistry,
  Rush-Presbyterian-St. Luke's Medical
  Center,
  1753 Congress Parkway
  Chicago, Illinois 60612, USA   *p. 62*

Matthaei, Heinrich
  Arbeitsgruppe Biochemie
  Max-Planck-Institut für
  experimentelle Medizin
  Hermann-Rein-Strasse 3
  D-3400 Göttingen, Germany   *p. 1901*

Maurer, Claus

Chirurgische Universitätsklinik
Klinisch-Chemische Abteilung
Kirschnerstrasse 1
D-6900 Heidelberg, Germany   *p. 1472*

Mayer, Dieter

Institut für Klinische Biochemie
und Physiologische Chemie der
Medizinischen Hochschule
Karl-Wiechert-Allee 9
D-3000 Hannover, Germany   *p. 1886*

Mecke, Dieter

Biochemisches Institut der
Universität Freiburg
Hermann-Herder-Strasse 7
D-7800 Freiburg i. Br., Germany   *p. 1716*

Mellanby, Jane

Department of Experimental Psychology
South Parks Road
Oxford, England   *p. 1836, 1840*

Michal, Gerhard

Boehringer Mannheim GmbH
Biochemica Werk Tutzing
D-8132 Tutzing/Obb., Germany   *p. 136,*
144, 158, 308, 1233, 1238, 1314, 1415, 1433,
1708, 1967, 2008, 2136

Möllering, Hans

Boehringer Mannheim GmbH
Biochemica Werk Tutzing
D-8132 Tutzing/Obb., Germany   *p. 136*
1222, 1243, 1520, 1538, 1589, 1696, 1772,
1813, 1919, 1959, 2073, 2078, 2132

Näher, Gotthilf

Boehringer Mannheim GmbH
Biochemica Werk Tutzing
D-8132 Tutzing/Obb., Germany
          p. 814, 1909

Nagel, Charles W.

Washington State University
Food Science Program
Department of Horticulture
Pullman, Washington 99163, USA
          p. 1299

Narins, Robert G.

University of Pennsylvania
Department of Medicine
Philadelphia, Pennsylvania 19104, USA
          p. 1580

Negelein, Erwin

Lindenberger Weg 74
1115 Berlin-Buch, DDR   *p. 1429*

Netheler, Heinrich G.

Eppendorf Gerätebau
Netheler & Hinz GmbH
Barkhausenweg 1
D-2000 Hamburg 63, Germany   *p. 181,*
184, 191, 193, 202, 203, 205

Newsholme, Eric A.

Department of Biochemistry,
South Parks Road
Oxford, England   *p. 283, 1409, 2144*

Noll, Franz

Akademie der Wissenschaften der DDR
Zentralinstitut für Molekularbiologie
Abteilung Zellphysiologie
1115 Berlin-Buch, DDR   *p. 1475*

Ohlenbusch, Hans-Dieter

Abteilung Physiologische Chemie der
Medizinischen Fakultät an der
Rhein.-Westf. Technischen Hochschule
D-5100 Aachen, Germany   *p. 923*

Osteux, Roger*

Laboratoire de Biochemie
Pharmaceutique
Faculté de Médecine et Pharmacie
Lille, France   *p. 1648*

* deceased

Otto, Peter

Medizinische Hochschule Hannover
Medizinische Klinik
Abteilung für Gastroenterologie
Podbielskistrasse 380
D-3000 Hannover, Germany   *p. 50*

Oudheusden, Antonius P. M. van

Sint Josef Ziekenhuis
Slingelaan 1
Doetinchem, Netherlands   *p. 971*

Packmann, Paul M.

Department of Pharmacology Psychiatry
Washington University
School of Medicine
St. Louis, Missouri 63110, USA   *p. 1346*

Passonneau, Janet V.

Section on Cellular Neurochemistry
Bethesda, Maryland 20014, USA   *p. 135,
1452, 1468, 1565, 1573, 1580, 1600,1608,
2059, 2229*

Pearson, David J.

Department of Biochemistry
University of Cambridge
Cambridge, England   *p. 1758*

Pfleiderer, Gerhard

Ruhr-Universität Bochum
Abteilung für Chemie
D-4630 Bochum/Westf., Germany
                             p. 1696

Pilz, Wolfgang

Institut für klinische Chemie
und analytische Chemie der ärztlichen
Abteilung
D-5090 Leverkusen-Bayerwerk, Germany
                             p. 806, 831

Poppendiek, Brunhilde

Chirurgische Universitätsklinik
Klinisch-Chemische Abteilung
Kirschnerstrasse 1
D-6900 Heidelberg, Germany   *p. 1472*

Preiss, Jack

University of California
Department of Biochemistry
and Biophysics
Davis, California 95616, USA
                             p. 2204, 2213

Pütter, Johann

Farbenfabriken Bayer A. G.
D-5600 Wuppertal-Elberfeld, Germany
                             p. 685

Rabinowitz, Jesse C.

University of California
Department of Biochemistry
Berkeley, California 94720, USA
                             p. 1546, 2110

Racker, Efraim

Cornell University
Division of Biological Sciences
Section of Biochemistry and Molecular
Biology
Ithaca, New York 14850, USA   *p. 1189,
1320, 1342, 1359, 1362, 1377, 1391, 1439*

Rauscher, Elli

Boehringer Mannheim GmbH
Biochemica Werk Tutzing
D-8132 Tutzing/Obb., Germany   *p. 890*

Rick, Wirnt

I. Medizinische Klinik der Universität
Moorenstrasse 5
D-4000 Düsseldorf 1, Germany   *p. 824,
885, 1006, 1013, 1046, 1864*

Rimbach, Erwin

Universitäts-Frauenklinik
D-7400 Tübingen, Germany   *p. 56*

Röschlau, Peter

Boehringer Mannheim GmbH
Biochemica Werk Tutzing
D-8132 Tutzing/Obb., Germany   *p. 1890*

Rosano, Carmen Louis

 Basic Science Research Laboratory
 Veterans Administration Hospital
 Albany, New York 12208, USA *p. 1723*

Rouayrenc, Jean-François

 Institut für Physiologische Chemie
 und Physikalische Biochemie der
 Universität München
 Goethestrasse 33
 D-8000 Munich 15, Germany *p. 254*

Samuelsson, Bengt

 Department of Chemistry
 Karolinska Institutet
 S-10401 Stockholm 60, Sweden *p. 1877*

Schaiberger, George E.

 Department of Microbiology
 University of Miami School of Medicine
 P. O. Box 875, Biscayne Annex
 Miami, Florida 33152, USA *p. 1701*

Scheibe, Peter

 Boehringer Mannheim GmbH
 Biochemica Werk Tutzing
 D-8132 Tutzing/Obb., Germany *p. 1951*

Scher, William

 Center for Experimental Cell Biology
 Mount Sinai School of Medicine
 Fifth Avenue and 100th Street
 New York, N.Y. 10029, USA *p. 1622*

Schievelbein, Helmut

 Institut für Klinische Chemie
 und Klinische Biochemie der
 Universität München
 Nußbaumstrasse 20
 D-8000 Munich 2, Germany *p. 1731, 1736*

Schlegel, Hans-Günter

 Institut für Mikrobiologie
 der Universität Göttingen
 Grisebachstrasse 8
 D-3400 Göttingen, Germany *p. 1081*

Schmid, Ella

 Laboratoire Central
 Hôpital Cantonal
 CH-1011 Lausanne, Switzerland *p. 721*

Schmidt, Ellen

 Medizinische Hochschule Hannover
 Medizinische Klinik
 Abteilung für Gastroenterologie
 Karl-Wiechert-Allee 9
 D-3000 Hannover-Kleefeld, Germany
         p. 6, 14, 650

Schmidt, Felix H.

 Boehringer Mannheim GmbH
 Abteilung Stoffwechsel
 Sandhofer Strasse
 D-6800 Mannheim 31, Germany
         p. 819, 1196

Schmidt, Friedrich W.

 Medizinische Hochschule Hannover
 Medizinische Klinik
 Abteilung für Gastroenterologie
 Podbielskistrasse 380
 D-3000 Hannover, Germany *p. 6, 14*

Schmidt, Helmuth

 II. Medizinische Universitätsklinik
 Martinistrasse 52
 D-2000 Hamburg 20, Germany *p. 1848*

Schoner, Wilhelm

 Institut für Biochemie
 und Endokrinologie
 Universität Giessen
 Frankfurter Strasse 110
 D-6300 Giessen, Germany *p. 1596, 1994*

Schormüller, Josef

 Technische Universität Berlin
 Institut für Lebensmittelchemie
 und Lebensmitteltechnologie
 Strasse des 17. Juni 135
 D-1000 Berlin 12, Germany *p. 71*

Schreiber, Gerhard
    Biochemisches Institut
    der Universität Freiburg
    Hermann-Herder-Strasse 7
    D-7800 Freiburg i. Br., Germany   p. 2194

Schütt, Christian
    Städtische Kliniken Darmstadt
    Institut für Laboratoriumsdiagnostik
    D-6100 Darmstadt, Germany
                                    p. 856, 860

Schulz, Demoy W.
    Department of Neurosurgery
    University of Colorado
    Medical School
    Denver, Colorado 80220, USA   p. 2229

Schwartz, Morton K.
    Memorial Hospital for Cancer
    and Allied Diseases
    New York, N.Y. 10021, USA   p. 768

Schweitzer, Gertraud
    Medizinische Hochschule Hannover
    Abteilung für Klinische Biochemie
    Roderbruchstrasse 101
    D-3000 Hannover, Germany   p. 1031

Seubert, Werner
    Physiologisch-Chemisches Institut
    der Georg-August Universität
    Humboldtallee 7
    D-3400 Göttingen, Germany
                                p. 1994, 2010

Siebert, Günther
    Lehrstuhl für Biologische Chemie
    und Ernährungswissenschaft
    Universität Hohenheim
    Garbenstrasse 30
    D-7000 Stuttgart 70, Germany   p. 1570

Siegel, Abraham L.
    University of Alabama
    Medical Center
    Birmingham, Alabama 35233, USA   p. 793

Staib, Wolfgang
    Physiologisch-Chemisches Institut II
    der Universität Düsseldorf
    Moorenstrasse 5
    D-4000 Düsseldorf 1, Germany
                                  p. 1858, 1868

Stamm, Dankwart
    Abteilung für Klinische Chemie
    Max-Planck-Institut für Psychiatrie
    Kraepelinstrasse 10
    D-8000 Munich 23, Germany   p. 318

Stegbauer, Hans-Peter
    Krankenhaus der Barmherzigen Brüder
    D-8400 Regensburg, Germany   p. 885

Stein, Philipp
    Behringwerke AG
    D-3550 Marburg/Lahn, Germany
                                        p. 1777

Stork, Harald
    Boehringer Mannheim GmbH
    Abteilung Stoffwechsel
    Sandhofer Strasse
    D-6800 Mannheim 31, Germany
                                   p. 819, 1196

Street, Harold V.
    Department of Forensic Medicine
    Medical School
    University of Edinburgh
    Edinburgh EH 8 9 AG, Scotland   p. 898

Strehler, Bernard L.
    University of Southern California
    Department of Biological Sciences
    Los Angeles, California 90007, USA
                                        p. 2112

Südhof, Heinrich*
    Robert-Koch-Krankenhaus des
    Landkreises Hannover
    Medizinische Klinik
    D-3011 Gehrden b. Hannover, Germany
                                        p. 1025

* deceased

Szasz, Gabor

Institut für Klinische Chemie
an den Universitätskliniken Giessen
Klinikstrasse 32 b
D-6300 Giessen, Germany   *p. 715, 1798*

Taniguchi, Shigehiko

Department of Biochemistry
University of Hiroshima
School of Dentistry
Hiroshima City, Japan   *p. 2260*

Trautschold, Ivar

Medizinische Hochschule Hannover
Abteilung für Klinische Biochemie
Roderbruchstrasse 101
D-3000 Hannover, Germany
                    p. 228, 1031, 1064, 2101

Tubbs, Philip K.

Department of Biochemistry
University of Cambridge
Cambridge, England   *p. 1758*

Ullrich, Johannes

Biochemisches Institut der
Universität Freiburg
Hermann-Herder-Strasse 7
D-7800 Freiburg i. Br., Germany
                               p. 2186

Vagelos, P. Roy

Washington University
School of Medicine
Department of Biological Chemistry
St. Louis, Missouri 63110, USA
                    p. 2005, 2031, 2038

Verdier, Carl-Henrie de

Dept. of Clinical Chemistry University
Hospital
S-75014 Uppsala 14, Sweden   *p. 1282*

Vögele, Peter

Henkel & Cie, GmbH
D-4000 Düsseldorf, Germany   *p. 923*

Voigt, Klaus-Dieter

Klinisch-chemische Abteilung
II. Medizinische Universitätsklinik
Martinistrasse 52
D-2000 Hamburg 20, Germany   *p. 1848*

Wahlefeld, August Wilhelm

Boehringer Mannheim GmbH
Biochemica Werk Tutzing
D-8132 Tutzing/Obb., Germany   *p. 136,*
894, 1464, 1585, 1604, 1786, 1831

Wallenfels, Kurt

Lehrstuhl Biochemie
Chemisches Laboratorium der
Universität Freiburg
Albertstrasse 21
D-7800 Freiburg i. Br., Germany
                          p. 1180, 1279

Waller, Hans Dierck

Medizinische Universitätsklinik
Hugstetter Strasse 55
D-7400 Tübingen, Germany   *p. 636*

Walter, Hans Elmar

Universität Regensburg
Fachbereich Biologie
Universitäts-Strasse 32
D-8400 Regenburg, Germany   *p. 1656*

Walter, Klaus

Institut für Laboratoriumsdiagnostik
Grafenstrasse 9
D-6100 Darmstadt, Germany
                          p. 856, 860

Warburg, Otto*

Max-Planck-Institut
für Zellphysiologie
Garystrasse 32
D-1000 Berlin 33 – Dahlem, Germany
                               p. 248

Weissbach, Arthur

National Institutes of Health
Bethesda, MD. 20014, USA   *p. 1333*

* deceased

Weisser, Herwig

    Medizinische Hochschule Hannover
    Institut für Klinische Biochemie und
    Physiologische Chemie
    Karl-Wiechert-Allee 9
    D-3000 Hannover-Kleefeld, Germany
                          p. 1777

Werle, Eugen

    Institut für Klinische Chemie
    und Klinische Biochemie der
    Universität
    Nussbaumstrasse 20
    D-8000 Munich 2, Germany
                 p. 660, 1031, 1064

Wharton, H. Whitney

    The Procter and Gamble Co.
    Winton Hill Technical Center
    Cincinnati, Ohio 45224, USA   *p. 1807*

Wieker, Hans-Joachim

    Max-Planck-Institut für
    Ernährungsphysiologie
    Rheinlanddamm 201
    D-4600 Dortmund, Germany   *p. 778*

Wieland, Otto

    Klinisch-chemisches Institut des
    Städtischen Krankenhauses
    München-Schwabing
    und Forschungsgruppe Diabetes
    D-8000 Munich 23, Germany
            p. 1404, 1442, 1483, 1611

Wieme, Roger Jozef

    Clinical Biochemistry
    Department Internal Medicine
    Academic Hospital
    De Pintelaan 115
    Ghent, Belgium   *p. 261, 593, 618, 745*

Wilkinson, J. Henry

    Department of Chemical Pathology
    Charing Cross Hospital
    Fulham Palace Road
    London W6 8 RF
    England   *p. 603*

Williamson, Dermot H.

    Metabolic Research Laboratory
    Nuffield Department
    of Clinical Medicine
    The Radcliffe Infirmary
    Oxford, England   *p. 1679*
    1727, 1836, 1840, 1844, 2041, 2266

Williamson, John R.

    Johnson Research Foundation
    University of Pennsylvania
    Philadelphia, Pennsylvania 19174, USA
                          p. 1616

Wilmanns, Wolfgang

    Medizinische Klinik der
    Universität Tübingen
    Auf dem Schnarrenberg
    D-7400 Tübingen, Germany   *p. 666, 1118*

Witt, Irene

    Universitäts-Kinderklinik
    Mathildenstrasse 1
    D-7800 Freiburg i. Br., Germany
             p. 1442, 1502, 1593, 1713

Wolf, Hans-Peter

    Klinische Forschung der
    E. Merck A.G.
    D-6100 Darmstadt, Germany   *p. 1109*

Wunderwald, Peter

    Boehringer Mannheim GmbH
    Biochemica Werk Tutzing
    D-8132 Tutzing/Obb., Germany   *p. 2136*

Zachau, Hans Georg

    Institut für Physiologische Chemie und
    Physikalische Biochemie der
    Universität München
    Goethestrasse
    D-8000 Munich, Germany   *p. 1894*

Zak, Bennie

Pathology Department
Wayne State University
School of Medicine
Detroit, Michigan 48207, USA   *p. 876*

Zankl, Gottfried

Boehringer Mannheim GmbH
Sandhofer Strasse
D-6800 Mannheim 31, Germany   *p. 557*

Ziegenhorn, Joachim

Boehringer Mannheim GmbH
Biochemica Werk Tutzing
D-8132 Tutzing/Obb., Germany   *p. 2034*

Zöllner, Nepomuk

Medizinische Poliklinik der
Universität München
Pettenkoferstrasse 8 a
D-8000 Munich 2, Germany

                                    p. 1151, 1288

Abbreviations

Abbreviations of Units of Mass and Constants

m.	Metre [m.]		g.	Gram [g.]
cm.	Centimetre [10^{-2} m.]		mg.	Milligram [10^{-3} g.]
mm.	Millimetre [10^{-3} m.]		μg.	Microgram [10^{-6} g.]
nm.	Nanometre [10^{-9} m.]		ng.	Nanogram [10^{-9} g.]

hr.	Hour		l.	Litre [l.]
min.	Minute		ml.	Millilitre [10^{-3} l.]
sec.	Second		μl.	Microlitre [10^{-6} l.]

t	Time [hr.] [min.] [sec.]
T	Temperature [° Kelvin]
V	Volume (usually volume of assay mixture) [ml.]
v	Volume (usually volume of sample in assay mixture) [ml.]
v	Rate of reaction, e. g. [μmole/min.]
MW	Molecular weight [g.]

c	Concentration [g./l.]; [mole/l.]
%	Percentage
%(v/v)	Percentage, volume related to volume
%(v/w)	Percentage, volume related to weight
%(w/v)	Percentage, weight related to volume
%(w/w)	Percentage, weight related to weight

d	Light path [cm.]
sp. gr.	Specific gravity at 20 °C relative to water at 4 °C
Ci	Curie

$[\alpha]_D^{20}$	Specific rotation (D-line at 20 °C)
cpm	Counts per minute [$min.^{-1}$]
rpm	Revolutions per minute [$min.^{-1}$]
g	Acceleration [$cm./sec.^2$]

ε	Extinction coefficient [$cm.^2/mole$], [$cm.^2/\mu mole$]
E	Extinction (absorbance)
OD	Optical density (Extinction)
F	Fluorescence
I	Light beam

k	Reaction constant
K	Equilibrium constant
K′	Apparent equilibrium constant
K_m	Michaelis constant [M]
K_i	Inhibitor constant [M]

pH	Hydrogen ion concentration ($-\log$)
pK	Acid dissociation constant ($-\log$)

$\bar{x}$	Mean value
s or SD	Standard deviation
CV	Coefficient of variation

M	Molar [mole/l.]
mM	Millimolar [mmole/l.], [10^{-3} mole/l.]
μM	Micromolar [μmole/l.], [10^{-6} mole/l.]
nM	Nanomolar [nmole/l.], [10^{-9} mole/l.]
pM	Picomolar [pmole/l.], [10^{-12} mole/l.]

U	International Unit (for enzymes)
mU	International milliunit [10^{-3} U]
IU	International inhibitor unit
ImU	International inhibitor milliunit [10^{-3} IU]

DN	Dibucaine number
FN	Fluoride number
RZ	Reinheitszahl (of peroxidase)

Abbreviations for Chemical and Biochemical Compounds

It is unavoidable with the numerous abbreviations in use that one abbreviation occasionally is used for different compounds. In such cases the correct meaning can be obtained from the text. Only the unequivocal abbreviations are used in the book without further explanation.

AA	Amino acid arylamidase (microsomal)	AK	Acetate kinase
		ALD	Fructose-1,6-diphosphate aldolase
γ-ABA-T	γ-Aminobutyric acid transaminase	Ammediol	2-Amino-2-methyl-propane-1,3-diol
ABTS®	2,2'-Azino-di-(3-ethylbenzthiazoline)-6'-sulphonate		
		AMP	Adenosine-5'-monophosphate
AcAc-CoA	Acetoacetyl-coenzyme A	A-2-MP	Adenosine-2'-monophosphate
Ac-CoA	Acetyl-coenzyme A	A-3-MP	Adenosine-3'-monophosphate
AChE	Acetylcholinesterase	A-3,2-MP	Adenosine-3'(2')-monophosphate
Ac-P	Acetyl phosphate	A-3:5-MP	Adenosine-3':5'-monophosphate, cyclic
ACT	Carnitine acetyltransferase		
ADA	Adenosine deaminase	A-5-MP	Adenosine-5'-monophosphate
ADH	Alcohol dehydrogenase	D-AOD	D-Amino acid oxidase
ADP	Adenosine-5'-diphosphate	L-AOD	L-Amino acid oxidase
A-2,5-DP	Adenosine-2',5'-diphosphate	AP	Alkaline phosphatase
A-3,5-DP	Adenosine-3',5'-diphosphate	APAD	Acetylpyridine-adenine dinucleotide
ADPG	Adenosine-5'-diphosphoglucose		
AGS	Amyloglucosidase	APADH	Acetylpyridine-adenine dinucleotide, reduced
AGT	Acylphosphate: D-glucose-6-phosphotransferase		
		ARS	Aryl sulphatase

ATCase	Aspartate transcarbamylase
ATP	Adenosine-5'-triphosphate
ATPase	Adenosine-5'-triphosphatase
BAEE	Benzoyl-L-arginine ethyl ester
BAPNA	N-Benzoyl-arginine-p-nitroanilide
BMTD	6-Benzamido-4-methoxy-m-toluidine-diazonium chloride
Bz-CoA	Benzoyl-coenzyme A
CA	Carbonic anhydrase
CAA	Carbamyl-L-aspartate
CAP	Carbamyl phosphate
CCE	Citrate cleavage enzyme
CCPN	N-3-(carboxypropionyl)-L-phenylalanine-p-nitroanilide
CDP	Cytidine-5'-diphosphate
CDPG	Cytidine-5'-diphosphoglucose
CE	Citrate condensing enzyme
Cellosolve	Ethylene glycol monomethyl ether
CHA	Cyclohexylammonium
CHE, ChE	Cholinesterase
CHTR	Chymotrypsin
CK (CPK)	Creatine kinase
CL	Citrate lyase
C-2-MP	Cytidine-2'-monophosphate
C-2:3-MP	Cytidine-2':3'-monophosphate, cyclic
C-3-MP	Cytidine-3'-monophosphate
C-3,2-MP	Cytidine-3'(2')- monophosphate
C-5-MP	Cytidine-5'-monophosphate
CoA, CoA-SH	Coenzyme A
CP	Creatine phosphate
CPK	Creatine kinase (CK)
CS	Citrate synthase
CTP	Cytidine-5'-triphosphate
Cyt-c	Cytochrome c
DAO	Diamine oxidase
DAP	Dihydroxyacetone phosphate
DEAE	Diethylaminoethyl
DFP	Diisopropyfluorophosphate
-DH	-Dehydrogenase
DIA	Diaphorase
DNase	Deoxyribonuclease
DNP	Dinitrophenylhydrazine
DTNB	5:5-Dithiobis-(2-nitrobenzoic acid)
EDTA	Ethylenediaminetetra-acetate
ENOL, ENO	Enolase

E-4-P	D-Erythrose-4-phosphate
ETF	Electron transferring flavoprotein
FAD	Flavin-adenine dinucleotide
FDH	Formate dehydrogenase
FDNB	1-Fluoro-2,4-dinitrobenzene
FDP (F-1,6-P_2)	D-Fructose-1,6-diphosphate
FDPase	Fructose- 1,6-diphosphatase
FH_2	Dihydrofolate
FH_4	Tetrahydrofolate
FIGLU	N-Formimino-L-glutamate
FMN	Flavin mononucleotide
FNR	Formate nitrate reductase
F-1-P	D-Fructose-1-phosphate
F-1,6-P_2	D-Fructose-1,6-diphosphate
F-6-P	D-Fructose-6-phosphate
F-6-PK	Fructose-6-phosphate kinase
FUM	Fumarase
GAD	General acyl-CoA dehydrogenase
Gal-DH	Galactose dehydrogenase
Gal-OD	Galactose oxidase
Gal-1-P	D-Galactose-1-phosphate
Gal-6-P	D-Galactose-6-phosphate
GAP	D-Glyceraldehyde-3-phosphate
GAPDH	D-Glyceraldehyde-3-phosphate dehydrogenase
GDH	L-Glycerol-3-phosphate dehydrogenase (glycerol-1-phosphate dehydrogenase; α-glycerophosphate dehydrogenase)
GDP	Guanosine-5'-diphosphate
GK	Glycerokinase
Gl-I	Glyoxalase I
GlDH (GluDH)	L-Glutamate dehydrogenase
Gly-R	Glyoxylate reductase (glycerate dehydrogenase)
GMP	Guanosine-5'-monophosphate
G-2-MP	Guanosine-2'-monophosphate
G-3-MP	Guanosine-3'-monophosphate
G-3,2-MP	Guanosine-3'(2')-monophosphate
G-3:5-MP	Guanosine-3:5-monophosphate, cyclic
G-5-MP	Guanosine-5'-monophosphate
GOD	Glucose oxidase
GOT	Glutamate-oxaloacetate transaminase

G-1-P	D-Glucose-1-phosphate	NBT	Nitro-BT-tetrazolium salt, 2,2'-
G-1,6-P$_2$	D-Glucose-1,6-diphosphate		di-p-nitrophenyl-5,5'-diphenyl-
G-6-P	D-Glucose-6-phosphate		3.3'-(-dimethoxy-4,4'-diphenylene)-
G6Pase	Glucose-6-phosphatase		ditetrazolium chloride
G6P-DH(ZF)	Glucose-6-phosphate dehydrogen-	NBTH	N-Methyl-2-benzothiazolone
	ase (Zwischenferment)		hydrazone
GPT	Glutamate-pyruvate transaminase	NDPK	Nucleoside diphosphate kinase
GR	Glutathione reductase	NMN	Nicotinamide mononucleotide
GRD	β-Glucuronidase	NMPK	Nucleoside monophosphate kinase
GSH	Glutathione	NP	Nucleoside phosphorylase
GSSG	Glutathione, oxidized		
GT	Glucuronyltransferase	OA	Oxaloacetate
γ-GT, GGTP	γ-Glutamyl transpeptidase	OCT	Ornithine-carbamyl transferase
GPT	Guanosine-5'-triphosphate	ODTG	Octadehydro-tetraguaiacol
		3-OH-A	3-Hydroxyanthranilic acid
Hb	Haemoglobin	3-OH-K	3-Hydroxykynurenine
HBDH	D-3-Hydroxybutyrate dehydrogen-	15-OH-PGDH	15-Hydroxyprostaglandin de-
	ase		hydrogenase
HK	Hexokinase	OxoG	2-Oxoglutaric acid
HMG-CoA	3-Hydroxy-3-methylglutaryl-	OxoG-DH	2-Oxoglutarate dehydrogenase
	coenzyme A		
HOADH	3-Hydroxyacyl-CoA dehydrogen-	PALP	Pyridoxal-5-phosphate
	ase	PAMP	Pyridoxamine-5-phosphate
HXM	Hypoxanthine	PChE	Pseudocholinesterase
		PDC	Pyruvate decarboxylase
ICDH	Isocitrate dehydrogenase	PDE	Phosphodiesterase
IDP	Inosine-5'-diphosphate	PEP	Phosphoenol pyruvate
I-5-MP	Inosine-5'-monophosphate	PFA	Fructose-1-phosphate aldolase,
INT	2-(p-Iodophenyl)-3-(p-nitro-		1-phosphofructoaldolase
	phenyl)-5-phenyltetrazolium	PFK	Phosphofructo-kinase, fructose-6-
	chloride		phosphate kinase
ISN	Inosine	PG	Prostaglandin
ITP	Inosine-5'-triphosphate	2-PG	2-Phosphoglycerate, D-glycerate-2-
			phosphate
		3-PG	3-Phosphoglycerate, D-glycerate-3-
LAP	Leucine aminopeptidase		phosphate
LDH	L-Lactate dehydrogenase	6-PG	6-Phosphogluconate, D-gluconate-
D-LDH	D-Lactate dehydrogenase		6-phosphate
MDH	L-Malate dehydrogenase	6-PG-DH	6-Phosphogluconate dehydrogen-
MK	Myokinase, adenylate kinase		ase
MPDH	Mannitol-1-P dehydrogenase	PGI, PHI	Phosphoglucose-isomerase,
			phosphohexose-isomerase
NAD	Nicotinamide-adenine dinucleotide	PGK	3-Phosphoglycerate kinase
NADH	Nicotinamide-adenine dinucleo-	PGluM	Phosphoglucomutase
	tide, reduced	PGM	Phosphoglycerate mutase
NADP	Nicotinamide-adenine dinucleo-	1,3-PGP	D-Glycerate-1,3-diphosphate,
	tide phosphate		1,3-Diphosphoglycerate
NADPH	Nicotinamide-adenine dinucleo-	2,3-PGP	D-Glycerate-2,3-diphosphate,
	tide phosphate, reduced		2,3-Diphosphoglycerate

P_i	Inorganic phosphate	TA	Transamidinase
PK	Pyruvate kinase	TA	Transaldolase
PL-A	Phospholipase A	dTDP	Deoxythymidine-5'-diphosphate
PL-D	Phospholipase D	dTDPG	Deoxythymidine-5'-diphospho-glucose
PMI	Phosphomannose isomerase		
PMS	Phenazine methosulphate	THF	Tetrahydrofolate
POD	Peroxidase	TIM	Triosephosphate isomerase
Poly-A	Polyadenylic acid	TK	Thiokinase
Poly-C	Polycytidylic acid	TK	Transketolase
Poly-I	Polyinosylic acid	TPP	Thiamine pyrophosphate
Poly-U	Polyuridylic acid	TR	Trypsin
DM-POPOP	1,4-bis-(4-methyl-5-phenyl-oxazolyl)-benzene	TRA	Triethanolamine
		Tris	Tris-hydroxymethyl-amino-methane
PPase	Pyrophosphatase, inorganic		
PP_i	Inorganic pyrophosphate	dTTP	Deoxythymidine triphosphate
PPO	2,5-Diphenyloxazole		
PTA	Phosphotransacetylase		
RDH	Ribitol dehydrogenase	UDP	Uridine-5'-diphosphate
RNA	Ribonucleic acid	UDPG	Uridine-5'-diphosphoglucose
sRNA	Soluble ribonucleic acid	UDPAG	Uridine-5'-diphospho-N-acetyl-glucosamine
tRNA	Transfer ribonucleic acid		
RNase	Ribonuclease	UDPGA	Uridine-5'-diphosphoglucuronate
R-1-P	D-Ribose-1-phosphate	UDPGal	Uridine-5'-diphosphogalactose
$R-1,5-P_2$	D-Ribose-1,5-diphosphate	UDPG-DH	Uridine-5'-diphosphoglucose dehydrogenase
R-5-P	D-Ribose-5-phosphate		
R5P-I	Ribose-5-phosphate isomerase	UDPGP	UDPG-pyrophosphorylase
Ru-1-P	D-Ribulose-1-phosphate	UMP	Uridine-5'-monophosphate
$Ru-1,5-P_2$	D-Ribulose-1,5-diphosphate	U-2-MP	Uridine-2'-monophosphate
Ru-5-P	D-Ribulose-5-phosphate	U-2:3-MP	Uridine-2':3'-monophosphate, cyclic
SBI	Soya bean inhibitor	U-3-MP	Uridine-3'-monophosphate
SD	Succinate dehydrogenase	U-3,2-MP	Uridine-3'(2')-monophosphate
SDH	Sorbitol dehydrogenase, polyol dehydrogenase	U-5-MP	Uridine-5'-monophosphate
		UT	Uridyltransferase
SDPase	Sedoheptulose-1,7-diphosphatase	UTP	Uridine-5'-triphosphate
$S-1,7-P_2$	D-Sedoheptulose-1,7-diphosphate		
S-7-P	D-Sedoheptulose-7-phosphate		
SSA-DH	Succinate semialdehyde dehydro-genase	XOD	Xanthine oxidase
		Xu-5-P	Xylulose-5-phosphate
20-StDH	$3\alpha,20\beta$-Hydroxysteroid dehydro-genase		
SUPHEPA	N-Succinyl-L-phenylalanine-p-nitroanilide	ZF (G6P-DH)	Zwischenferment, glucose-6-phosphate dehydrogenase

Section C

Methods for Determination of Enzyme Activities

Sorbitol Dehydrogenase

Ulrich Gerlach and Walter Hiby

Sorbitol dehydrogenase, SDH (L-Iditol:NAD 5-oxidoreductase, EC 1.1.1.14) is classified with the polyol dehydrogenases[1]. The enzyme was first partially purified in 1951 by *Blakley*[2] from rat liver. Since then SDH has been demonstrated in various human, animal and plant tissues[3-13]. *Smith* crystallized the enzyme in 1962[14]. It is mainly located in the cytoplasm and in the mitochondria[15,16] of liver, kidney and seminal vesicles[17-19].

Comparative studies have shown that SDH from *Acetobacter suboxydans*[12,13] and from liver can be differentiated by their substrate specificity[20]. Depending on the type of coenzyme used the dehydrogenases from *Acetobacter suboxydans* yield either D-fructose or L-sorbose as the oxidation product of D-sorbitol[21]. The molecular weight of SDH is not known. The *Michaelis-Menten* constant for sorbitol of the enzyme purified from liver is 0.7 mM at pH 8.7[2]. The pH optimum depends on the source of the enzyme and is between 6.1 and 8.1[2,22,23]. SDH is inhibited by borate, cyanide, monoiodoacetate and EDTA: 0.5 mM AgNO$_3$ or HgCl$_2$ cause 100% inhibition, 0.2 mM 2,3-dimercaptoethanol 91% inhibition[22]. For determination of the activity of the enzyme, measurement of the oxidation or reduction of NAD is preferable to the oxidation methods with periodic acid[24-26] or potassium ferricyanide[27,28], because of its accuracy and rapidity[29].

Application of Method: In biochemistry and clinical chemistry.

The clinical importance[17-19,33-37] of the assay of SDH is based on the finding that SDH is virtually absent from serum of healthy subjects, whereas it is detectable in liver damage (infectious, toxic or hypoxic). SDH activity in serum can therefore serve as a virtually organ-specific indicator of liver cell damage[17-19]. The physiological function[30-32] of cytoplasmic sorbitol dehydrogenase (equation 1) is possibly associated with a NADP-specific aldose reductase which converts glucose into sorbitol.

Principle

(1) $\qquad$ D-Sorbitol + NAD$^+$ $\xrightleftharpoons{\text{SDH}}$ D-Fructose + NADH + H$^+$

SDH activity can be measured in either direction. For measurements in serum the use of D(−)fructose as substrate is preferable. The decrease of the extinction at 340, 334, or 365 nm due to the oxidation of NADH is a measure of the SDH activity.

Optimum Conditions for Measurements

The relationship between the SDH activity and the concentration of D-fructose is shown in Fig. 1. The optimum concentration is ca. 0.4 M (in triethanolamine buffer, pH 7.4)[35,37]. The pH optimum of the reaction with fructose is pH 6.1 in triethanolamine buffer and tris-hydroxymethyl-aminomethane buffer (tris). The reaction in tris buffer is somewhat faster than in triethanolamine buffer, but tris requires a higher concentration of fructose to saturate the enzyme. In various buffers the SDH reaction is about 1−2 orders of magnitude faster with NADH than with NADPH.

Measurements at different temperatures may require different measuring conditions (cf. p. 127). Nevertheless, results obtained under the same measuring conditions but at different temperatures were formerly compared with each other ("conversion factors" were determined). Such conversion factors may be correct if determined with a relatively large proband collective; however, they cannot be applied generally to the individual case (cf. p. 129). The value of the following relative reaction rates thus lies in being able to appraise the temperature dependence of the reaction and at the most to compare qualitatively values up to the limit of normal.

°C	25	30	37	40
	1.00	1.23	1.63	1.74

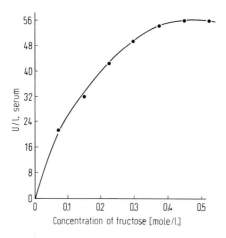

Fig. 1. Dependence of the SDH activity in serum on the fructose concentration.

Equipment

Spectrophotometer or spectrum-line photometer suitable for measurements at 340, 334 or 365 nm, preferably with constant temperature cuvette holder, glass cuvettes, 1 cm.; water bath (25 °C); stopwatch; centrifuge.

Reagents

1. Triethanolamine hydrochloride
2. Sodium hydroxide, 2 N
3. Reduced nicotinamide-adenine dinucleotide, NADH
   disodium salt, NADH-Na$_2$; commercial preparation, see p. 545.

4. D(−)-Fructose, crystalline, pure, C$_6$H$_{12}$O$_6$

Preparation of Solutions

Prepare all solutions with doubly distilled water.

  I. Triethanolamine buffer (0.2 M; pH 7.4):
     Dissolve 37.2 g. triethanolamine hydrochloride in distilled water, adjust to pH 7.4 with 2 N NaOH and dilute to 1 000 ml. with distilled water.
 II. Reduced nicotinamide-adenine dinucleotide (12 mM β-NADH):
     Dissolve 15 mg. NADH-Na$_2$ in 1.5 ml. 1% NaHCO$_3$ solution.·
III. D(−)-Fructose (4.0 M):
     Dissolve 72.06 g. D(−)-fructose in distilled water and make up to 100 ml.

Stability of Solutions

The triethanolamine buffer (I) is stable for about a year at room temperature and the D(−)-fructose solution (III) at 4 °C for about four weeks, providing that it is not contaminated with micro-organisms. The NADH solution (II) should be prepared freshly each week and stored at 4 °C.

Procedure

Collection, Treatment and Stability of Sample

Collect blood by venous or arterial puncture. Avoid the addition of anticoagulants, even though heparin does not affect the enzyme activity appreciably[36,37]. Centrifuge after coagulation and suck off serum. Serum from haemolysed blood can be analysed without any appreciable error because erythrocytes are low in sorbitol dehydrogenase[15]. The enzyme is thermolabile in serum. Table 1 shows the stability at different temperatures[36].

Table 1. Stability of SDH in serum at different temperatures[38], the initial value is the activity of fresh serum.

Period of storage	Loss of activity (% of initial value) after storage of serum at		
	21 °C	4 °C	−18 °C
24 hours	20.5	5.5	0
48 hours	49	10.6	0

Assay System

Wavelength: 340, Hg 334 or Hg 365 nm; light path: 1 cm.; final volume: 3.0 ml.; temperature: 25 °C (constant temperature cuvette holder), equilibrate the solutions to 25 °C before start of assay; read against air or water. Prepare a reagent blank (containing distilled water instead of serum) for each series of measurements.

Pipette into cuvettes:			Concentration in assay mixture
Triethanolamine buffer	(I)	1.6 ml.	ca. 107 mM
NADH solution	(II)	0.1 ml.	0.4 mM
Serum		1.0 ml.	
Mix and incubate for about 30 min. at 25 °C until the extinction is constant.			
D(−)-Fructose solution	(III)	0.3 ml.	400 mM
Mix and read the extinction at 60 sec. intervals for 5–8 min.			

The extinction change per minute at 365 nm should not be greater than 0.030. If necessary, dilute the serum 5- to 10-fold with physiological saline or read the extinction changes at shorter time intervals (30 sec.).

Calculations

The enzyme activity is calculated according to the formula (8) on p. 313. The following relationships hold for the present method:

Wavelength:	*334 nm*	*340 nm*	*365 nm*
Volume activity	$= 492 \times \Delta E/min.$	$482 \times \Delta E/min.$	$882 \times \Delta E/min.$ [U/l.]

The calculations can also be made graphically[15].

Precision of Method

With values around 12 U/l. the standard deviation s = 0.14 U/l. The coefficient of variation is 1.14%.

Normal Values

The SDH activity in the serum of healthy subjects is less than 1.5 U/l. The SDH activity in human organs is given in Table 2.

Table 2. SDH activity in human organs obtained at autopsy.

Organ	SDH activity	
	U/g. fresh wt.	U/g. dry wt.
Liver	5.216	20.57
Prostate	1.243	7.70
Kidney	1.108	5.27
Spleen	0.382	1.90
Testes	0.173	1.16
Lymph nodes	0.193	0.85
Heart, left ventricle	0,091	0.51
Skeletal muscle	0.121	0.45

Sources of Error

Effects of drugs and other therapeutic measures. These have no effect on the measured activity.

Interference in the assay: False results occur with insufficient pre-incubation before the start of the enzyme reaction because metabolites in serum, especially ketoses, can react with dehydrogenases in serum with resultant oxidation of NADH. The activity of SDH can be affected by the inhibitors listed above (see p. 569).
Old NADH preparations or solutions should not be used in kinetic assays because they can result in lower SDH activities.

Specificity of Method

SDH catalyses the following reactions in the presence of NAD or NADH: ribitol ⇌ D-ribulose; xylitol ⇌ D-xylulose; L-iditol ⇌ L-sorbose; allitol ⇌ D-allulose; L-gala-D-glucoheptitol ⇌ perseulose (L-gala-heptulose) and D-altro-D-glucoheptitol ⇌ sedoheptulose (D-altroheptulose). Only after sufficiently long preincubation and stabilization of the extinction is SDH activity measured specifically after the start of the reaction with D(−)-fructose.

Details for Measurements in Tissues

For the determination of SDH activity in tissue[1,4,17−19,32,35,38−40] the samples are homogenized and centrifuged in the cold at high speed. Care must be taken that the sample is worked up quickly, because under anaerobic and post-mortem conditions the concentration of sorbitol in tissues rises[28]. The clear supernatant fluid can be used directly for the assay, but the optimum conditions for human serum do not necessarily apply to tissue preparations; in particular, different conditions apply to purified SDH preparations[1,2,32,41,42]. With sorbitol as substrate the most favourable conditions[38] for crude rat liver extracts are tris buffer (pH 9) and a sorbitol concentration of 0.15 M. Proportionality between the activity and the amount of enzyme added as well as linear progress curves are obtained. In the reverse direction the reaction (with 0.4 M fructose) in triethanolamine buffer (pH 7.4) is about 8-fold faster; in tris buffer (pH 7.4) it is about 5-fold faster.

It should be noted that the determination of liver SDH usually includes the cytoplasmic SDH and the mitochondrial xylitol dehydrogenase. The enzymes are virtually homo-specific, but not identical[32].

References

1   *H. Holzer & H. W. Goedde*, Biochem. biophys. Acta *40*, 297 [1960].
2   *R. L. Blakley*, Biochem. J. *49*, 257 [1951].
3   *O. Hoffmann-Ostenhof*: Enzymologie, Springer Verlag, Vienna 1954, p. 485.
4   *H. Holzer, J. Haan & S. Schneider*, Biochem. Z. *326*, 451 [1955].
5   *H. G. Williams-Ashman & J. Banks*, Arch. Biochem. *50*, 513 [1954].
6   *H. G. Williams-Ashman, J. Banks & S. K. Wolfson jr.*, Arch. Biochem. *72*, 485 [1957].
7   *T. E. King & T. Mann*, Nature *182*, 868 [1958].
8   *J. McCorcindale*, Proc. Univ. Otago Med. School *31*, 7 [1953].
9   *J. McCorcindale & N. L. Edson*, Biochem. J. *57*, 518 [1954].
10 *R. M. Hann, E. B. Tilden & C. S. Hudson*, J. amer. chem. Soc. *60*, 1201 [1938].
11 *N. K. Richtmeyer, L. C. Stewart & C. S. Hudson*, J. amer. chem. Soc. *72*, 4934 [1950].
12 *A. C. Arcus & N. L. Edson*, Proc. Univ. Otago Med. School *32*, 6 [1954].
13 *A. C. Arcus & N. L. Edson*, Biochem. J. *64*, 385 [1956].
14 *M. G. Smith*, Biochem. J. *83*, 135 [1962].
15 *R. Richterich*: Klinische Chemie, Akad. Verlagsgesellschaft, Frankfurt 1965, p. 335.
16 *S. Hollmann & O. Touster*, J. biol. Chem. *225*, 87 [1957].
17 *U. Gerlach*, Klin. Wschr. *35*, 1144 [1957].
18 *U. Gerlach* in *W. H. Hauss & H. Losse*, Struktur und Stoffwechsel des Herzmuskels, Thieme Verlag, Stuttgart 1959, p. 148.
19 *U. Gerlach*, Klin. Wschr. *37*, 93 [1959].
20 *S. Hollmann*: Nichtglykolytische Stoffwechselwege der Glukose, Thieme Verlag, Stuttgart 1961, p. 23.
21 *J. T. Cummins, T. E. King & V. H. Cheldelin*, J. biol. Chem. *224*, 323 [1957].
22 *S. Hollmann* in *Hoppe-Seyler/Thierfelder*: Handbuch der physiologisch und pathologisch-chemischen Analyse. Springer Verlag, Berlin-Heidelberg-New York 1964, vol. VI, part A, p. 704.
23 *H. Reinauer & S. Hollmann* in *H. Bartelheimer, W. Heyde & W. Thorn*: D-Glucose und verwandte Verbindungen in Medizin und Biologie, Enke Verlag, Stuttgart 1966, p. 110.
24 *C. D. West & S. Rapoport*, Proc. Soc. exp. Biol. *70*, 141 [1949].
25 *F. Rapoport, I. Reifer & H. Weinmann*, Mikrochim. Acta *1*, 290 [1937].
26 *W. W. Smith, N. Finkelstein & H. Smith*, J. biol. Chem. *135*, 231 [1940].
27 *W. R. Todd, J. Vreeland, J. Myers & E. S. West*, J. biol. Chem. *127*, 269 [1939].
28 *H. G. Britton*, Biochem. J. *69*, 5P [1958].
29 *J. D. Anderson, P. Andrews & L. Hough*, Biochem. J. *72*, 9P [1959].
30 *H. G. Hers*, Biochim. biophys. Acta *22*, 202 [1956].
31 *H. G. Hers*, Proceedings of the International Symposium on Enzyme Chemistry (Tokyo and Kyoto 1957), Maruzen, Tokyo 1958, p. 109.
32 *S. Hollmann*, Hoppe-Seylers Z. Physiol. Chem. *317*, 193 [1959].
33 *U. Gerlach*: Praktische Enzymologie, Hans Huber Verlag, Bern und Stuttgart 1968.
34 *U. Gerlach & H. Kronsbein*, Klin. Wschr. *37*, 595 [1959].
35 *U. Gerlach & E. Schürmeyer*, Z. ges. exp. Med. *132*, 413 [1960].
36 *E. F. Schmidt, F. W. Schmidt & E. Wildhirt*, Klin. Wschr. *37*, 1221 [1959].
37 *H. Schön & H. Wüst*, Klin. Wschr. *38*, 497 [1960].
38 *U. Gerlach*, unpublished experiments.
39 *H. Kalk, E. Schmidt, F. W. Schmidt & E. Wildhirt*, Klin. Wschr. *38*, 421 [1960].
40 *E. Schmidt, F. W. Schmidt & E. Wildhirt*, Klin. Wschr. *37*, 1229 [1959].
41 *S. K. Wolfson & H. G. Williams-Ashman*, Proc. Soc. exp. Biol. *99*, 761 [1958].
42 *J. B. Wolf* in *S. P. Colowick & N. O. Kaplan*: Methods in Enzymology, Academic Press, New York 1955, vol. I, p. 348.

Lactate Dehydrogenase

Lactate dehydrogenase, LDH (L-Lactate: NAD oxidoreductase, EC 1.1.1.27), the "reduzierende Gärungs-ferment" *(Warburg)*[1] was first crystallized from rat muscle in 1943[2]. The most extensively studied lactate dehydrogenases are the enzymes from skeletal[3,4] and heart muscle[5]. Lactate dehydrogenases from bacteria[6] and yeast[7] are not linked to the pyridine nucleotide coenzymes. In human organs the LDH activity decreases in the following order[8] (g. fresh weight basis): kidney > heart > skeletal muscle > pancreas > spleen > liver > lung > serum.

The activity of LDH of animal origin can be measured spectrophotometrically[2] with pyruvate and NADH (equation 1). Measurements of the activity by the colour reaction[9] of the 2,4-dinitrophenylhydrazone formed from the unreacted pyruvate are difficult because the NADH also forms a hydrazone which absorbs in the same region.

In other methods the NADH formed from lactate and NAD is measured directly[10,11] or after reaction with phenazine-methosulphate[12-14] or diaphorase*[15] and a tetrazolium salt. The lactate dehydrogenase activity in serum results from the presence of different enzyme proteins with the same action and substrate specificity, but of different origin. The lactate dehydrogenase in serum, which may originate from liver, heart, skeletal muscle, erythrocytes, tumour, etc., are not only different from one another, but themselves consist of several enzymatically active fractions which can be separated from each other[16-32]. Such enzymes which differ in their protein structure and therefore in the optimum conditions for their action, but have the same specificity (in this case towards L-lactate) are termed "isoenzymes"[43]. A method is described below which gives approximately optimum conditions for the measurement of LDH from heart and liver (Fig. 1).

Application of Method: In biochemistry and clinical chemistry.

UV-Assay with Pyruvate and NADH

Hans Ulrich Bergmeyer and Erich Bernt

Principle

(1)
$$\text{Pyruvate} + \text{NADH} + \text{H}^+ \xrightleftharpoons{\text{LDH}} \text{Lactate} + \text{NAD}^+$$

The equilibrium is far on the side of lactate and NAD. The LDH activity is determined by the rate of oxidation of NADH. The change in extinction at 340 (334, 365) nm is measured.

Optimum Conditions for Measurements

The most important characteristics for the assay of activity of the individual lactate dehydrogenases are their different substrate and pH optima. Measurements which are not carried out under optimum conditions naturally result in values for the activity which are too low. The optimum conditions for the measurements of the enzyme in serum after myocardial infarction, in liver damage, blood diseases and tumours have been more or less established[20-29,34,35]. The results shown in Fig. 1 were obtained in phosphate buffer at 25 °C[36]. The optima of activity on variation of the pyruvate concentration are pH-dependent. Pyruvate concentrations between 0.3 and 0.6 mM at pH 7.5 give near-optimum activities in human serum for the enzymes from liver and heart. The temperature of the measurements is 25 °C and the NADH concentration 0.18 mM. The dependence of the LDH activity on the NADH concentration is not shown in Fig. 1. NADH over the range of about 0.05 to 0.5 mM shows a wide activity optimum. With higher temperatures, e. g. 37 °C, higher substrate concentrations are required for optimum activity.

---

* NADH: lipoamide oxidoreductase, EC 1.6.4.3.

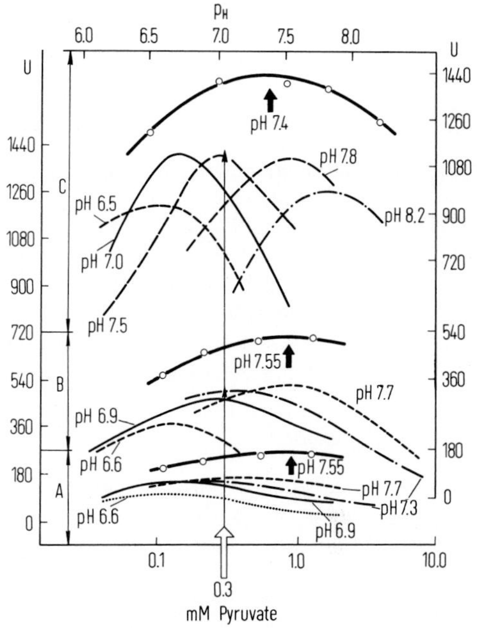

Fig. 1. Determination of optimum conditions for measurements of LDH activity in serum. 50 mM phosphate buffer; 25 °C.
Section A: Normal serum
Section B: Serum in hepatitis
Section C: Serum after myocardial infarction
Left hand and bottom co-ordinates (broken and thin-lined curves): Dependence of the activity on the pyruvate concentration with constant pH (shown on each curve). Right and upper co-ordinates (thick-lined curves o-o-o): Dependence of the activity on the pH with constant 0.3 mM pyruvate.

Measurements of different temperatures may require different measuring conditions (cf. p. 127). Nevertheless, results obtained under the same measuring conditions but at different temperatures were formerly compared with each other ("conversion factors" were determined). Such conversion factors may be correct if determined with a relatively large proband collective; however, they cannot be applied generally to the individual case (cf. p. 129). The value of the following relative reaction rates[37] thus lies in being able to appraise the temperature dependence of the reaction and at the most to compare qualitatively values up to the limit of normal.

°C	18°	19°	20°	21°	22°	23°	24°	25°	26°	27°
	1.95	1.8	1.65	1.5	1.35	1.2	1.08	*1.00*	0.92	0.85
°C	28°	29°	30°	31°	32°	33°	34°	35°	36°	37°
	0.79	0.73	0.67	0.62	0.58	0.54	0.50	0.46	0.43	0.40

Equipment

Spectrophotometer or spectrum-line photometer suitable for accurate measurements at 340, 334 or 365 nm, preferably with a constant temperature cuvette holder; water bath (25 °C); stopwatch.

Reagents*

1. Potassium dihydrogen phosphate, KH_2PO_4
2. Dipotassium hydrogen phosphate, K_2HPO_4
3. Sodium pyruvate commercial preparation, see p. 550.

4. Reduced nicotinamide-adenine dinucleotide, NADH disodium salt, NADH-Na_2; commercial preparation, see p. 545.
5. Sodium bicarbonate, A. R.

---

* Complete reagent kits are available commercially, see p. 558.

Purity of Reagents

All reagents must be A. R. quality or the purest grade available. The sodium pyruvate content should be at least 99%. Care should be taken that the NADH is free from inhibitors[37-39].

Preparation of Solutions (for ca. 25 determinations)

Prepare all solutions with fresh, doubly distilled water.

I. Phosphate/pyruvate (50 mM phosphate, pH 7.5; 0.63 mM pyruvate):
   Dissolve 700 mg. K_2HPO_4, 90 mg. KH_2PO_4 and 6.2 mg. Na pyruvate in distilled water and make up to 90 ml.

II. Reduced nicotinamide-adenine dinucleotide (ca. 11.3 mM β-NADH):
    Dissolve 14 mg. NADH-Na_2 and 15 mg. $NaHCO_3$ in 1.5 ml. distilled water.

Stability of Solutions

Store all solutions, stoppered, at 0–4 °C. Prepare the NADH solution (II) freshly each week. Deterioration of the buffer/substrate solution (I) is usually due to bacterial contamination, which can be prevented by addition of a few drops of chloroform.

Procedure

Collection, Treatment and Stability of Sample

Collection of sample:

Collect blood without venestasis. Addition of oxalate (1 mg./ml.), citrate (1 mg./ml.), fluoride (2 mg./ml.), heparin (0.2 mg./ml.) or EDTA (1 mg./ml.) has no adverse effects. Centrifuge at ca. 3000 g for 10 min. to obtain plasma or serum. Use only fresh serum or plasma completely free from haemolysis.

Stability of enzyme in sample:

Südhof et al.[40] have measured the loss of activity on storage of serum at various temperatures. Storage at 4 °C or freezing causes a 10–15% loss of activity in 12 hr. and 10–30% in 24 hr.; similar values are obtained at room temperature.

Assay System

Wavelength: 340 (Hg 334, Hg 365) nm; light path: 1 cm.; final volume: 3.15 ml.; 25 °C (constant temperature cuvette holder).
Bring the phosphate/pyruvate solution and the serum to 25 °C before the assay.

Pipette into cuvettes:			Concentration in assay mixture
Phosphate/pyruvate solution	(I)	3.00 ml.	48 mM buffer
			0.6 mM pyruvate
NADH solution	(II)	0.05 ml.	0.18 mM NADH
Serum		0.10 ml.	
Mix immediately, read extinction and start stopwatch. Repeat readings at exactly 1, 2 and 3 min. and calculate the mean extinction change.			

The ΔE/min. values at 365 nm should not be greater than 0.050. Otherwise dilute the serum 5–10-fold with physiological saline or read at shorter time intervals.

Calculations

The calculation formula (8) on p. 313 applies and therefore for this method the following relationships hold:

Wavelength:	334 nm	340 nm	365 nm
Volume activity	$= 5164 \times \Delta E$/min.	$5064 \times \Delta E$/min.	$9265 \times \Delta E$/min. [U/l.]

Precision of Method

With values around 200 U/l. the standard deviation is 10 U and the coefficient of variation 5%.

Normal Values

In human serum up to 195 U/l. (25 °C)[41]. In cerebrospinal fluid 4–10 U/l. (25 °C)[37].

Sources of Error

Effects of drugs and other therapeutic measures: None known.

Interference in the assay: With highly active serum a large proportion of the NADH can be oxidized between the addition of the serum and the first reading. The reaction then no longer proceeds under optimum conditions and too low activity is found. The first reading should therefore be made as rapidly as possible after addition of the serum. If the NADH contains inhibitors (p. 158), a progressive retardation of the reaction is observed. In this case the readings should be made at 15 or 30 sec. intervals.

Experience has shown that none of the substances present in blood interfere in the assay. The concentration of pyruvate in human serum is about 2 orders of magnitude lower than that in the assay mixture, and therefore contrary to several reports it cannot affect the optimum concentration.

The optimum concentration of pyruvate for serum LDH derived from other organs should be determined. For example, in carcinoma of the bronchus it is 2 mM[42].

Specificity of Method

A series of 2-oxo acids apart from pyruvate are reduced, and the rate decreases with increasing chain length[43]. Hydroxypyruvate reacts rapidly[44], phenylpyruvate and p-hydroxyphenylpyruvate only slowly, while oxaloacetate and 2-oxoglutarate are virtually inactive[44]. The relative reaction rates of various 2-hydroxy and oxo acids is different for the individual LDH isoenzymes[43,45]. LDH from spermatozoa reduces 2-oxobutyrate faster than pyruvate[46].

Details for Measurements in Tissues and Other Body Fluids

LDH is a cytoplasmic enzyme[42]; simple homogenization in a *Potter-Elvehjem* homogenizer (see p. 402) is sufficient to completely extract all the enzyme. The activity in tissues is determined in the supernatant fluid obtained after centrifugation of the homogenate at high speed; for measurements in, for example, liver needle biopsies 10 mg. fresh weight of tissue is sufficient[47].

The optimum conditions for human serum given in Fig. 1 do not necessarily hold for sera from other species or for organs or body fluids. The following concentrations are suitable for measurements on cerebrospinal fluid[48]: 0.8 to 20 mM NADH; 0.3 to 1 mM pyruvate; pH 6.5–7.4 (24 °C). Urine must be dialysed for at least 2 hr. before assay[49–51].

References

1 *O. Warburg:* Wasserstoffübertragende Fermente. Verlag Dr. W. Sänger, Berlin 1948, p. 40.
2 *F. Kubowitz & P. Ott,* Biochem. Z. *314,* 94 [1943].
3 *A. Kornberg* in *S. P. Colowick & N. O. Kaplan:* Methods in Enzymology. Academic Press, New York 1955, vol. I, p. 441.
4 *G. Beisenherz, J. H. Boltze, Th. Bücher, R. Czok, K. H. Garbade, E. Meyer-Arendt & G. Pfleiderer,* Z. Naturforsch. *8b,* 555 [1953].
5 *J. B. Neilands* in *S. P. Colowick & N. O. Kaplan:* Methods in Enzymology. Academic Press, New York 1955, vol. I, p. 449.
6 *J. Szulmajster, M. Gruenberg-Manago & C. Delavier-Klutekko,* Bull. Soc. Chim. biol. *35,* 1381 [1953].
7 *M. Dixon* in *S. P. Colowick & N. O. Kaplan:* Methods in Enzymology. Academic Press, New York 1955, vol. I, p. 444.
8 *F. Wroblewski,* Scand. J. Clin. & Lab. Invest. *10,* 230, Suppl. 31; Int. Congr. clin. Chem. Stockholm 1957.
9 *P. G. Cabaud, F. Wroblewski & V. Ruggiero,* Amer. J. clin. Pathol. *30,* 234 [1958].
10 *E. Amador, L. E. Dorfmann & W. E. C. Wacker,* Clin. Chem. *9,* 391 [1963].
11 *R. J. Gay, R. B. McComb & G. N. Bowers,* Clin. Chem. *14,* 740 [1968].
12 *M. M. Nachlas, S. J. Margulier, J. D. Goldberg & A. M. Seligman,* Anal. Biochem. *1,* 317 [1960].
13 *A. L. Babson & G. E. Phillips,* Clin. Chim. Acta *12,* 210 [1965].
14 *A. L. Babson,* Clin. Chim. Acta *16,* 121 [1967].
15 *W. J. Blaedel & G. P. Hicks,* Anal. Biochem. *4,* 476 [1962].
16 *Th. Wieland & G. Pfleiderer,* Biochem. Z. *329,* 112 [1957].
17 *G. Pfleiderer & D. Jeckel,* Biochem. Z. *329,* 370 [1957].
18 *Th. Wieland, G. Pfleiderer & F. Ortanderl,* Biochem. Z. *331,* 103 [1959].
19 *Th. Wieland, G. Pfleiderer, I. Haupt & W. Wörner,* Biochem. Z. *322,* 1 [1959].
20 *B. Hess,* Klin. Wschr. *36,* 985 [1958].
21 *B. Hess,* Ann. N. Y. Acad. Sci. *75,* 292 [1958].
22 *B. Hess* in *W. H. Hauss & H. Losse:* Struktur und Stoffwechsel des Herzmuskels. G. Thieme, Stuttgart 1959, p. 128.
23 *B. Hess & S. I. Walter,* Klin. Wschr. *38,* 1080 [1960].
24 *E. S. Vesell & A. G. Bearn,* Proc. Soc. exp. Biol. Med. *94,* 96 [1957].
25 *E. S. Vesell & A. G. Bearn,* J. clin. Invest. *37,* 672 [1958].
26 *E. S. Vesell & A. G. Bearn,* Ann. N. Y. Acad. Sci. *75,* 286 [1958].
27 *B. R. Hill,* Cancer Res. *16,* 460 [1956].
28 *F. W. Sayre & B. R. Hill,* Proc. Soc. exp. Biol. Med. *96,* 695 [1957].
29 *B.R.Hill,*Ann N. Y. Acad. Sci. *75,* 304 [1958].
30 *R. J. Wieme & L. Demeulenaere,* Acta gastro-ent. belg. *22,* 69 [1959].
31 *N. O. Kaplan, M. M. Ciotti, M. Hamolsky & R. E. Bieber,* Science (Washington) *131,* 392 [1960].
32 *R. Richterich, E. Gautier, W. Egli, K. Zuppinger & E. Rossi,* Klin. Wschr. *39,* 346 [1961].
33 *F. Wroblewski & K. Gregory:* Proc. 14th Internat. Congr. clin. Chem. Edinburgh, 1960. E. & S. Livinstone Ltd., Edinburgh & London 1961, p. 62.

34 *R. E. Thiers & B. Vallee*, Ann. N. Y. Acad. Sci. *75*, 214 [1957].
35 *E. Schmidt & F. W. Schmidt*, personal communication.
36 *H. U. Bergmeyer*, discourse on the Congr. f. Lab. & Med., Berlin, April 1961.
37 *J. King:* Practical Clinical Enzymology. D. van Nostrand Comp. Ltd., London 1965, p. 87.
38 *R. B. McComb & R. J. Gay*, Clin. Chem. *14*, 754 [1968].
39 *A. Haertel, R. Helger & H. Lang*, Z. klin. Chem. and Biochem. *6*, 259 [1968].
40 *H. Südhof & E. Woetzel*, Klin. Wschr. *38*, 1165 [1960].
41 *D. Amelung:* Fermentdiagnostik interner Erkrankungen. G. Thieme Verlag, Stuttgart 1964.
42 *Th. Buecher & P. Baum*, discourse Dtsch. Kongr. f. ärztl. Fortbildung, Berlin 1958.
43 *A. Meister*, J. biol. Chem. *184*, 117 [1950].
44 *H. A. Stafford, A. Mogaldi & B. Vennesland*, J. biol. Chem. *207*, 621 [1954].
45 *C. L. Markert & F. Moller*, Proc. Nat. Acad. Sci. USA *45*, 753 [1959].
46 *U. A. Withycombe & J. H. Wilkinson*, Biochem. J. *93*, 11 P [1964].
47 *E. Schmidt, F. W. Schmidt & E. Wildhirt*, Klin. Wschr. *36*, 172 [1958].
48 *H. A. Tyler & L. Bromberger*, J. nerv. ment. Dis. *130*, 54 [1960].
49 *M. F. Massod, R. J. Franey, M. E. Therrien, P. T. Rideout & M. T. Babcock*, Techn. Bull. Reg. Med. Technologists *34*, 177 [1964].
50 *L. E. Dorfman, E. Amador & W. E. C. Wacker*, J. Amer. med. Ass. *184*, 1 [1963].
51 *W. E. C. Wacker, E. Amador, L. E. Dorfman & Th. S. Zimmerman*, Ärztl. Lab. *11*, 204 [1965].

Colorimetric Assay with L-Lactate, NAD Phenazine Methosulphate and INT

Hans Ulrich Bergmeyer and Erich Bernt

Principle

(1) $$\text{Lactate} + NAD^+ \xrightleftharpoons{LDH} \text{Pyruvate} + NADH + H^+$$

(2) $NADH + \text{Phenazine methosulphate} + H^+ \rightarrow NAD^+ + \text{Reduced phenazine methosulphate}$

(3) Reduced phenazine methosulphate $+$ Tetrazolium salt $\rightarrow$ Formazan $+$ Phenazine methosulphate

Nachlas[1] and *Babson*[2,4] have described relatively simple methods in which the NADH formed in reaction (1) in the presence of phenazine methosulphate (PMS) and various tetrazolium salts is reduced to strongly coloured formazans. The most suitable salt is 2-(p-iodophenyl)-3-(p-nitrophenyl)-5-phenyltetrazolium chloride (INT)[2,3].

Optimum Conditions for Measurements

Optimum activity is obtained at pH 8.55 with 6 mM NAD and 45 mM L-lactate[4]. Optimum reaction rates in the indicator reaction (2) are obtained with 0.9 mM INT and 0.32 mM PMS[2]. According to [2] a concentration of 1.5 mM NAD is sufficient for this assay; excess has no further effect.

Equipment

Colorimeter suitable for measurements between 500 and 550 nm; water bath (37 °C); stop-watch.

Reagents*

1. Tris-hydroxymethyl-aminomethane, tris
2. L-Lactic acid, 1 M
3. Nicotinamide-adenine dinucleotide, NAD

   as free acid, commercial preparation, see p. 545.
4. 2-(p-Iodophenyl)-3-(p-nitrophenyl)-5-phenyltetrazolium chloride, INT
5. Phenazine methosulphate, PMS
6. Dipotassium oxalate, $K_2C_2O_4 \cdot H_2O$, A. R.
7. Ethylenediaminetetra-acetate disodium salt, EDTA-$Na_2H_2 \cdot 2H_2O$, A. R.
8. Hydrochloric acid, 0.5 N
9. Sodium hydroxide, 1 N

Purity of Reagents

All reagents must be A. R. grade or the purest available.

Preparation of Solutions

Prepare all solutions with fresh, doubly distilled water. Sterilize the containers first.

I. Tris buffer (1 M; pH 8.5):
   Dissolve 12.1 g. tris in 50 ml. distilled water, adjust to pH 8.5 with ca. 6.3 ml. 5 N HCl and dilute to 100 ml. with distilled water.
II. Substrate solution (0.1 M L-lactate):
   Adjust 10 ml. 1 M L-lactic acid to pH 5.5 with 1 N NaOH and dilute to 100 ml. with distilled water.
III. Colour reagent (7.5 mM NAD; 4.0 mM. INT; 1.6 mM PMS):
   Dissolve 50 mg. INT with stirring in 20 ml. distilled water. On complete solution, add 125 mg. NAD and 12.5 mg. PMS, dissolve and dilute to 25 ml. with distilled water.
IV. Blank solution (11 mM oxalate; 5.4 mM EDTA):
   Dissolve 0.2 g. $K_2C_2O_4 \cdot H_2O$ and 0.2 g. EDTA-$Na_2H_2 \cdot 2H_2O$ in distilled water and make up to 100 ml.

Stability of Solutions

Store all solutions, stoppered, in a refrigerator at ca. 4 °C. The colour reagent (III) is extremely sensitive to light and must be protected from it at all times. It is stable for several weeks. Preserve the tris buffer (I) and substrate solution (II) with a few drops of chloroform; they are stable for at least 4 weeks. The blank solution is stable for at least 6 months.

Procedure

Collection, Treatment and Stability

Collection of sample:
Collect blood without venestasis. Addition of 1 mg. oxalate/ml., 1 mg. citrate/ml., 2 mg. fluoride/ml., 0.2 mg. heparin/ml. or 1 mg. EDTA/ml. has no adverse effects. Centrifuge at ca. 3000 g to obtain plasma or serum. Use only fresh serum completely free from haemolysis.

Stability of enzyme in sample: See p. 576.

---

* Complete reagent kits are available commercially, see p. 558.

Assay System

Wavelength: 500–550 nm; light path: 1 cm.; final volume: 6.00 ml.; 37 °C; read against a blank, which contains blank solution (IV) instead of substrate solution (II).

Pipette into test tubes:			Concentration in assay mixture
Buffer solution	(I)	0.20 ml.	0.2 M tris
Serum		0.10 ml.	
Substrate solution	(II)	0.50 ml.	50 mM L-lactate
Mix and incubate for ca. 5 min. at 37 °C			
Colour reagent	(III)	0.20 ml.	1.5 mM NAD; 0.8 mM INT 0.32 mM PMS
Mix and incubate exactly for a further 5 min. at 37 °C.			
Hydrochloric acid 0.1 N		5.00 ml.	83 mM HCl
Mix and within 20 min. read the extinction against the blank.			

With results higher than 200 U/l. dilute the serum 1:5 with physiological saline and repeat the assay.

Calculations

The calculations are best made on the basis of control sera of known activity. As the standard curve is not strictly linear, it is necessary to use several control sera with different activities.

Precision of Method

With values around 100 U/l. the standard deviation is 5 U/l. The coefficient of variation is 5%.

Normal Values

In human serum 25 to 78 mU/ml. (37 °C)[5].

Sources of Error

Effects of drugs and other therapeutic measures: None known.

Interference in the assay: Not every batch of INT is suitable; a preliminary test should be made to check whether on reduction of the INT with ascorbic acid sufficient intensity of colour is obtained[2].
If diluted serum, urine or diluted tissue extract is used, the protein concentration is often not sufficient to hold the difficultly soluble formazan in solution. In this case 1% ethoxy oleyl alcohol must be added to buffer solution (I).

Specificity of Method

See "UV-Assay with Pyruvate and NADH", p. 574.

Details for Measurements in Tissues

See "UV-Assay with Pyruvate and NADH", p. 574.

References

1 *M. M. Nachlas, S. J. Margulier, J. D. Goldberg & A. M. Seligman,* Anal. Biochem. *1*, 317 [1960].
2 *A. L. Babson & G. E. Phillips,* Clin. Chim. Acta *12*, 210 [1965].
3 *A. L. Babson,* Clin. Chim. Acta *16*, 121 [1967].
4 *R. J. Gay, R. B. McComb & G. N. Bowers,* Clin. Chem. *14*, 740 [1968].
5 *R. O. Briere, J. A. Preston & J. G. Batsakis,* Am. J. Clin. Pathol. *45*, 544 [1966].

Method for Automatic Analysers

Bernard Klein

The measurement of lactate dehydrogenase activity in enzyme preparations and tissue extracts with automatic analysers was first developed by *Schwartz* et al.,[1]. *Strandjord* and *Clayson*[2] then described an automatic spectrophotometric method for serum that deviated in many respects from the flow system of the former method. In both methods the decrease in extinction due to oxidation of NADH in the reaction with pyruvate as substrate is measured. *Morgenstern* et al.[3] followed the reverse reaction, which over a wide range of lactate concentrations follows zero order kinetics, as *Amador* et al.[4] had shown previously.

(1) $$\text{Lactate} + \text{NAD}^+ \rightleftharpoons \text{Pyruvate} + \text{NADH} + \text{H}^+$$

All the more recent automated assay methods have employed this principle, irrespective of whether the assays are colorimetric[5,6] or fluorimetric[7,8].
Three automated spectrophotometric methods and a fluorimetric method are available.

Equipment

Sampler II, proportioning pump, heating bath with coil of suitable length and adjustable thermoregulator, photometer with flow-through cuvette (1.5 cm.) and recorder.

UV-Spectrophotometric Assay[3]

This method[3] has the simplest manifold system; the increase in extinction at 340 nm due to the formation of NADH is measured.

Reagents

1. L-(+)-Lactic acid, 85%, A. R.
2. 2-Amino-2-methyl-1-propanol, 50% (w/w).
3. Nicotinamide-adenine dinucleotide, NAD free acid, commercial preparation, see p. 545.
4. Reduced nicotinamide-adenine dinucleotide, NADH disodium salt, NADH-Na$_2$, commercial preparation, see p. 545.
5. Sodium hydroxide, 5 N
6. Hydrochloric acid, 6 N
7. Control serum

Preparation of Solutions

I. 2-Amino-2-methyl-1-propanol (0.75 M):
    Dilute 285 ml. 2-amino-2-methyl-1-propanol with distilled water to 1 000 ml.

II. 2-Amino-2-methyl-1-propanol buffer (0.67 M; pH 9.0):
    Adjust 89.6 ml. of the 0.75 M solution (I) to pH 9.0 with 6 N HCl and dilute to 100 ml. with distilled water.

III. Lactate control buffer (0.33 M lactate; pH 9.0):
    Mix 35.8 ml. 85% lactic acid with 896 ml. 2-amino-2-methyl-1-propanol buffer (solution I), adjust to pH 9.0 with 5 N NaOH and dilute to 1 000 ml.

IV. Lactate/NAD solution (82 mM lactate; 7.5 mM NAD; 188 mM buffer; pH 9.0):
    Dissolve 1.21 g. NAD in 250 ml. lactate control buffer (III).

V. NADH standard solutions (1.04 mM; 2.07 mM; 3.10 mM; 4.13 mM):
    Dissolve 16.25 mg. NADH-Na_2 in 5 ml. 2-amino-2-methyl-1-propanol buffer (solution II) (4.13 mM stock solution). Dilute 0.5 ml., 1.0 ml. and 1.5 ml. of this stock solution with 1.5 ml., 1.0 ml. and 0.5 ml. buffer (solution II).

VI. Enzyme control serum:
    Use the commercially available control sera according to the instructions of the manufacturers.
    Alternatively, according to *Amador* et al.[4] mixed serum can be used. This should be carefully diluted with physiological saline.

Stability of Solutions

The buffer solutions are stable at 0–4 °C. The lactate solutions are stable in a refrigerator, as long as bacterial contamination is avoided. Prepare only the daily requirement of lactate/NAD solution (IV). The standard NADH solution (V) can be stored for about 1 week in a refrigerator.

Procedure

For flow scheme, see Fig. 1. Use of recorder paper with extinction scale makes the calculations easier. Chart speed, 18 inch/hr. (45.6 cm./hr.). Determine the incubation time each day to allow for changes in the manifold system. The incubation time is the rate of flow of a coloured solution (e.g. 1% $K_2Cr_2O_7$) between points A and B; measure this with a stopwatch. Pump lactate control solution (III) for about 5 min. through the manifold, adjust the base line of the recorder to E = 0.010 and measure the NADH standard solutions (V) or samples at a rate of 40 samples/hr. After this control analysis pump through lactate/NAD solution (IV) instead of solution III and repeat the assay procedure. Check the correct functioning of the analyser by the assay of control sera (VI).

Calculations

The activity is expressed in μmole NAD reacting per min. per ml. (U/ml.). The extinctions measured in the samples with lactate/NAD solution minus those measured with lactate solution, namely ΔE, are used to obtain the NADH concentrations from the standard curve and these are divided by the incubation time.

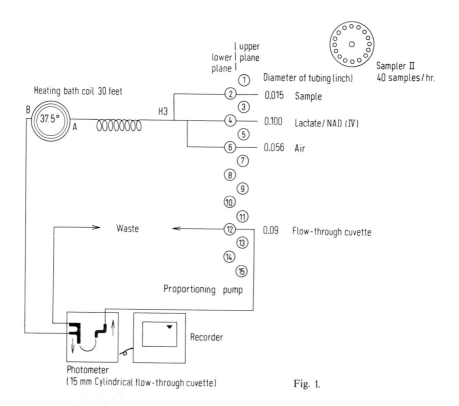

Fig. 1.

For example, if $\Delta E = 0.385$ corresponds to a concentration of 0.190 μmole NADH/ml. and the incubation time is 5 min., then the activity is 0.038 U/ml. (38 mU/ml.). With 0.1 ml. samples this is 770 mU/ml. sample (37.5 °C).

Method with Copper (Cu^{2+})/Neocuproin

Method of *Morgenstern* et al.[3]. The formation of a Cu^+-neocuproin chelate according to reactions (2) and (3) is measured at 455 nm.

(2) $$NADH + Cu^{2+} \rightarrow NAD^+ + Cu^+$$

(3) $$Cu^+ + Neocuproin \rightarrow Cu^+\text{-neocuproin chelate}$$

Reagents

Additional to those listed above (p. 582):
7. Sulphuric acid, 0.433 N
8. Copper sulphate, $CuSO_4 \cdot 5H_2O$

9. Neocuproin, 2,9-dimethyl-1,10-
   phenanthroline

Preparation of Solutions

Additional to solutions I–VI on p. 583:

VII. Copper (Cu^{2+})/neocuproin reagent:

Dissolve 1 g. $CuSO_4 \cdot 5 H_2O$ in 0.433 N H_2SO_4 and make up to 100 ml. Dilute 75 ml. of this solution with 0.433 N H_2SO_4 to about 950 ml., and then dissolve in this solution 1.74 g. neocuproin with stirring (magnetic) and then dilute to 1000 ml. with 0.433 N H_2SO_4. The solution is stable indefinitely.

Procedure

Flow scheme, see Fig. 2. The incubation time must be measured each day. Pump the lactate control solution (III) through the manifold system for about 5 min. and then suck through copper/neocuproin reagent (VII). When the combined reagent solutions pass through the flow-through cuvette, set the base line of the recorder to E = 0.010. Measure NADH standard solutions (V) and samples at a rate of 40 samples/hr. After this control analysis suck through lactate/NAD solution (IV) instead of solution III, adjust the base line of the recorder to E = 0.010 and repeat the measurements.

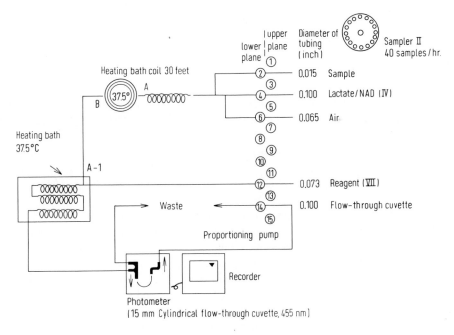

Fig. 2.

Calculations

The calculations are exactly as described for the UV-spectrophotometric method (583).

Method with Diaphorase and Tetrazolium Salt[6]

Capps et al.[5] use as electron carrier phenazine methosulphate (PMS) which reacts with a tetrazolium salt. The extinction of the resulting formazan is measured at 580 nm. This automated method has however some technical difficulties. We have modified the method which *Hochella* and *Weinhouse*[6] developed for urine for both single and four channel measurements of LDH activity in serum. Diaphorase is the intermediate electron carrier and the same tetrazolium salt is used, but the formazan formation is measured at 505 nm.

(4)   Tetrazolium salt $+$ NADH $+$ H$^+$ $\xrightarrow{\text{diaphorase/PMS}}$ NAD$^+$ $+$ Formazan

Reagents

1. DL-Lactic acid, 85%
2. Sodium hydroxide, 1 N
3. Potassium dihydrogen phosphate, KH$_2$PO$_4$
4. Tris-hydroxymethyl-aminomethane, tris
5. Hydrochloric acid, 1 N
6. Diaphorase
   e. g. from Worthington. Dissolve the contents of the ampoule in 5.5 ml. distilled water before use.
7. Bovine albumin
   fraction V, powder
8. Nicotinamide-adenine dinucleotide, NAD
   free acid; commercial preparation, see p. 545.
9. 3-(p-Nitrophenyl)-2-(p-iodophenyl)-5-phenyl tetrazolium salt (INT)
   Lyophilizate in ampoules
10. Triton X-100
11. Control serum

Preparation of Solutions

I. Phosphate buffer (1.0 M; pH 7.4):
Dissolve 136 g. KH$_2$PO$_4$ in 800 ml. distilled water. Dissolve in this solution 33.0 g. NaOH, allow to cool, check the pH and if necessary, adjust with 1 N NaOH or 1 N HCl and dilute to 1000 ml. with distilled water.

II. Phosphate control buffer (67 mM, pH 7.4; 0.15% albumin):
Dilute 67 ml. phosphate buffer (I) with 900 ml. distilled water; add 1.5 g. albumin and stir until completely dissolved. If necessary, adjust the pH and then dilute to 1000 ml. with distilled water.

III. Lactate/buffer solution (140 mM lactate; 100 mM tris, pH 8.8):
Dissolve 6.0 g. NaOH in about 50 ml. distilled water in a volumetric flask. Slowly allow 15 ml. lactic acid to run into the warm solution and stir magnetically for at least 30 min. Dilute with 500 ml. distilled water, slowly stir in 12.1 g. tris, dilute to 950 ml. with distilled water and adjust to pH 8.8 $\pm$ 0.05 (25 °C) with about 7.5 ml. 1 N HCl. Dilute to 1000 ml. with distilled water, add 1.5 ml. Triton X-100, mix, filter and store in a refrigerator.

IV. Diaphorase/nicotinamide-adenine dinucleotide (10 mM NAD; 1.5 mg. protein/ml.):
Stir 5.5 ml. diaphorase into 175 ml. control buffer (II), add 1.2 g. NAD, continue stirring until dissolved and make up to 200 ml. with buffer. Store the solution in an ice bath. This amount is sufficient for a 10 hr. period of measurements.

V. 3-(p-Nitrophenyl)-2-(p-iodiphenyl)-5-phenyl-tetrazolium chloride, INT (0.625 g./l.):
Dissolve 0.625 g. INT in distilled water and make up to 1000 ml.; store at room temperature in a brown flask.

Stability of Solutions

The buffered substrate (III) is stable for at least 2 weeks at room temperature. The control buffer containing albumin (solution II) should be prepared freshly each week or stored deep-frozen in suitable portions. The diaphorase/NAD solution (IV) should be prepared freshly each day. The INT solution (V) is stable for about 1 month if stored in a brown flask at room temperature.

Procedure

Flow scheme, see Fig. 3. Determine the incubation time each day. For other details, see method with Cu^{2+}/neocuproin, p. 585.

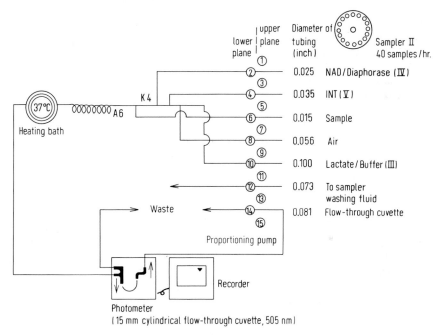

Fig. 3.

Calculations

See UV-spectrophotometric method, p. 583.

Fluorimetric Method[8]

The fluorimetric measurement of NADH is considerably more sensitive and has other advantages (*Lowry* et al.[9]). *Passen* and *Gennaro*[8] overcame the technical problems, which occur due to the fluorescence of serum proteins and other non-specific fluorescence; the enzymatically formed NADH is dialysed from the reaction mixture, before the fluorescence measurements are made.

Equipment

As described on p. 579, with the addition of a dialyser unit and fluorimeter with flow-through cuvette.

Reagents

1. Tris-hydroxymethyl-aminomethane, tris
2. Sodium lactate, syrup, 85%
3. Hydrochloric acid, 1 N
4. Hydroxylamine hydrochloride
5. Sodium hydroxide, 1 N
6. Brij-35
   from Technicon

7. Nicotinamide-adenine dinucleotide, NAD
   free acid, commercial preparation, see p. 545.
8. Control serum

Preparation of Solutions

I. Tris buffer (50 mM; pH 8.8):
   Dissolve 6.05 g. tris in 900 ml. distilled water, adjust to pH 8.8 with conc. HCl and dilute to 1000 ml. with distilled water.

II. Lactate/buffer solution (40 mM lactate; 35 mM tris, pH 8.8):
   Mix into 700 ml. tris buffer (I), 5.36 ml. lactic acid and 2.8 g. hydroxylamine hydrochloride. Adjust to pH 8.8 with 1.0 N NaOH and dilute to 1000 ml. with distilled water. Add 0.5 ml. Brij-35.

III. Nicotinamide-adenine dinucleotide, NAD (10 mM):
   Dissolve 330 mg. NAD in distilled water and make up to 50 ml.

Stability of Solutions

The buffer (I) and the lactate/buffer solution (II) are stable indefinitely, if stored in a refrigerator to prevent bacterial growth. The NAD solution (III) is stable for about 1 week.

Procedure and Calculations

Flow system, see Fig. 4. Pump the reagents through the analyser. As soon as the liquid passes through the flow-through cuvette adjust the base line of the recorder to 5 (arbitrary) units. Re-adjust after the instrument is steady. Prepare a standard curve according to[8]: dilute 0.1–0.9 ml. control serum with 0.8% sodium chloride solution to 1.0 ml. and measure. NADH standard solutions can also be used for standardization according to the method on p. 581. Plot the fluorescence values of these standards against their known LDH activity. Read off the LDH activity of unknown serum samples from this standard curve.

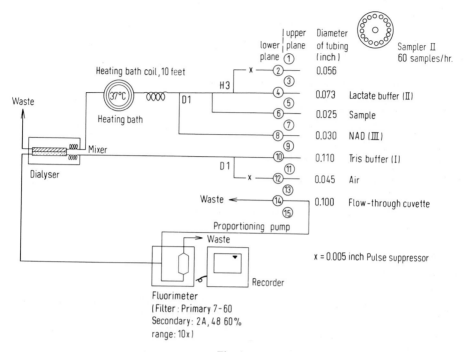

Fig. 4.

References

1 M. K. Schwartz, G. Kessler & O. Bodansky, J. biol. Chem., 236, 1207 [1961].
2 P. E. Strandjord & K. Clayson, Clin. Chem., 10, 635 [1964].
3 S. Morgenstern, R. Flor, G. Kessler & B. Klein, Anal. Biochem., 13, 149 [1965].
4 E. Amador, L. E. Dorfman & W. E. C. Wacker, Clin, Chem., 12, 406 [1966].
5 R. D. Capps, J. G. Batsakis, R. O. Briere & R. R. L. Calam, Clin. Chem., 12, 406 [1966].
6 N. Hochella & S. Weinhouse, Anal. Biochem., 13, 322 [1965]. Personal communication from J. Levine,
   Technicon Corporation, Tarrytown, New York, 10591.
7 L. Brooks & H. G. Olken, Clin. Chem., 11, 748 [1965].
8 S. Passen & W. Gennaro, Am. J. Clin. Pathol., 46, 69 [1966].
9 O. H. Lowry, N. R. Roberts & J. I. Kapphahn, J. biol. Chem., 224, 1047 [1957].

Lactate Dehydrogenase, Isoenzymes

The individual types of LDH proteins (see 574) can be separated from each other by electrophoresis[1-4] or chromatography[5-10]. Liver and skeletal muscle LDH, mainly LDH_4 and LDH_5, can be determined separately in serum even in the presence of LDH from heart, kidney and blood (mainly LDH_1 and LDH_2). In addition the LDH isoenzymes can be differentiated by heat denaturation[11-16] or by inactivation in the presence of high urea concentrations[17-22].

The best method of separating LDH_1 + LDH_2 from other isoenzymes is by adsorption on DEAE-Sephadex[23,24]. For comparative studies, see[25].

Application of Method: In biochemistry and clinical chemistry.

UV-Assay after Separation on DEAE-Sephadex

Hans Ulrich Bergmeyer and Erich Bernt

Principle

The LDH activity is measured before and after treatment of the sample with DEAE-Sephadex A-50. Under defined conditions DEAE-Sephadex A-50 adsorbs the heart muscle-type LDH protein, while the liver-type LDH remains in solution*. For the principle of the spectrophotometric assay, see p. 574.

Optimum Conditions for Measurements

The most important characteristics of LDH proteins in relation to the assay of their activities are their different substrate and pH optima. These have been studied, in particular by *Pfleiderer*[26] and *McComb*[27]. The activity is not very dependent on the NADH concentration. The optimum concentration for LDH_1, LDH_3 and LDH_5 is 0.15 mM. Activity is very dependent on the pyruvate concentration: LDH_1 requires 0.75 mM pyruvate, whereas LDH_5 requires 1.7 mM[27].

Equipment

Spectrophotometer or spectrum-line photometer suitable for accurate measurements at 340, 334 or 365 nm, preferably with constant temperature cuvette holder; water bath (25 °C); bench centrifuge; stopwatch.

Reagents**

Additional to 1–4 on p. 575:

5. Sodium dihydrogen phosphate, $NaH_2PO_4 \cdot H_2O$
6. Disodium hydrogen phosphate, $Na_2HPO_4 \cdot 12H_2O$

7. Sodium chloride, A. R.
8. DEAE-Sephadex A-50
   from *Serva*, Heidelberg; capacity ca. 3.5 mEquiv./g.

---

* The method is also suitable for the differentiation in aqueous tissue extracts of other enzymes and proteins apart from the LDH isoenzymes, providing that they are specifically adsorbed by DEAE-Sephadex. For example, serum free from α-globulin can be produced by this method.

** Or a complete reagent kit (see p. 558) from Boehringer Mannheim, GmbH. Other preparations have not been tested.

Purity of Reagents

All reagents must be A. R. grade or purest quality available. DEAE-Sephadex A-50 must have sufficient adsorbing capacity. NADH must be free from inhibitors.

Preparation of Solutions

Prepare all solutions with fresh, doubly distilled water.
Additional to I and II on p. 576.

III. Phosphate buffer (20 mM; pH 6.0):
Dissolve 0.885 g. $Na_2HPO_4 \cdot 12H_2O$ and 2.36 g. $NaH_2PO_4 \cdot H_2O$ with water, adjust to pH 6.0 with diluted HCl or NaOH, dilute to 1 000 ml. with distilled water.

IV. DEAE-Sephadex A-50 suspension (ca. 2%, w/v):
Suspend 1 g. DEAE-Sephadex A-50 in 50 ml. phosphate buffer (solution III) in a beaker, mix thoroughly, allow to sediment for ca. 45 min. and then decant the buffer from the sedimented material. Repeat the sedimentation procedure three times. Resuspend the uniformly fine sediment in phosphate buffer (solution III) to give a final volume of 50 ml.

Stability of Solutions

See p. 576. Store the DEAE-Sephadex A-50 at ca. 4 °C. Preserve the suspension with several drops of chloroform; it is stable for several months.

Procedure

Collection, Treatment and Stability of Sample

Collection of sample:

See UV-assay, p. 576.

Stability of enzyme in sample:

See UV-assay, p. 576.

Adsorption on DEAE-Sephadex A-50:

Suspend the DEAE-Sephadex evenly by shaking. Use pipettes with a wide (or broken) tip. In a 10 ml. centrifuge tube, thoroughly mix 1.00 ml. serum with 1.00 ml. DEAE-Sephadex A-50 suspension and allow to stand for 10 min. at 25 °C. Centrifuge at ca. 3000 rpm. for 5 min., carefully pour the supernatant fluid into a dry test tube and take 0.1 ml. for the assay.

Assay System

See UV-assay, p. 577.

Calculations

Use the formula on p. 577 to calculate the activity in serum and in the supernatant fluid after adsorption. The activity is obtained in U/l. of solution taken for assay.

As 1 g. DEAE-Sephadex A-50 binds 10 ml. of water, the "solute space" with 20 mg. DEAE-Sephadex in 2.0 ml. total volume is $2.0-0.2 = 1.8$ ml.

If A_1 = Activity per ml. serum

A_2 = Activity per ml. supernatant fluid,

the fraction of LDH activity not absorbed as a percentage of the total activity is

$$\% \, LDH_{liver-type} = \frac{100 \times 1.8 \, A_2}{A_1}$$

and the percentage of LDH adsorbed is

$$\% \, LDH_{heart-type} = 100 \times \left(\frac{1 - 1.8 \, A_2}{A_1} \right)$$

Precision of Method

If the adsorption is taken into account the coefficient of variation is ca. $\pm 6\%$. For the precision of the determination of activity, see p. 577.

Normal Values

The adsorption values for sera with normal LDH activity are between 30 and 60%[28].

Sources of Error

Effects of drugs and other therapeutic measures: None known.

Interference in the assay technique: Insufficient capacity of the DEAE-Sephadex leads to incomplete adsorption of the heart-type isoenzymes. Other sources of error, see p. 577.

Specificity of Method

See UV-assay p. 577.

References

1 *Th. Wieland & G. Pfleiderer*, Biochem. Z. *329*, 112 [1957].
2 *G. Pfleiderer & D. Jeckel*, Biochem. Z. *329*, 370 [1957].
3 *Th. Wieland, G. Pfleiderer & F. Ortanderl*, Biochem. Z. *331*, 103 [1959].
4 *Th. Wieland, G. Pfleiderer, I. Haupt & W. Woerner*, Biochem. Z. *332*, 1 [1959].
5 *B. Hess*, Klin. Wschr. *36*, 985 [1958].
6 *B. Hess*, Ann. N. Y. Acad. Sci. *75*, 292 [1958].
7 *B. Hess* in *W. A. Hauss & H. Losse:* Struktur und Stoffwechsel des Herzmuskels. G. Thieme Verlag, Stuttgart, 1959, p. 128.
8 *B. Hess & S. I. Walter*, Klin. Wschr. *38*, 1080 [1960].
9 *B. Hess & S. I. Walter*, Klin. Wschr. *39*, 213 [1961].
10 *B. Hess & S. I. Walter*, Ann. N. Y. Acad. Sci. *94*, 890 [1961].
11 *H. Wuest, H. Schoen & G. Berg*, Klin. Wschr. *40*, 1169 [1962].
12 *L. Paumier & A. W. Rotthauwe*, Enzymol. biol. clin. *3*, 87 [1963].
13 *A. v. Orelli & U. C. Dubach*, Klin. Wschr. *42*, 58 [1964].
14 *H. Wuest, E. Arnold & H. Schoen*, Klin. Wschr. *43*, 500 [1964].
15 *R. L. Bell*, Techn. Bull. *33*, 118 [1963].

16 *P. E. Strandjord & K. J. Clayson*, J. Lab. Clin. Med. *58*, 962 [1961].
17 *A. Konttinen & S. Lindy*, Nature *208*, 782 [1965].
18 *S. Lindy & A. Konttinen*, Nature *209*, 79 [1966].
19 *S. Lindy & A. Konttinen*, Clin. chim. Acta *14*, 615 [1966].
20 *A. Konttinen & S. Lindy*, Clin. chim. Acta *16*, 377 [1967].
21 *S. G. Welshman & E. C. Rixon*, Clin. chim. Acta *19*, 121 [1968].
22 *A. E. H. Emery, G. E. Moores & V. Hoaeson*, Clin. chim. Acta *19*, 159 [1968].
23 *R. Richterich & A. Burger*, Enzymol. biol. clin. *3*, 65 [1963].
24 *R. Richterich, P. Schafroth & H. Aebi*, Clin. chim. Acta *8*, 178 [1963].
25 *H. Wuest & G. Thusse*, Ärztl. Laboratorium *12*, 97 [1966].
26 *E. D. Wachsmuth & G. Pfleiderer*, Biochem. Z. *336*, 545 [1963].
27 *R. J. Gay, R. B. McComb & G. N. Bowers*, Clin. Chemistry *14*, 740 [1968].
28 *D. Amelung*, Dtsch. med. Wschr. *88*, 1940 [1963].

Measurements after Electrophoretic Separation

Roger Jozef Wieme

Lactate dehydrogenase, LDH (L-Lactate: NAD oxidoreductase, EC 1.1.1.27) was the first enzyme for which the existence of isoenzymes was demonstrated with certainty[1-5]. The elucidation of the structural[6-10] and functional[11-15] basis of this phenomenon was a decisive stage in the development of the isoenzyme concept. In virtually all extracts of tissues from higher animals it is possible to separate by electrophoresis 5 fractions with LDH activity. They are designated LDH 1, LDH 2, LDH 3, LDH 4, and LDH 5 in order of decreasing electrophoretic mobility at slightly alkaline pH. All 5 LDH isoenzymes have the same molecular weight of ca. 130000. As a rule they migrate equidistant from one another in an electrophoretic field; from this it can be concluded that the difference in charge from one fraction to the next is similar. *Markert*[16] was able to obtain a dissociation into subunits by freezing in 1 M NaCl, and after restoration of the original conditions these recombined to the original units. Dissociation of LDH fractions is also easily achieved with guanidine hydrochloride, preferably in the presence of β-mercaptoethanol[7].

From these observations and from studies of genetic variants[17] it is now generally accepted that multiplicity of LDH depends on the synthesis of two different subunits A and B under regulation of two structural genes. Immediately after their synthesis they randomly associate in groups of four subunits. The concentration ratio of the 5 fractions in a given cell is represented by a Newton binominal distribution of 4th power $(p+q)^4$, where p and q are the rates of synthesis of subunits A and B. The terms A and B refer to subunits which are found predominantly in liver and heart respectively. LDH 1 can therefore be represented by 4 B and LDH 5 by 4 A, while LDH isoenzymes 2, 3 and 4 have the structure 3 B 1 A, 2A 2B and 3A 1B. LDH 2. 3 and 4 are molecular hybrids with properties in agreement with this concept because they lie between those of LDH 1 and LDH 5.

If genetic variants occur in one of the subunits, as is the case in deer mouse[17], horse[18], humans[19-22], pigeon[23], primates[24], trout[25] and many other fish[26,27], complex situations can occur. If, for example 2 electrophoretically different types of subunit A are produced, there will be a total of 15 distinct LDH fractions: 4B, 3B 1A′ + 3B 1A′, 2B 2A + 2B 2A′ + 2B 1A 1A′, 1B 3A + 1B 3A′ + 1B 2A 1A′ + 1B 2A′ 1A, 4A + 4A′ + 3A 1A′ + 2A 2A′ + 1A 3A′.

The A- and B-subunits are distinct, immunologically different proteins. The A or B subunits of different animal species are very similar to one another and those of different tissues of a species are identical. However, in the mouse there appear to be two different types of the A subunit, which are not allele-determined, and are present in tissue-specific proportions[28].

The particular isoenzyme concentration ratio of a cell is stable, because under physiological conditions there appears to be no dissociation and reassociation. The concentration ratio in tissues is the sum of the concentration ratios in the individual cells, and therefore in a largely homogeneous cell population it is representative of those cells. On the other hand, the concentration ratio in body fluids is determined by the ratio in the tissues which have released LDH into the fluid. In addition, the half-life of LDH plays a role; this is different for each fraction, and in serum is shortest for LDH 5[29].

All 5 isoenzymes are typical freely soluble cytoplasmic enzymes, therefore effects of compartmentation play no role. *Kaplan*[13] and his group have related the rate of synthesis of the subunits A and B to the metabolic differentiation of the cells. In tissue culture, cells produce more B subunits when the oxygen concentration rises. LDH 1 has the highest activity at low pyruvate concentrations and with 1 mM pyruvate it is already strongly inhibited. At this concentration LDH 5 is still fully active. From this it has been concluded that in the presence of LDH 1 oxidative metabolism of pyruvate occurs, while in the presence of LDH 5 pyruvate is reduced to lactate. According to this hypothesis large amounts of LDH 5 indicate a predominantly anaerobic, glycolytic type of metabolism, and LDH 1 an oxidative type of metabolism.

There are however still objections to this hypothesis. The actual tissue concentrations of the substrate, and of NADH, are relatively low[30], whereas the enzyme is in great excess. *Vesell*[31,32] found that at 37 °C and physiological pH the relative inhibitions of LDH 1 and LDH 5 by lactate and pyruvate are very similar. In red cells of most animals LDH 1 predominates although the cells have a very low oxygen uptake. The lens of the eye also has a typical anaerobic metabolism, but has a high concentration of LDH 1. Even more peculiar is the liver which has a high oxygen uptake, but in which LDH 5 is the dominant isoenzyme. Our opinion is that the *Kaplan* hypothesis does not apply to non-nucleated cells (mature red cells, the eye lens and blood platelets) where LDH 1 is predominant and LDH 5 is absent. The absence of protein synthesis and the shorter half-life of LDH 5 may explain this anomaly. Recently *Kaplan*[33] put forward the important argument that even at high pyruvate concentrations LDH 5 can maintain glycolysis while the role of LDH 1 is less clear.

In mature male germ cells a sixth LDH occurs, the so-called LDH X[34,35]. Its electrophoretic mobility lies between LDH 3 and LDH 4[36]. The molecular weight is of the order of 130000. It is a tetrameric association of a subunit C[37]. In the pigeon the genetic site which controls the synthesis can cause allele-directed polymorphism[38]. A tendency to hybridization with B subunits is evident[39]. In fact its enzymatic properties are similar to LDH 1, especially the affinity for 2-oxobutyrate[40]. The substrate 2-oxovalerate is practically specific for this isoenzyme[41].

The electrophoretic separation of the LDH isoenzymes, at least in most species, is relatively simple. All media, even paper electrophoresis[42], give similar results. In starch-gel and polyacrylamide-gel a further differentiation (sub-bands), especially with mouse tissues, is obtained[43-45]. Its importance is not known and so far no clinical application has been described.

Application of Method:

The main interest in LDH differentiation lies in the clinical field, where it has become a corner stone of diagnostic enzymology. The importance depends on the more or less specific distribution of the LDH isoenzymes in tissues, which in certain situations give rise to typical changes in the LDH distribution pattern in serum. Three classes of tissue can be defined. The most important representatives are listed in Table 1. The tissue specificity appears to be low, but extremely useful information can be obtained from a combination of the serum data and the clinical picture. The clinical picture generally allows the elimination of the involvement of certain tissues which might otherwise fit the serum data. Tissue analysis is usually of limited interest, with the exception of cases of primary muscular dystrophy. In this case the analysis of a biopsy sample from a long, transversely striated muscle together with changes in the LDH activity in serum give information which is virtually specific[46].

The differentiation of serum LDH is particularly important with normal total LDH activity in serum; it is possible to detect slight variations in the smaller components, which pass unnoticed if only the total

Table 1. The 3 Main Types of LDH Isoenzymes in Tissues (with representative examples).

Type	Predominant fraction	Example
Heart muscle	LDH 1	Heart muscle
		Red blood cells
		Kidney glomerular cells
		Blood platelets
		Eye lens
Skeletal muscle	LDH 5	Skeletal muscle
		Liver
		Kidney tubule cells
		Granulocytes
		Malignant tumors
Smooth muscle	LDH 3	Smooth muscle
		Continuously contracting skeletal muscle

activity is measured. Combined fluctuations are important, e. g. the simultaneous rise of LDH 1 and LDH 5 in myocardial infarction with vascular shock. Measurements in cerebrospinal fluid [47,48], synovial fluid [49-52] and in urine [53] appear to be of little interest. Tables 2 and 3 give a summary of the numerous clinical applications of LDH measurements in serum; refer also to the chapter "Measurements of Enzyme Activities after Electrophoresis", p. 261, and to other publications [54-61].

Principle

The direct enzymoelectrophoretic method in which a tetrazolium staining reaction is used has superceded all other methods (elution, spectrophotometry *in situ*). The method described here is a modification of that proposed by *Van der Helm* [62]. The enzymoelectrophoretic separation is carried out in agar-gel. This is then covered with a second agar layer which contains L-lactate, NAD and a tetrazolium salt to make visible the enzymatic reduction of NAD. The activity zones are scanned at 546 nm.

Optimum Conditions for Measurements

The pH optimum for the conversion of lactate to pyruvate is between pH 8.3 and 8.9; 6 mM NAD is optimum for LDH 1 and LDH 5 [63]. The NAD concentration used here is on the low side. The choice of lactate concentration is critical. At 30 °C the optimum is 40 mM for LDH 1 and 70 mM or above for LDH 5. At 37 °C the difference appears to disappear [64], so that 50 mM L-lactate appears to be a good compromise. *Kreutzer* [65] examined the effect of temperatures above 37 °C on the area under the measured peaks. He found the largest value for LDH 5 at 40 °C and for LDH 1 at 62 °C. The temperature must therefore be carefully controlled. Great difficulties are caused in practice by the differential end-product inhibition resulting from the accumulation of pyruvate. According to Fig. 7, p. 279 this effect appears to be important only with LDH 1 and not with LDH 5 (at room temperature). At 37 °C during conversion of pyruvate to lactate, LDH 1 and LDH 5 are inhibited to the same slight extent by pyruvate concentrations over 2 mM [32].

Unlike most authors we use no cyanide in our assay. Instead we aid the development of the colour with EDTA, especially with LDH 4 and 5. For the mechanism of the reaction, see p. 274.

The volume of the substrate gel should be at least double that of the electrophoresis medium. The electrophoresis medium contains albumin to protect LDH 5 against inactivation during penetration into the agar gel [66].

Table 2. Diagnostic Application of LDH Differentiation in Serum.

	Tissue of origin	Notes	Probability of appearance (1 = always occurs)
Rise of LDH 1			
Myocardial infarction	Myocardium	Early or late sign	1
Haemolytic syndrome	Red cells	Also check haptoglobin level	1
Pernicious anaemia	Red cells		1
Dysgerminoma	Germ cells		?
Rise of LDH 5			
Liver damage	Liver cells	Massive necrosis causes a large rise (e. g. incubation phase of viral hepatitis)	1
Circulatory shock	Liver or muscle	Often together with rise of LDH 1 in severe myocardial infarction	1
Kidney tubule damage	Tubule cells	Only in tubule necrosis	1
Malignant prostate tumor	Neoplasm of prostate		0.5
Destruction of granulocytes	Granulocytes		0.7
Rise of LDH 3			
Primary muscular dystrophy	Modified skeletal muscle	Also check tissue distribution pattern	Initial: 0.5 Advanced: 1 Terminal: 0.5
Malignant tumors	Neoplasms	LDH 5 rise in serum is diminished on rapid removal	0.5
Diseases of kidney cortex	Kidney cortex	Especially in kidney infarction.	0.5

Table 3. Application of LDH Differentiation in Serum in Control of Progress of Disease.

Condition	Observations
Myocardial infarction	Should return to normal within a week. A fresh increase in LDH 1 indicates re-infarction.
Regression of tumors on cytostatic treatment	Rise of LDH 3 if tumor is sensitive
Haemodialysis	Increase of LDH 5 in pathological tubular conditions.
Viral hepatitis	LDH 5 should return to normal 2 weeks after onset of icteric attack.
Chronic liver diseases	Small rise of LDH 5 in necrotic attacks.
Treatment of pernicious anaemia	Should return to normal after 1 week.

Equipment

1. Electrophoresis apparatus for agar gel (e. g. Vitatron Type CTA/100).
2. Optical scanner with extinction recorder (e. g. Vitatron photometer Type UFD 100 with lin/log recorder Type UR 403).

Reagents

1. Special Agar-Noble
   from Difco, Detroit.
2. Sodium veronal (5,5-diethylbarbituric
   acid, sodium salt)
3. Hydrochloric acid, 1 N
4. DL-Lactic acid, ca. 85%
5. Nicotinamide-adenine dinucleotide,
   NAD
   free acid; commercial preparation, see p. 545.
6. 2-(p-Iodophenyl)-3-(p-nitrophenyl)-
   5-phenyl-tetrazolium chloride, INT
7. Phenazine methosulphate, PMS
8. Ethylenediaminetetra-acetic acid, EDTA
   disodium salt, EDTA-Na$_2$H$_2$·2H$_2$O
9. Albumin
   Human albumin, dry, purest grade.
10. Sodium hydroxide, 1 N
11. Acetic acid.

Preparation of Solutions

Prepare all solutions with fresh distilled water.

   I. Veronal buffer (pH 8.4; $\mu = 0.1$):
   Dissolve 17.0 g. sodium veronal in about 600 ml. distilled water, add 23.5 ml. N HCl
   and dilute to 1 000 ml. with distilled water.

  II. DL-Lactate (ca. 500 mM L-lactate):
   Neutralize 1 ml. 85% DL-lactic acid with 1 N NaOH.

 III. Phenazine methosulphate (3.27 mM):
   Dissolve 10 mg. PMS in 10 ml. distilled water, use directly for the preparation of substrate
   stock solution VI.

  IV. Nicotinamide-adenine dinucleotide (13 mM):
   Dissolve 100 mg. NAD in 10 ml. distilled water.

   V. 2-(p-Iodophenyl)-3-(p-nitrophenyl)-5-phenyl-tetrazolium chloride (1.97 mM):
   Dissolve 20 mg. INT in 20 ml. distilled water and use directly for the preparation of
   substrate stock solution VI.

  VI. Substrate stock solution (200 mM DL-lactate; 0.18 mM PMS; 2.9 mM NAD; 1.0 mM
   INT):
   Mix the solutions in the following order:

   DL-Lactate solution (II)   2.25 ml.
   PMS solution   (III)   0.60 ml.
   NAD solution   (IV)   2.25 ml.
   INT solution   (V)   6.00 ml.

   Store in a dark bottle.

 VII. Albumin (1% w/v):
   Dissolve 1 g. albumin in 100 ml. distilled water.

VIII. Fixing solution (0.34 N acetic acid):
   Dilute 2 ml. acetic acid with 100 ml. distilled water

  IX. EDTA stock solution (10 mM):
   Dissolve 372 mg. EDTA-Na$_2$H$_2$·2H$_2$O in 100 ml. distilled water.

   X. Agar stock solution (1.5% w/v):
   Dissolve 1.5 g. agar-Noble (Difco) in 50 ml. veronal buffer (I). Add 2 ml. EDTA stock
   solution (IX), dilute with distilled water to 100 ml. Heat in a boiling water bath for
   20 min. and while still warm distribute in 1.5 ml. portions in stoppered test tubes.

Stability of Solutions

Store all solutions at 0–4 °C. Solution I is stable indefinitely, the substrate stock solution VI is stable for at least 2 months in the dark; it should be discarded if a greenish colour appears. Solution VII is stable for several weeks. Store stock solution X in a refrigerator.

Preparation of Gels

1. Electrophoresis gel

The preparation is carried out as described under "Amylases" on p. 911, with 0.9 g. agar Noble (instead of 1 g. Ion agar) and veronal buffer (I) diluted with an equal volume of water. As soon as the solution has cooled to ca. 50 °C add 1 ml. albumin solution (VII) and 1 ml. EDTA stock solution (IX). Pour the plates as described in the cited method.

2. Substrate developer gel

Immediately before use place a test tube containing 1.5 ml. agar stock solution (X) in a boiling water bath until the contents are completely dissolved. Pour the warm solution into 1.2 ml. substrate solution (VI). Then proceed immediately according to the method on p. 911. Final concentration after dilution with agar stock solution: 47 mM L-lactate; 1.3 mM NAD; 80 μM PMS; 0.45 mM INT; 0.12 mM EDTA.

Procedure

Collection, Treatment and Stability of Sample

LDH 5 is more easily inactivated at higher and also lower temperatures than LDH 1. The liquid sample should not be frozen and it is better to store it at 15 °C than at the more usual 4 °C[67]. LDH appears to be more stable in frozen tissue, but even here a slow decrease of activity of LDH 5 occurs during the course of a few weeks. Serum should be tested within 48 hr. of collection. Haemolysed samples should be discarded because erythrocytes contain large amounts of LDH 1 and LDH 2. These conditions have no effect on the determination of LDH 5.

Electrophoresis

Carry out the electrophoretic separation according to p. 912 ("Amylases"). For routine separation a total of four samples can be placed in two groups on a single slide. With the Vitatron apparatus the separation requires 15 min. with a field intensity of 20 V/cm.

Incubation

It is essential that this is carried out in a room protected from direct sunlight. Immediately after completion of the electrophoresis lay the slides in a horizontal plane and place a rubber frame around the areas of interest. Pour on the substrate developer gel (see above) so that the free space is filled; leave for 2 min. Remove the rubber frame and cut the electrophoresis layer to the size of the substrate layer. Place the double layer in a small petri dish and incubate for 120 min. at 37 °C in a darkened incubator. Zones of activity are stained purple. It is useful to carry a control sample through the same procedure (without DL-lactate in the substrate layer).

Evaluation

The optical evaluation can be carried out on moist gel, but it is better on dried film. For this immerse the plates for 3 hr. in the fixing solution (VIII), then place on filter paper and dry overnight at 37 °C. Carry out the scanning at 546 nm.

Reproducibility of Method

The percentage values should be reproducible within the following 2s ranges: $2s < \pm 1\%$ for values of 15–60%, $2s < \pm 2\%$ for values of 0–15%. The quantitative relationships are discussed in the general chapter (p. 276).

Normal Values

Normal serum gives 5 fractions with virtually the same distance between each (Fig. 1). Their mr values, the percentage of their peak area as a proportion of the total and their 2s range are given in Table 4. Similar values have been found by *Van der Heiden*[68] for healthy children aged 4–13 years.

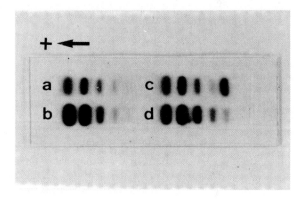

Fig. 1. Typical LDH separation according to the technique decribed here. Four samples of human serum have been analysed on one slide.
a) Normal serum, b) serum with raised LDH 1, c) serum with raised LDH 5, d) serum with raised middle fractions, especially LDH 3.

Table 4. Normal Values for LDH Activity in Serum from Adults.
The mr values indicate the electrophoretic mobility relative to pure human albumin.

	LDH 1	LDH 2	LDH 3	LDH 4	LDH 5
mr Values	0.93	0.69	0.45	0.22	0.02
Peak area as percentage of total	36%	42%	16%	4%	2%
$\pm 2s$	$\pm 4\%$	$\pm 4\%$	$\pm 2\%$	$\pm 2\%$	$\pm 2\%$

Sources of Error

If haemolysed samples are excluded and the sample is fresh, the non-specific staining of lipoproteins is the most important source of error. It can be avoided by prolonging the period of electrophoresis to 60 min. Then the lipoproteins are separated from the LDH isoenzymes and can be eliminated in the subsequent calculation of percentage fractions. For information on the so-called "nothing dehydrogenase" see p. 274; this effect particularly plays a role in concentrated tissue extracts.

Specificity of Methods

If interference from the "nothing dehydrogenase" is eliminated the method can be assumed to be specific for NAD-dependent LDH.

Other Methods

Methods of Class I

Of the other electrophoresis media cellulose acetate is also recommended for the clinical laboratory[69-74]. The electrophoretic separation can be carried out as for the serum proteins; the isoenzyme zones can be developed in a similar manner to that described here by placing the strip on a substrate layer. Good results have also been obtained with starch-gel[75] and polyacrylamide gel[76,77].
Differential adsorption of the LDH isoenzymes followed by the conventional LDH assay is described on p. 590.

Methods of Class II

LDH isoenzymes behave differently with NAD analogues which makes a differential assay feasible. This has been used to a great extent by *Kaplan* and his school, mainly for phylogenetic studies[7]. In the clinical field the so-called α-hydroxybutyrate assay of *Rosalki* and *Wilkinson*[78] is of more value. The total LDH activity is measured at room temperature with 10 mM 2-oxobutyrate and again with 0.7 mM pyruvate as substrate[79]. The ratio of the activities with 2-oxobutyrate and with pyruvate is calculated; it is normally 0.81 to 0.63. As LDH 1 is relatively more active with 2-oxobutyrate than LDH 5 the ratio activities rises when LDH 1 is released into the serum and falls when there is an increase of LDH 5 in the serum[80]. This method can easily be automated[81,82]. Prolonged storage of 2-oxobutyrate leads to the formation of a cyclic breakdown product which inhibits the LDH isoenzyme[83].
Also of interest are methods which use selective chemical inhibitors of the LDH isoenzymes. LDH 5 is more strongly inhibited than LDH 1 by 2 M urea[84]; with 0.2 mM oxalate the situation is reversed[85]. These methods are of clinical importance[86,87], especially in combination[88,89] or conjunction with alteration of lactate concentration[90,91]. Use of the substrate analogue glyoxylate[92] gives a poorer differentiation[93]. Differentiation by means of the different heat stability[94,95], which depends on the greater sensitivity of LDH 5 to heat, can be considered to have been superceded by other methods of class II. But even these, though simpler, are less direct, less sharp in their separation and more sensitive to interference than the methods of class I. These remain the methods of choice for LDH differentiation.

References

1 *J. B. Neilands,* J. biol. Chem. *199*, 373 [1952].
2 *E. S. Vesell & A. G. Bearn,* Proc. Soc. exp. Biol. Med. *94*, 96 [1957].
3 *F. W. Sayre & B. R. Hill,* Proc. Soc. exp. Biol. Med. *96*, 695 [1957].
4 *Th. Wieland & G. Pfleiderer,* Biochem. Z. *329*, 112 [1957].
5 *R. J. Wieme,* Behringwerk-Information *34*, 27 [1958].
6 *E. Appella & C. L. Markert,* Biochem. Biophys. Res. Comm. *6*, 171 [1961].
7 *R. D. Cahn, N. O. Kaplan, L. Levine & E. Zwilling,* Science *136*, 962 [1962].
8 *E. D. Wachsmuth & G. Pfleiderer,* Biochem. Z. *336*, 545 [1963].
9 *E. D. Wachsmuth, G. Pfleiderer & Th. Wieland,* Biochem. Z. *340*, 80 [1964].
10 *K. Rajewsky, S. Avrameas, P. Grabar, G. Pfleiderer & E. D. Wachsmuth,* Biochim. biophys. Acta *92*, 248 [1964].
11 *P. G. Pflagemann, K. F. Gregory & F. Wroblewski,* J. biol. Chem. *235*, 2288 [1960].
12 *C. L. Markert & H. Ursprung,* Developmental Biology *5*, 383 [1962].
13 *D. M. Dawson, T. L. Goodfriend & N. O. Kaplan,* Science *143*, 929 [1964].
14 *R. D. Cahn,* Developmental Biology *9*, 327 [1964].

15 *P. J. Fritz*, Science *150*, 364 [1965].
16 *C. L. Markert*, Science *140*, 1329 [1963].
17 *C. R. Shaw & E. Barto*, Proc. Natl. Acad. Sciences (USA) *50*, 211 [1963].
18 *N. Rauch*, Ann. N. Y. Acad. Sciences *151*, 672 [1968].
19 *S. H. Boyer, D. C. Fainer & E. J. Watson-Williams*, Science *141*, 642 [1963].
20 *W. E. Nance, A. Claflin & O. Smithies*, Science *142*, 1075 [1963].
21 *A. P. Kraus & C. L. Neely*, Science *145*, 595 [1964].
22 *R. G. Davidson, R. A. Fildes, A. M. Glen-Bott, H. Harris & E. B. Robson*, Ann. human Genet. *29*, 5 [1965].
23 *W. H. Zinkham, L. Kupchyk, A. Blanco & H. Isensee*, Nature *208*, 284 [1965].
24 *F. N. Syner & M. Goodman*, Science *151*, 206 [1966].
25 *E. Goldberg*, Science *151*, 1091 [1966].
26 *C. L. Markert & J. Faulhaber*, J. exp. Zoology *159*, 319 [1965].
27 *P. H. Odense, T. M. Allen & T. C. Leung*, Canad. J. Biochem. *44*, 1319 [1966].
28 *L. A. Costello & N. O. Kaplan*, Biochem. biophys. Acta *73*, 658 [1963].
29 *J. W. Boyd*, Biochim. biophys. Acta *132*, 221 [1967].
30 *E. S. Vesell & P. E. Pool*, Proc. Natl. Acad. Sciences (USA) *55*, 756 [1966].
31 *E. S. Vesell*, Science *150*, 1590 [1965].
32 *E. S. Vesell*, Ann. N. Y. Acad. Sciences *151*, 5 [1968].
33 *N. O. Kaplan, J. Everse & J. Admiraal*, Ann. N. Y. Acad. Sciences *151*, 400 [1968].
34 *A. Blanco & W. H. Zinkham*, Science *139*, 601 [1963].
35 *E. Goldberg*, Science *139*, 602 [1963].
36 *J. Clausen & B. Øvlisen*, Biochem. J. *97*, 513 [1965].
37 *W. H. Zinkham, A. Blanco & L. Kupchyk*, Science *142*, 1303 [1963].
38 *A. Blanco, W. H. Zinkham & L. Kupchyk*, J. exp. Zoology *156*, 137 [1964].
39 *W. H. Zinkham*, Ann. N. Y. Acad. Sciences *151*, 598 [1968].
40 *J. H. Wilkinson & W. A. Withycombe*, Biochem. J. *97*, 663 [1965].
41 *E. Goldberg*, Arch. Biochem. Biophys. *109*, 134 [1965].
42 *J. A. Morales-Malva, A. Magasich, J. M. Uribe-Echevarria & M. Sapag-Hagar*, Proc. Soc. exp. Biol. Med. *130*, 224 [1969].
43 *A. L. Koen*, Biochim. biophys. Acta *140*, 487 and 496 [1967].
44 *B. Fieldhouse & C. J. Masters*, Biochim. biophys. Acta *151*, 535 [1968].
45 *R. Stambaugh & J. Buckley*, J. biol. Chem. *242*, 4053 [1967].
46 *R. J. Wieme & J. E. Herpol*, Nature *194*, 287 [1962].
47 *H. J. Van der Helm, H. A. Zondag, H. A. Hartog & M. W. Van der Kooi*, Clin. chim. Acta *8*, 193 [1963].
48 *V. R. Cunningham, J. Phillips & E. J. Field*, J. clin. Pathology *18*, 765 [1965].
49 *H. N. Beaty & S. Oppenheimer*, New England J. Med. *279*, 1197 [1968].
50 *E. S. Vesell, K. C. Osterland, A. G. Bearn & H. G. Kunkel*, J. clin. Investigation *41*, 2012 [1962].
51 *H. Greiling, G. Engels & R. Kisters*, Klin. Wschr. *42*, 427 [1964].
52 *E. M. Veys & R. J. Wieme*, Ann. Rheumatic Diseases *27*, 569 [1968].
53 *U. C. Dubach*, Helv. med. Acta *33*, 139 [1966].
54 *B. Hess*: Enzymes in Blood Plasma, Academic Press, New York 1963.
55 *H. Mattenheimer*: Enzymologie für den praktischen Arzt, Verlag Hans Huber, Bern 1966.
56 *U. C. Dubach & D. Variakojis*, Schw. med. Wschr. *93*, 1224 [1963].
57 *L. Cohen, J. Djordjevich & V. Ormiste*, J. Lab. clin. Med. *64*, 355 [1964].
58 *E. S. Vesell*, Exp. Med. Surg. *23*, Supplement 10 [1965].
59 *R. J. Wieme*, Advances in Diagnostic Isoenzymology, in: Clinical Enzymology, Proc. Congr. Klin. Chemie, Munich 1966, Karger, Basel 1968, Vol. 2, p. 21.
60 *R. J. Wieme, W. Z. Van Hove & M. E. Van der Straeten*, Ann. N. Y. Acad. Sciences *151*, 213 [1968].
61 *L. Cohen*, Med. Clinics North Am. *53*, 115 [1969].
62 *H. J. Van der Helm*, Clin. chim. Acta *7*, 124 [1962].
63 *R. J. Gay, R. B. McComb & G. N. Bowers jr.*, Clin. Chem. *14*, 740 [1968].
64 *A. F. Krieg, S. Gorton & J. B. Henry*, Clin. chim. Acta *17*, 363 [1967].
65 *H. J. Kreutzer & H. H. Kreutzer*, Clin. chim. Acta *11*, 578 [1965].
66 *R. J. Wieme*, Clin. chim. Acta *13*, 138 [1966].
67 *H. H. Kreutzer & W. H. Fennis*, Clin. chim. Acta *9*, 64 [1964].
68 *C. Van der Heiden, J. Desplanque, J. W. Stoop & S. K. Wadman*, Clin. chim. Acta *22*, 409 [1968].
69 *H. Barnett*, Biochem. J. *84*, 83 P [1962].
70 *J. A. Preston, R. O. Briere & J. G. Batsakis*, Am. J. clin. Pathology *43*, 256 [1965].
71 *A. W. Opher, C. S. Collier & J. M. Miller*, Clin. Chem. *12*, 308 [1966].
72 *M. Mager, W. F. Blatt & W. H. Abelmann*, Clin. chim. Acta *14*, 689 [1966].
73 *B. H. Stagg & G. A. Whyley*, Clin. chim. Acta *19*, 139 [1968].

74 *G. M. Homer, B. Yott & J. G. Lim,* Tech. Bull. Registry Med. Technologists *39*, 11 [1969].
75 *I. H. Fine, N. O. Kaplan & D. Kuftinec,* Biochemistry *2*, 116 [1963].
76 *A. A. Dietz & T. Lubrano,* Analyt. Biochemistry *20*, 246 [1967].
77 *R. J. Albred & H. J. Keutel,* J. Lab. clin. Medicine *71*, 179 [1968].
78 *S. B. Rosalki & J. H. Wilkinson,* Nature *188*, 1110 [1960].
79 *K. Bickhardt,* Ärztl. Laboratorium *14*, 18 [1968].
80 *B. A. Elliott & J. H. Wilkinson,* Lancet 1961-I, 698.
81 *P. E. Strandjord & K. J. Clayson,* J. Lab. clin. Med. *67*, 131 [1966].
82 *V. Dube, D. T. Hunter & J. A. Knight,* Am. J. clin. Pathology *50*, 491 [1968].
83 *J. H. Wilkinson & F. P. Jenkins,* Clin. chim. Acta *19*, 397 [1968].
84 *R. Richterich & A. Burger,* Helv. physiol. Acta *21*, 59 [1963].
85 *D. T. Plummer & J. H. Wilkinson,* Biochem. J. *87*, 423 [1963].
86 *S. Lindy & A. Konttinen,* Clin. chim. Acta *17*, 223 [1967].
87 *S. G. Welshman & E. C. Rixon,* Clin. chim. Acta *19*, 121 [1968].
88 *P. M. Emerson & J. H. Wilkinson,* J. clin. Pathology *18*, 803 [1965].
89 *M. Rosnowska, Z. Sawicki & J. Krawczynski,* Clin. chim. Acta *20*, 7 [1968].
90 *A. L. Babson,* Clin. chim. Acta *16*, 121 [1967].
91 *M. Lubran & W. E. Jensen,* Clin. chim. Acta *22*, 125 [1968].
92 *S. Sawaki & K. Yamada,* Nature *210*, 91 [1966].
93 *M. R. Banner & S. B. Rosalki,* Nature *213*, 726 [1967].
94 *U. C. Dubach,* Schw. med. Wschr. *92*, 1436 [1962].
95 *L. Bell,* Am. J. clin. Pathology *40*, 216 [1963].

LDH$_1$ ("2-Hydroxybutyrate Dehydrogenase")*

UV-Assay

J. Henry Wilkinson

According to *Meister*[1], of the 2-oxo and 2,4-dioxo acids, only pyruvate and 2-oxobutyrate are rapidly reduced by lactate dehydrogenase (LDH) in the presence of NADH. This finding can be used for the differentiation of the LDH isoenzymes. The affinity of the anodic LDH components for 2-oxobutyrate is much greater than that of the cathodic fractions[2].

Heart muscle, erythrocytes, kidney and brain, the LDH$_1$-rich tissues, show high activity with 2-oxobutyrate as substrate, but relatively low activity with pyruvate[3,4]. In contrast, liver and skeletal muscle, which contain more LDH$_5$ show relatively little activity with the substrate analogue. The LDH$_x$ isoenzyme from human testis and spermatozoa[5-8] shows relatively high activity with 2-oxobutyrate[9,10], although its rate of electrophoretic migration lies between that of LDH$_3$ and LDH$_4$.

The LDH fractions which react with 2-oxobutyrate as substrate are termed "2-hydroxybutyrate dehydrogenase, 2-HBDH"[11]. However, this term should be used for diagnostic purposes only, because there is no evidence that an enzyme other than LDH is involved. The HBDH activity is usually measured spectrophotometrically with 2-oxobutyrate as substrate[2], but methods employing the reverse direction with L or DL-2-hydroxybutyrate have been described[4,12]. However, this latter compound is expensive, difficult to obtain and the high optimum concentration of 83 mM[4] excludes its use. A colorimetric method[13] depends on the reaction of the unreacted 2-oxobutyrate with 2,4-dinitrophenylhydrazine.

Application of Method: The determination is of clinical value in the diagnosis of myocardial infarction[11,14-26]. It is of particular value when two or more days have elapsed since the attack or when there is simultaneous liver damage. Raised values are also found in the severe sex-linked form *(Duchenne)* of progressive muscular dystrophy[16,27,28], in megaloblastic anaemia[27,29] and widely disseminated metastases[27].

The method described here was designed for measurements in human serum, but can also be used for tissue extracts.

Principle

(1) $CH_3-CH_2-CO-COO^- + NADH + H^+ \xrightleftharpoons{\text{2-HBDH}} CH_3-CH_2-CHOH-COO^- + NAD^+$

The equilibrium lies to the right like the LDH reaction with pyruvate. The oxidation of NADH per unit time, as determined by the extinction change at 340 (334, 365) nm is a measure of the activity.

Optimum Conditions for Measurements

The optimum 2-oxobutyrate concentration is 15 mM. The NADH concentration is optimum between 0.07 and 0.20 mM. Although with 15 mM 2-oxobutyrate the rate is ca. 25% higher the difference between LDH$_1$ and LDH$_5$ activities (LDH$_1$: LDH$_5$ ca. 10 : 6) is lower, so that the interpretation of the test is limited. It is better to use 0.12 mM NADH and pH 7.4 with suboptimum 2-oxobutyrate at 3.3 mM. These concentrations have been used in most of the comparative studies on isoenzymes of human and animal LDH, although there is a difference between the K_M values for the electrophoretically separated

---

* Synonym: α-Hydroxybutyrate dehydrogenase.

LDH_1 and LDH_5. At pH 7.4 and with 0.12 mM NADH the K_M of LDH_1 for 2-oxobutyrate is 0.63 mM, for LDH_5 it is 2.7 mM; the corresponding K_M values for pyruvate are 0.077 mM and 0.88 mM[3].
Measurements at different temperatures may require different measuring conditions (cf. p. 127). Nevertheless, results obtained under the same measuring conditions but at different temperatures were formerly compared with each other ("conversion factors" were determined). Such conversion factors may be correct if determined with a relatively large proband collective; however, they cannot be applied generally to the individual case (cf. p. 129). The value of the following relative reaction rates thus lies in being able to appraise the temperature dependence of the reaction and at the most to compare qualitatively values up to the limit of normal.

°C	25	27	30	32	34	37
Measured at 25 °C	1.00	1.08	1.19	1.25	1.31	1.37
Measured at 30 °C	0.84	0.91	1.00	1.05	1.10	1.15
Measured at 37 °C	0.73	0.79	0.87	0.91	0.96	1.00

Mean values for the ratios of the activities of different LDH isoenzymes from human tissues measured with 3.3 mM 2-oxobutyrate and 0.67 mM pyruvate are LDH_1 0.92; LDH_2 0.79; LDH_3 0.67; LDH_4 0.45 and LDH_5 0.30[3,9].

Equipment

Spectrophotometer or spectrum-line photometer for measurements at 340 (334, 365) nm, preferably with constant temperature cuvette holder. It is useful in addition to have a recorder connected to the photometer with a chart speed of 2 cm./min.; water bath (25 °C); stopwatch.

Reagents*

1. Potassium dihydrogen phosphate, KH_2PO_4, A. R.
2. Disodium hydrogen phosphate, A. R., Na_2HPO_4 or $Na_2HPO_4 \cdot 22H_2O$
3. 2-Oxobutyrate, sodium salt
4. Reduced nicotinamide-adenine dinucleotide
   sodium salt, $NADH$-Na_2; commercial preparation, see p. 545.

Purity of Reagents

After storage for more than two years, 2-oxobutyric acid can be transformed by a condensation reaction to 2-ethyl-3-methyl-tetrahydrofuran-4,5-dione which inhibits 2-HBDH. The sodium salt is more stable[30].

Preparation of Solutions

I. Phosphate buffer (67 mM; pH 7.4):
   Dissolve 128 mg. KH_2PO_4 and 853 mg. Na_2HPO_4 (or 961 mg. $Na_2HPO_4 \cdot 2H_2O$) in deionized and distilled water and make up to 100 ml. Check the pH at 25 °C.
II. 2-Oxobutyrate (0.1 M):
   Dissolve 144 mg. of the sodium salt in 10 ml. buffer (I).
III. Reduced nicotinamide-adenine dinucleotide, NADH (0.13 mM β-NADH):
   Dissolve 6 mg. $NADH$-Na_2 in 54 ml. buffer (I).

---

* Complete reagent kits are available commercially, see p. 558.

Stability of Solutions

The buffer (I) and the 2-oxobutyrate solution (II) are stable in stoppered flasks for about 3 months at 0–4 °C, providing that bacterial contamination does not occur. Prepare the NADH solution freshly each day.

Procedure

Collection, Treatment and Stability of Sample

Collection and treatment of sample:

Collect blood as usual. 2-HBDH is inhibited by anticoagulants like oxalate, citrate and fluoride. EDTA (1 mg./ml.) and heparin (0.2 mg./ml.) do not inhibit.

It is particularly important to avoid haemolysis during the collection of the blood and the serum, because erythrocytes contain about 100 times more LDH than normal serum (mainly anodic isoenzymes). For the same reason it is necessary to ensure that tissues are freed as completely as possible from blood before homogenization.

Stability of enzyme in sample:

2-HBDH is more stable than total LDH. After storage overnight at 4 °C or frozen at −18 °C there is ca. a 10% loss of activity. In frozen pooled serum there was no decrease of activity after 6 months and longer[31]. Tissue samples can be stored safely in the frozen state; dilute extracts, however, readily lose activity.

Assay System

Wavelength: 340 (Hg 334, Hg 365) nm; light path: 1 cm.; final volume: 3.0 ml.; 25 °C (constant temperature cuvette holder); read against air.

Pipette into a test tube:			Concentration in assay mixture
Serum		0.10 ml.	
NADH solution	(III)	2.80 ml.	0.12 mM NADH 62 mM phosphate
Equilibrate for 10–15 min. in a 25° water bath (non-specific oxidation of NADH comes to a stop)			
2-Oxobutyrate solution (equilibrated to 25 °C)	(II)	0.10 ml.	3.3 mM 2-oxobutyrate
Mix, pour immediately into a cuvette and read the extinction at 1 min. intervals for 3 to 5 min. The changes in $\Delta E/min.$ are used for the calculations.			

If $\Delta E/min.$ is $> 0.080/min.$ at 340 nm, repeat the measurements; dilute the serum 1 : 5 to 1 : 10 with buffer (I).

Calculations

Calculate the mean extinction change/min. ($\Delta E/min.$). In most cases it is possible to obtain sufficient points on the linear part of the progress curve.

The calculation formula (8) on p. 313 applies and therefore for this method the following relationships hold:

Wavelength:	*334 nm*	*340 nm*	*365 nm*
Volume activity $= 4918 \times \Delta E/min$		$4823 \times \Delta E/min$	$8824 \times \Delta E/min$ [U/l.]

Precision of Method

With a mean value of 150 U/l. serum a standard deviation of 7.5 U/l. and a coefficient of variation of 5% was found.

Normal Values

In human serum the normal range is 56 to 125 U/l.[18].

Sources of Error

Effects of drugs and other therapeutic measures: No effects of drugs on the assay are known.

Interference in the assay technique: As long as the sample is not too active there is no interference. For the effects of enzyme inhibitors in impure NADH preparations, see p. 158.

Specificity of Method

The determination of 2-HBDH activity is selective rather than specific for LDH_1. Other LDH isoenzymes also show lower activity with 2-oxobutyrate as substrate. The ratio of the activities with different LDH isoenzymes measured as 2-HBDH or as LDH are as follows at 25 °C:

	LDH_1	LDH_2	LDH_3	LDH_4	LDH_5
2-HBDH/LDH:	0.92	0.78	0.55	0.39	0.25

The above assay is specific for LDH.

References

1 *A. Meister*, J. biol. Chem. *184*, 117 [1950].
2 *S. B. Rosalki & J. H. Wilkinson*, Nature (London) *188*, 1110 [1960].
3 *D. T. Plummer, B. A. Elliot, K. B. Cooke & J. H. Wilkinson*, Biochem. J. *87*, 416 [1963].
4 *D. T. Plummer & J. H. Wilkinson*, Biochem. J. *87*, 423 [1963].
5 *A. Blanco & W. H. Zinkham*, Science *139*, 601 [1963].
6 *E. Goldberg*, Science *139*, 602 [1963].
7 *W. H. Zinkham, A. Blanco & L. Kupchyk*, Science *142*, 1303 [1963].
8 *J. Clausen & B. Øvlisen*, Biochem. J. *97*, 513 [1965].
9 *J. H. Wilkinson & W. A. Withycombe*, Biochem. J. *97*, 663 [1965].
10 *R. Stambaugh & J. Buckley*, J. biol. Chem. *242*, 4053 [1967].
11 *B. A. Elliott & J. H. Wilkinson*, Lancet *1*, 698 [1961].
12 *J. M. Allen*, Ann. N. Y. Acad. Sci. *94*, 937 [1961].
13 *S. B. Rosalki*, Clin. chim. Acta *8*, 415 [1962].
14 *A. Konttinen*, Lancet *2*, 556 [1961].
15 *L. Pagliaro & A. Notarbartolo*, Lancet *2*, 1261 [1961].
16 *L. Pagliaro & A. Notarbartolo*, Lancet *1*, 1043 [1962].
17 *B. A. Elliott & J. H. Wilkinson*, Lancet *2*, 71 [1962].
18 *B. A. Elliott, E. M. Jepson & J. H. Wilkinson*, Clin. Sci. *23*, 205 [1962].

19 A. Hansson, B. Johannsson & J. Sievers, Lancet 1, 167 [1962].
20 A. Konttinen & P. I. Halonen, Amer. J. Cardiol. 10, 525 [1962].
21 S. B. Rosalki, Brit. Heart J. 26, 795 [1963].
22 P. L. Bigazzi & G. P. Ciampi, Progr. Med. 19, 590 [1963].
23 J. H. Wilkinson & S. B. Rosalki, Diag. Terap. 1, 309 [1963].
24 J. A. Preston, J. G. Batsakis & R. O. Briere, Amer. J. clin. Path. 41, 237 [1964].
25 S. B. Rosalki & J. H. Wilkinson, J. Amer. med. Assoc. 189, 61 [1964].
26 A. F. Smith, Lancet 2, 178 [1967].
27 B. A. Elliott & J. H. Wilkinson, Clin. Sci. 24, 343 [1963].
28 H. A. Johnston, J. H. Wilkinson, W. A. Withycombe & S. Raymond, J. clin. Path. 19, 250 [1966].
29 P. M. Emerson & J. H. Wilkinson, Brit. J. Haemat. 12, 678 [1966].
30 J. H. Wilkinson, F. P. Jenkins & G. A. P. Tuey, Clin. Chim. Acta 19, 397 [1968].

Colorimetric Assay[1]

John King

The reaction is linear with time and amount of enzyme up to 60% conversion of substrate. A fixed time period can therefore be used for the measurement of enzyme activity. The enzyme is relatively stable in serum, only above 50 °C does it show signs of inactivation; it can therefore be safely measured at 37 °C.

Principle

See p. 603. 2-Oxobutyrate and NADH form 2,4-dinitrophenylhydrazones, which absorb in alkaline solution at 430 or 400 nm respectively[2]. The enzyme activity is determined at 37 °C by measurement of the hydrazone concentration at 430 nm before and after the reaction[3]. A standard curve is used.

Optimum Conditions for Measurements

Refer also to p. 603. Although the 2-oxobutyrate concentration must be decreased so that readable extinctions can be obtained, the concentration is near to the optimum one. The optimum pH for the LDH reactions changes not only with the direction of the reaction and the buffer used, but also with the substrate concentration (see Fig. 1, p. 575); which in turn is temperature dependent. With 0.58 mM 2-oxobutyrate and 37 °C Pottage[1] found a pH optimum of 5.6 in phthalate buffer; activity was maximal in phosphate buffer at pH 6.4. Under these conditions 0.46 mM NADH is optimum (K_M is 0.1 mM). The measurements can be made at 436 nm (Hg line) instead of 430 nm; the difference is < 4%. The activities obtained at 25 °C, 30 °C and 37 °C by this method are related as follows: 1 : 1.40 : 1.85.

Equipment

Spectrophotometer or spectrum-line photometer suitable for measurements at 430 (436) nm; 37 °C water bath.

Reagents

1. Disodium hydrogen phosphate,
   $Na_2HPO_4 \cdot 2H_2O$, A. R.
2. Potassium dihydrogen phosphate,
   KH_2PO_4, A. R.
3. 2-Oxobutyrate
   sodium salt, anhydrous

4. Reduced nicotinamide-adenine
   dinucleotide, NADH
   sodium salt, $NADH-Na_2$; commercial preparation, see 545.
5. 2,4-Dinitrophenylhydrazine, A. R.
6. Hydrochloric acid, 1 N, A. R.
7. Sodium hydroxide, 0.4 N, A. R.

Preparation of Solutions

Use only doubly distilled water.

  I. Phosphate buffer (67 mM; pH 6.4):
     Dissolve 3.171 g. $Na_2HPO_4 \cdot 2H_2O$ and 6.654 g. KH_2PO_4 in distilled water and make
     up to 1 000 ml.
 II. 2-Oxobutyrate (0.75 mM):
     Dissolve 18.6 mg. 2-oxobutyrate in 200 ml. phosphate buffer (I).
III. Reduced nicotinamide-adenine dinucleotide (3 mM):
     Dissolve 5 mg. $NADH-Na_2$ in distilled water and make up to 2 ml.
 IV. Ketone reagent (1 mM):
     Dissolve 200 mg. 2,4-dinitrophenylhydrazine in hot 1 N HCl, cool and dilute to 1 000 ml.
     with 1 N HCl.
  V. Standard solution (0.75 mM):
     Dissolve 13.3 mg. $NADH-Na_2$ in 2-oxobutyrate solution (II) and make up to 20 ml.

Stability of Solutions

The sodium hydroxide and ketone reagent are stable indefinitely. The phosphate buffer is stable indefinitely
at 0 °C after the addition of several drops of chloroform to prevent the growth of micro-organisms and the
2-oxobutyrate is stable for a month. The NADH solution is stable in the frozen state for a month. Prepare
the standard solution freshly just before use.

Procedure

Collection, Treatment and Stability of Sample

Collect blood without venestasis and obtain plasma or serum as quickly as possible. Avoid
haemolysis because it causes false results. Heparin, EDTA, citrate or fluoride can be used as
anti-coagulants; oxalate gives low values.
The serum enzyme is stable for 48 hr. at room temperature, and for at least 7 days at 4 °C.
In the frozen state no loss of activity was detected within 4 weeks[4].

Assay System

Wavelength: 430 (Hg 436) nm; light path: 1 cm.; incubation volume: 1.3 ml.; 37 °C. Volume for colorimetric measurements: 12.3 ml.; read against distilled water.

Pipette into test tubes:		Test	Blank	Concentration in assay mixture
2-Oxobutyrate solution	(II)	1.0 ml.	–	0.58 mM;
Sample (serum)		0.1 ml.	0.1 ml.	51 mM phosphate
Equilibrate at 37 °C in water bath.				
NADH solution	(III)	0.2 ml.	0.2 ml.	0.46 mM
Mix and incubate for exactly 15 min.				
Ketone reagent	(IV)	1.0 ml.	1.0 ml.	
2-Oxobutyrate solution	(II)	–	1.0 ml.	
Mix, incubate for 15 min. and then take tubes out of bath.				
NaOH, 0.4 N		10.0 ml.	10.0 ml.	
Mix and measure extinctions. Calculate difference between blank and test.				

If the extinction of the blank is > 0.800 read against dilute ketone reagent instead of against water. A 1 : 10 dilution of ketone reagent gives an extinction of 0.155 and a 1 : 100 dilution an extinction of 0.070 (these extinctions are dependent on the H$^+$ ion concentration, see Fig. 1). Although the difference in extinction between the blank and test changes with time, the error 60 min. after addition of NaOH is < 3%. With extinction changes of > 0.400 repeat the assay with dilute sample.

Standard curve

Pipette into each test tube the following solutions and then proceed as for the above protocol starting with addition of ketone reagent (IV).

Tube No.	1	2	3	4	5	6	7	8	9
Standard solution (V)	1.0	0.9	0.8	0.7	0.6	0.5	0.4	0.3	0.2
Phosphate buffer (I)	0.3	0.4	0.5	0.6	0.7	0.8	0.9	1.0	1.1
U/l. (37 °C)	0	50	100	150	200	250	300	350	400

Subtract the extinctions of tubes 2–9 from that of tube 1. Plot these values (ordinate) against U/l. (abscissa). The standard curve is slightly non-linear.

Calculations

The difference in extinction between standards 1 and 2 represents a decrease of $0.1 \times 0.75/1000$ mmole 2-oxobutyrate and NADH. If this change is brought about by 0.1 ml. serum in 15 min. it corresponds to $0.1 \times 0.75 \times 1000000/0.1 \times 15 \times 1000 = 50$ nmole/min./ml. $= 50$ U/l.

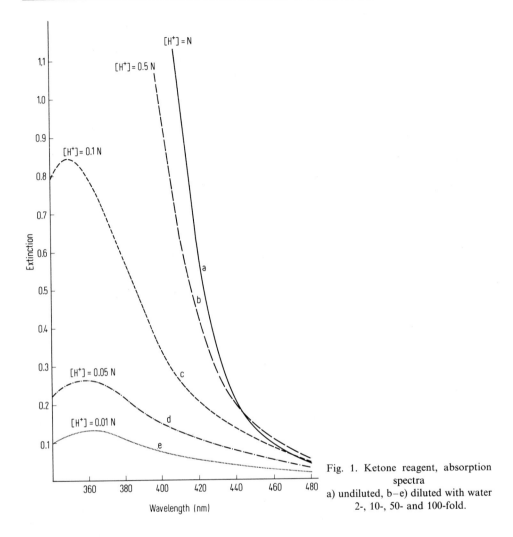

Fig. 1. Ketone reagent, absorption spectra
a) undiluted, b–e) diluted with water
2-, 10-, 50- and 100-fold.

Precision of Method

For activities of 160 U/l. ± 15.5 U/l. the coefficient of variation was 4.8%.

Normal Values

See p. 606. For serum of healthy adults: 40–135 U/l. (37 °C). Much higher values are found in cord blood: 105–255 U/l.[1].

Sources of Error

For simplicity an NADH solution which is equimolar with the 2-oxobutyrate solution is used for the standard curve. Although this is more concentrated than in the test the resulting error is negligible.

Specificity of Method

By addition of NADH to the blank the reduction of endogenous pyruvate by LDH is eliminated. The assay is therefore specific for the isoenzymes which have the highest affinity for 2-oxobutyrate[5], namely LDH$_1$ and LDH$_2$.

References

1 *J. Pottage:* Thesis, Institute of Medical Laboratory Technology, London [1968].
2 *J. King:* Practical Clinical Enzymology, D. Van Nostrand Co., Ltd., [1965] p. 55, 57.
3 *B. A. Elliott & J. H. Wilkinson,* Lancet *1,* 698 [1961].
4 *A. D. Clarke,* J. med. Lab. Technol. *21,* 21 [1964].
5 *R. J. Wieme,* Lancet *2,* 304 [1962].

UV-Assay, Automated Method

Günter Bechtler

This method is essentially the same as the manual method described on p. 603, therefore only the differences will be described here.

Equipment

Eppendorf-Automat 5010 for the spectrophotometric determination of enzymatic activities[1].

Reagents, see p. 604.

Preparation of Solutions

The volumes used are different from the manual method (p. 604). To maintain the same substrate concentration another 2-oxobutyrate solution is prepared:

II. 2-Oxobutyrate (ca. 90 mM):
Dissolve 130 mg. of the sodium salt in 10 ml. buffer (I).

Prepare solutions I and III as described on p. 604.

Procedure

Collection, Treatment and Stability of Sample, see p. 605.

Preparation of Automat*

Programmer	Dispenser Sample	Reagent	Incubator	Dispenser Reagent	Photometer	Analogue printer
Analysis time	Cylinder "10"	Cylinder "100"	15 min.	Cylinder "10"	Filter Hg 334 nm	Extinction 0–1 (1–2)
30 sec.	Serum 10 μl.	NAD solution 25 °C (III) 500 μl.		2-Oxobutyrate solution (II) 20 μl.		Chart speed 1 cm./min.

Assay System

Wavelength: Hg 334 nm; light path: 1 cm.; final volume: 530 μl.; temperature: 25 °C. Read against air; the solutions must not be equilibrated.

Into the reaction cuvettes are automatically pipetted:			Concentration in assay mixture
Serum		10 μl.	
NADH solution	(III)	500 μl.	63 mM phosphate 0.12 mM NADH
Incubation 15 min. at 25 °C (automatic)			
2-Oxobutyrate solution	(II)	20 μl.	3.4 mM
Mix, first measurement 46 sec. after addition and a total of 7 measurements in 154 sec.			

If the activity is more than 350 U/l. repeat the assay with serum diluted 1:10.

Calculations

The activity is calculated from the slope[2] $\alpha\left(tg\,\alpha = \dfrac{\Delta E}{\Delta t}\right)$ according to the following relationship:

Volume activity $= 435 \times tg\,\alpha$ [U/l.]

Precision of Method

The standard deviation in the normal range is 5 U/l.

References

1 *G. Bechtler,* Ärztl. Lab. *15,* 86 [1969].
2 *H. Weber* & *R. Richterich,* Klin. Wschr. *41,* 665 [1963].

---

* Consult the information leaflet B 5010 of the Eppendorf Gerätebau Netheler & Hinz, GmbH, Hamburg, Germany.

Malate Dehydrogenase

Malate dehydrogenase, MDH, (L-Malate:NAD oxidoreductase, EC 1.1.1.37) was discovered by *Thunberg*[1] and *Batelli* and *Stern*[2] in 1910, and isolated in pure state from pig heart by *Straub*[3]. The enzyme occurs in animal and plant tissues and in microorganisms. As a constituent of the citric acid cycle it is found in large amounts in mitochondria and sarcosomes[4]. *Bücher* et al[5,6] showed that MDH from mitochondria has a different pH optimum and substrate affinity from the cytoplasmic enzyme. The distribution of the two enzymes between cytoplasm and mitochondria varies from organ to organ; in heart muscle virtually all the MDH is located in the cytoplasm. The absolute activity in cytoplasm is greatest in liver, followed by heart, skeletal muscle and brain.

The concentration of malate dehydrogenase in the cell is several orders of magnitude higher than in the extracellular space. The large concentration gradient means that when the cell membrane is damaged more MDH appears in the serum. *Hess* et al.[7,8], *Wacker* et al.[9] and *Siegel* et al.[10] were first to measure MDH activity in serum in various diseases. MDH activity can be measured by the Thunberg techniques manometrically or, preferably, spectrophotometrically. The activity which appears in serum is due to the presence of several isoenzymes[11,12] from different sources and of different activities, as shown by *Vesell* et al.[13], *Hess*[14], *Schmidt* et al.[15], *Tsao*[16]. Generally, the enzyme found in the serum is the cytoplasmic enzyme, but in severe cell damage the mitochondrial enzyme also occurs.

Application of Method: In biochemistry and in clinical chemistry.

UV-Assay

Hans Ulrich Bergmeyer and Erich Bernt

Principle

(1) $\qquad$ L-Aspartate + 2-Oxoglutarate $\xrightarrow{\text{GOT*}}$ L-Glutamate + Oxaloacetate

(2) $\qquad$ Oxaloacetate + NADH + H$^+$ $\xrightarrow{\text{MDH}}$ L-Malate + NAD$^+$

The equilibrium of reaction (2) at neutral pH is far to malate and NAD[3]. According to[17] $K' = [\text{oxalo-acetate}] \times [\text{NADH}]/[\text{L-malate}] \times [\text{NAD}^+] = 2.33 \times 10^{-5}$ at pH 7.4 and 22 °C. The measurements are therefore made with oxaloacetate as substrate and NADH as coenzyme[18].

As oxaloacetate is unstable in aqueous solution and is partially decarboxylated to pyruvate, lactate dehydrogenase activity of the serum is measured[14] if old oxaloacetate solutions are used. This difficulty can be avoided if the optimum amount of oxaloacetate is produced in the cuvette shortly before the MDH assay from 2-oxoglutarate and L-aspartate with glutamate-oxaloacetate transaminase (GOT)[19].

The amount of oxaloacetate reacting per unit time, measured by the decrease in extinction due to the oxidation of NADH, is a measure of the MDH activity.

Optimum Conditions for Measurements

The most important characteristics of MDH proteins for measurement of their activity are their different substrate and pH optima. These have been studied in particular by *Schmidt*[15]. The dependence of the reaction on the NADH concentration is low; at pH values around 7.5 the following oxaloacetate concentrations are optimum for measurements in serum: in acute hepatitis 1.7 mM; in myocardial infarction

---

* L-Aspartate: 2-oxoglutarate aminotransferase, EC 2.6.1.1

0.8 mM; in haemolytic anaemia 1.4 mM; in bronchial carcinoma 3.7 mM. If the MDH activity is measured in serum several days after release of MDH from a certain organ has occurred, the optimum oxaloacetate concentration is now different, i. e. values which are too low are now obtained with the original optimum oxaloacetate concentration[15]. Research and discussion on this point are still in progress.

In the following method 1 mM oxaloacetate, 0.2 mM NADH and pH 7.4 are used as these concentrations and pH approximate to the optimum conditions for measurements in serum after myocardial infarction and hepatitis.

Measurements at different temperatures may require different measuring conditions (cf. p. 127). Nevertheless, results obtained under the same measuring conditions but at different temperatures were formerly compared with each other ("conversion factors" were determined). Such conversion factors. may be correct if determined with a relatively large proband collective; however, they cannot be applied generally to the individual case (cf. p. 129). The value of the following relative reaction rates[20] thus lies in being able to appraise the temperature dependence of the reaction and at the most to compare qualitatively values up to the limit of normal.

°C	18	19	20	21	22	23	24	25	26	27
	1.80	1,65	1.52	1.39	1.28	1.18	1.09	*1.00*	0.92	0.86
°C	28	29	30	31	32	33	34	35	36	37
	0.80	0.74	0.68	0.63	0.58	0.54	0.50	0.46	0.43	0.40

Equipment

Spectrophotometer or spectrum-line photometer suitable for accurate measurements at 340, 334 or 365 nm, preferably use a constant temperature cuvette holder. – Water bath (25 °C); stopwatch.

Reagents*

1. Postassium dihydrogen phosphate, KH_2PO_4
2. Dipotassium hydrogen phosphate, K_2HPO_4
3. L-Aspartate, sodium salt
4. 2-Oxoglutarate

   free acid or disodium salt, commercial preparation, see p. 548.
5. Sodium hydroxide, 1 N
6. Reduced nicotinamide-adenine dinucleotide, NADH

   sodium salt, $NADH-Na_2$; commerical preparation, see p. 545.

7. Glutamate-oxaloacetate transaminase, GOT

   from pig heart, suspension in 3 M ammonium sulphate solution; $\geqq$ 180 U/mg. (25 °C), containing 2.5 mM 2-oxoglutarate and 50 mM maleate[21,22] for stabilization; commercial preparation, see p. 462.
8. Sodium hydrogen carbonate, $NaHCO_3$, A.R.

Purity of Enzyme Preparation

GOT must be free from MDH. Contamination with glutamate dehydrogenase, lactate dehydrogenase and oxaloacetate decarboxylase should be < 0.05% (relative to the GOT activity).

---

* Complete reagent kits are available commercially, see p. 558.

Preparation of Solutions (for ca. 25 assays)

Prepare all solutions with fresh, doubly distilled water.
  I. Phosphate/aspartate (0.1 M phosphate buffer, pH 7.4; 42 mM aspartate):
      Dissolve 0.2 g. KH_2PO_4 + 1.5 g. K_2HPO_4 + 0.66 g. Na-L-aspartate or 0.56 g. L-aspartic
      acid in 50 ml. distilled water, adjust to pH 7.4 with 0.1 N NaOH and dilute to 100 ml. with
      distilled water.
 II. 2-Oxoglutarate (66 mM):
      Dissolve 19 mg. Na_2-2-oxoglutarate in 1.5 ml. distilled water or 14.5 mg. 2-oxoglutaric acid
      in ca. 1 ml. distilled water, neutralize with ca. 0.2 ml. 1 N NaOH and dilute to 1.5 ml. with
      distilled water.
III. Reduced nicotinamide-adenine dinucleotide (12 mM β-NADH):
      Dissolve 15 mg. NADH-Na_2 and 15 mg. $NaHCO_3$ in 1.5 ml. distilled water.
IV. Glutamate-oxaloacetate transaminase, GOT (1 mg. protein/ml.):
      If necessary, dilute the stock suspension accordingly with 3 M ammonium sulphate solution.

Stability of Solutions

Store all solutions at 0–4 °C. The phosphate/aspartate solution (I) is stable providing that bacterial
contamination does not occur. Prepare the 2-oxoglutarate and NADH solution every month. The GOT
suspension keeps for several months.

Procedure

Collection and Stability of Sample

Collection of sample:

Collect blood without venestasis. Addition of 1 mg. oxalate/ml., 1 mg. citrate/ml., 2 mg.
fluoride/ml., 0.2 mg. heparin/ml. or 1 mg EDTA/ml. have no adverse effects. Centrifuge at ca.
3 000 g for 10 min. to collect plasma or serum. Use only fresh, non-haemolysed serum or plasma.

Stability of enzyme in sample:

According to[23] the enzyme in serum loses ca. 17% of its activity in 24 hr. at room temperature,
ca. 11% at 4 °C and ca. 2% in the frozen state. This does not take into account the possible
changes in optimum substrate concentration due to ageing of the enzyme[15].
According to[20] the enzyme in human serum is stable for at least 48 hr. at 20 °C and at least 2
weeks at 4 °C.

Assay System

Wavelength: 340 (Hg 334, Hg 365) nm; light path: 1 cm.; final volume: 2.75 ml.; 25 °C. (constant temperature cuvette holder). A blank is unnecessary; read against air. Bring the solutions to 25 °C before the assay.

Pipette into cuvettes:			Concentration in assay mixture
Phosphate/aspartate solution	(I)	2.50 ml.	91 mM phosphate 38 mM aspartate
2-Oxoglutarate solution	.(II)	0.05 ml.	1.2 mM
NADH solution	(III)	0.05 ml.	0.22 mM
GOT suspension	(IV)	0.05 ml.	18 μg./ml. $\geqq$ 3.3 U/ml.
Mix and allow to stand for 5 min. Oxaloacetate is formed from aspartate (optimum concentration for the MDH reaction).			
Sample (serum, cerebrospinal fluid, etc.)		0.10 ml.	
Mix, read extinction and start stopwatch. Repeat readings at exactly 1, 2 and 3 min.			

The ΔE/min. values at 365 nm should not be greater than 0.030, otherwise dilute the serum 5- to 10-fold with physiological saline or read at shorter time intervals.

Calculations

The calculation formula (8) on p. 313 applies and therefore the following relationships hold:

Wavelength:	*334 nm*	*340 nm*	*365 nm*
Volume activity =	4508 $\times$ ΔE/min.	4421 $\times$ ΔE/min.	8088 $\times$ ΔE/min. [U/l.]

Precision of Method

With values around 100 U/l. a standard deviation of 5 U/l. was found. The coefficient of variation is 5%.

Normal Values

In human serum 48–96 U/l. (25 °C)[24]. For assays with 0.5 mM oxaloacetate *King* and *Morris*[25] give values for normal adults of 12.5–50 U/l. and double this range for the new-born.
Potter[26] has published values for the MDH activity of several organs (aqueous homogenates) of laboratory animals.

Sources of Error

Effects of drugs and other therapeutic measures: None known.

Interference in the assay technique: Possible interference due to the decarboxylation of the substrate oxaloacetate is reduced to a minimum in the assay described here. For the effects of enzyme inhibitors in NADH preparations of insufficient purity, see p. 158.

Specificity of Method

As the oxoglutarate added reacts nearly completely before the start of the MDH reaction the presence of glutamate dehydrogenase in the sample does not interfere. The MDH activity is measured specifically.

Details for Measurements in Tissues

The total cell content of malate dehydrogenase is determined only after optimum homogenization of the tissue[5,6,26], because a portion of the activity is located in the mitochondria. It is possible to differentiate between cytoplasmic and mitochondrial MDH by variation of the homogenization technique. As the optimum pH and substrate concentrations for malate dehydrogenase differ from tissue to tissue, they should be determined in preliminary experiments.

References

1 *T. Thunberg*, Scand. Arch. Physiol. *24*, 23 [1910].
2 *F. Batelli & L. Stern*, Biochem. Z. *31*, 478 [1911].
3 *F. B. Straub*, Hoppe-Seylers Z. physiol. Chem. *275*, 63 [1942].
4 *E. P. Kennedy & A. L. Lehninger*, J. biol. Chem. *179*, 957 [1949].
5 *Th. Bücher & M. Klingenberg*, Angew. Chem. *70*, 552 [1958].
6. *A. Delbrück, E. Zebe & Th. Bücher*, Biochem. Z. *331*, 273 [1959].
7 *B. Hess & E. Gehm*, Klin. Wschr. *33*, 91 [1955].
8 *B. Hess & R. Raftopoulo*, Dtsch. Arch. klin. Med. *204*, 97 [1957].
9 *W. E. C. Wacker, D. D. Ulmer & B. L. Vallee*, New England J. Med. *255*, 449 [1956].
10 *A. Siegel & R. J. Bing*, Proc. Soc. exp. Biol. Med. *91*, 604 [1956].
11 *C. L. Markert & F. Møller*, Proc. nat. Acad. Sci. USA *45*, 753 [1959].
12 *F. Wroblewski & K. Gregory:* Proc. 14th Internat. Congr. Clin. Chem. Edinburgh, 1960. E. & S. Livingstone Ltd., Edinburgh and London 1961, p. 62.
13 *E. S. Vesell & A. G. Bearn*, Ann. New York Acad. Sci *75*, 286 [1958].
14 *B. Hess*, Ann. New York Acad. Sci. *75*, 292 [1958]·
15 *E. Schmidt & F. W. Schmidt*, Klin. Wschr. *38*, 810 [1960].
16 *M. U. Tsao*, Arch. Biochem. Biophysics *90*, 234 [1960].
17 *J. R. Stern, S. Ochoa & F. Lynen*, J. biol. Chem. *198*, 313 [1952].
18 *A. M. Hehler, A. Kornberg, S. Grisola & S. Ochoa*, J. biol. Chem. *174*, 961 [1948].
19 *R. Ordell:* Intern. Congr. Clin. Chem., Stockholm 1957, Summaries and Abstracts, p. 116.
20 *J. King:* Practical Clinical Enzymology, D. Van Nostrand Comp. Ltd., London 1965, p. 93.
21 *W. T. Jenkins & J. W. Sizer*, J. Amer. chem. Soc. *79*, 2655 [1957].
22 *W. T. Jenkins, D. A. Yphantis & J. W. Sizer*, J. biol. Chem. *234*, 50 [1959].
23 *H. Südhof & E. W. Wötzel*, Klin. Wschr. *38*, 1165 [1960].
24 *G. Laudahn*, personal communication, 1964
25 *J. King & M. B. Morris*, Arch. Dis. Childh. *36*, 604 [1961].
26 *V. R. Potter*, J. biol. Chem. *165*, 311 [1946].

Assay after Electrophoretic Separation

Roger Jozef Wieme

As shown by *Bücher*[1] and his colleagues, NAD-dependent malate dehydrogenase (MDH) exists in two forms which differ in their pH optimum and in their substrate affinities. They occur in the cytoplasmic and mitochondrial compartment. The M-enzyme is characterized by inhibition by oxaloacetate concentrations above 0.1 mM, while the C-enzyme is not inhibited under these conditions. This holds for all cells of many plant and animal species[2,3].

The two enzymes are different proteins[4,5] with different amino acid composition[6]. In all higher animals and plants they have a molecular weight of 70000, which indicates a dimeric structure[7] that is essential for the catalytic activity[8]. In some micro-organisms, such as *Bacillus subtilis*[9] and *Neurospora*[10], MDH with a tetrameric structure has been found. Hybrids from C and M enzymes should not occur *in vivo*[11], although they can be prepared *in vitro*[12].

The first electrophoretic separation of MDH was described by *Vessell* and *Bearn*[13], who used starch-block electrophoresis followed by elution. Since then many conflicting results have been published, particularly on the heterogeneity of the M-enzyme. The C-enzyme behaves as a virtually homogeneous entity in all electrophoretic media and in all animal species examined. Under the usual electrophoretic conditions it migrates like a β-protein. In contrast, the M-enzyme shows complex and inconsistent behaviour. A number of contradictory results have been published[14-19]. A fundamental study was carried out by *Thorne*[20] who separated the M-enzyme into 6 fractions by means of starch-gel electrophoresis at pH 7.0 (buffer: 1.4 mM sodium citrate + 8.6 mM sodium phosphate). This separation could not be obtained in *Poulik* buffer or in 50 mM veronal buffer (both at pH 8.6). The bands of M-MDH are close to each other in the γ-globulin area. *Kaplan* and his colleagues[21] considered them to be conformational variants on the basis of observations on the conversion of one form into the other by denaturation at pH 2 and renaturation[12]. Other workers have not been able to reproduce these experiments[22,23].

The M-enzyme from tuna fish cannot be further separated under the conditions of *Thorne*; it migrates before the C-enzyme to the anode[4].

According to our experience the M-enzyme from human tissue extracts migrates rapidly to the anode as a striated zone just before albumin, providing that agar electrophoresis in veronal buffer (pH 8.4; $\mu = 0.05$) is used. The mobility decreases with increasing concentration. In addition, there are some weaker components which appear in the α- and especially in the slower γ-globulin zone. We have found that the behaviour of the M-enzyme depends to a large extent on the ionic strength. In veronal buffer, pH 8.4 but with $\mu = 0.2$ the M-enzyme forms a compact band with mr = 0.05. In starch-gel with the discontinuous buffer of *Poulik* the M-enzyme migrates as a wide zone which extends from the point of application to the anode, an indication of poor penetration in the gel. The mobility therefore appears to be greatly influenced by aggregation phenomena and by instability of the conformation of the M-enzyme.

As with many other isoenzymes, the elution analysis first used by *Vesell*[13] is being replaced by enzyme-electrophoretic methods (zymogram). However, it should always be borne in mind that several factors can interfere with the correct interpretation of a zymogram and are responsible for confused findings in the literature. If oxaloacetate is used as substrate (forward reaction), bands with LDH activity are also detected due to formation of pyruvate by the decarboxylation of oxaloacetate. With this method a maximum of 6 fractions have been described in human tissues, serum or cerebrospinal fluid[24]. Even the "back" reaction is not free from interference of the "nothing dehydrogenase" class (see p. 274). In human serum non-enzymatic reduction of the tetrazolium salt occurs in the albumin and lipoprotein bands. In addition, in concentrated tissue extracts there appears to be a considerable amount of lactate bound to LDH isoenzymes. These zones appear as coloured bands without addition of substrate. As MDH activity in tissue extracts is much lower than that of LDH, this form of interference cannot be avoided by dilution of the sample. It is therefore important that all enzyme-electrophoretic methods are tested for the presence of "nothing dehydrogenase".

The most important electrophoretic media for the study of MDH are agar gel[16,24] and cellulose acetate[25], or starch gel[14,20] and polyacrylamide gel[18,19,26,27].

Application of Method

MDH isoenzymes have been studied in particular in tissue extracts, because the zymogram serves as guide to phylogeny[28] and ontogeny[29-32]. The enzymatic properties and electrophoretic mobility of the C-enzyme have changed little during evolution. The zymograms from different tissues of the same species are similar to each other so that no tissue-specific changes in serum pattern are to be expected after necrosis of an organ. *Schmidt* et al.[33] showed by chromatography that the M-MDH in serum increases with mitochondrial damage, and that it has a remarkably long half-life. With their chromatographic method they found that M-MDH made up about 20% of the total MDH of normal serum. M-MDH in normal human serum cannot be detected with certainty by electrophoresis. *Yakulis*[16] was unable to obtain a consistent pattern in pathological conditions. With the method described below (veronal buffer; pH 8.4; $\mu = 0.05$) the C-enzyme is always clearly discernible; it appears in the β-globulin area (mr = 0.45). In our studies it increases in all cases of raised total MDH in serum. The diagnostic importance of the modification of the M-enzyme deserves further study.

A genetically determined polymorphism of M-MDH has been found in leucocytes and placenta of humans. In electrophoretic studies under the conditions of *Thorne*, about 1% of an American population showed an abnormally strong intensity of the 3 slowest bands in the γ-globulin region[34]. With the C-enzyme a genetic variant has been found only in one of the 300 subjects studied[35].

Principle

The electrophoretic separation is carried out in agar gel. This is then covered with a second agar gel layer which contains L-malate, NAD and a tetrazolium system for revealing the NADH formed in the reaction. A purple colour occurs at the areas of activity and these can be evaluated by scanning at 546 nm.

Optimum Conditions for Measurements

The L-malate concentration chosen is a little lower than usual, so as to avoid inhibition of the C-enzyme[36]. At a concentration of 50 mM malate the M-enzyme is still fully active[37]. EDTA is necessary to prevent interference with the colour reaction by Cu^{2+}. It considerably increases the sensitivity of the staining reaction (see p. 274) so that the use of cyanide can be avoided. The ionic strength of 0.1 used here instead of the more usual 0.05 gives a clearer separation of the M-enzyme.

Equipment

1. Electrophoresis apparatus for agar gel (e.g. Vitatron type CTA/100).
2. Optical scanning apparatus with extinction recorder (e.g. Vitatron photometer type UFD 100 with lin/log. recorder type UR 403).

Reagents

1. Special Agar-Noble (Difco-Detroit)

2. Sodium veronal (5,5-diethylbarbituric acid, sodium salt)

3. Hydrochloric acid, 1 N
4. DL-Malic acid
5. Nicotinamide-adenine dinucleotide, NAD
   free acid; commercial preparation, see p. 545.
6. 2-(p-Iodophenyl)-3-(p-nitrophenyl)-5-phenyl-tetrazolium chloride, INT

7. Phenazine methosulphate, PMS
8. Ethylenediaminetetra-acetic acid, EDTA disodium salt, EDTA-$Na_2H_2 \cdot 2H_2O$.
9. Albumin
   human albumin, dry, purest grade.
10. Sodium hydroxide, 32% (w/v), about 8 N
11. Acetic acid

Preparation of Solutions

Prepare all solutions with fresh distilled water.

I. Veronal buffer (pH 8.4; $\mu = 0.1$):
   Dissolve 17.0 g. sodium veronal in about 600 ml. distilled water, add 23.5 ml. 1 N HCl and dilute to 1000 ml. with distilled water.

II. DL-Malate (1 M):
   Dissolve 1.34 g. DL-malic acid in about 8 ml. distilled water, adjust to pH 7.0 with 32% NaOH, dilute to 10 ml. with distilled water. This solution is 0.5 M with respect to L-malate.

III. Phenazine methosulphate (3.27 mM):
   Dissolve 10 mg. PMS in 10 ml. distilled water, and use directly for the preparation of substrate stock solution VI.

IV. Nicotinamide-adenine dinucleotide (13 mM):
   Dissolve 100 mg. NAD in 10 ml. distilled water.

V. 2-(p-Iodophenyl)-3-(p-nitrophenyl)-5-phenyl tetrazolium chloride (1.97 mM):
   Dissolve 20 mg. INT in 20 ml. distilled water and use directly for preparation of substrate stock solution VI.

VI. Substrate stock solution (202 mM DL-malate; 0.18 mM PMS; 2.9 mM NAD; 1.0 mM INT):
   Mix the solutions in the following order:

DL-Malate solution	(II)	2.25 ml.
PMS solution	(III)	0.60 ml.
NAD solution	(IV)	2.25 ml.
INT solution	(V)	6.00 ml.

   Store in a dark bottle at 4 °C.

VII. Albumin (1% w/v):
   Dissolve 1.0 g. albumin in 100 ml. distilled water.

VIII. Fixing solution (0.3 N acetic acid):
   Dilute 2 ml. acetic acid with 100 ml. distilled water.

IX. EDTA stock solution (10 mM):
   Dissolve 372 mg. EDTA-$Na_2H_2 \cdot 2H_2O$ in 100 ml. distilled water.

X. Agar stock solution (1.5% w/v):
   Dissolve 1.5 g. Agar-Noble (Difco) in 50 ml. veronal buffer (I), add 2 ml. EDTA stock solution and dilute to 100 ml. with distilled water. Heat for 20 min. in a boiling water bath; while still warm distribute in 1.5 ml. portions in stoppered test tubes.

Stability of Solutions

Store all solutions at 0–4 °C. Solution I is stable indefinitely, the substrate stock solution VI is stable for at least 2 months (in dark); it should be discarded if a greenish colour appears. Solution VII is stable for weeks.

Preparation of Gels

1. Electrophoresis gel

The preparation is carried out as described under "Amylases" on p. 911, but 1 g. of Ion- agar is replaced by 0.9 g. Agar-Noble (Difco) and veronal buffer (I) is used. As soon as the solut- ion has cooled to 50 °C, add 1 ml. albumin solution (VII) and 1 ml. EDTA stock solution (IX). Pour the plates as described in the method.

2. Substrate developer gel

Immediately before use immerse a test tube containing 1.5 ml. agar stock solution (X) in a boiling water bath until the contents are completely dissolved. Pour the warm solution into 1.2 ml. substrate stock solution (VI). Then proceed exactly as described in the method on p. 911. Final concentrations after dilution with the agar stock solution: 47 mM L-malate; 1.3 mM NAD; 80 μM PMS; 0.45 mM INT; 0.12 mM EDTA.

Procedure

Collection, Treatment and Stability of Sample

MDH is not considered to be particularly unstable. However, according to our experience the electrophoretic mobility of M-MDH alters after about a week, especially on repeated freezing and thawing.

Electrophoresis

Carry out the electrophoretic separation according to p. 912 ("Amylases").

Incubation

It is essential that the operations are carried out in a room protected from direct sunlight. Immediately on completion of the electrophoresis place the slide in a horizontal plane and place a rubber frame around the area of interest. Pour on the substrate developer solution (see above), so that the free space is filled and allow to stand for 2 min. Remove the rubber frame and cut the electrophoresis layer to the same size as the substrate layer. Place the double layer in a small petri dish and incubate this for 120 min. at 37 °C, in a darkened incubator. The zones of activity appear stained purple. It is necessary to treat a control sample in the same way (without DL-malate in the substrate layer).

Evaluation

The optical scanning can be carried out on moist gel, but is better on a dry film. For this immerse the plate after the incubation for 3 hr. in fixing solution (VIII), then place on filter paper and dry overnight at 37 °C. Carry out the evaluation at 546 nm.

Precision of Method

As the assay has mainly been used for purposes of separation, no quantitative data are available. Comparison with studies on LDH suggest that the area under the peaks is related to the enzyme activity (see p. 280).

Normal Values

In normal human serum only 1 peak occurs at mr = 0.45 (Fig. 1). In addition "nothing dehydrogenase" (see p. 274) occurs in the area of the lipoproteins (red-orange colour) and of albumin (purple colour). In tissue extracts a more complicated picture is obtained with a well-defined C-enzyme always found at mr = 0.45. The M-enzyme gives up to 7 bands. In the more severe cases of muscular dystrophy the M-enzyme can be found in serum (Fig. 1).

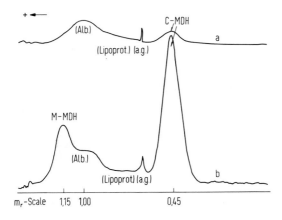

Fig. 1. Example of a MDH separation by this method.
a) Normal human serum (total MDH 78 U/l.); b) serum of a patient with primary muscular dystrophy (total activity 980 U/l.). Optical evaluation at 546 nm with a Vitatron photometer, type UR 403. "Nothing dehydrogenase" activity (see p. 274) in (alb.) and (lipoprot.). Starting point at a.g. ("application groove"). Relative electrophoretic mobility is given on the mr scale.

Sources of Error

The "nothing dehydrogenase" activity can be very misleading if it is not taken into account. This applies in particular to tissue extracts, where in addition the LDH isoenzymes can interfere (see p. 274). The ionic strength should be controlled precisely, because it has a very marked effect on the mobility and number of bands of the M-enzyme. Haemolysis only affects the C-peak, because erythrocytes contain only this type of MDH[38].

Specificity of Method

With sufficient control of the "nothing dehydrogenase" effect this method can be considered to be specific for NAD-linked malate dehydrogenase.

Details for Measurements in Tissues

We found that the M-enzyme can be extracted selectively by simple extraction with 1-butanol. The tissue is homogenized with 2 volumes isotonic sodium chloride and then 1 volume of 1-butanol is added. The homogenate is centrifuged for 30 min. at 20000 g, and the clear supernatant fluid stored at 4 °C. Repeated freezing and thawing is to be avoided. In an ultrasonic extract of human placenta a C/M ratio of about 1/2 has been measured.

Other Methods

Mainly, class II methods have been used (see p. 261). Coenzyme analogues have been employed to a large extent by *Kaplan* and his group[39] for the study of phylogenetic relationships. The monofluoro- and difluoroderivatives of oxaloacetate have been used for a differential test[40].

References

1 A. Delbrück, H. Schimassek, K. Bartsch & Th. Bücher, Biochem. Z. 331, 297 [1959].
2 N. O. Kaplan in N. V. Thoai & J. Roche: Homologous enzymes and biochemical evolution. Gordon and Breach, New York 1968, p. 405.
3 I. Witt, R. Kronau & H. Holzer, Biochim. biophys. Acta 128, 63 [1966].
4 G. B. Kitto & R. G. Lewis, Biochim. biophys. Acta 139, 1 [1967].
5 G. B. Kitto, Biochim. biophys. Acta 139,16 [1967].
6 T. Dévényi, S. J. Rogers & R. G. Wolfe, Nature 210, 489 [1966].
7 W. H. Murphy, G. B. Kitto, J. Everse & N. O. Kaplan, Biochemistry 6, 603 [1967].
8 K. Harada & R. G. Wolfe, J. biol. Chem. 243, 4131 [1968].
9 W. H. Murphy, C. Barnaby, F. J. Lin & N. O. Kaplan, J. biol. Chem. 242, 1548 [1967].
10 K. D. Munkres, Ann. N. Y. Acad. Sci. 151, 294 [1968].
11 N. O. Kaplan, Ann. N. Y. Acad. Sci. 151, 382 [1968].
12 O. P. Chilson, G. B. Kitto, J. Pudles & N. O. Kaplan, J. biol. Chem. 241, 2431 [1966].
13 E. S. Vesell & A. G. Bearn, J. clin. Inv. 37, 672 [1958].
14 M. U. Tsao, Arch. Biochem. Biophys. 90, 234 [1960].
15 M. van Sande, D. Karcher & A. Lowenthal in H. Peeters: Protides of the biological fluids, Symposium Bruges 1960, Elsevier Amsterdam 1961, p. 108.
16 V. J. Yakulis, C. W. Gibson & P. Heller, Am. J. clin. Pathol. 38, 378 [1962].
17 J. Kamarýt & Z. Zázvorka, Clin. Chim. Acta 9, 559 [1964].
18 M. Sims, Nature 207, 757 [1965].
19 G. R. Honold, V. Macko & M. A. Stahmann, Naturwissenschaften 7, 169 [1967].
20 C. J. R. Thorne, L. I. Grossman & N. O. Kaplan, Biochim. biophys. Acta 73, 193 [1963].
21 G. B. Kitto, P. M. Wassarman & N. O. Kaplan, Proc. Natl. Acad. Sci. (U.S.) 56, 578 [1966].
22 K. G. Mann & C. S. Vestling, Biochim. biophys. Acta 159, 567 [1968].
23 A. N. Schechter & C. J. Epstein, Science 159, 997 [1968].
24 A. Lowenthal, M. van Sande & D. Karcher, Ann. N. Y. Acad. Sci. 94, 988 [1961].
25 S. Sawaki, N. Morikawa & K. Yamada, Nature 207, 523 [1965].
26 E. Goldberg, Science 139, 602 [1963].
27 Y. Rabinowitz & A. A. Dietz, Blood 29, 182 [1967].
28 G. B. Kitto & A. C. Wilson, Science 153, 1408 [1966].
29 B. Wiggert & C. A. Villee, Science 138, 509 [1962].
30 R. D. Billiar, J. C. Brungard & C. A. Villee, Science 146, 1464 [1964].
31 G. W. Patton jr., L. Mets & C. A. Villee, Science 156, 400 [1967].
32 C. A. Villee, Ann. N. Y. Acad. Sci. 151, 222 [1968].
33 E. Schmidt, W. Schmidt & P. Otto, Clin. Chim. Acta 15, 283 [1967].
34 R. G. Davidson & J. A. Cortner, Science 157, 1569 [1967].
35 R. G. Davidson & J. A. Cortner, Nature 215, 761 [1967].
36 S. Englard & H. H. Breiger, Biochim. biophys. Acta 56, 571 [1962].
37 L. Siegel & S. Englard, Biochim. biophys. Acta 54, 67 [1961].
38 E. Shrago, Arch. Biochem. Biophys. 109, 57 [1965].
39 N. O. Kaplan & M. M. Ciotti, Ann. N. Y. Acad. Sci. 94, 701 [1961].
40 E. Kun & P. Volfin, Biochem. biophys. Res. Commun. 22, 187 [1966].

Isocitrate Dehydrogenase

Isocitrate dehydrogenase, ICDH (*threo*-D$_s$-Isocitrate: NADP oxidoreductase, decarboxylating, EC 1.1.1.42) was discovered by *Martius*[1-3]. It was soon shown that the enzyme was also able to decarboxylate oxalosuccinate[4,5]. With highly purified enzyme preparations it has been shown that the same protein is responsible for the dehydrogenase and decarboxylase activity[6-9].

ICDH is widely distributed in Nature; heart muscle is a particularly rich source. By starch-gel electrophoresis *Tsao*[10] and *Bell*[11] obtained isoenzyme fractions from rat liver, kidney and brain or from heart, liver, kidney and skeletal muscle respectively. According to *Goebell*[12] it is possible to differentiate exactly between extra- and intramitochondrial activity. In muscle tissue 15–25% of the total activity is present in the extramitochondrial compartment.

The main interest of ICDH determinations in serum is in liver diseases. The determination in heart and blood diseases is of lesser interest.

Application of Method: In biochemistry and clinical chemistry.

UV-Assay

Erich Bernt and Hans Ulrich Bergmeyer

Principle

(1)   2-Oxoglutarate $+ CO_2 +$ NADPH $+ H^+ \xrightleftharpoons[Mn^{2+}]{ICDH}$ Isocitrate $+$ NADP$^+$

The equilibrium is completely to the left at pH 7.5. The equilibrium constant K', [isocitrate] × [NADP]/ [2-oxoglutarate] × [CO$_2$] × [NADPH] is 1.3×10^{-4} litre/mole at pH 7.0 and 22 °C[13]. The assay is carried out with isocitrate as substrate and NADP as coenzyme[6].

The amount of isocitrate oxidized, as determined by the increase of extinction due to formation of NADPH, is a measure of the ICDH activity.

Optimum Conditions for Measurements

The enzyme from human serum has the highest activity[14,15] at pH 7.5 with 3–4 mM DL-isocitrate and 2–4 mM Mn^{2+}.

Measurements at different temperatures may require different measuring conditions (cf. p. 127). Nevertheless, results obtained under the same measuring conditions but at different temperatures were formerly compared with each other ("conversion factors" were determined). Such conversion factors may be correct if determined with a relatively large proband collective; however, they cannot be applied generally to the individual case (cf. p. 129). The value of the following relative reaction rates[16] thus lies in being able to appraise the temperature dependence of the reaction and at the most to compare qualitatively values up to the limit of normal.

°C	18	19	20	21	22	23	24	*25*	26	27
	1.75	1.65	1.5	1.4	1.3	1.2	1.1	*1.0*	0.93	0.85
°C	28	29	30	31	32	33	34	35	36	37
	0.78	0.72	0.67	0.62	0.57	0.52	0.46	0.42	0.39	0.36

Equipment

Spectrophotometer or spectrum-line photometer suitable for accurate measurements at 340, 334 or 365 nm; preferably with constant temperature cuvette holder; water bath (25 °C); stopwatch.

Reagents*

1. Triethanolamine hydrochloride
2. Sodium hydroxide, 1.0 N
3. Sodium chloride, NaCl, A. R.
4. DL-Isocitrate,
   trisodium salt·$2H_2O$

5. Nicotinamide-adenine dinucleotide phosphate, NADP
   disodium salt NADP-Na_2H; commercial preparation, see p. 545.
6. Manganous sulphate, $MnSO_4 \cdot H_2O$, A. R.

Purity of Reagents

All reagents must be A. R. grade or the purest quality available. NADP-Na_2H should contain at least 82% enzymatically active NADP.

Preparation of Solutions (for ca. 25 determinations)

Prepare all solutions with fresh, doubly distilled water.

I. Buffer/substrate (0.1 M triethanolamine buffer, pH 7.5; 4.6 mM DL-isocitrate; 52 mM NaCl):
   Dissolve 1.40 g. triethanolamine hydrochloride, 225 mg. NaCl and 100 mg. DL-isocitrate-$Na_3 \cdot 2H_2O$ in 50 ml. distilled water, adjust to pH 7.5 with ca. 2 ml. 1 N NaOH and dilute to 75 ml. with distilled water.

II. Nicotinamide-adenine dinucleotide phosphate/$MnSO_4$ (10 mM NADP; 0.12 M $MnSO_4$):
   Dissolve 26 mg. NADP-Na_2H and 60 mg. $MnSO_4 \cdot H_2O$ in 3 ml. distilled water.

Stability of Solutions

The buffer/substrate solution is stable for at least 3 months at 4 °C if bacterial contamination is avoided, similarly the NADP/Mn^{2+} solution is stable for 4 weeks at 4 °C.

Procedure

Collection, Treatment and Stability of Sample

Collection of sample:

Collect blood without venestasis. Addition of citrate (1 mg./ml. blood) or EDTA (1 mg./ml. blood) has no adverse effects. With fluoride (2 mg./ml. blood) there is a 15% inhibition. Oxalate interferes because it causes turbidity in the reaction mixture. Obtain plasma or serum by centrifugation for 10 min. at ca. 3000 g. Use only fresh, non-haemolysed serum or plasma. Turbidity in the assay system is prevented by addition of NaCl.

---

* Complete reagents kits are available commercially, see p. 558.

Stability of enzyme in serum:

According to[14,15] the enzyme is stable for up to 14 days at 4 °C. However, according to our studies there is already a ca. 30% loss of activity after 3 days at 4 °C. The enzyme cannot be reactivated by SH-reagents.

Assay System

Wavelength: 340 (Hg 334, Hg 365) nm; light path: 1 cm.; final volume: 3.10 ml.; 25 °C (constant temperature cuvette holder). A blank is unnecessary; read against air. Bring the solutions to 25 °C before the start of the assay.

Pipette into cuvettes:			Concentration in assay mixture
Buffer/substrate solution	(I)	2.50 ml.	80 mM triethanolamine 3.7 mM DL-isocitrate 42 mM NaCl
Sample		0.50 ml.	
Mix and allow to incubate at 25 °C for ca. 5 min.			
NADP/Mn^{2+} solution	(II)	0.10 ml.	0.32 mM NADP 3.9 mM Mn^{2+}
Mix, read the extinction and start a stopwatch. After exactly 1, 2 and 3 min. read again and calculate the mean of the extinction changes (ΔE/min.).			

The values for ΔE/min. at 365 nm should not be greater than 0.050, otherwise dilute the serum 5- to 10-fold with physiological saline.

Calculations

The calculation formula (8) on p. 313 applies and therefore the following relationships hold.

Wavelength:	*334 nm*	*340 nm*	*365 nm*
Volume activity =	$1016 \times \Delta$E/min.	$997 \times \Delta$E/min.	$1797 \times \Delta$E/min. [U/l.]

Precision of Method

With values around 20 U/l. serum a standard deviation of 2 U/l. was found. The coefficient of variation is 10%.

Normal Values

In human serum from adults 1–4 U/l.; from new-born 3–8 U/l. (25 °C)[14].

Sources of Error

Effects of drugs: None known.

Interference in the assay technique: The enzyme has very reactive SH groups. Samples should be absolutely fresh and traces of metals must be rigorously excluded.

Specificity of Method

The enzyme reacts specifically with D-isocitrate and NADP. L-Isocitrate and *cis*-aconitate cannot replace D-isocitrate, likewise NAD cannot be substituted for NADP.

Details for Measurements in Tissues

The total ICDH content of the cell is only obtained after optimum homogenization of the tissue. Data concerning the mitochondrial or particulate-bound location of ICDH in different animal organs can be found in[17-20].

References

1 C. Martius, Hoppe-Seyler's Z. physiol. Chem. 247, 104 [1937].
2 C. Martius, Hoppe-Seyler's Z. physiol. Chem. 257, 29 [1939].
3 C. Martius & G. Schorre, Z. Naturforsch. 5b, 170 [1950].
4 F. Lynen & H. Scherer, Liebig's Ann. Chem. 560, 163 [1948].
5 S. Ochoa in Sumner & Myrbäck: Enzymes, Vol. II/2, p. 929.
6 G. Siebert, J. Dubuc, R. C. Warner & G. W. E. Plaut, J. biol. Chem. 226, 965 [1957].
7 G. Siebert, M. Carsiotis & G. W. E. Plaut, J. biol. Chem. 226, 977 [1957].
8 J. Moyle & M. Dixon, Biochem. J. 63, 548 [1956].
9 J. Moyle, Biochem. J. 63, 552 [1956].
10 M. U. Tsao, Arch. Biochem. 90, 234 [1960].
11 J. L. Bell & D. N. Baron, Biochem. J. 82, 5P [1962].
12 H. Goebell & D. Pette, Enzym. biol. clin. 8, 161 [1967].
13 S. Ochoa, J. biol. Chem. 174, 133 [1948].
14 S. K. Wolfson jr. & H. G. Williams-Ashman, Proc. Soc. Exp. Biol. Med. 96, 231 [1957].
15 G. Ellis & D. M. Goldberg, Clin. Biochem. 2, 175 [1971].
16 J. King: Practical Clinical Enzymology, D. Van Nostrand Comp. Ltd., London 1965, p. 78.
17 P. V. Vignais & P. M. Vignais, Biochim. biophys. Acta 47, 515 [1961].
18 C. H. Callagher, J. D. Judah & K. R. Rees, Proc. R. Soc. London [B] 145, 134 [1956].
19 H. F. DeLuca & H. Steenbock, Science, N. Y. 126, 258 [1957].
20 H. Gutfreund, K. E. Ebner & L. Mediola, Nature 192, 820 [1961].

Colorimetric Assay[1]

John King

Under optimum conditions the reaction is linear until 50% of the substrate has been converted, therefore within this limit the reaction product can be measured colorimetrically after a fixed incubation time[2,3]. The enzyme is stable for 60 min. at 55 °C; the assay can be carried out at 37 °C to obtain sufficiently high rates.

Principle

Equation, see p. 624. Both reaction products, 2-oxoglutarate and NADPH, form 2,4-dinitrophenyl-hydrazones which absorb in alkaline solution at 385 nm and 420 nm respectively[4]. The enzyme activity (mU/ml.) is obtained by means of a standard curve.

Optimum Conditions for Measurements

The pH optimum varies with the buffer used, but at pH 7.2–8.2 the variation is least. We use triethanol-amine buffer with manganese as activator. EDTA must be added to avoid the precipitation of manganese hydroxide in the alkaline medium. In triethanolamine buffer manganese behaves better than in other buffers. We find optimum activity at 37 °C with 2.5 mM DL-isocitrate (K_M 0.2 mM), 1.25 mM NADP (K_M 0.14 mM) and 2.5 mM Mn^{2+} (K_M 0.18 mM). More than 95% of this activity is found with 0.8 mM NADP[1]. With optimum Mg^{2+} (7mM) only 80% of the value with Mn^{2+} is found.

Measurements at different temperatures may require different measuring conditions (cf. p. 127). Nevertheless, results obtained under the same measuring conditions but at different temperatures were formerly compared with each other ("conversion factors" were determined). Such conversion factors may be correct if determined with a relatively large proband collective; however, they cannot be applied generally to the individual case (cf. p. 129). The value of the following relative rates[5,6] thus lies in being able to appraise the temperature dependence of the reaction and at the most to compare qualitatively values up to the limit of normal.

°C	25	30	37
	1	1.66	2.87

Equipment

Spectrophotometer or spectrum-line photometer suitable for measurements at 390 (405) nm; 37 °C water bath.

Reagents

1. Triethanolamine hydrochloride
2. Sodium hydroxide, A. R., 0.1 N and 0.4 N
3. Isocitric acid,
   trisodium salt
4. Manganous sulphate, A. R., $MnSO_4 \cdot 4H_2O$
5. Nicotinamide-adenine dinucleotide phosphate, NADP
   disodium salt, NADP-Na_2H; commercial preparation, see p. 546.
6. 2,4-Dinitrophenylhydrazine, A. R.
7. Hydrochloric acid, A. R., 1 N
8. Ethylenediaminetetra-acetate, EDTA, A. R.
   disodium salt, EDTA-$Na_2H_2 \cdot 2H_2O$
9. Reduced nicotinamide-adenine dinucleotide phosphate, NADPH
   tetrasodium salt, NADPH-Na_4 or disodium salt, NADH-Na_2; commercial preparation, see p. 547.
10. 2-Oxoglutaric acid
    Commercial preparation, see p. 548.

Preparation of Solutions

Use only fresh, doubly distilled water.

    I. Triethanolamine hydrochloride buffer (0.1 M; pH 7.75):
        Dissolve 1.875 g. triethanolamine hydrochloride in 40 ml. 0.1 N NaOH and make up with distilled water to 100 ml.

    II. Isocitrate (50 mM):
        Dissolve 130 mg. DL-isocitrate in 10 ml. triethanolamine buffer (I).

    III. Manganous sulphate (50 mM):
        Dissolve 1.11 g. $MnSO_4 \cdot 4H_2O$ in distilled water and make up to 100 ml.

IV. Substrate solution (5 mM isocitrate, 5 mM Mn^{2+}):
Mix buffer (I), isocitrate solution (II) and manganous sulphate solution (III) in the ratio
8:1:1.

V. Nicotinamide-adenine dinucleotide phosphate (5.6 mM):
Dissolve 5 mg. NADP-Na_2H in 1.0 ml. distilled water.

VI. Ketone reagent (1 mM):
Dissolve 200 mg. 2,4-dinitrophenylhydrazine in hot 1 N HCl, cool and dilute to 1000 ml.
with 1 N HCl.

VII. Ethylenediaminetetra-acetate (0.1 M):
Dissolve 3.7 g. EDTA-$Na_2H_2 \cdot 2H_2O$ in distilled water and make up to 100 ml.

VIII. 2-Oxoglutarate (1.2 mM):
Dissolve 17.5 mg. 2-oxoglutarate in buffer solution (I) and make up to 100 ml.

IX. Standard solution (1.2 mM):
Dissolve 12.2 mg. NADPH-Na_4 or 10.6 mg. NADH-Na_2 in 2-oxoglutarate solution
(VIII) and make up to 10 ml.

Stability of Solutions

Sodium hydroxide, manganous sulphate and ketone reagent are stable indefinitely. Store the other
solutions in a refrigerator at 0–4 °C. The EDTA solution is stable for 6 months; if too high an extinction
is obtained, prepare afresh. Add a few drops of chloroform to the isocitrate solution to prevent the growth
of micro-organisms; it is stable for 6 months. The substrate solution (IV) and 2-oxoglutarate solution
(VIII) are stable for 3 months. The NADP solution is stable for one month. Prepare the standard solution
just before use.

Procedure

Collection, Treatment and Stability of Sample

Obtain plasma or serum as rapidly as possible. Avoid haemolysis, which gives high values.
Heparin, oxalate, citrate and fluoride can be added to blood; EDTA results in low values.
Low values are also obtained with lipaemic serum.

The enzyme in serum is stable for two days at room temperature, for seven days at 4 °C, and
for at least 10 days frozen. The stability of the enzyme in plasma is lower than in serum. The
enzyme in cerebrospinal fluid is stable for at least 4 days at 4 °C[7].

Assay System

Wavelength: 390 (405) nm; light path: 1 cm.; 37 °C; read against water. Blank containing water instead of NADP solution.

Pipette into a test tube:			Concentration in assay mixture
Buffer solution	(I)	0.8 ml.	64 mM
Isocitrate solution	(II)	0.1 ml.	3.6 mM
Mn^{2+} solution	(III)	0.1 ml.	3.6 mM
Sample (serum)		0.2 ml.	
Equilibrate in a water bath at 37 °C.			
NADP solution	(V)	0.2 ml.	0.8 mM
Mix, incubate exactly for 60 min. in a water bath.			
Ketone reagent	(VI)	1.0 ml.	
EDTA solution	(VII)	0.5 ml.	
Mix, incubate for 20 min. in a water bath.			
NaOH 0.4 N		10.0 ml.	
Mix and read extinctions.			

With extinction changes of > 0.450 repeat the assay with dilute sample.

Standard Curve

Pipette into each test tube 0.1 ml. isocitrate solution (II), 0.1 ml. $MnSO_4$ solution (III) and the following solutions. Then proceed according to the above protocol starting with addition of ketone reagent (VI). Read against tube 1.

Tube No.	1	2	3	4	5	6	7
Standard solution (IX) ml.	0	0	0.1	0.2	0.3	0.4	0.5
NADP solution (V) ml.	0	0.2	0.2	0.2	0.2	0.2	0.2
Buffer solution (I) ml.	1.2	1.0	0.9	0.8	0.7	0.6	0.5
U/l. (37 °C)		0	10	20	30	40	50

Plot the extinctions (ordinate) against the U/l. (abscissa). The standard curve is slightly concave downwards.

Calculations

The difference in extinction between tube 2 and 3 represents 0.1 ml. of a 1.2 mM solution of the reaction products. If this value is given by 0.2 ml. serum in 60 min. it corresponds to $0.1 \times 1.2 \times 1000 \times (1/0.2) \times (1/60) = 10$ nmole per min. per ml. or 10 U/l.

Precision of Method

For activities of ca. 15.5 U/l. ± 1.1 U/l. the coefficient of variation is 3.6%.

Normal Values

Serum values for healthy adults are 2.0–8.7 U/l. at 37 °C, mean value 4.75 U/l. and standard deviation 1.65 U/l. In serum from cord blood 3.7–25.4 U/l. are normal, mean 12.7 U/l.
This increases in the new-born on the second day of life to 23.7 U/l. and decreases to 9.8 U/l. on the 9th day.

Sources of Error

For simplicity the NADP concentration is not varied in preparation of the standard curve. Neither this nor the substitution of NADH for the more expensive NADPH results in an error of $> 3\%$.

Specificity of Method

There are no factors known which affect the specificity of the method. The amino acid concentration in serum is so low that the possibility of errors due to transamination is excluded.

References

1 *J. King*, Thesis, Institute of Medical Laboratory Technology, London [1967].
2 *T. H. Taylor* & *M. E. Friedman*, Clin. Chem. 6, 208 [1960].
3 *J. L. Bell* & *D. N. Baron*, Clin. Chim. Acta 5, 740 [1960].
4 *J. King*, J. Med. Lab. Technol. 17, 89 [1960].
5 *G. N. Bowers, Jr.*, Clin. Chem. 5, 509 [1957].
6 *J. King:* Practical Clinical Enzymology. D. Van Nostrand Co. Ltd., London 1965, p. 78.
7 *M. van Rymenant* & *J. Robert*, Cancer 13, 878 [1960].

6-Phosphogluconate Dehydrogenase

John King

6-Phosphogluconate dehydrogenase, 6-PG-DH (6-Phospho-D-gluconate: NADP 2-oxidoreductase, EC 1.1.1.44) was discovered by *O. Warburg*[1] in animal tissues and yeast. As an enzyme of the pentose phosphate cycle 6-PG-DH is a cytoplasmic enzyme and is widely distributed. It occurs in large amounts in adrenal cortex, liver, lung, lymphatic tissues, kidney, erythrocytes and heart; in lower amounts in skeletal muscle of various mammals[2]. *Wolfson* and *Williams-Ashman*[3] were first to report on the serum enzyme and on the 450-fold higher amount in erythrocytes. The determination of 6-PG-DH activity in serum[4-7] and in vaginal secretion[8-14] is of clinical importance.

Until recently isoenzymes of 6-PG-DH were unknown, but *Fildes* and *Parr*[15] have shown heterogeneity of the enzyme from human erythrocytes by gel-electrophoresis. These genetically-determined qualitative differences[16,17] have been thoroughly studied[18-24]. Variants of the enzyme have also been shown to occur in tissue extracts[20]; they can be distinguished by heat treatment[18], or by the action of urea or iodoacetate[19]. The enzyme activity can be followed directly at 340 nm by the formation of NADPH[3,25-27] or at 600 nm with phenazine methosulphate and the reduction of 2,6-dichlorophenolindophenol[14].

Application of Method: In biochemistry and clinical chemistry.

Principle

(1) 6-Phosphogluconate + NADP$^+$ $\xrightleftharpoons{\text{6-PG-DH}}$ Ribulose-5-phosphate + CO_2 + NADPH + H$^+$

The equilibrium of the reaction is far to the right; the reaction is linear up to 40% conversion[16]. The increase of extinction at 340 (334 or 365) nm is a measure of the activity.

Optimum Conditions for Measurements

The rate of the reaction is increased[15] by Mg^{2+} or Mn^{2+} and by chelating agents such as glycylglycine, cysteine[3,17] or EDTA[28]. The optimum pH depends on the buffer and the chelating agent[12,26,28]. For serum and glycylglycine buffer, pH 7.6 is optimum; 6.5 mM cysteine increases this activity by 20%, while at pH 8.6 the activity increases by a factor of 2.3 and at pH 9.6 by a factor of 3.4. In the presence of cysteine the pH optimum is broader. The activity is optimum and constant over the range 0.5 to 20 mM 6-phosphogluconate[16]. Nothing is known about the affinity of the isoenzymes for substrate and coenzyme. The reaction is inhibited by > 20 mM Mg^{2+}. Measurements at different temperatures may require different measuring conditions (cf. p. 127). Nevertheless, results obtained under the same measuring conditions but at different temperatures were formerly compared with each other ("conversion factors" were determined). Such conversion factors may be correct if determined with a relatively large proband collective; however, they cannot be applied generally to the individual case (cf. p. 129). The value of the following relative reaction rates[27] thus lies in being able to appraise the temperature dependence of the reaction and at the most to compare qualitatively values up to the limit of normal.

°C	18	19	20	21	22	23	24	25	26	27
	1.50	1.40	1.30	1.24	1.18	1.12	1.06	*1.00*	0.95	0.90
°C	28	29	30	31	32	33	34	35	36	37
	0.85	0.80	0.76	0.72	0.68	0.65	0.62	0.59	0.56	0.53

Equipment

Spectrophotometer or spectrum-line photometer suitable for accurate measurements at 340, 334 or 365 nm, preferably with constant temperature cuvette holder (25 °C); stopwatch.

Reagents

1. Glycylglycine
2. Sodium hydroxide, 0.1 N
3. 6-Phosphogluconate
   trisodium salt ·2H$_2$O; commercial preparation, see p. 535.
4. Magnesium chloride, MgCl$_2$ · 6H$_2$O
5. L-Cysteine hydrochloride
6. Nicotinamide-adenine dinucleotide phosphate
   disodium salt, NADP-Na$_2$H; commercial preparation, see p. 546.

Purity of Reagents

The 6-phosphogluconate must be free from glucose-6-phosphate.

Preparation of Solutions

Use only doubly distilled water.

  I. Glycylglycine buffer (0.1 M; pH 8.6):
     Dissolve 1.32 g. glycylglycine in 60 ml. 0.1 N NaOH and make up to 100 ml. with distilled water.
 II. Substrate solution (ca. 30 mM 6-PG):
     Dissolve 65 mg. 6-PG-Na$_2$·2H$_2$O in 5 ml. buffer I.
III. Magnesium chloride (0.3 M):
     Dissolve 6.1 g. MgCl$_2$ · 6H$_2$O in distilled water and make up to 100 ml.
 IV. Cysteine (0.1 M):
     Dissolve 160 mg. cysteine hydrochloride in 10 ml. 0.1 N NaOH.
  V. Coenzyme solution (ca. 2.4 mM):
     Dissolve 10 mg. NADP-Na$_2$H in distilled water and make up to 5 ml.

Stability of Solutions

The MgCl$_2$ solution is stable indefinitely. The buffer, substrate and coenzyme solutions are stable for several weeks at 0–4 °C. Prepare the cysteine solution immediately before use.

Procedure

Collection, Treatment and Stability of Sample

Collection of sample:
Obtain serum as rapidly as possible; avoid haemolysis, because it results in high values. Plasma is unsuitable because low and irreproducible values are obtained[6]. Addition of heparin requires that the erythrocytes must be washed several times with sodium chloride before haemolysis for electrophoretic studies[24].

Stability of enzyme in serum:
There is no change of activity within 5 hr. at room temperature; after 24 hr. a 20% loss of activity occurs and after 3 days complete loss[27]. *Wolfson* and *Williams-Ashman*[3] report a 50% loss of activity in serum after 4 days at 4 °C. For electrophoretic studies whole blood can be stored for 2–3 weeks at 4 °C.

Assay System

Wavelength: 340 (Hg 334, Hg 365) nm; light path: 1 cm.; final volume: 3.1 ml.; 25 °C (constant temperature cuvette holder). Read against air. When carrying out measurements on haemolysates, prepare a control cuvette containing distilled water instead of substrate solution II. Bring all solutions to 25 °C before the measurements.

Pipette into cuvettes:			Concentration in assay mixture
Glycylglycine buffer	(I)	1.3 ml.	50 mM
Mg^{2+} solution	(III)	0.2 ml.	20 mM
Cysteine solution	(IV)	0.2 ml.	6.5 mM
Coenzyme solution	(V)	0.2 ml.	ca. 1.5 mM
Sample (serum or 1 : 100 dilution stroma-free haemolysate)		1.0 ml.	
Mix and follow the extinction until constant.			
Substrate solution	(II)	0.2 ml.	ca. 2 mM
Mix, read extinction at 2 min. intervals for 12 to 20 min. $\Delta E/min.$ is used for the calculations.			

With $\Delta E/min.$ values $> 0.040/min.$ at 340 nm read the extinctions at smaller time intervals.

Calculations

The calculation formula (8) on p. 313 applies and the following relationships hold:

Wavelength:	*334 nm*	*340 nm*	*365 nm*
Volume activity	$= 508 \times \Delta E/min.$	$498 \times \Delta E/min.$	$899 \times \Delta E/min.$ [U/l.]

For haemolysates (concentration measured at 540 nm) the following applies (340 nm):

$$\text{Specific activity} = \frac{69 \times \Delta E/min.}{E_{Haemolysate}} \text{ [U/g. haemoglobin}[16]]$$

Precision of Method

For activities of 7.3 U/l. ± 0.6 U/l. the coefficient of variation is 4%.

Normal Values

In serum of healthy adults 1.5–7.5 U/l. (25 °C). Haemolysates from normal blood have 2.2–4.5 U/g. haemoglobin.

Sources of Error

Effects of drugs and other therapeutic measures: Desforges et al.[29] report competitive and non-competitive inhibition of the enzyme from erythrocytes *in vitro* by drugs, e. g. menadione, sulphanilamide and tolbutamide.

Interference in the assay technique: In extreme cases a prolonged "lag phase" of up to 6 min. can occur.

Specificity of Method

Re-oxidation of NADPH by glucose-6-phosphate dehydrogenase can be ignored. Providing the 6-phospho-gluconate contains no glucose-6-phosphate the reaction is specific.

Details for Measurements in Tissues

Glock and *McLean*[26] used glycylglycine buffer, pH 9.0 for measurements on extracts of animal tissues, but most measurements on haemolysates are carried out at pH 8.0[16]. According to *Muir*[12], vaginal secretion contains three isoenzymes with pH-optima at 7.6, 8.3–8.6 and 9.0. The requirement for chelating agents and the pH optimum should be determined in preliminary experiments[28].

References

1 *O. Warburg, W. Christian & A. Griese*, Biochem. Z. *282*, 157 [1935].
2 *G. E. Glock & P. McLean*, Biochem. J. *56*, 171 [1954].
3 *S. K. Wolfson, jr. & H. G. Williams-Ashman*, Proc. Soc. exptl. Biol. Med. *96*, 231 [1957].
4 *S. K. Wolfson, jr., J. A. Spencer, R. L. Sterkel & H. G. Williams-Ashman*, Ann. N. Y. Acad. Sci. *75*, 260 [1958].
5 *E. Schmidt, F. W. Schmidt & E. Wildhirt*, Klin. Wschr. *36*, 280 [1958].
6 *P. Heller, H. G. Weinstein, M. West & H. J. Zimmerman*, J. Lab. Clin. Med. *55*, 425 [1960].
7 *A. Merten & H. G. Solbach*, Klin. Wschr. *39*, 222 [1961].
8 *D. G. Bonham & D. F. Gibbs*, Brit. med. J. *2*, 823 [1962].
9 *G. G. Muir, G. Canti & D. Williams*, Brit. med. J. *2*, 1563 [1964].
10 *H. J. Nerdrum*, Scand. J. clin. Lab. Invest. *16*, 565 [1964].
11 *C. B. Cameron & O. A. N. Husain*, Brit. med. J. *1*, 1529 [1965].
12 *G. G. Muir*, Clin. Chim. Acta *14*, 748 [1966].
13 *G. G. Muir & G. Canti*, J. Obstet. Gynaec. Brit. Cwlth. *73*, 611 [1966].
14 *D. F. Gibbs*, J. clin. Path. *21*, 189 [1968].
15 *R. A. Fildes & C. W. Parr*, Nature *200*, 890 [1963].
16 *C. W. Parr & L. I. Fitch*, Biochem. J. *93*, 28C [1964].
17 *G. J. Brewer & R. J. Dern*, Clin. Res. *12*, 215 [1964].
18 *C. W. Parr & I. B. Parr*, Biochem. J. *95*, 16P [1965].
19 *N. D. Carter, S. R. Gould, C. W. Parr & P. H. Walter*, Biochem. J. *99*, 17P [1966].
20 *C. W. Parr*, Nature *210*, 487 [1966]
21 *R. J. Dern, G. J. Brewer, R. E. Tashian & T. B. Shows*, J. Lab. clin. Med. *67*, 255 [1966].
22 *H. Gordon, M. M. Keraan & M. Vooijs*, Nature *214*, 466 [1967].
23 *C. W. Parr & L. I. Fitch*, Ann. Hum. Genet. *30*, 339 [1967].
24 *N. D. Carter, R. A. Fildes, L. I. Fitch & C. W. Parr*, Acta Genet. *18*, 109 [1968].
25 *B. L. Horecker & P. Z. Smyrniotis*, J. biol. Chem. *193*, 371 [1951].
26 *G. E. Glock & P. McLean*, Biochem. J. *55*, 400 [1953].
27 *J. King*: Practical Clinical Enzymology, D. Van Nostrand Co. Ltd., London 1965, p. 100.
28 *L. J. Greenberg & D. Glick*, J. biol. Chem. *235*, 3028 [1960].
29 *J. F. Desforges, E. Kalaw & P. Gilchrist*, J. Lab. Clin. Med. *55*, 757 [1960].

Glucose-6-phosphate Dehydrogenase

Georg Wilhelm Löhr and Hans Dierck Waller

Glucose-6-phosphate dehydrogenase, G6P-DH*, was first isolated from erythrocytes and from fermenting yeast by *O. Warburg* et al.[1-5], who carried out an extensive purification and characterization of the enzyme. It has been demonstrated in almost all animal tissues and micro-organisms. Blood cells[6-11], adipose tissue[12] and lactating mammary gland[13,14] are especially rich sources of the enzyme. Less occurs in liver, pancreas, kidney, lung, brain and gastric mucosa, while only traces are found in skeletal and heart muscle and virtually none in serum[12]. Some human and animal tumors contain high activity of the enzyme[12,15-17].

There are several methods[18] for the determination of G6P-DH activity of which two are mentioned here:

1. Manometric measurement of the oxygen uptake of cytolysates on addition of G-6-P, NADP and "old yellow enzyme" (FMN).
2. Spectrophotometric determination of the rate of NADPH formation from the increase in extinction at 340, 334 or 366 nm.

Application of Method: In biochemistry and clinical chemistry.

Principle

(1)   Glucose-6-phosphate $+$ NADP$^+$ $\xrightleftharpoons{\text{G6P-DH}}$ 6-Phosphogluconate $+$ NADPH $+$ H$^+$

The rate of formation of NADPH is a measure of the enzyme activity and it can be followed by means of the increase in extinction at 340, 334 or 365 nm[3].

Optimum Conditions for Measurements

The pH optimum for the G6P-DH reaction is 8.3 for the enzyme from yeast or blood cells (Fig. 1); between pH 7.4 and 8.6 there is little change in the enzyme activity. The measurements are made at pH 7.5, because this is near to physiological conditions and allows comparison to be made with other enzyme activities which are usually measured at this pH.

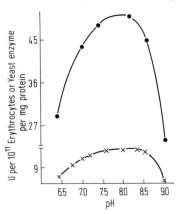

Fig. 1. The dependence of the activity of G6P-DH from yeast (. _ . _ .) and erythrocytes ($-\times-\times-\times-$) on pH.

---

* D-Glucose-6-phosphate: NADP 1-oxidoreductase, EC 1.1.1.49

Phosphate buffer must be avoided because 0.1 M phosphate completely inhibits the enzyme[4]. Triethanol-amine buffer (50 mM, pH 7.5) containing 5 mM EDTA has proved best.

Table 1. Michaelis constants of G6P-DH from different sources.

Source of enzyme	Michaelis constant for	
	G-6-P	NADP
	μM	μM
Yeast	69	50
Erythrocytes (human)	7.4	12
Leucocytes (human)	5.6	13
Paramyeloblasts (acute leukaemia, human)	18	9.1
Lymphocytes (chronic lymphadenoma, human)	23	12
Liver (human)	33	23

Measurements of activity in cytolysates and cell homogenates are not very accurate because the presence of 6-phosphogluconate dehydrogenase (additional reduction of NADP) results in too high activity being found. NADPH oxidizing reactions (glutathione reductase, methaemoglobin reductase and other flavo-proteins) tend to compensate for this. Nevertheless, the measurement of G6P-DH activity in biological material is liable to error. A more accurate, but more complicated method of assay is to remove the inter-fering 6-phosphogluconate dehydrogenase* by adsorption on $Ca_3(PO_4)_2$ gel[19]. Magnesium ions activate G6P-DH in glycylglycine buffer, but not in phosphate or triethanolamine buffer[19].
The substrate affinity of G6P-DH from different cell types for glucose-6-phosphate and NADP is given in Table 1.

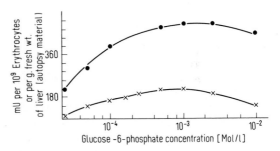

Fig. 2. Dependence of the G6P-DH activity in human liver homogenates (.–.–.) and erythrocyte haemolysates (–×–×–) on the glucose-6-phosphate concentration. 50 mM triethanolamine buffer, pH 7.5; 25 °C; 0.5 mM NADP.

Measurements are made on tissue samples with 0.67 mM G-6-P and 0.5 mM NADP, which are optimum concentrations for the enzyme from erythrocytes (see Fig. 2).

Equipment

Spectrophotometer or spectrum-line photometer suitable for measurements at 340, 334 or 365 nm; laboratory centrifuge; apparatus for counting blood cells; glass homogenizer.

---

* Editorial note: This enzyme can be completely inhibited by ca. 4 mM maleinimide; see p. 1200.

Reagents

For preparation of sample

1. Triethanolamine hydrochloride
2. Ethylenediaminetetra-acetate
   disodium salt, EDTA-Na$_2$H$_2$·2H$_2$O
3. Ethylenediaminetetra-acetate
   magnesium-dipotassium salt,
   EDTA-Mg·K$_2$·2H$_2$O
4. Sodium citrate, A. R.
5. Sodium chloride, A. R.
6. Potassium hydroxide, A. R., 1 N
7. Sodium hydroxide, A. R., 0.1 N
8. Ammonium chloride, A. R., anhydrous

9. Potassium dihydrogen phosphate, A. R.,
   KH$_2$PO$_4$
10. Disodium hydrogen phosphate, A. R.,
    Na$_2$HPO$_4$ · 2H$_2$O
11. Potassium chloride, A. R.
12. Magnesium chloride, A. R.,
    MgCl$_2$ · 6H$_2$O
13. Sodium hydrogen carbonate
14. Glucose
15. Digitonin
16. Silicone oil*
17. Toluene

For measurements**

No. 1, 2, 7 and 13, also:
18. Glucose-6-phosphate, G-6-P
    sodium salt, NADP-Na$_2$H; commercial preparation, see p. 538.

19. Nicotinamide-adenine dinucleotide
    phosphate, NADP
    sodium salt, NADP-NaH$_2$; commercial preparation, see p. 546.

Preparation of Solutions

Prepare all solutions with glass distilled water.

For preparation of samples

For erythrocytes:
  I. Citrate (3.8% w/v):
     Dissolve 3.8 g. sodium citrate in distilled water and make up to 100 ml.
 II. Physiological saline (0.9% w/v):
     Dissolve 9 g. NaCl in distilled water and make up to 1 000 ml.
III. Triethanolamine buffer (50 mM; pH 7.5):
     Dissolve 0.93 g. triethanolamine hydrochloride and 0.2 g. EDTA-Na$_2$H$_2$ · 2H$_2$O in
     ca. 50 ml. distilled water, adjust to pH 7.5 with 0.1 N NaOH and dilute to 100 ml. with
     distilled water.
 IV. Digitonin solution (saturated):
     Add ca. 1 g. digitonin to 100 ml. distilled water, shake well and filter off precipitate.

Additional for leucocytes:
  V. EDTA-MgK$_2$ (0.115 M; pH 7.4):
     Dissolve 4.917 g. EDTA-MgK$_2$ · 2H$_2$O in a little distilled water, adjust to pH 7.4 and
     dilute with distilled water to 100 ml.
 VI. Ammonium chloride (0.87% w/v):
     Dissolve 8.7 g. NH$_4$Cl (anhydrous) in distilled water and make up to 1 000 ml.

---

* e. g. Silicone "Wacker S. W. 60", Wacker-Chemie GmbH, Munich, Germany.
** Complete reagent kits are available commercially, see p. 558.

VII. Phosphate buffer/NaCl (1.33 mM phosphate; 0.88% w/v NaCl; pH 7.4):
Mix 28 ml. of a solution containing 9.078 g. $KH_2PO_4/1\,000$ ml. with 72 ml. of a solution containing 11.876 g. $Na_2HPO_4 \cdot 2H_2O/1\,000$ ml. To 20 ml. of this mixture add 4.27 g. $EDTA\text{-}MgK_2 \cdot 2H_2O$ and dilute to $1\,000$ ml. with 0.9% Na Cl solution (II).

VIII. Tyrode solution, calcium-free:
Dissolve 8.00 g. NaCl; 0.20 g. KCl; 0.10 g. $MgCl_2 \cdot 6H_2O$; 0.05 g. $Na_2HPO_4 \cdot 2H_2O$; 1.00 g. glucose, 1.00 g. $NaHCO_3$ in distilled water and make up to $1\,000$ ml. To prevent bacterial growth add a few drops of toluene and store in a dark bottle.

Additional to solutions I–IV for platelets:

IX. $EDTA\text{-}Na_2H_2$ (1% w/v $EDTA\text{-}Na_2H_2 \cdot 2H_2O$):
Dissolve 1 g. $EDTA\text{-}Na_2H_2 \cdot 2H_2O$ in 100 ml. physiological saline (II).

For liver homogenates only:

X. Physiological saline containing 0.66 mM EDTA:
Dissolve 0.25 g. $EDTA\text{-}Na_2H_2 \cdot 2H_2O$ in physiological saline and make up to $1\,000$ ml.

For measurements

Solution I and

XI. Glucose-6-phosphate (ca. 40 mM G-6-P):
Dissolve 130 mg. $G\text{-}6\text{-}P\text{-}Na_2$ in 10 ml. distilled water.

XII. Nicotinamide-adenine dinucleotide phosphate (ca. 30 mM β-NADP):
Dissolve 25 mg. $NADP\text{-}Na_2H$ in 1.0 ml. 1% $NaHCO_3$ solution.

Stability of Solutions

All solutions should be stored stoppered, in a refrigerator at 0–4 °C. The NADP and glucose-6-phosphate solutions are stable for 2–3 weeks under these conditions, but in the frozen state they keep considerably longer.

Procedure

Collection, Treatment and Stability of Sample

Use only fresh serum, absolutely free from haemolysis; blood cells are rich in G6P-DH.

Erythrocytes: Take 0.5 ml. venous blood into a syringe containing 0.5 ml. citrate solution (I), centrifuge at ca. $1\,000$ g on a bench centrifuge and wash cells twice with 5 ml. physiological saline (II). Suspend the sediment in 1 ml. physiological saline, mix well by rotation and count the erythrocytes twice in a Zeiss-Thoma chamber (about $2 \times 10^6/\mu l$).

Haemolysis: Mix in a centrifuge tube:
1.0 ml. erythrocyte suspension
1.0 ml. distilled water
0.7 ml. triethanolamine buffer (solution III)
0.3 ml. digitonin solution (IV).

Allow to stand for 15 min. in a refrigerator at 4 °C, centrifuge off the insoluble material (15 min. at $1\,000$ g) and discard.

Leucocytes: Isolation of leucocytes: In a boiling tube mix

> 45 ml. venous blood
> 5 ml. EDTA-MgK$_2$ solution (V)

To sediment the erythrocytes allow the tube to stand in an inclined position for 30 min. in an incubator at 37 °C. Carefully suck off the supernatant fluid containing the leucocytes from the erythrocyte layer with a bulb pipette and transfer to a 10 ml. centrifuge tube.

Removal of erythrocytes: Mix

> 1 vol. leucocyte-containing supernatant fluid
> 3 vol. ammonium chloride solution (VI).

Allow to stand for exactly 5 min. and then centrifuge off the leucocytes at low speed (100 to 200 g) for 3 min. Carefully suck off the supernatant fluid and discard (it contains haemolysed erythrocytes and platelets).
Wash the sediment three times with phosphate buffer/NaCl solution, centrifuge each time at low speed (100 g) in the cold. After the last washing suspend the sediment in 5 ml. ice-cold Tyrode solution (VIII). Carry out a leucocyte count (in quadruplicate) in a Zeiss-Thoma counting chamber. The cell count should be above 10000/μl.

Cytolysis: In a centrifuge tube mix

> 5 ml. leucocyte suspension
> 2 ml. distilled water
> 2 ml. triethanolamine buffer (solution III)
> 1 ml. digitonin solution (IV)

Allow to stand for 60 min. in a refrigerator at 0–4 °C and then centrifuge off the insoluble material in the cold (15 min. at 3000 g). Discard the sediment.

Platelets[9]: Take 18.00 ml. of venous blood using a siliconized V2A cannula and a graduated, siliconized syringe which contains 2.00 ml. EDTA-Na solution (IX). Use only siliconzied tubes, pipettes, etc., for all operations. Immediately centrifuge the blood in pre-cooled 8 ml. centrifuge tubes for 10 min. at 4 °C and 100 g. Carefully pipette off the supernatant plasma containing the platelets, combine in pre-cooled centrifuge tubes and centrifuge for 15 min. at 4 °C and 1040 g. Decant the supernatant plasma which contains few platelets, add to the sediment 6 ml. physiological saline (solution II), carefully stir with a wooden rod and then centrifuge at 4 °C and 1040 g. Suspend the platelets in 2 ml. physiological saline (solution II). Carry out a duplicate platelet count with a phase contrast microscope using the technique of

Feissly and *Lüdin*[20] (ca. 2 × 10^6 platelets/μl).

Cytolysis: Mix in a centrifuge tube

> 2.0 ml. platelet suspension
> 1.0 ml. distilled water
> 0.7 ml. triethanolamine buffer (solution III)
> 0.3 ml. digitonin solution (IV)

Allow to stand for 60 min. at 4 °C (refrigerator), centrifuge off the insoluble material (15 min. at 1000 g and 4 °C). Discard the sediment.

Liver tissue[21]. Immediately blot liver biopsies (at least 10 mg. wet weight) obtained by needle puncture on a filter paper to remove most of the blood and weigh on a torsion balance. Add the tissue and EDTA-physiological saline solution (X) (0.04 ml./mg. wet weight) to an ice-cold

Potter-Elvehjem homogenizer (see p. 402) and homogenize for 2 min. in an ice bath (stop-watch). Centrifuge for 20 min. at 0–1.5 °C and 15000 rpm. and decant the clear supernatant fluid. The time between the liver biopsy and the start of the centrifugation should not be more than 5 min.

The accuracy of the determination of activity in liver tissue can be increased if the haemo-globin content of the supernatant fluid is determined and on the basis of this estimation the additional G6P-DH due to the blood cells is calculated. This value is then subtracted from the total activity of the liver homogenate.

Stability of the enzyme in the sample: In the living organism the half-life of G6P-DH in the erythrocytes is 60 days[8]. In digitonin haemolysates containing triethanolamine buffer (pH 7.5) half of the activity is lost in 2 days; G6P-DH from erythrocytes has a half-life in serum of 1 day. On account of the instability of the enzyme the G6P-DH activity in haemolysates, cytolysates, serum and plasma should be determined within a few hours after preparation.

Assay System

Wavelength: 340, Hg 334 or Hg 365 nm; light path: 1 cm.; temperature: 25 °C; (constant temperature cuvette holder); final volume: 3.0 ml. The increase in extinction should not be greater than 0.30/min. (measured at 365 nm); otherwise add less or dilute the sample.

Serum

1.00 ml. sample + 1.90 ml. buffer (III). Read against distilled water or air.

Erythrocytes

0.05 ml. sample + 2.85 ml. buffer (III). Prepare a blank containing buffer solution (III) instead of NADP solution because of the high extinction of the sample due to blood pigments. Read against this blank.

Leucocytes

0.20 ml. sample + 2.70 ml. buffer (III). Prepare a blank as described under "Erythrocytes". Measure against this blank

Platelets and liver tissue

0.50 ml. sample + 2.40 ml. buffer (III). Prepare a blank as described under "Erythrocytes". Read against this blank.

Pipette into cuvettes:			Concentration in assay mixture
Triethanolamine buffer + sample	(III)	2.90 ml.	31–48 mM
NADP solution	(XII)	0.05 ml.	0.5 mM
Mix and incubate for 5 min. at 25 °C.			
G-6-P solution	(XI)	0.05 ml.	0.67 mM
Mix, wait for an extinction increase of about 0.020, start a stopwatch and read the extinction at 2 min. intervals for 10 min. Mean the extinction increases/ 2 min. and divide by 2: ΔE/min. is used for the calculations.			

Calculations

The calculation formula (8) on p. 313 applies. The G6P-DH activity contained in 1 ml. of sample (serum, haemolysate, cytolysate or tissue homogenate supernatant fluid) is calculated as follows:

Serum

1 ml. serum in 3 ml. assay mixture.

Wavelength:	334 nm	340 nm	365 nm
Volume activity =	492 × ΔE/min.	482 × ΔE/min.	870 × ΔE/min. [U/l.]

Erythrocyte suspension

0.05 ml. Haemolysate is added, which has been diluted 3-fold on haemolysis. The total dilution factor is therefore 3 × 20 = 60.

Wavelength:	334 nm	340 nm	365 nm
Volume activity =	29 508 × ΔE/min.	28 938 × ΔE/min.	52 173 × ΔE/min. [U/l.]

If the values for the erythrocyte suspension are divided by the erythrocyte count/ml. and then multiplied by 10^9 the G6P-DH activity is obtained in mU/10^9 erythrocytes.

Leucocyte suspension

Dilution factor: 2 × 5 = 10.

Wavelength:	334 nm	340 nm	365 nm
Volume activity =	4918 × ΔE/min.	4823 × ΔE/min.	8695 × ΔE/min. [U/l.]

For conversion to number of leucocytes see "Erythrocytes".

Platelet suspension

Dilution factor = 4.

Wavelength:	334 nm	340 nm	365 nm
Volume activity =	1967 × ΔE/min.	1929 × ΔE/min.	3478 × ΔE/min. [U/l.]

For conversion to the number of platelets see "Erythrocytes".

Liver tissue

The G6P-DH activity in liver tissue is related either to mg. soluble protein (determined by the biuret method, see p. 174) in the homogenate supernatant fluid or to g. fresh weight. Calculation formula as for platelets.

Normal Values

Serum	0–0.18 U/l.
Erythrocytes	0.131 ± 0.013 U/10^9 cells
Granulocytes	9.20 ± 0.33 U/10^9 cells
Lymphocytes	3.37 ± 0.20 U/10^9 cells
Platelets	0.073 ± 0.007 U/10^9 cells
Liver	0.855 ± 0.031 U/g. fresh wt.

Sources of Error

G6P-DH is inhibited by primaquine[11] and other 8-aminoquinolines (antimalarial drugs) in millimolar concentration, as well as by phenylhydrazine. Nevertheless, the therapeutic concentration of these substances is more than ten-fold lower and therefore they have no significant effect on the measurements.

References

1 *O. Warburg & W. Christian*, Biochem. Z. *242*, 206 [1931].
2 *O. Warburg & W. Christian*, Biochem. Z. *254*, 438 [1932].
3 *O. Warburg, W. Christian & A. Griese*, Biochem. Z. *282*, 157 [1935].
4 *E. Negelein & E. Haas*, Biochem. Z. *282*, 206 [1935].
5 *E. Negelein & W. Gerischer*, Biochem. Z. *284*, 289 [1936].
6 *H. D. Waller, G. W. Löhr & M. Tabatabai*, Klin. Wschr. *1957*, 1022.
7 *G. W. Löhr & H. D. Waller*, Klin. Wschr. *1958*, 865.
8 *G. W. Löhr & H. D. Waller*, Klin. Wschr. *1959*, 833.
9 *H. D. Waller, G. W. Löhr, F. Grignani & R. Gross*, Thromb. Diath. haem. *3*, 520 [1959].
10 *G. W. Löhr, H. D. Waller & H. E. Bock*, Verh. dtsch. Ges. inn. Med. *66*, 1045 [1960].
11 *G. W. Löhr & H. D. Waller*, Dtsch. med. Wschr. *1961*, 27, 87.
12 *E. Schmidt & F. W. Schmidt*, Klin. Wschr. *1960*, 957.
13 *E. E. Glock & P. McLean*, Biochim. biophys. Acta *15*, 590 [1953].
14 *G. E. Glock & P. McLean*, Biochem. J. *56*, 171 [1954].
15 *A. Delbrück, H. Schimassek, K. Bartsch & Th. Bücher*, Biochem. Z. *331*, 297 [1959].
16 *Th. Bücher & M. Klingenberg*, Angew. Chem. *70*, 552 [1958].
17 *H. J. Hohorst* in *H. Wilmanns:* Chemotherapie der Tumoren. Schattauer-Verlag, Stuttgart 1960.
18 *E. Bernt* in *E. Deutsch, E. Gerlach & K. Moeser:* I. Intern. Symp. über Stoffwechsel- und Membran-permeabilität Wien 1968, Georg Thieme Verlag, Stuttgart 1968.
19 *A. Kornberg & B. L. Horecker* in *S. P. Colowick & N. O. Kaplan:* Methods in Enzymology. Academic Press, New York 1955, Vol. I, p. 323.
20 *R. Feissly & H. Lüdin*, Helv. Physiol. Arch. *7*, 9 [1949].
21 *E. Schmidt, F. W. Schmidt & E. Wildhirt*, Klin. Wschr. *1958*, 171.

Xanthine Oxidase (Xanthine Dehydrogenase)

Rainer Fried and Lygia W. Fried*

Xanthine oxidase, XOD (Xanthine: oxygen oxidoreductase, EC 1.2.3.2) is a metal-flavoprotein containing FAD, molybdenum and iron in the ratio of 2 : 2 : 8. Xanthine oxidase can react with various classes of substrate, but its main role is to oxidize hypoxanthine and xanthine to uric acid according to reactions (1) and (2).

(1) $$\text{Hypoxanthine} + O_2 + H_2O \xrightarrow{\text{XOD}} \text{Xanthine} + H_2O_2$$

(2) $$\text{Xanthine} + O_2 + H_2O \xrightarrow{\text{XOD}} \text{Uric acid} + H_2O_2$$

It also oxidizes aldehydes to the corresponding acids and other substances, including pterins, purines, and certain drugs such as allopurinol and 6-mercaptopurine. Molecular oxygen, dyes, nitrate and cytochrome c can serve as electron acceptors.

Xanthine oxidase is the last enzyme in the pathway of the degradation of purine derivatives from nucleic acids and is assumed to be a rate-limiting step in purine metabolism[1]. It is also assumed that it takes part in alcohol metabolism[2,3]; it plays a role in the incorporation of iron in ferritin[4]. Its role in milk (cream) is not known. The enzyme is non-specifically inhibited by cyanide and other inhibitors, and specifically by pteridyl-6-aldehyde, purine-6-aldehyde and allopurinol.

The enzyme occurs in high concentration in the fatty particles of milk, and in large amounts in mammalian liver; other organs and serum contain much less or no activity[5-7].

High concentrations of enzyme have also been found in the intestinal mucosa; this enzyme contains copper instead of molybdenum[8]. Chicken liver and kidney have no xanthine oxidase activity, but have high dehydrogenase activity[9,10]. The activity of xanthine oxidase should be measured by several different methods, because the predominance of the oxidase or dehydrogenase activity depends on the source of the enzyme. Endogenous inhibitors can affect the two types of enzyme differently. The enzyme also occurs in bacteria, but appears to be different from the enzyme in mammalian tissues and cream. The intramolecular transport in xanthine oxidase appears to be very complex, and varies with the substrate and electron acceptor. Xanthine oxidase has been studied as a model for mitochondrial electron transport and the enzyme has been the subject of many reviews[11-18].

Xanthine oxidase can be determined by a multiplicity of methods: e. g. manometrically[19], spectrophotometrically[20] in the ultraviolet range (decrease of xanthine and hypoxanthine or formation of uric acid), fluorimetrically[21] and colorimetrically[22-24] (with the aid of redox dyes: methylene blue, 2,6-dichlorophenolindophenol or tetrazolium salts). The fluorimetric method is the most sensitive, the spectrophotometric method the most usual. These methods can be combined with isotopic methods[25]. The colorimetric method is rapid and simple to carry out.

Application of Method: In biochemistry and clinical biochemistry; in foodstuff chemistry.

Principle

(3) $$\text{Xanthine} + \text{Tetrazolium salt (yellow)} \xrightarrow{\text{XOD}} \text{Uric acid} + \text{Formazan (violet)}$$

The increase in intensity of colour with time, as determined at 530–580 nm, is a measure of the enzyme activity.

---

* The authors have been in part supported by Milheim Foundation for Cancer Research and Searle & Co.

Optimum Conditions for Measurements

Exclusion of air is not necessary with the tetrazolium method. The method described here[24] is based on another developed for reductases[26,27], in which the precipitation of the formazan is prevented with gelatine. The extinction of the transparent emulsion is measured in the usual way. With nitro-BT-tetrazolium salt there is a broad absorption maximum between 530 and 580 nm. A linear relationship exists between the extinction and the amount of enzyme. After a short lag period the reaction is linear. With excess of enzyme parabolic curves are obtained with increasing substrate concentration[28]. The reason for this type of kinetics is not known.

Xanthine oxidase has a substrate optimum between 0.1 and 0.2 mM xanthine or hypoxanthine. The enzyme concentration should be such that an extinction change of 0.050–0.100/min. is obtained at 540 nm. Gelatine has a double function: it keeps the insoluble formazan in solution and in some unknown way increases the rate of the reaction[24,27]. Gelatine cannot be replaced by EDTA; frequently these two reagents have an additive activating effect and so therefore must act via different mechanisms. Phenazine methosulphate affects the rate of the reaction; a 20% activation has been found over a wide concentration range. The extent of the activation by phenazine methosulphate varies with the age and method of preparation of the enzyme, but this can usually be ignored.

If the XOD activity measured at 25 °C is considered to be 1, then activity measured at 30 °C is 1.38-fold higher and at 37 °C 2.08-fold (see also Fig. 1).

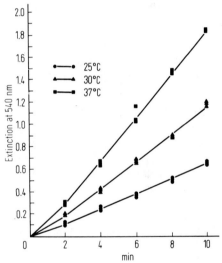

Fig. 1. Xanthine oxidase (xanthine dehydrogenase) from milk (diluted 1 : 100) measured according to the tetrazolium method, pH 7.8.

Equipment

Spectrophotometer suitable for measurements between 530 and 580 nm. As the assay system contains light-sensitive components a covered cuvette holder should be used. Most of the assays of the authors were carried out with a Beckman DU spectrophotometer. Stopwatch.

Reagents

1. Disodium hydrogen phosphate, $Na_2HPO_4 \cdot 7H_2O$
2. Gelatine (the best quality available)

3. Ethylenediaminetetra-acetate, EDTA EDTA-$Na_2H_2 \cdot 2H_2O$ or EDTA-$Na_4 \cdot H_2O$

4. Phenazine methosulphate, PMS
   (light sensitive)
5. Nitro-BT-tetrazolium salt, NBT
   (light sensitive) 2,2'-di-p-nitrophenyl-5,5'-
   diphenyl-3,3'-(3,3'-dimethoxy-4,4'-diphenylene)
   ditetrazolium chloride, e. g. from Sigma Chemical Co., St. Louis, Mo., USA, grade III.

6. Hypoxanthine
7. Xanthine or its disodium salt
8. Sodium hydroxide, 0.1 N
9. Hydrochloric acid, 0.1 N

Preparation of Solutions

Prepare all solutions with distilled water.

   I. Phosphate buffer (0.1 M; pH 7.8):
      Dissolve 26.8 g. $Na_2HPO_4 \cdot 7H_2O$ in ca. 800 ml. distilled water, adjust the pH to 7.8
      with 0.1 N HCl and dilute to 1000 ml. with distilled water.
  II. Ethylenediaminetetra-acetate, EDTA (10 mM):
      Dissolve 3.8 g. $EDTA-Na_4 \cdot H_2O$ in ca. 800 ml. distilled water, adjust to pH 7.8 with
      0.1 N HCl and dilute to 1000 ml. with distilled water.
 III. Gelatine (1% w/v):
      Dissolve 1 g. gelatine in 100 ml. boiling phosphate buffer (I) and allow to cool.
  IV. Phenazine methosulphate, PMS (0.2 mg./ml.):
      Dissolve 10 mg. PMS in 50 ml. buffer solution (I). Weigh in subdued light. Pour solution
      into a dark bottle. When a strong green colour appears, prepare a fresh solution.
   V. Nitro-BT-tetrazolium salt (4 mg./ml.):
      Dissolve 200 mg. NBT in 50 ml. buffer. Weigh out in subdued light. Store in a dark
      bottle. When a precipitate occurs, prepare the solution afresh.
  VI. Xanthine solution (1 mM):
      Dissolve 19.6 mg. xanthine, disodium salt in 20 ml. 0.01 N NaOH (stock solution 5 mM).
      Dilute the stock solution 1 : 5 with phosphate buffer (solution I) (working solution, 1mM).
      Prepare the working solution freshly before each experiment.

Procedure

Collection, Treatment and Stability of Sample

The enzyme in milk is bound to the fat droplets, from which it can be released with detergents,
organic solvents like butanol or by enzymatic treatment. For assay of milk proceed as follows:
dialyse milk in a cold room three times for 30 min. against 100 volumes phosphate buffer
(solution I). Add 1.0 ml. of the dialysed milk to the assay. Commercial milk and cream have
high XOD activity which is inactivated by heating for 15 min. in a boiling water bath. The
rate of inactivation of XOD in milk at lower temperatures has been studied by [29,30].

The liver enzyme occurs in the supernatant fluid after cell fractionation by repeated centrifugation in 0.25 M sucrose[31]. It can be isolated by acidification of the homogenate to pH 4.8
with 4 N acetic acid and fractionation of the neutral supernatant with ammonium sulphate.
The precipitate between 20 and 40% saturation contains xanthine oxidase[32].

The enzyme is inhibited by high concentrations of low-molecular weight compounds which
are normal constituents of tissues: xanthine, hypoxanthine or uric acid, folic acid and its

derivatives. If too low activity of XOD is obtained these compounds should be removed by dialysis.

A non-dialysable, heat-labile inhibitor of the tetrazolium reduction has recently been isolated from rat liver; it appears to be normally masked, but can be activated during the purification process[33,45].

Stability of enzyme: The enzyme can be kept for about two weeks in a refrigerator with only slight loss of activity. It is stable for about a month in the frozen state. Several reagents stabilize the enzyme, e. g. ammonium sulphate, phosphate and salicylic acid salts. In dilute solutions the stability decreases. Freezing and solvent treatments affect the activity of this enzyme selectively[33a].

Assay System

Wavelength: 530–580 nm, preferably 540 nm; or for Hg filter photometer 546 and 578 nm; light path: 1 cm.; final volume: 3.0 ml.; temperature: 25 °C (constant temperature cuvette holder). Read against blank without xanthine.

Prepare the following reagent mixture (subdued light):

Phosphate buffer	(I)	6 parts	
EDTA solution	(II)	5 ,,	
Gelatine solution	(III)	5 ,,	
PMS solution	(IV)	1 ,,	
NBT solution	(V)	3 ,,	
		18 parts	
Sample		2 ,,	
		20 parts	

Mix, incubate this solution for 5 min. and then use for the assay.

Pipette into cuvettes:			Concentration in assay mixture
Reagent mixture + sample		2.0 ml.	100 mM phosphate 0.86 mM EDTA 1.4 mg. gelatine/ml. 5.7 μg. PMS/ml.
Phosphate buffer	(I)	0.5 ml.	342 μg. NBT/ml.
Xanthine solution	(VI)	0.5 ml.	0.14 mM xanthine
Mix, read at 2 min. intervals for 10 min. Use only the linear part of the reaction curve (from ca. 2 min.) for the calculations. The ΔE/min. is used for the calculations.			

Calculations

The calculation formula (8) on p. 313 applies. The extinction coefficient of the reduced NBT-tetrazolium salt at 540 nm is 7.2 cm.^{2}/μmole. Under the conditions described here (F = dilution factor for sample, v = sample volume in test):

Wavelength: *540 nm*   *546 nm*   *578 nm*

Volume activity $= \dfrac{0.417 \times F}{v} \times \Delta E/min. \; \dfrac{0.417 \times F}{v} \times \Delta E/min. \; \dfrac{0.443 \times F}{v} \times \Delta E/min. \; [U/l.]$

Precision of Method

The reproducibility of the method is good. With purified XOD the values vary by about $\pm 5\%$. For XOD from milk (1 : 100 dilution) we found a mean extinction change (540 nm) per 10 min. of 0.895 $\pm$ 0.030 (s) for 9 determinations. Coefficient of variation is 3.35%.

Normal Values

Human blood or serum contains no xanthine oxidase activity[6,34]. In human organs slight activity has been found in kidney, spleen, skeletal muscle and heart (0.03 to 0.4 mU/g. protein) and higher activity in liver (42 to 250 mU/g. protein) and in the jejunal mucosa (80 to 400 mU/g. protein[34]). For XOD values in animal organs, see[6,7,35].

Pathological Values

Mazur and *Sackler*[47] report a range of 5.49–1.92 units of xanthine oxidase (μmole of substrate oxidized/g. tissue protein/hr.) in samples obtained from normal human livers, while very low values or no activity was found in livers of cirrhotic patients (1.01; 0.08; 0.04; 3 with no measurable activity) and in cases of haemochromatosis (1.46; 0.36; 0.10; 0.03; 0.00). Laboratory animals whose brain and lungs have been infiltrated with viruses show increased XOD activity[36–38]. In inoculated tumours the XOD activity is lower or not present[39–43]. Other factors can also affect the XOD activity, especially in liver[12]: XOD in rat liver decreases rapidly when the animals are deficient in riboflavin, protein, iron, molybdenum or fed a diet rich in tungsten. XOD is an adaptive enzyme; its concentration can be increased by administration of high doses of xanthine or by feeding folic acid deficient diets.

Sources of Error

Effects of drugs and other therapeutic measures: XOD is inhibited by very small doses of allopurinol[25]. This also applies to xanthine dehydrogenase when it is measured with the tetrazolium reduction method (*R. Fried*, et al.[45]). Other drugs such as disulphiram, metronidazole, 6-mercaptopurine, etc., in high concentration inhibit the enzyme. Frequently the inhibition depends on the experimental system used; the dehydrogenase activity can be inhibited without effect on the oxidase activity and *vice versa*[32,33,44]. The mechanism of the selective inhibition of the two activities of the same enzyme is not known.

Interference in the assay technique: In the presence of uricase too high values are obtained, because uricase can also transfer electrons to tetrazolium salts (*R. Fried*, unpublished). Interference by other reactions which reduce tetrazolium salts can be avoided by dialysis or salting out with saturated ammonium sulphate. Prolonged dialysis does not decrease the XOD activity. A protein has been isolated from liver which blocks tetrazolium reduction[45]; it is probably related to or identical with superoxide dismutase[46,48].

Specificity of Method

The method is specific for xanthine oxidase or, better, xanthine dehydrogenase.

Details for Measurements in Tissues

It is recommended that the enzyme activity is determined after high speed centrifugation or dialysis; virtually all the xanthine oxidase activity is found in the supernatant fluid[31].

References

1 *F. Bergel:* "Chemistry of Enzymes in Cancer", Thomas, Springfield, Ill. [1961].
2 *D. Keilin & E. F. Hartree,* Biochem. J. *39,* 293 [1945].
3 *R. Lowy & G. Griffaton,* Biol. Med. *54,* 279 [1965].
4 *A. Mazur, S. Baez & E. Shorr,* J. biol. Chem. *213,* 147 [1955].
5 *E. Morgan,* Biochem. J. *20,* 1282 [1926].
6 *U. A. S. al-Khalidi & T. H. Chaglassian,* Biochem. J. *97,* 318 [1965].
7 *W. W. Westerfeld & D. A. Richert,* Proc. Soc. Expt. biol. Med. *71,* 181 [1949].
8 *G. G. Roussos & B. H. Morrow,* Arch. Biochem. Biophys. *114,* 599 [1966].
9 *C. N. Remy, D. A. Richert, R. J. Doisy, I. C. Wells & W. W. Westerfeld,* J. biol. Chem. *217,* 293, [1955].
10 *E. J. Landon & C. E. Carter,* J. biol. Chem. *235,* 819 [1960].
11 *H. R. Mahler* in *F. F. Nord:* Adv. Enzymol., *17,* 233 [1956].
12 *E. C. deRenzo* in *F. F. Nord:* Adv. Enzymol., *17,* 293 [1956].
13 *R. C. Bray* in *P. D. Boyer, H. A. Lardy & K. Myrbäck:* The Enzymes, 2nd edn., Academic Press, New York, vol. *7,* 533 [1963].
14 *G. Schmidt* in *E. Chargaff & J. N. Davidson:* The Nucleic Acids, Academic Press, N. Y., 1955, p. 555, 609.
15 *R. C. Bray, G. Palmer & H. Beinert* in *T. King, H. S. Mason & M. Morrison:* Oxidases and Related Redox Systems, Wiley, New York, 1965.
16 *H. C. Bray, A. J. Chisholm, L. I. Hart, L. S. Meriwether & D. C. Watts:* Symposium on Flavins and Flavoproteins, Elsevier, Amsterdam [1965].
17 *P. Handler, K. V. Rajagopalan & V. Aleman,* Fed. Proc. *23,* 30 [1964].
18 *W. W. Westerfeld,* Fed. Proc. *20,* suppl. *10,* 158 [1961].
19 *E. G. Ball,* J. biol. Chem. *121,* 51 [1939].
20 *H. E. Kalckar,* J. biol. Chem. *167,* 461 [1947].
21 *O. H. Lowry* in *S. Colowick & N. O. Kaplan:* Methods of Enzymology, vol. *4,* p. 380. Academic Press, New York, 1957.
22 *D. E. Green,* Biochem. J. *28,* 1550 [1934].
23 *P. G. Avis, F. Bergel & R. C. Bray,* J. Chem. Soc. *1956,* 1219.
24 *R. Fried,* Anal. Biochem. *16,* 427 [1966].
25 *J. R. Klineberg, S. Goldfinger, K. H. Bradley & J. E. Seegmiller,* Clin. Chem. *13,* 554 [1967].
26 *M. M. Nachlas, S. I. Margulies & A. M. Seligman,* J. biol. Chem. *235,* 499 [1960].
27 *M. M. Nachlas, S. I. Margulies, J. D. Goldberg & A. M. Seligman,* Anal. Biochem. *1,* 317 [1960].
28 *R. Fried & L. W. Fried,* This book, p. 1945.
29 *C. A. Zittle, E. S. Della Monica, J. H. Custer & R. K. Rudd,* J. Dairy Sci. *39,* 522 [1956].
30 *J. Pien,* Lait *25,* 311 [1945].
31 *G. G. Villela, E. Mitideri & A. Alfonso,* Nature *175,* 1087 [1955].
32 *R. Fried & L. W. Fried,* Biochem. Pharmacol. *15,* 1890 [1966].
33 *R. Fried & L. W. Fried,* Fed. Proc. *26,* 837 [1967]; *27,* 785 [1968].
33a *F. Stirpe & E. Della Corte,* J. biol. Chem. *244,* 3855 [1969].
34 *R. W. E. Watts, J. E. M. Watts & J. E. Seegmiller,* J. Lab. Clin. Med. *66,* 688 [1965].
35 *E. Morgan,* Biochem. J. *20,* 1282 [1926].
36 *D. J. Bauer & P. L. Bradley,* Brit. J. Exptl. Pathol. *37,* 447 [1956].
37 *M. I. Sellers & G. J. Jann,* Proc. Soc. Exp. Biol. Med. *86,* 205 [1954].
38 *M. I. Sellers,* Proc. Soc. Exp. Biol. Med. *91,* 457 [1957].
39 *F. Bergel, R. C. Bray, A. Haddow, I. Lewin* in *G. E. W. Wolstenholme & C. M. O'Connor:* The Chemistry and Biology of Purines, Ciba Symposium 256 [1957].
40 *G. de Lamirande, C. Allard & A. Cantero,* Cancer Res. *18,* 952 [1958].
41 *I. Lewin, R. Lewin & R. C. Bray,* Nature *180,* 763 [1957].
42 *J. S. Colter, H. H. Bird & H. Koprowski,* Cancer Res. *17,* 815 [1957].
43 *P. Feigelson, J. E. Ultman, S. Harris & T. Dashman,* Cancer Res. *19,* 1230 [1959].
44 *R. J. Doisy, D. A. Richert & W. W. Westerfeld,* J. biol. Chem. *217,* 303 [1955].
45 *R. Fried, L. W. Fried & D. Babin,* Eur. J. Biochem. *16,* 399 [1970].
46 *I. Fridovich,* J. biol. Chem. *245,* 6049 [1970].
47 *A. Mazur & M. Sackler,* Lancet *1,* 254 [1967].
48 *R. Fried, L. W. Fried & D. R. Babin,* Europ. J. Biochem. [1973], in press.

Glutamate Dehydrogenase

UV-Assay

Ellen Schmidt

Glutamate dehydrogenase, GlDH (L-Glutamate: NAD oxidoreductase, deaminating, EC 1.4.1.2; L-Glutamate: NAD(P) oxidoreductase, deaminating, EC 1.4.1.3; L-Glutamate: NADP oxidoreductase, deaminating EC 1.4.1.4) is a widely distributed enzyme. GlDH 1.4.1.2 occurs in higher plants, yeasts and the cytoplasm of fusaria. GlDH 1.4.1.4 occurs in yeasts, in mitochondria of fusaria and in bacteria, e. g. *E. coli*[1-12]. GlDH 1.4.1.3 is the enzyme of warm-blooded animals[13-17]. Only this enzyme will be considered here. It was crystallized in 1920 by *Thunberg*[18] and in 1952/53 by *Strecker*[14] and by *Olson* and *Anfinsen*[13] from ox liver. Liver[17,19,20] (Table 1) has the highest activity of all tissues. Because of its easy availability liver GlDH is one of the best studied enzymes[21].
GlDH is located within the mitochondrial matrix[22-26]. Measurement of GlDH activity can therefore be used to check the purity of non-mitochondrial fractions during cell fractionation.
Normal serum contains very low GlDH activity (below 3 mU/ml.). Only after severe cell damage does the GlDH activity rise in serum[27-34].
GlDH is measured in the spectrophotometric assay of *Warburg*: of the 4 possible assays (2 coenzymes, 2 directions) the best for the measurement of warm-blooded GlDH is the rate of oxidation of NADH (limitation: the very sharp optimum concentration range for NADH[35,36]). With extracts of human liver and under optimum conditions the activities relative to activity with NADH were: 50% with NADPH, 20% with NAD and only 3% with NADP[37].

Application of Method: In serum in clinical chemistry, in liver disease, especially for the differential diagnosis of jaundice; in serum and tissues in biochemistry, toxicology and experimental medicine.

Principle

(1) $2\text{-Oxoglutarate} + \text{NADH} + \text{NH}_4^+ \rightleftharpoons \text{L}(+)\text{-Glutamate} + \text{NAD}^+ + \text{H}_2\text{O}$

The equilibrium of the reaction lies far in favour of glutamate formation. $K = [\text{OxoG}] \times [\text{NH}_4^+] \times [\text{NADH}]/[\text{Glutamate}] \times [\text{H}_2\text{O}] \times [\text{NAD}]$ is between 4.0×10^{-14} and 2.5×10^{-13} at pH 6.4 − 7.6 and 25–30 °C[14,38,39]. The measurements are therefore made with OxoG and NH_4^+ as substrates and NADH as coenzyme. The oxidation of NADH is directly proportional to the reaction of the substrate and serves as a measure of the activity. The pyruvate content of the sample is removed by a 5-min-preincubation with lactate dehydrogenase (LDH)*.

Optimum Conditions for Measurements

The relationship between enzyme activity in serum from patients with liver disease and substrate, coenzyme and pH is shown in Fig. 1. From this it follows that the following concentrations are optimum for measurements in serum at 25 °C and triethanolamine buffer, pH 8.0: 0.16 mM NADH, 6.9 mM OxoG, 100 mM NH_4^+, 2.5 mM EDTA. Alterations of the optimum substrate concentrations in aged sera have not so far been observed. Addition of 1 mM ADP increases GlDH activity 1.86 (± 0.51) fold. Measurements at different temperatures may require different measuring conditions (cf. p. 127). Nevertheless, results obtain-

---

* L-Lactate: NAD oxidoreductase, EC 1.1.1.27.

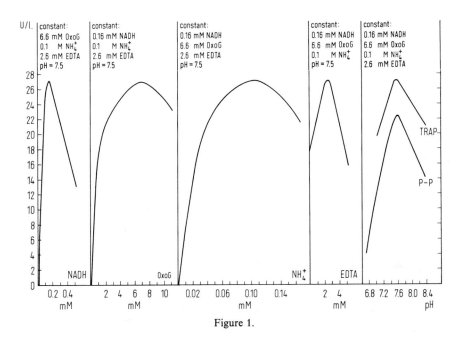

Figure 1.

ed under the same measuring conditions but at different temperatures were formerly compared with each other ("conversion factors" were determined). Such conversion factors may be correct if determined with a relatively large proband collective; however, they cannot be applied generally to the individual case (cf. p. 129). The value of the following relative reaction rates[37] thus lies in being able to appraise the temperature dependence of the reaction and at the most to compare qualitatively values up to the limit of normal.

°C	26	27	28	29	30	31	32	33	34	35	36	37
	0.96	0.92	0.88	0.84	0.81	0.78	0.75	0.72	0.68	0.66	0.64	0.62

Equipment

Spectrophotometer or spectrum-line photometer suitable for accurate measurements at 334, 340 or 365 nm; constant temperature cuvette holder, water bath (25 °C), stopwatch or recorder.

Reagents

1. Triethanolamine hydrochloride, TRA-HCl
2. Sodium hydroxide, 2 N, A. R.
3. Reduced nicotinamide-adenine dinucleotide, NADH
   sodium salt, NADH-Na$_2$; commercial preparation, see p. 545.
4. 2-Oxoglutaric acid, OxoG
5. Ammonium acetate, A. R.

6. Ethylenediaminetetra-acetate, EDTA
   disodium salt, EDTA-Na$_2 \cdot 2 H_2O$
7. Adenosine-5'-diphosphate, ADP
   disodium salt, ADP-Na$_2$; commercial preparation, see p. 525.
8. Lactate dehydrogenase, LDH
   from pig muscle, solution in 50% (v/v) Glycerol; $\geqq 500$ U/mg. (25 °C); commercial preparations see p. 482.

Purity of Reagents

All the necessary reagents are commercially available in A. R. or biochemical reagent grade and require no further purification.

Preparation of Solutions (for ca. 100 assays with a final volume of 1.0 ml.)

Prepare all solutions with doubly distilled water.

   I. Triethanolamine buffer (70 mM; pH 8.0; 3.6 mM EDTA):
      Dissolve 1.3 g. TRA-HCl and 134 mg. EDTA-$Na_2H_2 \cdot 2H_2O$ in ca. 80 ml. distilled water, add ca. 2.2 ml. 2 N NaOH, adjust pH to 8.0 (pH meter) and dilute to 100 ml.
  II. NADH/ADP (10.25 mM β-NADH; 50 mM ADP):
      Dissolve 17.5 mg. NADH-Na_2 and 54 mg. ADP-Na_2 in 2 ml. distilled water.
 III. Ammonium acetate (3.3 M):
      Dissolve 1.28 g. ammonium acetate in 5 ml. distilled water.
 IV. Lactate dehydrogenase, LDH (100 U/l.):
      If necessary, dilute the stock solution accordingly with 50% glycerol.
  V. 2-Oxoglutarate (233 mM OxoG):
      Dissolve 104 mg. OxoG in 2 ml. distilled water, adjust to pH 6.8–7.0 with ca. 0.06 ml. 2 N NaOH and dilute to 3.0 ml. with distilled water.

Stability of Solutions

Store NADH/ADP, LDH, oxoglutarate solution and buffer at 4 °C. The NADH solution is stable for about a week, the oxoglutarate solution for about 4 weeks. The other solutions are stable virtually indefinitely.

Procedure

Collection, Treatment and Stability of Sample

Collection of sample

Preferably collect blood without venestasis. Slight haemolysis does not interfere, but there is an increase in the non-specific preliminary reaction. Addition of anticoagulants at the usual concentrations (ca. 2 mM EDTA, ca. 10 mM citrate, ca. 7.5 μM heparin) does not interfere with the assay. Centrifuge blood for 10–15 min. at ca. 3000 g. Store serum or plasma in a refrigerator until the assay.

Stability of enzyme in sample

GlDH activity in serum as % of the activity on 1st. day ($\pm$ S. D.)[37,40]:

	2nd day	3rd day	5th day	7th day	12th–16th day
+ 4 °C	100 $\pm$ 5	95 $\pm$ 5	87 $\pm$ 8	74 $\pm$ 11	70 $\pm$ 21
+25 °C	90 $\pm$ 7	85 $\pm$ 6	76 $\pm$ 6	70 $\pm$ 8	—
−38 °C	122 $\pm$ 1	112 $\pm$ 5	104 $\pm$ 4	102 $\pm$ 3	—

There is no decrease of GlDH activity in homogenates of human and rat liver up to 24 hr. after preparation.

Assay System

Wavelength: 340 (Hg 334, Hg 365) nm; light path: 1 cm.; final volume: 1.0 ml.; temperature: 25 °C; read against air; adjust to 25 °C before the start of the assay. With extinction recorder: chart speed 1 cm./min.

Pipette into semi-micro cuvettes:			Concentration in assay mixture
NADH solution	(II)	0.02 ml.	0.2 mM NADH, 1 mM ADP
Buffer solution	(I)	0.70 ml.	50 mM TRA
			2.5 mM EDTA
Ammonium acetate solution	(III)	0.03 ml.	100 mM
Sample (serum)		0.20 ml.	
LDH solution	(IV)	0.02 ml.	2 U LDH/ml.
Mix, read extinction and start stopwatch. Read extinctions at 1 min. intervals for 10 min. (non-specific preliminary reaction) $\Delta E/\text{min.}$ of the linear part of the reaction $= \Delta E_1$. With measurements on a recorder: $\text{tg}\alpha$ of the linear part of the reaction $= \text{tg}\alpha_1$.			
2-Oxoglutarate solution	(V)	0.03 ml.	7 mM
Mix, read extinction and incubate for 5 min. Start stopwatch. Read extinctions at 1 min. intervals for 10 min. $\Delta E/\text{min.} = \Delta E_2$. With measurements on a recorder: $\text{tg}\alpha = \text{tg}\alpha_2$. $\Delta E_2 - \Delta E_1 = \Delta E_{\text{GlDH}}$ or $\text{tg}\alpha_2 - \text{tg}\alpha_1 = \text{tg}\alpha_{\text{GlDH}}$ is used for the calculations.			

The non-specific preliminary reaction may stop after several minutes (ΔE_1 or $\alpha_1 = 0$). If the extinction change exceeds 0.100 in the first 15 min., a further 0.01 ml. NADH solution (II) must be added before the start of the main reaction.

If the following values are exceeded in the main reaction:

	334 nm	340 nm	365 nm
$\Delta E/\text{min.}$	0.030	0.030	0.020
$\text{tg}\alpha_2$	40	40	20

or if the extinction changes do not progress in a linear way, the sample must be diluted 2- or 5-fold with buffer solution I[37].

Calculations

The calculation formula (8) on p. 313 applies and therefore the following relationships hold for this method:

Wavelength:	334 nm	340 nm	365 nm
Volume activity	$= \Delta E_{\text{GlDH}} \times 820$	$\Delta E_{\text{GlDH}} \times 804$	$\Delta E_{\text{GlDH}} \times 1471$ [U/l.]
Volume activity	$= \text{tg}\alpha_{\text{GlDH}} \times 40.98$	$\text{tg}\alpha_{\text{GlDH}} \times 40.2$	$\text{tg}\alpha_{\text{GlDH}} \times 73.53$ [U/l.]

Precision of Method

For measurements in serum with GlDH values from 1 to 20 U/l. a coefficient of variation of 5.2% was obtained (day to day measurements). For measurements in liver homogenates with GlDH values around 200 U/l. (0.02 ml. homogenate added) a coefficient of variation of 4% was found (2 experienced analysts, series of 20 assays each on the same day).

Normal Values

In serum of adults[37] $\bar{x} \pm 2s$ = 0.3 U/l. to 4.1 U/l. for men and $\bar{x} \pm 2s$ = 0.4 U/l. to 2.9 U/l. for women were found.

In aqueous tissue extracts the following GlDH activities (in U/g. fresh wt.) have been obtained with comparable methods.

		Liver	Heart	Skeletal muscle	Kidney cortex	Cerebrum
Human[19]		92	1.1	0.5	6.7	4.1
Horse[41]		61	0.5	0.2	—	—
Dog[42]		74	—	—	—	—
Guinea pig[42]		130	—	—	—	—
Marmoset[42]	ri.	39				
	le.	61	0	0.08	19.8	9.0
Rat[20,34]	ri.	51				
	le.	44	1.9	0.3	40	—

These values have been obtained by the assay without ADP. The values are increased by a factor of 1.5 to 2 with ADP (method described here). ri = right lobe; le = left lobe (in the rat = caudate lobe).

Sources of Error

Influence of drugs and other therapeutic measures: No effect of therapeutic measures on the actual assay is known. The GlDH activity in serum decreases with corticosteroid therapy (as do other enzymes)[32]. Increases of GlDH in liver and kidney have been described after administration of cortisone, glucagon, thyroxine or protein-rich diets[20,43-46]. Sulphonyl-ureas inhibit GlDH[47].

Interference in the assay technique: Like the deficiency of NADH already metioned, too high a concentration of NADH results in low values because of the extremely narrow concentration optimum. Other possible sources of error are eliminated by subtraction of the preliminary reaction.

Specificity of Method

The main reaction is specific for GlDH activity because the amino acid concentrations in serum or tissue extracts are not high enough under the assay conditions to result in appreciable transamination and the slight non-specific reactions are corrected for by measurement of the preliminary reaction. With the generally low GlDH activities in serum the non-specific reaction cannot be disregarded.

Results for 408 sera (GlDH activity 0.2–1400 U/l.)[37]

Non-specific reaction	% of sera
0	39
10% of the activity	29
11–20% of the activity	13
21–30% of the activity	8
30% of the activity	11

Of the sera for which without subtraction of the non-specific reaction the result of the GlDH activity calculation would be more than 30% too high, in 98% of the cases the activity is less than 4 U/l, i.e. within the range or limit region of normal.

Details for Measurements in Tissues

The intramitochondrial location of GlDH means that the extracting agent and the degree of mechanical disruption of the mitochondria are of great importance for the quantitative determination of the enzyme in tissues. Immediate centrifugation of a liver homogenate prepared in 0.15 M NaCl with a glass/glass or Teflon/glass homogenizer gives less than 20% of the total activity in the supernatant fluid. The yield increases to 60% after 24 hr. standing before centrifugation. If distilled water is used instead of NaCl then about 80% of the GlDH activity is detectable in the supernatant fluid after standing for 2 hr. Homogenization for 2 min. in an Ultra-Turrax results in 92–97% of the activity being found in the supernatant fluid after immediate centrifugation, and the total activity after standing for 1 hr. before centrifugation. A determination in duplicate on liver requires 1 mg. fresh wt.[48-50].

If extracts of human liver are separated on a DEAE-cellulose column at pH 6, the main fraction of GlDH activity (75–85%) appears with the 4th protein peak (0.05 M phosphate buffer + 0.05 M NaCl). A small fraction is only eluted with 0.1 M phosphate buffer + 0.1 M NaCl. Both GlDH fractions show the same affinity for oxoglutarate, but the fraction which is more difficult to elute has higher K_M values for NH_4^+ and NADH[51].

The following conditions have been described for the determination of GlDH activity in livers from various species (concentrations in μmole/ml. assay mixture):

Species	Buffer		pH	NADH	OxoG	NH_4^+	pH	NAD	Gluta-mate	EDTA	Ref.
Cattle	a, b)	Phosphate					7.6	0.1	33.0		52
Chicken	a, b)	Tris	7.6	0.15	11.1	150	8.0	0.2	13.3		15
Cattle	b)	Phosphate					8.0	8.3	11.0		53
Rat	a)	Phosphate	7.7	0.28	10.0	50	7.7	1.4	13.0	+	26
Cattle	b)	Tris	8.0	0.10	50.0	100	8.0	3.3	50.0	+	35
Human	a)	TRA	8.0	0.13	8.0	70	8.0	3.3	60.0	2.6	36, 37
	b)	TRA	7.6	0.24	5.0	75	8.0	2.6	40.0	2.6	37
				NADPH				NADP			
Human	a)	TRA	8.0	0.22	10.0	120	8.0	1.8	25.0	2.6	37
	b)	TRA	7.6	1.5	6.8	75	8.0	1.4	70.0	1.3	36

a) Crude or fractionated tissue extracts
b) Purified or crystalline enzyme preparations.

References

1 H. v. Euler, E. Adler & T. Steenhoff-Eriksen, Hoppe-Seylers Z. physiol. Chem. 248, 227 [1937].
2 E. Adler, V. Hellström, G. Günther & H. v. Euler, Hoppe-Seylers Z. physiol. Chem. 255, 14 [1938].
3 E. Adler, G. Günther & J. E. Everett, Hoppe-Seylers Z. physiol. Chem. 255, 27 [1938].
4 M. Damodaran & K. R. Nair, Biochem. J. 32, 1064 [1938].
5 S. Barban, J. Bacteriol. 68, 493 [1954].
6 B. Nisman, Bacteriol. Rev. 18, 16 [1954].
7 B. A. Fry, Biochem. J. 60, 6 [1955].
8 J. T. Wachsman, J. biol. Chem. 223, 19 [1956].
9 W. A. Bulen, Arch. Biochem. Biophys. 62, 173 [1956].
10 J. R. S. Fincham, Biochem. J. 65, 721 [1957].
11 H. Holzer & S. Schneider, Biochem. Z. 329, 361 [1957].
12 B. D. Sanwal, Arch. Biochem. 93, 377 [1961].

13 *J. A. Olson & C. B. Anfinsen,* J. biol. Chem. *197,* 67 [1952].
14 *H. J. Strecker,* Arch. Biochem. Biophys. *46,* 128 [1953].
15 *J. E. Snoke,* J. biol. Chem. *223,* 271 [1956].
16 *J. B. Solomon,* Biochem. J. *66,* 264 [1957].
17 *Ch. D. Kochakian, B. R. Endahl & G. L. Endahl,* Amer. J. Physiol. *197,* 129 [1959].
18 *T. Thunberg,* Scand. Arch. Physiol. *40,* 1 [1920].
19 *E. Schmidt & F. W. Schmidt,* Klin. Wschr. *38,* 957 [1960].
20 *J. E. Wergedahl & A. E. Harper,* Proc. Soc. exper. Biol. Med. *116,* 600 [1964].
21 *C. Frieden* in: The Enzymes, Academic Press, New York and London 1963, Vol. 7, p. 3.
22 *G. H. Hoogeboom & W. C. Schneider,* J. biol. Chem. *204,* 233 [1953].
23 *G. S. Christie & J. D. Judah,* Proc. Soc. (London) Ser. B *141,* 420 [1953].
24 *C. de Duve, C. Pressman, R. Gianetto, R. Wattiaux & F. Appelmans,* Biochem. J. *60,* 604 [1955].
25 *C. Allard, G. de Lamiranda & A. Cantero,* Exp. Cell. Res. *13,* 69 [1957].
26 *H. Beaufay, D. S. Bendall, P. Baudhuin & C. de Duve,* Biochem. J. *73,* 623 [1959].
27 *U. Gerlach,* Klin. Wschr. *35,* 1144 [1957].
28 *E. Schmidt, F. W. Schmidt & E. Wildhirt,* Klin. Wschr. *36,* 280 [1958].
29 *E. Schmidt & F. W. Schmidt,* Klin. Wschr. *40,* 962 [1962].
30 *G. Filippa,* Enzym. biol. clin. *3,* 97 [1963].
31 *G. Laudahn,* Klin. Wschr. *41,* 618 [1963].
32 *E. Schmidt & F. W. Schmidt,* Enzym. biol. clin. *3,* 1 [1963].
33 *U. Gerlach* in: Praktische Enzymologie, H. Huber, Bern 1968, p. 165.
34 *E. Schmidt, F. W. Schmidt & C. Herfarth,* Enzym. biol. clin. *7,* 53, 167 and 185 [1966].
35 *C. Frieden,* J. biol. Chem. *234,* 809 [1959].
36 *E. Schmidt & F. W. Schmidt,* Enzym. biol. clin. *2,* 201 [1962/63].
37 *E. Schmidt & F. W. Schmidt,* unpublished results.
38 *J. A. Olson & C. B. Anfinsen,* J. biol. Chem. *202,* 841 [1953].
39 *K. Burton & H. A. Krebs,* Biochem. J. *54,* 94 [1953].
40 *S. Feissli, G. Forster, G. Laudahn, E. Schmidt & F. W. Schmidt,* Klin. Wschr. *44,* 390 [1961].
41 *H. Hörnicke, E. Schmidt & F. W. Schmidt,* unpublished results.
42 *J. Möhr, J. R. Möhr, H. Mattenheimer, A. W. Holmes, F. Deinhardt & F. W. Schmidt,* Enzyme, *12,* 99 [1971].
43 *P. McLean & M. W. Gurney,* Biochem. J. *87,* 96 [1963].
44 *E. Hirschberg, D. Snider & M. Osaro* in: Adv. in Enzyme Regulation, The Macmillan Co., New York 1964, Vol. 2, p. 301.
45 *M. T. Nishikawara & J. G. Bricker,* Amer. J. Physiol. *210,* 586 [1966].
46 *M. T. Nishikawara,* Endocrinology *79,* 997 [1966].
47 *K. Wallenfels & H. D. Summ,* Klin. Wschr. *35,* 849 [1957].
48 *E. Schmidt & F. W. Schmidt,* Enzymol. biol. clin. *2,* 223 [1962/63].
49 *G. L. Endahl & Ch. D. Kochakian,* Proc. Soc. exper. Biol. Med. *94,* 192 [1957].
50 *D. Pette,* in: Praktische Enzymologie, H. Huber, Berne 1968, p. 15.
51 *E. Schmidt, F. W. Schmidt & C. Herfarth,* Klin. Wschr. *40,* 1133 [1962].
52 *H. J. Strecker* in: Methods in Enzymology, Academic Press, New York 1955, Vol. 2, p. 220.
53 *S. J. Adelstein & B. L. Vallee,* J. biol. Chem. *234,* 824 [1959].
54 Empfehlungen der Deutschen Gesellschaft für Klinische Chemie, Z. Klin. Chem., Klin. Biochem. *10,* 182 [1972].

Colorimetric Assay[1]

John King

Even at suboptimum substrate concentrations the GlDH activity measured according to equation (1), p. 650 is linearly proportional with time and enzyme concentration up to 50% conversion of substrate. It is therefore possible to use a fixed time interval for measurements of the activity. GlDH is relatively thermolabile; it is immediately inactivated in serum at 50 °C. Inactivation can even occur at 37 °C if the incubation is prolonged; but time periods below 1 hr. are safe.

Principle

See p. 650. Both substrates, 2-oxoglutarate and NADH, form 2,4-dinitrophenylhydrazones, which absorb at 385 and 400 nm respectively in alkaline solution[2]. The enzyme activity is determined by measurements of the hydrazone concentration before and after the reaction. A standard curve is used.

Optimum Conditions for Measurements

The optimum pH depends on the direction of the reaction and varies with the buffer and the temperature. We use phosphate buffer, pH 7.0. Several anions, e. g. nitrate and chloride, inhibit, therefore we use ammonium sulphate; 100 mM $(NH_4)_2SO_4$ is optimum at 37 °C ($K_M = 10$ mM). The optimum concentration range for NADH at 25 °C is very narrow, while at 37 °C it is broader; we use 0.6 mM NADH ($K_M = 0.12$ mM). NADPH (0.6 mM) gives only 60% of the optimum activity with NADH. To obtain extinctions which are readable suboptimum concentrations of 2-oxoglutarate must be used.
The ratios of activity at 25 °C, 30 °C and 37 °C with this method (1 hr. incubation) are $1:1\cdot32:1\cdot67$ (see p. 651).

Equipment

Spectrophotometer or spectrum-line photometer suitable for measurements at 390 (405) nm; 37 °C water bath.

Reagents

1. Disodium hydrogen phosphate, $Na_2HPO_4\cdot2H_2O$, A. R.
2. Potassium dihydrogen phosphate, KH_2PO_4, A. R.
3. 2-Oxoglutaric acid
   Commercial preparation, see p. 548.
4. Ammonium sulphate, $(NH_4)_2SO_4$, A. R.

5. Reduced nicotinamide-adenine dinucleotide, NADH
   disodium salt, NADH-Na_2. Commercial preparation, see p. 545.
6. 2,4-Dinitrophenylhydrazine, A. R.
7. Hydrochloric acid, A. R., 1 N
8. Sodium hydroxide, A. R., 0.4 N.

Preparation of Solutions

Use only fresh, doubly distilled water.

I. Phosphate buffer (0.067 M; pH 7.0):
   Dissolve 7.25 g. $Na_2HPO_4\cdot2H_2O$ and 3.53 g. KH_2PO_4 in distilled water and make up to 1 000 ml.

II. 2-Oxoglutarate (0.96 mM):
   Dissolve 14.0 mg. 2-oxoglutarate in phosphate buffer (I) and make up to 100 ml.

III. Ammonium sulphate (0.3 M):
   Dissolve 3.96 g. ammonium sulphate in phosphate buffer (I) and make up to 100 ml.

IV. Reduced nicotinamide-adenine dinucleotide (ca. 3 mM):
   Dissolve 2.5 mg. NADH-Na_2 in 1.0 ml. distilled water.

V. Ketone reagent (1 mM):
   Dissolve 200 mg. 2,4-dinitrophenylhydrazine in hot 1 N HCl, cool and dilute to 1 000 ml. with 1 N HCl.

VI. Standard solution (0.96 mM):
   Dissolve 8.5 mg. NADH-Na_2 in 10 ml. 2-oxoglutarate solution (II).

Stability of Solutions

Sodium hydroxide and the ketone reagent are stable indefinitely. The phosphate buffer and ammonium sulphate solution are stable for two months if stored in a refrigerator at 0–4 °C with the addition of several drops of chloroform to prevent the growth of micro-organisms. It is best to prepare the NADH solution just before use; it is stable in the frozen state for a month[3]. Prepare the standard solution freshly just before use.

Procedure

Collection, Treatment and Stability of Sample

Use only fresh plasma or serum. Heparin, oxalate, citrate, EDTA or fluoride can be added to blood. Avoid haemolysis: it does not affect the results, but the measurements must be made against a blank containing a suitable dilution of the ketone reagent.

The enzyme in serum is stable for 48 hr. in the frozen state, but loses activity in 24 hr. at room temperature[1].

Assay System

Wavelength: 390 (Hg 405) nm; light path: 1 cm.; incubation volume: 1.4 ml.; 37 °C; volume for colorimetric assay: 12.4 ml. read against water.

If the extinction of the blank is > 0.800 read against ketone reagent (V) diluted with water (1 : 50 dilution has an extinction of 0.160 and 1 : 100 an extinction of about 0.095)*.

With extinction changes of > 0.300 repeat the assay with less sample. The extinctions change with time, but the error of the difference between the blank and test values is < 5% within 30 min. of addition of NaOH.

Pipette into test tubes:		Test	Blank	Concentration in assay mixture
2-Oxoglutarate solution	(II)	0.5 ml.	—	0.34 mM
				47.5 mM phosphate
$(NH_4)_2SO_4$ solution	(III)	0.5 ml.	0.5 ml.	107 mM
Sample		0.2 ml.	0.2 ml.	
Equilibrate in a water bath to 37 °C.				
NADH solution	(IV)	0.2 ml.	0.2 ml.	0.4 mM
Mix and incubate for exactly 60 min. in the water bath.				
Ketone reagent	(V)	1.0 ml.	1.0 ml.	
2-Oxoglutarate solution	(II)	—	0.5 ml.	
Mix, incubate for 20 min. in the water bath and then remove tubes from bath.				
0.4 N NaOH		10.0 ml.	10.0 ml.	
Mix and measure the extinctions. Calculate the difference between the blank and test.				

---

* See p. 609.

Standard Curve

Pipette into each tube 0.5 ml. $(NH_4)_2SO_4$ solution (III), 0.2 ml. pooled serum or water, 1.0 ml. ketone reagent (solution V) and the following solutions. Then proceed as for the protocol above, starting with 20 min. incubation. Read against water.

Tube No.	1	2	3	4	5	6	7	
Standard solution (VI)	—	0.05	0.10	0.15	0.20	0.25	0.30	ml.
Phosphate buffer (I)	0.50	0.45	0.40	0.35	0.30	0.25	0.20	ml.
U/l. (37 °C)	0	4	8	12	16	20	24	

Subtract the extinctions of tubes 2–7 from the extinction of tube 1. Plot these values (ordinate) against U/l. (abscissa). The standard curve is slightly curved.

Calculations

The extinction difference between tubes 1 and 2 of the standards represents a change in 2-oxoglutarate concentration of $0.05 \times 0.96/1\,000$ mmole. If this change is caused by 0.2 ml. serum in 60 min. then this is $(0.05 \times 0.96/1\,000) \times (1\,000\,000/60 \times 0.2) = 4$ nmole/ml. per min. or 4 U/l.

Precision of Method

For values around 16 U/l. ± 1.4 U/l. the coefficient of variation is 4.3%.

Normal Values

In normal serum the values are around zero; the upper limit is taken to be 2.5 U/l. (see p. 654). In cord blood up to 4 U/l. is normal.

Sources of Error

For simplicity the NADH and 2-oxoglutarate concentrations are equal in the standard curve, although the former should be lower. However, the resulting error is negligible.

Specificity of Method

Addition of NADH to the blank allows for the reaction of other substrates with other dehydrogenases contained in the sample. The possibility that serum transaminases may decrease the 2-oxoglutarate concentration can be ignored. GlDH is determined specifically. In the reverse direction, the effect of transamination (GPT) is significant[1].

References

1 *J. King,* Thesis, Institute of Medical Laboratory Technology, London [1967].
2 *J. King,* J. med. Lab. Technol. *17,* 89 [1960].
3 *J. Pottage,* Thesis, Institute of Medical Laboratory Technology, London [1968].

Diamine Oxidase

Wilfried Lorenz, Jürgen Kusche and Eugen Werle

Best[1] described in 1929 a histamine-inactivating enzyme which was called histaminase[2,3]. *Zeller* named it diamine oxidase, DAO (Amine: oxygen oxidoreductase, deaminating, pyridoxal-containing, EC 1.4.3.6) because the enzyme from pig kidney also oxidatively deaminated putrescine, cadaverine and agmatine[4]. Histamine reacts because it is a substituted, cyclic diamine. Although the identity of DAO and histaminase has not yet been firmly established, the two names are frequently used synonymously. So far only the enzyme from pig kidney, pig plasma and human placenta has been purified to a state of homogeneity and characterized as diamine oxidase[5-7]. A recent classification differentiates amine oxidases according to their preferred substrate: benzylamine oxidase in pig plasma reacts preferentially with benzylamine, but also attacks histamine and other biogenic amines[9-11]. "Diamine oxidase" from pig[5,7] and dog kidney[11] as well as from pea seedlings[12] preferentially deaminate cadaverine and putrescine. "Histaminase" from animal and human salivary glands reacts preferentially with histamine[11]. Other enzymes with different substrate specificity, e. g. "putrescine oxidase" have been found in micro-organisms[13-15].

Clinical Biochemistry

An increase in DAO activity in human serum has been described in pregnancy[11,16-18] and in several diseases[19]. The placenta, which has a very high DAO activity[21,22,24,25], is considered to be the source of raised DAO activity in serum during pregnancy[20-23]. During normal pregnancy the DAO level in serum begins to rise from the 2nd. to 3rd. month, and reaches a maximum by the 5th. to 7th. month and remains at this level until parturition. The DAO activity falls within a few days *post partum* to the very low levels of normal human serum[21,26]. Measurement of DAO activity is of prognostic value in threatened abortion: if abortion occurs the DAO values are considerably lower than in gravidae of the same age, whereas if it does not the values are normal or only slightly lower[21,27,28]. In the more severe stages of pregnancy toxemia, e. g. hyperemesis gravidarum, pre-eclampsia and eclampsia, the DAO activity of serum falls markedly[20,21,29], while the histamine content of blood is raised[29]. If only a small portion of the placenta or hydatidiform mole remain in the uterus the DAO activity after parturition does not return to the normal values of healthy, non-pregnant women[21,27,28]. An increase of DAO activity in serum has been observed in cases of malignant tumors of the uterus and ovaries (corpus carcinoma of the uterus, myosarcoma of the uterus, granulosa cell tumor)[30]. The serum DAO activity is also raised in bronchial carcinoma[31,32], in anaphylactic shock[33,34,35] and after intravenous administration of heparin[36].

Methods for Determination of DAO Activity

Due to the relatively large number of substrates and reaction products many methods are available for the assay of DAO activity.

With histamine as substrate: a) biological assay of the residual histamine by the guinea pig ileum method[37] or by the blood pressure changes with anaesthetized cats[38]; b) fluorimetric, polarographic[39], or spectrophotometric assay[40]; c) measurements of the O_2 consumption manometrically[41] or spectrophotometrically (haemoglobin formation[42]). With cadaverine, putrescine or hexamethylenediamine as substrates: spectrophotometric determination of the aldehyde after cyclization and condensation with o-aminobenzaldehyde[43]. Ammonia formation measured according to *Van Slyke* and *Cullen*[44], *Folin*[45], *Parnas* vacuum distillation[4] or *Conway* diffusion analysis[12,46]. Measurement with hydrogen peroxide by means of the decolorization time required for a given amount of indigo[47], colorimetric determination of the residual dye[48], titration with $KMnO_4$[49] and spectrophotometric determination of the colour formed with o-dianisidine[50]. Radiochemical method with [^{14}C]-putrescine as substrate[51]. Of these numerous assay methods the one described here is distinguished for its high sensitivity, specificity and simplicity. The ammonia formed in the DAO reaction is determined enzymatically with glutamate dehydrogenase, GlDH (L-Glutamate: NAD(P) oxidoreductase, deaminating, EC 1.4.1.3). The enzymatic determination of ammonia was first described by *Kirsten* et al.[52], while *Lorenz* et al.[11,53] were first to apply this method to the measurement of the activity of enzymes concerned in the liberation of ammonia (DAO, histidase and urease).

Application of Method: In biochemistry and clinical chemistry.

Principle

(1) $$R–CH_2–NH_2 + O_2 + H_2O \xrightarrow{\text{DAO}} R–CHO + NH_3 + H_2O_2$$

(2) $$NH_3 + \text{2-Oxoglutarate} + NADH + H^+ \xrightarrow{\text{GlDH}} \text{Glutamate} + NAD^+ + H_2O$$

The equilibrium of reaction (1) lies completely on the right; the back reaction has not been demonstrated. Due to the position of the equilibrium of reaction (2)

$$K = \frac{[\text{2-Oxoglutarate}]\,[NH_3]\,[NADH]\,[H^+]}{[\text{Glutamate}]\,[NAD^+]\,[H_2O]} = 1.8 \times 10^{-13}\ M$$

the ammonia formed reacts virtually quantitatively. The ammonia formation per unit time, as determined by the decrease in extinction due to oxidation of NADH, is a measure of the DAO activity.

Optimum Conditions for Measurements

The following concentrations are optimum for the assay of DAO activity[53]: 3.2 U GlDH/assay; 0.19 mM NADH (higher concentrations decrease the activity of GlDH[54]); 5.7 mM 2-oxoglutarate. The pH optimum of the coupled system is pH 7.4, and the reaction is somewhat slower at pH 8.0[53,55]. The most suitable buffer concentration is 0.2 M. The optimum substrate concentrations for pea seedling DAO are: cadaverine 0.3 mM, putrescine 8 mM, hexamethylenediamine 14 mM, benzylamine 16 mM and histamine 1 mM. As each amine oxidase shows different optimum substrate concentrations these must be determined in each particular situation.

Equipment

Spectrophotometer or spectrum-line photometer suitable for precise measurements at 340, 334 or 365 nm; preferably with a constant temperature cuvette holder (25 °C) and a recorder. Stopwatch.

Reagents

1. Potassium dihydrogen phosphate, KH_2PO_4
2. Disodium hydrogen phosphate, $Na_2HPO_4 \cdot 2\,H_2O$
3. Glutamate dehydrogenase, GlDH
   NH_4^+-free, solution in 50% glycerol; ≥ 90 U/mg. (25 °C); commercial preparation, see p. 461.
4. 2-Oxoglutaric acid
   free acid or sodium salt; commercial preparation, see p. 548.

5. Reduced nicotinamide-adenine dinucleotide, NADH
   disodium salt, NADH-Na_2; commercial preparation, see p. 545.
6. Substrates:
   Putrescine, cadaverine, hexamethylenediamine and histamine as dihydrochlorides, benzylamine.

Purity of Enzyme Preparation

GlDH must be free from ammonia; the content of LDH and MDH should not exceed 0.2% (relative to the specific activity of GlDH).

Preparation of Solutions (for ca. 25 determinations)

Prepare all solutions with fresh, doubly distilled water.

I. Phosphate buffer (0.2 M; pH 7.4):
   (a) Dissolve 68.05 g. KH_2PO_4 in distilled water and make up to 1000 ml. (b) Dissolve 89.0 g. $Na_2HPO_4·2H_2O$ in distilled water and make up to 1000 ml. Mix 9.1 ml. solution (a) with 40.9 ml. solution (b) and dilute with distilled water to 125 ml.

II. 2-Oxoglutarate (171 mM):
   Dissolve 97.5 mg. Na_2-2-oxoglutarate in 3 ml. distilled water, or 75 mg. 2-oxoglutaric acid in 1 ml. distilled water, titrate with 0.3 N NaOH to pH 7.4 and dilute to 3 ml. with distilled water.

III. Reduced nicotinamide-adenine dinucleotide (5.7 mM β-NADH):
   Dissolve 12.1 mg. NADH-Na_2 in 3 ml. 1% $NaHCO_3$ solution.

IV. Substrate solution (240 mM putrescine*):
   Dissolve 15.9 mg. putrescine dihydrochloride in 3 ml. distilled water. Other substrates: 9 mM cadaverine dihydrochloride (4.72 mg./3 ml.); 420 mM hexamethylenediamine dihydrochloride (23.7 mg./3 ml.); 640 mM benzylamine (1.57 ml./3 ml., diluted 1 : 100); 30 mM histamine dihydrochloride (1.66 mg./3 ml.).

V. Glutamate dehydrogenase, GlDH (10 mg. protein/ml.):
   If necessary, dilute the stock solution with 50% glycerol.

Stability of Solutions

Store all solutions at 0–4 °C. Prepare the 2-oxoglutarate, NADH and substrate solutions freshly each week. GlDH in glycerol does not lose significant activity within 6 months at 4 °C.

Procedure

Collection, Treatment and Stability of Sample

Venous blood: Plasma or serum can be used. Heparin (3 USP units Liquemin /ml.) is recommended as anticoagulant; oxalate affects the DAO activity[56]; EDTA inhibits DAO[8]. Addition of fluoride or citrate has no effect[56].

Animal tissues[11]: Homogenize the tissue in 0.1 M phosphate buffer (solution I diluted 1+1) in the proportion 1+2 and centrifuge at 100000 g at 0–4 °C for 30 min. Chromatograph the supernatant fluid on Sephadex G 50. Concentrate the protein peak of the resulting filtrate by stirring in dry Sephadex G 25 and then centrifuge for a short period in sieve tubes. The concentrate is used as the enzyme preparation. Homogenates and enzyme preparations stored

---

* Cadaverine has proved the most suitable substrate for human serum (especially during pregnancy).

deep-frozen at -14 to -20 °C remain stable for weeks. Using the o-aminobenzaldehyde method[43], which is also suitable for crude homogenates, it was established that this method of concentration resulted in no loss of activity of dog kidney enzyme. After filtration on Sephadex G 50 the whole activity was $45 \pm 5\%$ higher than that of the crude homogenate. Concentration with Sephadex G 25 resulted in a loss of about 20%. The increase in activity after gel filtration may be due to the removal of low-molecular weight inhibitors, as has been described by *Southren* et al.[57].

Assay System

Wavelength: 340 (Hg 334, Hg 365) nm; light path: 1 cm.; final volume: 3 ml.; 25 °C (constant temperature cuvette holder); read against a blank containing water instead of substrate. Bring the solutions to 25 °C before starting the measurements.

Pipette successively into cuvettes:			Concentration in assay mixture
Phosphate buffer	(I)	1.65-2.55 ml.	ca. 0.15 M
GlDH solution	(V)	0.05 ml.	15 U/ml.
2-Oxoglutarate solution	(II)	0.10 ml.	5.7 mM
NADH solution	(III)	0.10 ml.	0.19 mM
Enzyme sample		0.1–1.0 ml.	
Mix and allow to stand for 10 min. The ammonia already present in the mixture reacts.			
Substrate solution	(IV)	0.1 ml.	8 mM putrescine*
Mix and after 2 min. read the extinction against the blank. Depending on the activity, read at 2 min. intervals for 15–45 min.			

For the exact determination of the difference between test and blank it is recommended to use a photometer with automatic cuvette changer and recorder. With the above substrate concentrations the reaction with 25–100 mU DAO/assay is linear from the start; up to 450 mU the reaction proceeds in the form of a consecutive reaction: induction period up to 3 min., linear curve up to 7 min. and finally a plateau due lack of NADH[53].

Calculations

The calculation formula (8) on p. 313 applies. For this method (1 ml. enzyme sample) the following relationships hold

Wavelength:	*334 nm*	*340 nm*	*365 nm*
Volume activity	$491.8 \times \Delta E/\text{min.}$	$482.3 \times \Delta E/\text{min.}$	$882.4 \times \Delta E/\text{min.}$ [U/l.]

---

* Or 0.3 mM cadaverine, 14 mM hexamethylenediamine, 16 mM benzylamine, 1 mM histamine.

Precision of Method

With appropriate expansion of the recorder scale the method can detect 3×10^{-9} moles NH_4^+ [11], and the decrease in extinction of NADH is directly proportional to the amount of NH_4^+ added[53]. In 10 assays with a purified DAO from pea seedlings the coefficient of variation was 0.3% at a ΔE of 1.07 $\pm$ 0.03.

Normal Values

The DAO activity in human serum of men and non-pregnant women is 18–37 [U/l.] (37 °C)[36]. In pregnant women serum values between 100 [U/l.] in the 16th. week of pregnancy and 870 [U/l.] in the 28th. week have been found[11].

Sources of Error

Interference due to high blanks or "creep" is most likely with crude samples. It usually results in considerable oxidation of NADH before the start of actual assay. The following remedies can be tried: a) increase the amount of NADH solution up to 0.2 ml./cuvette; b) dilute the sample; c) purify the sample on Sephadex G 50.

Specificity of Method

The enzymatic determination of the liberated ammonia by the GlDH reaction confers a high specificity. The glutamate dehydrogenase method is also suitable for the determination of monoamine oxidase, urease and histidase[11,53].

References

1   C. H. Best, J. Physiol. 67, 256 [1929].
2   E. W. McHenry & G. Gavin, Biochem. J. 29, 622 [1935].
3   C. H. Best & E. W. McHenry, J. Physiol. 70, 1349 [1930].
4   E. A. Zeller, Helv. chim. Acta 21, 880–890 [1938].
5   R. Kapeller-Adler & H. MacFarlane, Biochim. biophys. Acta 67, 542–565 [1963].
6   R. Kapeller-Adler, Clin. chim. Acta 11, 191–193 [1965].
7   B. Mondovi, G. Rotilio, A. Finazzi & A. Scioscia-Santoro, Biochem. J. 91, 408–415 [1964].
8   F. Buffoni, Pharm. Rev. 18, 1163–1199 [1966].
9   F. Buffoni & H. Blaschko, Proc. roy. soc. 161, 153–167 [1964].
10 H. Blaschko, Advanc. Comp. Physiol. Biochem. 1, 67–116 [1962].
11 W. Lorenz, J. Kusche, H. Hahn & E. Werle, Z. Analyt. Chem. 243, 259 [1968].
12 E. Werle, I. Trautschold & D. Aures, Hoppe-Seyler's Z. Physiol. Chem. 326, 200 [1961].
13 U. Bachrach, J. biol. Chem. 237, 3443–3447 [1962].
14 H. Yamada, O. Adachi & K. Ogata, Agr. biol. Chem. (Tokyo) 29, 117–123 [1965].
15 H. Yamada, A. Tanaka & K. Ogata, Agr. biol. Chem. (Tokyo) 29, 260–261 [1965]; Chem. Research
     Institute for Food Science N. 26, 1–9 [1965].
16 Y. Kobayashi, J. Lab. clin. Med. 62, 699–702 [1963].
17 A. L. Southren, Y. Kobayashi, P. H. Sherman, L. Levine, G. Gordon & A. B. Weingold, Surg. Forum 14,
     395–397 [1963].
18 E. Werle & G. Effkemann, Arch. Gynaekol., 170, 82 [1940].
19 F. C. Code, M. M. Hurn & R. G. Mitchell, Mayo Clinic Proceedings 39, 715 [1964].
20 R. Kapeller-Adler, Biochem. J. 38, 270–274 [1944].
21 A. Ahlmark, Acta physiol. scandinav. 9 (suppl. 28), 1–107 [1944].
22 G. V. Anrep, G. S. Barsoum & A. Ibrahim, J. Physiol. 106, 379–393 [1947].
23 Lindberg, Acta obst. et gynec. scandinav. 42, (suppl. 1) 26–34 [1963].
24 H. Swanberg, Acta physiol. scandinav. 23, (suppl. 79) 1–69 [1950].
25 E. A. Zeller, B. Schaer & Staehlin, Helv. chim. Acta 22, 837–850 [1929].

26 E. A. Zeller, Schweizer mediz. Wchschrft. 71, 1 349–1 351 [1941].
27 N. E. Borglin & B. Willert, Acta obst. gynec. scandinav. 36, 382–397 [1957].
28 Genell & Sune, Acta obst. gynec. scandinav. 30, (suppl. 7) 413–421 [1950].
29 R. Kapeller-Adler, Lancet 2, 745–747 [1949].
30 N. E. Borglin & B. Willert, Cancer 15, 271–275 [1962].
31 G. Casati, M. Carbone, M. Lops & R. Italia, Giornale ital. Tuberkulosi 17, 8 10 [1963].
32 K. W. Starr, J. Gibbons & J. C. Clandatus, Nature (London) 195, 1010 [1962].
33 R. K. Bernauer, H. Giertz, F. Hahn, W. Schmutzler, G. Seseke & B. U. Sievers, Naturwissenschaften 17, 412–413 [1964].
34 G. B. Logan, Proc. soc. exp. Biol. N. Y. 107, 466–469 [1961].
35 G. B. Logan, Proc. soc. exp. Biol. N. Y. 111, 171–174 [1962].
36 O. Dahlbaeck, R. Hansson, G. Tibbling & N. Tryding, Scand. J. Lab. Invest 21, 17–25 [1968].
37 S. Edlbacher & E. A. Zeller, Helv. chim. Acta 20, 717 [1937].
    F. Wicksell, Acta physiol. scandinav. 17, 359 [1949];
    A. Ahlmark, Acta physiol. scandinav. 9, (suppl. 28) [1944];
    G. V. Anrep, M. S. Ayadi, G. S. Barsoum, J. R. Smithu & N. M. Talaat, J. Physiol. 103, 155 [1944];
    F. Hahn, W. Schmutzler, G. Seseke, H. Giertz & W. Bernauer, Biochem. Pharmacol. 15, 155 [1966];
    E. Werle & G. Effkemann, Arch. Gynaekol. 170, 82 [1940];
    R. M. Gesler, M. Matsuba & C. A. Dragstedt, J. Pharmacol. exp. Therapeut. 116, 356 [1956].
38 C. H. Best, J. Physiol. 67, 256 [1929];
    G. Albus, Klin. Wschr. 24, 858 [1939];
    N. Emmelin, G. Kahlson & F. Wicksell, Acta physiol. scandinav. 22, 123 [1941].
39 K. Uozumi, J. Nakahara, T. Higashin & Y. Sakamoto, J. Biochem. (Tokyo) 56, 601 [1964].
40 C. A. Dodge, Amer. J. Ostetr. Gynecol. 63, 1213 [1952].
41 C. H. Best & E. W. McHenry, J. Physiol. 70, 1 349 [1930]; E. Gebauer-Füllnegg & A. C. Alt, Proc. Soc. exp. Biol. Med. 29, 531 [1932]; E. A. Zeller, H. Birkhäuser, H. Nislin & M. Wenk, Helv. Chim. Acta 22, 1 381 [1939].
42 B. Mondovi, G. Rotilio & M. T. Costa, Proc. Symp. Chem. Biol., p. 415, Pergamon Press Oxford 1963; M. Lawskowski, J. biol. Chem. 145, 457 [1942].
43 B. Holmstedt & R. Tham, Acta physiol. scandinav. 45, 152 [1959].
44 E. W. McHenry & G. Gavin, Biochem. J. 26, 1365 [1932].
45 S. Edlbacher & E. A. Zeller, Helv. chim. Acta 20, 717 [1937].
46 E. A. Zeller, Klin. Wchschrft. 20, 220 [1941];
    G. C. Cotzias & V. P. Dole, J. biol. Chem. 196, 235 [1952];
    R. Kapeller-Adler, Biochem. J. 44, 70 [1949];
    C. M. McEwen, J. biol. Chem. 240, 2003 [1915];
    M. Laskowski, J. M. Lenleg & C. K. Keith, Arch. Biochem. 6, 105 [1945].
47 E. A. Zeller, Helv. chim. Acta 21, 1645 [1938].
48 E. A. Zeller, Helv. chim. Acta 23, 1502 [1940].
    Schweiz. med. Wschr. 71, 1349 [1941];
    B. B. Lozzio, A. D. Marenci & M. Royer, Rev. farmaceutica (Buenos Aires) 102, 53 [1960].
49 R. Kapeller-Adler, Biochim. biophys. Acta (Amsterdam) 22, 291 [1956];
    R. Kapeller-Adler & Renswick, Clin chim. Acta (Amsterdam) 1, 197 [1956].
50 P. N. Aarsen & H. Kemp, Nature (London) 204, 1195 [1964].
51 R. Okuyama & Y. Kobayashi, Arch. Biochem. Biophys. 95, 242 [1961].
52 E. Kirsten, C. Gerez & R. Kirsten, Biochem. Z. 337, 312 [1963].
53 W. Lorenz, J. Kusche & E. Werle, Hoppe-Seyler's Z. Physiol. chem. 348, 561–567 [1967].
54 E. Baesler in Hoppe-Seyler-Thierfelder (eds.), Handbuch d. physiol. u. pathol.-chem. Analyse, vol. 6a, p. 683, Springer Verlag Berlin-Heidelberg-New York 1964.
55 B. Mondovi, G. Rotilio, A. Finazzi & M. T. Costa, Biochim. Biophys. Acta 132, 521 [1967].
56 E. A. Zeller, Advanc. Enzymol. 2, 93 [1942].
57 A. L. Southren, Y. Kobayashi, N. C. Carmody & A. B. Weingold, Amer. J. Obstet. Gynec. 95, 615 [1966].

Dihydrofolate Reductase

(Tetrahydrofolate Dehydrogenase)

Wolfgang Wilmanns

Dihydrofolate reductase (5,6,7,8-Tetrahydrofolate: NADP oxidoreductase, EC 1.5.1.3) was purified in 1957 by *Futterman*[1], in 1958 by *Osborn* and *Huennekens*[2], in 1959 by *Peters* and *Greenberg*[3] and by *Zakrzewski* and *Nichol*[4]. Sources of the enzyme were chicken, sheep and pigeon liver. *Blakley* and *McDougall*[5] isolated the enzyme from *Streptococcus faecalis* and *Nath* and *Greenberg*[6] from calf thymus. The enzyme has been detected in humans in leukaemic cells by *Bertino, Gabrio* and *Huennekens*[7] and by *Wilmanns*[8,9]. According to [10] dihydrofolate reductase also occurs in the myeloid precursors of normal leucocytes. Only slight enzyme activity has been found in lymphocytes and in lymphatic cells in chronic lymphatic leukaemia. The enzyme is located in the cytoplasm of the cells. It has not been detected in the extracellular space. *Jaenicke* and *Scholz*[11] observed a large increase in enzyme activity during the period of DNA synthesis in synchronized yeast cultures.

The determination of the activity of dihydrofolate reductase in cytolysates of leucocytes and bone marrow cells is described here. This method is not applicable to erythrocytes because of the interference from high concentrations of haemoglobin.

Application of Method: In biochemistry, biochemical haematology, experimental tumour research and as a complement to studies on cell kinetics.

Principle

(1)
$$FH_2 + NADPH + H^+ \xrightleftharpoons[\text{reductase}]{\text{dihydrofolate}} FH_4 + NADP^+$$

The equilibrium of the reaction lies far to the right. The decrease of extinction at 340 nm with time is a measure of the dihydrofolate reductase activity. This decrease in extinction is due to the oxidation of NADPH ($\varepsilon = 6.22$ cm.^{2}/μmole) and reduction of dihydrofolate ($\varepsilon = 5.05$ cm.^{2}/μmole). The sum of these two values ($\varepsilon = 11.27$ cm.^{2}/μmole) is used for this enzyme reaction as described by *Misra* et al.[13].

Optimum Conditions for Measurements

In all tissues studied the enzyme has two pH optima. One optimum is at pH 7.5. The highest activity is measured at lower pH values. The optima in this range vary with the type of tissue studied. The enzyme purified from animal liver has its maximum activity below pH 5.0. In leucocyte cytolysates it is between pH 5.0 and 5.4. We use citrate buffer, pH 5.4. In spite of the considerable destruction of NADPH in acid solution (see also p. 160) it is possible with the appropriate blanks and exact pipetting to obtain reproducible and accurate measurements. The equilibrium constant of reaction (1) is 5.6×10^4 (enzyme purified from chicken liver)[12]; the Michaelis constant for dihydrofolate is 5.0×10^{-7} M. In studies with leucocyte cytolysates the K_M for dihydrofolate was found to be 1.3×10^{-5} M and for NADPH 4×10^{-5} M[9].

The incubation mixture contains 2-mercaptoethanol because reduced folate derivatives are easily oxidized.

Equipment

Spectrophotometer suitable for accurate measurements at 340 nm, preferably with constant temperature cuvette holder; water bath (25 °C); stopwatch.

Reagents

1. Ethylenediaminetetra-acetate magnesium-dipotassium salt, EDTA-MgK$_2$ · 2 H$_2$O
2. Sodium hydroxide, A. R., 1 N
3. Potassium hydroxide, A. R., 1 N
4. Ammonium chloride, A. R., anhydrous
5. Potassium dihydrogen phosphate, A. R., KH$_2$PO$_4$
6. Dipotassium hydrogen phosphate, A. R., K$_2$HPO$_4$
7. Potassium chloride, A. R.
8. Sodium chloride, A. R.
9. Magnesium chloride, A. R., MgCl$_2$ · 6 H$_2$O
10. Sodium hydrogen carbonate, A. R., NaHCO$_3$
11. D-Glucose
12. Silicone oil "Wacker SW 60", Wacker-Chemie GmbH, Munich, Germany
13. Carbon tetrachloride, CCl$_4$
14. Citric acid monohydrate, A. R., C$_6$H$_8$O$_7$ · H$_2$O
15. Mercaptoethanol
16. Reduced nicotinamide-adenine dinucleotide phosphate, NADPH tetrasodium salt, NADPH-Na$_4$; commercial preparation, see p. 547.
17. Dihydrofolic acid preparation, see Appendix, p. 671.

Preparation of Solutions

Prepare all solutions with doubly distilled water.

For preparation of sample

Ia. Ringer solution:
Dissolve 6.2 g. NaCl, 0.2 g. KCl, 0.1 g. MgCl$_2$ · 6 H$_2$O and 2.0 g. NaHCO$_3$ in distilled water and make up to 1 000 ml.

Ib. Ringer phosphate-glucose solution:
Mix 45 ml. Ringer solution with 5 ml. 67 mM phosphate buffer (solution IV). Dissolve in this solution 100 mg. glucose. Prepare freshly each day.

II. Ethylenediaminetetra-acetate (0.1 M; pH 7.4):
Dissolve 4.267 g. EDTA-MgK$_2$ · 2 H$_2$O in distilled water, adjust to pH 7.4 with 1 N KOH and dilute to 100 ml. with distilled water.

III. Ammonium chloride (0.83% w/v):
Dissolve 8.3 g. NH$_4$Cl in distilled water and make up to 1 000 ml.

IV. Potassium phosphate buffer (67 mM; pH 7.4):
Mix 80.0 ml. K$_2$HPO$_4$ solution (1.16 g./100 ml.) with 19.2 ml. KH$_2$PO$_4$ solution (0.91 g./100 ml.) and adjust pH to 7.4.

V. Potassium phosphate buffer (1 mM; pH 7.4):
Dilute phosphate buffer (IV) 1 :67 with distilled water.

VI. Silicone (2%):
Dissolve 2 ml. silicone oil in carbon tetrachloride and make up to 100 ml.

For assay

VII. Citrate buffer (0.15 M; pH 5.4):
Dissolve 42 g. citric acid monohydrate in 400 ml. 1 N NaOH and dilute with distilled water to 1 000 ml. Dilute 75 ml. of this solution with 2.5 ml. 0.2 N NaOH and adjust to pH 5.4.

VIII. 2-Mercaptoethanol (0.3 M):
   Dilute 1 ml. 2-mercaptoethanol with 45.5 ml. distilled water.
  IX. Reduced nicotinamide-adenine dinucleotide phosphate (10 mM):
   Dissolve 10 mg. NADPH-Na$_4$ in 1.2 ml. 50 mM KHCO$_3$.
   X. Dihydrofolic acid (50 mM):
   Dilute the crystalline suspension in HCl with 50 mM KHCO$_3$ immediately before use.
   FH$_2$ goes into solution. Determine the concentration of the solution spectrophoto-
   metrically at 283 nm ($\varepsilon = 22$ cm.^{2}/μmole; dilute accordingly).

Procedure

Collection, Treatment and Stability of Sample

Isolation and cytolysis of leucocytes:

Collect 20–40 ml. venous blood into 2–4 ml. EDTA solution (II) and carefully mix. Use
siliconized test tubes. Slant the tubes and allow the cells to sediment for 30 min. at 37 °C.
Suck off the supernatant layer of leucocytes, platelets and some erythrocytes with a siliconized
pipette and centrifuge in cellulose nitrate tubes in a refrigerated centrifuge at 175 g and 0 °C.
Carry out all the following operations at 0–3 °C. Carefully suck off the supernatant with a
pipette and discard. Suspend the sediment in 3 ml. ammonium chloride solution (III) and
allow to stand for 3 min. to haemolyse the remaining erythrocytes. Centrifuge again, wash
the sediment three times with calcium-free Ringer-phosphate-glucose solution (Ib). Adjust the
last suspension to give a cell count of about 10^8 leucocytes/ml. (quadruplicate count in a
Zeiss-Thoma or Neubauer chamber). Centrifuge again. To cytolyse the sediment suspend in
the same volume of phosphate buffer (V) as for the last suspension and after standing at 0 °C
for 1 hr. centrifuge for 30 min. at 38 000 g to remove the cell stroma (refrigerated centrifuge).
Use the supernatant fluid for the enzyme assay.

Isolation and cytolysis of bone marrow cells:

Aspirate 1–2 ml. sternum marrow with a siliconized syringe and immediately add to a cellulose-
nitrate centrifuge tube containing 1.0 ml. Ringer-phosphate-glucose solution (Ib) and 0.2 ml.
EDTA solution (II). Centrifuge for 10 min. at 175 g in a refrigerated centrifuge. Carry out
the haemolysis of the erythrocytes, isolation of nucleated cells and their cytolysis as described
for leucocytes.

Stability of enzyme in the cytolysates:

The enzyme activity must be determined within 4 hr. of completion of the cell isolation (later
the activity decreases considerably); the samples must be stored at 0–3 °C before the assay.

Assay System

Wavelength: 340 nm; light path: 1 cm.; final volume: 1.25 ml.; 25 °C. For each series of measurements prepare a blank containing distilled water instead of sample. Read against (also blank) a control containing distilled water instead of dihydrofolate solution (X).

Pipette into cuvettes:			Concentration in assay mixture
Citrate buffer	(VII)	1.00 ml.	120 mM
2-Mercaptoethanol solution	(VIII)	0.05 ml.	12 mM
NADPH solution	(IX)	0.05 ml.	0.4 mM
Dihydrofolic acid	(X)	0.05 ml.	2 mM
Mix and allow to stand for 5 min.			
Sample (cytolysate)		0.10 ml.	equivalent to ca. 2×10^7 cells
Mix. Read the extinctions against the control for 30 min. to check the progress (linear) of the reaction: every 2 min. for the first 10 min., then every 5 min.			

Calculations

Subtract the $\Delta E/30$ min. value of the blank (0.010 ± 0.009) from the extinction decrease $\Delta E/30$ min. of test. This corrected $\Delta E/30$ min. value lies generally between 0.050/30 min and 0.300/30 min., and depends on the type and number of cells.

The enzyme activity is expressed in $U/10^{10}$ cells and is calculated on the basis of $\varepsilon = 11.27$ cm.$^2/\mu$mole. According to p. 313 the following relationship holds for the conditions described here:

$$\text{Mean cell activity} = \frac{1.25 \times 10^{10} \times F}{0.1 \times 11.27 \times C} \times \Delta E/\text{min} = \frac{1.109 \times F}{C} \times 10^{10} \times \Delta E/\text{min} \ [U/10^{10} \text{ cells}]$$

F = Factor regarding the dilution during cytolysis.
C = Number of cells taken for assay.

The enzyme activity can also be related to mg. protein content, but for clinical biochemical problems the number of cells is a better reference system.

Normal Values

Activities[14] determined in bone marrow cells and peripheral leucocytes as well as in leukaemia are given in Table 1.

Table 1. Activities of dihydrofolate reductase in different blood and bone marrow cells.

Cells	N	$U/10^{10}$ cells
		$(\bar{x} \pm s)$
Normal bone marrow cells	16	0.37 ± 0.12
Normal leucocytes (periph. cells)	29	$0 \ (\pm 0.05)$
Acute leukaemia (periph. cells)	50	0.48 ± 0.33
marrow cells	14	0.48 ± 0.3
Chronic myeloleukaemia (periph. cells)	19	0.3 ± 0.16
Blast crisis in chronic myeloleukaemia (periph. cells)	5	0.52 ± 0.35
Chronic lymphatic leukaemia (periph. cells)	14	$0 \ (0.07 \pm 0.07)$

N = number of cases; $\bar{x}$ = mean value; s = standard deviation.

Sources of Error

Effects of drugs and other therapeutic measures: Dihydrofolate reductase is inhibited by 0.01 μM aminopterin and amethopterin (Methotrexate)[15-17]. Addition of these folic acid antagonists to cell cultures and treatment of human leucocytes and leukaemia cells with Methotrexate later results in increased activity of the dihydrofolate reductase which at first is completely inhibited. This increase in activity can exceed that measured before the action of the inhibitor by several-fold[13,18-22]. The extent of the inhibition and the rate of increase of enzyme activity after a therapeutic single intravenous injection of Methotrexate give information on the sensitivity or resistance of leukaemic cells and normal bone marrow cells to folic acid antagonists.

The inhibition of dihydrofolate reductase by aminopterin and amethopterin is maximum at pH 5.9. It is caused because the extremely strong binding of the antagonists to the enzyme is stoichiometric. Therefore it is possible to determine the concentration of folic acid antagonists in various tissues by titration with purified dihydrofolate reductase. An acetone powder of chicken liver is a suitable source of the enzyme[23].

Interference in the assay technique: Spontaneous oxidation of NADPH in acid solution*. This source of error can be eliminated by use of a blank without sample to correct the values for the test.

Interference with the enzyme reaction in crude extracts by NADP reductase: No interfering reduction of NADP in the assay has been found using cytolysates of leucocytes and bone marrow by the method described here.

Specificity of Method

The reductase activity is reduced to about 1/5 by substitution of folic acid for dihydrofolic acid. Under the above assay conditions no reduction of folic acid by human leucocytes and leukemic cells can be demonstrated.

Other Methods for Determination of Dihydrofolate Reductase Activity

The spectrophotometric assay method described here is applicable to measurements of activity of dihydrofolate reductase in homogenates of chicken, pigeon, sheep and rat liver, and cytolysates of white blood cells and bone marrow cells, which have been obtained by the method described above. With extracts of acetone powders of ascites tumour cells and leucocytes, however, the assay can only be carried out after preliminary fractionation. In this case other assay methods should be considered:

1. Combination with tetrahydrofolate formylase[7]. For principle see "Tetrahydrofolate Formylase", p. 1118
2. Spectrophotometric assay[24] by measurement of the extinction decrease at 283 nm. This method has the advantage that NADP reductase contained in crude enzyme extracts does not interfere. However, as dihydrofolic acid and tetrahydrofolic acid have adjacent absorption maxima[25] (283 nm and 298 nm) the extinction coefficient in this case for the reduction of dihydrofolate is $\varepsilon = 3.36$ cm.^{2}/μmole. The sensitivity of the assay is therefore reduced to 1/3 of the method described here.
3. By use of tritium-labelled folic acid the sensitivity of the assay can be increased. *Rothenberg*[26] separates the resulting folic acid derivates electrophoretically. *Roberts*[27] has described a method which is based on the fact that in contrast to folic acid the tritium label of tetrahydrofolic acid is labile to oxidizing agents. The tritium label can be quantitatively split from the tetrahydrofolic acid by treatment with an incubation mixture containing trichloroacetic acid and KNO_2. After adsorption of the excess labelled tritium folic acid compounds on animal charcoal, the tritium can be determined as tritiated water.

---

* Does not occur at pH values > 7, but the results are then very much lower (e. g. 2- to 3-fold).

Appendix

Dihydrofolic acid

Folic acid is reduced to dihydrofolic acid according to[1,14].

Additional Reagents

18. L-(+)-Ascorbic acid, A. R.
19. Folic acid
20. Sodium dithionite, A. R.,
21. Hydrochloric acid, A. R., 1 N

Method

Dissolve 1 g. ascorbic acid in ca. 4 ml. distilled water in a 25 ml. flask with stirring (magnetic stirrer). Slowly add 1 N NaOH until the pH reaches 6.0 (continual measurement of pH with glass electrode) and then add 10 ml. distilled water. Dissolve 38.2 mg. folic acid in 1.6 ml. 1 N NaOH and add to the sodium ascorbate solution. Stir in 400 mg. sodium dithionite, after complete solution slowly stir for 5 min. at room temperature, then cool in an ice bath to below 5 °C with stirring. Carry out the following steps in an ice bath. Drop in 1 N HCl from a burette until the pH reaches 2.8 (continual pH control); stir for a further 5 min. Centrifuge off the precipitate in a refrigerated centrifuge ("Sorvall" with SS-34-rotor) for 5 min. at 1 000 g and 0 °C and resuspend in 10 ml. 10% sodium ascorbate solution. Stir and again add 1 N NaOH until the pH is 6.0. Slowly drop in 1 N HCl, dihydrofolic acid crystallizes out. The crystallization is complete 5 min. after attainment of pH 2.8. Centrifuge for 5 min. at 1 000 g and 0 °C. Wash the precipitate 3 times with ca. 10 ml. cold 0.005 N HCl. Suspend the crystals in 4 ml. 0.005 N HCl and store in the dark at 0 °C.

Dihydrofolic acid dissolved in 0.01 N KOH has an absorption maximum at 283 nm. The suspension of dihydrofolic acid in HCl is stable for several months.

References

1　S. Futterman, J. biol Chem. 228, 1031 [1957].
2　M. J. Osborn & F. M. Huennekens, J. biol. Chem. 233, 969 [1958].
3　J. M. Peters & D. M. Greenberg, Biochim. Biophys. Acta 32, 273 [1959].
4　S. F. Zakrzewski & C. A. Nichol, Biochim. Biophys. Acta 27, 425 [1958].
5　R. L. Blakley & B. M. McDougall, J. biol. Chem. 236, 1163 [1961].
6　R. Nath & D. M. Greenberg, Biochemistry 1, 435 [1962].
7　J. R. Bertino, B. W. Gabrio & F. M. Huennekens, Biochem. biophys. Res. Comm. 3, 461 [1960].
8　W. Wilmanns, Klin. Wschr. 39, 884 [1961].
9　W. Wilmanns, Klin. Wschr. 40, 533 [1962].
10　W. Wilmanns, Med. Welt 52, 2667 [1963].
11　K. Scholz & L. Jaenicke: Europ. J. Biochemistry 4, 448 [1968].
12　C. K. Mathews, K. G. Scrimgeour & F. M. Huennekens in S. P. Colowick & N. O. Kaplan: Methods in Enzymology, vol. VI, p. 364, Academic Press New York 1963.
13　D. K. Misra, S. P. Humphreys, M. Friedkin, A. Goldin & E. J. Crawford, Nature 189, 39 [1961].
14　R. L. Blakeley, Nature 40, 1684 [1961].
15　S. Futterman & M. Silverman, J. biol. Chem. 224, 31 [1957].
16　M. J. Osborn, M. Freeman & F. M. Huennekens, Proc. Soc. Exp. Biol. Med. 97, 429 [1958].
17　W. C. Werkheiser, Cancer Res. 23, 1277 [1963].
18　G. A. Fischer, Biochem. Pharmacol 7, 75 [1961].
19　M. T. Hakala, S. F. Zakrzewski & C. A. Nichol: J. biol. Chem. 236, 952 [1961].

20 *J. R. Bertino, D. M. Donohue, B. W. Gabrio, R. Silber, A. Alenty, M. Meyer* & *F. M. Huennekens,*
    Nature *193,* 140 [1962].
21 *W. Wilmanns,* 17. Mosbacher Colloquium, Springer, Berlin-Heidelberg-New York 1966.
22 *W. Wilmanns* & *H. Martin,* Klin. Wschr. *46,* 281 [1968].
23 *S. F. Zakrzewski,* J. biol. Chem. *235,* 1776 [1960].
24 *D. K. Misra,* Blood *23,* 572 [1964].
25 *L. Jaenicke* & *C. Kutzbach,* Fortschr. d. Chemie org. Naturstoffe, vol. XXI, p. 184, Springer Ed.,
    Vienna 1963.
26 *O. O. Rothenberg,* Anal. Biochem. *13,* 530 [1965].
27 *D. W. Roberts,* Biochemistry *5,* 3549 [1966].

Catalase

Hugo Aebi

Catalase (Hydrogen-peroxide : hydrogen-peroxide oxidoreductase, EC 1.11.1.6) was recognized as being widely distributed in nature by *O. Loew* (1901)[1] although the H_2O_2-cleaving activity of various tissues had already been described in 1819 by *Thénard*[2] and erroneously considered to be a general property of all enzymes by *Schönbein*[3]. Catalase was first isolated and obtained in crystalline form from ox liver (*Sumner and Dounce*, 1937)[4], and later from blood and other sources (*Bonnichsen*[5], *Herbert* and *Pinsent*[6], *Laskowski* and *Sumner*[7], *Agner*[8]). The enzyme contains 4 ferriprotoporphyrin groups per molecule (molecular weight 240 000) which corresponds to a protohaem content of 1.1% and an iron content of 0.09%. The extinction at 405 nm (Soret band) is used to determine the concentration of catalase. The millimolar extinction coefficient is 380–400 per mole of enzyme or 100 per haem group. The specific activity and the ratio E_{405}/E_{280} can be used as an index of the purity.

The catalase activity of tissues varies greatly; it is highest in liver and kidney and low in connective tissue. In tissues it is mainly particle-bound (in mitochondria[9] and peroxisomes [10]), whereas it exists in a soluble state in erythrocytes[11]. The catalase activity of blood is practically all due to the erythrocytes. Human erythrocytes are normally rich in catalase, while those of the duck are virtually catalase-free. Catalase can be separated from haemoglobin either by the classical precipitation with ethanol-chloroform[12] or better by chromatography on DEAE-cellulose[13] or by gel filtration[14].

Catalase has a double function, because it catalyses the following reactions: (1) decomposition of H_2O_2 to give H_2O and O_2 (catalase activity; see equation 1); (2) oxidation of H donors, for example, methanol, ethanol, formic acid, phenols, with the consumption of 1 mole of peroxide (peroxidase activity; see equation 2).

(1)
$$2\ H_2O_2 \xrightarrow{\text{catalase}} 2\ H_2O + O_2$$

(2)
$$ROOH + AH_2 \xrightarrow{\text{catalase}} H_2O + ROH + A$$

The predominating reaction depends on the concentration of H donor and the steady-state concentration or rate of production of H_2O_2 in the system. In both cases the active catalase-H_2O_2-complex I is formed first. The decomposition of H_2O_2, in which a second molecule of H_2O_2 serves as H donor for complex I, proceeds exceedingly rapidly (rate constant $k \sim 10^7$ sec.$^{-1}$ mole^{-1}), whereas peroxidative reactions proceed relatively slowly ($k \sim 10^2 - 10^3$).

The physiological function of catalase is still obscure, although various theories have been put forward[15,16,17,18]. Probably the catalase located in the cell organelles plays the role of a specific peroxidase. The enzyme pattern of the peroxisomes is noteworthy for the simultaneous presence of H_2O_2-producing (e. g. D-amino acid oxidase, uricase) and consuming enzymes (catalase). In erythrocytes catalase-like glutathione peroxidase exerts a protective function for haemoglobin and other SH-proteins (enzymes, stroma), the importance of which can vary with the species and the experimental conditions[19,20]. The lower the catalase activity of the erythrocytes the more effective is the action of oxidizing agents (H_2O_2, ascorbic acid, methylhydrazine) or of X-rays on methaemoglobin formation[21].

Catalase activity can be measured by following either the decomposition of H_2O_2 or the liberation of O_2. The method of choice for biological material is the UV spectrophotometric method. The titrimetric methods are suitable for comparative studies, while for large series of measurements there are simple screening tests, which give a rapid indication of the approximate catalase activity[22,23,24].

Catalase Kinetics

The kinetics of catalase do not obey the normal pattern. On the one hand it is not possible to saturate the enzyme with "substrate" within the feasible concentration range (up to 5 M H_2O_2), and on the other there is a rapid inactivation of catalase at H_2O_2 concentrations above 0.1 M, when the active enzyme-H_2O_2-complex I is converted to the inactive complexes II or III. Measurement of enzyme activity at substrate saturation or determination of the K_s is therefore impossible. In contrast to reactions proceeding at substrate saturation, the enzymatic decomposition of H_2O_2 is a first order reaction, the rate of which is always proportional to the peroxide concentration present. Consequently, to avoid a rapid decrease in the initial rate of the reaction, the assay must be carried out with relatively low concentrations of H_2O_2 (ca. 0.01 M). As the activation energy for the decomposition of H_2O_2 catalysed by catalase is very low (600–1 700 cal./mole), there is only slight dependence on temperature ($Q_{10} = 1.05$–1.12). The decomposition of H_2O_2 initially (ca. 0–30 sec.) follows that of a first order reaction with H_2O_2 concentrations between 0.01 and 0.05 M. The rate constant (k) for the overall reaction is given by:

$$(3) \qquad\qquad k = \frac{1}{\varDelta t} \times \ln \frac{S_1}{S_2} = \frac{2.3}{\varDelta t} \log \frac{S_1}{S_2}$$

Where $\varDelta t = t_2 - t_1$ = measured time interval; S_1 and S_2 = H_2O_2 concentrations at times t_1 and t_2. The constant k (dimension: sec.$^{-1}$) can be used as a direct measure of the catalase concentration. For the determination of catalase activity in blood or haemolysates, the haemoglobin content is usually chosen as the reference unit[25,26]. In studies with purified enzyme preparations the specific activity (k'_1) is obtained by dividing k by the molar concentration of catalase (e).

$$(4) \qquad\qquad k'_1 = k/e \quad (M^{-1} \text{ sec.}^{-1})$$

The value for k'_1 for pure catalase from human erythrocytes is 3.4×10^7 (M^{-1} sec.$^{-1}$)[6]. This value is used to calculate the absolute content of enzyme in blood and tissues[25,27].

UV-Assay

Application of Method: In biochemistry and haematology, occasionally in clinical chemistry.

Principle

In the ultraviolet range H_2O_2 shows a continual increase in absorption with decreasing wavelength. The decomposition of H_2O_2 can be followed directly by the decrease in extinction at 240 nm ($\varepsilon_{240} = 40.0$ cm^2/μmole). The difference in extinction ($\varDelta E_{240}$) per unit time is a measure of the catalase activity.

Optimum Conditions for Measurements

To avoid inactivation of the enzyme during the assay (usually ca. 30 sec.) or formation of bubbles in the cuvette due to the liberation of O_2, it is necessary to use a relatively low H_2O_2 concentration (10 mM). The H_2O_2 concentration is critical in so far as there is direct proportionality between the substrate concentration and the rate of decomposition. Dependence of the assay on the temperature is low ($Q_{10} < 1.1$) so that measurements can be carried out at room temperature (20 °C). The pH activity curve relative to V_0 has a fairly broad pH optimum (pH 6.8–7.5): measurements are made at pH 7.0.

Equipment

Spectrophotometer suitable for accurate measurements at 240 nm connected to a recorder (e.g. Hi-speed recorder). Quartz cuvettes (1 cm. light path).

Reagents

1. Potassium dihydrogen phosphate, KH_2PO_4
2. Disodium hydrogen phosphate, $Na_2HPO_4 \cdot 2H_2O$

3. Hydrogen peroxide, about 30% w/v (e.g. "Perhydrol", Merck, A.R.)

Purity of Reagents

Glassware, buffer and substrate should be free from heavy metals (catalytic decomposition of H_2O_2).

Preparation of Solutions

I. Phosphate buffer (50 mM; pH 7.0):
   a) Dissolve 6.81 g. KH_2PO_4 in distilled water and make up to 1000 ml.
   b) Dissolve 8.90 g. $Na_2HPO_4 \cdot 2H_2O$ in distilled water and make up to 1000 ml.
   Mix the solutions a) and b) in the proportion 1:1.55.
II. Hydrogen peroxide (30 mM):
   Dilute 0.34 ml. 30% hydrogen peroxide with phosphate buffer (solution I) to 100 ml.

Stability of Solutions

The phosphate buffer is stable as long as bacterial contamination is avoided; store at 2 °C. Prepare the buffered H_2O_2 solution (II) freshly each day.

Procedure

Collection, Treatment and Stability of Sample

Collection:

Venous blood: centrifuge venous blood containing heparin or citrate and take off plasma and leucocyte layer. Wash the erythrocyte sediment 3 times with isotonic NaCl. Prepare a stock haemolysate containing ca. 5 g. Hb/100 ml. by the addition of 4 parts by volume of distilled water. Prepare a 1 : 500 dilution of this concentrated haemolysate with phosphate buffer immediately before the assay and determine in duplicate its Hb content (e.g. by the method of *Drabkin*[28]).

Capillary blood: haemolyse 0.1 or 0.02 ml. of blood in 250 or 50 ml. distilled water. If the haemoglobin content of the blood is required as reference point it must be determined in a separate sample of blood.

Stability of enzyme in sample:

Although catalase in intact erythrocytes and in concentrated haemolysates is quite stable at 2 °C for several days, there is a relatively rapid loss of activity in dilute haemolysates. This instability is more likely due to decomposition of the enzyme into subunits than to proteolytic changes. No general rules can be made about the stability of the enzyme in dilute haemolysates. *Hübl* and *Bretschneider*[29] state that haemolysate samples should be analysed within 5–10 min. of dilution. The concentration dependence of this inactivation is shown in Fig. 1.

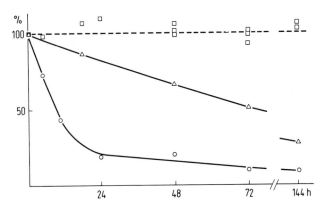

Fig. 1. Effect of haemolysate concentration on the catalase activity in normal human blood during storage (2 °C). Activity determined by method A (spectrophotometric).
a) □ 60 mg. Hb/ml.
b) △ 1.2 mg. Hb/ml.
c) ○ 0.06 mg. Hb/ml.

Assay System

Wavelength: 240 nm; light path: 1 cm.; final volume: 3.0 ml. Read at 20 °C ($\sim$ room temperature) against a reference cuvette containing enzyme solution or haemolysate but no substrate.

Pipette successively into cuvettes:		Reference cuvette	Test cuvette	Concentration in assay mixture
Phosphate buffer	(I)	1.0 ml.	—	50 mM
Sample (haemolysate)		2.0 ml.	2.0 ml.	—
H_2O_2 solution	(II)	—	1.0 ml.	10 mM
Start the reaction by addition of H_2O_2. Mix well with a plastic paddle; follow the decrease in extinction with a recorder for ca. 30 sec.				

If a recorder is not available, take readings at 5 or 10 sec. intervals ("tracking technique") see *Beers* and *Sizer*[30]. The values for $E_{240}/15$ sec. should not be greater than 0.10 and not smaller than 0.02.

Calculations

Definition of international catalase units (U) according to the recommendations of the IUB is not simple because of the abnormal kinetics (but see p. 674). It is therefore understandable that for this enzyme there are a number of differently defined units and different methods of evaluation in use (refer to p. 681). It is recommended to use the rate constant of a first order reaction (k). The rate constant related to the haemoglobin content (k/g. Hb) can serve as a measure of the specific activity of erythrocyte catalase.

Equation (3) on p. 674 applies in this case. If the extinction decrease is recorded, the value of $\log \frac{E_1}{E_2}$ for a measured time interval or the time required for a certain decrease in extinction can be determined.

a) For a time interval of 15 sec. the following relationship is obtained according to equation (3):

$$(5) \qquad k = \frac{2.3}{15} \times \log \frac{E_1}{E_2} = 0.153 \times \log \frac{E_1}{E_2} \ [sec.^{-1}]$$

To calculate k/ml. or k/g. Hb proceed as follows:

$$(6) \qquad k/ml. = k \times a$$

$$(7) \qquad k/g.\ Hb = k/ml. \frac{1000}{b} = \frac{2.3}{15} \times \frac{a}{b} \times \log \frac{E_1}{E_2}\ [sec.^{-1}]$$

Where E_1 is E_{240} at $t = 0$; E_2 is E_{240} at $t = 15$ sec.

$$a = \text{dilution factor} = \frac{\text{Hb concn. in blood or erythrocyte sediment (mg. Hb/ml.)}}{\text{Hb concn. in cuvette (mg. Hb/ml.)}}$$

b = Hb content of blood or erythrocyte sediment (g./l.).

b) For the difference in extinction of 0.450—0.400 (log $E_1/E_2 = 0.05115$) the following relation holds:

$$(8) \qquad k = \frac{2.3}{\Delta t} \times \log \frac{E_1}{E_2} = \frac{0.1175}{\Delta t}\ [sec.^{-1}]$$

Precision of Method

With values around 300 k/g. Hb a precision of 10 k/g. Hb was found. The coefficient of variation is 2–3%.

Normal Values

The catalase activity in blood of 37 normal subjects (students) was found to be 313 ± 96 k/g. Hb $(x \pm 2\ SD)$[31].

Sources of Error

In the determination of catalase activity in haemolysates or tissue homogenates the following sources of interference must be considered:

a) Lability of catalase in dilute solution. Avoid this by dilution of the stock solution just before the assay.

b) Low activity because of restricted permeability due to the binding of catalase to cell structures, e.g. incomplete haemolysis, presence of intact mitochondria or peroxisomes. Avoid this by addition of saponin (0.2%), Triton X-100 (1%)[32], or by freezing and thawing (three times) the undiluted samples[27].

c) Interference in the assay by strongly absorbing substances or precipitation in the sample. This is particularly troublesome when the sample cannot be diluted greatly because of the low catalase activity (e.g. blood samples from carriers of the enzyme defect acatalasia[31]. In such cases the titrimetric assay is recommended.

d) Bacterial contamination: store samples in frozen state.

e) The presence of catalase inhibitors in samples of biological material is less likely (e.g. cyanide, azide, hydroxylamine, 3-amino-1,2,4-triazole).

Specificity of Method

Any substance which catalyses the decomposition of H_2O_2 is determined. As the activity of other haem compounds is several orders of magnitude smaller $(10^3 - 10^4)$[33,34,35], the method can be considered specific for catalase. In doubtful cases, the addition of catalase inhibitors (e.g. 0.1 mM Na azide) provides information as to whether the observed decomposition of H_2O_2 is catalysed by catalase or a haem compound.

Details for Measurements in Tissues

Catalase in tissues containing relatively high activity, such as liver and kidney, can be determined spectro-photometrically, if it is possible to obtain complete lysis of all organelles and clear (or only slightly coloured) solutions or extracts. It is necessary to use a detergent (e.g. 1% Triton-X-100) in the preparation of the stock homogenate (1:10 or 1:20). Further dilutions can be made with phosphate buffer, pH 7.0 (1:100 to 1:500 according to the tissue and the species). The catalase activity of tissue samples is normally expressed on a mg. wet weight or mg. total-N basis. A convenient method for the measurement of catalase activity in tissue extracts has recently been described by *Cohen* et al [64].

Titrimetric Method

Application of Method: The assay of catalase activity by titration is necessary when high UV absorption, pigmentation or precipitation of the sample does not allow use of the spectrophotometric method. This is the case with homogenates of tissues containing low catalase activity (e.g. brain, fibroblasts, tumours), with milk, and with concentrated extracts of plant or bacterial origin.

Principle

The decomposition of H_2O_2 is followed by measurement of the peroxide still present in the mixture after a certain time by back-titration, e. g. with permanganate. Portions of the assay mixture can be taken after 10, 20 and 30 sec. or the reaction in the whole mixture can be stopped by addition of acid.

Optimum Conditions for Measurements

See p. 674. Titrimetric methods with incubation times of longer than 30 sec. give only comparative values. The preparation of progress curves requires a considerable expenditure of time and effort with a large series of measurements. Perborate, a more stable substrate, is best for routine studies; the inactivation of the enzyme is somewhat slower. The results obtained with H_2O_2 and perborate are of the same order of magnitude. In practice the method of *Feinstein*[36] is suitable, in so far as the assay conditions are modified according to the recommended procedure of *Bonnichsen*[37] (i. e. 30 sec. incubation time at pH 7.0 and 20 °C).

Equipment

Thermostatic water bath (20 °C) with rotating shaking attachment.

Reagents

1. Sodium perborate, $NaBO_3 \cdot 4H_2O$, A.R.
2. Potassium permanganate, $KMnO_4$, A.R.
3. Sulphuric acid, A. R., 2N

4. Hydrochloric acid, A.R., diluted 1:5
5. Primary and secondary phosphates for preparation of buffer, see p. 675.

Purity of Reagents

See remarks on p. 675.

Preparation of Solutions

  I. Sodium perborate (100 mM; pH 7.0):
     Dissolve 7.694 g. $NaBO_3 \cdot 4H_2O$ in ca. 20 ml. 1:5 dilute HCl, add ca. 400 ml. distilled water, adjust with HCl to pH 7.0 and make up to 500 ml. with distilled water.
 II. Phosphate buffer (50 mM; pH 7.0): see p. 675.
III. Potassium permanganate (0.05 N):
     Dissolve 1.58 g. $KMnO_4$ in distilled water and make up to 1 000 ml.

Stability of Solutions

Buffer, see p. 675, the perborate solution is stable for several days at 2 °C. Always check titer with permanganate.

Procedure

Collection, Treatment and Stability of Sample, see p. 675.

Assay System

Incubation at 20 °C; final volume: 5.0 ml.

Pipette successively into test tubes:		Blank	Test*	Concentration in assay mixture
Phosphate buffer	(II)	1.0 ml.	1.0 ml.	10 mM
Na perborate solution	(I)	3.0 ml.	3.0 ml.	60 mM
Preincubate for 10 min. at 20 °C.			.	
Water		1.0 ml.	—	
Sample** (haemolysate)		—	1.0 ml.	
Stop the reaction after 30 sec. by addition of				
2 N H_2SO_4		3.0 ml.	3.0 ml.	
The remaining perborate is back-titrated with permanganate solution (III).				

Calculations

A. Titration results, especially those which have been obtained with different incubation times, can be calculated in the same way as the spectrophotometric method according to equation (3) and (4) on p. 674. Because of the progressive inactivation of the enzyme the calculated k values for the various time intervals must be extrapolated to t = 0[37,38]. The values obtained in this way for the rate constant k are somewhat lower[39].

B. For comparative purposes the results can also be expressed in arbitrarily defined "units", e.g. the number of milliequivalents of Na perborate decomposed under the standard experimental conditions related to mg. wet weight of tissue (or g. haemoglobin, etc.) ("perborate units"[36]).

---

 * To construct a progress curve prepare several assay mixtures and stop the reaction at 10, 20 and 30 sec.
** The concentration of the enzyme solution should be such that after 30 sec. not more than 50% and not less than 10% of the perborate is decomposed. If the catalase activity in the sample is low, the incubation time should be increased to 1 min. or even to 5 min.

Precision of Method

3–5% according to the type and activity of the sample.

Sources of Error

In the titration of concentrated homogenates or blood samples the end-point is not sharp, because the protein in the sample slowly reacts with permanganate.

If the titration is carried out rapidly and always to the same end-point (relative excess of $KMnO_4$), the resulting error is small. A correction can be applied by titration of an additional control mixture containing no perborate or by deproteinization of the incubated reaction mixtures with trichloroacetic acid. Oxidizable substances (e.g. tris) must not be used as components of buffers if catalase activity is determined by the titrimetric method.

Specificity of Method

Refer to p. 677.

Other Methods of Determination

A number of the methods for determination of catalase in common use are summarized in Table 1. Recently introduced automatic methods (using the *Technicon AutoAnalyzer®*) are available for large series of samples[27,55].

Method	Reference	Material
A. Determination of H_2O_2 removal		
1. Titrimetric methods		
a) Iodometric	Bonnichsen et al., (1947)[40]	Tissues, Blood
b) Permanganometric	Feinstein (1949)*[36]	Tissues, Blood
	Takahara et al., (1960)[41]	Tissues, Blood
2. Spectrophotometry (E_{240})	Bergmeyer (1955)[42]	Tissues
	Werner and Heider (1963)[26]	Blood
3. Photometry (E_{405} to E_{415})		
a) Titanium sulphate	Hübl and Bretschneider (1964)[29]	Tissues, Blood
b) Titanium tetrachloride	Pilz and Johann (1965)*[43]	Blood
c) Vanadic acid	Warburg and Krippahl (1963)[44]	Tissues
4. Fluorimetry		
a) Scopoletin	Perschke and Broda (1961)[45]	Aqueous
(decrease of fluorescence)	Aebi (1963)[46]	solutions
b) Diacetyldichlorofluorescin	Keston and Brandt (1965)[47]	
(increase of fluorescence)		
B. Determination of O_2 production		
1. Polarography	Jacob (1964)[48]	Micro-organisms
2. Oxygen electrode	Ogata (1964)[49]	Blood
	Rørth and Jensen (1967)[50]	Blood
3. Manometry		
a) with the van Slyke apparatus	Kirk (1963)[51]	Blood, Tissues
b) with floating filter paper	Gagnon et al., (1959)[52]	Blood, Tissues
C. Immunoprecipitation		
(with anti-catalase)	Higashi et al., (1961)[53]	Blood, Tissues
	Ben-Yoseph and Shapira (1973)[65]	
D. Measurement of heat production	Landahl (1953)[54]	Blood

* In these methods Na perborate was used as substrate, in all others the substrate was hydrogen peroxide.

Screening Test

To obtain a rough estimate of catalase activity in blood, especially to detect individuals with abnormally low blood catalase (heterozygote or homozygote carriers of the enzyme defect acatalasia) several screening tests are available[22,23,24].

The test of *Gross* and *Wüst*[24] depends on the liberation of O_2 from H_2O_2 i.e. the rate of froth production: take 1–2 drops of blood from the fingertip and take up in a polyethylene tube of 3 mm internal and 5 mm external diameter and 20 cm. long. Press the end of the tube which contains the blood into the hole of a polyacrylic block which is filled with 5% H_2O_2. The height of the froth produced is measured after 10 sec. and serves as an index of the catalase activity of the blood.

The height of the froth is only slightly dependent on the amount of blood trapped in the polyethylene tube, but there is a direct proportionality to the H_2O_2 concentration. There is a linear regression between the catalase activity determined titrimetrically and the height of the froth (normal height: 14–17 cm; hypocatalasaemia: < 12 cm.; acatalasaemia: ~ 1 cm.). The error of a single determination depends on the skill of the operator $\pm$ 13–20% (with duplicate determinations $\pm$ 9–14%). The test can be standardized by the parallel determination (with the titrimetric and screening methods) of a series of blood samples of different activity (e.g. normal blood containing varying amounts of azide).

Other Catalase Units

The rate constant, k, calculated according to equation (3) and related to a suitable reference unit (e.g. g. Hb, ml. blood or mg. protein) is the prefered catalase unit[26,56,57]. Other units can be obtained from the k value as follows:

Absolute enzyme concentration

According to equation (4) the following relation $e = k/k'_1$ holds between the rate constant (k), the specific activity of the pure enzyme (k'_1) and the molar catalase concentration (e). If the specific activity of the enzyme is known (e.g. human erythrocyte catalase[6]: $k'_1 = 3.4 \times 10^7 \, M^{-1} \, sec.^{-1}$) it is possible to calculate the molar enzyme concentration in a particular blood sample (range: $3–4.5 \times 10^{-9}$ moles/ml. erythrocytes[25,27,58]).

Catalase Units according to Bergmeyer

A unit[42] is the amount of enzyme which liberates half the peroxide oxygen from a H_2O_2 solution of any concentration (ca. 10 mM) in 100 sec. at 25 °C. This unit is therefore related to the half-life time τ of a first order reaction:

$$(9) \qquad\qquad \tau = \frac{\ln 2}{k} = \frac{0.693}{k}$$

The relationship between the observed half-life time (τ observed) and the enzyme activity (k observed) is:

$$(10) \qquad\qquad 1 \text{ unit} = \frac{100}{\tau \text{ observed}} = \frac{k \text{ observed}}{6.93 \times 10^{-3}}$$

Therefore according to equation (8):

(11)
$$\frac{0.1175}{\Delta t \times 6.93 \times 10^{-3}} = \frac{17}{\Delta t} = \text{units/assay mixture}$$

To interconvert k values and units according to *Bergmeyer*:

$$\text{Units according to } \textit{Bergmeyer} = \frac{k}{6.93 \times 10^{-3}}$$

Katalase Fähigkeit (Kat. f.)

This unit is replaced by k or k'_1[37,39]. It is still, however, occasionally used in data on purity or specific activity.
Definition according to *von Euler*[59,60]:

(12)
$$\text{Kat. f.} = \frac{K \, (\min.^{-1})}{\text{g. material (dry wt.) in 50 ml. assay mixture}}$$

(13)
$$\text{Kat. f.} = \frac{60 \, k \, (\sec.^{-1})}{2.3 \times 10^{-3} \times 16.7a} = 1\,565 \, k/\text{mg. material (dry wt.)}$$

Explanation of the factors used:
a = number of mg. material (dry wt.) in 3 ml. reaction mixture; 60: dimension of k is $\sec.^{-1}$ instead of $\min.^{-1}$; 2.3: log instead of ln; k instead of K; amount of material present in reaction expressed in mg. instead of g. (factor 10^{-3}) and related to 3 ml. instead of 50 ml. (factor 16.7). This equation does not take into account differences in experimental conditions (e. g. temperature).

International Units

An international unit is the amount of enzyme which decomposes 1 μmole H_2O_2 per minute at 25 °C under strictly defined conditions, especially with regard to the H_2O_2 concentration. Concentrations of 12.5 mM[61] and 5.9 mM[62] have been proposed for this purpose. As there is a direct proportionality between the rate of the reaction and the H_2O_2 concentration the conversion factor depends on the particular H_2O_2 concentration used.

Other Units

For information refer to the original literature: Catalase number *(Lück*[63]*)*, catalase index *(Werner and Heider*[26]*)*, and perborate units *(Feinstein*[36]*)*.

References

1 *O. Loew*, U.S. Dept. Agr. Report No. *68*, 47 [1901].
2 *L. J. Thénard*, Ann. chim. Phys. *11*, 85 [1819].
3 *C. F. Schönbein*, J. prakt. Chemie *89*, 323 [1863].
4 *J. B. Sumner & A. L. Dounce*, J. biol. Chem. *121*, 417 [1937].
5 *R. K. Bonnichsen*, Arch. Biochem. Biophys. *12*, 83 [1947].
6 *D. Herbert & J. Pinsent*, Biochem. J. *43*, 203 [1948].
7 *M. Laskowski & J. B. Sumner*, Science *94*, 615 [1941].

8 *K. Agner*, Arkiv. Kemi Mineral. Geol. *16A*, No. 6 [1942].
9 *D. Neubert, A. B. Wojtczak & A. L. Lehninger*, Proc. nat. Acad. Sci. U.S. *48*, 1651 [1962].
10 *C. de Duve & P. Baudhuin*, Physiol. Rev. *46*, 323 [1966].
11 *H. Aebi, E. Bossi, M. Cantz, S. Matsubara & H. Suter:* V. Berliner Symposium über Struktur und Funktion der Erythrocyten 1967, Humboldt Universität Berlin, DDR.
12 *M. Tsuchihashi*, Biochem. Z. *140*, 63 [1923].
13 *O. A. Thorup, J. T. Carpenter & P. Howard*, Brit. J. Haematol. *10*, 542 [1964].
14 *H. Aebi, C. H. Schneider, H. Gang & U. Wiesmann*, Experientia *20*, 103 [1964].
15 *O. Warburg, W. Schröder & H. W. Gattung*, Z. Naturforsch. *15b*, 196 [1960].
16 *G. Cohen & P. Hochstein*, Science *134*, 1 756 [1961].
17 *G. Cohen & P. Hochstein*, Biochemistry *2*, 1 420 [1963].
18 *P. Nicholls*, Biochem. Biophys. Acta *99*, 286 [1965].
19 *H. Aebi, J. P. Heiniger & E. Lauber*, Helv. chim. Acta *47*, 1 428 [1964].
20 *H. Aebi*, Exposés annuels de Biochimie Médicale [1969].
21 *H. Aebi & H. Suter*, Humangenetik *2*, 328 [1966].
22 *H. B. Hamilton, J. V. Neel, T. Y. Kobara & K. Ozaki*, J. clin. Invest. *40*, 2199 [1961].
23 *R. N. Feinstein, J. B. Howard, L. B. Ballonoff & J. E. Seaholm*, Anal. Biochem. *8*, 277 [1964].
24 *J. Groß & E. Wüst:* V. Berliner Symposium über Struktur und Funktion der Erythrocyten 1967, Humboldt Universität Berlin, DDR.
25 *A. R. Tarlov & R. W. Kellermeyer*, J. Lab. & Clin. Med. *58*, 204 [1961].
26 *E. Werner & H. Heider*, Z. klin. Chem. *1*, 115 [1963].
27 *J. N. Lamy, J. Lamy-Provansal, R. Jund & J. D. Weill*, Ann. Biol. clin. *26*, 417 [1968].
28 *D. L. Drabkin & J. H. Austin*, J. biol. Chem. *112*, 51 [1935].
29 *P. Hübl & R. Bretschneider*, Hoppe Seyler's Z. physiol. Chem. *335*, 146 [1964].
30 *R. F. Beers, Jr. & J. W. Sizer*, J. biol. Chem. *195*, 133 [1952].
31 *H. Aebi & H. Suter* in *J. J. Yunis:* Biochemical Methods in red cell genetics, Academic Press, New York 1969.
32 *R. N. Feinstein, J. T. Braun & J. B. Howard*, Arch. Biochem. Biophys. *120*, 165 [1967].
33 *A. Krause*, Monatsheft für Chemie *93*, 955 [1963].
34 *A. Krause, F. Domka, E. Kukielka & I. Plura*, Monatsheft für Chemie *94*, 466 [1963].
35 *A. Krause & Z. Winowski*, Monatsheft für Chemie *94*, 470 [1963].
36 *R. N. Feinstein*, J. biol. Chem. *180*, 1 197 [1949].
37 *R. Bonnichsen* in *S. P. Colowick & N. O. Kaplan:* Methods in Enzymology, Academic Press, New York 1955, Vol. II, p. 781–784.
38 *H. von Euler & K. Josephson*, Just. Lieb. Ann. Chem. *452*, 158 [1927].
39 *P. Nicholls & G. R. Schonbaum* in *P. D. Boyer, H. Lardy & K. Myrbäck:* The Enzymes (Vol. 8), Academic Press, New York 1963, p. 147–225 (see Tab. III, p. 157).
40 *R. K. Bonnichsen, B. Chance & H. Theorell*, Acta chem. Scand. *1*, 685 [1947].
41 *S. Takahara, H. B. Hamilton, J. V. Neel, T. Y. Kobara, Y. Ogura & E. T. Nishimura*, J. clin. Invest. *39*, 610 [1960].
42 *H. U. Bergmeyer*, Biochem. Z. *327*, 255 [1955].
43 *W. Pilz & J. Johann*, Z. analyt. Chem. *210*, 358 [1965].
44 *O. Warburg & G. Krippahl*, Z. Naturforschung *18b*, 340 [1963].
45 *H. Perschke & E. Broda*, Nature *190*, 257 [1961].
46 *H. Aebi*, Radiation Res. Suppl. *3*, 130 [1963].
47 *A. S. Keston & R. Brandt*, Anal. Biochem. *11*, 1 [1965].
48 *H. E. Jacob*, Z. Chem. *4*, 189 [1964].
49 *M. Ogata:* Symposium on Genetics and Biochemistry of Acatalasemia, IX Annual Meeting of the Japan Society of Human Genetics at Wakayama Medical College (in press).
50 *M. Rørth & P. K. Jensen*, Biochem. Biophys. Acta *139*, 171 [1967].
51 *J. E. Kirk*, Clin. Chem. *9*, 763 [1963].
52 *M. Gagnon, W. M. Hunting & W. B. Esselen*, Anal. Chem. *31*, 144 [1959].
53 *T. Higashi, M. Yagi & H. Hirai*, J. Biochem. Tokyo *49*, 707 [1961].
54 *H. D. Landahl*, Proc. Soc. exp. Biol. Med. *84*, 74 [1953].
55 *F. Leighton, B. Poole, H. Beaufay, P. Baudhuin, J. W. Coffey, S. Fowler & C. de Duve*, J. Cell Biol. *37*, 482 [1968].
56 *B. Chance & A. C. Maehly* in *S. P. Colowick & N. O. Kaplan:* Methods in Enzymology, Academic Press, New York 1955, Vol. II, p. 764–775.
57 *K. G. Paul & L. M. Engstedt*, Scand. J. clin Lab. Invest. *10*, 26 [1958].
58 *A. C. Maehly & B. Chance* in *D. Glick:* Methods of Biochemical Analysis (Vol. 1), Interscience Publishers, Inc., New York 1954, p. 357–408.
59 *H. von Euler & K. Josephson*, Chem. Ber. *59*, 770 [1926].

60 *H. von Euler:* Festschrift Arthur Stoll 1957, Sandoz A. G. Basel.
61 *H. Lück* in *H. U. Bergmeyer:* Methoden der enzymatischen Analyse (1st. edition), Verlag Chemie Weinheim 1962, p. 885–894.
62 Information leaflet "Catalase", Worthington Biochemical Corporation, Freehold N. J. 1968.
63 *H. Lück,* Biochem. Z. *329,* 165 [1957].
64 *G. Cohen, D. Dembiec & J. Marcus,* Anal. Chem. *34,* 30 [1970].
65 *Y. Ben-Yoseph & E. Shapira,* J. Lab. Clin. Med., in press [1973].

Peroxidases

Johann Pütter

The term *peroxidase* (POD) in its widest sense includes a group of specific enzymes such as NAD-POD, NADP-POD, fatty acid-POD, cytochrome-POD and glutathione-POD as well as a group of very non-specific enzymes from different sources, which are simply known as POD (donor: H_2O_2-oxidoreductase, EC 1.11.1.7). Only the latter group will be considered in this chapter. POD catalyses the dehydrogenation of a large number of organic compounds such as phenols and aromatic amines, hydroquinones and hydro-quinoid amines, especially benzidine derivatives. In particular, should be mentioned o-cresol[1], o-toluidine[2], guaiacol[3-5], pyrogallol[6], homovanillinic acid[7], p-hydroquinone[8], o- or p-phenylenediamine[9,10], leuco-malachite green[11], reduced 2,6-dichlorophenolindophenol[12,13], 4,4′-diaminodiphenylamine[14], benzidine[15], o-tolidine[16], di-o-anisidine[14,17-19], and some azo dyes derived from these[14].

With few exceptions the typical POD belonging to group 1.11.1.7 are haemoproteins[20]. Although the real POD reaction consists of the transfer of hydrogen from a donor to H_2O_2, there are examples of POD acting like oxidases[20-23] ($SH_2 + O_2 \rightarrow S + H_2O_2$) and mono-oxygenases[24-26] (e. g. $S-H + O_2 + NADPH \rightarrow S-OH + NADP^+ + OH^-$). On the other hand, apart from the true POD, peroxidative reactions can be catalysed by catalase with certain substrates, e. g. phenols, alcohols and several inorganic compounds[27-30], as well as by haemoglobin and some of its break-down products with typical POD substrates[31,32]. Finally, oxidases can in many cases react like POD and use H_2O_2 as a source of oxygen[33]. Although in the classical POD reactions the *specificity* for the hydrogen donor is very low, that for the peroxide is much higher. It appears that apart from H_2O_2, only compounds having the group $-O-OH$, e. g. acetyl-, methyl- and ethyl-hydroperoxide[34-36] can act as substrates[37].

Haemoprotein POD *occur* in animals, in higher plants, e.g. horse radish, pineapples, figs, potatoes, legumes, corn, root vegetables, tobacco plants[6,38-48], in yeasts[37-49], in moulds[50] and in bacteria[20]. The longest and the best studied is horse radish POD. In mammals POD occur in leucocytes[20,51,52], milk[53], liver[54], spleen[55], uterus[56], salivary glands[57], stomach wall[55], intestinal mucosa[20], lung[55], thyroid glands[58], etc. They have been found in mammalian cells in the supernatant, microsomal and mitochondrial fractions.

POD can be determined by the decrease of H_2O_2 or the hydrogen donor or the formation of the oxidized compound[37]. Usually the third method is employed, and many different substrates have been used. Very accurate values are obtained with di-o-anisidine[14], but the use of this compound should be limited because of its potential carcinogenic activity. The older method for the assay of POD with guaiacol[3] is therefore recommended here.

A new POD-substrate that has recently achieved considerable importance for the determination of blood glucose is 2,2′-azino-di-[3-ethyl-benzothiazoline-(6)-sulphonic acid][58a,58b].

Application of POD and the POD assay:

a) "Pseudoperoxidative" reaction of the blood pigments (detection of occult blood[59]).
b) Differential staining of leucocytes[59].
c) As auxiliary enzyme in the determination of hydrogen peroxide[60], catalase[61], oxidases[62], glucose[18,19], galactose[63], etc.
d) For the characterization of disease states in experimental pathology (e. g.[64]).
e) In general biochemistry.

Principle

The POD reaction consists of 2 successive steps each involving 1 electron[65]. A general equation for POD catalysed reactions cannot be formulated because the course of the reaction depends on the type of substrate. In the simplest case the same molecule is hydrogen donor for both steps. The equation of the overall reaction is usually:

(1) $$H_2O_2 + DH_2 \xrightarrow{\text{POD}} 2H_2O + D$$

The intermediate DH is in many cases detectable[14]. Often the intermediate product radicals can give rise to complicated secondary reactions. An example of a complicated reaction is the peroxidative oxidation of guaiacol. As the literature about the resulting dehydrogenation product is somewhat contradictory[66,67] and as probably more than one compound results from the reaction of guaiacol with H_2O_2 and peroxidase[67], a definite stoichiometric formula cannot be given here. Possibly the nature of the reaction product depends on the reaction conditions. Under the best conditions described below, a stoichiometric reaction proceeds in so far as one mole H_2O_2 oxidizes one mole guaiacol. In this contribution the resulting end product is called GDHP (guaiacol dehydrogenation product). The rate of formation of GDHP in the guaiacol assay is a measure of the POD activity and can be determined spectrophotometrically. The extinction coefficient for GDHP at 436 nm is 6.39 cm.^{2} per μmole guaiacol oxidized or per μmole H_2O_2 consumed.

The kinetics of the various POD are not uniform (e.g.[68,69]). Generally it holds that for H_2O_2 there is a definable Michaelis constant which is dependent on the concentration of the donor. Whether a Michaelis constant can be obtained for the donor is a matter of controversy[33,70,71]. In any case, under the usual conditions there is considerable dependence of the rate of the reaction on the concentration of the donor, while it is hardly affected by changes in the H_2O_2 concentration. In order to obtain a valid and linear relationship between the measurements and the enzyme activity, it is necessary to express the enzyme activity as a reciprocal of the time required for a fixed conversion (constant increase in extinction). Even here it is possible to convert the results to international units. The rate of reaction for various donors is different; POD from different sources differ in regard to relative reaction rates with different donors[37]. The expression of POD activity in μmole substrate converted per min. is therefore not generally valid, but only applies for a particular substrate and particular concentration of substrate.

Optimum Conditions for Measurements

The pH optima of different POD with guaiacol as hydrogen donor are not the same. However, as most POD are active over a relatively broad range of pH, assay of activity at pH 7.0 is possible in practically all cases. In addition, the temperature dependence of plant and animal POD is different; because of the general applicability and the technical simplicity it is proposed that 25 °C should be used. Saturation of enzyme with H_2O_2 or with substrate is not achieved under our conditions; the concentrations given are based on the apparent kinetics of the reaction[68].

The extinction maximum of GDHP is at 418 nm. At 436 nm the extinction is not essentially different; measurement at this wavelength has the advantage that it can be carried out with the usual filter photometers. The brown colour of GDHP is not stable for long: in the first 10 min. after formation it decreases by 4–5%. For accurate measurements, it is therefore recommended to add sufficient enzyme so that the time required for the reaction does not exceed 5 min.

Equipment

Potter-Elvehjem homogenizer. Spectrophotometer or filter photometer suitable for measurements at 436 nm, preferably with constant temperature cuvette holder. Water bath (25 °C); stopwatch.

Reagents

1. Potassium dihydrogen phosphate, KH_2PO_4
2. Dipotassium hydrogen phosphate, $K_2HPO_4 \cdot 3H_2O$

3. Guaiacol, synthetic, cryst. DAB 6
4. Hydrogen peroxide solution, 30% (w/v).

Preparation of Solutions

I. Phosphate buffer (0.1 M; pH 7.0):
a) Dissolve 13.61 g. KH_2PO_4 in doubly distilled water and make up to 1 000 ml.; – b) dissolve 22.82 g. $K_2HPO_4 \cdot 3H_2O$ in doubly distilled water and make up to 1 000 ml.; mix 39 ml. solution a) and 61 ml. solution b).

II. Guaiacol solution (20.1 mM):
Dissolve 249 mg. guaiacol in doubly distilled water and make up to 100 ml.

III. Hydrogen peroxide solution (0.042% = 12.3 mM):
Dilute 0.14 ml. 30% H_2O_2 to 100 ml. with doubly distilled water. The extinction of this solution should be 0.485 (± 0.020) at 240 nm and 1 cm. light path. If no UV-spectro-photometer is available, the peroxide content of the solution can be determined by titration with 0.01 N $KMnO_4$.

Stability of Solutions

The guaiacol solution is stable for at least 24 hr. in a cold room; in the frozen state it is stable for several months. The stability of the dilute H_2O_2 solution depends on various factors; it is best to determine its content daily by measurement of the extinction (see above).

Procedure

Collection, Treatment and Stability of Sample

Collection of sample: It depends on the type of experimental material. Blood must be removed from organs of experimental animals.

Treatment: Fluids require no special treatment. Homogenize tissues with a *Potter-Elvehjem* homogenizer. Refer to the appropriate methods (e. g. [58]) for the determination in different cell fractions (see p. 407). Suspensions of cell particles can generally be added directly to the cuvette.

The stability of enzyme in sample: Depends on situation, but in any case it is recommended that during the work up and storage of the sample it should be kept at 0–4 °C. If the stability of the sample has not been specially studied, the assay should be carried out within 5 hr. of collection of sample.

Assay System

Wavelength: Hg 436 nm; light path: 1 cm.; final volume: 3.18 ml.; temperature: 25 °C. Read against distilled water instead of H_2O_2 solution (III). Bring buffer solution (I) to 25 °C before the assay.

Pipette into cuvettes:			Concentration in assay mixture
Phosphate buffer	(I)	3.00 ml.	0.1 M
Guaiacol solution	(II)	0.05 ml.	0.316 mM
Sample		0.10 ml.	
H_2O_2 solution	(III)	0.03 ml.	0.116 mM
Mix; wait until the extinction has increased by 0.050, start stopwatch and note time for a further increase in extinction of $\Delta E = 0.100$.			

During the measured time interval (i. e. to attain the extinction increase of 0.100) the mean concentration for guaiacol is 0.3 mM and for H_2O_2 is 0.1 mM.

Calculations

According to equation (8) from p. 313 with $\varepsilon_{436\,nm} = 6.39$ cm.^{2}/μmole and under the conditions described here*:

$$\text{Volume activity} = \frac{3.18 \times 0.100 \times 1000}{6.39 \times 1 \times \Delta t \times 0.100} = \frac{500}{\Delta t} \text{ [U/l.]}$$

Precision of Method

The most accurate values are obtained when the time required is between 1 and 3 min. If the solution contains 250 U/l. (t = 2 min.), the standard deviation is 2 U/l. The coefficient of variation is about 1.03%.

Normal Values

Information on the normal values for POD can be obtained from the references cited in the Introduction under the section on occurrence of enzyme.

Sources of Error

Effects on POD activity in vivo: Hormones can sometimes affect POD activity in hormone-dependent tissues (e. g.[64]); certain drugs can decrease POD activity. In certain cases of poisoning there is decreased activity. Malignant tumours usually have lower POD activity than the organ of origin (e. g.[72]).

Interference in the assay technique: By pseudoperoxidative reactions other haemoproteins (haemoglobin) or even haem in the presence of protein can simulate activity in the assay of POD in tissues (see e. g.[58]). Cyanide inhibits all POD; this inhibition can sometimes be used to identify "true" POD activity.

---

* 25 °C, pH 7.0, 0.3 mM guaiacol and 0.1 mM H_2O_2.

Specificity of Method

Apart from the above-mentioned pseudoperoxidative reactions, oxidation of guaiacol by H_2O_2 in the absence of POD rarely occurs.

Details of Measurements in Tissues

For accurate assays it is important to ensure that removal of blood from the samples is as complete as possible (exsanguination on decapitation of animals; perfusion of organs with buffer solution) because of the POD activity of leucocytes and the pseudoperoxidative action of haemoglobin in erythrocytes. As a large portion of POD is located in cell particles the total content of POD is only obtained after extensive homogenization.

For histochemical detection of POD, which is important for the differentiation of white cells[59], refer to the appropriate clinical and histochemical handbooks.

References

1 *W. Bansi & H. Ucko*, Hoppe-Seylers, Z. physiol. Chem. *157*, 192 [1926].
2 *A. Purr*, Biochem. Z. *321*, 1 [1950].
3 *E. Lépinois*, Compt. rend. Soc. biol. *51*, 428 [1899].
4 *A. Bach & S. Zubkowa*, Biochem. Z. *125*, 282 [1921].
5 *A. C. Maehli* in *D. Glick:* Methods of biochemical Analysis, Interscience Publishers, New York 1954, Vol. 1, p. 357.
6 *R. Willstätter & A. Stoll*, Liebigs Ann. Chem. *416*, 21 [1918].
7 *G. G. Guilbault, P. Brignac & M. Zimmer*, Analyt. Chem. *40*, 190 [1968].
8 *Z. Rzymskowski*, Z. Elektrochem. *31*, 371 [1925].
9 *R. Dupony*, Compt. rend. Soc. biol. *55*, 1000 [1903].
10 *J. S. Wallerstein, R. T. Alba, M. G. Hale & H. Levy*, Biochim. biophys. Acta *1*, 327 [1947].
11 *R. Willstätter & H. Weber*, Liebigs Ann. Chem. *449*, 156 [1926].
12 *L. S. Malowan*, Enzymologia 7, 193 [1939].
13 *A. Clark & B. G. Timms*, Clin. chim. Acta *20*, 352 [1968].
14 *J. Pütter*, Habilitationsarbeit Univ. Bonn [1964].
15 *K. L. Zirm, R. Reuter, H. Willstädt*, Biochem. Z. *245*, 290 [1932].
16 *J. E. Middleton & W. E. Griffiths*, Brit. Med. J. *2*, 1525 [1957].
17 *A. S. Keston*, Abstr. Am. chem. Soc. *129th* Meeting, Dallas 31 c [1957].
18 *A. S. G. Huggett & D. A. Nixon*, Lancet *273*/II, 368 [1957].
19 *J. Pütter & R. Strufe*, Clin. chim. Acta *15*, 159 [1967].
20 *K. G. Paul* in *P. D. Boyer, H. Lardy & K. Myrbäck:* The Enzymes, Academic Press, London 1963, 2nd. Edn. Vol. 8, p. 227.
21 *H. Theorell & B. Swedin*, Naturwiss. *27*, 95 [1939].
22 *R. H. Kenten*, Biochem. J. *61*, 353 [1955].
23 *B. A. Rubin, L. A. Voronkw, G. I. Kapustina*, Biokhimiya *33*, 121 [1968].
24 *D. R. Buhler & H. S. Mason*, Arch. Biochem. Biophys. *92*, 424 [1961].
25 *H. S. Mason, I. Onopyrenko & D. Buhler*, Biochim. biophys. Acta *24*, 225 [1957].
26 *I. Yamazaki, H. S. Mason & L. Piette*, J. biol. Chem. *235*, 2444 [1960].
27 *P. Nicholls & G. R. Schonbaum* in *P. D. Boyer, H. Lardy & K. Myrbäck:* The Enzymes, Academic Press, London 1963, 2nd. Edn., Vol. 8, p. 147.
28 *P. George*, Biochem. J. *52*, XIX [1952].
29 *B. Chance*, J. biol. Chem. *194*, 471 [1952].
30 *D. Keilin & P. Nicholls*, Biochim. biophys. Acta *29*, 302 [1958].
31 *F. Leuthard:* Lehrbuch der physiologischen Chemie, Verlag de Gruyter, Berlin, 1963, 15th Edn., p. 234, 632.
32 *M. J. Smith & W. S. Beck*, J. clin. Invest. *45*, 1074 [1966].
33 *M. Dixon & E. C. Webb*, Enzymes, Longmans, Green a. Co. Ltd., London 1964, 2nd. Edn.
34 *K. G. Stern*, Nature *136*, 335 [1935].
35 *B. Chance*, Arch. Biochem. *21*, 416 [1949].
36 *H. Wieland & H. Sutter*, Ber. dtsch. chem. Ges. *63*, 66 [1930].

37 *A. C. Maehli & B. Chance* in *D. Glick:* Methods of Biochemical Analysis, Interscience Publishers, New York 1954, Vol. I, p. 357.
38 *C. Beaudrau & K. T. Yasonobu,* Biochemistry *5,* 1405 [1966].
39 *J. B. Sumner & S. F. Howell,* Enzymologia *1,* 133 [1936].
40 *K. Kondo & Y. Morita,* Bull. Res. Inst. Food, Sci. Ygoto-Univ. *10,* 33 [1952].
41 *Y. Morita,* Bull. Res. Inst. Food. Sci. Ygoto-Univ. *15,* 56 [1954].
42 *P. K. Macnicol,* Arch. Biochem. Biophys. *117,* 347 [1966].
43 *P. Penon, M. Teissere, J. P. Cecchini, J. Nari & J. Ricard,* Compt. rend. *265,* 276 [1967].
44 *K. Tagawa & M. Chin,* J. Biochem. (Tokio) *46,* 803 [1959].
45 *M. M. El Fouly & J. Jung,* Naturwiss. *53,* 586 [1966].
46 *I. Yamazaki, K. Fujinaga, I. Takehara & H. Takahashi,* J. Biochem. (Tokio) *43,* 377 [1956].
47 *G. Mozza, M. Teissere, C. Charles, P. Penon & J. Ricard,* Compt. rend. *264,* 2679 [1967].
48 *F. Solymosy, I. Szirmai, L. Becner & G. L. Farkas,* Virology *32,* 117 [1967].
49 *A. M. Altschul, R. Abrams & T. R. Hogness,* J. biol. Chem. *136,* 777 [1940].
50 *B. Haccius & J. Reiss,* Arch. Microbiol. *58,* 53 [1967].
51 *K. Agner,* Acta Chem. Scand. *12,* 89 [1959].
52 *S. John & J. Schultz,* Abstr. Papers. Am. Chem. Soc. *1965,* No. 150, 18c.
53 *H. Theorell & A. Akeson,* Arkiv Kemi, Mineral. Geol. *17 B,* 122 [1943].
54 *M. J. Hunter* in *S. P. Colowick & N. O. Kaplan:* Methods in Enzymology, Academic Press Inc., New York 1955, Vol. II, p. 791.
55 *H. A. Neufeld, A. N. Levay, F. V. Lucas, A. P. Martin & E. Stotz,* J. biol. Chem. *233,* 209 [1958].
56 *K. G. Paul, A. Kumlien, S. Jakobsson & S. Brody,* Scand. J. Clin. Lab. Invest. *20,* 11 [1967].
57 *J. Thomson & D. B. Morell,* J. Biochem. *62,* 483 [1967].
58 *T. Hosoya & M. Morrison,* Biochemistry *6,* 1021 [1967].
58a *K. Gawehn, H. Wielinger & W. Werner,* Z. Anal. Chem. *252,* 222 [1970].
58b *W. Werner, H. Rey & H. Wielinger,* Z. Anal. Chem. *252,* 224 [1970].
59 *F. Müller, O. Seifert & H. v. Kress* in *H. v. Kress:* Taschenbuch der medizinisch-klinischen Diagnostik, Verlag J. F. Bergmann, Munich 1962, 68. Edn.
60 *P. Glogner, H. P. Wolf & H. Holzer,* Biochem. Z. *332,* 407 [1960].
61 *J. Pütter,* Z. physiol. Chem. *329,* 40 [1962].
62 Biochemica Boehringer, Information leaflet: "Peroxidase".
63 *C. H. Verdier & M. Hjelm,* Clin. chim. Acta *7,* 742 [1962].
64 *K. B. Paul, A. Kumlien & S. Brody,* Experientia *22,* 799 [1966].
65 *B. Chance,* Arch. Biochem. Biophys. *41,* 416 [1952].
66 *G. Bertrand,* Ann. Inst. Pasteur *18,* 116 [1904].
67 *H. Booth & B. C. Sounders,* J. chem. Soc. p. 940 [1956].
68 *B. Chance & A. C. Maehli* in *S. P. Colowick & N. O. Kaplan:* Methods in Enzymology, Academic Press Inc., New York 1955, Vol. II, p. 764.
69 *R. N. Hati, M. Bal & A. G. Datta,* Biochem. biophys. Res. Comm. *31,* 392 [1968].
70 *B. Chance* in *E. S. Barron:* Modern Trends in Physiology and Biochemistry, Academic Press, New York 1952, p. 25.
71 *W. Heinmann & K. Wisser,* Biochem. Z. *332,* 573 [1960].
72 *J. F. Townsend, J. H. Owens, F. Cavazos, D. G. Hall & F. V. Lucas,* Am. J. Obstet, Gynecol. *100,* 98 [1968].

Ornithine Carbamoyltransferase

Giovanni Ceriotti

Ornithine carbamoyltransferase, OCT (Carbamoylphosphate : L-ornithine carbamoyltransferase, EC 2.1.3.3) was discovered by *Grisolia* and *Cohen*[1] in 1952 and purified from liver. It is the enzyme that catalyses transfer of an "active" carbamoyl group to the amino group of ornithine in the urea cycle of *Krebs* and *Henseleit*[2]. *Jones* et al.[3] showed that the active compound was carbamoyl phosphate. OCT is identical with the enzyme that catalyses the arsenolysis and phosphorolysis of citrulline[4]. Like carbamoylphosphate synthetase it is located in the mitochondria[4-6]. In mammals the highest concentration of the enzyme occurs in the liver[4,7]; there are much smaller amounts in the intestine, while in all other organs and tissues it is virtually absent[8,9]. It has not been found in avian liver, but does occur in many micro-organisms[4,10,11] and in plants[12].

The virtually exclusive presence of this enzyme in high concentration in the liver, with low serum values, results in a large increase in OCT in serum after cytolytic and mitochondrial changes in the liver cells brought about by infectious, degenerative or toxic factors. The assay of OCT activity in serum is therefore a good diagnostic and prognostic tool in various liver diseases[13-19]. Two assay methods can be used. The first is based on the arsenolytic activity of the enzyme: citrulline is converted to ornithine $+ CO_2 + NH_3$. The CO_2 can be measured by the isotope method of *Reichard*[20-22], or the NH_3 can be determined by diffusion followed by the *Nessler*[21,23] or *Berthelot*[16,24] reactions. The second method[13,24-28] which is described here measures the true transferase reaction.

Application of Method: In clinical chemistry, biochemistry, experimental pathology, toxicology and pharmacology.

Manual Method

Principle

(1)   Carbamoylphosphate + Ornithine $\xrightleftharpoons{\text{OCT}}$ Citrulline + P_i

The equilibrium of the reaction lies far on the side of citrulline[29,30]. The amount of citrulline formed per unit time is a measure of the OCT activity. After destruction of the urea in the sample with urease the citrulline is determined in the diacetylmonoxime-antipyrine reaction[31].

Optimum Conditions for Measurements

The favourable position of the equilibrium permits the assay to be carried out under optimum experimental conditions, to keep to a short reaction time and have a sensitive, specific and easy assay. The type of buffer, the pH and the substrate concentration are the most important variables which must be strictly controlled[32]. Below pH 7 the activity decreases rapidly; above pH 7 it increases, but the blank also increases because carbamoylphosphate decomposes, especially in glycylglycine and tris buffers[33,34]. In addition these buffers inhibit OCT[32-34]. To avoid this, the substrate concentration must be decreased and a lower rate of reaction must be accepted[33]. A suitable compromise is pH 7.0 and phosphate buffer[27]. With these conditions the optimum concentration of 12.5 mM carbamoylphosphate can be used without any increase in the blank[28]. These conditions are also optimum for the urease activity, which destroys the urea contained in serum[35].

Measurements at different temperatures may require different measuring conditions (cf. p. 127). Nevertheless, results obtained under the same measuring conditions but at different temperatures were formerly compared with each other ("conversion factors" were determined). Such conversion factors may be correct if determined with a relatively large proband collective; however, they cannot be applied generally to the individual case (cf. p. 129). The value of the following relative reaction rates thus lies in being able to appraise the temperature dependence of the reaction and at the most to compare qualitatively values up to the limit of normal.

°C	25	26	27	28	29	30	31	32	33	34	35	36	*37*
	2.46	2.29	2.14	2.00	1.87	1.74	1.61	1.49	1.39	1.29	1.19	1.09	*1.00*

Equipment

Normal laboratory equipment; 37 °C water bath; spectrophotometer for accurate measurements at 460 nm. For the micro-method the micro equipment of *Sanz* or *Eppendorf* is necessary.

Reagents

All reagents should be A.R. quality.

1. Disodium hydrogen phosphate,
   $Na_2HPO_4 \cdot 2H_2O$
2. Potassium dihydrogen phosphate,
   KH_2PO_4
3. Carbamoylphosphate
   dilithium salt; commercial preparation,
   see p. 528.
4. L-Ornithine monohydrochloride
5. Citrulline

6. Urease
   dry powder; 5 U/mg. (30 °C); commercial preparation, see p. 517.
7. Trichloroacetic acid
8. Antipyrine
9. Diacetylmonoxime
10. Ferric sulphate, $Fe_2(SO_4)_3 \cdot 9H_2O$
11. Sulphuric acid, conc.
12. Acetic acid
13. Ethylene glycol

Preparation of Solutions

Use doubly distilled water.

    I. Phosphate buffer (67 mM; pH 7.0):
        a) Dissolve 9.078 g. KH_2PO_4 in 1 000 ml. distilled water;
        b) Dissolve 11.876 g. $Na_2HPO_4 \cdot 2H_2O$ in 1 000 ml. distilled water; mix 38.8 ml. solution
        a) with 61.2 ml. solution b), check pH with glass electrode.
    II. Urease (0.5 mg./ml.):
        Dissolve 25 mg. urease in phosphate buffer (I) and make up to 50 ml.
    III. Urease/substrate solution (12.5 mM carbamoylphosphate; 25 mM ornithine; 0.5 mg. urease/ml.):
        Dissolve 20 mg. carbamoylphosphate, dilithium salt, and 42.5 mg. ornithine monohydrochloride in 20 ml. urease solution (II).
    IV. Citrulline standard solution (10 mM):
        Dissolve 17.5 mg. citrulline in 10 ml. distilled water; store in a refrigerator. Immediately before use dilute 1 ml. to 20 ml. with distilled water (0.5 mM).

V. Trichloroacetic acid (10% w/v):
Dissolve 10 g. trichloroacetic acid in distilled water and make up to 100 ml.

VI. Antipyrine/ferric sulphate solution:
Add carefully and slowly with cooling, 400 ml. conc. H_2SO_4 to about 500 ml. distilled water. Dissolve in this solution 50 mg. $Fe_2(SO_4)_3 \cdot 9H_2O$ and 4 g. antipyrine; after cooling dilute to 1 000 ml. with distilled water.

VII. Acetic acid (5% v/v):
Dilute 50 ml. acetic acid with distilled water to 1 000 ml.

VIII. Diacetylmonoxime (0.5% w/v):
Dissolve 2.5 g. diacetylmonoxime in 500 ml. 5% acetic acid.

IX. Colour reagent:
Immediately before use mix 2 volumes solution VI with 1 volume solution VIII.

Stability of Solutions

Solutions II and III are unstable; they must therefore be prepared immediately before use. Portions can be frozen in tightly stoppered tubes and thawed just before use. The reagents VI and VIII are stable indefinitely even at room temperature. The colour reagent IX should be prepared just before use.

Procedure

Collection, Treatment and Stability of Sample

The assay is usually carried out on serum from venous blood. Plasma from blood to which oxalate, citrate or heparin have been added can also be used. Haemolysis does not interfere. With the micro-method it is preferable and easier[35] to use whole blood. In this case the values must be related to the plasma content.

According to *Reichard* and *Reichard*[21] the enzyme is stable in serum for at least a week at 4 °C, and at −15 °C for longer than a year. We found [36,37] that, under sterile conditions venous, blood stored at 25 °C showed a loss of activity only after 7 days.

Assay System

Incubation temperature: 37 °C; incubation volume 0.9 ml. Colorimetric assay at room temperature; wavelength: 460 nm; final volume: 3.2 ml. Read against blank containing buffer (I) instead of sample.

The citrulline content of the sample (serum) must be determined separately (tube "citrulline"); read against blank containing buffer (I) instead of sample.

To measure the extinction coefficient or as reference standard add 0.1 ml. 0.5 mM citrulline standard solution (IV), equivalent to 50 nmole citrulline, instead of sample. Read against a blank containing 0.9 ml. buffer (I).

Incubate all blanks.

Pipette into centrifuge tubes:		OCT	Serum citrulline	Concentration in assay mixture
Sample (serum)		0.1 ml.	0.1 ml.	
Urease/substrate solution	(III)	0.8 ml.	—	400 μg. urease/ml.
Urease solution	(II)	—	0.8 ml.	67 mM phosphate
Mix and incubate for exactly 15 min.				
Trichloroacetic acid	(V)	1.1 ml.	1.1 ml.	
Mix, centrifuge for 10 min. at 3000 r.p.m. Use the supernatant fluid.				
Pipette into test tubes:				
Supernatant fluid		1.5 ml.	1.5 ml.	
Colour reagent	(IX)	1.5 ml.	1.5 ml.	
Mix with a mechanical mixer (or stopper with rubber bung and shake; do not stopper tubes with thumb, because human skin contains urea); place for 25 min. in a boiling water bath.				
Ethyleneglycol		0.2 ml.	0.2 ml.	
Allow to cool to room temperature and read extinctions. $E_{OCT} - E_{Citrulline} = \Delta E$.				

If the extinction is > 0.800, repeat the measurements with dilute sample.

Micro-method

Add one-tenth of the above volumes. After incubation use 100 μl trichloroacetic acid, centrifuge and add 100 μl supernatant to 100 μl colour reagent IX fluid; addition of ethyleneglycol is not necessary.

Calculations

To calculate the OCT activity* the nmole of citrulline liberated per minute must be obtained. Under the conditions given here (37 °C; t = 15 min.; concentration of standard solution 500 nmole/ml.) the following relationship holds for the sample analysed:

$$\text{Volume activity} = \frac{\Delta E}{15 \times E_{Standard}} \times 500 = \frac{\Delta E}{E_{Standard}} \times 33.5 \text{ [U/l.] (37 °C)}$$

Precision of Method

The coefficient of variation is 5%.

---

* At variance with the international unit (U) we have defined our unit as one μmole substrate reacting per hour at 37 °C[27,28,35]. The units given by us elsewhere are 60 times larger than the international U.

Normal Values

The normal values measured under the conditions described here are between 0.1 and 3.5 U/l. serum[28]. The OCT activity of various organs of dog and humans have been measured by *H. Reichard*[8,9]; apart from liver only intestine contains detectable amounts of enzyme.

Sources of Error

No effects of therapeutic measures have been observed. Contamination of the assay mixture by urea from the skin of the fingers or incomplete destruction of the urea in the serum due to inactive urease can give false values. Under the conditions described here the urease activity is in excess and can hydrolyse even high urea concentrations in serum[35]. The urease activity of the preparation should be checked before use in the assay. Carbamoylphosphate is rather unstable. Even in the crystalline state the preparation must be stored in a stoppered bottle in the cold. The purity of commercial preparations should be checked each time, because variations in concentration in the assay can result in false values.

Specificity of Method

The reaction is specific for citrulline in the absence of urea.

Measurements in Tissues

OCT is a mitochondrial enzyme, therefore for complete extraction the mitochondrial membrane must be destroyed. This can be effected by homogenization with distilled water in a blendor[8,9]; we prefer, particularly with small samples, to grind with quartz sand in a centrifuge tube, extract with salt solution[35] and dilute accordingly with phosphate buffer (solution I) to the expected activity[35].

Determination with Automatic Analysers

The OCT activity can be determined[38,39] automatically with the AutoAnalyzer® if the above manual method[27,28] is slightly modified. A similar, but somewhat more complicated method has been described by *Strandjord* and *Clayson*[33].

Application of Method: The automated method is especially suitable for screening in social and preventive medicine (viral hepatitis epidemics, occupational diseases).

Principle

Reaction equation, see p. 691. The citrulline formed in 10 min. by OCT is dialysed into a diacetylmonoxime solution and determined in the colorimetric assay with antipyrine-H_2SO_4. Urea in the serum is destroyed with urease as in the manual method.

Equipment

AutoAnalyzer® with sampler II; proportioning pump; 37 °C water bath; dialyzer type C; 95 °C water bath, colorimeter with interference filter for 460 nm; recorder.

Reagents

In addition to those listed on p. 692:

14. Brij 35
    from Technicon

Preparation of Solutions

Use only fresh distilled water.

Of the solutions listed on p. 692 the following are required:

  I. Phosphate buffer (67 mM; pH 7.0)
 II. Urease (0.5 mg./ml.):
     use 10 times the volume; 0.5 ml. Brij per litre.
III. Urease/substrate solution:
     use 10 times the volume: 0.5 ml. Brij per litre.
  V. Antipyrine/ferric solution.

Solutions of different composition:

VII. Diacetylmonoxime (0.5% w/v):
     Dissolve 2.5 g. diacetylmonoxime in 500 ml. physiological saline (0.85% NaCl).

 IX. Citrulline standard solutions:
     Dissolve 17.5 mg. citrulline in distilled water and make up to 100 ml. (1 000 nmole/ml.).
     Prepare further dilutions of 50, 100, 200, 400, 600 and 800 nmole/ml.

Additional solutions:

  X. Standard serum.
     Human serum as secondary standard, activity determined with the manual method.

Stability of Solutions

Solutions II and III are unstable and should be prepared immediately before use. During the assay store the containers in ice water.

Procedure

Flow scheme, see Fig. 1; 40 samples per hr. Sample and substrate solution (III) are mixed in the mixing spiral and run through the 37 °C water bath for 10 min.*.

With each series of measurements assay a series of standards using citrulline standard solutions IX.

To determine the citrulline content of the sample use solution (II) instead of urease/substrate solution (III). The relationship between extinction: nmole citrulline is linear up to 912 nmole

---

* The incubation time can be determined as follows: add haemolysed blood; measure the time required from its entry into the water bath to its entry in the dialyzer. The time can be determined more exactly by measurement of the activity of a standard serum, see under "Calculations".

(160 μg.) citrulline/ml. It is however advisable to dilute with buffer solution (I) samples which liberate more than 500 nmole citrulline in 10 min.

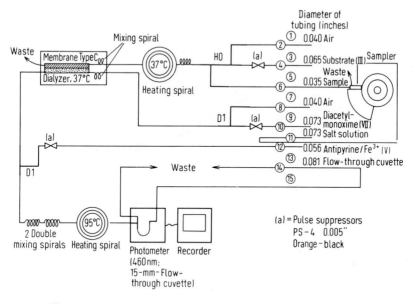

Fig. 1. Flow scheme for the automated determination of OCT activity.

Calculations

To calculate the OCT activity (formation of nmole citrulline/min.) it is necessary to determine exactly the reaction time t and the concentration of citrulline after incubation with and without substrate. The following formula holds for the sample:

$$\text{Volume activity} = \frac{C_{OCT} - C_{Citr.}}{t} \ [U/l.]; \ 37\ °C$$

C_{OCT} citrulline concentration after enzymatic reaction [nmole/ml.].
$C_{Citr.}$ citrulline concentration of sample without substrate [nmole/ml.].

Obtain the citrulline concentration from the standard curve (e. g. with a Technicon *Chart Reader*). The incubation time t can be determined most accurately with a standard serum of known activity. For this

$$t = \frac{C_{OCT} - C_{Citr.}}{[U/l.]_{manual}}$$

Normal Values

See p. 695.

Sources of Error

Carbamoylphosphate is unstable in solution. Prolonged storage of the carbamoylphosphate solutions leads to an increase of the blank. It is therefore advisable to prepare an amount which will be used in 2 hr. The urease solution should be clear to avoid blockage of the dialysis membrane, therefore use highly purified urease as in the manual method.

References

1   S. Grisolia & P. P. Cohen, J. biol. Chem. 198, 561 [1952].
2   H. A. Krebs & K. Henseleit, Z. physiol. Chem. 210, 33 [1932].
3   M. E. Jones, L. Spector & F. Lipman, J. Am. Chem. Soc. 77, 819 [1955].
4   H.A. Krebs, L. V. Eggleston & V. A. Knivett, Biochem. J. 59, 185 [1955].
5   S. Grisolia & P. P. Cohen, J. biol. Chem. 204, 753 [1953].
6   P. P. Cohen & H. J. Sallach, Metabolic Pathways 2, 1 Academic Press, New York [1962].
7   S. Grisolia & R. O. Marshall, Recent Advances in Citrulline Biosynthesis. A Symposium on Amino Acid Metabolism. The John Hopkins Press, 258 [1955].
8   H. Reichard, J. Lab. Clin. Med. 3, 417 [1959].
9   H. Reichard, J. Lab. Clin. Med. 56, 218 [1960].
10 B. D. Davis, Symposium on Microbiol. Metabolism Suppl. Rendiconti Istituto Superiore di Sanita p. 23 [1953].
11 R. L. Ory, D. W. Hood, & C. M. Lyman, J. biol. Chem. 207, 267 [1954].
12 K. Kleczkowski & P. P. Cohen, Arch. Biochem. Biophys. 107, 271 [1964].
13 R. W. Brown & S. Grisolia, J. Lab. Clin. Med. 54, 617 [1959].
14 H. Reichard, Acta Med. Scandinav. 172, Suppl. 390 [1962].
15 H. Reichard, Acta Med. Scandinav. 172, 723 [1962].
16 G. F. Moretti, R. Mahon, J. Staeffen, P. Ballan, G. Catanzaro & M. Vandendriessche, Ann. Biol. Clin. 21, 573 [1963].
17 G. F. Moretti, J. Staeffen, P. Ballan & G. Catanzaro, Presse Med. 72, 325 [1964].
18 G. F. Moretti, J. Staeffen & P. Ballan, Presse Med. 72, 3109 [1964].
19 B. Kylin, H. Reichard, I. Sumegi & S. Yllner, Acta pharmacol. et toxicol 20, 16 [1963].
20 H. Reichard, Scand. J. Clin. Lab. Invest. 9, 103 [1957].
21 H. Reichard & P. Reichard, J. Lab. Clin. Med. 52, 709 [1958].
22 H. Reichard, J. Lab. Clin. Med. 63, 1061 [1964].
23 H. Reichard, Scand. J. Lab. Clin. Invest. 9, 311 [1957].
24 L. Girard, F. Rousselet, M. Koch, Ann. Biol. Clin. 21, 557 [1963].
25 G. Leluan, Ann. Biol. Clin. 22, 343 [1964].
26 V. Kulhanek & V. Vojtiskova, Clin. Chim. Acta 9, 95 [1964].
27 G. Ceriotti & A. Gazzaniga, Clin. Chim. Acta 14, 57 [1966].
28 G. Ceriotti & A. Gazzaniga, Clin. Chim. Acta 16, 436 [1967].
29 P. Reichard, Acta Chem. Scand. 11, 523 [1957].
30 G. H. Burnett & P. P. Cohen, J. biol. Chem. 229, 337 [1957].
31 G. Ceriotti & L. Spandrio, Clin. Chim. Acta 11, 519 [1965].
32 R. L. Joseph, D. C. Watts & E. Baldwin, Comp. Biochem. and Physiol. 11, 119 [1964].
33 P. E. Strandjord & K. J. Clayson, J. Lab. Clin. Med. 67, 154 [1966].
34 P. J. Snodgrass, Federation Proc. 26, 762 [1967].
35 G. Ceriotti & A. Gazzaniga, Epatologia 13, 1009 [1967].
36 G. Ceriotti, VIIth. Int. Congr. Clin. Chem. Geneva, Sept. 1969 Abstracts, 344.
37 G. Ceriotti, C. Franzini, P. A. Bonini & A. Gazzaniga, 1st. Congr. Soc. Ital. Biochim. Clin., Stresa, April 1970; Ann. Ist. Sup. Sanita 7, 158 [1971].
38 B. Lollis, A. De Nadai Frank & G. Ceriotti, Technicon Symp., Rome, Oct. 1969.
31 G. Ceriotti, B. Lollis & A. De Nadai Frank, Clin. Chim. Acta 33, 69 [1971].

Transamidinase

Ulrich C. Dubach

Transamidinase, TA (L-Arginine: glycine amidinotransferase, EC 2.1.4.1) activity was simultaneously and independently demonstrated in 1940 by *Borsook* et al.[1] and *Bloch* et al.[2]. These workers showed how the synthesis of guanidinoacetate, a precursor of creatine, occurs from arginine and glycine in homogenates and slices of mammalian kidneys. The pH optimum is 7.0–7.5. Anaerobiosis and potassium cyanide do not affect TA activity[1]. A method for the partial purification (80-fold) from pig kidney has been described by *Ratner* et al.[3], while *Conconi* et al.[4] have achieved a 900-fold purification. The enzyme occurs in significant amounts only in mammalian kidneys[1,5] and pig pancreas[6]. TA activity is present in heart, skeletal muscle, spleen, testis, brain, thymus, lung, decidua and erythrocytes, and the sum of the total activity in spleen, skeletal muscle, lung, brain and testis is the same as that in kidney and pancreas[7]. No isoenzymes are known.

This selective distribution in mammals suggests that measurement of the serum activity in kidney disease could be used for diagnostic purposes. *Levy* et al.[8] and *Horner* et al.[9] made the first studies on the activity in serum. The activity is inhibited by p-chloromercuribenzoate and this inhibition is reversed by glutathione, cysteine or dimercaptoethanol. TA is therefore considered to be a sulphydryl enzyme; the activity is dependent on sources of exogenous protein[10].

TA activity in tissues can be measured by a variety of methods; that developed by *Walker*[11] uses canavanine and ornithine as substrates. The arginine formed is measured with the *Sakaguchi* reaction as modified by *Sakate* et al.[8,12]. This procedure, and that of *Izumi*[13,14] gave poor reproducibility in our hands with homogenates of rat tissues and with rat sera. We also found the method of *Albanese* et al.[15] to be unsatisfactory. Reproducible results were obtained with the procedure of *Ratner* et al.[3] and *Chinard*[16] with modification of the arginine and glycine concentrations; determination of the ornithine formed is less liable to interference than that of arginine with the *Sakaguchi* reaction.

Application of Method: In biochemistry and in clinical chemistry (on trial).

Principle

(1) $$\text{L-Arginine} + \text{Glycine} \xrightleftharpoons{\text{TA}} \text{L-Ornithine} + \text{Guanidinoacetate}$$

At pH 7.5 the reaction is six times more rapid from left to right; the equilibrium constant is 1.1[3]. The amount of ornithine formed per unit time, determined by the chromogen formation with ninhydrin, is a measure of the TA activity.

Optimum Conditions for Measurements

These have not been studied for human serum.

Equipment

Spectrophotometer, spectrum-line photometer or colorimeter suitable for accurate measurements at 546 nm (500–550 nm); water bath (100 °C); stopwatch.

Reagents

1. Potassium dihydrogen phosphate,   5. Sodium azide
   KH_2PO_4 6. Trichloracetic acid
2. Dipotassium hydrogen phosphate,   7. Ninhydrin
   K_2HPO_4 8. Phosphoric acid, sp. gr. 1.17
3. L-(+)-Arginine, monohydrochloride   9. Acetic acid
4. Glycine   10. L-Ornithine, monohydrochloride.

Preparation of Solutions (for ca. 50 determinations)

Only use fresh, doubly distilled water.

I. Buffer-substrate solution (17 mM arginine; 0.114 M glycine in 75 mM phosphate buffer; pH 7.5):
   Dissolve 1.500 g. L-arginine hydrochloride, 0.855 g. glycine, 0.081 g. KH_2PO_4, 1.188 g. K_2HPO_4 and 0.100 g. sodium azide in 100 ml. distilled water.

II. Trichloroacetic acid (0.62 M):
   Dissolve 10 g. trichloroacetic acid in distilled water and make up to 100 ml.

III. Chromogen solution (2.5% ninhydrin in acetic acid/phosphoric acid):
   Dissolve 2.5 g. ninhydrin in a mixture of 23.5 ml. 85% phosphoric acid, 16.5 ml. distilled water and 60 ml. acetic acid. Warm to ca. 70 °C to dissolve and then cool.

IV. Standard solution (0.6 mM ornithine):
   Dissolve 0.100 g. L-ornithine monohydrochloride and 0.500 g. sodium azide in 1 000 ml. distilled water.

Stability of Solutions

Solutions I, III and IV are stable for 3–4 weeks at 0–4 °C. The chromogen solution III must be stored in a dark bottle.

Procedure

Collection, Treatment and Stability of Sample

Collection of sample:

Collect blood without venestasis. Do not add anticoagulants. Centrifuge for 10 min. at 3000 g to obtain serum or plasma. Use only non-haemolysed serum or plasma within two hours of collection.

Stability of enzyme in sample:

No information is available for human serum.

Assay System

Wavelength: 546 (500–550) nm; light path: 1 cm.; incubation volume: 1.5 ml.; 25 °C; volume for colorimetric measurements: 5 ml. For each series of measurements analyse a reagent blank containing water instead of sample and a standard containing 0.50 ml. standard solution (IV). Read against reagent blank. Bring solutions to 20 to 25 °C before start of assay.

Pipette into test tubes:		Test	Control	Concentration in assay mixture
Buffer-substrate solution	(I)	1.00 ml.	1.00 ml.	1.1 mM arginine 76 mM glycine 50 mM phosphate
Sample (serum)		0.50 ml.	—	
Mix and incubate for 30 min.				
Trichloroacetic acid solution	(II)	1.50 ml.	1.50 ml.	0.31 M
Sample (serum)		—	0.50 ml.	
Mix and centrifuge for 10 min. at 3000 g.				
Supernatant		1.00 ml.	1.00 ml.	
Chromogen solution	(III)	1.00 ml.	1.00 ml.	
Acetic acid		3.00 ml.	3.00 ml.	
Mix, place in a boiling water bath for 60 min. and cool to room temperature. Read extinctions against blank. E_{Test}, $E_{St.}$ and $E_{Con.}$ are used for the calculations.				

Calculations

The following formula is used:

$$\text{Volume activity} = \frac{(E_{Test} - E_{Con.}) \times 0.1 \times 3 \times 1000}{E_{St.} \times 30 \times 0.5} \ [U/l.]$$

where

E_{Test}	= extinction of sample (test)
$E_{Con.}$	= extinction of control
$E_{St.}$	= extinction of standard
0.1	= μmole standard
3	= volume of assay mixture after addition of trichloroacetic acid
30	= incubation time
0.5	= volume of sample
1000	= conversion from U/ml. to U/l.

Precision of Method

A standard deviation of 0.5 U/l. was found with a homogenate containing 5.0 U/l.

Normal Values

No detectable activity was found in human serum in chronic renal diseases[9]. Of 164 patients at the Medizinische Universitätspoliklinik, Basel, 108 were negative; 41 of the 56 positives had renal disease, while in 15 cases there was no evidence clinically or on past history. The mean activity of the 41 subjects with suspected renal disease was 2.04 U/l. (range 0.6–11.3 U/l.)[17]. The highest value was in a case of chronic urinary with interstitial nephritis. In rat, activity is higher in kidneys from males than from females[18].

Sources of Error

Effects of drugs and other therapeutic measures: None known.

Interference in the assay: The determination is not affected by citrate (up to 10 mg./ml. serum), heparin (up to 2 mg./ml. serum) or sodium azide (up to 1 mg./ml. buffer). Oxalate, EDTA and fluoride inhibit the reaction. The TA activity of rat tissues is dependent on the concentration of creatinine[19]. Haemolysed serum cannot be used because erythrocytes contain TA.

Specificity of Method

The enzyme is not specific for arginine and glycine. Arginine can be replaced by homoarginine, canavanine and guanidinoacetate, while ornithine, canaline and hydroxylamine can be substituted for glycine[3].

References

 1 *H. Borsook & J. W. Dubnoff*, J. biol. Chem. *138*, 389 [1941].
 2 *K. Bloch & R. Schoenheimer*, J. biol. Chem. *138*, 167 [1941].
 3 *S. Ratner & O. Rochovansky*, Arch. Biochem. Biophys. *63*, 277 [1956].
 4 *F. Conconi & E. Grazi*, J. biol. Chem. *240*, 2461 [1965].
 5 *J. F. van Pilsum, D. A. Berman & E. A. Wolin*, Proc. Soc. Exp. Biol. Med. *95*, 96 [1956].
 6 *J. B. Walker*, Proc. Soc. Exp. Biol. Med. *98*, 7 [1958].
 7 *J. F. van Pilsum, R. M. Warkol & R. B. McHugh*, J. Nutr. *91*, 391 [1967].
 8 *S. Levey, L. Persky & N. Czernecki*, Arch. Surg. *86*, 209 [1963].
 9 *W. H. Horner, J. F. Chambliss & M. Dershananand*, Proc. Soc. Exp. Biol. Med. *118*, 65 [1965].
10 *J. F. van Pilsum, D. A. Berman & E. A. Wolin*, Proc. Soc. Exp. Biol. Med. *95*, 96 [1956].
11 *J. B. Walkner*, J. biol. Chem. *218*, 549 [1956].
12 *K. Sakata & J. M. Luck*, Bull. Soc. Chim. Biol. *40*, 1743 [1958].
13 *Y. Izumi*, Ann. Biochem. *10*, 218 [1965].
14 *Y. Izumi*, Ann. Biochem. *12*, 1 [1965].
15 *A. A. Albanese & J. E. Frankstone*, J. biol. Chem. *159*, 185 [1945].
16 *B. Chinard*, J. biol. Chem. *199*, 91 [1952].
17 *U. C. Dubach*, unpublished experiments.
18 *J. F. van Pilsum & F. Ungar*, Arch. Biochem. Biophys. *124*, 372 [1968].
19 *F. Ungar & J. F. van Pilsum*, Endocrinology *79*, 1143 [1966].

Transketolase

Myron Brin*

Transketolase, TK (Sedoheptulose-7-phosphate: D-glyceraldehyde-3-phosphate glycolaldehyde trans-ferase, EC 2.2.1.1), is an enzyme of the pentose phosphate cycle. It occurs in animals, plants and micro-organisms; preparative procedures have been described for spinach[1,2] and yeast[3,4] as the starting material. In rat tissues the activity decreases in the following order: liver, kidney, spleen, intestine, lung, brain, heart, skeletal muscle and erythrocytes[5,6]. As a soluble enzyme it occurs in the cellular and extra-cellular fluid[6-9]. It contains thiamine pyrophosphate (TPP) and requires Mg^{2+} ions for activity[10]. The TK level in serum is of diagnostic interest in liver diseases and cancer[8], while changes in the activity of this enzyme are of interest in erythrocytes and tissues in thiamine deficiency[7,9,11-13]. This is known as the "TPP effect", because the percentage increase in enzyme activity is measured after addition of TPP to the assay mixture.

Application of Method: In biochemistry and clinical chemistry.

Principle**

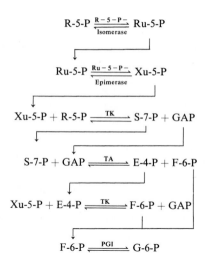

R-5-P and Xu-5-P are the substrates for TK, the preceding reactions (1) and (2) form Xu-5-P from R-5-P added to the assay. The two enzymes required for reactions (1) and (2) are present in sufficient excess in erythrocytes and serum (see below).

---

* This work was carried out while the author was at the Department of Nutrition, College of Agriculture and Environmental Sciences, University of California, Davis, California 95616, USA.

** Further enzymes required: R-5-P isomerase = D-Ribose-5-phosphate ketol-isomerase, EC 5.3.1.6; Ru-5-P-epimerase = D-Ribulose-5-phosphate 3-epimerase, EC 5.1.3.1; TA = transaldolase, Sedo-heptulose-7-phosphate: D-glyceraldehyde-3-phosphate dihydroxyacetone transferase, EC 2.2.1.2; PGI = phosphoglucoisomerase, D-Glucose-6-phosphate ketol-isomerase, EC 5.3.1.9; GDH = glycerol-1-phosphate dehydrogenase, sn-Glycerol-3-phosphate: NAD 2-oxidoreductase, EC 1.1.1.8; GAPDH = D-glyceraldehyde-3-phosphate dehydrogenase, D-Glyceraldehyde-3-phosphate: NAD oxidoreductase (phosphorylating), EC 1.2.1.12.

Numerous methods have been described for the determination of TK activity:
Measurement of
    Decrease of pentose phosphates[8,11–13];
    Formation of S-7-P[6,7,14,18];
    Formation of GAP[2,4,15–17] (enzymatic spectrophotometric assay)
    Formation of hexose phosphates[11–13].
For discussion of the methods, see also[19]. Several methods are given below.

Optimum Conditions for Measurements

The kinetic behaviour of the assay system is complicated. The preceding reactions (1) and (2), which form the substrate Xu-5-P, are apparently not rate-limiting, because the activity of both enzymes in blood and serum is about 1000-fold higher than that of TK[7]. Saturation of TK with substrate is obtained with 2 mM R-5-P[7]. Addition of Xu-5-P generally results in no increase in activity (unpublished findings).

From a kinetic stand-point the continuous measurement of a product of the TK reaction, e. g. of GAP with GAPDH[15,16] or with GDH[2,4,17] is more favoured than the determination of a reaction product at the end of an incubation period. This also applies to dilute tissue extracts, but with erythrocyte haemolysates interference from blood pigments often occurs[19].

As a rule therefore the TK reaction is stopped by deproteinization after a fixed time and a reactant determined in a second separate reaction. In this case GAP is less suitable, because it does not accumulate quantitatively, but partially reacts further. For the same reason S-7-P is not a suitable product.

Even the hexose phosphates are not true end-products, because they slowly react with the glycolytic enzymes. In the case of the pentose phosphates there is the difficulty of reliably determining three different compounds. The most frequently used method with orcinol gives different intensities of colour with the three pentose phosphates. In spite of this theoretical limitation good proportionality to the amount of enzyme has been obtained with different methods under standardized conditions. Often it is possible to demonstrate the dependence of the reaction rate on the TPP concentration. As this is the cofactor for TK, it is a further indication that TK is really the limiting enzyme in the assay.

Apart from enzymatic methods[20], a large range of colorimetric reactions, e. g. the orcinol reaction[21] for pentose phosphates[18] and S-7-P[7,18], as well as the anthrone reaction for hexose phosphates, are available for determination of the reactants after a defined period of incubation. In the following the incubation mixture and the orcinol and anthrone reactions are briefly described. Information on the enzymatic determinations are included. These assays also allow measurement of the TPP effect.

Equipment

Photometer or spectrophotometer suitable for measurements at 620 nm (anthrone method) or 670 nm (orcinol method) or 334, 340, 365 nm (enzymatic UV-method). Constant temperature water bath (38 °C).

Reagents

For incubation
1. Sodium chloride, A. R.
2. Potassium chloride, A. R.
3. Dipotassium hydrogen phosphate, K_2HPO_4, A. R.
4. Hydrochloric acid, 1 N, A. R.

5. Magnesium sulphate, $MgSO_4 \cdot 7H_2O$, A. R.
6. Thiamine pyrophosphate, cocarboxylase, TPP tetrahydrate, $TPP \cdot 4H_2O$; commercial preparation, see p. 553.

7. Ribose-5-phosphate, R-5-P
monobarium salt, R-5-P-Ba; commercial preparation, see p. 551.
8. Trichloroacetic acid, A. R.
9. Sodium sulphate, $Na_2SO_4 \cdot 10H_2O$, A. R.
10. Potassium hydroxide, 5 N, A. R.

For anthrone method

11. D-Glucose, anhydrous, A. R.
12. Anthrone

13. Thiourea, A. R.
14. Sulphuric acid, A.R., 66% (w/w), sp. gr. 1.565

For orcinol method

15. D-Ribose
16. Orcinol, crystalline
17. Ferric chloride, $FeCl_3 \cdot 6H_2O$, A. R.
18. Hydrochloric acid, A.R., 30% (w/w), sp. gr. 1.15

Preparation of Solutions

For incubation
  I. Buffer (4 mM Na^+; 115 mM K^+; 20 mM PO_4^{3-}; 5 mM Mg^{2+}; pH 7.4): Mix 40 ml. 0.9% NaCl solution, 1030 ml. 1.15% KCl solution, 200 ml. 1.75% K_2HPO_4 solution (adjusted to pH 7.4 with 1 N HCl) and 10 ml. 3.82% $MgSO_4 \cdot 7H_2O$ solution. If necessary, adjust to pH 7.4.
 II. Thiamine pyrophosphate solution (0.26 mM):
Dissolve 29 mg. $TPP \cdot 4H_2O$ in 25 ml. buffer (I). Dilute 1 ml. of this with 8 ml. buffer (I).
III. Ribose-5-phosphate (47 mM):
Dissolve 3.24 g. R-5-P-Ba in 8.5 ml. 1 N HCl, dilute to 45 ml. with distilled water and slowly add 8 ml. saturated sodium sulphate solution. Allow precipitate to settle in the cold and centrifuge off. Adjust supernatant fluid to pH 7.4 with 5 N KOH. Determine the ribose content (e. g. with the orcinol reaction, see below), and then adjust to exactly 7 mg. ribose/ml. (47 mM).
IV. Trichloroacetic acid (7.5% w/v, ca. 0.45 M):
Dissolve 75 g. trichloroacetic acid in distilled water and make up to 1000 ml.

For anthrone method
  V. Hexose standard solution (0.55 mM):
Dissolve 25 mg. D-glucose in 25 ml. distilled water. Dilute 5 ml. of this to 50 ml. with trichloroacetic acid solution (IV): this solution contains 100 μg. glucose/ml.
 VI. Anthrone reagent (2.5 mM anthrone; 0.13 M thiourea):
Dissolve 0.5 g. anthrone and 10 g. thiourea in ca. 200 ml. 66% H_2SO_4 by warming to 60–70 °C. Allow to cool and dilute to 1000 ml. with 66% H_2SO_4. Allow to stand for at least 24 hr. in the cold before use.

For orcinol method
 VII. Pentose standard solution (67 mM):
Dissolve 25 mg. D-ribose in 25 ml. distilled water. Dilute 1 ml. of this to 100 ml. with trichloroacetic acid solution (IV); this solution contains 10 μg. ribose/ml.
VIII. Orcinol reagent (14 mM orcinol; 062 mM $FeCl_3$):
Dissolve 4.0 g. orcinol and 335 mg. $FeCl_3 \cdot 6H_2O$ in distilled water and make up to 100 ml., dilute to 2000 ml. with 30% HCl.

Stability of Solutions

Store solutions I, IV, VI and VIII at ca. 4 °C and solutions II, III, V and VII at -20 °C. Solution III is stable for about 3 months and the other solutions are stable indefinitely.

Procedure

Collection, Treatment and Stability of Sample

Collection and treatment:

Treat blood with anticoagulants (oxalate, citrate, heparin, EDTA), centrifuge for 30 min. and discard plasma. Weigh the cells in the centrifuge tube, add the same volume of water and mix. For better haemolysis store overnight in the frozen state (alternatively the sample can be frozen 3 times in dry ice/alcohol and thawed).
Homogenize animal organs (fresh or frozen) in buffer (I). Use a fifty-fold volume of buffer for rat liver and kidney, and ten-fold volume for spleen, intestine, lung, brain, heart and muscle.

Stability of sample:

The TK activity in frozen tissue is stable for at least 2 months. Fresh blood can be stored for up to 3 days in a refrigerator before haemolysis, while the haemolysate can be stored for ca. 3 months.

Incubation System

Macro Method

Apart from the "test" a "blank 1" (without substrate) is required. If TPP effect is also to be measured (see Introduction) an additional tube "TPP test" (as for "test" with addition of TPP) should be prepared. If the orcinol reaction (decrease of pentoses) is to be used, a "substrate blank" is also required.
Incubation volume: 1.15 ml.; incubation time: 60 min.; temperature: 38 °C; volume after deproteinization: 7.15 ml.

Pipette into test tubes:		Test	Blank 1	TPP test*	Substrate blank*
Sample		0.5 ml.	0.5 ml.	0.5 ml.	—
Buffer	(I)	0.45 ml.	0.65 ml.	—	0.95 ml.
TPP solution	(II)	—	—	0.45 ml.	—

Mix. Only when the TPP test is analysed are all tubes incubated for 30 min. at 38 °C, otherwise proceed directly.

R-5-P solution	(III)	0.2 ml.	—	0.2 ml.	0.2 ml.

Mix and incubate for 60 min. at 38 °C. Stop reaction:

Trichloroacetic acid solution	(IV)	6.0 ml.	6.0 ml.	6.0 ml.	6.0 ml.

Mix, centrifuge off precipitate and use supernatant fluid for assay. It can be stored for up to 5 days in a refrigerator.

The concentrations of R-5-P and TPP in the test before the addition of trichloroacetic acid are 8.2 mM and 0.1 mM respectively.

---

* As required, see above.

Semi-micro method

Dilute 6.8 ml. R-5-P solution (III) to 10 ml. with buffer (I), dilute the TPP stock solution 1 + 16 with buffer (I) instead of 1 + 8; add 5% trichloroacetic acid. Prepare test with 0.1 ml. sample, 0.4 ml. buffer (I), 0.1 ml. R-5-P solution and 3 ml. trichloroacetic acid. Prepare other tubes accordingly. Length of incubation and temperature as for macro-method. The same TPP effects are measured with this method but often the TK activities are slightly higher than with the macro method.

Measurements with Anthrone Method

Wavelength: 620 nm; light path: 1 cm.; final volume: 11 ml.; room temperature. Read against blank 2 (trichloroacetic acid solution (IV) instead of samples). Standardization with standard solution (V).

Pipette into test tubes:		Test & Blank 1	Standard	Blank 2
Supernatants after incubation		1.0 ml.	—	—
Hexose standard solution	(V)	—	1.0 ml.	—
Trichloroacetic acid	(IV)	—	—	1.0 ml.
Anthrone, precooled	(VI)	10.0 ml.	10.0 ml.	10.0 ml.

Add solution VI with continual stirring, heat tubes for 10 min. in a boiling water bath, then cool for 5 min. in a cold water bath. Allow to stand for 20 min. in the dark and read the extinctions against blank 2. Subtract the extinction of blank 1 from the test, and where appropriate also from the TPP test. The corrected ΔE values are used for the calculations.

Measurements with Orcinol Method

Wavelength: 620 nm; light path: 1 cm.; final volume: 11 ml.; room temperature. Read against blank 2 (water instead of sample). Standardization with standard solution (VII).

Pipette into test tubes:		Test & Blank 1	Substrate blank	Standard	Blank 2
Supernatants after incubation		0.2 ml.	0.1 ml.	—	—
Pentose standard solution	(VII)	—	—	1.0 ml.	—
Distilled water		1.3 ml.	1.4 ml.	0.5 ml.	1.5 ml.
Orcinol reagent	(VIII)	4.5 ml.	4.5 ml.	4.5 ml.	4.5 ml.

Mix thoroughly, place tubes for 20 min. in a boiling water bath and then cool for 5 min. in a cold water bath. Read extinctions against blank 2. Double the values obtained for the substrate blank (half the amount taken). Subtract blank 1 *only from the test values*. The ΔE values obtained are used for the calculations.

Measurements with Enzymatic Assay

Neutralize the supernatant fluid after trichloroacetic acid deproteinization and determine F-6-P and G-6-P by the method described on p. 1238.

Other enzymatic methods can be coupled directly to the TK reaction during the incubation; refer to the original references[2,4,15-17]. Difficulties arising in the assay of erythrocyte haemolysates have been discussed under "Optimum Conditions for Measurements".

Calculations

The following equations hold for the sample:

Anthrone method

$$\text{Volume activity} = \frac{\Delta E_{Sample} \times C_{Standard} \times 7.15 \times 1\,000}{\Delta E_{Standard} \times 60 \times 1.0 \times 0.5} = 238 \times \frac{\Delta E_{Sample}}{\Delta E_{Standard}} \times C_{Standard} \; [U/l.]$$

$C_{Standard}$ = concentration in standard solution (V) in μmole/ml.

Orcinol method

$$\text{Volume activity} = \frac{\Delta E_{Sample} \times C_{Standard} \times 7.15 \times 1\,000}{\Delta E_{Standard} \times 60 \times 0.2 \times 0.5} = 1\,190 \times \frac{\Delta E_{Sample}}{\Delta E_{Standard}} \times C_{Standard} \; [U/l.]$$

$C_{Standard}$ = concentration of standard solution (VIII) in μmole/ml.

Semi-micro method

Substitute in the above formula 3.6 and 0.1 for 7.15 and 0.5 respectively.

TPP effect

$$\text{TPP effect (\%)} = \frac{(\text{Test with TPP}) - (\text{Test without TPP})}{(\text{Test without TPP})} \times 100$$

Precision of Method

Duplicate assays can differ by 5%, while determinations carried out at different times can vary by 10%.

Normal Values

Most normal blood samples have values between 75–92 U/l.* There is no sex difference in the values.

The TPP effect gives the following values:

Group	TPP effect
Normal	0–14%
Borderline deficiency	15–24%
Acute TPP deficiency, usually with clinical signs	$\geq 25\%$

With TPP-deficient patients the TK activity generally returns to normal 2 hr. after administration of thiamine (5 mg. thiamine·HCl, intramuscular). Occasionally there are cases in which the TPP effect disappears after therapy but the TK activity remains low for up to 2 weeks. Generally these are extremely

---

* Measured with the anthrone method

undernourished patients, who apart from a deficiency in coenzyme have a deficiency of apo-transketolase[22]. The values after thiamine administration are however valid because the TPP effect measures the amount of *reactive* apo-TK which has lost its coenzyme.

Specificity and Sources of Error

The test values do not solely represent the activity of TK in the sample (for theory see above), but they are good indications. It is certainly true that in the strict sense the methods described here are not assays of the activity of a single enzyme. The values for enzyme activity and TPP effect obtained by the hexose determination method fit the clinical and subjective findings on patients better than those obtained by the determination of pentose phosphates.

References

1 *B. L. Horecker & P. Smyrniotis*, J. Am. Chem. Soc. *75*, 1009 [1953].
2 *B. L. Horecker, P. Smyrniotis & J. Hurwitz*, J. biol. Chem. *223*, 1009 [1956].
3 *E. Racker, G. de la Haba & I. G. Leder*, J. Am. Chem. Soc. *75*, 1010 [1953].
4 *G. de la Haba, I. G. Leder & E. Racker*, J. biol. Chem. *214*, 409 [1955].
5 *M. Brin*, Israel J. Med. Sci. *3*, 792 [1967].
6 *M. Brin*, J. Nutr. *78*, 179 [1962].
7 *F. H. Bruns, E. Dunwald & E. Noltmann*, Biochem. Z. *330*, 497 [1958].
8 *M. I. Mello*, Proc. Intern. Symp. Enzyme Chem. Tokio Kyoto 1967. Maruzen, Tokio 1958, p. 106.
9 *M. Brin, S. S. Shohet & C. S. Davidson*, J. biol. Chem. *230*, 319 [1958].
10 *A. G. Datta & E. Racker*, J. biol. Chem. *236*, 617 [1961].
11 *M. Brin, M. Tai, A. S. Ostashever & H. Kalinski*, J. Nutr. *71*, 273 [1960].
12 *M. Brin*, Ann. N. Y. Acad. Sci *98*, 528 [1962].
13 *M. Brin*, J. Am. Med. Assoc. *187*, 762 [1964].
14 *P. M. Dreyfus*, N. Engl. J. Med. *267*, 596 [1962].
15 *N. J. Benevenga, W. J. Stielau & R. A. Freedland*, J. Nutr. *84*, 345 [1964].
16 *C. H. Cheng & R. E. Shank*, Fed. Proc. *24*, 690 [1965].
17 *C. J. Gubler* in *G. E. W. Wolstenholme & M. O'Connor:* Thiamine Deficiency, Ciba Foundation Study Group No. 28, Churchill, London 1967, p. 54.
18 *B. L. Horecker, P. Z. Smyrniotis & H. Klenow*, J. biol. Chem. *205*, 661 [1953].
19 *M. Brin* in *G. E. W. Wolstenholme & M. O'Connor:* Thiamine Deficiency, Ciba Foundation Study Group No. 28, Churchill, London 1967, p. 82.
20 *J. R. Cooper* in *G. E. W. Wolstenholme & M. O'Connor:* Thiamine Deficiency, Ciba Foundation Study Group No. 28, Churchill, London 1967, p. 112.
21 *Z. Dische*, J. biol. Chem. *204*, 983 [1953].
22 *J. Fennelly, O. Frank, H. Baker & C. M. Leevy*, Am. J. Clin. Nutr. *20*, 946 [1967].

Transaldolase

Karl Brand

Transaldolase, TA (Sedoheptulose-7-phosphate: D-glyceraldehyde-3-phosphate dihydroxyacetone transferase, EC 2.2.1.2) was first described by *Horecker* and *Smyrniotis*[1] in 1953. The enzyme was crystallized from *Candida utilis* by *Pontremoli* et al.[2] in 1961. Transaldolase occurs in animal[3-6] and plant tissues[4,7] and in micro-organisms[4,8,9]. As an enzyme of the pentose phosphate cycle it is found in the cytoplasmic compartment of the cell.

A survey of the distribution of the activities of transaldolase, transketolase, fructose-1,6-diphosphate aldolase and fructose-1,6-diphosphatase in rabbit tissues[10] is given in Table 1. Although the enzymes of glycolysis and gluconeogenesis (aldolase and fructose-1,6-diphosphatase) are present in the individual tissues in different amounts, the enzymes of the pentose phosphate cycle show only slight differences in activity from organ to organ. In normal and pathological human sera there is extremely low transaldolase activity.

Table 1. Activities of transaldolase, transketolase, fructose-1,6-diphosphate aldolase, fructose-1,6-diphosphatase in rabbit tissues. (I = mU/g. fresh wt.; II = mU/mg. extract protein; 25 °C)

Tissue	Transaldolase		Transketolase		F-1,6-DP-aldolase		F-1,6-DPase	
	I	II	I	II	I	II	I	II
Lung	465	8	—	—	490	6	70	1
Stomach	515	16	295	9	900	27	160	5
Liver	705	6	355	2	1 300	22	2 000	18
Kidney	645	11	430	7	2 200	63	2 440	42
Brain	300	10	230	8	3 600	115	10	0.3
Bone marrow	480	12	—	—	1 080	26	65	0.15
Pancreas	450	7	120	0.2	670	11	475	8
Adrenal	580	32	1 160	13	2 400	125	—	—
Thyroid	255	12	85	3	3 350	136	295	10
Testicle	595	11	435	8	650	12	50	1
Prostate	320	23	125	9	2 250	195	215	15
Mammary gland	160	7	—	—	10 800	455	255	11
Mammary gland during pregnancy	335	9	195	5	6 200	146	280	7
Placenta	225	5	60	1	1 000	18	70	1

Frozen tissue was homogenized in a blade homogenizer (3 × 1 min.) with the addition of washed glass beads (0.17–0.18 mm. diameter). Bone marrow and pancreas were homogenized in a Teflon homogenizer. The enzyme activities were measured in the supernatant fluid after centrifugation at 12 000 g : transketolase by a modification of the method of *Horecker* et al.[13], F-1,6-P$_2$-aldolase by a modification of the method of *Racker*[14], F-1,6-diphosphatase by a modification of the method of *Pontremoli* et al.[15]. Protein was determined as described by *Bücher*[16].

Candida utilis is particularly suitable for the isolation of the enzyme because it has a high transaldolase activity. In the crystallization of the enzyme from this yeast it appears that only part of the activity can be obtained in crystalline form, the major part cannot be crystallized. This different behaviour can be explained by the work of *Tsolas* and *Horecker*[11], who have demonstrated the presence of 3 forms of the enzyme which can be separated by chromatography, and which have been designated types I, II and III on the basis of their elution pattern from a DEAE-Sephadex column. They showed that types I and III were isoenzymes and that type II was a hybrid form of I and III. So far only type III has been obtained in crystalline form by the procedure of *Tchola* and *Horecker*[12].

Properties: Transaldolase type I has a Michaelis constant (K_M) for fructose-6-phosphate (F-6-P) of 0.53 mM and for D-erythrose-4-phosphate (E-4-P) of 0.02 mM. The corresponding K_M values for typeIII are 0.71 mM and 0.019 mM respectively[12]. D-Fructose-6-phosphate and D-sedoheptulose-7-phosphate are the most active donor substrates for dihydroxyacetone; D-glyceraldehyde-3-phosphate and D-erythrose-4-phosphate are the most active acceptor aldehydes[4]. Octulose-8-phosphate[17], sorbose-6-phosphate[18] and free fructose[19] are less effective as donor substrates, while free glyceraldehyde[19], L-glyceraldehyde-3-phosphate[18] and ribose-5-phosphate[17] are less effective as acceptor substrates.

The molecular weights as determined by a sedimentation equilibrium method are 76 100 for type I and 65 900 for type III[20]. The yeast enzyme does not have a prosthetic group and does not require a cofactor for its catalytic activity.

Application of Method: In biochemistry.

Principle

(1) $$\text{F-6-P} + \text{E-4-P} \xrightleftharpoons{\text{TA}} \text{S-7-P} + \text{GAP}$$

(2) $$\text{GAP} \xrightleftharpoons{\text{TIM}^*} \text{DAP}$$

(3) $$\text{DAP} + \text{NADH} + \text{H}^+ \xrightleftharpoons{\text{GDH}^{**}} \text{Glycerol-3-P} + \text{NAD}^+$$

Transaldolase (TA) catalyses the transfer of dihydroxyacetone, which is liberated by aldol cleavage of fructose-6-phosphate (F-6-P), to erythrose-4-phosphate (E-4-P) with the formation of sedoheptulose-7-phosphate (S-7-P) and glyceraldehyde-3-phosphate (GAP).

For the determination of transaldolase activity the GAP formed per unit time from F-6-P according to equations (2) and (3) is measured. Under the conditions described below the rate of NADH oxidation is proportional to the TA activity. The decrease of extinction at 340 (334 or 365) nm per min. is measured. According to *Racker*[7] the equilibrium constant $K = [\text{S-7-P}] \times [\text{GAP}]/[\text{F-6-P}] \times [\text{E-4-P}] = 0.95$. The further reactions of GAP and DAP in the auxiliary and indicator reactions give a quantitative conversion of F-6-P and E-4-P.

Optimum Conditions for Measurements

The pH optimum for transaldolase lies between 7.3 and 8.1 with a steep decrease on either side. For routine determinations it is recommended to work at 25 °C, but the enzyme is stable up to 40 °C. Metal ions or other cofactors are not required for the catalytic activity of the yeast enzyme[4]. Transaldolase is inhibited by > 0.1 M phosphate[21], pyrophosphate or sulphate[22].

Equipment

Spectrophotometer or spectrum-line photometer suitable for accurate measurements at 340, 334 or 365 nm and constant temperature cuvette holder; water bath (25 °C); stopwatch.

---

*   Triosephosphate isomerase (D-Glyceraldehyde-3-phosphate ketol-isomerase, EC 5.3.1.1).

** Glycerophosphate dehydrogenase (*sn*-Glycerol-3-phosphate: NAD 2-oxidoreductase EC 1.1.1.8).

Reagents

1. Triethanolamine hydrochloride, TRA
2. Ethylenediaminetetra-acetic acid
   disodium salt, EDTA-Na$_2$H$_2$·2H$_2$O
3. D-Fructose-6-phosphate, F-6-P
   disodium salt, F-6-P-Na$_2$; commercial preparation, see p. 535.
4. D-Erythrose-4-phosphate, E-4-P
   Synthesis according to the method of *Baxter* et
   al.[23] by oxidation of G-6-P with lead tetra-
   acetate; store as a 10 mM solution at pH 2–3
   in the cold. Commercial preparations (see 531)
   can also be used.

5. Reduced nicotinamide-adenine
   dinucleotide, NADH
   disodium salt, NADH-Na$_2$; commercial preparation, see p. 545.
6. Glycerophosphate dehydrogenase, GDH
   from rabbit muscle, crystalline suspension in
   3.2 M ammonium sulphate solution; ≥ 40 U/mg.
   (25 °C); commercial preparation, see p. 468.
7. Triosephosphate isomerase, TIM
   from rabbit muscle, crystalline suspension in
   3.2 M ammonium sulphate solution; ≥ 5000
   U/mg. (25 °C); commercial preparation, see p.
   515.
8. Sodium hydrogen carbonate, 1% (w/v)
9. Sodium hydroxide, 1 N

Preparation of Solutions (for ca. 20 determinations)

Use only doubly distilled water.

    I. Triethanolamine buffer (0.1 M; pH 7.6; 10 mM EDTA):
       Dissolve 1.857 g. triethanolamine hydrochloride and 0.372 g. EDTA-Na$_2$H$_2$ · 2H$_2$O in
       80 ml. distilled water, adjust to pH 7.6 with 1 N NaOH and dilute to 100 ml. with distilled
       water.
   II. Fructose-6-phosphate (0.15 M):
       Dissolve 130 mg. F-6-P-Na$_2$ (70% F-6-P) in 2.0 ml. distilled water.
  III. Erythrose-4-phosphate (10 mM):
       Determine the E-4-P concentration enzymatically according to p. 1391 and dissolve or
       dilute accordingly with distilled water. The pH of the solution should be between 2 and 3.
  IV. Reduced nicotinamide-adenine dinucleotide (7.5 mM β-NADH):
       Dissolve 12.5 mg. NADH-Na$_2$ in 2 ml. 1% NaHCO$_3$ solution.
   V. Glycerophosphate dehydrogenase/triosephosphate isomerase, GDH/TIM (ca. 0.9 mg.
       GDH/ml.; ca. 0.1 mg. TIM/ml.):
       Dilute commercial GDH/TIM crystalline suspensions (10 mg./ml.; mixed ratio GDH:
       TIM ca. 10:1 relative to protein, ca. 1:6 relative to activities) 1 + 9 with 3.2 M ammonium
       sulphate solution.

Stability of Solutions

Store all solutions at 0 to 4 °C. The E-4-P solution (pH 2–3) and the F-6-P solution are stable for long
periods, the NADH solution should be prepared freshly each week. The GDH/TIM mixed suspension
is stable for longer than a year.

Procedure

Stability of enzyme in sample:

Crystalline transaldolase from *Candida utilis* suspended in 60% saturated ammonium sulphate
solution is stable for more than 1 year. Crude extracts of animal and plant tissues and of
micro-organisms can be stored at −20 °C for several months without loss of activity.

Assay System

Wavelength: 340 (Hg 334, Hg 365) nm; light path: 1 cm.; final volume: 2.75 ml.; 25 °C constant temperature cuvette holder. Read against air. Bring the solutions to 25 °C before the assay.

Pipette into cuvettes:			Concentration in assay mixture
Triethanolamine buffer	(I)	2.50 ml.	90 mM TRA 90 mM EDTA
F-6-P solution	(II)	0.05 ml.	2.7 mM
E-4-P solution	(III)	0.05 ml.	0.18 mM
NADH solution	(IV)	0.05 ml.	0.14 mM
GDH/TIM suspension	(V)	0.05 ml.	16 μg. GDH/ml. $\simeq$ 0.6 U/ml. 1.8 μg. TIM/ml. $\simeq$ 9 U/ml.
Mix, wait for 2 min. until GAP and DAP in the F-6-P and E-4-P preparations are reduced with NADH.			
Sample		0.05 ml.	
Mix. Read extinction and start stopwatch. Repeat readings at 1, 2, 3, 4, and 5 min.			

The values ΔE/min. at 340 nm should not be larger than 0.060/min., otherwise dilute the sample with buffer solution I and take the dilution factor into account in the calculations.

Calculations

The calculation formula (8) on p. 313 applies and therefore in this method the following relationships hold:

Wavelength:	334 nm	340 nm	365 nm
Volume activity	9016 $\times$ ΔE/min.	8842 $\times$ ΔE/min.	16176 $\times$ ΔE/min. [U/l.]

Precision of Method

With values around 300 U/l. s = 18 U/l. was found. The coefficient of variation is 3.3%.

Sources of Error

Contamination by GAP and DAP is rapidly and completely removed in the preliminary reaction before addition of sample, so that under the conditions described above the TA activity is measured specifically. In homogenates and extracts from cells and tissues which have been incubated with an excess of glucose, NADH is also oxidized by the continuation of glycolytic reactions and the added TIM/GDH mixture. This source of error can be avoided by removal of the glycolytic substrates from the sample by dialysis.

References

1 *B. L. Horecker & P. Z. Smyrniotis,* J. Am. Chem. Soc. *75,* 2021 [1953].
2 *S. Pontremoli, B. D. Prandini, A. Bonsignore & B. L. Horecker,* Proc. Natl. Acad. Sci. *47,* 1942 [1961].
3 *Z. Dische & E. Pollaczek,* Abstracts, 2nd Intl. Cong. of Biochem., Paris p. 289.

4 *B. L. Horecker & P. Z. Smyrniotis*, J. biol. Chem. *212*, 811 [1955].
5 *G. A. Calabria & N. Orzalesi*, Boll. Soc. Ital. Biol. Sper. *40*, 1674 [1964] (C. A. 62, 16694f.).
6 *W. Chefurka*, Can. J. Biochem. Physiol. *36*, 83 [1958].
7 *E. Racker* in *P. D. Boyer, H. Lardy & K. Myrbäck:* The Enzymes, vol. 5, p. 407, 2nd. Edn., Academic Press, New York.
8 *D. Couri & E. Racker*, Arch. Biochem. Biophys. *83*, 195 [1959].
9 *P. Srere, J. R. Cooper, M. Tabachnick & E. Racker*, Arch. Biochem. Biophys. *74*, 295 [1958].
10 *K. Brand, L. Davis & B. L. Horecker*, unpublished results.
11 *O. Tsolas & B. L. Horecker*, Arch. Biochem. Biophys. *136*, 287 [1970].
12 *O. Tchola & B. L. Horecker* in *Willis A. Wood:* Methods in Enzymology, vol. IX, p. 499, Academic Press, New York 1966.
13 *B. L. Horecker, P. Z. Smyrniotis & J. Hurwitz*, J. biol. Chem. *223*, 1009 [1956].
14 *E. Racker*, J. biol. Chem. *167*, 843 [1947].
15 *S. Pontremoli, S. Traniello, B. Luppis & W. A. Wood*, J. biol. Chem. *240*, 3459 [1965].
16 *T. Bücher*, Biochim. Biophys. Acta *1*, 292 [1947].
17 *E. Racker & E. A. R. Schröder*, Arch. Biochem. Biophys. *66*, 241 [1957].
18 *R. Venkataraman, A. G. Datta & E. Racker*, Fed. Proc. *19*, 82 [1960].
19 *A. Bonsignore, S. Pontremoli, E. Grazi & M. Mangiarotti*, Biochem. Biophys. Research Communs. *1*, 79 [1959].
20 *O. Tsolas & B. L. Horecker*, Arch. Biochem. Biophys. *136*, 303 [1970].
21 *A. Bonsignore, S. Pontremoli, E. Grazi & B. L. Horecker*, J. biol. Chem. *235*, 1888 [1960].
22 *P. T. Rowley, O. Tchola & B. L. Horecker*, Arch. Biochem. Biophys. *107*, 305 [1964].
23 *J. N. Baxter, A. S. Perlin & F. J. Simpson*, Can. J. Biochem. Physiol. *37*, 199 [1959].

γ-Glutamyltranspeptidase

Gabor Szasz

γ-Glutamyltranspeptidase*, γ-GT was discovered in 1950 by *Hanes* et al.[1,2] and isolated in pure form from ox kidneys in 1963 by *Szewczuk* and *Baranowski*[3]. The enzyme contains SH-groups and is a glucoproteide containing 20% carbohydrate[3]. γ-GT has been found in a number of tissues: kidney, pancreas, mammary gland, liver, intestine, lung, spleen, thyroid glands, bone marrow and lens[4-7]. In human tissues the greatest activity has been found in the proximal tubules and in the loops of *Henle* in the kidney, and in the epithelium of the intrahepatic bile ducts and the pancreatic ducts[8-10]. γ-GT occurs part bound to the cell structure and part in a soluble form. It is the latter which appears in serum and urine[11].

An increase in γ-GT activity in human serum has been observed virtually only with diseases of the liver, the bile ducts, and the pancreas. Extremely high values are generally indicative of cholestasis without the need for further differentiation[39,44]. In the case of anicteric patients the assay of γ-GT activity is particularly useful as a screening test for liver and bile duct diseases[12-16,39,45,47]. The activities of alkaline phosphatase, leucine aminopeptidase and γ-GT are usually correlated in hepatobiliary diseases, but changes of the latter are by far the most sensitive[17-21,39-41,44,45]. The γ-GT appears to have particular significance in liver complaints[40,43,46] due to alcohol and in the detection of liver metastases[39,40,42]. The γ-GT activity found in serum is due to the presence of several isoenzymes, which can be separated electrophoretically and by column chromatography[22-26]. The γ-GT activity can be measured chromatographically[1,2], manometrically[27] or preferably colorimetrically[4,28-34].

Application of Method: In biochemistry and in clinical chemistry.

Principle

$$HOOC-CHNH_2-CH_2-CH_2-CO \qquad + H_2N \cdot CH_2 - CONH - CH_2 - COOH$$

HN⟨◯⟩NO$_2$

γ-Glutamyl-p-nitroanilide   Glycylglycine

$$\xrightarrow{\gamma-GT} HOOC-CHNH_2-CH_2-CH_2-CO \qquad\qquad + H_2N⟨◯⟩NO_2$$

HN-CH$_2$-CONH-CH$_2$-COOH

γ-Glutamyl-glycylglycide   p-Nitroaniline

p-Nitroaniline has an absorption maximum around 400 nm, while the substrate does not absorb at this wavelength. The γ-GT activity is directly proportional to the amount of p-nitroaniline liberated per unit time[32].

Optimum Conditions for Measurements

The γ-GT in human serum reacts most rapidly with L-γ-glutamyl-p-nitroanilide at pH 8.2[34]. The same activity is found in ammediol, diethanolamine, triethanolamine and tris buffers[34]. The enzyme is saturated at a substrate concentration of 4.0 mM[34]. The highest activity is obtained with glycylglycine as the acceptor

---

* (γ-Glutamyl)-peptide: amino-acid γ-glutamyltransferase, EC 2.3.2.2.

for the γ-glutamyl residue[4]. The optimum concentration of glycylglycine is 50 mM. Magnesium ions have no effect on the activity[14,34,35], but appear to favour the solubilization of the substrate.

Measurements at different temperatures may require different measuring conditions (cf. p. 127). Nevertheless, results obtained under the same measuring conditions but at different temperatures were formerly compared with each other ("conversion factors" were determined). Such conversion factors may be correct if determined with a relatively large proband collective; however, they cannot be applied generally to the individual case (cf. p. 129). The value of the following relative reaction rates[34] thus lies in being able to appraise the temperature dependence of the reaction and at the most to compare qualitatively values up to the limit of normal.

°C	25	30	37
	1.00	0.80	0.63

Equipment

Spectrophotometer or spectrum-line photometer suitable for measurements at 405 nm, preferably with automatic cuvette changer (constant temperature cuvette holder) and recorder.

Reagents*

1. 2-Amino-2-methyl-propan-1,3-diol, Ammediol, ca. 95%
2. Hydrochloric acid, A. R. 1 N
3. L-γ-Glutamyl-p-nitroanilide

4. Glycylglycine, ca. 99%
5. Magnesium chloride, $MgCl_2 \cdot 6H_2O$, A. R.

Purity of Reagents

L-γ-Glutamyl-p-nitroanilide crystallizes with $^1/_2$ mole water and should be at least 90% pure.

Preparation of Solutions (for ca. 50 determinations)

  I. Ammediol buffer (50 mM, pH 9.3):
     Dissolve 526 mg. ammediol in 50 ml. doubly distilled water, adjust to pH 9.3 with 1 N HCl (about 0.6 ml.) and dilute to 100 ml. with distilled water.
 II. Substrate solution (4.2 mM L-γ-glutamyl-p-nitroanilide; 52.5 mM glycylglycine; 10.5 mM $MgCl_2$):
     Dissolve 120.5 mg. L-γ-glutamyl-p-nitroanilide + 694 mg. glycylglycine + 213 mg. $MgCl_2 \cdot 6H_2O$ in solution I at between 50 and 60 °C with constant stirring and make up to 100 ml. This solution is ca. pH 8.2 and has an absorption of 0.4 to 0.6 at 405 nm when read in a 1 cm. cuvette against solution I.

Stability of Solutions

Solution I is stable for several months at 4 °C. Store solution II at room temperature. The solution is supersaturated, but as a rule flocculation occurs only after 3–5 days. The colour of solution II increases daily by 15–20%.

---

* Complete reagent kits are available commercially, see p. 558.

Procedure

Collection, Treatment and Stability of Sample

Collection:

Collect venous blood and centrifuge at 3000 g for 10 min. to obtain serum. Haemolysis (up to 0.5 g% haemoglobin) does not affect the activity[34].

Stability of enzyme in sample:

The enzyme in human serum is stable for at least a week at between −20 °C and +20 °C[14,34].

Assay System

Wavelength: Hg 405 nm; light path: 1 cm.; final volume: 2.1 ml.; 25 °C (constant temperature cuvette holder); bring the substrate solution to 25 °C before the start of the assay; prepare a blank cuvette (substrate solution without sample) for each series of measurements; read against air.

Pipette into cuvettes:			Concentration in assay mixture
Sample (serum)		0.1 ml.	
Substrate solution	(II)	2.0 ml.	4.0 mM L-γ-glutamyl-p-nitroanilide 50 mM glycylglycine 10 mM $MgCl_2$ 48 mM ammediol buffer
Mix, read extinction and start timer. After exactly 1, 2 and 3 min. read again. ΔE/min. is used for the calculations.			

The values for ΔE/min. should not be larger than 0.060. If necessary, dilute the serum 5- to 10-fold with physiological saline or read at shorter time intervals.

Calculations

The calculation formula (8) on p. 313 applies and therefore for this method the following relationship holds (wavelength 405 nm):

$$\text{Volume activity} = 2120 \times \Delta E/\text{min. [U/l.]}$$

The spontaneous hydrolysis of L-γ-glutamyl-p-nitroanilide may amount to a ΔE/min. of 0.001 and must be determined for each series of measurements by means of a blank. If necessary, a correction should be made in the calculations.

Precision of Method

With values around 20 or 40 U/l. a range of 0.7–1.1 or 1.1–2.1 U/l. was found which corresponds to a coefficient of variation of 3.8–5.5%.

Normal Values

The normal values in human serum using L-γ-glutamyl-p-nitroanilide as substrate are 4–18 U/l. for women and 6–28 U/l. for men (25 °C)[34]. In new-born babies the activity is substantially higher (10–100

	U/l.	U/g. fresh wt.	U/10^{11} cells	U/g. Hb	n	s ±	Range
Human							
Serum	8.1				16	5.5	2.8–25.0
Erythrocytes				1.9	5	0.5	1.3–2.5
Leucocytes			45.6		8	14.7	25.3–66.4
Thrombocytes			1.9		5	0.4	1.3–2.5
Dog							
Serum	2.2				16	1.1	0.6–4.8
Lymph	1.4				10	0.7	0.0–2.6
Erythrocytes				1.3	13	0.6	0.5–2.6
Leucocytes			116		7	29	81 –153
Thrombocytes			0.13		6	0.10	0.02–0.27
Liver		0.9			4	0.3	0.6–1.4
Kidney cortex		86.1			6	7.9	76.0–97.8
Kidney medulla		19.1			6	8.9	9.0–31.0
Kidney papilla		3.0			6	1.5	1.0–4.5
Skeletal muscle		0.0			1	—	—
Lung		0.14			1	—	—
Spleen		0.15			1	—	—
Intestinal muscul.		0.15			1	—	—
Intestinal mucosa		1.5			1	—	—
Lymph nodes		0.8			1	—	—
Rabbit							
Serum	1.7				8	0.6	1.2–2.7
Erythrocytes				0.7	7	0.3	0.2–1.2
Leucocytes			89.2		6	31.9	44.4–131
Thrombocytes			0		7	0	—
Rat							
Serum	0.6				6	0.5	0.0–1.1
Erythrocytes				1.0	6	0.6	0.4–2.1
Leucocytes			64.2		4	10.1	51.5–73.1
Thrombocytes			0		5	0	—
Liver		0.13			3		0.10–0.16
Skeletal muscle		0			2		—
Heart		0			2		
Spleen		0.28			2		0.26–0.30
Colon		1.2			2		0.92–1.4
Lung		0.72			2		0.68–0.75
Kidney cortex		189			1		—
Kidney medulla		325			1		—
Marmoset							
Serum	8.3				12	2.5	5.6–14.1
Erythrocytes				0.61	9	0.17	0.28–0.88
Thrombocytes			0		5	0	—
Liver		1.3			7	0.6	0.55–2.0
Kidney cortex		148			3		116 –168
Kidney medulla		116			3		67.4–188
Skeletal muscle		0			3		—
Heart		0			3		—
Lung		0.48			3		0.21–0.95
Spleen		5.4			1		—
Colon		5.5			3		3.2–7.2

U/l.)[48] and drops continuously during infancy[48,49]. The normal range for young children and children of school age is 4–13 U/l. (25 °C)[50]. The activity in urine is 2- to 4-fold higher than in serum[31]. The excretion in 8 hr. night urine for women is 2 130–12 800 and for men 3 880–17 900 mU/8 hr. (25 °C)[37]. In cerebrospinal fluid the γ-GT activity is extremely low[36]. *Friedel & Mattenheimer*[38] found the following γ-GT activities (assay conditions: 0.1 M tris‑buffer, pH 8.5; 3.5 mM glutamyl-p-nitroanilide, 50 mM glycylglycine; 25 °C).

Sources of Error

Effects of drugs and other therapeutic measures: None known. Bromosulphalein does not inhibit the activity at a serum concentration of 0.10–0.15 mM[34].

Interference in the assay: Has not been observed.

Specificity of Method

The specificity of γ-GT is limited to the γ-glutamyl portion, the residual part of the substrate molecule merely affects the rate of the reaction[31]. In the absence of an acceptor either transpeptidization between two substrate molecules[32] or hydrolysis[4] occurs; higher pH values favour transpeptidization[31].

Other Assay Methods

Apart from L-γ-glutamyl-p-nitroanilide, L-γ-glutamylnaphthylamide[31,33] and L-γ-glutamylanilide[4,14] can be used to determine γ-GT activity. A semi-automatic kinetic method with L-γ-glutamyl-p-nitroanilide allows an assay rate of 60 per hour[34].

Determination of Activity in Tissues and other Body fluids

The soluble and insoluble forms of γ-GT can be determined separately or together depending on the preliminary treatment of the tissue. After centrifugation of the tissue homogenate for 30 min. at 100 000 g. only the soluble form is found in the supernatant fluid[3,11].
Urine contains dialysable inhibitors[37].

References

1 *C. S. Hanes, F. J. R. Hird & F. A. Isherwood,* Nature *166*, 288 [1950].
2 *C. S. Hanes, F. J. R. Hird & F. A. Isherwood,* Biochem. J. *51*, 25 [1952].
3 *A. Szewczuk & T. Baranowski,* Biochem. Z. *338*, 317 [1963].
4 *J. A. Goldbarg, O. M. Friedman, E. P. Pineda, E. E. Smith, R. Chatterji, E. H. Stein & A. M. Rutenburg,* Arch. Biochem. Biophys. *91*, 61 [1960].
5 *S. Szmigielski, J. Litwin & B. Zupanska,* J. clin. Path. *18*, 244 [1965].
6 *E. E. Cliffe & C. S. Waley,* Biochem. J. *79*, 118 [1961].
7 *E. Greenberg, E. E. Wollaeger, G. A. Fleisher & G. W. Engstrom,* Clin. chim. Acta *16*, 79 [1967].
8 *Z. Albert, M. Orlowski & A. Szewczuk,* Nature *191*, 767 [1961].
9 *G. G. Glenner & J. E. Folk,* J. Histochem. Cytochem. *9*, 624 [1961].
10 *G. G. Glenner, J. E. Folk & P. J. McMillan,* J. Histochem. Cytochem. *10*, 481 [1962].
11 *A. Szewczuk,* Clin. chim. Acta *14*, 608 [1966].
12 *E. Szczeklik, M. Orlowski, A. Szewczuk & B. Kolaczkowska,* Intern. Congr. Castroenterol., Leyden 1960. Excerpta med., Amsterdam 1961.
13 *E. Szczeklik, M. Orlowski & A. Szewczuk,* Gastroenterology *41*, 353 [1961].
14 *J. A. Goldbarg, E. P. Pineda, E. E. Smith, O. M. Friedman & A. M. Rutenburg,* Gastroenterology *44*, 127 [1963].
15 *A. M. Rutenburg, J. A. Goldbarg & E. P. Pineda,* Gastroenterology *45*, 43 [1963].

16 *F. Kokot, J. Kuska & J. Maraszek*, Z. inn. Med. *18*, 851 [1963].
17 *K. Gibiński, R. Szatoń & J. Maraszek*, Gastroenterologia *99*, 237 [1963].
18 *K. F. Aronsen, A. Hanson & B. Nosslin*, Acta Chir. Scand. *130*, 92 [1965].
19 *L. Villa, N. Dioguardi, A. Agostini, G. Ideo & R. Stabilini*, Enzymol. biol. clin. *7*, 109 [1966].
20 *S. Lukasik, R. Richterich & J.-P. Colombo*, Schweiz. med. Wschr. *98*, 81 [1968].
21 *G. Szasz, P. Rosenthal & W. Fritzsche*, Schweiz. med. Wschr. *99*, 606 [1969].
22 *F. Kokot & J. Kuska*, Clin. chim. Acta *11*, 118 [1965].
23 *M. Orlowski & A. Szczeklik*, Clin. chim. Acta *15*, 387 [1967].
24 *A. M. Rutenburg, E. E. Smith & J. W. Fischbein*, J. Lab. clin. Med. *69*, 504 [1967].
25 *K. Jacyszyn & T. Laursen*, Clin. chim. Acta *19*, 345 [1968].
26 *F. Kokot & J. Kuska*, Enzymol. biol. clin. *9*, 59 [1968].
27 *E. G. Ball, J. P. Revel & O. Cooper*, J. biol. Chem. *221*, 895 [1956].
28 *J. H. Kinoshita & E. G. Ball*, J. biol. Chem. *200*, 609 [1953].
29 *F. J. R. Hird & P. H. Springell*, Biochem. J. *56*, 417 [1954].
30 *A. Szewczuk & M. Orlowski*, Clin. chim. Acta *5*, 680 [1960].
31 *M. Orlowski & A. Szewczuk*, Clin. chim. Acta *7*, 755 [1962].
32 *M. Orlowski & A. Meister*, Biochem. Biophys. Acta *73*, 679 [1963].
33 *V. Kulhanek & D. M. Dimov*, Clin. chim. Acta *14*, 619 [1966].
34 *G. Szasz*, Clin. Chem. *15*, 124 [1969].
35 *M. Orlowski & A. Szewczuk*, Acta Biochim. Polon. *8*, 189 [1961].
36 *J. Swinnen*, Clin. chim Acta *17*, 255 [1967].
37 *G. Szasz*, Z. clin. Chem. & clin. Biochem. *8*, 1 [1970].
38 *R. Friedel & H. Mettenheimer*, unpublished results.
39 *G. Szasz, P. Rosenthal & W. Fritzsche*, Dtsch. med. Wschr. *94*, 1911 [1969]
40 *M. Zein & G. Discombe*, Lancet *2*, 748 [1970].
41 *C. Kammeraat*, Ned. T. Geneesk *114*, 1814 [1970].
42 *K. F. Aronsen, B. Nosslin & B. Pihl*, Acta Chir. Scand. *136*, 17 [1970].
43 *S. B. Rosalki, D. Rau, D. Lehmann & M. Prentice*, Ann. clin. Biochem. *7*, 143 [1970].
44 *G. Lum & S. R. Gambino*, Clin. Chem. *18*, 358 [1972].
45 *R. Schläger, R. Schenzer & R. Kattermann*, Med. Klinik *67*, 521 [1972].
46 *N. Kathke*, Münch. med. Wschr. *114*, 1151 [1972].
47 *K. Mayr*, Wien. klin. Wschr. *85*, 83 [1973].
48 *H. Bartels & D. Kleist*, Mschr. Kinderheilk. *119*, 334 [1971].
49 *F. C. Sitzmann, K. Kellerer & M. Bierschenk*, Arch. Kinderheilk. *183*, 276 [1971].
50 *G. Szasz & H. W. Rautenburg*, Z. Kinderheilk. *111*, 233 [1971].

UDP-Glucuronyltransferase

Jörg Frei, Ella Schmid and Heidi Birchmeier

Important biological compounds, such as bilirubin, steroid hormones, thyroid hormones, phenols produced by the intestinal flora, drugs and other exogenous substances or their metabolic products, can be conjugated in the organism by glucuronyltransferase, GT (UDP glucuronate β-glucuronosyl-transferase, acceptor-unspecific, EC 2.4.1.17) to glucuronides (conjugated glucuronic acids) and excreted in this form in the bile and urine. GT catalyses the transfer of a glucuronyl residue from uridinediphosphoglucuronate. UDPGA (activated glucuronic acid) to an aglycone with the formation of the corresponding glucuronide and uridine diphosphate.

In the cell the enzyme is bound to the microsomes[1,2]. GT is mainly a liver parenchymal cell enzyme, but is also found in other tissues, namely kidney[3], small intestine [4,5], intestinal mucosa[6], brain[3] and also probably in the cells of the histio-phagocytic series[7]. On the other hand GT is not present in muscle, spleen[3] and leucocytes[7]. An enzyme is present in cartilage tissue which incorporates a glucuronyl residue into chondroitin sulphate; it is not known whether or not this enzyme, which is concerned with the synthesis of certain mucopolysaccharides, is identical with GT[8].

So far the purification of GT has only been partial, mainly because of its relative instability. *Isselbacher* et al.[9] and *Tomlinson* et al.[10] were able to obtain a soluble and purified fraction by treatment of liver parenchymal microsomes with *Trimesurus flaviridis* toxin or with deoxycholate and precipitation with ammonium sulphate. GT activity can be determined both with physiological (bilirubin, steroid and thyroid hormones) and non-physiological aglycones (o-aminophenol, phenolphthalein, p-nitrophenol, 4-methylumbelliferone, anthranilic acid). To determine the activity of this enzyme in very small amounts of tissue, such as that obtained from needle biopsy material, only microanalytical, chemical or radio-chemical methods are suitable. The assay of GT activity with 4-methylumbelliferone as substrate is described here.

Application of Method: In clinical chemistry. The assay of GT allows examination of an important detoxification process of the liver. Sensitive microanalytical methods have been developed for the assay of the activity of this enzyme in the smallest biopsies of human liver.

Principle

(1) $\qquad$ Aglycone + UDPGA $\xrightarrow{\text{GT}}$ Glucuronide + UDP

The equilibrium of the reaction is practically completely to the right at pH 7.5. 4-Methylumbelliferone (as aglycone) fluoresces at alkaline pH (excitation maximum 340 nm, emission maximum 440 nm), whereas the corresponding glucuronide has no fluorescence under the same conditions. Consequently, the disappearance of fluorescence of 4-methylumbelliferone in alkaline solution is measured after the incubation. The method described here is based on that of *Perona* et al.[11]. It was first used by *Arias*[12].

Optimum Conditions for Measurements

Perona et al.[11] give the following conditions as being optimum: 0.36 mM 4-methylumbelliferone, 1.6 mM UDPGA, 12 mM Mg^{2+}, pH 7.5. The optimum amount of liver homogenate depends on the activity of the sample. With liver of humans and rats the activity at 37 °C (incubation time of 15 min.) is proportional to the amount of homogenate up to a protein content of 0.68 mg./ml. assay mixture.

Equipment

Spectrophotofluorimeter or photometer equipped with a Hg lamp, e.g. *Farrand* Mod. A (primary filter Corning 5860, secondary filter Corning 3387 + 4308 + 5562); glass hand microhomogenizer Ultra-Turrax Type 18/2*; 37 °C water bath with shaker; disposable polypropylene micro tubes (550 μl. capacity)**; microcentrifuge *Greiner***, *Spinco-Beckman**** or *Runne*****; constriction or other micro pipettes; stopwatch; ice bath; electromagnetic (*Cahn's*[+]) or torsion balance of suitable accuracy in the range 1–10 mg.

Reagents

1. Tris-hydroxymethyl-aminomethane, tris
2. Magnesium oxide, A.R.
3. Hydrochloric acid, A.R., 1 N
4. 4-Methylumbelliferone
   e.g. from Fluka, Buchs, St. Gallen, Switzerland.
5. Uridinediphosphoglucuronate, UDPGA disodium salt, UDPGA-Na$_2$; commercial preparation, see p. 555.
6. Sodium tungstate, Na$_2$WO$_4 \cdot 2$H$_2$O, A.R.
7. Sulphuric acid, A.R., 0.66 N
8. 2-Amino-2-methyl-1-propanol

Preparation of Solutions

Use only doubly distilled water.

I. Tris buffer (0.15 M; pH 7.5):
   Dissolve 1.81 g. tris in ca. 40 ml. distilled water, adjust to pH 7.5 with 1 N HCl and dilute to 100 ml. with distilled water.

II. Magnesium chloride (0.4 M):
   Dissolve 1.61 g. MgO in 1 N HCl, neutralize and dilute to 100 ml. with distilled water.

III. 4-Methylumbelliferone (1 mM):
   Dissolve 17.6 mg. 4-methylumbelliferone in 100 ml. boiling water and store in the dark at 37 °C.

IV. Uridinediphosphoglucuronate (8 mM):
   Dissolve 2.5 mg. UDPGA Na$_2$ in 500 μl. tris buffer (I); store at −25 °C for not longer than 4–5 days.

V. Sodium tungstate (10% w/v):
   Dissolve 10 g. Na$_2$WO$_4 \cdot 2$H$_2$O in distilled water and dilute to 100 ml.

VI. Deproteinization mixture
   Mix 1 part tungstate solution (V), 1 part 0.66 N H$_2$SO$_4$ and 7.5 parts distilled water.

VII. Aminomethylpropanol buffer (0.1 M; pH 10.3):
   Dissolve 8.9 g. base in ca. 500 ml. distilled water, adjust to pH 10.3 with 1 N HCl and dilute with distilled water to 1 000 ml.

---

* Janke and Kunkel, Stauffen i. Br., Germany
** Milian Instruments SA, Bd. Helvetique 26, Geneva, Switzerland.
*** Spinco-Beckman, Palo Alto, Calif. U.S.A.
**** Fr. Runne Nachf., Zentrifugenbau, Heidelberg-Rohrbach, Germany.
[+] Cahn Instrument Co., Downey, Calif., USA.

Stability of Solutions

UDPGA solution (IV) is stable for only a few days even in the deep-freeze. All other solutions are stable virtually indefinitely.

Procedure

Collection, Treatment and Stability of Sample

Cool liver biopsies to 0 °C in a small tube immediately after collection. Rapidly wash with ice-cold physiological saline to remove any blood which may be present, dry on filter paper and deep-freeze. The piece of tissue can be stored for several weeks at $-20°$ to -30 °C without loss of activity. Treat other animal tissues in the same way. To completely extract the enzyme freezing of the tissue samples is recommended even if they are to be worked up immediately. Before homogenization thaw the tissue at just above 0 °C. Weigh $2-6$ mg. sample on a torsion or *Cahn* electromagnetic balance and homogenize with a hand microhomogenizer in tris buffer (solution I) to 2.5% (w/v) for ca. 2 min. in ice. For larger amounts of tissue homogenize with an Ultra-Turrax (3 times for 15 sec. at 0 °C and 25000 rpm.); in this case previous freezing is not necessary.

Assay System

Incubation. Temperature: 37 °C; volume 20 μl. in polypropylene microtubes. To check the kinetics incubate for several different periods with a duplicate for each time. For the zero time sample (initial tube), first add deproteinization mixture and then sample.
Fluorescence measurements. Primary wavelength: 340 nm; secondary wavelength: 440 nm; light path: $0.8-1$ cm.; room temperature; final volume: 1.01 ml. Use the zero time sample as the standard. Subtract the fluorescence of the buffer solution as a blank.

Reagent mixture

Tris buffer	(soln. I)	5 volumes	
MgCl₂ solution	(II)	1 volume	This solution is stable in an
4-Methylumbelliferone solution	(III)	9 volumes	ice bath for ca. 2 hr.
UDPGA solution	(IV)	5 volumes	

Pipette into ice-cold microtubes:		Concentration in assay mixture during incubation
Reagent mixture	16 μl.	30 mM tris buffer 16 mM MgCl 0.36 mM 4-methylumbelliferone 1.6 mM UDPGA
Sample	4 μl.	
Mix, incubate in a thermostat with shaker. At 10, 20, 30 and 40 min. remove 2 tubes and proceed as indicated:		
Deproteinization mixture (IV)	400 μl.	
Mix, immediately place in an ice bath; centrifuge for 5 min.		
Supernatant after deproteinization Aminomethylpropanol buffer (VII)	10 μl. 1000 μl.	ca. 0.1 M
Measure fluorescence.		

Calculations

The zero time value serves as the standard. Correct the fluorescence values for the blank (fluorescence of the buffer solution).

F_0 Fluorescence at zero time

F_t Fluorescence at time t

G_0 4-Methylumbelliferone content of the zero time tube (standard) in μmole; e.g. as stated above 0.36 mM or 0.0072 μmole/mixture of 20 μl.

t   Incubation time in min.

$$\text{Volume activity in homogenate} = \frac{(F_0 - F_t) \times G_0}{F_0 \times t} \times 250000 \ [\text{U/l.}]$$

Precision of Method

In duplicate experiments the accuracy is better than 5%; no statistical evaluation is yet available.

Normal Values

Activity (U/g. protein*)

Human liver	10.1 ($\pm$1.8)	Mouse liver	22.8 ($\pm$1.0)
Rat liver	20.7 ($\pm$1.7)	Guinea pig liver	20.9 ($\pm$1.4)

In brackets: standard deviation of the mean.

The GT activity in human liver is significantly decreased in *Gilbert's* disease[14,15,16] in cases of *Crigler-Najjar* disease[17], in viral hepatitis[14,16] and in drug-induced hepatitis[16], while the activity is only moderately decreased in cirrhosis and steatosis[16]. Foetal liver is practically inactive[16,18]. The activity of GT is very low in homozygous *Gunn* rats[19-22].

---

* Determined by method of *Lowry* et al.[13].

Sources of Error

GT is inhibited by various SH reagents (organic mercurials, N-ethylmaleinimide, organic arsenicals, iodoacetamide, iodosobenzoate, Lewisite)[23]. Cysteine and glutathione protect the enzyme from these inhibitors. The conjugation of bilirubin is inhibited non-competitively by Novobiocin[10,24]. The conjugation of certain aglycones can be inhibited either competitively or non-competitively by other aglycones[10,25]. Calcium or magnesium ions may either activate or inhibit depending on the type of acceptor. Less is known about direct effects on GT activity *in vivo*. Certain drugs appear to affect the synthesis of the enzyme: synthesis of GT is promoted by phenobarbital[26] and testosterone[27] and inhibited by oestradiol[27]. The activity of GT is lower after administration of thioacetamide[28].
It is not known whether β-glucuronidase (EC 3.2.1.31) has an antagonistic action. Similarly the destruction of the substrates, particularly UDPGA, by side reactions has not been studied in detail.

Specificity

A wide variety of compounds can be conjugated as glucuronides: alcohols, phenols, organic acids[29,30], aromatic amines[31]. It is now known that the latter are conjugated by a special enzyme[32]. It is not known whether one or more glucuronyltransferases are concerned in the conjugation of the other aglycones. *Tomlinson* et al.[10] and *Cotte* et al.[17] have concluded, on the basis of inhibition and activation studies with Mg^{2+}, that bilirubin and p-nitrophenol are cunjugated by two different enzymes.

Other Methods of Determination

Methods using the following substrates have been described: o-aminophenol[17,33], anthranilic acid[10], bilirubin[34,35], isotope methods[14,36,37] with p-nitrophenol[9,14,38].

References

1 *R. Schmid & L. Hammaker*, New Engl. J. Med. *260*, 1310 [1959].
2 *L. M. Arias*, J. Histochem. Cytochem. *7*, 250 [1959].
3 *G. M. Grodsky & J. V. Carbone*, J. biol. Chem. *226*, 449 [1958].
4 *G. J. Dutton*, Biochem. J. *69*, 39 P [1958].
5 *K. J. V. Hartiala, K. Leikkola & P. Savola*, Acta Physiol. Scand. *42*, 36 [1958].
6 *W. Hoffmann & H. Brener*, Z. Klin. Chem. *6*, 85 [1968].
7 *J. Frei & L. Falcão*, Helv. Physiol. Acta *24*, C 84 [1966].
8 *A. J. Bollet, J. F. Goodwin & A. K. Brown*, J. Clin. Invest. *38*, 451 [1959].
9 *K. Isselbacher, M. F. Chrabas & R. C. Quinn*, J. biol. Chem. *237*, 3033 [1962].
10 *G. A. Tomlinson & S. J. Yaffe*, Biochem. J. *99*, 507 [1966].
11 *G. Perona, C. Frezza, R. Dalla & G. De Sandre*, Clin. Chim. Acta *10*, 513 [1964].
12 *I. M. Arias*, Bull. N. Y. Acad. Med. *35*, 450 [1959].
13 *O. H. Lowry, N. J. Rosebrough, A. L. Farr & R. J. Randall*, J. biol. Chem. *193*, 265 [1951].
14 *W. R. Metge, C. A. Owen, W. T. Foulk & H. N. Hoffmann*, J. Lab. Clin. Med. *64*, 89 [1964].
15 *I. M. Arias*, Science *126*, 563 [1957].
16 *Z. Madarasz, P. Magnenat & J. Frei*, in preparation.
17 *J. Cotte, M. Mathieu, J. P. André, C. Collombel & L. Padis*, Enzymol. Biol. Clin. *8*, 387 [1967].
18 *G. M. Grodsky, J. V. Carbone & R. Fanska*, Proc. Soc. Exp. Biol. & Med. *97*, 291 [1958].
19 *J. V. Carbone & G. M. Grodsky*, Proc. Soc. Exp. Biol. & Med. *94*, 461 [1957].
20 *R. Schmid, J. Axelrod, L. Hammaker & R. C. Swarm*, J. Clin. Invest. *37*, 1123 [1958].
21 *G. H. Lathe & M. Walker*, Biochem. J. *66*, 9 P [1957].
22 *J. Frei & Z. Madarasz*, unpublished results.
23 *I. D. E. Storey*, Biochem. J. *95*, 201 [1965].
24 *T. Hargreaves & J. B. Holton*, Lancet, i. 839 [1962].
25 *G. H. Lathe & M. Walker*, Biochem. J. *70*, 705 [1958].

26 *S. J. Yaffe, G. Levy, T. Matsuzava & T. Baliah*, New Engl. J. Med. *275*, 1461 [1966].
27 *J. K. Inscoe & J. Axelrod*, J. Pharm. Exp. Therapeutics *129*, 128 [1960].
28 *C.-H. Hamma & W. Prellwitz*, Enzymol. Biol. Clin. *8*, 203 [1967].
29 *G. J. Dutton*, Biochem. J. *60*, XIX [1955].
30 *G. J. Dutton & J. M. Spencer*, Biochem. J. *60*, 8 [1956].
31 *I. D. E. Storey*, Biochem. J. *95*, 209 [1965].
32 *I. M. Arias*, Biochem. Biophys. Res. Comm. *6*, 81 [1961].
33 *J. Dutton & I. D. E. Storey*, in *Colowick & Kaplan:* Methods in Enzymology Academic Press Inc., New York, N. Y., Bd. Vol. p. 159 [1962].
34 *F. P. Van Roy & K. P. M.* Heirweigh, Biochem. J. *107*, 507 [1968].
35 *J. Frei, H. Birchmeier & E. Schmid*, Enzym. Biol. Clin. *11*, 385 [1970].
36 *W. R. Metge, C. A. Owen, W. T. Foulk & H. N. Hoffmann*, J. Lab. Clin. Med. *64*, 335 [1964].
37 *M. Menken, P. V. D. Barrett & N. I. Berlin*, Clin. Chim. Acta *14*, 777 [1966].
38 *B. M. Pogell & L. F. Leloir*, J. biol. Chem. *236*, 293 [1961].

Glutamate-Oxaloacetate Transaminase

The enzyme glutamate-oxaloacetate transaminase, GOT (L-Aspartate: 2-oxoglutarate aminotransferase, EC 2.6.1.1) has been demonstrated in micro-organisms and in all animal and human tissues so far investigated. It is most active in heart muscle, then follow* in humans[1]: brain, liver, gastric mucosa, adipose tissue, skeletal muscle, kidney, etc. and finally serum with considerably smaller amounts.

There are several methods for the determination of the activity[2]: paper chromatography of substrates or reaction products after the incubation (see equation 1); spectrophotometric determination of oxalo-acetate formation at 280 nm; manometric determination, e. g. of the glutamate formed with glutamate decarboxylase; photometric assay of oxaloacetate formed from aspartate and 2-oxoglutarate: a) with malate dehydrogenase** as indicator enzyme and NADH, b) with 2,4-dinitrophenylhydrazine as ketone reagent and c) with 6-benzamido-4-methoxy-m-toluidine diazonium salt. The UV-assay has proved most popular. For comparison of methods, see[3].

The enzyme requires pyridoxal phosphate as coenzyme[4,5]. This is usually present in sufficient amounts in serum and in all tissues. However, pyridoxal phosphate should be added to the serum of older subjects[6] or of chronic alcoholics, or in thyrotoxicosis or intermittent porphyria. According to[7] the activity should be determined in every case in the presence of 25 μM pyridoxal phosphate, also to protect the enzyme for inactivation.

Application of Method: In biochemistry and clinical chemistry.

UV-Assay, Manual Method

Hans Ulrich Bergmeyer and Erich Bernt

Principle

(1)   L-Aspartate + 2-Oxoglutarate $\xrightarrow{\text{GOT}}$ Oxaloacetate + L-Glutamate

(2)   Oxaloacetate + NADH + H$^+$ $\xrightarrow{\text{MDH}}$ L-Malate + NAD$^+$

The equilibrium of the reaction (2) lies far to the right[8]. The equilibrium of reaction (1) is not important because oxaloacetate reacts immediately in the next reaction. The activity of GOT is therefore determined by the rate of NADH oxidation in reaction (2). The following method for the assay in serum is based on that of *Karmen*[9], except that optimum substrate concentrations are used.

Optimum Conditions for Measurements

The optimum pH and optimum substrate concentrations have been investigated by several authors[9-13]. In human serum the following relationship has been established[10] at 25 °C between the variables for the enzyme originating from heart (after myocardial infarction) and liver (in hepatitis):

In the pH range 6.5–9.0 the activity is dependent on the aspartate concentration, but scarcely dependent on the 2-oxoglutarate concentration. The influence on the activity by the chosen type of buffer is only small; the differences vary within a range of about 10%[14]. Triethanolamine buffer (50 mM, pH = 7.5) gives the

---

* mU/mg. tissue protein; if related to the fresh weight of tissue the order is different.
** Malate dehydrogenase, MDH (L-Malate: NAD oxidoreductase, EC 1.1.1.37).

highest activity[14]. Phosphate buffer is to be preferred, however, since it decreases the GlDH activity*
by 50%. This activity is unavoidably measured at the same time, if e.g. ammonia-containing enzyme
preparations are used. The pH activity curve shows a very flat peak in phosphate buffer between pH 7.2
and 8.0. Activities decrease with increasing phosphate concentration. However, a phosphate buffer
concentration of 80 mM is necessary to keep the pH constant.

In 80 mM phosphate buffer, pH 7.4, optimum values are obtained with 2-oxoglutarate concentrations of
6 to 20 mM and L-aspartate concentrations between 200 mM and 400 mM. Variation of the L-aspartate
concentration from 30 mM to 300 mM only results in a slight alteration of optimum activity in relation
to the 2-oxoglutarate concentration and vice versa. For the indicator reaction 0.18 mM NADH and 600
units malate dehydrogenase per litre assay mixture are sufficient.

Optimum and technically most favourable conditions for assays in normal serum, in serum after myocardial
infarction and in hepatitis serum (final concentrations in the test system) are:

> 80   mM phosphate buffer, pH 7.4
> 12   mM 2-oxoglutarate
> 200   mM L-aspartate
> 0.18 mM NADH
> 600   U malate dehydrogenase per litre assay mixture

1200 U lactate dehydrogenase** per litre assay mixture guarantee a fast and complete removal of the
pyruvate from the sample before the start of the GOT reaction.

Measurements at different temperatures may require different measuring conditions (cf. p. 127). Nevertheless, results obtained under the same measuring conditions but at different temperatures were formerly
compared with each other ("conversion factors" were determined). Such conversion factors may be
correct if determined with a relatively large proband collective; however, they cannot be applied generally
to the individual case (cf. p. 129). The value of the following relative reaction rates thus lies in being able
to appraise the temperature dependence of reaction and at the most to compare qualitatively values up
to the limit of normal.

°C	25	30	37
	1.00	0.70	0.46

Equipment

Spectrophotometer or spectrum-line photometer suitable for accurate measurements at 340,
334 or 365 nm, preferably with constant temperature cuvette holder; water bath (25 °C);
stopwatch.

Reagents***

1. Potassium dihydrogen phosphate,   3. Aspartic acid
   KH_2PO_4 sodium salt or free acid.
2. Dipotassium hydrogen phosphate,
   K_2HPO_4

---

  * Glutamate dehydrogenase (L-Glutamate: NAD(P) oxidoreductase, deaminating, EC 1.4.1.3). This
    enzyme catalyzes the reaction 2-Oxoglutarate $+$ NADH $+$ NH_4^+ $\rightleftharpoons$ Glutamate $+$ NAD^+ $+$ H_2O. –
    As a further safeguard to suppress this reaction, the indicator enzyme MDH (and LDH) must be
    free from NH_4^+ ions.
 ** L-Lactate: NAD oxidoreductase, EC 1.1.1.27.
*** Complete reagent kits are available commercially, see p. 558.

4. 2-Oxoglutaric acid
   free acid or dipotassium salt, commercial
   preparation, see p. 548.
5. Reduced nicotinamide-adenine dinucleotide, NADH
   sodium salt, NADH-Na$_2$; commercial preparation, see p. 545.
6. Malate dehydrogenase, MDH
   from pig heart, suspension in 3.2 M ammonium
   sulphate solution, or solution in 50% (v/v)
   glycerol, $\geq$1100 U/mg. (25 °C). Commercial
   preparation, see p. 485.

7. Lactate dehydrogenase, LDH
   from skeletal muscle, crystalline suspension in
   3.2 M ammonium sulphate solution or solution
   in 50% (v/v) glycerol; $\geq$550 U/mg. (25 °C);
   commercial preparation, see p. 481.
8. Sodium hydroxide, 5 N
9. Glycerol, A. R.
10. Sodium hydrogen carbonate, A. R.

Purity of Reagents

Use reagents of the purest available grade. The contamination of MDH (relative to the specific activity of MDH) with GOT should not exceed 0.01% (measured with ca. 0.2 μg. pyridoxal phosphate per assay) and 0.03% with glutamate dehydrogenase. MDH must not contain any apo-GOT.

Preparation of Solutions (for ca. 20 determinations):

To prevent the growth of micro-organisms in the solutions, sterilize the containers. Prepare all solutions with fresh, doubly distilled water.
   I. Phosphate/aspartate (0.1 M phosphate buffer, pH 7.4; 0.25 M aspartate):
      Dissolve 0.150 g. KH$_2$PO$_4$, 1.580 g. K$_2$HPO$_4$ and ca. 3.9 g. Na-L-aspartate or 3.3 g.
      L-aspartic acid in distilled water and make up to 100 ml. If free aspartic acid is used,
      adjust the pH to 7.6 with ca. 22 ml. 1 N NaOH before dilution.
  II. Reduced nicotinamide-adenine dinucleotide (13 mM β-NADH):
      Dissolve 16 mg. NADH-Na$_2$ and 15 mg. NaHCO$_3$ in 1.5 ml. distilled water.
 III. Malate dehydrogenase/lactate dehydrogenase, MDH/LDH (each 0.5 mg. protein/ml.):
      Mix the enzyme suspensions in ammonium sulphate solution and dialyse for three
      periods of 4 hr. at 0 °C against 200 volumes of 10 mM potassium phosphate buffer,
      pH 7.6. Dilute the contents of the dialysis sac with an equal volume of glycerol, A. R.
      and adjust with 50% glycerol to give 0.5 mg. of each protein/ml. – Or dilute commercial
      MDH and LDH solutions in glycerol with 50% (v/v) glycerol.
  IV. 2-Oxoglutarate (ca. 0.45 M):
      Dissolve 200 mg. 2-oxoglutaric acid in ca. 2 ml. distilled water, adjust pH to 7.0 with ca.
      0.5 ml. 5 N NaOH and make up to 3 ml. with water. – Or dissolve 260 mg. of the dipotassium
      salt to 3 ml. with water.

Stability of Solutions

Store all solutions, stoppered, in a refrigerator at 0–4 °C. Prepare the NADH solution II and the 2-oxo-glutarate solution IV freshly every 4 weeks. The other solutions are stable for at least 6 months. Deterioration of the solutions, especially the phosphate/aspartate solution, is usually due to bacterial contamination.

This can be prevented by addition of 0.3 ml. chloroform. Pour out the day's requirement of the stock solutions; do not use a pipette.

Procedure

Collection, Treatment and Stability of Sample

Collection and treatment of sample:

Collect blood without venestasis. Addition of 1 mg. oxalate/ml., 1 mg. citrate/ml., 2 mg. fluoride/ml., 0.2 mg. heparin/ml. or 1 mg. EDTA/ml. is quite safe. Centrifuge whole blood for 10 min. at ca. 3000 g. to obtain plasma or serum. Use only fresh serum free from haemolysis.

Stability of enzyme in sample:

According to[15-18] serum loses 10–15% of its GOT activity within 14 days at −20 °C. At 0–4 °C there is a 15% loss after 24 hr. and a 25% loss after 48 hr. At room temperature the activity decreases by 10 to 20%.

Assay System

Wavelength: 340 (Hg 334, Hg 365) nm; light path: 1 cm.; final volume: 3.7 ml.; 25 °C (constant temperature cuvette holder); read against air. Adjust the solutions to 25 °C before the assay.

Pipette into cuvettes:			Concentration in assay mixture
Phosphate/aspartate solution	(I)	3.00 ml.	80 mM phosphate 200 mM L-aspartate
NADH solution	(II)	0.05 ml.	0.18 mM
MDH/LDH solution	(III)	0.05 ml.	7.5 U MDH/ml. 3.7 U LDH/ml.
Serum		0.50 ml.	
Mix and allow to stand for 5 min.*			
2-Oxoglutarate solution	(IV)	0.10 ml.	12 mM
Mix, read extinction and start stopwatch. Repeat readings after exactly 1, 2 and 3 min. and calculate mean extinction difference.			

The values of ΔE/min. at 365 nm should not be greater than 0.080, otherwise dilute the serum 5- to 10-fold with physiological saline.

---

* Pyruvate, oxaloacetate and other substrates in serum react with NADH and enzymes contained in serum. After the preliminary incubation only the GOT reaction occurs on addition of 2-oxoglutarate.

Modification of the Procedure

Prepare reagent mixture:

Phosphate/aspartate solution (I)	30.0 Vol.	Stable at 25 °C
NADH solution (II)	0.5 Vol.	for 12 hr.
MDH/LDH solution (III)	0.5 Vol.	
	31.0 Vol.	

For the assay mix 3.10 ml. reagent mixture + 0.5 ml. serum in the cuvette and then proceed according to the above protocol.

Calculations

The calculation formula (8) on p. 313 applies and therefore for this method the following relationships hold:

Wavelength:	334 nm	340 nm	365 nm
Volume activity	$= 1213 \times \Delta E/min.$	$1190 \times \Delta E/min.$	$2176 \times \Delta E/min.$ [U/l.]

Precision of Method

With values around 15 U/l. the standard deviation is 0.8 U/l., the coefficient of variation 5.5%. It is lower when activity in the serum is high.

Normal Values

Laudahn et al.[19] were first to note the relationship between transaminase activities and the anthropometric data of sex, age and body weight, and to publish the appropriate normal values.

Table 1. Quantiles and medians for the relationships between age and body weight. GOT [U/l.] acc. to[21].

Age (Years)	Men Relative body weight* ≤1.2	>1.2	Mean	Women Relative body weight* ≤1.2	>1.2	Mean
≤30	7.4–18.1 10.2	7.8–30.2 14.05	7.4–23.8 10.2	4.0–13.9 9.65	—	4.0–13.9 9.65
31–40	7.9–18.1 10.4	9.0–19.2 12.0	8.0–18.2 11.1	5.9–15.0 8.5	5.6–16.8 8.6	5.7–15.8 8.6
41–50	7.2–19.3 11.05	7.8–18.3 11.9	7.3–19.0 11.7	6.1–13.7 8.5	5.8–13.9 9.3	6.1–13.9 8.95
51–60	7.2–18.9 10.3	8.2–18.1 11.1	7.4–18.1 11.0	7.0–16.8 9.8	6.1–16.0 9.45	6.1–16.8 9.6
>60	7.6–19.5 10.9	6.8–22.0 10.75	6.8–21.6 10.9	7.0–14.0 9.5	6.2–14.6 10.0	6.35–14.55 9.8
Mean	7.2–18.7 10.8	7.8–19.3 11.5	7.4–18.9 11.1	6.1–14.5 9.0	6.0–15.1 9.4	6.1–15.1 9.2
n	395	313	708	265	403	668

* Definition, see p. 757.

In the most recent studies [20-23] the criteria for the selection of "normals" has been refined. Probands with pathological values sufficiently significant to affect the results were eliminated. The following findings were unanimous: a) the distribution curves could be considered logarithmic – normal distribution; b) the upper limits of normal for men are significantly higher than for women; c) the dependence of the activities on body weight is less pronounced; d) differences in GOT activity due to age are slight and can be ignored.

The mean upper limit of normal for GOT activity in serum from men is around 19 U/l. (25 °C) and for women is 15 U/l. (25 °C).

Sources of Error

Effects of drugs and other therapeutic measures: Numerous investigations with different methods have been made. It is not evident, whether drugs are harmful to any organ or whether they influence the assay system.

Interference in the assay technique: The presence of glutamate dehydrogenase in the sample interferes, because it catalyses the oxidation of NADH by 2-oxoglutarate. Glutamate dehydrogenase is barely detectable in normal serum, but may be present in pathological serum in significant amounts. If the presence of ammonium ions in the assay mixture is avoided (by use of a solution of MDH and LDH in ca. 50% glycerol), the glutamate dehydrogenase reaction cannot proceed. The Michaelis constant of GlDH for NH_4^+ ions is so large (56 mM) that the enzyme remains inactive even with the raised ammonia concentrations which occur in some pathological sera.

With highly active sera the major part of the NADH may be oxidized between the addition of the 2-oxoglutarate solution (IV) and the first reading. The reaction then no longer proceeds under optimum conditions and too low or no activity is found. The first reading should therefore be made as rapidly as possible after the addition of the 2-oxoglutarate solution.

The assay is not inhibited by any physiological compounds which may occur in blood. Pyruvate, oxaloacetate and other substrates which oxidize NADH react in the preliminary incubation.

Specificity of Method

Apart from aspartate, glutamate can also act as an amino donor to 2-oxoglutarate[21,22]. DL-threo-β-Methylaspartate is a more active amino donor than aspartate, and methyloxaloacetate is a better acceptor than oxaloacetate[23]. However, these compounds either do not occur in serum or occur in such low concentration that there is no interference.

Details for Measurements in Tissues

According to *Bücher* et al.[24] GOT is located in both the intra- and extra-mitochondrial compartments of the cell. Simple homogenization in a *Potter-Elvehjem* (see p. 402) is not sufficient to completely extract the enzyme. The activity is therefore determined in whole homogenate[25], but the units are related to the soluble protein in the supernatant fluid as determined by the biuret method after high-speed centrifugation. For measurements on, for example, liver needle biopsies, 1 mg. fresh wt. is sufficient.

The optimum conditions for human serum are not necessarily valid for sera from other species or for tissues. In preliminary experiments on mouse liver homogenate[9] two to five-times higher concentrations of L-aspartate and 2-oxoglutarate were necessary to achieve optimum activity.

Animal tissues, especially liver, kidney and brain[1], are rich in glutamate dehydrogenase. It is therefore necessary to determine the amount of interference due to this enzyme, since it occurs in spite of the use of ammonia-free reagents: the phosphate-aspartate buffer is replaced by one containing 2-oxoglutarate and the GOT reaction is started with L-aspartate after measurement of the glutamate dehydrogenase activity. The difference between the $\Delta E/min.$ values is used for the calculation of GOT activity.

References

1 *F. W. Schmidt*, Ref. Med. Ges. Marburg/Lahn, December 1959.
2 Vgl. *P. P. Cohen* in *S. P. Colowick & N. O. Kaplan:* Methods in Enzymology. Academic Press, New York 1955, Vol. II, p. 178.
3 *G. Giusti, G. Ruggiero & L. Cacciatore*, Enzymol. biol. chim. *10*, 17 [1969].
4 *D. E. Green, L. F. Leloir & V. Nocito*, J. biol. Chem. *161*, 559 [1945].
5 *D. O'Kane & I. C. Gunsalus*, J. biol. Chem. *170*, 425 [1947].
6 *A. Hamfelt*, Scand. J. Clin. Lab. Invest. *18*, Suppl. 92 [1966].
7 *R. Rej, C. F. Fasce & R. E. Vanderlinde*, Clin. Chemistry *19*, 92 [1973].
8 *F. B. Straub*, Hoppe-Seylers Z. physiol. Chem. *275*, 63 [1942].
9 *A. Karmen*, J. clin. Invest. *34*, 131 [1955].
10 *H. U. Bergmeyer & E. Bernt* in *H. U. Bergmeyer:* Methoden der enzymatischen Analyse, 1. edn., p. 837, Verlag Chemie, Weinheim 1962.
11 *R. I. Henry, N. Chiamori, O. I. Golub & S. Berkman*, Amer. J. Clin. Pathol. *34*, 381 [1960].
12 *P. Trinder & I. F. Kirkland*, Clin. Chim. Acta, *16*, 287 [1967].
13 Recommendations of the Dt. Ges. Klin. Chem., Z. Klin. Chem. and Klin. Biochem. *10*, 182 [1972].
14 *E. Schmidt & F. W. Schmidt*, Z. analyt. Chem. *243*, 398 [1968].
15 *H. Südhof & E. Woetzel*, Klin. Wschr. *38*, 1165 [1960].
16 *M. M. Friedman & T. H. Taylor* in *M. Rainer & D. Seligson:* Standard Methods of Clinical Chemistry, Vol. III, p. 207, New York 1961.
17 *T. Laursen & G. Espersen*, Scand. J. clin. Lab. Invest., *11*, 61 [1959].
18 *A. Karmen, F. Wróblewski & I. S. LaDue*, J. clin. Invest. *34*, 126 [1955].
19 *G. Laudahn, E. Hartmann, E. M. Rosenfeld, H. Weyer & H. W. Muth*, Klin. Wschr. *48*, 838 [1970].
20 *E. Schmidt & F. W. Schmidt:* Kleine Enzymfibel, Boehringer Mannheim GmbH, 1973.
21 *W. Thefeld, H. Hoffmeister, E. W. Busch, P. U. Koller & J. Vollmar*, Deutsche Med. Wochenschr. *99*, 343 [1974].
22 *D. Weisshaar, R. Wolfer, E. Gossrau, K. U. Bäcker & B. Schwarz*, Medizinische Welt *25*, 351 [1974].
23 *H. Schlebusch, W. Rick, H. Lang & M. Knedel*, in preparation.
24 *W. T. Jenkins, D. A. Yphantis & I. W. Sizer*, J. biol. Chem. *234*, 1179 [1959].
25 *S. F. Velick & I. Vavra*, J. biol. Chem. *237*, 2109 [1962].
26 *C. Gilvarg*, J. biol. Chem. *233*, 1501 [1958].
27 *Th. Bücher & P. Baum*, Vortrag Dtsch. Kongr. f. ärztl. Fortbildung, Berlin 1958.
28 *E. Schmidt, F. W. Schmidt & E. Wildhirt*, Klin. Wschr. *36*, 179 [1958].

UV-Assay, Automated Method

Günter Bechtler

This method corresponds in the essential details to the manual method described on p. 727 so therefore only the differences are described here.

Equipment

Eppendorf-Automat 5010 for the spectrophotometric determination of enzyme activity[1].

Reagents, see p. 728.

Preparation of Solutions

Use solutions I to IV from p. 729. Before the start of the assays prepare a reagent mixture:
V. Reagent mixture:

Number of assays	Phosphate/aspartate solution (I)	NADH solution (II)	MDH/LDH solution (III)
20	12.00 ml.	0.20 ml.	0.20 ml.
60	30.00 ml.	0.50 ml.	0.50 ml.
120	60.00 ml.	1.00 ml.	1.00 ml.

Stability of Solutions

The reagent mixture (V) can be safely used up to 12 hr. after preparation. For other details, see p. 729.

Procedure

Collection, Treatment and Stability of Sample, see p. 730.

Preparation of Automat*

Pro-grammer	Sample	Reagent dispenser	Incubator	Reagent dispenser	Photometer	Analogue printer
Assay time 30 sec.	Cylinder "10" Serum 100 μl.	Cylinder "100" Reagent mixture (V) 500 μl.	15 min. 25 °C	Cylinder "10" 2-Oxoglutarate (IV) 20 μl.	Filter Hg 334 nm	Extinction 0–1 (1–2) Chart speed 2 cm./min.

Assay System

Wavelength: Hg 334 nm; light path: 1 cm.; final volume: 620 μl.; temperature: 25 °C. Read against air; the solutions need not be equilibrated.

The following are automatically pipetted into reaction cuvettes:		Concentration in assay mixture
Serum	100 μl.	
Reagent mixture (V)	500 μl.	78 mM phosphate 200 mM L-aspartate 0.16 mM NADH 6.5 μg. MDH & LDH/ml.
Incubation for 15 min. at 25 °C (automatically)		
2-Oxoglutarate solution (IV)	20 μl.	14.5 mM
Mix, 1st. reading 46 sec. after addition and a total of 7 readings in 154 sec.		

If the activity is more than 170 U/l. repeat the determination with 10 μl. serum.

---

* Consult the information leaflet B 5010 of the Eppendorf Gerätebau Netheler & Hinz GmbH, 2000 Hamburg 63, Barkhausenweg 1, Germany.

Calculations

The activity is determined from the slope of the reaction curve[2] $\alpha\left(tg\alpha = \dfrac{\Delta E}{\Delta t}\right)$. The results are either read directly from the scale calibrated in mU/ml. or the activity is calculated from the angle found on the degree scale, according to the following relationship:

Sample volume:	100 μl.	10 μl.
Volume activity $= 102 \times tg\alpha$		$869 \times tg\alpha$ [U/l.]

Precision of Method

The standard deviation over the normal range is 0.5 to 1 U/l.

Sources of Error

If the activity is over 800 U/l., it can appear on the recorder chart as a sample with very low activity, because of the extensive consumption of the NADH. To detect this error all sera with an activity <3 U/l. are repeated with a 10 μl. sample (dilution 1:8.55).

References

1 G. Bechtler, Ärztl. Lab. 15, 86 [1969].
2 H. Weber & R. Richterich, Klin. Wschr. 41, 665 [1963].

Colorimetric Assay of Reitman and Frankel[1]

Hans Ulrich Bergmeyer and Erich Bernt

The GOT activity can be measured colorimetrically by the use of two points. The first colorimetric assay by this technique was described by *Tonhazy* et al.[2] in which the reaction product oxaloacetate is quantitatively decarboxylated to pyruvate with aniline citrate as catalyst and the pyruvate is then determined as the 2,4-dinitrophenylhydrazone. Some later workers (e.g.[1]) rejected this method in favour of a simpler procedure, although others (e.g.[3-5]) retained it. The simplified procedure is described here[1].

Principle

After a fixed time the 2,4-dinitrophenylhydrazone of the reaction product, oxaloacetate, formed according to equation (1) p. 727 is determined colorimetrically in alkaline solution.

Some of the oxaloacetate spontaneously decarboxylates to pyruvate. The assay mixture therefore contains oxaloacetate, pyruvate and 2-oxoglutarate, all of which form 2,4-dinitrophenylhydrazones with absorption maxima at different wavelengths (Fig. 1). During the reaction the concentration of 2-oxoglutarate decreases, while that of oxaloacetate and pyruvate increases. To keep low the contribution of the 2-oxoglutarate hydrazone to the colour, the measurements are made at wavelengths (about 500–550 nm) higher than the absorption maximum which allows the greatest differentiation between the extinctions of the three hydrazones.

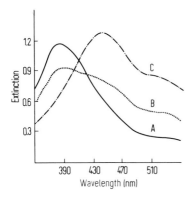

Fig. 1. Absorption spectra of equimolar alkaline solutions of the 2,4-dinitrophenylhydrazones of (A) 2-oxoglutarate, (B) oxaloacetate and (C) pyruvate (according to[23]).

Conditions for Measurements

See "UV-Assay, Manual Method", p. 727. As 2-oxoglutarate also reacts with 2,4-dinitrophenylhydrazine the measurements must be made with suboptimum 2-oxoglutarate concentration so that the blanks are not too high.

Equipment

Photometer suitable for measurements at 500 and 550 nm; water bath (37 °C); stopwatch.

Reagents*

1. Potassium dihydrogen phosphate, KH_2PO_4
2. Dipotassium hydrogen phosphate, K_2HPO_4
3. L-Aspartic acid
   sodium salt or free acid.

4. 2-Oxoglutaric acid
   free acid, commercial preparation, see p. 548.
5. Sodium pyruvate
   commercial preparation, see p. 550.
6. 2,4-Dinitrophenylhydrazine, A. R.
7. Hydrochloric acid, 1 N
8. Sodium hydroxide, A. R., pellets

Purity of Reagents

All reagents must be A. R. or purest grade available. Sodium pyruvate must have a purity of 98–100%.

Preparation of Solutions (for ca. 50 determinations)

To prevent the growth of micro-organisms in the solutions, sterilize the containers. Prepare all solutions with fresh, doubly distilled water.

  I. Buffer/substrate (0.1 M phosphate buffer, pH 7.4; 0.1 M aspartate; 2 mM 2-oxoglutarate): Dissolve 1.50 g. K_2HPO_4, 0.20 g. KH_2PO_4, 30 mg. 2-oxoglutaric acid, 1.57 g. L-aspartate, mono-sodium salt (or 1.32 g. L-aspartic acid) in 70 ml. distilled water, check pH with glass electrode, if necessary, adjust to pH 7.4 with NaOH (solution III) and dilute to 100 ml. with distilled water.

---

* Complete reagent kits are available commercially, see p. 558.

II. Chromogen (1 mM 2,4-dinitrophenylhydrazine):
   Dissolve 20 mg. 2,4-dinitrophenylhydrazine in 1 N HCl and make up to 100 ml.
III. Sodium hydroxide (0.4 N):
   Dissolve 16 g. NaOH in distilled water and make up to 1000 ml.
IV. Pyruvate (2 mM):
   Dissolve 22.0 mg. Na pyruvate in distilled water and make up to 100 ml.

Stability of Solutions

NaOH (III) and chromogen solution (II) are stable indefinitely if well stoppered. Store buffer-substrate solution (I) and pyruvate solution (IV) at ca. 4 °C. After addition of a few drops of chloroform to prevent bacterial growth these solutions are stable for more than two months.

Procedure

Collection, Treatment and Stability of Sample

Collection of sample:

See "UV-Assay, Manual Method", p. 730.

Stability of enzyme in sample:

See "UV-Assay, Manual Method", p. 730.

Assay System

Wavelength: 500–550 nm; light path: 1 cm.; 37 °C; incubation volume: 1.20 ml.; final volume: 12.2 ml.; read against blank containing distilled water instead of sample.

Pipette into a test tube:			Concentration in assay mixture
Buffer/substrate solution (I)		1.00 ml.	80 mM phosphate; 80 mM L-aspartate 1.6 mM 2-oxoglutarate
Serum		0.20 ml.	
Mix and incubate for exactly 60 min. at 37 °C in water bath.			
Chromogen solution (II)		1.00 ml.	0.45 mM
Mix and allow to stand for 20 min. at room temperature.			
NaOH (III)		10.00 ml.	0.33 mM
Mix and after 5 min. read extinction against blank.			

With results over 70 U/l. serum dilute 1:10 with physiological saline and repeat measurements.

Calculations

It is not possible to use the extinction coefficients of the 2,4-dinitrophenylhydrazones of pyruvate and oxaloacetate to calculate the results (see p. 312). The method is best standardized with the UV-assay with MDH as indicator enzyme (see above p. 709) or the extinction is related to that of a control serum of known GOT activity. However, as the activity curves are non-linear several control sera of different activities are required. For routine work it is sufficient to prepare several standards with different amounts of pyruvate but a constant sum of pyruvate + 2-oxoglutarate. The standard curves (abscissa: GOT activity; ordinate: extinction) are non-linear. Oxaloacetate is not suitable as a standard because of its instability. As in all methods of this type the error is unusually large.

Standard Curve and Table of Values:

Pipette successively into test tubes:

Test tube No.	Na pyruvate solution (IV) ml.	Buffer/substrate solution (I) ml.
1	0.00	1.00
2	0.05	0.95
3	0.10	0.90
4	0.15	0.85
5	0.20	0.80
6	0.25	0.75

Pipette into each tube 0.2 ml. distilled water and 1.0 ml. chromogen solution (II), mix and after 20 min. add 10 ml. NaOH (III). Mix and after 5 min. read the extinctions of tubes 2–6 against tube 1. Plot the extinctions (ordinate) against mU/ml. (abscissa).
By comparison with the UV method the following relationship was found:

Tube No. 2 = 10.5 U/l. serum
Tube No. 3 = 21   U/l. serum
Tube No. 4 = 32   U/l. serum
Tube No. 5 = 48   U/l. serum
Tube No. 6 = 70   U/l. serum

By direct comparison of the two methods the following table was constructed for measurements at 546 nm:

Extinction	U/l.	Extinction	U/l.
0.020	4	0.160	35
0.040	8	0.180	41
0.060	12	0.200	50
0.080	16	0.220	59
0.100	20	0.240	70
0.120	24	0.260	83
0.140	30		

Evaluation

When the measurements are made at 546 nm, obtain the U/l. from the above Table.
When a standard curve has been prepared with pyruvate solution (IV), convert the extinctions obtained for serum into U/l.
If control sera of different activities have been used, draw a standard curve (abscissa: U/l.; ordinate: extinctions) and convert the extinctions obtained for serum to U/l. with the aid of this curve.

Precision of Method

With values around 20 U/l. the standard deviation is 4 U/l. The coefficient of variation is 20%.

Normal Values

See "UV-Assay, Manual Method", p. 731.

Sources of Error

Effects of drugs and other therapeutic measures: See p. 732.

Interference in the assay technique: All compounds which form hydrazones with 2,4-dinitrophenylhydrazine interfere if they are present in high concentration. Pyruvate only interferes above 2.5 mg. %. With higher concentrations it is necessary to prepare a blank for the sample in which the sample is pipetted in immediately after addition of chromogen solution (II).

Specificity of Method

See "UV-Assay, Manual Method", p. 732.

Details for Measurements in Tissues

See "UV-Assay, Manual Method", p. 732.

References

1 *S. Reitman & S. Frankel,* Amer. J. clin. Pathol. *28,* 56 [1956].
2 *N. E. Tonhazy, N. G. White & W. W. Umbreit,* Arch. Biochem. Biophys. *28,* 36 [1950].
3 *P. Cabaud, R. Leeper & F. Wroblewski,* Amer. J. clin. Pathol. *26,* 1101 [1956].
4 *U. C. Dubach,* Schweiz. med. Wschr. *87,* 185 [1957].
5 *D. F. Ashman,* Acta ci. venezolana *10,* 14 [1959].

Colorimetric Assay of Tonhazy[1]

Hans Ulrich Bergmeyer and Erich Bernt

Principle

The oxaloacetate formed after a fixed time according to equation (1) on p. 727 is quantitatively converted to pyruvate with aniline citrate, and the pyruvate together with the excess 2-oxoglutarate is converted to the 2,4-dinitrophenylhydrazones. After selective extraction of the pyruvate hydrazone with toluene the colour is measured at 500–550 nm[1].

Optimum Conditions for Measurements

See "UV-Assay, Manual Method", p. 727.

Equipment

See "Colorimetric Assay of Reitman & Frankel", p. 736.

Reagents

1. Dipotassium hydrogen phosphate,
   K_2HPO_4
2. Potassium hydroxide, A. R., pellets
3. L-Aspartic acid,
   free acid.
4. 2-Oxoglutaric acid,
   free acid, commercial preparation, see p. 548.

5. Aniline
6. Citric acid, monohydrate, pure
7. Trichloroacetic acid, A. R.
8. 2,4-Dinitrophenylhydrazine, A. R.
9. Hydrochloric acid, conc., A. R.
10. Toluene
11. Ethyl alcohol, 95%, not denatured
12. Potassium hydroxide, A. R., 0.5 N

Preparation of Solutions (for ca. 50 determinations):

Prepare all solutions with fresh, doubly distilled water.

   I. Buffer/substrate solution (0.1 M phosphate buffer, pH 7.4; 0.1 M L-aspartate):
      Dissolve 0.87 g. K_2HPO_4 and 0.66 g. L-aspartic acid in ca. 25 ml. distilled water, adjust
      to pH 7.4 on a pH meter with 0.5 N KOH and make up to 50 ml. with distilled water.

  II. 2-Oxoglutarate solution (0.1 M):
      Dissolve 0.146 g. 2-oxoglutaric acid in a little distilled water, adjust to pH 7.0 with
      0.5 N KOH and dilute to 10 ml. with distilled water.

 III. Trichloroacetic acid (6.2 M):
      Dissolve 100 g. trichloroacetic acid in distilled water and make up to 100 ml.

 IV. Aniline citrate (5.5 M aniline; 2.4 M citric acid):
      Dissolve 5.0 g. citric acid monohydrate in 5 ml. distilled water and immediately before
      use mix in 5.0 ml. aniline.

  V. Chromogen (5 mM 2,4-dinitrophenylhydrazine):
      Dissolve 0.10 g. 2,4-dinitrophenylhydrazine in a mixture of 20 ml. conc. HCl and 50 ml.
      distilled water.

 VI. Toluene, saturated with water:
      Shake 500 ml. toluene vigorously in a 1 litre separating funnel with 100 ml. distilled
      water. After separation of the phases, run off lower phase and discard. Filter upper
      phase through a dry filter paper.

VII. Alcoholic KOH (0.45 M):
      Dissolve 2.5 g. KOH in 100 ml. 95% ethyl alcohol.

Stability of Solutions

The citric acid solution, aniline, trichloroacetic acid solution (III), chromogen solution (V), toluene (VI) and ethanolic-KOH (VI) are stable at room temperature. Store buffer/substrate solution (I) and 2-oxo-glutarate solution (II) at ca. 4 °C. After addition of a few drops of chloroform to prevent bacterial growth both solutions are stable for more than two months.

Procedure

Collection, Treatment and Stability of Sample, see p. 730.

Assay System

Wavelength: 500–550 nm; light path: 1 cm.; 37 °C; incubation volume: 0.90 ml.; final volume: 7.0 ml.; read against blank to which the serum is added after the trichloroacetic acid.

Pipette into a 10 ml. centrifuge tube:			Concentration in assay mixture
Buffer/substrate solution	(I)	0.50 ml.	55 mM phosphate; 55 mM L-aspartate
Serum		0.20 ml.	
Mix and equilibrate for 4–5 min. at 37 °C.			
2-Oxoglutarate solution	(II)	0.20 ml.	22 mM
Mix and incubate for exactly 10 min. at 37 °C.			
Trichloroacetic acid	(III)	0.10 ml.	0.62 mM
Shake vigorously.			
Aniline citrate	(IV)	0.20 ml.	0.9 M aniline 0.4 M citric acid
Mix and allow to stand for 10 min.			
Chromogen solution	(V)	1.00 ml.	2.3 mM
Mix and incubate for 5 min. at 37 °C.			
Toluene, saturated with water	(VI)	2.00 ml.	
Shake vigorously, allow to stand for 5 min. and then centrifuge for 5 min. at 3000 rpm. Pipette into cuvettes:			
Supernatant fluid		1.00 ml.	0.37 M
Alcoholic KOH	(VII)	5.00 ml.	
Mix and allow to stand for 5 min.			
Distilled water		1.00 ml.	
Mix and read extinction against blank.			

Calculations

It is best to compare the results with those of control sera of known activity. Use the standard curve obtained with the control sera (abscissa: U/l.; ordinate: extinctions) to convert the extinctions obtained with the serum samples to U/l.

Precision of Method

The precision of the method is better than the colorimetric assay of *Reitman* and *Frankel* (p.735).

Normal Values

See "UV-Assay, Manual Method", p. 731.

Sources of Error

Effects of drugs and other therapeutic agents: See p. 732.

Interference in the assay technique: As the hydrazone of pyruvate is selectively extracted and the sample is measured against a serum blank the interference described on p. 739 does not occur.

Specificity of Method

See "UV-Assay, Manual Method", p. 732.

Details for Measurements in Tissues

See "UV-Assay, Manual Method", p. 732.

References

1 *N. E. Tonhazy, N. E. White & W. W. Umbreit,* Arch. Biochem. Biophys. *28,* 36 [1950].

Colorimetric Assay with 6-Benzamido-4-methoxy-m-toluidine Diazonium Chloride

Hans Ulrich Bergmeyer and Erich Bernt

Principle

The oxaloacetate formed in a fixed time according to equation (1), p. 727 is coupled with a stable diazonium salt. The resulting colour is proportional to the amount of oxaloacetate present and can be measured at 500–550 nm[1-3]. Use of N^1-butyl-4-methoxy-m-anilamide diazonium salt (True Ponceau L or True Red PDC) has the advantage of better linearity of the reaction[4].

Optimum Conditions for Measurements

See "UV-Assay, Manual Method", p. 727.

Equipment

Photometer suitable for measurements between 500 and 550 nm; water bath (37 °C); stopwatch.

Reagents*

1. Dipotassium hydrogen phosphate, K_2HPO_4
2. Potassium dihydrogen phosphate, KH_2PO_4
3. 2-Oxoglutaric acid
   commercial preparation, see p. 548.
4. L-Aspartic acid

* Complete reagent kits are available commercially, see p. 558.

5. Ethylenediaminetetra-acetate, EDTA
   tetra sodium salt
6. 6-Benzamido-4-methoxy-m-toluidine
   diazonium chloride, BMTD
   Fast violet salt B

7. Polyvinylpyrrolidone
8. Oxaloacetic acid
9. Sodium pyrosulphite, $Na_2S_2O_5$, pure
10. Sodium hydroxide, 0.1 N
11. Hydrochloric acid, 0.1 N
12. Hydrochloric acid 0.01 N

Purity of Reagents

All reagents must be A. R. or purest grade available. The 2-oxoglutaric acid, L-aspartic acid and oxalo-acetic acid must be $98-100\%$ pure.

Preparation of Solutions

Prepare all solutions with fresh, doubly distilled water. Sterilize the containers.

I. Buffer/substrate solution (0.2 M phosphate buffer, pH 7.4; 5 mM 2-oxoglutarate, 17.2 mM L-aspartate):
    Dissolve 0.146 g. 2-oxoglutaric acid, 0.532 g. L-aspartic acid, 6.70 g. K_2HPO_4, 0.20 g. KH_2PO_4, 2.0 g. polyvinylpyrrolidone and 0.20 g. EDTA in 150 ml. distilled water, adjust to pH 7.4 with 0.1 N NaOH or 0.1 N HCl and make up to 200 ml. with distilled water.

II. Chromogen solution (ca. 17 mM BMTD):
    Dissolve 50 mg. 6-benzamido-4-methoxy-m-toluidine diazonium chloride, 25 mg. EDTA and 50 mg. polyvinylpyrrolidone in 10 ml. distilled water.

III. Control buffer solution (0.2 M phosphate buffer, pH 7.4; 5 mM 2-oxoglutarate):
     Prepare as for solution I, but omit L-aspartic acid.

IV. Pyrosulphite solution (2.6 mM $Na_2S_2O_5$):
    Dissolve 50 mg. $Na_2S_2O_5$ in 100 ml. distilled water.

V. Oxaloacetic acid standard solution (5 mM stock solution):
    Dissolve 66.0 mg. oxaloacetic acid in 100 ml. 0.01 N HCl (stock solution). Add to 0, 1, 2, 4, 6 and 8 ml. of this solution 10, 9, 8, 6, 4, and 2 ml. 0.01 N HCl and mix. These dilute standard solutions contain 0, 0.1, 0.2, 0.4, 0.6, and 0.8 μmole oxaloacetic acid in 0.2 ml.

Stability of Solutions

The buffer/substrate solution (I) and the control buffer solution (III) are stable for two months at 4 °C with the addition of several drops of chloroform.
Store the chromogen solution (II) and pyrosulphite solution (IV) at ca. 4 °C and prepare freshly each week. Prepare the oxaloacetic acid standard solutions (V) just before use.

Procedure

Collection, Treatment and Stability of Sample

Collection of sample:

See "UV-Assay, Manual Method", p. 730.

Stability of enzyme in sample:

See "UV-Assay, Manual Method", p. 730.

Assay System

Wavelength: 500–550 nm; light path: 1 cm.; 37 °C; incubation volume: 1.20 ml.; final volume: 7.20 ml.; read against blank containing physiological saline instead of serum. Adjust solutions to 37 °C before the start of the experiments.

Pipette into a test tube:			Concentration in assay mixture
Buffer/substrate solution	(I)	1.00 ml.	0.17 M phosphate buffer; 4.2 mM 2-oxoglutarate; 14.3 mM L-aspartate
Serum		0.20 ml.	
Mix and incubate for exactly 20 min. at 37 °C.			
Chromogen solution	(II)	1.00 ml.	ca. 8 mM
Mix and incubate for a further 10 min. at 37 °C.			
Pyrosulphite solution	(IV)	5.00 ml.	1.8 mM
Read the extinction of the sample against the blank within 1 hr.			

If the serum is lipaemic or icteric read against a serum blank containing control buffer solution (III) instead of buffer/substrate solution (I). The 20 min. incubation can be omitted.

Calculations

Use an oxaloacetate standard curve. Mix 0.2 ml. of each of the dilute oxaloacetic acid standard solutions with 1.0 ml. control buffer solution (III), equilibrate to 37 °C and add 1.0 ml. chromogen solution (II). After exactly 10 min. dilute with 5.0 ml. pyrosulphite solution (IV) and read the extinctions against the solution without oxaloacetic acid as described above.

Under the assay conditions the various oxaloacetic acid concentrations correspond to the following U/l.

μmole oxaloacetic acid/assay:	0	0.1	0.2	0.4	0.6	0.8
U/l.:	0	25	52	116	209	367

It is best also to assay control sera of known activity and to relate the extinction of the serum samples to these values.

Precision of Method

With values around 25 U/l. the standard deviation is 2 U/l. The coefficient of variation is 8%.

Normal Values

Range with 20 healthy subjects was 4–26 U/l. (37 °C)[3].

Sources of Error

Effects of drugs and other therapeutic agents: see p. 732.

Interference in the assay technique: As oxaloacetate is very unstable in aqueous solution, low values are found with solutions which are more than 2 hr. old. In addition the quality of the chromogen has a marked effect on the extinction. It is therefore essential to prepare a new standard curve for each batch of chromogen.

Specificity of Method

It is not known whether there are other substances in serum which react with BMTD. See also p. 732.

Details for Measurements in Tissues

See "UV-Assay, Manual Method", p. 732.

References

1   *A. L. Babson, P. O. Shapiro, P. A. R. Williams* & *G. E. Phillips,* Clin. Chim. Acta 7, 199 [1962].
2   *A. L. Babson* & *P. O. Shapiro,* Clin. Chim. Acta 8, 326 [1963].
3   *M. Turuno* & *A. Sheena,* Clin. Chemistry *11,* 23 [1965].
4   *S. M. Sax* & *J. J. Moore,* Clin. Chemistry *13,* 175 [1967].

Determination after Electrophoretic Separation

Roger Jozef Wieme

The electrophoretic heterogeneity of glutamate-oxaloacetate transaminase, GOT (aspartate aminotranferase) was first demonstrated by paper electrophoresis followed by fractional elution[1,2]. The direct zymogram technique is the method of choice, although chromatographic methods can also be used[3,4]. Most of the usual media for electrophoresis have been used (starch block[5], starch gel[6], agar gel[7], cellogel[8], cellulose acetate[9], polyacrylamide gel[10]); the results are comparable. Two main components can be separated: GOT 1 (mobility of α/β-globulin) and GOT 2 (mobility of slow γ-globulin). They correspond to the cytoplasmic and mitochondrial enzymes described by *Bücher* et al.[11]. The two isoenzymes are different proteins with different immunological specificity. This property has been used to separate them[12,13]. Although the electrophoretic mobility is species-specific, the ratio of GOT 1 : GOT 2 (1 : 3) is virtually the same in all tissues.

In all animal species studied GOT 2 has higher K_M values for 2-oxoglutarate and lower for L-aspartate than GOT 1. GOT 2 is also heat-labile and more sensitive to product inhibition by oxaloacetate[7]. *Boyde*[14] has shown that GOT 2 in human serum is bound to an α_2-globulin, probably α_2-macroglobulin. With suitable conditions a total of three bands can be demonstrated. With starch gel electrophoresis GOT 1 can be separated into sub-bands[15]. This separation is strongly dependent on the pH. For example, with pig heart GOT 1, one band is obtained at pH 8.9, while three bands are obtained at pH 8.0[16]. With enzyme-electrophoretic methods the assay described by *Karmen* has been used: the oxidation of NADH is determined visually in ultra-violet light or by UV-photography[6,7]. The bands can also be scanned at 365 nm. *Boyde*[10] proposed an incubation mixture for the easier detection of GOT 2, which is described in detail here.

The assay method of *Babson*[17], in which the diazonium salt of "Azoene Fast Violet B" (6-benzamido-4-methoxy-m-toluidine diazonium chloride) is immediately coupled with the oxaloacetate to form a soluble blue dye, should give better localization of the bands and higher sensitivity[15,18], but this has not been confirmed by other workers[19]. *Banks*[16] detected GOT by coupling the transaminase reaction with tetrazolium reduction via glutamate dehydrogenase as the intermediary enzyme.

Application of Method: The assay of GOT isoenzymes has proved of particular value in the detection of mitochondrial damage. However, the isoenzyme GOT 2 does not appear to be a sensitive indicator for tissue necrosis because of its remarkably short half-life in serum (dog[20]). GOT 2 increases in serum only in the severest cases of liver or heart damage. Consequently, the increase of GOT in serum in myocardial infarction[6], muscular dystrophy[21] and hepatitis[4] is virtually all due to a rise of GOT 1. The observation of *Boyde*[14] on the presence of bound GOT 2 even in normal human serum may revive interest in this field.

Principle

The method described here which is most suitable for the detection of GOT 2, is a combination of polyacrylamide gel electrophoresis[22] with a modification of the *Karmen* assay[10]. Bands of activity appear as dark spots on a fluorescent background; they can be photographed or the decrease of extinction at 340 or 365 nm can be evaluated by spectrophotometric scanning.

This electrophoretic technique has been chosen because it is an example of a polyacrylamide method which is very suitable for enzyme studies. All soluble components employed in the polymerization of the support material are excluded. Agar gel is just as suitable for the electrophoresis[7].

Optimum Conditions for Measurements

Both GOT 1 and GOT 2 are strongly inhibited by oxaloacetate and therefore it should not be allowed to accumulate. As the K_M for 2-oxoglutarate and for L-aspartate is very dependent on ionic composition

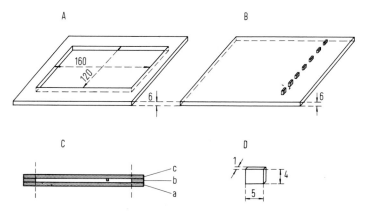

Fig. 1. Apparatus for preparation of polyacrylamide plates.
A: Plexiglass frame which is filled with the solution for gel formation.
B: Plexiglass lid with ridge of pegs.
C: Complete assembly: a) base plate which is stuck to frame; b) leaving room in the middle for the solution;
c) lid with the ridged teeth pointing below.
D: measurements of a peg (in mm.).

of the medium, the choice of buffer is critical. Neither the conditions of *Karmen* nor those of *Reitman* & *Frankel* are optimum for GOT 2. Phosphate buffer should not be used[23,24]; the 2-oxoglutarate concentration has been carefully adjusted to give the highest sensitivity in the detection of GOT 2[10].

Equipment

1. Plexiglass frame with ridge of pegs
2. Thin-layer electrophoresis apparatus
3. Direct current power supply (300 V, 50 mA)
4. UV-Lamp for study or photography of the zymogram
5. UV apparatus (340 or 365 nm), suitable for the measurement of negative peaks
6. Whatman No. 3 paper
7. Polyester film (ICI, London)
8. Rubber frames to surround the area to be developed.

Reagents

1. Boric acid, H_3BO_3
2. Sodium hydroxide, 1 N, and 32% (w/v) ca. 8 N
3. Acrylamide*
4. N,N'-Methylene-bis-acrylamide, "Bis"*
5. N,N,N',N'-Tetramethylethylenediamine, "TEMED"**
6. Ammonium persulphate, $(NH_4)_2S_2O_8$
7. Agarose***
8. Tris-hydroxymethyl-aminomethane, tris

9. Acetic acid
10. Malate dehydrogenase, MDH
    from pig heart, crystalline suspension in 3.2 M ammonium sulphate solution; ≥ 1100 U/mg. (25 °C). Commercial preparation, see p. 485.
11. L-Aspartic acid
12. 2-Oxoglutaric acid
13. Reduced nicotinamide-adenine dinucleotide, NADH
    disodium salt, NADH-Na_2; commercial preparation, see p. 545.

Preparation of Solutions

I. Borate buffer for electrophoresis:
   a) Stock buffer (0.5 M):
      Mix 170 ml. 1 N NaOH with 800 ml. distilled water, add 61.8 g. boric acid and with stirring heat to dissolve. Cool and dilute with distilled water to 2000 ml.
   b) Working buffer (25 mM, pH 8.4):
      Dilute 100 ml. stock buffer to 2000 ml. with distilled water.

II. Polyacrylamide gel:
   a) Stock mixture of the monomers:
      Mix thoroughly 95 g. acrylamide and 5 g. "Bis", store in plastic flasks. Avoid inhalation of the toxic dust.
   b) Solution for gel formation:
      Dissolve 9 g. of the stock mixed monomers in 200 ml. distilled water. Immediately before use add 0.20 ml. ammonium persulphate and 0.20 ml. "TEMED", then deaerate for a few seconds and pour the plates directly.

---

  * Commercial preparation from British Drug Houses Ltd., (BDH), Poole, England.
 ** Commercial preparation from Fluka, Buchs, St. Gallen, Switzerland.
*** Commercial preparation from Industrie Biologique Francaise, 35, Quai du Moulin de Cage, Boite Postale 48, 92-Gennevilliers, France.

III. Agarose solution:
    a) In distilled water (2%, w/v):
       Add agarose to fifty volumes of distilled water and dissolve by immersion in a boiling
       water bath (20 min.).
    b) To fifty volumes working buffer for electrophoresis add agarose (2%, w/v) and dissolve
       by immersion in boiling water bath (20 min.).
IV. Incubation buffer (0.2 M tris; pH 7.4):
    Mix 9.4 ml. acetic acid with about 500 ml. distilled water. Dissolve 24.2 g. tris in this
    solution and dilute to 1 000 ml. with distilled water.
 V. L-Aspartate (0.5 M):
    Suspend 1.33 g. L-aspartic acid in about 8 ml. distilled water. Titrate with 1 N NaOH
    until neutral when the aspartic acid dissolves. Dilute to 20 ml. with distilled water.
VI. 2-Oxoglutarate (0.1 M):
    Dissolve 1.46 g. 2-oxoglutaric acid in about 40 ml. distilled water. Titrate until neutral with
    0.2 N NaOH and dilute to 100 ml. with distilled water.

Stability of Solutions

Store all solutions at 0 to 4 °C. Solutions Ia, IIIa and IV are stable indefinitely, solutions V and VI are stable for a week. Prepare the other solutions immediately before use.

Preparation of Gel Plates

Pour the solution for gel formation (IIb) into the flat Plexiglass form. Push the lid with ridged pegs pointing below lightly over the frame, so that the arrangement is completely closed (Fig. 1c). Allow to stand for 2 hr. for gel formation. Transfer the gel with frame into a large flat vessel containing distilled water. Remove the gel from the frame under water, suck off water and replace with working buffer for electrophoresis (Ib). Allow gel to equilibrate in this buffer for 24 hr. Repeat the process twice. Place the gel in the frame again under water, if necessary, cut to size. Dry the surface and remove the liquid from the application grooves.

Procedure

Collection, Treatment and Stability of Sample

See p. 730. No difference in the stability of the isoenzymes of GOT is known and therefore no special precautions are required.

Electrophoresis

Mix serum samples with an equal volume of agarose solution (IIIa) and samples of low conductivity with an equal volume of agarose solution IIIb. Melt agarose solution in boiling water bath and transfer to a water bath at 45 °C. Bring sample and a capillary pipette to this temperature. Mix equal volumes of agarose solution and sample, and transfer to the groove with the capillary pipette.

Place plate on the electrode vessels, make the junction with 6 layers Whatman No. 3 paper and cover with polyester film. The final assembly is shown in Fig. 1 on p. 746. Fill the electrode containers with working buffer for electrophoresis (Ib). Carry out the run overnight in a cold room (4 °C, 2 V/cm. in gel).

Developer Reaction

Immediately before use mix the following for 20 ml. developer solution:

a) Incubation buffer (IV)   4 ml.
    NADH   10 mg.
    L-Aspartate solution (V)   2 ml.
    2-Oxoglutarate solution (VI)   10 ml.
    MDH suspension   0.05 ml.

Place in a 40 °C water bath:

b) warm agarose solution in distilled water (IIIa)   4 ml.

Mix solutions a) and b)*, place a rubber frame on gel and fill the frame with the developer solution. Wait for gel to form, cover with polyester foil and incubate for 120 min. at 37 °C.

Evaluation

Scan at 365 nm. Set base line on an extinction of 0.7. Activity zones appear as a decrease of the base line extinction. The inspection of the plate can be carried out in ultra-violet light. Activity zones appear as dark spots on a whitish-green background. A permanent record of the results can be obtained by photography.

Normal Picture

In normal human serum after polyacrylamide gel electrophoresis there is significant activity only in the slow migrating α_2-globulin area. Under the conditions of *Boyde* a weak additional zone of activity occurs in the area of α_2-macroglobulin. Exact quantitative details are not available. In some pathological sera there is an additional band with the mobility of γ-globulin in the area of the application groove; it corresponds to free GOT 2. If the separation is carried out in agar gel GOT 1 and GOT 2 appear in the α/β and in the slow-migrating γ-area respectively (Fig. 2).

Sources of Error

In studies on serum, haemolysis interferes only with the assay of GOT 1: mature erythrocytes contain no GOT 2[8].

Specificity of Method

The method appears to be specific for GOT.

---

* Final concentrations in incubation solution: 50 mM L-aspartate; 50 mM 2-oxoglutarate; 0.75 mM NADH; 6 μg. MDH/ml. (ca. 4.4 U/ml.).

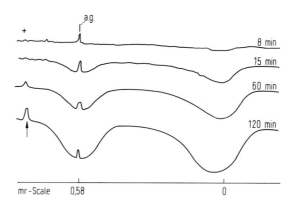

Fig. 2. Successive curves of the development reaction of GOT isoenzymes. Human liver extract diluted
1 : 100 with isotonic sodium chloride solution. Electrophoresis in agar gel (veronal buffer, pH 8.4; $\mu = 0.05$)
on microscope slides. *Boyde*[10] method of detection. Optical evaluation with Vitatron spectrophotometer
(UFD 100 + 200) with recorder (UR 403) at 365 nm; a. g. = application groove. The arrow shows a place
where an air bubble developed in the gel during the incubation. Relative electrophoretic mobilities
(mr values) are given.

Details for Measurements in Tissues

Generally extracts are prepared in the usual 0.25 M sucrose solution. However, *Boyd*[25] showed that the
yield of GOT 1 can be considerably increased if 1-butanol is used (20 % 1-butanol in the extraction mixture,
shake for 15 min., centrifuge off insoluble material, then remove butanol by dialysis against the buffer
medium to be used subsequently).

Other Methods of Detection

Boyde and *Latner*[6] proposed to make the reaction visible by a second incubation with a paper impregnated
with a tetrazolium salt. Activity zones appear as clear areas on a coloured background on reduction
of the tetrazolium salt by contact with NADH.
Class II methods (see p. 261) have also been used with success. *Fleisher*[26] has introduced a double assay:
at pH 6.0 and lower aspartate concentration (5 mM) where only GOT 2 is active and pH 7.5 and higher
aspartate concentration (100 mM) where both GOT react. A heat lability test has also been developed[27,28].

References

 1 *R. Emmrich & S. Zimmermann*, Klin. Wschr. *37*, 935 [1959].
 2 *G. A. Fleisher, C. S. Clarence & K. G. Wakim*, Proc. Soc. exptl. Biol. Med. *103*, 229 [1960].
 3 *A. Reith, J. Möhr, E. Schmidt, F. W. Schmidt & E. Wildhirt*, Klin. Wschr. *42*, 909 [1964].
 4 *E. R. Gabrieli & A. Orfanos*, Proc. Soc. exptl. Biol. Med. *128*, 803 [1968].
 5 *E. R. Gabrieli & A. Orfanos*, Proc. Soc. exptl. Biol. Med. *127*, 766 [1968].
 6 *T. R. C. Boyde & A. L. Latner*, Biochem. J. *82*, 51 P [1962].
 7 *J. W. Boyd*, Clin. Chim. Acta *7*, 424 [1962].
 8 *P. M. Manucci & N. Dioguardi*, Clin. Chim. Acta *14*, 215 [1966].
 9 *L. Körmendy, G. Gantner & R. Hamm*, Biochem. Z, *342*, 31 [1965].
10 *T. R. C. Boyde*, Z. klin. Chem. klin. Biochem. *6*, 431 [1968].
11 *A. Delbrück, H. Schimmassek, K. Bartsch & Th. Bücher*, Biochem. Z. *331*, 297 [1959].
12 *N. Lang & S. Massarrat*, Klin. Wschr. *43*, 597 [1965].

13 *S. Massarrat* & *N. Lang,* Klin. Wschr. *43*, 602 [1965].

14 *T. R. C. Boyde* & *J. F. Pryme,* Clin. Chim. Acta *21*, 9 [1968].

15 *L. E. Decker* & *M. Rau,* Proc. Soc. exptl. Biol. Med. *112*, 144 [1963].

16 *B. E. C. Banks, S. Doonan, A. J. Lawrence* & *C. A. Vernon,* Europ. J. Biochem. *5*, 528 [1968].

17 *A. L. Babson, P. O. Shapiro, P. A. R. Williams* & *G. E. Phillips,* Clin. Chim. Acta *7*, 199 [1962].

18 *M. K. Schwartz, J. S. Nisselbaum* & *O. Bodansky,* Amer. J. clin. Pathol. *40*, 103 [1963].

19 *W. D. Block, R. Carmichael* & *C. E. Jackson,* Proc. Soc. exptl. Biol. Med. *115*, 941 [1964].

20 *G. A. Fleisher* & *K. G. Wakim,* J. Lab. clin. Invest. *61*, 98 [1963].

21 *N. C. Kar* & *C. M. Pearson,* Proc. Soc. exptl. Biol. Med. *116*, 733 [1964].

22 *R. J. Wieme* in *H. Peeters:* Protides of the biological fluids, Symposium Bruges 1962, Elsevier, Amsterdam 1963, p. 309.

23 *T. R. C. Boyde,* Biochem. J. *106*, 581 [1968].

24 *J. S. Nisselbaum,* Analyt. Biochem. *23*, 173 [1968].

25 *J. W. Boyd,* Biochim. biophys. Acta *113*, 362 [1966].

26 *G. A. Fleisher* & *K. G. Wakim,* Proc. Soc. exptl. Biol. Med. *106*, 283 [1961].

27 *J. Kellen* & *V. Romančik,* Z. klin. Chem. *4*, 78 [1966].

28 *Z. Zázvorka,* Z. klin. Chem. *4*, 79 [1966].

Glutamate-Pyruvate Transaminase

The glutamate-pyruvate transaminase, GPT (L-Alanine: 2-oxoglutarate aminotransferase, EC 2.6.1.2) content of human tissues decreases in the following order[1,2]: liver, kidney, heart, skeletal muscle, pancreas, spleen, lung, serum (activity related to fresh weight).

The activity can be determined by various methods: paper chromatography of the substrates or reaction products; manometric determination of the glutamate formed with glutamate decarboxylase; determination of the pyruvate formed with salicylaldehyde. Most popular has proved the measurement of the pyruvate formed from alanine and 2-oxoglutarate: a) enzymatically with lactate dehydrogenase* as indicator enzyme and NADH, b) in a colorimetric assay with 2,4-dinitrophenylhydrazine. According to[3] the nicotinamide-adenine dinucleotide (NAD) formed in the indicator reaction (equation 2) can be determined fluorimetrically. For a comparison of the methods, see[4]. GPT requires pyridoxal phosphate as coenzyme[5]; this is very tightly bound to the enzyme (in contrast to glutamate-oxaloacetate transaminase)[6], so that there is no need to add pyridoxal phosphate to the assay system.

Application of Method: In biochemistry and clinical chemistry.

UV-Assay, Manual Method

Hans Ulrich Bergmeyer and Erich Bernt

This method was first published by *Henley* et al.[7]. The method described here is based on that of *Wroblewski* and *LaDue*[2].

Principle

(1) $\qquad$ L-Alanine + 2-Oxoglutarate $\xrightleftharpoons{\text{GPT}}$ Pyruvate + L-Glutamate

(2) $\qquad$ Pyruvate + NADH + H$^+$ $\xrightleftharpoons{\text{LDH}}$ L-Lactate + NAD$^+$

The equilibrium of reaction (2) lies far to the right. The pyruvate formed in reaction (1) is therefore immediately converted to L-lactate. The activity of GPT is determined from the rate of NADH oxidation in reaction (2).

Optimum Conditions for Measurements

The optimum pH and optimum substrate concentrations have been measured for the GPT reaction in serum[3], but they have been rarely investigated systematically with regard to their dependence on each other or comparisons made between normal and pathological serum. Until recently no published assay method gave the optimum conditions. The values given in the literature are therefore generally too low by more than 50%. Only now have numerous studies been made under optimum and standard conditions, and thus direct comparisons with other enzymes, e.g. GOT, have become possible.

In human serum the following relationships have been established at 25 °C between the variables for the enzymes originating from heart (after myocardial infarction) and liver (in hepatitis). The highest activity

---

* Lactate dehydrogenase, LDH (L-Lactate: NAD oxidoreductase, EC 1.1.1.27).

of the enzyme is measured with 50 mM triethanolamine buffer[8] (pH 8.0). Nearly the same activities are measured in phosphate and in tris buffer. Phosphate buffer is to be preferred, however, because it decreases the GlDH* activity to half. This activity is unavoidably measured at the same time, if ammonia-containing enzyme preparations are used. The pH activity curve is very flat in phosphate buffer. The optimum is between pH 7.3 and 7.8 depending on the substrate concentration. The activity decreases with increasing phosphate concentration. However, a phosphate buffer concentration of 80 mM is necessary to keep the pH constant.

In 80 mM phosphate buffer, pH 7.4, the optimum activity of normal serum is obtained with 3 mM to 0.3 M 2-oxoglutarate and with L-alanine concentrations of 30 mM to 1 M. There are hardly any differences over these ranges of concentration and occasionally there are none. In hepatitis serum significant differences are always observed; we found optimum values at more than 15 mM 2-oxoglutarate. Variation of the L-alanine concentration at constant 18 mM 2-oxoglutarate gave an optimum concentration of 800 mM to 1 M L-alanine.

In the indicator reaction 0.18 mM NADH and 1 200 units lactate dehydrogenase per litre assay mixture are sufficient.

Optimum conditions for the measurements of activity at 25 °C are as follows[9] (final concentrations):

$$
\begin{array}{ll}
80 & \text{mM phosphate buffer, pH 7.4} \\
18 & \text{mM 2-oxoglutarate} \\
800 & \text{mM L-alanine} \\
0.18 & \text{mM NADH} \\
1\,200 & \text{U lactate dehydrogenase/1 000 ml. assay mixture}
\end{array}
$$

Other conditions apply for other buffers and especially for different temperatures (e.g. lower L-alanine concentration at elevated temperature).

Measurements at different temperatures may require different measuring conditions (cf. p. 127). Nevertheless, results obtained under the same measuring conditions but at different temperatures were formerly compared with each other ("conversion factors" were determined). Such conversion factors may be correct if determined with a relatively large proband collective; however, they cannot be applied generally to the individual case (cf. p. 129). The value of the following relative reaction rates[9] thus lies in being able to appraise the temperature dependence of the reaction and at the most to compare qualitatively values up to the limit of normal.

°C	25	30	37
	1.00	0.75	0.52

Equipment

Spectrophotometer or spectrum-line photometer suitable for precise measurements at 340, 334 or 365 nm, preferably with constant temperature cuvette holder; water bath (25 °C); stopwatch.

Reagents**

1. Potassium dihydrogen phosphate,
   KH_2PO_4

2. Dipotassium hydrogen phosphate,
   K_2HPO_4

---

* Glutamate dehydrogenase (L-Glutamate: NAD(P) oxidoreductase, deaminating, EC 1.4.1.3). This enzyme catalyses the reaction: 2-Oxoglutarate $+$ NADH $+$ NH_4^+ $\rightleftharpoons$ Glutamate $+$ NAD^+ $+$ H_2O. – As a further safe-guard to suppress this reaction, the indicator enzyme LDH must also be free from NH_4^+ ions.
** Complete reagent kits are available commercially, see p. 558).

3. L-Alanine

4. 2-Oxoglutaric acid
   free acid or disodium salt; commercial preparation, see p. 548.

5. Reduced nicotinamide-adenine dinucleotide, NADH
   disodium salt, NADH-Na$_2$; commercial
   preparation, see p. 545.

6. Lactate dehydrogenase, LDH
   from skeletal muscle, crystalline suspension in
   3.2 M ammonium sulphate solution or solution
   in 50% (v/v) glycerol, $\geqq$ 550 U/mg. (25 °C),
   commercial preparation, see p. 481.

7. Sodium hydroxide, 5 N

8. Glycerol, A. R.

9. Sodium hydrogen carbonate, A. R.

Purity of Reagents

All reagents must be purest quality available. The LDH should not contain more than 0.01% GPT and
0.03% glutamate dehydrogenase (relative to the specific activity of the LDH).

Preparation of Solutions (for ca. 25 determinations)

To avoid bacterial contamination sterilize the containers. Prepare all solutions with fresh,
doubly distilled water.

I. Phosphate/alanine (0.1 M phosphate buffer, pH 7.4; 1.0 M L-alanine).
   Dissolve 0.2 g. KH$_2$PO$_4$, 1.5 g. K$_2$HPO$_4$ and 8.90 g. L-alanine in distilled water and make
   up to 100 ml. Check pH, and if necessary adjust to pH 7.4 with 0.1 N NaOH or 0.1 N HCl.

II. Reduced nicotinamide-adenine dinucleotide (ca. 13 mM β-NADH):
   Dissolve 16 mg. NADH-Na$_2$ and 15 mg. NaHCO$_3$ in 1.5 ml. distilled water.

III. Lactate dehydrogenase, LDH (0.5 mg. protein/ml.):
   Dialyse the enzyme suspension in ammonium sulphate solution three times for 4 hr. against
   200 volumes 10 mM potassium phosphate, pH 7.4 at 4 °C. Mix the contents of the dialysis
   sac with an equal volume of glycerol, A. R. and dilute to 0.5 mg. protein/ml. with 50%
   glycerol. Or dilute commercial LDH solutions in glycerol with 50% glycerol.

IV. 2-Oxoglutarate (0.66 M):
   Dissolve 290 mg. 2-oxoglutaric acid in ca. 2 ml. distilled water, adjust to pH 7.0 with
   1 N NaOH in an ice bath and make up to 3 ml. with distilled water. Using disodium salt,
   dissolve 375 mg. with distilled water ad 3 ml.

Stability of Solutions

Store all solutions, stoppered, in a refrigerator at 0–4 °C. Prepare the NADH solution II and the 2-oxo-
glutarate solution IV freshly every 4 weeks. The other solutions are stable for at least 6 months. Deterioration of the solutions, especially the phosphate/alanine solution is usually due to bacterial contamination.
This can be prevented by the addition of 0.3 ml. chloroform. Pour out the day's requirement of solutions;
do not pipette.

Procedure

Collection, Treatment and Stability of Sample

Collection of sample:

Obtain blood without venestasis. Addition of oxalate (1 mg./ml.), citrate (1 mg./ml.), fluoride (2 mg./ml.), heparin (0.2 mg./ml.) or EDTA (1 mg./ml.) is quite safe. Centrifuge for 10 min. at ca. 3000 g to obtain plasma or serum. Use only fresh serum or plasma free from haemolysis.

Stability of enzyme in sample:

The GPT activity in serum decreases by about 15% in 24 hr. at room temperature, by about 11% at 4 °C and by about 10% at -20 °C[10].
According to[11,12] there is no significant loss after 72 hr. at 4 °C.

Assay System

Wavelength: 340 (Hg 334, Hg 365) nm.; light path: 1 cm.; final volume: 3.70 ml.; 25 °C (constant temperature cuvette holder); read against air. Bring solutions to 25 °C before the start of each assay.

Pipette into cuvettes:			Concentration in assay mixture
Phosphate/alanine solution	(I)	3.00 ml.	80 mM phosphate buffer; 0.8 M L-alanine
NADH solution	(II)	0.05 ml.	0.18 mM
LDH solution	(III)	0.05 ml.	6.8 μg./ml. $\geqq$ 3.7 U/ml.
Serum		0.50 ml.	
Mix thoroughly and allow to stand for 3 min.*.			
2-Oxoglutarate solution	(IV)	0.10 ml.	18 mM
Mix, read extinction and start stopwatch. Repeat readings at exactly 1, 2 and 3 min. and calculate the mean change in extinction.			

The ΔE/min. values should not exceed 0.080/min. at 366 nm., otherwise dilute the serum 5- to 10-fold with physiological saline.

Modification of Procedure

Prepare a reagent mixture:

Phosphate/alanine solution	(I)	30.0 Vol.	
NADH solution	(II)	0.5 Vol.	Stable at 25 °C
LDH solution	(III)	0.5 Vol.	for ca. 12 hr.
		31.0 Vol.	

---

* Pyruvate, oxaloacetate and other substrates contained in serum react with enzymes in serum to oxidize NADH. Only the GPT reaction occurs after the preliminary incubation on the addition of 2-oxoglutarate.

For the assay mix 3.10 ml. reagent mixture +0.5 ml. serum in the cuvettes and then proceed according to the above scheme.

Calculations

The calculation formula (8) on p. 313 applies and therefore the following relationships hold for this method:

Wavelength:	*334 nm.*	*340 nm.*	*365 nm.*
Volume activity =	$1213 \times \Delta E/min.$	$1190 \times \Delta E/min.$	$2196 \times \Delta E/min.$ [U/l.]

Precision of Method

With values around 15 U/l. the standard deviation was 0.8 U/l. The coefficient of variation is 5.5%. It decreases to 2–4% with sera of higher activity.

Normal Values

Laudahn et al.[13] were first to note the relationship between transaminase activities and the anthropometric data of sex, age and body weight, and to publish the appropriate normal values.

In the most recent studies[14–17] the criteria for the selection of "normals" has been refined. Probands with pathological values sufficiently significant to affect the results have been eliminated. The selected groups of probands contained 2040 or 3927 persons respectively[21,22].

The following findings were unanimous: a) The distribution curves for GPT (and also for GOT and γ-GT) can be considered logarithmic – normal distribution. b) The upper limits of normal of the enzyme activities measured are significantly higher for men than for women. c) For both sexes there exists a marked relationship between enzyme activity and body weight (also for γ-GT). d) Differences in GPT (and GOT) activity due to age are slight and can be ignored.

Table 1. Quantiles and medians for the relationships between age and body weight. GPT [U/l.] acc. to[15].

Age (Years)	Men Relative body weight $\leqslant 1.2$	> 1.2	Mean	Women Relative body weight $\leqslant 1.2$	> 1.2	Mean
$\leqslant 30$	5.8–21.8 9.8	8.2–28.2 14.0	5.8–26.8 9.8	4.2–10.5 8.8	—	4.2–10.5 8.8
31–40	7.5–21.0 11.5	9.6–38.6 16.05	7.8–33.8 13.1	5.1–18.3 8.6	5.3–20.9 9.3	5.1–20.9 9.0
41–50	6.8–25.2 12.02	8.5–28.0 14.5	7.0–26.9 13.1	4.9–17.3 8.05	5.3–17.0 9.0	5.0–17.3 8.6
51–60	5.3–24.7 11.35	7.0–25.7 12.05	6.8–24.8 11.95	5.7–25.1 8.5	5.0–20.2 9.9	5.0–22.2 9.8
> 60	6.2–15.8 10.0	5.9–28.0 13.3	5.9–25.0 11.8	4.6–12.9 8.5	4.0–15.9 11.0	4.3–15.55 9.95
Mean	6.1–22.3 11.1	7.6–28.5 14.0	6.8–27.2 12.2	5.0–18.2 8.3	5.2–18.1 9.8	5.0–18.1 9.05
n	395	313	708	265	403	668

The "relative body weight" given in Table 1 is related to the "ideal weight". This has been taken from the Tables of the Metropolitan Life Insurance Company[18]. Overweight has been defined as a relative body weight of > 1.2.

The dependence of GPT activity on body weight is statistically significant. The upper limit for men of normal weight is between 22 and 23 U/l. (25 °C) and for women is 18 U/l. (25 °C).

Certain men in middle-age with marked overweight show values up to 39 U/l. The dependence of GPT values on weight in women is seen by the displacement of the median. The upper limits of normal only change slightly. It is notable that women up to 30 years virtually never show values higher than 11 U/l.

Sources of Error

Effects of drugs and other therapeutic measures: Numerous investigations with different methods have been made (e. g.[15]). It is not evident, whether drugs are harmful to any organ or whether they influence the assay system.

Interference in the assay technique: Animal tissues, especially liver, kidney and brain are rich in glutamate dehydrogenase[15]. In spite of the use of ammonia-free reagents the resulting interference must be determined: the alanine in phosphate buffer (solution I) is replaced by 2-oxoglutarate and the GPT reaction is started with alanine after measurements of the glutamate dehydrogenase activity. The difference between the $\Delta E/$ min. values is used for the calculation of GPT activity. With highly active sera a considerable proportion of the NADH can be oxidized in the time between the addition of the 2-oxoglutarate solution (IV) and the first reading. The reaction no longer proceeds under optimum conditions and too low or no activity is obtained, consequently first reading should be made as soon as possible after the addition of 2-oxoglutarate.

Experience has shown that compounds which occur in blood do not interfere with the assay. Pyruvate, oxaloacetate and other substrates which can oxidize NADH react during the preliminary incubation.

Specificity of Method

L-Alanine can be replaced by 3-aminobutyric acid, but the rate is considerably lower[17]. 2-Oxoglutarate cannot be replaced by the oxo analogues of valine, norvaline, leucine or other amino acids[17-19].

Details for Measurements in Tissues

GPT is one of the enzymes which is only partly found in the supernatant fluid after high-speed centrifugation of rat liver homogenate. With human liver 96–100% is found in the supernatant fluid, while with rat liver it is 65–70%[20]. Therefore on the basis of preliminary experiments GPT activity is measured in either the whole homogenate or the supernatant fluid.

The optimum conditions for human serum need not necessarily apply to sera or organs from other species; they may differ considerably.

References

1 *F. Wróblewski & J. S. LaDue*, Ann. intern. Med. *45*, 801 [1956].
2 *F. Wróblewski & J. S. LaDue*, Proc. Soc. exp. Biol. Med. *91*, 569 [1956].
3 *T. Laursen & P. F. Hansen*, Scand. J. Clin. Lab. Invest. *10*, 53 [1958].
4 *G. Giusti*, Enzymol. biol. clin. *10*, 17 [1969].
5 *D. E. Green, L. F. Leloir & V. Nocito*, J. biol. Chem. *161*, 559 [1945].
6 *L. Grein & G. Pfleiderer*, Biochem. Z. *330*, 433 [1958].
7 *K. S. Henley & H. M. Pollard*, J. Lab. clin. Med. *46*, 785 [1955].

8 *E. Schmidt & F. W. Schmidt*, Z. analyt. Chem. *243*, 398 [1968].
9 Empfehlungen der Dt. Ges. Klin. Chem., Z. Klin. Chem., Klin. Biochem. *10*, 182 [1972].
10 *H. Südhof & E. Wötzel*, Klin. Wschr. *38*, 1165 [1960].
11 *T. Bücher & P. Baum*, Vortrag Dtsch. Kongreß f. ärztl. Fortbildung, Berlin 1958.
12 *G. W. Mosley*, Techn. Bull. Registry of Med. Technol. *135*, 183 [1965].
13 *G. Laudahn, E. Hartmann, E. M. Rosenfeld, H. Weyer & H. W. Muth*, Klin. Wschr. *48*, 838 [1970].
14 *E. Schmidt & F. W. Schmidt:* Kleine Enzymfibel, Boehringer Mannheim GmbH, 1973.
15 *W. Thefeld, H. Hoffmeister, E. W. Busch, P. U. Koller & J. Vollmar*, Deutsche Med. Wochenschr., *99*, 343 [1974].
16 *D. Weisshaar, R. Wolfer, E. Grossrau, K. U. Bäcker & B. Schwarz*, Medizinische Welt, *25*, 351 [1974].
17 *H. Schlebusch, W. Rick, H. Lang & M. Knedel*, in preparation.
18 Metropolitan Life Insurance Company: Statistical Bulletin *40* [1959].
19 *E. Schmidt, F. W. Schmidt & E. Wildhirt*, Klin. Wschr. *36*, 172 [1958].
20 *H. L. Segal, D. S. Beattie & S. Hoppers*, J. biol. Chem. *237*, 1914 [1962].
21 *S. Hoppers & H. C. Segal*, Fed. Proc. *21*, 245 [1962].
22 *P. P. Cohen*, J. biol. Chem. *136*, 565 and 585 [1940].
23 *E. Schmidt, F. W. Schmidt & E. Wildhirt*, Klin. Wschr. *37*, 1221 [1959].

UV-Assay, Automated Method

Günter Bechtler

The essential details of the method are as for the manual method described on p. 752, and therefore only the differences are given here.

Equipment

Eppendorf-Automat 5010 for the spectrophotometric determination of enzyme activities[1].

Reagents, see p. 753–754.

Preparation of Solutions

Use solutions I to IV on p. 754. Prepare the following reaction mixture before the start of the assays.

V. Reaction mixture:

Number of determinations	Phosphate/alanine solution	NADH solution (II)	LDH solution (III)
20	12.00 ml.	0.20 ml.	0.20 ml.
60	30.00 ml.	0.50 ml.	0.50 ml.
120	60.00 ml.	1.00 ml.	1.00 ml.

Stability of Solutions

The reaction mixture (V) can be used safely for up to 12 hr. after preparation. For other details, see p. 754.

Procedure

Collection, Treatment and Stability of Sample

Preparation of Automat*

Programmer	Dispenser		Incubator	Dispenser Reagent	Photometer	Analogue printer
	Sample	Reagent				
Assay time	Cylinder "10"	Cylinder "100"	15 min.	Cylinder "10"	Filter Hg 334 nm	Extinction 0–1 (1–2)
30 sec.	Serum 100 µl	Reagent mixture (V) 500 µl.	25 °C	2-Oxogluta- rate (IV) 20 µl.		Chart speed 2 cm./min.

Assay System

Wavelength: Hg 334 nm; light path: 1 cm.; final volume: 620 µl.; temperature: 25 °C; read against air; the solutions need not be equilibrated.

The following are pipetted automatically into the cuvettes:		Concentration in assay mixture
Serum	100 µl.	
Reagent mixture (V)	500 µl.	78 mM phosphate 0.78 M L-alanine (optimum) 0.16 mM NADH 6.5 µg. LDH/ml.
Incubate for 15 min. at 25 °C (automatically).		
2-Oxoglutarate solution (IV)	20 µl.	17.8 mM
Mix, 1st. reading 46 sec. after addition, with a total of 7 readings in 154 sec.		

If the activity is more than 170 U/l. repeat the determination with 10 µl. serum.

Calculations

Determine the activity from the angle of the enzyme reaction curve[2] $\alpha \left(\text{tg } \alpha = \dfrac{\Delta E}{\Delta t} \right)$. The results are read off directly from the scale calibrated in U/l. or calculated from the angle of the progress curve according to the following relationship:

Sample volumes	100 µl.	10 µl.
Volume activity =	$102 \times \text{tg } \alpha$	$869 \times \text{tg } \alpha$ [U/l.]

Precision of Method

The standard deviation in the normal range is 0.5 to 1 U/l.

---

* See information leaflet B 5010 of Eppendorf Gerätebau Netheler & Hinz GmbH, 2000 Hamburg 63, Barkhausenweg 1, Germany.

Sources of Error

If the activity exceeds 800 U/l. (conventional method) it can appear on the recorder chart as sample with very low activity, because of the considerable oxidation of the NADH. To detect this error all sera with an activity < 3 U/l. should be repeated with a 10 μl. sample (dilution 1:8.55).

References

1 *G. Bechtler*, Ärztl. Lab. *15*, 86 [1969].
2 *H. Weber & R. Richterich*, Klin. Wschr. *41*, 665 [1963].

Colorimetric Assay of Reitman and Frankel[1]

Hans Ulrich Bergmeyer and Erich Bernt

Like the GOT activity the GPT activity can be measured by use of two reference points. The first colorimetric assay was described by *Green* et al.[2]. The most popular is the assay with 2,4-dinitrophenylhydrazine[1,3] The method described here is based on that of *Reitman* and *Frankel*[1].

Principle

After a fixed time the pyruvate formed from L-alanine and 2-oxoglutarate according to equation 1 (p. 752) is determined colorimetrically by treating the 2,4-dinitrophenylhydrazone with alkali. The residual 2-oxo-glutarate also forms a hydrazone, but its absorption maximum in alkaline solution is different from that of the pyruvate hydrazone (refer to Fig. 1 on p. 736). To keep the contribution of the 2-oxoglutarate hydrazone colour to the extinction low, the measurements are made between 500 and 550 nm instead of at the absorption maximum of the pyruvate hydrazone.

The method is either standardized by direct comparison with the assay of GPT with LDH as indicator enzyme (see p. 752) or (in routine work) with standards containing different amounts of pyruvate, but with a constant molecular amount of pyruvate + 2-oxoglutarate. The standard curves (GPT activity against extinction) are non-linear; it is best to use the extinction of a control serum of known GPT activity. However, even these reaction curves are non-linear, so that it is essential to use several control sera of different activity.

Conditions for Measurements

The principle of the assay requires that a relatively low 2-oxoglutarate concentration is used (1.7 mM instead of the optimum 18 mM) and consequently the conditions are not optimum. This error can be eliminated only if the method is simultaneously standardized by the GPT assay with LDH as indicator enzyme (see above). A standard curve prepared with known amounts of pyruvate/2-oxoglutarate does not eliminate this error.

Equipment

Photometer suitable for measurements between 500 and 550 nm.; water bath (37 °C); stop-watch.

Reagents *

1. Potassium dihydrogen phosphate, KH_2PO_4
2. Dipotassium hydrogen phosphate, K_2HPO_4
3. DL-Alanine
4. 2-Oxoglutaric acid
   free acid, commercial preparation, see p. 548.

5. Sodium pyruvate
   commercial preparation, see p. 550.
6. 2,4-Dinitrophenylhydrazine
7. Hydrochloric acid, 1 N
8. Sodium hydroxide, A. R., as pellets

Purity of Reagents

Only use reagents of A. R. or purest quality available. Pyruvate must be 98–100% pure.

Preparation of Solutions (for ca. 50 determinations)

Prepare all solutions with fresh, doubly distilled water.

   I. Buffer/substrate solution (0.1 M phosphate buffer, pH 7.4; 0.2 M DL-alanine; 2 mM 2-oxoglutarate):
Dissolve 1.50 g. K_2HPO_4, 0.20 g. KH_2PO_4, 0.030 g. 2-oxoglutaric acid and 1.78 g. DL-alanine in distilled water and make up to 100 ml. Check the pH with a pH meter, if necessary, adjust to pH 7.4 with NaOH (solution III).

  II. Chromogen solution (1 mM 2,4-dinitrophenylhydrazine):
Dissolve 20 mg. 2,4-dinitrophenylhydrazone in 1 N HCl and make up to 100 ml.

 III. Sodium hydroxide (0,4 N):
Dissolve 16 g. NaOH in distilled water and make up to 1000 ml.

 IV. Pyruvate solution (2 mM):
Dissolve 22.0 mg. Na pyruvate in distilled water and make up to 100 ml.

Stability of Solutions

NaOH (III) and chromogen solution (II) are stable indefinitely, if well stoppered. Store the buffer/substrate solution (I) and pyruvate solution (IV) at ca. 4 °C. As long as bacterial growth is prevented (by addition of a few drops of chloroform) the solutions are stable for longer than two months.

Procedure

Collection, Treatment and Stability of Sample

Collection of sample:

See "UV-Assay, Manual Method", p. 755.

Stability of enzyme in sample:

See "UV-Assay, Manual Method", p. 755.

---

* Complete reagents kits are available commercially, see p. 558.

Assay System

Wavelength: 500–550 nm; light path: 1 cm.; incubation temperature: 37 °C; incubation volume: 1.20 ml.; final volume: 12.2 ml.; room temperature; read against a blank containing distilled water instead of serum.

Pipette into a test tube:			Concentration in assay mixture
Buffer/substrate solution (I)		1.00 ml.	80 mM phosphate; 0.166 M DL-alanine; 1.6 mM 2-oxoglutarate
Serum		0.20 ml.	
Mix and incubate for exactly 30 min. at 37 °C in a water bath.			
Chromogen solution (II)		1.00 ml.	0.45 mM
Mix and allow to stand for 20 min. at room temperature.			
Sodium hydroxide (III)		10.00 ml.	0.33 M
Mix and after 5 min. read extinction against blank.			

With results above 70 U/l. dilute the serum 1:10 with physiological saline and repeat the assay.

Calculations

For the calculations of the results it is best to standardize the method by the UV-assay with LDH as indicator enzyme (see p. 752); or with a control serum of known GPT activity. However, as the reaction curves are non-linear several control sera of different activity are required. For routine work it is sufficient to use standards containing different amounts of pyruvate, but with a constant molecular amount of pyruvate + 2-oxoglutarate. The standard curves (abscissa: GPT activity; ordinate: extinction) are non-linear. As in all methods of this type the error is considerable.

Standard Curve and Table of Values

Pipette into test tubes:

Test tube No.	Pyruvate solution (IV) (ml.)	Buffer/substrate solution (I) (ml.)
1	0.0	1.0
2	0.1	0.9
3	0.2	0.8
4	0.3	0.7
5	0.4	0.6
6	0.5	0.5

Pipette into each tube 0.2 ml. distilled water and 1.0 ml. chromogen solution (II), mix and after 20 min. at room temperature add 10.0 ml. NaOH solution (III). Mix and after 5 min. read the extinctions of test tubes

2–6 against tube 1. Plot extinctions (ordinate) against GPT units (abscissa). The following relationship was found by direct comparison with the UV method (lactate dehydrogenase as indicator enzyme):

Test tube No. 2 = 13 U/l. serum
Test tube No. 3 = 28 U/l. serum
Test tube No. 4 = 48 U/l. serum
Test tube No. 5 = 78 U/l. serum
Test tube No. 6 = 102 U/l. serum

By direct comparison of the two methods the following Table was constructed for measurements at 546 nm:

Extinction	U/l.	Extinction	U/l.
0.025	2.5	0.225	35
0.050	5.5	0.250	41
0.075	9.0	0.275	47
0.100	12	0.300	54
0.125	17	0.325	61
0.150	21	0.350	70
0.175	25	0.375	80
0.200	30		

Evaluation

If the measurements are made at 546 nm read off the U/l. from the above Table. If the standard curve has been prepared with pyruvate solution (IV) convert the extinction obtained for serum to U/l. with the aid of this standard curve. If control sera of different activity have been used, plot the standard curve (abscissa: U/l., ordinate) extinction and convert the extinctions obtained for the serum samples to U/l. with the aid of this standard curve.

Precision of Method

With values around 20 U/l. the standard deviation is 4 U/l. The coefficient of variation is 20%.

Sources of Error

Effects of drugs and other therapeutic measures: See p. 757.

Interference in the assay technique: All compounds which form 2,4-dinitrophenylhydrazones interfere if they are present in high enough concentration. Pyruvate interferes only at concentrations of 2.5 mg.% and higher. With high concentrations of possible interfering compounds it is necessary to prepare a blank for the sample in which the sample is pipetted immediately after addition of the chromogen solution (II).

Specificity of Method

See "UV-Assay, Manual Method", p. 757.

Details for Measurements in Tissues

See "UV-Assay, Manual Method", p. 757.

References

1 *S. Reitman* & *S. Frankel*, Amer. J. clin. Pathol. *28*, 56 [1957].
2 *D. E. Green, L. F. Leloir* & *V. Nocito*, J. biol. Chem. *161*, 559 [1945].
3 *F. Wroblewski* & *P. Cabaud*, Amer. J. clin. Pathol. *27*, 235 [1957].

Colorimetric Assay of Tonhazy[1]

Hans Ulrich Bergmeyer and Erich Bernt

Principle

The pyruvate formed according to equation 1 on p. 752 after a fixed time and the residual 2-oxoglutarate are converted to the corresponding 2,4-dinitrophenylhydrazones. After selective extraction of the pyruvate hydrazone with toluene its colour is measured at 500–550 nm.[1-3] This method has the advantage that the assay can be carried out with an optimum 2-oxoglutarate concentration.

Optimum Conditions for Measurements

See "UV-Assay, Manual Method", p. 752

Equipment, see p. 753.

Reagents

1. Dipotassium hydrogen phosphate,
   K_2HPO_4
2. Potassium hydroxide, KOH, pellets
3. L-Alanine
4. 2-Oxoglutaric acid
   free acid, commercial preparation, see p. 548.

5. Trichloroacetic acid, A. R.
6. 2,4-Dinitrophenylhydrazine, A. R.
7. Hydrochloric acid, conc., A. R.
8. Toluene
9. Ethyl alcohol, 95%, not denatured

Purity of Reagents

All compounds should be A. R. or purest quality available.

Preparation of Solutions

Use fresh, doubly distilled water.
  I. Buffer/substrate solution (0.1 M phosphate buffer; 0.8 M L-alanine; pH 7.4):
     Dissolve 0.87 g. K_2HPO_4 and 3.55 g. L-alanine in ca. 45 ml. distilled water, adjust to pH 7.4
     on pH meter with dilute KOH and dilute to 50 ml. with distilled water.
 II. 2-Oxoglutarate solution (0.1 M):
     Dissolve 0.146 g. 2-oxoglutaric acid in a little distilled water, adjust to pH 7.0 with dilute
     KOH and make up to 10 ml. with distilled water.
III. Trichloroacetic acid (6.2 M):
     Dissolve 100 g. trichloroacetic acid in distilled water and make up to 100 ml.
 IV. Chromogen solution (5 mM 2,4-dinitrophenylhydrazine):
     Dissolve 0.10 g. 2,4-dinitrophenylhydrazine in a mixture of 20 ml. conc. HCl and 80 ml.
     distilled water.
  V. Toluene saturated with water:
     Shake 500 ml. toluene with 100 ml. distilled water vigorously in a 1-litre separating funnel.
     On separation of the phases, run off the lower phase and discard. Filter the upper phase
     through a dry filter paper.
 VI. Alcoholic KOH (0.45 M):
     Dissolve 2.5 g. KOH in 100 ml. 95% ethyl alcohol.

Stability of Solutions

Trichloroacetic acid solution (III), chromogen solution (IV), toluene (V) and alcoholic KOH (VI) are stable
indefinitely at room temperature.
Store buffer/substrate solution (I) and 2-oxoglutarate solution (II) at 4 °C. After addition of a few drops of
chloroform to prevent bacterial growth both solutions are stable for longer than two months.

Procedure

Collection, Treatment and Stability of Sample, see p. 755.

Assay System

Wavelength: 500–550 nm; light path: 1 cm.: 37 °C; incubation volume: 0.90 ml.: final volume 7.0 ml.; read against a blank in which the trichloroacetic acid is added before the serum.

Pipette into a 10 ml. centrifuge tube:			Concentration in assay mixture
Buffer/substrate solution	(I)	0.50 ml.	55 mM phosphate; 0.44 M L-alanine
Serum		0.20 ml.	
Mix and equilibrate 4–5 min. at 37 °C.			
2-Oxoglutarate solution	(II)	0.20 ml.	22 mM
Mix and incubate for exactly 10 min. at 37 °C.			
Trichloroacetic acid	(III)	0.10 ml.	0.62 M
Shake vigorously			
Chromogen solution	(IV)	1.00 ml.	2.5 mM
Add, mix and incubate for 5 min. at 37 °C.			
Toluene, saturated with water	(V)	2.00 ml.	
Shake vigorously, allow to stand for 5 min. and then centrifuge for 5 min. at 3000 rpm.			
Supernatant fluid		1.00 ml.	
Alcoholic KOH	(VI)	5.00 ml.	0.37 M
Mix and allow to stand for 5 min.			
Distilled water		1.00 ml.	
Add, mix and read extinction against blank.			

Calculations

The calculations are best made by comparison with control sera of different activity. From the standard curve obtained with control sera (abscissa: U/l., ordinate: extinctions) convert the extinctions obtained with the serum samples to U/l.

Precision of Method

No studies have been made.

Normal Values

See "UV-Assay, Manual Method", p. 756.

Sources of Error

Effects of drugs and other therapeutic measures: See p. 757.

Interference in the assay technique: As the pyruvate hydrazone is selectively extracted and the sample is measured against a serum blank, the type of interference described on p.763 does not occur.

Specificity of Method

See "UV-Assay, Manual Method", p.757.

Details for Measurements in Tissues

See "UV-Assay, Manual Method", p.757.

References

1 *N. E. Tonhazy, N. G. White & W. W. Umbreit,* Arch. Biochem. *27,* 36 [1950].
2 *E. F. Caldwell & E. W. McHenry,* Arch. Biochem. *45,* 97 [1953].
3 *G. H. Beaton, D. M. Curry & M. J. Vean,* Arch. Biochem. *70,* 288 [1957].

GOT and GPT, Assay with Automatic Analysers*

Morton K. Schwartz and Oscar Bodansky

Automated methods for the determination of transaminase activities are based on the manual methods (spectrophotometric[1], fluorimetric[2], colorimetric[3]). The first depends on a coupled enzyme reaction in which the decrease of extinction due to the oxidation of NADH is measured spectrophotometrically at 340 nm; the fluorimetric method makes use of the fact that NADH, in contrast to NAD, fluoresces strongly at 340 nm. An automated fluorimetric method[4] has been in use in our laboratory for years and is described here. Other automated methods for the determination of GOT activity depend on the formation of coloured complexes between oxaloacetate and diazonium salts[5]. One of these methods is also described here.

Fluorimetric Method for GOT and GPT[4]

Equipment

AutoAnalyzer® with 37 °C water bath, dialyser and fluorimeter. The fluorimeter is equipped with a 7–60 primary filter (360 nm, narrow pass) and No 8 secondary filter (485 nm, sharp cut). Flow diagram, see Fig. 1.

Reagents

1. Potassium dihydrogen phosphate, KH_2PO_4
2. Sodium hydroxide
3. 2-Oxoglutaric acid
4. L-Aspartic acid
5. L-Alanine
6. Reduced nicotinamide-adenine dinucleotide, NADH
   disodium salt NADH-Na$_2$; commercial preparation, see p. 545.
7. Albumin
   from bovine serum albumin, fraction V
8. Triton X-405**

9. Malate dehydrogenase, MDH
   from pig heart, suspended in 3.2 M ammonium sulphate solution; $\geq$ 1100 U/mg. (25 °C); commercial preparation, see p. 485.
10. Lactate dehydrogenase, LDH
    from rabbit muscle, crystalline suspension in 3.2 M ammonium sulphate solution; $\geq$ 550 U/mg. (25 °C); commercial preparation, see p. 481.
11. GOT and GPT standard
    Control serum, e.g. Versatol E***. Check the activity with the manual method.

Purity of Reagents

MDH must be free from GOT, otherwise a correction must be made for the GOT content.

---

*This work was partly supported by Grant CA-08748 of the National Cancer Institute, National Institute of Health, and Grant T-432 of the American Cancer Society.
**Rohm and Haas Company, Philadelphia, USA.
***General Diagnostics Division, Warner-Chilcott Co., USA.

Preparation of Solutions

Use only fresh distilled water

I. Phosphate buffer (1.0 M; pH 7.4):
Dissolve 132 g. KH_2PO_4 + 33 g. NaOH in ca. 800 ml. distilled water. Adjust the pH to 7.4 (glass electrode) and dilute to 1 000 ml. with distilled water.

II. Phosphate buffer (0.1 M; pH 7.4):
Dilute solution I 10-fold with distilled water. Add 1 ml. Triton X-405.

III. Albumin (0.15% in 0.1 M phosphate buffer, pH 7.4):
Dilute 50 ml. phosphate buffer (solution I) to 500 ml. with distilled water and dissolve 0.75 g. albumin in this solution.

IV. Reduced nicotinamide-adenine dinucleotide (0.4 mM β-NADH):
Dissolve 17.5 mg. NADH-Na$_2$ in 50 ml. albumin solution (III).

V. Malate dehydrogenase (3 U/ml.):
Dilute the stock suspension with albumin solution (III) to 9 U/ml. Freeze at $-20\,°C$ in small portions; stable for at least 1 month. Immediately before use thaw out and dilute to 3 U/ml. with solution III.

VI. Lactate dehydrogenase (39 U/ml.):
Dilute the stock suspension to 117 U/ml. with albumin solution III. Freeze at $-20\,°C$ in small portions; stable for at least 1 month. Immediately before use dilute to 39 U/ml. with solution III.

VII. GOT substrate (139 mM L-aspartate; 18 mM 2-oxoglutarate):
Dilute 100 ml. phosphate buffer (I) to 800 ml. with distilled water, and dissolve in this 18.5 g. L-aspartate and 2.63 g. 2-oxoglutarate. Add 128 ml. 1 N NaOH, adjust to pH 7.4 using a glass electrode and dilute to 1 000 ml. with distilled water. Immediately before use add 1 ml. Triton X-405.

VIII. GPT substrate (246 mM L-alanine; 11.8 mM 2-oxoglutarate):
Dilute 100 ml. phosphate buffer (I) to 800 ml. with distilled water, and dissolve in this 27.7 g. L-alanine and 1.73 g. 2-oxoglutarate. Adjust to pH 7.4 using a glass electrode and dilute to 1 000 ml. with distilled water. Immediately before use add 1 ml. Triton X-405.

IX. Standards (0–200 U/l.; 37 °C):
Reconstitute Versatol E according to the instructions of the manufacturer and determine the activity[1] (see p. 727 & 752). For large amounts reconstitute 10 bottles of Versatol E, combine, determine the activity and dilute 2-, 3-, 4-, 5-, 10- and 20-fold with 0.9% NaCl: final volume of each dilution, 20 ml. Divide each dilution into 0.5 ml. portions and freeze at $-20\,°C$. Thaw out the daily requirement. If a large amount is required mix portions of the same concentration. Set up 6 standard values for each series of assays.

Stability of Solutions

Unless otherwise stated store all solutions at 4 °C. The substrate solutions are stable providing bacterial contamination does not occur. This can be prevented by addition of 0.5 ml. chloroform and occasional shaking. Prepare the NADH solution freshly and store in an ice bath. Also store the thawed MDH and LDH solutions in an ice bath. The diluted Versatol solutions are stable for at least 1 month at $-20\,°C$.

Procedure

Collection, Treatment and Stability of Sample, see p. 755.

Assay System

See Fig. 1. 40 Samples can be analysed per hour. A blank is not necessary for GOT, but is for GPT because serum contains pyruvate. The blank contains phosphate buffer (solution II) instead of substrate solution.

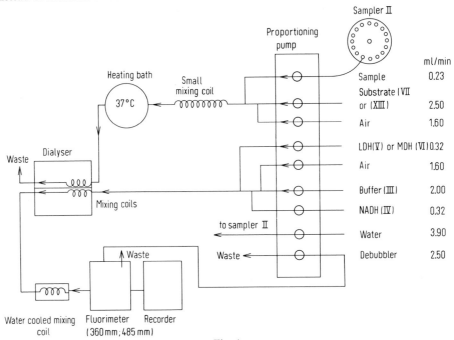

Fig. 1.

First aspirate distilled water through all tubes and with an opaque aperture blocking the light path set the recorder to 5% transmission.

Rinse the clean tubes with the appropriate reagents and by the appropriate combination of slit and light adjustment (usually 3 × light adjustment and slit No. 3) obtain a base line transmission of 90%. This represents the maximum fluorescence of the NADH of the reaction mixture, when excited with primary filter 360 nm and measured with the secondary filter 485 nm. The activity of the samples is seen as a decrease in transmission.

The following are the final concentrations in the assay system:

	GOT	GPT
NADH	47 μM	47 μM
2-Oxoglutarate	16.5 mM	10.7 mM
Aspartate	125 mM	—
MDH	0.53 U/ml. (25 °C)	—
Alanine		214 mM
LDH	—	6.9 U/ml. (25 °C)

Calculations

Standard curve: Plot the % transmission (ordinate) against U/l. of the standards. As the fluorescence is linear it is not necessary to plot the values as extinctions. The transmissions are linearly proportional to the activities between 0 and 200 U/l. (37 °C).

Precision of Method

Serum aliquots measured on 11 successive days gave a mean of 17 U/l. (37 °C); standard deviation 0.9 U/l. The coefficient of variation is 5%.

Normal Values

The normal values obtained with this method are similar to those obtained with the manual method. The upper limit of the normal value for GOT is 23 U/l. (37 °C) adults[6] and for GPT is 37 U/l. for men and 27 U/l. (37 °C) for woman[6].

Sources of Error

Effects of drugs and other therapeutic measures: See p. 757.

Interference in the assay technique: The dialysis removes the need for a blank for GOT, because it excludes interference from fluorescent compounds in the sample and in the enzyme which can compete for NADH. The serum concentration of oxaloacetate is so low that it need not be considered here. However, the pyruvate concentration is large enough to necessitate a blank for the determination of GPT activity.

Colorimetric Assay for GOT

Equipment

AutoAnalyser® with 45 °C water bath for enzyme incubation, 37 °C water bath for colour development, dialyser and colorimeter with 455 nm filter. Flow scheme, see Fig. 2.

Reagents

1. Dipotassium hydrogen phosphate, K_2HPO_4
2. Potassium dihydrogen phosphate, KH_2PO_4
3. L-Aspartic acid
4. 2-Oxoglutaric acid
5. Ethylenediaminetetra-acetate, EDTA tetrasodium salt, EDTA-Na_4
6. Citric acid
7. Sodium citrate
8. Fast Ponceau L
9. Triton X-405
10. Versatol E

Preparation of Solutions

Use only fresh distilled water.
 I. Citrate buffer (0.2 M; pH 4.5):
   Dissolve 22.48 g. citric acid and 27.36 g. sodium citrate in 800 ml. distilled water, adjust pH to 4.5 using a glass electrode and dilute to distilled water.

II. GOT substrate (53 mM L-aspartate; 6.8 mM 2-oxoglutarate; 0.001 mg. % EDTA):
Dissolve 33.5 g. K_2HPO_4 + 1.0 g. KH_2PO_4 + 7.05 g. L-aspartic acid + 1.0 g. 2-oxo-
glutaric acid + 1 mg. EDTA in distilled water, adjust pH to 7.4 using a glass electrode and
dilute to 1000 ml. with distilled water.
III. Diazonium salt:
Dissolve 0.45 g. Fast Ponceau L in 100 ml. citrate buffer (solution I).
IV. Triton X-405 (0.1% v/v):
Dilute 1 ml. Triton X-405 in distilled water and make up to 1000 ml.
V. GOT Standard (0 to 200 U/l.; 37 °C):
Preparation, see p. 769.

Stability of Solutions

Store all solutions in a refrigerator at 4 °C, unless otherwise stated. Prepare the diazonium solution
freshly each day and protect from light.

Procedure

Collection, Treatment and Stability of Sample, see p. 755.

Assay System

Flow scheme, see Fig. 2. Forty samples can be analysed per hour. A blank is not necessary.
Use sampler II with a 1 : 1 wash ratio. Pump the substrate for 15 min. through the system,
then add the diazonium solution (III). When the complete reaction mixture reaches the
flow-through cell, adjust the base line transmission to 99%. Then aspirate the samples and

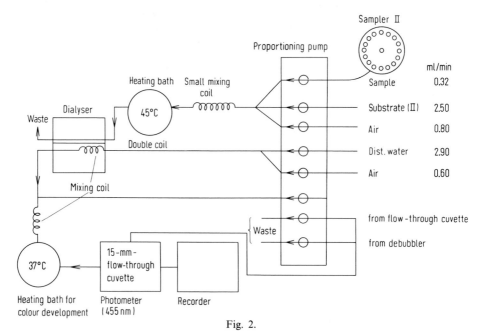

Fig. 2.

standards. Every 2 hours the system must be cleaned; for this rinse the tube for the diazonium solution with the following cleaning solution of 5 ml. 45% (w/v) KOH diluted to 100 ml. with 95% (v/v) ethanol. Then wash through with distilled water. The concentrations in the reaction system are as follows: 47 mM L-aspartate, 6.05 mM 2-oxoglutarate, 0.178 M phosphate buffer.

Calculations

As described for the automated fluorimetric method on p. 771. Although the incubation is carried out at 45 °C the results apply for 37 °C, because the standards are standardized manually at 37 °C.

Precision of Method

The reproducibility of the method with repeated analyses is good and the error is less than 2%. The mean deviation on two successive determinations on 20 sera was 2.1%.

Note

The Technicon method SMA 12/60 for GOT is based on the method described here, with the exception that the diazonium salt Azoene Fast Red is used and the colour is read at 460 nm. The azoene procedure for GOT has been found to yield artefactually elevated GOT values in serums containing excessive concentrations of ketone bodies[7].

References

1 A. Karmen, J. Clin. Invest. 34, 131 [1955].
2 L. Brooks & H. G. Olken, Clin. Chem. 11, 748 [1965].
3 A. L. Babson, P. O. Shapiro, P. A. R. Williams & G. E. Phillips, Clin. Chim. Acta 7, 199 [1962].
4 J. B. Levine & T. B. Hill in: Automation in Analytical Chemistry. Technicon Symposium 1965, Mediad New York 1966, p. 569.
5 S. Morgenstern, M. Oklander, J. Auerbach, J. Kaufman & B. Klein, Clin. Chem. 12, 95 [1966].
6 M. K. Schwartz: Methods in Enzymology. vol. 17 B, p. 866. Academic Press, New York.
7 J. J. Moore & S. M. Sax, Clin. Chem. 15, 730 [1969].

Pyruvate Kinase

Assay in Serum and Erythrocytes

Ingeborg Gutmann and Erich Bernt

Pyruvate kinase, PK (ATP: pyruvate 2-O-phosphotransferase. EC 2.7.1.40) was discovered by *Lohmann* and *Meyerhof*[1,2] and in 1942 first crystallized from rat muscle by *Negelein*[3].

As a glycolytic enzyme it occurs in the cytoplasm, although brain mitochondria also contain glycolytic enzymes and 25% of the total activity of PK has been found in the mitochondria[4].

In the rat the pyruvate kinases from skeletal muscle, heart muscle and brain differ from those from liver and kidney. The PK from a particular organ gives only one band on electrophoresis, and therefore there are no isoenzymes but rather different enzymes[4,5].

The importance of PK in clinical chemistry was described by *Tanaka* et al.[6,7] in 1961. In non-sphereocytic haemolytic anaemia a deficiency of PK in the erythrocytes was established. Since then further cases of PK-deficiency anaemias have been described[8]. The enzyme defect is found in erythrocytes and not in leucocytes[8]. *Bigley* et al.[9] have demonstrated that the PK from erythrocytes and leucocytes are different enzymes. The disease is genetically determined and appears to be autosomal recessive. In homozygotes the PK-deficiency goes hand in hand with the clinical picture of anaemia resulting from erythrocyte destruction. *Wiesmann* et al.[8] was not able to demonstrate any difference in the kinetic behaviour and coenzyme specificity of the pyruvate kinases from normal subjects, a patient and two heterozygotes.

PK activity can be measured spectrophotometrically by the formation of NAD in the lactate dehydrogenase, LDH (L-lactate : NAD oxidoreductase, EC 1.1.1.27) coupled reaction[10] or directly by the decrease in extinction at 230 nm due to the removal of phosphoenolpyruvate (PEP)[11].

Application of Method: In biochemistry and clinical chemistry.

Principle

(1)
$$\text{PEP} + \text{ADP} \xrightarrow[\text{Mg}^{2+}, \text{K}^+]{\text{PK}} \text{Pyruvate} + \text{ATP}$$

(2)
$$\text{Pyruvate} + \text{NADH} + \text{H}^+ \xrightarrow{\text{LDH}} \text{L-Lactate} + \text{NAD}^+$$

The equilibrium of reaction (1) lies on the side of pyruvate and ATP with an equilibrium constant K of 2×10^3 (at 30 °C)[12]. Pyruvate is rapidly removed in the indicator reaction (2). The amount of PEP converted to pyruvate per unit time, as determined by the decrease of extinction due to oxidation of NADH, is a measure of the PK activity.

Optimum Conditions for Measurements

The method described here is based on that of *Beisenherz* et al.[10]. The concentrations of PEP and ADP used for the assay are optimum.

Equipment

Spectrophotometer or spectrum-line photometer suitable for accurate measurements at 340, 334 or 365 nm, preferably with constant temperature cuvette holder; water bath (25 °C); stopwatch.

Reagents*

1. Triethanolamine hydrochloride
2. Sodium chloride, A. R., NaCl
3. Potassium chloride, A. R., KCl
4. Magnesium sulphate, A. R.,
   $MgSO_4 \cdot 7H_2O$
5. Sodium bicarbonate, A. R., $NaHCO_3$
6. Ethylenediaminetetra-acetic acid, EDTA
   disodium salt, EDTA-$Na_2H_2 \cdot 2H_2O$
7. Adenosine-5'-diphosphate, ADP
   disodium salt, ADP-Na_2; commercial preparation, see p. 525.

8. Reduced nicotinamide-adenine
   dinucleotide, NADH
   disodium salt, NADH-Na_2; commercial preparation, see p. 545.
9. Phosphoenolpyruvate, PEP
   tricyclohexylammonium salt, PEP·$(CHA)_3$;
   commercial preparation, see p. 548.
10. Lactate dehydrogenase, LDH
   from rabbit muscle, crystalline suspension in
   3.2 M ammonium sulphate solution; ≥ 360
   U/mg. (25 °C); commercial preparation, see p.
   481.

Purity of Reagents

LDH must not contain more than 0.01% PK; the Boehringer preparation conforms to this requirement.

Preparation of Solutions

Prepare all solutions with fresh, doubly distilled water. To prevent the growth of bacteria
sterilize the containers.

 I. Triethanolamine buffer (0.16 M triethanolamine; 0.12 M KCl; 21 mM $MgSO_4$; 1.3 mM
    EDTA; pH 7.5):
    Dissolve 2.2 g triethanolamine hydrochloride + 0.7 g. KCl + 0.4 g. $MgSO_4 \cdot 7H_2O$ + 40
    mg. EDTA-Na_2H_2 in 50 ml. distilled water adjust to pH 7.5 with 0.1 N NaOH and dilute
    to 75 ml. with distilled water.
 II. NADH/PEP (6 mM NADH; 32 mM PEP):
    Dissolve 10 mg. NADH-Na_2, 45 mg. PEP-$(CHA)_3$ and 10 mg. $NaHCO_3$ in 3 ml. distilled
    water.
III. LDH (0.5 mg./ml.):
    Dilute the stock suspension with 3.2 M ammonium sulphate solution.
 IV. ADP (0.1 M):
    Dissolve 162 mg. ADP-Na_2 and 30 mg. $NaHCO_3$ in 3 ml. distilled water.
  V. Physiological saline (0.9% NaCl):
    Dissolve 0.9 g. NaCl in 100 ml. distilled water.

Stability of Solutions

Solution V is stable for a year and solution I for one month at room temperature, suspension III is stable
for a year at 4 °C. Solutions II and IV are stable for 3 weeks at 4 °C.

---

* Complete reagent kits are available commercially, see p. 558.

Procedure

Collection, Treatment and Stability of Sample

Collection of sample:

Collect blood without venestasis. Addition of citrate (1 mg./ml.), fluoride (2 mg./ml.), heparin (0.2 mg/ml.) or EDTA (1 mg./ml.) is safe; oxalate (1 mg./ml.) inhibits.

Treatment:

Centrifuge whole blood for 10 min. at ca. 3000 g to obtain serum. Use only serum which is completely free from haemolysis. To prepare red cell haemolysates, wash 0.2 ml. blood three times with 2 ml. saline solution (V). After each washing centrifuge for 10 min. at ca. 3000 g. Suspend the washed, centrifuged erythrocytes in 2.0 ml. ice-cold doubly distilled water, allow to stand for 15 min. at 4 °C and then centrifuge. Use 0.10 ml. of the supernatant fluid for the assay.

Stability of enzyme in sample:

The enzyme is very unstable. About 50% of the activity is lost in 24 hr. at 4 °C. The assay of activity must therefore be carried out on fresh serum or haemolysate. The PK activity in a *Potter* extract of human liver decreases just as rapidly after 4 hr.[13].

Assay System

Wavelength: 340 (Hg 334, Hg 365) nm; light path: 1 cm.; final volume: 3.25 ml.; temperature: 25 °C (constant temperature cuvette holder); a blank is not required; read against air or dilute picric acid solution (1–2 drops 1.2% picric acid to 100 ml. distilled water). Bring the solutions to 25 °C before the start of the assay.

Pipette into test tubes:		Serum	Haemolysate	Concentration in assay mixture
Buffer	(I)	2.50 ml.	2.00 ml.	123 (97.5) mM TRA 92.5 (74) mM KCl 16.2 (13) mM $MgSO_4$
Doubly distilled water		—	0.90 ml.	
NADH/PEP solution	(II)	0.10 ml.	0.10 ml.	185 μM NADH 1 mM PEP
Serum		0.50 ml.	—	
Haemolysate			0.10 ml.	
LDH suspension	(III)	0.05 ml.	0.05 ml.	7.7 μg./ml. $\geqq$ 2.5 U/ml.
Mix, incubate for ca. 5 min. in a 25 °C water bath. Pour into cuvettes, read extinction E_1 and continue incubation at 25 °C. Exactly 10 min. after the first reading read extinction E_2.				
ADP solution	(IV)	0.10 ml.	0.10 ml.	3 mM
Mix and measure extinction E_3. Incubate at 25 °C and exactly 10 min. after third reading read extinction E_4. $\Delta E = (E_3 - E_4) - (E_1 - E_2)$.				

The assay of activity in haemolysates can also be carried out as follows: Add 0.10 ml. ADP solution (IV) 5 min. after addition of LDH (III), mix and pour into cuvettes. Read extinction and start stopwatch. Repeat readings at exactly 1, 2, 3 and 4 min. Calculate the mean of the extinction changes/min. and multiply this by 10 and use in the calculation formula given for haemolysates.

The values for $\Delta E/10$ min. at 366 nm should not exceed 0.300/min. otherwise dilute the serum or haemolysate 5- to 10-fold with physiological saline.

Calculations

The calculation formula (8) on p. 313 applies in this case. The dilution factor on haemolysis is 10.5. The following relationships hold for this method:

Wavelength:	334 nm	340 nm	365 nm	
Serum: volume activity	$= 106.6 \times \Delta E$	$104.5 \times \Delta E$	$191.2 \times \Delta E$	[U/l.]
Erythrocyte: volume activity	$= 5594 \times \Delta E$	$5486 \times \Delta E$	$10037 \times \Delta E$	[U/l. blood]

Precision of Method

With activities around 25 U/l. the standard deviation is 0.7 U/l. The coefficient of variation is 3%.

Normal Values

In human serum up to 25 U/l. (25 °C), see also[14]; in erythrocytes 60–220 mU/10^9 erythrocytes (25 °C), which corresponds to 2–7 U/g. Hb^8.

Sources of Error

Effects of drugs and other therapeutic measures: None known.

Interference in the assay technique: None known.

Specificity of Method

As the reaction is started with ADP solution all interfering compounds can react before the PK reaction and therefore the PK assay is specific.

References

1 *K. Lohmann & O. Meyerhof*, Biochem. Z. *273*, 60 [1943].
2 *O. Meyerhof, P. Ohlmeyer, W. Gentner & H. Maier-Leibnitz*, Biochem. Z. *298*, 396 [1938].
3 *E. Negelein*, see *Th. Bücher & G. Pfleiderer* in *S. P. Colowick & N. O. Kaplan:* Methods in Enzymology, Vol. I, p. 435, 436, 440, Academic Press, New York 1955.
4 *R. von Fellenberg, R. Richterich & H. Aebi*, Enzymol. biol. clin. *3*, 240 [1963].
5 *T. Tanaka* et al., Biochem. Biophys. Res. Commun. *21*, 55 [1965].
6 *W. N. Valentine, K. R. Tanaka & S. Miwa*, Trans. Assoc. Am. Physicans *74*, 100 [1961].
7 *K. R. Tanaka, W. N. Valentine & S. Miwa*, Blood *19*, 267 [1962].
8 *U. Wiesmann, O. Tönz, R. Richterich & P. Verger*, Klin. Wschr. *43*, 1311 [1965].
9 *R. D. Kohler, R. H. Bigley, R. T. Jones, D. A. Rigas, P. Vanbellinghen & P. Tompson:* Pyruvate kinase: molecular differences between human red cell and leucocyte enzyme. Cold Spr. Harb. Symp. quant. Biol. June 5.–11.1964.
10 *G. Beisenherz, H. J. Boltze, Th. Bücher, R. Czok, K. H. Garbade, E. Meyer-Arendt & G. Pfleiderer*, Z. Naturforsch. *8b*, 515 [1953].

11 *N. G. Pon* & *R. J. L. Bondar*, Analytical Biochemistry *19*, 272 [1967].
12 *O. Meyerhof* & *P. Oesper*, J. biol. Chem. *179*, 1371 [1949].
13 *E. Schmidt* & *F. W. Schmidt*, Enzymol. biol. clin. *3*, 80 [1963].
14 *P. Otto*, *E. Schmidt* & *F. W. Schmidt*, Klin. Wschr. *42*, 75 [1964].

Pyruvate Kinase from Yeast

Benno Hess and Hans-Joachim Wieker

Yeast pyruvate kinase*, PK, was first purified from bakers' yeast by *Washio* et al.[1,2] in 1959 and obtained in pure form from brewers' yeast by *Hess* et al.[3] and *Hunsley* and *Suelter*[4]. Isoenzymes of pyruvate kinase do not occur in yeast.

The values for the molecular weight vary between 138 000[4] (determined with the ultracentrifuge), 150 000[3] (calculated from the amino acid composition) and 200 000[3] (determined by gel filtration). Studies on the properties of pyruvate kinase from yeast show that the following ligands are allosteric activators[3]: phosphoenolpyruvate ($n_H = 2.6$)**, F-1,6-P_2 ($n_H = 2.7$), Mg^{2+} ($n_H = 2.7$), Rb^+ ($n_H = 2.7$). Allosteric inhibitors are: Ca^{2+} ($n_H = 2.1$), citrate ($n_H = 3$), NADP ($n_H = 6.3$), ATP ($n_H = 5$). CTP, UTP, GTP, ITP, AMP and cyclic AMP also inhibit. In contrast to muscle pyruvate kinase the yeast enzyme is strongly activated by F-1,6-P_2[3,4,5]. F-1,6-P_2 affects the activation by monovalent ions and considerably decreases the $K_{1/2}$ value*** for phosphoenolpyruvate; the sigmoid activity curve becomes hyperbolic (plot of the activity against the phosphoenolpyruvate concentration), while the V_{max} is unchanged[3]. With physiological phosphoenolpyruvate concentrations the activation constant is about 1 700[6]. Only one isoenzyme (type L) of the liver pyruvate kinases is activated by F-1,6-P_2[7,15].

Application of Method: In biochemistry.

Principle

(1)   Phosphoenolpyruvate + ADP $\xrightarrow[(Mg^{2+}, K^+)]{PK}$ Pyruvate + ATP

(2)   Pyruvate + NADH + H^+ $\xrightarrow{LDH}$ Lactate + NAD^+

The amount of PEP reacting per unit time is determined by the decrease in extinction of NADH. This coupled assay is suitable for both the determination of activity and for kinetic measurements[8].

Optimum Conditions for Measurements

The optimum pH depends on the phosphoenolpyruvate concentration[3]. At low concentrations it is around pH 5.3; with higher concentrations there is a second maximum at pH 7.0. The pH optimum is 6.3 at the saturating concentration of phosphoenolpyruvate (5–8 mM)[16]. The ratio of the activities of yeast pyruvate kinase to LDH should be about 1 : 150, because then the transition time to the steady state condition is less than 50 msec. as determined by *Hess* and *Kleinhans*[9,17] with stopped-flow measurements.

With the coupled assay described here a linear relationship between the rate of the reaction (v) and the enzyme concentration (e) was found up to a value for e of 80 µg./ml. with a highly purified PK preparation[10]. With slightly different conditions the specific activity is independent of concentration in the range 2.5×10^{-10} M to 5×10^{-6} M PK[10].

---

  * Pyruvate kinase (ATP: pyruvate 2-*O*-phosphotransferase, EC 2.7.1.40).
 ** n_H = Hill coefficient.
*** $K_{1/2}$ is the molar concentration of a ligand at which half maximum activity is observed.

Equipment

Spectrophotometer or spectrum-line photometer suitable for measurements at 365 nm (or 340, 334 nm) and with constant temperature cuvette holder; water bath at 25 °C.

Reagents

1. Potassium dihydrogen phosphate, KH_2PO_4
2. Dipotassium hydrogen phosphate, $K_2HPO_4 \cdot 3H_2O$
3. Magnesium sulphate, $MgSO_4 \cdot 7H_2O$
4. Sodium hydrogen carbonate, $NaHCO_3$
5. Adenosine-5'-diphosphate, ADP
   disodium salt, ADP-Na_2; commercial preparation, see p. 525.
6. Phosphoenolpyruvate, PEP
   tricyclohexyl-ammonium salt; commercial preparation, see p. 548.

7. Fructose-1,6-diphosphate, F-1,6-P_2
   trisodium salt; commercial preparation, see p. 534.
8. Reduced nicotinamide-adenine-dinucleotide, NADH
   disodium salt, NADH-Na_2; commercial preparation. see p. 545.
9. Lactate dehydrogenase, LDH
   crystalline from rabbit muscle, suspension in 3.2 M ammonium sulphate solution $\geq$ 360 U/mg. (25 °C); commercial preparation, see p. 481.

Preparation of Solutions

Prepare all solutions in volumetric flasks and use only fresh, doubly distilled water.

I. Phosphate buffer (0.1 M; pH 6.0):
   Dissolve 1.20 g. KH_2PO_4 + 0.28 g. $K_2HPO_4 \cdot 3H_2O$ in distilled water and make up to 100 ml.

II. Magnesium sulphate (0.3 M):
   Dissolve 740 mg. $MgSO_4 \cdot 7H_2O$ in distilled water and make up to 10 ml.

III. Adenosine-5'-phosphate, ADP (0.1 M):
   Dissolve 541 mg. ADP-Na_2 in distilled water and make up to 10 ml.

IV. Phosphoenolpyruvate, PEP (0.1 M):
   Dissolve 465 mg. PEP (tricyclohexylammonium salt) in distilled water and make up to 10 ml.

V. Fructose-1,6-diphosphate (0.1 M):
   Dissolve 406 mg. F-1,6-P_2 (trisodium salt) in distilled water and make up to 10 ml.

VI. Reduced nicotinamide-adenine-dinucleotide, NADH (10 mM):
   Dissolve 71 mg. NADH-Na_2 in 1% $NaHCO_3$ solution and make up to 10 ml.

VII. Lactate dehydrogenase, LDH (10 mg. protein/ml.):
   Use the stock suspension.

Check the concentrations of solutions III–VI enzymatically (see Section B) and if necessary adjust accordingly. Store solutions III–VI and suspension VII at 0 to 4 °C. Prepare solutions IV and VI freshly each week.

Assay of Optimum PK Activity

Assay System for 25 determinations

Wavelength: 340 (Hg 334, Hg 365) nm; light path: 1 cm.; temperature: 25 °C (bring the solutions to 25 °C before the assay); final volume: 2.02 ml.; read against air.

Reagent mixture:

Pipette into a 50 ml. volumetric flask:

MgSO₄ solution	(II)	5.0 ml.

$MgSO_4$ solution   (II)   5.0 ml.
ADP solution   (III)   5.0 ml.
PEP solution   (IV)   2.5 ml.
NADH solution   (VI)   1.25 ml.
LDH suspension   (VII)   0.5 ml.
Phosphate buffer (I) up to 50   ml.

Pipette into cuvettes:		Concentration in assay mixture
Reagent mixture	2.00 ml.	30.00 mM Mg^{2+} 10.00 mM ADP 0.10 mg. LDH/ml. $\cong$ 36 U/ml. 5.00 mM PEP 0.25 mM NADH
Sample	0.02 ml.	
Mix. Measure the change of extinction with time.		

With a recording spectrophotometer obtain the value for $\Delta E/min.$ from the linear decrease in extinction at the start of the reaction. If the extinction measurements are made manually the $\Delta E/min.$ should be less than 0.5/min., otherwise dilute the sample or add a smaller volume.

Calculations

The formula (8) on p. 313 applies in this case. The following relationships hold with this method:

Wavelength:	*334 nm*	*340 nm*	*365 nm*
Activity:	$16557 \times \Delta E/min.$	$16238 \times \Delta E/min.$	$29706 \times \Delta E/min.$ [U/l.]

If a different sample volume to that stated is taken this must be allowed for by use of the following factor:

$$\frac{2.0 + \text{sample volume}}{101 \times \text{sample volume}}$$

Determination of Activation Factor for F-1,6-P₂

(Determination of Cellular PK Activity)

A characteristic of yeast pyruvate kinase is the considerable activation by F-1,6-P₂ (see p. 778), so that in many cases it is of interest to determine both the activity and the activation factor in extracts or during purification procedures. It is also possible with this method to determine the type L isoenzyme of liver pyruvate kinase (activated by F-1,6-P₂) separately from other isoenzymes (type M)[7].

In the following assay system (cellular PK)* the same conditions and solutions are used as for the optimum PK assay.

---

* This assay is termed "cellular" because the substrates are added at about the physiological concentrations.

Assay System for ca. 25 determinations

Wavelength: 340 (Hg 334, Hg 365) nm; light path: 1 cm.; temperature: 25 °C (bring solutions to 25 °C before the assay); final volume: 2.05 ml.; read against air.

Reagent mixture:

Pipette into a 50 ml. volumetric flask:

MgSO₄ solution	(II)	0.40 ml.
ADP solution	(III)	0.25 ml.
PEP solution	(IV)	0.25 ml.
NADH solution	(VI)	1.25 ml.
LDH suspension	(VII)	0.50 ml.
Phosphate buffer	(I) up to 50	ml.

Pipette into cuvette:		Concentration in assay mixture
Reagent mixture	2.00 ml.	2.40 mM Mg^{2+} 0.50 mM PEP
		0.50 mM ADP
		0.25 mM NADH
Sample	0.002 ml.	0.10 mg. LDH/ml. $\cong$ 36 U/l.
Mix. Record the extinction changes for 1 min.		
F-1,6-P₂ solution (V)	0.050 ml.	2.50 mM F-1,6-P₂
Mix. Record the extinction changes.		

Use a recording spectrophotometer to determine the activation factor.
Dilute the sample so that the extinction change ΔE/min. before the addition of F-1,6-P₂ is between 0.05/min. and 0.1/min.

Calculations

The formula for calculating the activation factor (AF), which is independent of the wavelength used, is as follows:

$$AC = 1.025 \times \frac{\Delta E/\text{min. with F-1,6-P}_2}{\Delta E/\text{min. without F-1,6-P}_2}$$

Determination of Kinetic Constants

The conditions described for the optimum assay can also be used to measure the relationship between the rate of the reaction and the substrate concentration and thus determine V_{max}, $K_{1/2}$ and n_H*. The stock solutions II–VI are prepared in the same way except that the components are dissolved in buffer (I) instead

---

* V_{max} = maximum velocity; $K_{1/2}$ = ligand concentration at which $v = \frac{1}{2} V_{max}$; n_H = Hill coefficient.

of water (if necessary the pH of the solutions should be adjusted). The concentration of all solutions should be determined (see Section B) and if necessary the volumes described below corrected accordingly. The NADH solution (at pH < 7.5) should be prepared freshly each day.

Assay System

Wavelength: 340 (Hg 334, Hg 365) nm; light path: 1 cm.; temperature: 25 °C (bring the solutions to 25 °C before the assay); final volume: 2.01 ml.; read against air.

Reagent mixture:

Pipette into a 50 ml. volumetric flask:

MgSO$_4$ solution	(II)	10.0 ml.
NADH solution	(VI)	2.5 ml.
LDH suspension	(VII)	1.0 ml.
ADP or PEP solution (III)		
	or (IV)	10.0 ml.
Phosphate buffer	(I) up to 50 ml.	

Pipette into cuvettes:			Concentration in assay mixture
Reagent mixture		1.00 ml.	30.00 mM Mg^{2+} 0.25 mM NADH 0.10 mg. LDH/ml. $\cong$ 36 U/l. 10.00 mM ADP or PEP
PEP or ADP (2nd. substrate)		x ml.	variable
Modifier, e. g. F-1,6-P$_2$		y ml.	variable
Phosphate buffer	(I)	(1 − x − y) ml.	
Mix.			
PK solution		0.01 ml.	
Mix and record the extinction changes.			

With a recording spectrophotometer obtain the value for ΔE/min. from the linear decrease in extinction at the start of the reaction. Choose the amounts of PK solution so that with the highest substrate concentration the Δ E/min. is ∼0.5/min. (dilute if necessary). The volume of PK solution added to the assay mixture should not exceed 0.01 ml. to avoid significant concentration changes due to increase in volume.

Calculations

In addition to the extinction change ΔE/min. the protein content is determined (see p. 171 et seq.). The specific activity is calculated as follows:

$$\text{Specific activity} = \frac{\Delta E \times V}{\Delta t \times \varepsilon \times v \times p \times d} \ [U/mg.]$$

Where

p = protein content of the enzyme solution taken for assay in mg./ml.

v = volume of the enzyme solution taken for assay in ml.

Wavelength:	*334 nm*	*340 nm*	*365 nm*
Specific activity:	$\dfrac{0.330}{v \times p} \times \Delta E/\Delta t$	$\dfrac{0.323}{v \times p} \times \Delta E/\Delta t$	$\dfrac{0.591}{v \times p} \times \Delta E/\Delta t$

Evaluation

The determination of V_{max}, $K_{1/2}$ and n_H can be carried out by the usual linear transformations of the rate equation. However, because yeast PK shows a sigmoidal saturation curve and substrate inhibition at high concentrations, extrapolation by the methods described in the literature results in inaccurate constants. The compensation method in conjunction with a computer programme (*Wieker, Johannes & Hess*[11]) has proved most suitable.

Precision of Method

The accuracy of the measurements with a recording spectrophotometer is at least $\pm 3\%$[10]. The coupled assay described here gives the same kinetic constants as the non-coupled pH-stat method[10] (see p. 254).

Other Methods of Determination

The following assay methods have also been used:

1. A titrimetric method in which the proton removal in the reaction is measured (*Melchior*[12], *Suelter*[13], *Hess*[10]).

2. An optical method in which the disappearance of the enol band at 230 nm is measured (*Hess* et al.[3,5], *Pon* and *Bondar*[14]).

References

1 *S. Washio, Y. Mano, N. Shimazono,* J. Biochemistry (Tokyo) *46,* 1661, [1959].
2 *S. Washio, Y. Mano,* J. Biochemistry (Tokyo), *48,* 874 [1960].
3 *R. Haeckel, B. Hess, W. Lauterborn, K.-H. Wüster,* Hoppe Seyler's Z. Physiol. Chem. *349,* 699, [1968].
4 *J. R. Hunsley, C. H. Suelter,* Federat. Proc. *26,* 559, [1967].
5 *B. Hess, R. Haeckel & K. Brand,* Biochem. Biophys. Res. Commun. *24,* 824 [1966].
6 *B. Hess & R. Haeckel,* Nature (London) *214,* 848 [1967].
7 *T. Tanaka, F. Sue & H. Morimura,* Biochem. Biophys. Res. Commun. *29,* 444 [1967].
8 *T. Bücher, W. Luh & D. Pette* in *Hoppe-Seyler-Thierfelder* (eds.): Handbuch der physiologischen und patholigschen chemischen Analyse, 10th edition, vol. VI A, p. 292, Springer Verlag, Berlin-Heidelberg-New York 1964.
9 *H. Kleinhaus,* Studienarbeit, Staatl. Ingenieurschule, Essen 1967.
10 *B. Hess, H.-J. Wieker,* unpublished.
11 *H.-J. Wieker, K. J. Johannes & B. Hess,* FEBS Letters *8,* 178 [1970].
12 *J. Melchior,* Biochemistry, *4,* 1518 [1965].
13 *F. J. Kayne & C. H. Suelter,* J. Am. Chem. Soc. *87,* 897 [1965].
14 *N. G. Pon & R. J. L. Bondar,* Anal. Biochem. *19,* 272 [1967].
15 *B. Hess & G. Kutzbach,* Hoppe Seyler's Z. Physiol. Chem. *352,* 453 [1971].
16 *H.-J. Wieker & B. Hess,* Biochemistry *10,* 1243 [1971].
17 *B. Hess & B. Wurster,* FEBS Letters *9,* 73 [1970].

Creatine Kinase

Georg Forster, Erich Bernt and Hans Ulrich Bergmeyer

As first shown by *Lohmann*[1] skeletal muscle extracts catalyse the phosphorylation of creatine by ATP. This so-called *Lohmann reaction* is reversible[2]. The terms "forward" and "back-reaction" are usually used to denote the two directions of the reaction, but these terms have not been used consistently in the literature. According to the systematic nomenclature of the IUB (ATP: creatine *N*-phosphotransferase, EC 2.7.3.2) and *Kuby* et al.[3] the synthesis of creatine phosphate is designated as the forward-reaction, and its cleavage as the back-reaction. The turnover number of the enzyme for the latter at optimum pH is 150 000 which is six-fold higher than that of the forward reaction. Mg^{2+} ions are required for full activity. The assay of activity with creatine phosphate as substrate (see p. 789) is more sensitive and less liable to interference. The biological importance of creatine kinase* lies in the synthesis of phosphocreatine as energy store and the rapid provision of ATP when required, thus CK maintains an "ATP reservoir".

Banga[4] partially purified the enzyme from rabbit muscle and *Kuby, Noda* and *Lardy*[5] were first to crystallize CK from this source. Its molecular weight is 81 000. The enzyme has two active centres each with a reactive SH group (*Kuby* et al.)[3]. As expected from the dimeric structure[6] three isoenzymes can be distinguished on electrophoresis[7-15]: an enzyme in brain (BB) which migrates rapidly to the anode, a slow migrating, cathodic fraction in white muscle (MM) and an intermediate fraction (MB) which can be distinguished by different Michaelis constants and differences of amino acid composition, but not of molecular weight[12]. Heart muscle contains the slow migrating isoenzyme MM and smaller amounts of the intermediate type MB. Although CK is mainly found in the cytoplasm of the cell, *Kleine*[16], *Jacobs*[17,18], and *Pette*[19] have demonstrated activity in mitochondrial fractions of muscle and brain.

CK is found in order of decreasing activity in the following human organs: skeletal muscle, heart muscle, cerebral cortex, smooth muscle, thyroid glands, kidney and liver[9,16,20]. Human erythrocytes and normal human serum have no, or only very slight, CK activity. *Dreyfus* and *Schapira*[21-23] and *Forster* and *Escher*[24] observed an increased activity of the enzyme in serum in myopathies and myocardial infarction. *Ebashi* and *Toyokura*[25] and *Colombo, Richterich, Aebi* et al.[20,26] found raised values in serum in progressive muscular dystrophy. Carriers of the *Duchenne* type of hereditary muscular dystrophy can be detected by an increased CK activity in serum[27-30]. For further references to the clinical application of the CK assay in serum, see p. 31.

In clinical studies on the activity in serum using the method of *Tanzer* and *Gilvarg*[31] CK was found to be unstable. *Rotthauwe* et al.[32,33] and *Forster*[24,34] observed a rapid decrease in activity even if the serum was stored in a refrigerator at 4 °C. This rules out reliable assays in serum samples which have to be sent into the laboratory from outside. The reason for this loss of activity has been investigated[24]: the activity in a CK-rich serum (addition of 1 : 1000 heart homogenate) decreased more rapidly than the corresponding dilution of the homogenate in 1.1 % KCl. Some retardation of the inactivation was obtained by dilution of an active serum with physiological KCl or NaCl solution or by addition of EDTA. The activity of CK in serum appears to increase with dilution[35]. Serum apparently contains factors which rapidly inactivate CK. The inactivation of CK can be slowed by addition of a little EDTA to the tube before collection of the blood (*Wilson*[36]). SH-Reagents prevent the inactivation (the activity may even increase five to ten-fold), so that the loss of activity may be due to the reversible oxidation by serum oxidases or heavy metal ions of 2 SH-groups at the active centre of CK. The serum oxidase, caeruloplasmin may play an important role in this oxidative inactivation. Evidence for this is provided by the rise in oxidase activity in serum after myocardial infarction where the peak of caeruloplasmin activity in serum is related in time to the steep decline in CK activity. The observation of especially low CK values in hyperthyroid states and high values in myxoedema[37-40] underlines this relationship.

---

* Synonyms: Creatine phosphokinase, ATP-creatine transphosphorylase.

Application of Method: In biochemistry and in clinical chemistry for the diagnosis of myocardial infarction and of myopathies, in particular progressive muscular dystrophy and dermatomyositis.

The assay of SH-reactivated CK (addition of GSH) in serum has the advantage in the diagnosis of myocardial infarction that it not only shows a steep rise in activity to higher absolute values, but also the increase is maintained for 5 to 6 days.

Determination with Creatine as Substrate

The method for determination of CK activity in the forward reaction described here is based on that of *Tanzer* and *Gilvarg*[31]: the auxiliary and indicator enzymes are pyruvate kinase, PK (ATP: pyruvate 2-*O*-phosphotransferase, EC 2.7.1.40) and lactate dehydrogenase, LDH (L-Lactate: NAD oxidoreductase, EC 1.1.1.27). The stabilization or reactivation of the enzyme is based on the modification of this method described by *Forster*[24,41,42].

Principle

(1) $$\text{Creatine} + \text{ATP} \xrightleftharpoons{\text{CPK}} \text{Creatine phosphate} + \text{ADP}$$

(2) $$\text{ADP} + \text{Phosphoenolpyruvate} \xrightleftharpoons{\text{PK}} \text{ATP} + \text{Pyruvate}$$

(3) $$\text{Pyruvate} + \text{NADH} + \text{H}^+ \xrightleftharpoons{\text{LDH}} \text{Lactate} + \text{NAD}^+$$

The rate of removal of NADH is measured as the extinction change at 340 (334, 365) nm and is proportional to the CK activity.

Optimum Conditions for Measurements

The pH optimum for the phosphorylation of creatine is pH 9.0 at 30 °C (pH 7.0 for the back reaction). Under these conditions the Michaelis constants for the crystalline enzyme are as follows[43]: 0.5 mM for ATP; 16 mM for creatine. The CK activity is dependent on the ATP/Mg^{2+} ratio and the optimum molar ratio is 1/1: each should be about 4 mM with 24 mM creatine in ca. 0.1 M glycine buffer[44]. Few studies have been made of the optimum assay conditions for human serum[41,42].

The measurements are carried out at 25 °C, pH 9.0 and at the following final concentrations: 4 mM ATP; 4 mM MgCl$_2$; 33 mM creatine; 0.44 M glycine and 10 mM GSH. The high concentration of buffer is necessary to overcome the buffering capacity of serum. In the auxiliary and indicator reactions 0.39 mM PEP, 0.25 mM NADH and 100 μg. PK and LDH are used per assay.

Equipment

Spectrophotometer or spectrum-line photometer for precise measurements at 340, 334 or 365 nm, preferably with constant temperature cuvette holder. Water bath (25 °C), stop watch or linear recorder.

Reagents*

1. Creatine
2. Glycine
3. Magnesium chloride, $MgCl_2 \cdot 6H_2O$
4. Sodium carbonate, A. R., anhydrous
5. Phosphoenolpyruvate, PEP
   cyclohexylammonium salt; commercial preparation, see p. 548.
6. Reduced nicotinamide-adenine dinucleotide, NADH
   disodium salt, $NADH\text{-}Na_2$; commercial preparation, see p. 545.
7. Adenosine-5'-triphosphate, ATP
   disodium salt, $ATP\text{-}Na_2H_2 \cdot 3H_2O$; commercial preparation, see p. 527.

8. Glutathione, GSH
   Commercial preparation, see p. 538.
9. Lactate dehydrogenase, LDH
   crystalline from skeletal muscle; suspension in 3.2 M ammonium sulphate solution ≥ 300 U/mg. (25 °C); commercial preparation, see p. 481.
10. Pyruvate kinase, PK
    crystalline from skeletal muscle, suspension in 3.2 M ammonium sulphate solution ≥ 150 U/mg. (25 °C); commercial preparation, see p. 509.

Purity of Reagents

LDH and PK must be free of phosphatases, CK and ATPase. To avoid a large blank oxidation of NADH the ATP should be reasonably free from ADP and PEP free from pyruvate.

Preparation of Solutions (for ca. 10 determinations)

Prepare all solutions with fresh doubly distilled water

I. Buffer/coenzyme mixture (1.8 M glycine buffer, pH 9.0; 1.3 mM β-NADH; 16.3 mM ATP; 1.6 mM PEP; 16.3 mM $MgCl_2$):
   Dissolve 2.02 g. glycine; 0.60 g. Na_2CO_3; 12.5 mg. $NADH\text{-}Na_2$; 150 mg. $ATP\text{-}Na_2H_2$. $\cdot 3H_2O$, 11 mg. PEP (cyclohexylammonium salt) and 50 mg. $MgCl_2 \cdot 6H_2O$ in doubly distilled water and make up to 15 ml.

II. Lactate dehydrogenase/pyruvate kinase, LDH/PK (each 2 mg. protein/ml.):
    If necessary, dilute the stock suspensions with 3.2 M ammonium sulphate solution to 4 mg. protein/ml. and mix them in the ratio $1+1$ by volume.

III. Glutathione (0.285 M GSH):
     Dissolve 88 mg. GSH in 1.0 ml. distilled water.

IV. Creatine/glycine buffer (63 mM creatine in 0.1 M glycine buffer; pH 9.0):
    Dissolve 350 mg. creatine, 300 mg. glycine and 90 mg. Na_2CO_3 in distilled water and make up to 40 ml.

V. Glycine buffer (0.1 M; pH 9.0):
   Dissolve 300 mg. glycine and 90 mg. Na_2CO_3 in distilled water and make up to 40 ml.

Stability of Solutions

Store all solutions stoppered in a refrigerator at 0 to 4 °C. Prepare the buffer/coenzyme mixture (I) and the GSH solution (III) each week, creatine/glycine buffer (IV) and glycine buffer (V) each month. The enzyme suspension (II) is stable for about a year.

---

* Complete reagent kits are available commercially, see p. 558.

Procedure

Collection, Treatment and Stability of Sample

Collection of sample:

Use fresh serum. Slight haemolysis does not interfere, as erythrocytes contain no detectable CK[24,45,46].

Stability of enzyme in sample:

The CK activity of serum decreases very rapidly[33,34,41]. The loss amounts to 30–70% in 24 hr., even if the serum is stored at 4 °C. Addition of SH-compounds to the assay results in complete reactivation of the enzyme[33,34,41,47–49].

Assay System

Wavelength: 340 (Hg 334, Hg 365) nm; light path: 1 cm.; final volume: 2.85 ml.; temperature 25 °C (constant temperature cuvette holder). Read against a blank containing all the solutions with glycine buffer (V) instead of creatine/glycine buffer (IV). Adjust the solutions before measurement to 25 °C.

Pipette successively into cuvettes:			Concentration in assay mixture
Serum		0.50 ml.	
Buffer/coenzyme mixture	(I)	0.70 ml.	0.44 M glycine buffer; 0.25 mM β-NADH; 4 mM ATP; 4 mM Mg^{2+}; 0.39 mM PEP;
LDH/PK suspension	(II)	0.05 ml.	35 μg. LDH/ml. $\geq$ 10 U/ml. 35 μg. PK/ml. $\geq$ 5.3 U/ml.
GSH solution	(III)	0.10 ml.	10 mM GSH
Mix. allow to stand ca. 15 min. at 25 °C. (Pyruvate formed from PEP, and ADP from ATP react with oxidation of NADH).			
Creatine-glycine buffer	(IV)	1.75 ml.	33 mM creatine
Mix, set the extinction of the blank cuvette to 0.300 on the photometer scale and read the extinction of the test cuvette exactly after 2, 4 and 6 min. (stop watch). Reset the extinction of the blank to 0.300 and read the extinctions of the test once again. The mean value of the extinction differences ($\Delta E/2$ min.) is used for the calculations.			

If $\Delta E/2$ min. exceeds 0.060/2 min. (365 nm) dilute the serum accordingly with 0.9% NaCl and repeat the assay.

Calculations

The formula (8) on p. 313 is used. The following relationships hold for this method:

Wavelength	334 nm	340 nm	365 nm
Volume activity =	$934 \times \Delta E/2$ min.	$916 \times \Delta E/2$ min.	$1676 \times \Delta E/2$ min. [U/l.]

Precision of Method

With values around 8 mU/ml. the standard deviation is 0.5 U/l. The coefficient of variation is 6.2%.

Normal Values

Numerous authors have been concerned with the tabulation of normal values. However, the various work-ers have used different substrate concentrations, different pH values, with and without SH-compounds. The normal range (using 1.7 mM ATP; 31 mM creatine; 11 mM Mg^{2+}; 3 mM GSH; 25°C; pH 9) is 1.2–8 U/l.[34]. According to [35] (using 4 mM ATP; 75 mM creatine; 4 mM Mg^{2+}; 38–40 °C; pH 9) the normal values in fresh sera from adults, but not reactivated with SH-compounds, is 1–3 U/l. The normal range is somewhat dependent on the age and sex. According to [41] (using 4 mM ATP; 5 mM Mg^{2+}; 37 mM creatine; 12 mM cysteine; 37 °C; pH 9) the normal range for women is 4–14 U/l. and for men 4–30 U/l. In the new-born these values can rise to 42 U/l.

Sources of Error

Effects of drugs and other compounds: Increased CK activity in serum has been observed in hypothyroid states[37-40], after severe physical exercise or prolonged sporting activities[24,50-53] and muscular trauma (e. g. after electric shock treatment for defibrillation[24]), after epileptic fits[24] and repeated intramuscular injections of various drugs, especially psychotic drugs[24,54].

Interference in the assay technique: Alkaline phosphatase (forms pyruvate from PEP), ATPase and myo-kinase (form ADP from ATP) and NADH oxidase (oxidizes NADH) interfere with the assay. They are eliminated by the blank. As far as is known no other serum enzyme interferes in the reaction in the form described here.
Sometimes the activity of dilute serum is significantly higher in comparison to undiluted serum[35]. This is presumably due to the presence of inhibitors in the serum, which are less active on dilution.

Specificity of Method

CK reacts specifically with creatine. Neither ADP nor ITP can act as phosphate donor.

Details for Measurements in Tissues

Most of the CK in tissues is cytoplasmic[16] with a small fraction in the mitochondria (*Jacobs*[17,18], *Pette*[19]), and therefore the total content of the cell is only obtained after optimum homogenization. Consequently it is best to either assay whole homogenate[51] or the high-speed supernatant after thorough disintegration of all cellular particles[31].

Determination with Creatine Phosphate as Substrate

Principle

(1)   Creatine phosphate $+$ ADP $\underset{\text{CK}}{\rightleftharpoons}$ Creatine $+$ ATP

(2)   ATP $+$ Glucose $\underset{\text{HK}^*}{\rightleftharpoons}$ ADP $+$ Glucose-6-P

(3)   Glucose-6-P $+$ NADP$^+$ $\underset{\text{G6P-DH}^{**}}{\rightleftharpoons}$ Gluconate-6-P $+$ NADPH $+$ H$^+$

Optimum Conditions of Measurements

The pH optimum of reaction (1) is at 6.9–7.0[43, 56]. The optimum ADP concentration is 1 mM[55] and the optimum creatine phosphate concentration 35 mM. A sufficiently rapid auxiliary reaction (2) is given with 20 mM glucose and 7 U HK/assay. For reaction (3) 3.5 U G6P-DH/assay and 1 mM NADP are sufficient to convert the G-6-P immediately to 6-phosphogluconate. For complete activation or re-activation concentrations of cysteine, GSH or mercaptoethanol between 0.5 and 10 mM are suitable[49]. Further details on the activation and the necessary concentrations of SH-compounds can be found in [34,47,57]. According to [58], GSH should not be used ro reactivate the CK because the oxidation product GSSG reacts with glutathion reductase which may be present in serum and affects NADPH consumption. A too low CK activity is simulated.

As myokinase, MK (ATP : AMP phosphotransferase, EC 2.7.4.3) cannot be excluded from the sample, adenosine-5'-monophosphate is added in a concentration of 10 mM to inhibit this enzyme[55]. Measurements at different temperatures may require different measuring conditions (cf. p. 127). Nevertheless, results obtained under the same measuring conditions but at different temperatures were formerly compared with each other ("conversion factors" were determined). Such conversion factors may be correct if determined with a relatively large proband collective; however, they cannot be applied generally to the individual case (cf. p. 129). The value of the following relative reaction rates [57] thus lies in being able to appraise the temperature dependence of the reaction and at the most to compare qualitatively values up to the limit of normal.

$^\circ C$	24°	26°	27°	28°	29°	30°	31°
	1.00	0.92	0.85	0.79	0.73	0.68	0.63
$^\circ C$	32°	33°	34°	35°	36°	37°	
	0.58	0.54	0.50	0.46	0.43	0.40	

Equipment

Spectrophotometer or spectrum-line photometer suitable for accurate measurements at 340, 334 or 365 nm, preferably with a constant temperature cuvette holder; water bath (25 °C); stopwatch.

Reagents****

1. Imidazole

2. Magnesium acetate, $(CH_3 \cdot COO)_2 Mg$ $\cdot 4H_2O$

---

  *   Hexokinase, HK (ATP: D-hexose-6-phosphotransferase, EC 2.7.1.1).
 **   Glucose-6-phosphate dehydrogenase, G6P-DH (D-Glucose-6-phosphate: NADP 1-oxidoreductase, EC 1.1.1.49).
***   Glutathione reductase, GR (NAD(P)H: oxidized-glutathione oxidoreductase, EC 1.6.4.2).
****   Complete reagents kits are available commercially, see p. 558.

3. Glucose, monohydrate
4. Creatine phosphate, CP
   disodium salt, commercial preparation, see p. 529.
5. Adenosine-5'-diphosphoric acid, ADP
   free acid, ADP; commercial preparation, see p. 525.
6. Adenosine-5'-monophosphate, AMP
   disodium salt, AMP-Na$_2$ · 6H$_2$O; commercial preparation, see p. 526.
7. Nicotinamide-adenine dinucleotide phosphate, NADP
   disodium salt, NADP-Na$_2$H; commercial preparation, see p. 546.

8. Hexokinase, HK
   from yeast, suspension in 3.2 M ammonium sulphate solution; $\geqq$ 140 U/mg. (25 °C); commercial preparation, see p. 473.
9. Glucose-6-phosphate dehydrogenase, G6P-DH
   from yeast, suspension in 3.2 M ammonium sulphate; $\geqq$ 140 U/mg. (25 °C); commercial preparation, see p. 458.
10. N-Acetylcysteine, NAC
11. Acetic acid
12. Bovine serum albumin, pure
13. Glycerol, A. R.

Purity of Reagents

CP, ADP and AMP must be at least 90% pure and must contain no ATP. HK and G6P-DH must be completely free from myokinase. All other reagents must be A. R. or purest quality available.

Preparation of Solutions

Prepare all the solutions with fresh doubly distilled water.
  I. Reaction mixture (0.11 M imidazole buffer, pH 6.9; 22 mM glucose; 11 mM Mg^{2+}; 1.1 mM ADP; 11 mM AMP; 0.8 mM NADP; 38 mM CP):
     Dissolve 750 mg. imidazole, 435 mg. glucose, 235 mg. Mg acetate·4H$_2$O, 53 mg. ADP, 550 mg. AMP-Na$_2$·6H$_2$O, 70 mg. NADP-Na$_2$H and 1.38 g. CP-Na$_2$·6H$_2$O in 70 ml. distilled water, adjust to pH 6.9 with ca. 3 ml. 2 N CH$_3$COOH and dilute to 100 ml.
 II. Hexokinase/glucose-6-phosphate dehydrogenase (each 1 mg./ml. protein):
     Mix the stock suspensions, add sufficient bovine serum albumin, so that a 10-fold excess is present, relative to the amount of enzyme protein, and dialyse for 5 hr. against ice-cold distilled water. Change the water every hour. After the dialysis dilute the solution with glycerol to 2 mg. enzyme protein/ml.
III. N-Acetyl cysteine (0.27 M NAC):
     Dissolve 220 mg. N-Acetyl-cysteine (NAC) in 5 ml. distilled water.

Stability of Solutions

Store all solutions, stoppered, at ca. 4 °C. The reaction mixture (I) and the NAC solution (III) are stable for at least 4 weeks, and the HK/G6P-DH solution for at least 6 months.

Procedure

Collection, Treatment and Stability of Sample

Collection of sample:
See determination with creatine as substrate, p. 787.

Stability of sample:
See determination with creatine as substrate, p. 787.

Assay System

Wavelength: 340 (Hg 334, Hg 365) nm; light path: 1 cm.; final volume: 2.72 ml.; 25 °C (constant temperature cuvette holder). Bring reaction mixture (I) to 25 °C before use.

Pipette into cuvettes:			Concentration in assay mixture
Reaction mixture	(I)	2.50 ml.	100 mM Imidazole-buffer; 20 mM glucose; 10 mM Mg^{2+}; 1 mM ADP; 10 mM AMP; 0.7 mM NADP; 35 mM CP;
HK/G6P-DH	(II)	0.02 ml.	7.5 μg. HK/ml. $\leq$ 1 U/ml.; 7.5 μg. G6P-DH/ml. $\leq$ 1 U/ml.
NAC solution Serum	(III)	0.10 ml. 0.10 ml.	10 mM NAC
Mix and incubate for 5 min. at 25 °C, then read extinction and start stopwatch. Repeat readings at exactly 1, 2, 3, 4 and 5 min. and calculate the mean extinction change.			

The extinction change Δ E/min. at 365 nm should not exceed 0.030/min. otherwise dilute the serum 5–10-fold with 0.9% NaCl solution and repeat the measurements.

Calculations

The calculation formula (8) on p. 313 applies and therefore the following relationships hold for this method:

Wavelength:	*334 nm*	*340 nm*	*365 nm*
Volume activity =	4459 × Δ E/min.	4373 × Δ E/min.	7884 × Δ E/min. [U/l.]

Precision of Method

With values around 80 U/l. the standard deviation is 4.5 U/l. and therefore the coefficient of variation is 5.6%.

Normal Values

The normal ranges given by various workers differ considerably. *Rosalki*[57] gives 12–100 U/l. for men at 37 °C and 10–60 U/l. for women.

According to[59] the normal range is between 0–40 U/l. at 30 °C. In the most recent, as yet unpublished studies[60], the upper limit of normal for measurements at 25 °C is given as 50 U/l. Slight differences between men and women were also observed in this study.

Sources of Error

Effects of drugs and other therapeutic measures: See p. 788.

Interference in the assay technique: Sometimes use of dilute serum gives higher values in comparison to undiluted serum[35,59]. This is presumably due to the presence of inhibitors in the serum which are less active on dilution. In this case the serum is diluted by inactivated human serum.

Specificity of Method

CK reacts specifically with creatine phosphate.

Details for Measurements in Tissues

See determination with creatine as substrate, p. 788.

References

1 *K. Lohmann*, Biochem. Z. *271*, 264 [1934].
2 *H. Lehmann*, Biochem. Z. *281*, 271 [1935].
3 *S. A. Kuby* & *E. A. Noltmann*, ATP: Creatine Transphosphorylase, in: *P. D. Boyer, H. Lardy* & *K. Myrbäck:* The Enzymes, Vol. 6, p. 515, Acad. Press, New York/London 1962.
4 *I. Banga*, Stud. Inst. med. Chem. Univ. Szeged *3*, 59 [1943].
5 *S. A. Kuby, L. Noda* & *H. A. Lardy*, J. biol. Chem. *209*, 191 [1954].
6 *D. M. Dawson, H. M. Eppenberger* & *N. O. Kaplan*, Biochem. Biophys. Res. Comm. *21*, 346 [1965].
7 *A. Burger, R. Richterich* & *H. Aebi*, Biochem. Z. *339*, 305 [1964].
8 *A. Burger, M. Eppenberger, U. Wiesmann* & *R. Richterich*, Helv. physiol. pharmacol. Acta *21*, C 6 [1963].
9 *D. M. Dawson* & *I. H. Fine*, Arch. Neurol. *16*, 175 [1967].
10 *D. H. Deul* & *J. F. L. Van Breemen*, Clin. Chim. Acta *10*, 276 [1964].
11 *H. M. Eppenberger, M. Eppenberger, R. Richterich* & *H. Aebi*, Developmental Biol. *10*, 1 [1964].
12 *H. M. Eppenberger, D. M. Dawson* & *N. O. Kaplan*, J. Biol. Chem. *242*, 204 & 210 [1967].
13 *S. B. Rosalki*, Nature *207*, 414 [1965].
14 *K. Sjoevall* & *A. Voigt*, Nature *202*, 701 [1964].
15 *K. J. van der Veen* & *A. F. Willebrands*, Clin. Chim. Acta *13*, 312 [1966].
16 *T. O. Kleine*, Klin. Wschr. *43*, 504 [1965].
17 *H. Jacobs* & *H. W. Heldt*, Bull. Soc. Chim. Biol. *46*, 188 [1964].
18 *H. Jacobs, H. W. Heldt* & *M. Klingenberg*, Biochem. Biophys. Res. Comm. *16*, No. 6 [1964].
19 *D. Pette:* Mitochondrial enzyme activities, in: *J. M. Tager, S. Papa, E. Quagliariello* & *E. C. Slater*, Regulation of metabolic processes in mitochondria p. 28, Elsevier Publ. Comp. Amsterdam 1966.
  — Aktivitätsmuster und Ortsmuster von Enzymen des energieliefernden Stoffwechsels, in: Praktische Enzymologie, Verlag H. Huber, Bern 1968.
20 *J. P. Colombo, R. Richterich* & *E. Rossi*, Klin. Wschr. *40*, 37 [1962].
21 *J. C. Dreyfus* & *G. Schapira*, Rev. franc. Etud. clin. biol. *5, 384* & *386* [1960].
22 — Arch. Mal. coeur *2*, 187 [1960].
23 *G. Schapira* & *J. C. Dreyfus*, Rev. franc. Etud. clin. biol. *5*, 990 [1960].
24 *G. Forster:* Die Enzymdiagnostik des Herzinfarktes. Habil.-Schrift, Zürich 1967.
25 *S. Ebashi* & *Y. Toyokura*, J. Biochem. (Tokyo) *46*, 103 [1959].
26 *F. Vassella, R. Richterich* & *E. Rossi*, Pediatrics *35*, 322 [1965].
27 *U. Aebi, R. Richterich, J. P. Colombo* & *E. Rossi*, Enzymol. Biol. Clin. *1*, 61 [1961/62].
28 *R. Richterich, S. Rosin, H. Aebi* & *E. Rossi*, Amer. J. hum. Genet. *15*, 133 [1963].
29 *H. W. Rotthauwe* & *S. Kowalewski*, Klin. Wschr. *43*, 150 [1965].
30 *U. Wiesmann, H. Moser, R. Richterich* & *E. Rossi*, Klin. Wschr. *43*, 1015 [1965].
31 *M. L. Tanzer* & *C. Gilvarg*, J. biol. Chem. *234*, 3201 [1959].
32 *H. W. Rotthauwe* & *M. Cerqueiro*, Klin. Wschr. *41*, 876 [1963].
33 *H. W. Rotthauwe* & *S. Kowalewski*, Klin. Wschr. *45*, 387 [1967].
34 *G. Forster*, Schweiz. med. Wschr. *97*, 329 [1967].

35 *F. A. Graig, J. C. Smith & F. F. Foldes,* Clin. Chim. Acta *15*, 107 [1967].
36 *T. G. G. Wilson,* Clin. Res. *13*, 223 [1965].
37 *G. A. Fleisher & W. M. McConahey,* J. Lab. Clin. Med. *64*, 857 [1964].
38 *G. A. Fleisher, W. M. McConahey & M. Pankow,* Proc. Mayo Clin. *40*, 300 [1965].
39 *F. A. Graig & G. Ross,* Metabolism *12*, 57 [1963].
40 *F. A. Graig & J. C. Smith,* J. clin. Endocrin. *26*, 723 [1965].
41 *U. Wiesmann, J. P. Colombo, A. Adam & R. Richterich,* Enzymol. biol. clin. *7*, 266 [1966].
42 *M. Feraudi & K. Harm,* Z. klin. Chem. &. klin. Biochem. *5*, 270 [1967].
43 *S. A. Kuby, L. Noda & H. A. Lardy,* J. biol. Chem. *210*, 65 [1954].
44 *S. Okinaka & H. Sugita,* 84th Ann. Meeting Amer. Neur. Ass. Atlantic City 1959.
45 *E. Bernt,* unpublished results.
46 *R. Richterich,* Klinische Chemie, Akadem. Verlagsgesellschaft Frankfurt a. M. 1968, 2. Edition, p. 310.
47 *N. C. Kar & C. M. Pearson,* Proc. Soc. Exp. biol. Med. *118*, 662 [1965].
48 *J. H. Hess, K. J. Murdock & G. J. W. Natho,* Amer. J. clin. Pathol. *50*, 89 [1968].
49 *S. Okinaka, H. Sugita, H. Momoi, Y. Toyokura, T. Watanabe, F. Ebashi & S. Ebashi,* J. Lab. Clin. Med. *64*, 299 [1964].
50 *P. Baumann, J. Escher & R. Richterich,* Schweiz. Z. f. Sportmedizin *10*, 33 [1962].
51 *P. D. Griffiths,* Clin. Chim. Acta (Amst.) *13*, 413 [1966].
52 *J. M. Pearce & P. D. Griffiths,* Bio. Med. J. 1965 II, 167.
53 *A. Vejjajiva & G. M. Teasdale,* Brit. med. J. 1965 I, 1933.
54 *R. Flammer, H. Weber & T. Wegmann,* Ther. Umsch. *22*, 237 [1965].
55 *I. T. Oliver,* Biochem. J. *61*, 116 [1955].
56 *P. Stein & W. Lamprecht,* Klin. Wschr. *40*, 177 [1962].
57 *S. B. Rosalki,* J. Lab. Clin. Med. *69*, 696 [1967].
58 *G. Weidemann,* Z. klin. Chem. & klin. Biochem. *11*, 134 [1973].
59 *J. W. Hess, R. P. MacDonald, G. J. W. Natho & K. J. Murdock,* Clin. Chem. *13*, 994 [1967].
60 *G. Szasz, E. W. Busch & H. B. Fahros,* Dtsch. med. Wschr. *95*, 829 [1970].

Determination with Automatic Analysers

Abraham L. Siegel and Patricia S. Cohen

The method[1] described here for the assay of creatine kinase, CK (ATP: creatine *N*-phosphotransferase, EC 2.7.3.2) activity in serum with automatic analysers is of particular value when a large series of assays are required for "screening" purposes. In our laboratory the method has been used for the assay of CK activity in serum of patients after heart operations and in serum of relatives of muscular dystrophy patients.

Principle

(1) $\qquad$ Creatine phosphate + ADP $\xrightleftharpoons{\text{CK}}$ Creatine + ATP

The creatine formed in the reaction is measured as a pink-coloured complex which forms on the addition of diacetyl and α-naphthol in alkaline conditions[2,3]. This is also the basis of the automated method of *Fleisher*[4]. *Daly* and *Levine*[5] have described an automated procedure in which the colour is developed with orcinol instead of α-naphthol.

Equipment

Standard Autoanalyser®* with 37 °C heating bath, heating coil and photometer with a 15 mm cylindrical flow-through cuvette and filter for 520 nm.

---

* Technicon Coporation, Tarrytown, N. Y., USA.

Reagents

1. Imidazole
2. Acetic acid, A. R.
3. Creatine phosphate, CP
   sodium salt; commercial preparation, see p. 529.
4. Adenosine-5'-diphosphate, ADP
   disodium salt, ADP-Na$_2$; commercial preparation, see p. 525.
5. 2-Mercaptoethanol
   commercial preparation, e. g. Eastman Kodak
6. Magnesium sulphate, MgSO$_4 \cdot 7H_2O$

7. Brij-35
   from Pierce Chemical Company
8. Malonic acid
9. Sodium hydroxide, 10 N
10. Sodium carbonate, Na$_2$CO$_3$
11. N-Ethylmaleimide
    commercial preparation, e. g. Sigma Chemical Company
12. α-Naphthol
13. Diacetyl (2.3-butanedione)
    e. g. Eastman Kodak, 1591
14. Creatine monohydrate

Preparation of Solutions

Use distilled or deionized water for preparation of solutions.

   I. Imidazole buffer (0.2 M; pH 6.8):
      Dissolve 1.36 g. imidazole in ca. 80 ml. distilled water, adjust to pH 6.8 with acetic acid and dilute to 100 ml. with distilled water.
  II. Substrate mixture* (2.90 mM CP; 2.02 mM ADP; 10 mM 2-mercaptoethanol; 3.05 mM MgSO$_4$; 0.16% Brij-35):
      Dissolve 136 mg. creatine phosphate, 137 mg. ADP-Na$_2$, 0.08 ml. 2-mercaptoethanol, 93 mg. MgSO$_4 \cdot 7H_2O$ and 0.20 ml. Brij-35 in 75 ml. cold imidazole buffer (I) and dilute to 125 ml. with cold distilled water.
 III. Malonate (0.1 M):
      Dissolve 1.04 g. malonic acid in about 50 ml. distilled water, neutralize with 10 N NaOH and dilute to 100 ml. with distilled water.
  IV. Alkali reagent (1.5 N NaOH; 1.18 M Na$_2$CO$_3$):
      Dissolve 60 g. NaOH and 128 g. Na$_2$CO$_3$ in distilled water and make up to 1 000 ml.
   V. N-Ethylmaleimide (18.5 mM):
      Dissolve 230 mg. N-ethylmaleimide in 100 ml. distilled water and add 0.2 ml. Brij-35.
  VI. α-Naphthol (0.1 M):
      Dissolve 1.5 g. α-naphthol in 100 ml. alkali reagent (IV), filter and store in a dark bottle under a 2 cm. layer of mineral oil.
 VII. Diacetyl:
      Dissolve 0.025 ml. diacetyl in 25 ml. distilled water and store at 4 °C.
VIII. Creatine standard solution (6.8, 3.4, 1.7 and 0.85 μmole/ml.):
      Dissolve 25.4 mg. creatine in 25 ml. distilled water (stock solution containing 6.8 μmole/ml.); dilute this solution 1 + 1, 1 + 3 and 1 + 7 with distilled water

Stability of Solutions

Store all solutions at 0–4 °C. The substrate mixture II is stable for several hours, prepare solution VI freshly each day. Solution VII is stable for at least 2 weeks and the other solutions are stable indefinitely providing that no bacterial contamination occurs.

---

* for ca. 60 assays at 50 assays/hr.

Procedure

Fill the stock container of sampler II with 0.5% Brij-35 solution as washing solution. Place a loose glass wool plug in the suction tube of the α-naphthol stock container to avoid the precipitation of oxidized material. For flow scheme, see Fig. 1. Before the start of the assay measure the time taken for the incubation: pump a dilute solution of Evans Blue through the tube for the sample solution and pump water through the other manifolds, then measure the time required for passage through points A and B. The incubation time is about 10 min.; it varies little from day to day.

The sample solution is added to substrate mixture II, which is kept at 0 °C. After the incubation the reaction mixture is dialysed through a type C membrane. The creatine formed is taken up by the N-ethylmaleimide stream. This removes sulphydryl groups and avoids interference in the subsequent colour development. The dialysate is first mixed with α-naphthol and then with diacetyl. Three double mixing coils ensure efficient mixing and allow enough time for development of colour. The coloured solution then flows through the cylindrical flow-through cuvette of the photometer.

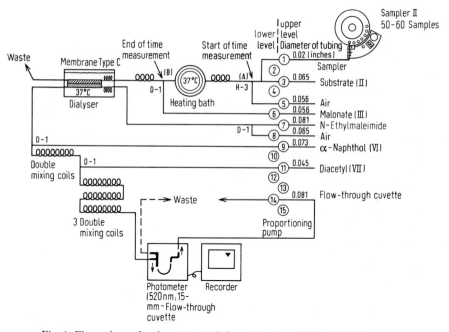

Fig. 1. Flow scheme for the automated determination of CK activity in serum.

In our experience and for our studies it is not necessary to run blanks, however if alkaline phosphatase is greatly increased in the serum it is necessary to prepare blanks containing a substrate mixture without ADP.

If the CK activity of the samples is greater than 150 U/l. the assays should be repeated with dilute samples, because under the above conditions the reaction is no longer linear at this level of activity. A typical recorder tracing is shown in Fig. 2 which was obtained with a through-put of 50 assays/hr. The reproducibility is sufficient; there is no detectable overlapping of the absorption peaks.

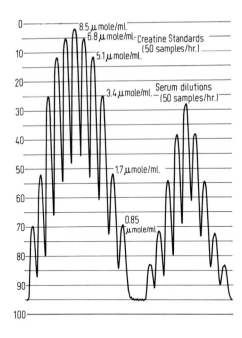

Fig. 2. Tracing of creatine standards and a four-fold
diluted serum sample with high CK activity.

Calculations

The enzyme activity is expressed as U/1 serum (37 °C). The concentration c of the creatine [μmole/ml.]
formed is read off from a standard curve in which c is plotted against the logarithm % transmission (Fig. 3).

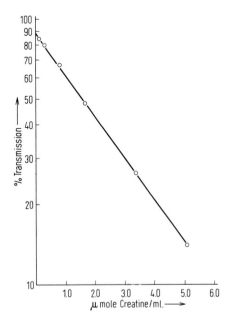

Fig. 3. Creatine standard curve.

Therefore:

$$\text{Volume activity} = c \times \frac{1\,000}{t} \quad [\text{U/l.}]; 37\,°C$$

where t = incubation time in min.

Normal Values

This method gives a mean normal value for human serum of 30.0 ± 12.4 U/l. (37 °C).

References

1 *A. L. Siegel* & *P. S. Cohen*, Technicon Symposium "Automation in Analytical Chemistry", New York 1966.
2 *A. H. Ennor* & *H. Rosenberg*, Biochem. J. *57*, 203 [1954].
3 *B. P. Hughes*, Clin. Chim. Acta *11*, 951 [1962].
4 *G. Fleisher*, Clin. Chim. *13*, 233 [1967].
5 *J. Daly* & *J. Levine*, Clin. Chem. *14*, 797 [1968].

Phosphoglucomutase

John King

Phosphoglucomutase, PGluM (α-D-Glucose-1,6-bisphosphate: α-D-glucose-1-phosphate phosphotransferase, EC 2.7.5.1) activity was first found by the *Coris*[1,2] in animal tissues and yeast extracts. The requirement for glucose-1,6-diphosphate[3] was confirmed by *Leloir*[4], who also elucidated the mechanism of the reaction.

The apparent intramolecular transfer of phosphate from C_1 to C_6 is in reality an intermolecular transfer of phosphate from glucose-1,6-diphosphate to glucose-1-phosphate with the formation of new G-1,6-P_2 and G-6-P (see equation 1).

As a glycolytic enzyme phosphoglucomutase is widely distributed and occurs in the cytoplasm. PGluM is found in human serum; the relationship between its presence and disease has been investigated[5-17]. *Spencer* et al.[18] have demonstrated the heterogeneity of PGluM with starch gel electrophoresis and have found three genetic patterns in human haemolysates.

The activity of the enzyme is often determined by measurement of the acid-labile phosphate[19] of G-1-P before and after the reaction[12,20-22]. The difficulty of the assay until recently was the lack of the required coenzyme G-1,6-P_2. This was usually present in G-1-P preparations in more or less sufficient amounts[5,18,21] or was added in the form of a heated mouse liver extract[8]. Today both G-1,6-P_2-free G-1-P and pure G-1,6-P_2 are available commercially[2] (see p. 537).

Methods for the measurement of the initial reaction rates use glucose-6-phosphate dehydrogenase, G6P-DH (D-Glucose-6-phosphate: NADP 1-oxidoreductase, EC 1.1.1.49) as indicator enzyme[23-25].

Application of Method: In biochemistry and clinical chemistry.

Principle

(1) $$\text{G-1-P} + \text{G-1,6-}P_2 \xrightarrow{\text{PGluM}} \text{G-1,6-}P_2 + \text{G-6-P}$$

(2) $$\text{G-6-P} + \text{NADP}^+ \xrightarrow{\text{G6P-DH}} \text{6-Phosphogluconolactone} + \text{NADPH} + \text{H}^+$$

The equilibrium of the reactions lies on the side of 6-PG (95%); the reaction is linear up to 60% conversion of G-1-P^{20}.

The amount of NADPH formed per unit time, as determined by the extinction change at 340 (334, 365) nm, is the measure of the activity.

Optimum Conditions for Measurements

Divalent cations, preferably magnesium, and a sulphydryl compound, cysteine[20,24], histidine[12,22] or glutathione[25] are necessary for maximum activity. The optimum pH for the PGluM reaction is pH 7.4–7.6. Optimum activity in serum is obtained with 5 mM G-1-P, 1.5 mM Mg^{2+}, 25 mM histidine and about 8 μM G-1,6-P_2.

Measurements at different temperatures may require different measuring conditions (cf. p. 127). Nevertheless, results obtained under the same measuring conditions but at different temperatures were formerly compared with each other ("conversion factors" were determined). Such conversion factors may be correct if determined with a relatively large proband collective; however, they cannot be applied generally to the individual case (cf. p. 129). The value of the following relative reaction rates thus lies in being

able to appraise the temperature dependence of the reaction and at the most to compare qualitatively
values up to the limit of normal.

°C	20	21	22	23	24	25	26	27	28
	1.55	1.42	1.3	1.2	1.1	1.0	0.92	0.835	0.76

°C	29	30	31	32	33	34	35	36	37
	0.685	0.625	0.57	0.52	0.475	0.44	0.41	0.39	0.37

Equipment

Spectrophotometer or spectrum-line photometer suitable for accurate measurements at 340
(334, 365) nm, preferably with constant temperature cuvette holder; centrifuge; stopwatch.

Reagents

1. Tris-hydroxymethyl-aminomethane, tris
2. Hydrochloric acid, 0.1 N
3. Glucose-1-phosphate, G-1-P
   dipotassium salt, $G-1-P-K_2 \cdot 2H_2O$; commercial
   preparation, see p. 537.
4. Magnesium chloride, $MgCl_2 \cdot 6H_2O$, A. R.
5. L-Histidine, monohydrochloride
6. Sodium hydroxide, 1 N
7. Glucose-1,6-diphosphate, $G-1,6-P_2$
   cyclohexylammonium salt $\cdot 4H_2O$; commercial
   preparation, see p. 537.

8. Glucose-6-phosphate dehydrogenase,
   G6P-DH
   from yeast, suspension in 3.2 M ammonium
   sulphate solution, $\geqq 140$ U/mg (25 °C); commercial preparation, see p. 458.
9. Nicotinamide-adenine dinucleotide phosphate, NADP
   disodium salt, $NADP-Na_2H$; commercial preparation, see p. 546.

Preparation of Solutions

Prepare all solutions with doubly distilled water.
   I. Tris buffer (0.1 M; pH 7.6):
      Dissolve 1.21 g. tris in 78 ml. 0.1 N HCl and dilute with distilled water to 100 ml.
  II. Substrate solution (77.5 mM G-1-P):
      Dissolve 290 mg. $G-1-P-K_2 \cdot 2H_2O$ in 10 ml. tris buffer I.
 III. Magnesium chloride (22.5 mM):
      Dissolve 460 mg. $MgCl_2 \cdot 6H_2O$ in distilled water and make up to 100 ml.
  IV. Histidine (0.2 M; pH 7.6):
      Dissolve 383 mg. histidine hydrochloride in 1.75 ml. 1 N NaOH and make up to 10 ml.
      with tris buffer I.
   V. Glucose diphosphate (0.125 mM):
      Dissolve ca. 1 mg. $G-1,6-P_2$ in 10 ml. tris buffer I.
  VI. Glucose-6-phosphate dehydrogenase, G6P-DH (0.1 mg. protein/ml., 14 U/ml.):
      Dilute 0.1 ml. stock suspension with 0.9 ml. 3.2 M ammonium sulphate solution.
 VII. Nicotinamide-adenine dinucleotide phosphate (6 mM β-NADP):
      Dissolve 5 mg. $NADP-Na_2H$ in 1 ml. distilled water.

Stability of Solutions

The buffer and magnesium solutions are stable indefinitely. The substrate, glucose diphosphate, histidine and NADP solutions are stable for several weeks at 4 °C. Prepare the G6P-DH solution freshly each day from the stock suspension.

Procedure

Collection, Treatment and Stability of Sample

Use fresh serum or heparinized plasma free from haemolysis. Addition of EDTA, oxalate or fluoride as anticoagulants results in lower activity in plasma[22].

The enzyme in serum is stable for at least 8 hr. at room temperature, two days at 4 °C and 4 days at -20 °C[12,22].

Assay System

Wavelength: 340 (Hg 334, Hg 365) nm; light path: 1 cm.; 25 °C (constant); final volume: 3.1 ml.; read against water.

Pipette into cuvettes:			Concentration in assay mixture
Sample (serum)		0.5 ml.	
Buffer	(I)	1.4 ml.	66 mM
MgCl$_2$ solution	(III)	0.2 ml.	1.5 mM
Histidine solution	(IV)	0.4 ml.	26 mM
G-1,6-P$_2$ solution	(V)	0.2 ml.	8 μM
G6P-DH suspension	(VI)	0.1 ml.	0.45 U/ml.
NADP solution	(VII)	0.1 ml.	0.2 mM
Mix and equilibrate the cuvette contents to 25 °C.			
Substrate solution	(II)	0.2 ml.	5 mM
Mix, read extinction and start stopwatch. Repeat readings every 2 min. for 12–20 min. Δ E/min. is used for the calculations.			

With values of Δ E/min. > 0.040/min. (340 nm) read at shorter time intervals or dilute the serum 5- to 10-fold with buffer solution I.

Calculations

The calculation formula (8) on p. 313 applies and therefore the following relationships hold for this method:

Wavelength:	*334 nm*	*340 nm*	*365 nm*
Volume activity	$= 1016 \times \Delta$ E/min.	$997 \times \Delta$ E/min.	$1797 \times \Delta$ E/min. [U/l.]

Precision of Method

For activities of 10.1 U/l. $\pm$ 0.5 U/l. the coefficient of variation is 2.4 %.

Normal Values

Serum values for healthy adults are 0.5–6.3 U/l. (25 °C); serum from cord blood has higher activity (*Ivie*[22]). The activity in cerebrospinal fluid of normal protein content is < 1 U/l.[22]

Sources of Error

Effects of drugs and other therapeutic measures: None known.

Interference in the assay technique: Several minutes are required after the start of the reaction for the indicator reaction to reach equilibrium, consequently the initial ΔE values may be too low.

Specificity of Method

The PGluM activity is measured specifically.

Details for Measurements in Tissues

The above assay can be used virtually unchanged for homogenates[20,21] although *Bodansky*[26] recommends the determination of the optimum concentrations for each tissue.

References

1 *C. F. Cori* & *G. T. Cori*, Proc. Soc. exptl. Biol. Med. *34*, 702 [1936].
2 *G. T. Cori, S. P. Colowick* & *C. F. Cori*, J. biol. Chem. *123*, 375 [1938].
3 *L. P. Kendal* & *L. H. Strickland*, Biochem. J. *32*, 572 [1938].
4 *L. F. Leloir, R. E. Trucco, C. E. Cardini, A. Paladini* & *R. Caputto*, Arch. Biochem. *19*, 339 [1948].
5 *J.-C. Dreyfus* & *G. Schapira*, Compt. rend. Soc. Biol. *147*, 1145 [1953].
6 *J.-C. Dreyfus, G. Schapira, F. Schapira* & *J. Demos*, Clin. Chim. Acta *1*, 434 [1956].
7 *M. Coltorti* & *G. Giusti*, Boll. Soc. Ital. Biol. sper. *32*, 384 [1956].
8 *F. De Ritis, G. Giusti* & *M. Coltorti*, Boll. Soc. Ital. Biol. sper. *32*, 386 [1956].
9 *F. De Ritis, G. Giusti* & *M. Coltorti*, Minerva Med. *48*, 3 [1957].
10 *F. De Ritis, G. Giusti* & *M. Coltorti*, Experentia *13*, 81 [1957].
11 *F. De Ritis, M. Coltorti* & *G. Giusti*, Clin. Chim. Acta *4*, 213 [1959].
12 *O. Bodansky*, Cancer *10*, 859 [1957].
13 *O. Bodansky*, Cancer *10*, 865 [1957].
14 *E. Noltmann* & *F. H. Bruns*, Z. Physiol. Chem. *313*, 194 [1958].
15 *R. Merten* & *H. G. Solbach*, Klin. Wschr. *39*, 222 [1961].
16 *G. E. Joplin* & *K. A. Jegatheesan*, Brit. med. J. *1*, 827 [1962].
17 *K. A. Jegatheesan* & *G. E. Joplin*, Brit. med. J. *1*, 831 [1962].
18 *N. Spencer, D. A. Hopkinson* & *H. Harris*, Nature *204*, 742 [1964].
19 *K. Lohmann*, Biochem. Z. *194*, 306 [1928].
20 *V. A. Najjar*, J. biol. Chem. *175*, 281 [1948].
21 *C. Milstein*, Biochem. J. *79*, 574 [1961].
22 *M. P. Ivie:* Thesis. Institute of Medical Laboratory Technology, London, 1964.
23 *H. Klenow* & *R. Emberland*, Arch. Biochem. Biophys. *57*, 276 [1955].
24 *O. Bodansky*, J. biol. Chem. *236*, 328 [1961].
25 *U. Stave*, Enzymol. biol. clin. *8*, 21 [1967].
26 *O. Bodansky*, J. biol. Chem. *232*, 859 [1958].

Uridyl Transferase

Kurt J. Isselbacher

The enzyme uridyl transferase (UDP glucose: α-D-galactose-1-phosphate uridylyl transferase, EC 2.7.7.12) occurs in many mammalian tissues (e.g. erythrocytes, liver, mammary gland, brain). It is also found in bacteria, especially in *Escherichia coli*. It catalyses the reation.

$$\text{Gal-1-P} + \text{UDPG} \rightleftharpoons \text{UDPGal} + \text{G-1-P}$$

(Gal-1-P = galactose-1-phosphate; G-1-P = glucose-1-phosphate; UDPG = uridinediphosphate glucose; UDPGal = uridinediphosphate galactose).

There are several methods for the determination of uridyl transferase activity: either the decrease of UDPG concentration is determined with UDPG dehydrogenase (UDPglucose: NAD 6-oxidoreductase, EC 1.1.1.22)[1] or the formation of G-1-P is measured with phosphoglucomutase, PGluM (α-D-Glucose-1,6-bisphosphate : α-D-glucose-1-phosphate phosphotransferase, EC 2.7.5.1) and glucose-6-phosphate dehydrogenase, G6P-DH (D-Glucose-6-phosphate: NADP 1-oxidoreductase, EC 1.1.1.49)[2]. The first method is often used for the diagnosis of galactosaemia.

UDPGal-4-epimerase interferes, but in the absence of nicotinamide-adenine dinucleotide (NAD) erythrocytes do not show any epimerase activity.

The second method, which is described here, is not affected by UDPGal-4-epimerase.

Application of Method: In biochemistry and clinical chemistry.

Principle

(1) $\qquad$ Gal-1-P + UDPG $\xrightarrow[\text{transferase}]{\text{uridyl}}$ UDPGal + G-1-P

(2) $\qquad$ G-1-P $\xrightarrow[\text{G}-1,6-\text{P}_2]{\text{PGluM}}$ G-6-P

(3) $\qquad$ G-6-P + NADP$^+$ $\xrightarrow{\text{G6P}-\text{DH}}$ 6-PG + NADPH + H$^+$

One μmole NADPH is formed for each μmole hexose phosphate. The increase in extinction at 340 (334, 365) nm due to the formation of NADPH is measured.

Optimum Conditions for Measurements

Uridyl transferase from mammalian tissues and bacteria has an activity optimum[2,3] at pH 8.7. Substrates and indicator enzymes are added in excess.

Equipment

Spectrophotometer or spectrum-line photometer suitable for accurate measurements at 340, 334 or 365 nm; stopwatch.

Reagents*

1. Glycine
2. Cysteine hydrochloride · H_2O
3. Magnesium chloride, $MgCl_2 \cdot 6H_2O$
4. Sodium hydroxide, A. R., 5 N
5. Sodium sulphate, A. R.,
   $Na_2SO_4 \cdot 10H_2O$, 10% solution
6. Galactose-1-phosphate, Gal-1-P
   barium or potassium salt; prepared according
   to[4] or commercial preparation, see p. 535.
7. UDP-Glucose
   sodium salt; commercial preparation, see p. 555.
8. Nicotinamide-adenine dinucleotide
   phosphate, NADP
   sodium salt, NADP-Na_2H; commercial preparation, see p. 546.

9. Phosphoglucomutase, PGluM
   prepared from rabbit muscle according to[5] or
   commercial preparation, see p. 499; ca. 200
   U/mg. (25 °C).
10. Glucose-6-phosphate dehydrogenase,
    G6P-DH
    prepared from yeast according to[6] or commer-
    cial preparation, see p. 458; ca. 140 U/mg.
    (25 °C).
11. Glucose-1,6-diphosphate, G-1,6-P_2
    crystalline tetra-cyclohexylammonium salt
    ·$4H_2O$; commercial preparation, see p. 537.

Purity of Enzyme Preparations

The indicator enzymes must not be contaminated with 6-phosphogluconate dehydrogenase. This is checked with known amounts of G-1-P and G-6-P. Only 1 μmole NADPH should be formed per μmole hexose phosphate. Direct assay for 6-phosphogluconate dehydrogenase is recommended. Although the phosphoglucomutase prepared according to[5] contains G-1,6-P_2 it is preferable to add more. Commercial preparation, see p. 537.

Preparation of Solutions

I. Glycine buffer (1 M; pH 8.7):
   Dissolve 7.5 g. glycine in 75 ml. distilled water, adjust to pH 8.7 with ca. 1.4 ml. 5 N NaOH and dilute to 100 ml. with distilled water.
II. Cysteine (ca. 0.2 M):
   Dissolve 350 mg. cysteine hydrochloride · H_2O in 9 ml. distilled water. Immediately before use adjust to pH 8.5 with ca. 0.7 ml. 5 N NaOH (pH paper).
III. Magnesium chloride (0.1 M):
   Dissolve 2.03 g. $MgCl_2 \cdot 6H_2O$ in 100 ml. distilled water.
IV. Galactose-1-phosphate, Gal-1-P (10 mM):
   Dissolve 34 mg. potassium salt in 10 ml. distilled water or dissolve 40 mg. barium salt in 5 ml. distilled water, add ca. 0.4 ml. 10% Na_2SO_4 solution until no further precipitate forms. Centrifuge off the precipitate, wash with water and combine the washing with the supernatant fluid. Dilute to 10 ml. with distilled water.
V. UDP-Glucose (10 mM; pH 8.7):
   Dissolve 6 mg. sodium salt in 1 ml. distilled water.
VI. Nicotinamide-adenine dinucleotide phosphate (25 mM β-NADP):
   Dissolve 20 mg. NADP-Na_2H in 1 ml. distilled water.

---

* Complete reagent kits are available commercially, see p. 558.

VII. Phosphoglucomutase, PGluM (1 U/ml.):
    Dilute the product prepared from rabbit muscle[5] or the commercial preparation with
    3.2 M ammonium sulphate solution. Add 6 mg. G-1,6-P_2 per ml.
VIII. Glucose-6-phosphate dehydrogenase, G6P-DH (ca. 1 U/ml.):
    Dilute the product prepared from yeast[6] or the commercial preparation with 3.2 M
    ammonium sulphate solution.

Stability of Solutions

The galactose-1-phosphate, buffer and $MgCl_2$ solutions and the suspensions of PGluM and G6P-DH are
stable for months at 0–4 °C. Prepare the UDPG, NADP and cysteine solutions freshly each week and
store cold or frozen.

Procedure

Collection, Treatment and Stability of Sample

Use erythrocyte haemolysates (for preparation, see p. 639) or soluble fraction of rat liver (supernatant
fluid after centrifugation of an homogenate at ca. 100 000 g.).
The enzyme is relatively stable at −10 °C. If the enzyme is stored lyophilized and in a vacuum it appears
to be stable for several months. Glutathione increases the stability[2].

Assay System

Wavelength: 340 (Hg 334 or Hg 365) nm; light path: 1 cm.; cuvette volume: 1 ml.; final volume:
0.62 ml.; temperature: 25 °C; read against water. Control cuvette containing distilled water
instead of Gal-1-P solution (IV).

Pipette into cuvettes:			Concentration in assay mixture
Cysteine solution	(II)	0.03 ml.	ca. 10 mM
$MgCl_2$ solution	(III)	0.01 ml.	ca. 1.6 mM
Buffer	(I)	0.06 ml.	ca. 0.1 M
NADP solution	(VI)	0.01 ml.	ca. 0.4 mM
UDPG solution	(V)	0.02 ml.	ca. 0.32 mM
PGluM suspension	(VII)	0.01 ml.	ca. 16 mU/ml.
G6P-DH suspension	(VIII)	0.01 ml.	ca. 16 mU/ml.
Sample + water		0.44 ml.	
Mix and follow extinction until constant (usually 2 min.).			
Gal-1-P solution	(IV)	0.03 ml.	ca. 0.5 mM
Mix and read extinction at 30 sec. intervals for 3 min. Calculate the increases in extinction for the experimental and control cuvettes per min. The difference between the two is ΔE/min.; use this for the calculations.			

Calculations

The calculation formula (8) on p. 313 applies for the volume activity of the sample.

Wavelength: *334 nm*   *340 nm*   *365 nm*

Volume activity $= \dfrac{101.64}{v} \times \varDelta E/\text{min.}$ $\dfrac{99.67}{v} \times \varDelta E/\text{min.}$ $\dfrac{179.71}{v} \times \varDelta E/\text{min.}$

v = volume of sample in assay.

Normal Values

Rat liver: 1.4 ± 0.5 U/g.; standard deviation of each sample in duplicate is ± 0.13 U.
Human erythrocytes: The activity depends on the age and sex of subject, and age of blood cells. Normal range is about 0.16–0.67 U/g. haemoglobin. Standard deviation for each sample in duplicate is ± 0.02 U. Some of the values in the literature refer to units measured at 37 °C and related to 60 min. (instead of 25 °C and 1 min.; these values are > 60-fold higher.

Specificity of Method

The method described here is specific for uridyl transferase.

References

1 *E. P. Anderson, H. M. Kalckar, K. Kurahashi & K. J. Isselbacher,* J. Lab. clin. Med. *50*, 469 [1957].
2 *K. Kurahashi & E. P. Anderson,* Biochim. biophys. Acta *29*, 498 [1958].
3 *H. M. Kalckar, K. Kurahashi & E. Jordan,* Proc. nat. Acad. Sci. USA *45*, 1776 [1959].
4 *S. P. Colowick,* J. biol. Chem. *124*, 557 [1938].
5 *V. A. Najjar* in *S. P. Colowick & N. O. Kaplan:* Methods in Enzymology. Academic Press, New York 1955, Vol. I, p. 294.
6 *A. Kornberg & B. L. Horecker* in *S. P. Colowick & N. O. Kaplan:* Methods in Enzymology. Academic Press, New York 1955, Vol. I, p. 323.

Arylesterases

Wolfgang Pilz

It has been known since 1947 that human serum has the ability to hydrolyse short-chain fatty acid esters of aromatic hydroxyl compounds. *Huggins* and *Lapides*[1] and *Mounter* and *Whittaker*[2] demonstrated that human serum can hydrolyse some esters of p-nitrophenol. Other workers (e. g. *Zeller* et al.[3]) found that the p-nitrophenyl ester was hydrolysed by several enzymes in human serum. *Aldridge*[4] found that serum or plasma of rat, rabbit or horse also contained esterase activity for p-nitrophenyl ester.

Various authors since 1949 have studied the hydrolysis of the β-naphthol esters of fatty acids[5-11]. *Augustinsson*[12] first used phenyl esters to determine this enzyme and proposed the name arylesterase (EC 3.1.1.2). From the numerous studies of *Augustinsson* and his school (for review, see [13]) a clear picture has emerged concerning the arylesterases which occur in human serum and serum from other animals.

After starch-gel electrophoresis we found two separate arylesterases in human serum. Arylesterase I migrates with albumin, arylesterase II migrates between albumin and α_1-globulin[14]. The two enzymes are different in other ways: arylesterase I is not inhibited by phosphoric acid esters. The optimum chain length of the β-naphthyl fatty acid esters is C_3, propionic acid, of the phenyl esters it is C_2, acetic acid[14]. In agreement with[13] we found that serum saturated with E 600* (and therefore only containing specific arylesterase I) showed very different activity with phenyl acetate and β-naphthyl-propionate[15]. In contrast, arylesterase II is not specific and was soon designated carboxyesterase (EC 3.1.1.1); this enzyme is inhibited by organic phosphoric acid esters. As a true enzyme of fatty acid metabolism only arylesterase I will be considered here. The physiological function of arylesterases in human serum was for long unknown. While *Erdös*[16] proposed that the physiological function of the enzyme was to hydrolyse aryl phosphates, we showed that arylesterases were unable to hydrolyse organic phosphoric acid esters[15,27]. The arylesterases are not identical with the enzymes described by *Krisch*[17]. In the meantime we demonstrated the presence of arylesterases in various experimental animals, e. g. rat[18]. Human serum from cord blood contains 12 different arylesterases[19]. In 1964 it was discovered that arylesterase I from human serum could catalyse an exchange of ester radicals: β-naphthylpropionate in the presence of the sodium salt of a long chain fatty acid with the liberation of free propionate[20]. The reaction could be followed quantitatively and the new β-naphthyl ester obtained in preparative amounts. In 1966 we discovered that a fraction from human liver (after column chromatography on DEAE-Sephadex) was able to convert the β-naphthyl ester of a long-chain fatty acid to β-naphthylpropionate[21]. These reactions can also be carried out with phenyl esters. Thus in the human organism there occurs an arylesterase system which can be represented in a simplified form as follows:

Serum: Phenyl ester short chain fatty acids + free long-chain fatty acids = phenyl ester long-chain fatty acids + free short-chain fatty acids.

Liver: Phenyl ester long-chain fatty acids + free short-chain fatty acids = phenyl ester short chain fatty acids + free long-chain fatty acids (for details, see [21]).

The specific substrates for arylesterase in human serum are lipoproteins in which the tyrosine constituent of the intact protein is esterified with short-chain fatty acids[22]. The arylesterases therefore catalyse a

---

* E 600 = O–O–diethyl–O–(p-nitrophenyl)–phosphate ("Paraoxon").

transport to the liver of long-chain free fatty acids, which arise by hydrolysis of lipoproteins in serum, in heart and in lung[23]. This system has so far only been extensively studied in man and rabbit[22,24]. Arylesterase I has been obtained preparatively from human serum (starch-gel electrophoresis[31]). It was chromatographically, electrophoretically and immunochemically homogeneous and hydrolysed phenyl acetate and β-naphthylpropionate at very different rates[15]. The hydrolytic activity with the two substrates was a measure for the rate of ester exchange reactions in the different lipoprotein fractions[32].

For the assay of the serum enzymes therefore both β-naphthylpropionate and phenyl acetate should be used as substrates. Both are synthetic substrates with high specificity. In each case one of the reaction products is determined (β-naphthol[25] or phenol[26]). Both methods were considered as purely analytical problems before their introduction into enzymatic analysis[25,26].

Application of Method: In biochemistry (mainly research on lipid metabolism), in clinical chemistry.

Measurements with Phenylacetate as Substrate

Arylesterase I has apparently 2 active centres. One hydrolyses phenylacetate and the other β-naphthyl-propionate. The hydrolytic activity with phenylacetate is a measure of the ester exchange reactions in the pre-albumin fraction and in the α-lipoproteins.

Principle

(1)
$$\text{Phenylacetate} + H_2O \xrightleftharpoons[\text{esterase I}]{\text{aryl}-} \text{Phenol} + \text{Acetic acid}$$

(2)

4-Aminoantipyrine   (R)

The condensation product R is extracted with n-pentanol (pentan-1-ol) and determined colorimetrically. Under the conditions of the reaction the equilibrium lies completely to the right.

Optimum Conditions for Measurements

The optimum chain length for the phenyl esters of fatty acids is C_2 (phenyl acetate)[13]. The optimum substrate concentration is between 1.0 and 1.5 mM, the pH optimum is between pH 7.2 and 8.6[14].

Measurements at different temperatures may require different measuring conditions (cf. p. 127). Nevertheless, results obtained under the same measuring conditions but at different temperatures were formerly compared with each other ("conversion factors" were determined). Such conversion factors may be correct if determined with a relatively large proband collective; however, they cannot be applied generally to the individual case (cf. p. 219). The value of the following relative reaction rates[27] thus lies in being able to appraise the temperature dependence of the reaction and at the most to compare qualitatively values up to the limit of normal.

°C	18	20	25	30	37	45
	1.4	1.3	1.2	1.1	1.0	ca. 1.9
						(start of denaturation of enzyme)

Equipment

Constant temperature incubator; mixer; spectrophotometer for the visible range (accurate measurements).

Reagents

1. Sodium veronal (sodium barbiturate)
2. Sodium acetate, cryst.
3. Hydrochloric acid, 1 N
4. 4-Aminoantipyrine (4-aminophenazone)

5. n-Pentanol (pentan-1-ol)
6. Phenylacetate (acetic acid phenyl ester)*
7. Potassium ferricyanide, $K_3[Fe(CN)_6]$
8. Ethanol, pure

Preparation of Solutions

 I. Veronal buffer (0.1 M; pH 8.6):
    Dissolve 49.2 g. sodium veronal and 32.4 g. sodium acetate in about 3 000 ml. distilled water and after addition of 30 ml. N HCl dilute to 5 000 ml. with distilled water
 II. 4-Aminoantipyrine solution (98.5 mM):
    Dissolve 20 g. 4-aminoantipyrine in distilled water and make up to 1 000 ml.
 III. Potassium ferricyanide solution (0.243 M):
    Dissolve 80 g. $K_3[Fe(CN)_6]$ in distilled water and make up to 1 000 ml.
 IV. Phenylacetate stock solution (200 mM):
    Dissolve 1.361 g. phenylacetate in pure alcohol and make up to 50 ml.
 V. Substrate solution (1.33 mM):
    Homogenize 150 ml. solution I with 1 ml. solution IV in a mixer at the highest speed possible.

Stability of Solutions

With the exception of substrate solution (V) which must be prepared freshly each day, all solutions are stable for 6−8 weeks at room temperature in the dark.

Procedure

Collection, Treatment and Stability of Sample

Collection of sample:

Collect blood without venestasis from the *vena cubitalis*. Centrifuge for 10 min. at ca. 3 000 g to obtain serum. Use only fresh serum. Slight haemolysis is of no consequence because the enzyme is not present in erythrocytes.

Stability of enzyme in sample:

The enzyme is stable for 24 hr. at 4 °C; after this period a decrease in activity may occur.

---

* It is necessary to check the commercial phenylacetate for its ester content. The methods in[28,29] are best.

Assay System

Enzyme reaction in incubator at 37 °C; reaction volume: 25.01 ml.; reaction time: 30 min. Prepare a control without sample and a blank without sample and without substrate for each series of experiments. Wavelength: 465 nm (463 to 467 nm); light path: 0.5 cm.; room temperature; read against blank.

Pipette into 100 ml. volumetric flasks	Sample	Control	Blank	Concentration in assay mixture
Substrate solution (IV)	25 ml.	25 ml.	—	1.33 mM
Serum	0.01 ml.	—	—	
Incubate for 30 min. at 37 °C.				
Veronal buffer (I)	—	—	25 ml.	71.4 mM
4-Aminoantipyrine				
solution (II)	5 ml.	5 ml.	5 ml.	14.05 mM
$K_3[Fe(CN)_6]$ solution (III)	5 ml.	5 ml.	5 ml.	34.70 mM
Allow to stand for 15 min. at room temperature.				
n-Pentanol	25 ml.	25 ml.	25 ml.	
Shake vigorously, allow to separate, pour off upper organic phase and centrifuge for 10 min. at 3000 g. Use clear solution for colorimetric measurements. Read E_S (sample) and E_C (control) against blank. $E_S - E_C = \Delta E$ is used for the calculations.				

If the pentanol extracts are too intense for the colorimetric measurements ($\Delta E > 0.800$) dilute all solutions including blank with pentanol. Take the dilution factor into account in the calculations.

Calculations

For measurements at 465 nm the extinction coefficient of the dye is 21.7 cm.^{2}/μmole. Therefore according to equation (2) on p. 312 the amount of dye formed from phenol (in 25 ml. pentanol extract) in the indicator reaction (2):

$$c = \frac{\Delta E \times 25}{21.7 \times 0.5} \qquad [\mu mole/25\ ml.]$$

This amount is equivalent to the phenylacetate reacting in 30 min. in the enzymatic reaction (1). For the above conditions the arylesterase activity at 37 °C is given by:

$$\text{Volume activity} = \frac{\Delta E \times 25}{21.7 \times 0.5} \times \frac{1000}{0.01 \times 30} = \Delta E \times 7683 \quad [U/l.]$$

Precision of Method

Using this method a standard deviation of 1.13 U/l. was found for a mean value of 12 U/l. The coefficient of variation is 9.21%.

Normal Values

12000 ± 6000 U/l. serum.

Sources of Error

Effects of drugs and other therapeutic measures: None known.

Interference in the assay technique: Trouble-free results are obtained if veronal or tris-acetate buffer [30], pH 8.6 are used. Interference occurs with other buffers and pH values.

Specificity of Method

As phenylacetate is hydrolysed only by arylesterase I of serum[15] and the substrate is not cleaved by any other serum enzyme the method is specific.

Details for Measurements in Tissues

Phenyl ester hydrolysing enzymes occur in many organs, tissues, etc. Most of the tissue enzymes have the same pH optimum as the serum enzyme, but different specificity with regard to the chain length of the fatty acids. The assay technique is independent of the chain length of the fatty acid, because the hydrolysis product phenol is determined.

Measurements with β-Naphthylpropionate as Substrate

The hydrolytic activity of arylesterase I with β-naphthylpropionate (second active centre of the enzyme, see p. 806) is a measure of the ester exchange activity of the β-lipoprotein fraction and the pre-β-lipoprotein fraction[32].

(3) $\beta\text{-Naphthylpropionate} + H_2O \xrightleftharpoons[\text{esterase I}]{\text{aryl}-} \beta\text{-Naphthol} + \text{Propionic acid}$

(4)

β-Naphthol   Diazonium   Azo dye A
                    Solution

The azo dye A is extracted from neutral solution (NaHCO$_3$) with n-pentanol (pentan-1-ol) and determined colorimetrically. The equilibrium of reaction (2) under these conditions lies completely to the right.

Optimum Conditions for Measurements

For the serum enzyme the optimum chain length of the fatty acid β-naphthyl ester is C$_3$ (β-naphthylpropionate)[14], for other details, see p. 807.

Equipment

As described on p. 808.

Reagents

1. Sodium veronal (sodium barbiturate)
2. Sodium acetate, cryst.
3. Hydrochloric acid, 1 N
4. 4-Aminophenetol, b. p. 111 °C (5 mm)
5. Sodium nitrite
6. Sulphaminic acid

7. β-Naphthylpropionate*
8. Ethanol, pure
9. Sodium hydrogen carbonate, NaHCO₃, A. R.
10. n-Pentanol (pentan-1-ol)
11. Gum arabic.

Preparation of Solutions

I. Veronal buffer (0.1 M; pH 8.6):
   Prepare as described on p. 808.

II. Sodium nitrite solution (1.45 N):
   Dissolve 10 g. sodium nitrite in distilled water and make up to 100 ml.

III. Sulphaminic acid solution (0.876 M):
   Dissolve 10 g. sulphaminic acid in distilled water and make up to 100 ml.

IV. Diazonium solution:
   Dissolve 0.3 ml. 4-aminophenetol in 5 ml. 1 N HCl in a volumetric flask, add 5 ml. $NaNO_2$ solution (II), shake and stand for ca. 10 min. Slowly add 20 ml. sulphaminic acid solution (III) (vigorous frothing) and after shaking vigorously dilute to the mark with distilled water.

V. β-Naphthylpropionate stock solution (200 mM):
   Dissolve 2.01 g. β-naphthylpropionate in a 50 ml. volumetric flask with pure ethanol (slight warming) and dilute to the mark with ethanol.

VI. Substrate (1.33 mM):
   Homogenize 150 ml. veronal buffer (I) with 0.5 g. gum arabic in a mixer at the fastest speed possible; at the same time slowly drop in 1 ml. substrate solution (V).

VII. Sodium hydrogen carbonate solution, NaHCO₃ (0.5 M):
   Dissolve 42.0 g. NaHCO₃ in distilled water in a 1 000 ml. volumetric flask and dilute to the mark.

Stability of Solutions

Solutions IV and VI must be prepared freshly each day. The stability of the other solutions is as described for method A.

Procedure

Collection, Treatment and Stability of Sample: as described on p. 808.

---

* Commercial β-naphthylpropionate must be recrystallized from alcohol. The compound can easily be prepared from β-naphthol and propionic anhydride.

Assay System

Wavelength: 465 nm (463–467 nm); light path: 0.5 cm.; room temperature. Read against blank.

Enzyme reaction in an incubator at 37 °C; reaction volume: 25.01 ml.; reaction time: 30 min. Prepare a control without sample and a blank without sample and without substrate for each series of measurements.

Pipette into 100 ml. volumetric flasks:	Sample	Control	Blank	Concentration in assay mixture
Substrate solution (VI)	25 ml.	25 ml.	—	1.33 mM
Serum	0.01 ml.	—	—	
Incubate for 30 min. at 37 °C.				
Diazonium solution (IV)	5 ml.	5 ml.	5 ml.	
NaHCO$_3$ solution (VII)	10 ml.	10 ml.	10 ml.	125 mM
Allow to stand for 20 min. at room temperature.				
n-Pentanol	25 ml.	25 ml.	25 ml.	
Shake vigorously, allow phases to separate and pour off the upper organic phase. Centrifuge for 10 min. at 3000 g. Use the clear solution for the colorimetric measurements. Read the E$_S$ (sample) and E$_C$ (control) against the blank. E$_S$ − E$_C$ = ΔE is used for the calculations.				

If the pentanol extracts are too dense for colorimetric measurements (ΔE > 0.800), dilute all solutions including the blank with pentanol. Take the dilution into account in the calculations.

Calculations

For measurements at 465 nm the extinction coefficient of the dye is 12.5 cm.^{2}/μmole. Therefore according to equation (2) on p. 312 the amount of dye (in 25 ml. pentanol extract) formed from β-naphthol in indicator reaction (4) is given by:

$$c = \frac{\Delta E \times 25}{12.5 \times 0.5} \quad [\mu\text{mole/25 ml.}]$$

This is equivalent to the μmole β-naphthylpropionate converted in enzymatic reaction (3) in 30 min. Under the above conditions the arylesterase I activity in serum at 37 °C is:

$$\text{Volume activity} = \frac{\Delta E \times 25}{12.5 \times 0.5} \times \frac{1000}{0.01 \times 30} = \Delta E \times 13339 \ [\text{U/l.}]$$

Precision of Method

Using this method a standard deviation of 0.15 U/l. serum was found for a mean value of 5 U/l. The coefficient of variation is 3.07%.

Normal Values

5000 ± 2500 U/l. serum.

Sources of Error

Effects of drugs and other therapeutic measures: None known.

Interference in the assay technique: The reaction mixture must be pH 7.5 before the extraction (if necessary, add more $NaHCO_3$) although the type of buffer does not matter.

Specificity of Method

As β-naphthylpropionate is hydrolysed only by arylesterase I[14,15] and, as the substrate is not cleaved by any other serum enzyme, the method is specific.

Details for Measurements in Tissues, see p. 810.

References

1 Ch. Huggins & J. Lapides, J. biol. Chem. *170*, 467 [1947].
2 L. A. Mounter & V. P. Whittaker, Biochem. J. *54*, 551 [1953].
3 E. A. Zeller, G. A. Fleischer, R. A. McNaughton & J. S. Schweppe, Proc. Soc. exp. Biol. Med., *71*, 526 [1949].
4 W. N. Aldridge, Biochem. J. *53*, 110 [1953].
5 M. M. Nachlas & A. M. Seligman, J. nat. Cancer Inst. *9*, 415 [1949].
6 M. M. Nachlas & A. M. Seligman, J. biol. Chem. *181*, 343 [1949].
7 A. M. Seligman, M. M. Nachlas & M. C. Mollomo, Amer. J. Physiol. *159*, 337 [1949].
8 A. M. Seligman & M. M. Nachlas, J. clin. Invest *29*, 31 [1950].
9 A. A. Delcourt, C. E. Rubin, W. L. Palmer & J. B. Kirschner, J. Lab. clin. Med. *42*, 310 [1953].
10 R. A. Ravin & A. M. Seligman, Arch. Biochem. Biophysics, *42*, 337 [1953].
11 S. Katz, Amer. J. Gastroenterol. *27*, 479 [1957].
12 K. B. Augustinsson, Nature (London) *181*, 1786 [1958].
13 K. B. Augustinsson, Ann. N. Y. Acad. Sci. *94*, 844 [1961].
14 W. Pilz, Hoppe-Seyler's Z. physiol. Chem. *328*, 1 [1962].
15 W. Pilz, Hoppe-Seyler's Z. physiol. Chem. *328*, 247 [1962].
16 E. Erdös, personal communication.
17 K. Krisch, Z. Klin. Chem. Klin. Biochem. *6*, 41 [1968].
18 W. Pilz & G. Kimmerle, Hoppe-Seyler's Z. physiol. Chem. *329*, 20 [1962].
19 W. Pilz, Hoppe-Seyler's Z. physiol. Chem. *335*, 221 [1964].
20 W. Pilz & H. Hörlein, Hoppe-Seyler's Z. physiol. Chem. *335*, 221 [1964].
21 W. Pilz, H. Hörlein & E. Stelzl, Hoppe-Seyler's Z. physiol. Chem. *345*, 65 [1966].
22 W. Pilz, Z. Klin. Chem. Klin. Biochem. *6*, 337 [1968].
23 H. Hörlein & W. Pilz, Hoppe-Seyler's Z. physiol. Chem. *327*, 256 [1962].
    W. Pilz & J. Johann, Hoppe-Seyler's Z. physiol. Chem. *348*, 73 [1967].
24 W. Pilz, E. Stelzl & I. Johann, Enzym. biol. clin. *9*, 97 [1968].
25 W. Pilz, Mikrochim. Acta *1961*, 614.
26 W. Pilz & I. Johann, Z. analyt. Chem. *212*, 410 [1965].
27 W. Pilz, Z. physiol. Chem. 1973, in preparation.
28 W. Pilz, Z. analyt. Chem. *162*, 81 [1958].
29 W. Pilz, Z. analyt. Chem. *166*, 190 [1959].
30 W. Pilz & I. Johann, Z. analyt. Chem. *215*, 105 [1966].
31 W. Pilz, Z. analyt. Chem. *243*, 587 [1968].
32 W. Pilz, European J. Biochem. 1973, in press.

Lipase

Titrimetric Assay

Gotthilf Näher

Lipase (Triacylglycerol acylhydrolase, EC 3.1.1.3) hydrolyses emulsified triglycerides[1-3] of the long-chain fatty acids. The site of the action of lipase is the interface between the oil drops and the aqueous phase, so that the degree of emulsification plays an important part in establishing the active substrate concentration[4]. This distinguishes lipases from esterases, which can react with water soluble substrates. The concentration of lipase in normal serum is low[2,5-8]. In acute pancreatitis and in cases of pancreatic carcinoma[5,9-12] a rise in serum lipase activity occurs, which has the same diagnostic significance as a rise in amylase activity. The lipase activity in acute pancreatitis can rise to 200-fold the upper limit of normal, the mean increase being about 50-fold[12]. A rise in the lipase content of serum is also observed in acute and chronic renal diseases[9,13].

In pathological serum the lipase activity is pancreatic in origin. In pancreatic and duodenal juice[5] the lipase concentration is several orders of magnitude higher than the activity measured in serum. Apart from pancreatic lipase, there are also lipases in adipose tissue[14,15] and milk[16,17]. In cases of pancreatitis no lipase activity can be detected in urine[2,12].

Application of Method: In biochemistry, clinical chemistry, in pharmaceutical chemistry as a control of preparations containing pancreatic extracts[18], and in foodstuff chemistry[16,17].

Principle[9]

In each step catalysed by lipase one fatty acid is liberated.

By titration at the pH optimum the formation of free fatty acids per unit time is measured. Under the conditions described here the assay is linear from the 2nd to the 6th min. An olive oil emulsion is used as substrate. The number of fatty acid ester bonds hydrolysed per unit time, as determined by the amount of NaOH required to maintain a constant pH, is a measure of the lipase activity.

Optimum Conditions for Measurements

The pH optimum for pancreatic lipase is pH 8.6 to 9.0. If a lipase from another source is to be measured then the pH optimum must be determined.

As the active concentration of the substrate depends on the water-oil interface, the substrate must be prepared as an emulsion which will be stable for the period of the assay. Most workers use gum arabic as a protective colloid for the emulsion in the titrimetric determination of lipase. The present method is essentially based on that of *Marchis-Mouren, Sarda* and *Desnuelle*[19].

With measurements in the lower range of the sensitivity of the method there is a slight alkaline hydrolysis of the gum arabic which can lead to errors because it is not linear in the first 4 min. For the accurate determination of low activity we therefore recommend a 4 min. preliminary incubation of the emulsion at pH 9.0; this can be omitted with highly active samples (e.g. pancreatic extracts).

Sodium deoxycholate is used as an emulsifier because it is obtainable at higher purity than sodium tauro-cholate recommended by other authors[18,19]. The earlier reported[20] activation of lipase by Ca^{2+} gives variable values with the titrimetric determination at pH $9.0^{2,21}$.

Pre-neutralization of the olive oil is absolutely necessary, because the presence of free oleic acid affects the uniformity of the emulsion.

If the method described here is modified as outlined below, it then corresponds to the recommendations of Federation Internationale Pharmaceutique for the quality control of pancreatin[18]:

Replace sodium deoxycholate by sodium taurocholate (FIP standard); add 48.5 mg. tris-hydroxymethyl-amino-methane, A.R. to solution III; carry out the assay at 37 °C.

Equipment

1. Direct reading pH-meter
2. Syringe burette (e. g. Multidosimat E 415 from *Metrohm* with 10 ml. bulb). A micro burette can be used instead of a syringe burette. In this case the tip is connected via tubing (ca. 1 mm. diameter) to a micro proportioning pump (e. g. peristaltic pump from *LKB Produkter*). The syringe burette or the proportioning pump is connected to a pressure button so that the NaOH addition can be regulated by the pH reading. A soda-lime tube should be on the burette or on the NaOH stock container.
3. Water bath (25 °C) with circulating pump.
4. Magnetic stirrer.
5. Mixer.
6. Double-walled reaction vessel made of glass or plastic, volume ca. 50 ml. Double mantle with warm water entry and exit. The reaction vessel contains a Teflon-covered magnet (ca. 15–20 mm.). The cover of the vessel has three holes. The first hole is for the electrode of the pH meter, the second for a glass tube drawn out to a capillary (0.5–1.0 mm. diameter) for gassing with nitrogen. The third hole is for the NaOH delivery tube from the syringe burette or the micro-pump. One of the openings must have sufficient play so that the nitrogen can escape.
7. Gas flowmeter (0–100 l./hr.).
8. Stopwatch.

Reagents

1. Olive oil, (e. g. U.S.P. XVIII)
   first cold pressing. Saponification number 187 to 196
2. Gum arabic, (e. g. Acacia, U.S.P XVIII) powdered
3. Sodium deoxycholate, A. R.
4. Sodium hydroxide, 0.1 N and 0.01 N
5. Sodium chloride, A. R.
6. Nitrogen, CO_2-free
7. Phenolphthalein
8. Ether
9. Ethanol

Preparation of Solutions (for ca. 10 determinations)

I. Gum arabic (10% w/v):
   Dissolve 50 g. gum with ca. 200 ml. distilled water and make up to 500 ml.

II. Neutralized olive oil:

Immediately before the preparation of the emulsion stir the calculated amount of 0.1 NaOH into 20 ml. olive oil. To determine the required amount: dissolve 5 ml. olive oil in a mixture of 40 ml. equal parts ether and ethanol neutralized with NaOH to a phenolphthalein end-point and titrate with 0.1 N NaOH until it gives a permanent colour. Multiplication of the amount of NaOH required by 4 gives the amount needed for 20 ml. oil. The determination usually requires to be repeated with each batch of oil only once, because if the oil is kept cool the acid content remains constant for several months.

III. Deoxycholate/NaCl (1.6% sodium deoxycholate; 32 mM sodium chloride):

Dissolve 1.60 g. Na deoxycholate and 187 mg. NaCl in doubly distilled water and make up to 100 ml.

IV. Substrate emulsion*:

Blend 165 ml. gum arabic solution (I), 15 g. broken ice, (minus the caustic solution necessary for neutralization under II; volume $\approx$ weight) 20 ml. neutralized oil (II) for 15 min. in a mixer at medium speed (position 2). The size of the oil droplets should be between 2 and 3 μ, although some droplets up to a maximum of 10 μ are permissible (check size with a microscope).

Stability of Solutions

Store all solutions at 0–4 °C. The substrate emulsion (IV) is stable for two days, but it is advisable with a large series of measurements to prepare freshly each day. The other solutions are stable for several months providing that growth of micro-organisms does not occur.

Procedure

Collection, Treatment and Stability of Sample

Serum: Add undiluted serum free from haemolysis. No decrease in lipase activity has been observed after four weeks storage at 4 °C. Samples stored frozen at -20 °C have been stable for 3 years.

Urine: Use undiluted.

Duodenal juice and pancreatic juice: Immediately before the assay dilute 1 : 50 with cold doubly distilled water and mix thoroughly for 2 min.

Milk: Use undiluted.

Pancreatin and pharmaceuticals containing pancreatic extracts: dissolve away the covering of coated preparations with distilled water, dry residue on filter paper and finally dry in a stream of cold air. Weigh the residue and powder in a mortar. Grind 200 mg. powder with ca. 10 ml. doubly distilled water at ca. 5 °C in a mortar for 10 min., rinse into a volumetric flask and dilute to 100 ml. with cold doubly distilled water. Shake the suspension for ca. 2 min. and allow the large particles to settle out. Decant a portion of the slightly turbid supernatant fluid, equilibrate to 20 °C and use for the assay. Dilution factor 1 : 500.

---

* A stabilized dry preparation which after mixing with water gives a reconstituted olive oil emulsion (use immediately for tests) has been described by *A. Hagen* and *G. Michal*[22].

Assay System

Equilibrate the solutions to 25 °C before the assay.
Equilibrate the reaction vessel to 25 °C by circulation of warm water. Carry out assay under nitrogen (exclusion of CO_2).

Pipette successively into the reaction vessel:			Concentration in assay mixture
Substrate emulsion	(IV)	10.00 ml.	31.4 μl./ml. oil as emulsion equivalent to ca. 750 cm.^{2}/ml. oil-water interface.
Deoxycholate/NaCl	(III)	10.00 ml.	1.25 mM deoxycholate 1.0 mM NaCl
Doubly distilled water		10.00 ml.	
Adjust the electrode of the pH meter; it should be immersed ca. 25 mm in the solution. Bring the solution to approximately pH 8.8 with 0.1 NaOH from a pipette. Introduce the nitrogen capillary, which should be immersed ca. 5 mm. Add NaOH from the bulb burette or with a micro-pump. Start the gassing with nitrogen (ca. 50 l./hr.). Adjust to exactly pH. 9.0 with 0.01 N NaOH. Hold the pH at exactly pH 9.0 for 8 min. by addition of NaOH, start stopwatch and read burette. Maintain at pH 9.0 for 4 min. and read off volume of NaOH required V_1.			
Sample		1.0 ml.	
Adjust again to exactly pH 9.0 with 0.01 N NaOH and maintain there for 1 min. Read burette and maintain at pH 9.0 for a further 4 min. Read volume V_2.			

The volume of 0.01 N NaOH should not be greater than 8 ml. otherwise repeat the assay with dilute sample.

Calculations

The consumption of 1 ml. 0.01 N NaOH is equivalent to 10 μmole fatty acid liberated. From this it follows for the lipase activity of the sample:

$$\text{Volume activity} = \frac{(V_2 - V_1) \times 10 \times 10^3}{4} \text{ [U/l.]; 25 °C}$$

Micro-Method

With a micro-electrode and a micro dispenser (e.g. micro-dosimat from *Metrohm* or micrometer bulb pipette) and smaller reaction vessel the assay can be scaled down by a factor of 5 without loss of accuracy.

Automation of Assay

For a large number of assays automation by inclusion of a pH-stat is an advantage. For low activities and for the micro-method the Titrigraph of Radiometer is recommended[18]. A combination of *Impulsomat* E 473 with recorder and *Microdosimat* from *Metrohm* is also suitable. With higher activities (pancreatin, duodenal juice) a simpler and economic pH-stat, e. g. the apparatus of *WTW, Weilheim/Obb.*, Germany can be used.

Precision of Method

With values around 10000 U/l. a standard deviation of 850 U/l. was found. The variance coefficient is 9.7%.

Normal Values

In human serum 11–138 U/l. (25 °C); according to[2].

Sources of Error

Effects of drugs and other therapeutic measures: Lipases are inhibited by quinine, various aldehydes and eserine[7].

Interference in the assay technique: Possible interference from the introduction of CO_2 into the reaction mixture or the NaOH used for titration is reduced to a minimum in the method described here. Errors are to be expected if an unsteady or incorrectly calibrated pH-meter or pH-stat is used; similar interference is encountered if the electrode is not defatted between assays.

Specificity of Method

In contrast to the various short-chain fatty acid esters, which are also hydrolysed, sometimes preferentially, by esterases, olive oil (triolein) is a specific substrate for lipases. A substrate with the specificity of olive oil must be used for the determination of lipase activity in the presence of relatively high esterase activity (e.g. as in human serum)[3].

References

1 *P. Desnuelle* in *F. F. Nord:* Advances in Enzymology *23*, 121 [1961].
2 *W. Rick*, Z. klin. Chem. & klin. Biochem. *7*, 530 [1969].
3 *W. Rick*, Enzym. biol. clin. *10*, 350 [1969b].
4 *P. Desnuelle, J. B. Reboud & A. B. Abdeljlil*, Pure appl. Chem. *3*, 423 [1961].
5 *W. Rick*, Der Internist *11*, 110–117 [1970].
6 *W. C. Vogel & L. Zieve*, Clin. Chem. *9*, 168 [1963].
7 *L. D. Bunch & R. L. Emerson*, Clin. Chem. *2*, 75 [1956].
8 *R. P. MacDonald & R. O. Le Fave*, Clin. Chem. *8*, 509 [1962].
9 *N. W. Tietz & E. A. Fiereck* in Standard Methods of Clinical Biochemistry, Vol. 7, ed. in chief *G. R. Cooper*, Academic Press, New York & London [1971], p. 19.
10 *N. W. Tietz & E. A. Fiereck*, Clin. chim. Acta *13*, 352 [1966].
11 *J. King:* Practical Clinical Enzymology, D. Van Nostrand Company Ltd. London [1965] p. 252.
12 *W. Rick*, Verh. dtsch. Ges. inn. Med. *74*, 230 [1968].
13 *A. Pasternak, B. Kuhlbäck & L. G. Tallgreen*, Acta med. scand. Suppl. *412*, 87 [1964].
14 *P. Nilsson-Ehle, H. Torquist & P. Belfrage*, Clin. chim. Acta *42*, 383 [1972].
15 *M. A. Rizack*, J. biol. Chem. *239*, 392 [1964].
16 *R. C. Chandan & K. M. Shahani*, J. Dairy, Sci. *49*, 356 [1966].
17 *C. Litchfield*, Analysis of Triglycerides, Academic Press, New York & London [1972], p. 183.
18 Federation International Pharmaceutique, International Commission for the Standardization of Pharmaceutical Enzymes, Fourth Report, J. mond. Pharm. *3*, 11 [1968].
19 *G. Marchis-Mouren, L. Sarda & P. Desnuelle*, Arch. Biochem. Biophys. *83*, 309 [1959].
20 *R. Willstätter, E. Waldschmidt-Leitz & F. Memmen*, Hoppe-Seyler's, Z. physiol. Chem. *125*, 93 [1923].
21 *P. Desnuelle, M. J. Constantin & J. Baldy*, Bull. Soc. Chim. Biol. *37*, 285 [1955].
22 *A. Hagen & G. Michal*, German Patent No. 1961983 [1972].

Photometric Assay

Felix H. Schmidt, Harald Stork and Katharina von Dahl

Until recently lipase activity (Triacylglycerol acyl-hydrolase, EC 3.1.1.3) was determined exclusively by titrimetric methods[1] with unspecific chromogenic substrates[2]. In many biological samples difficulties are encountered with this technique. A colorimetric method is described here which allows the relatively rapid and sensitive assay of lipase activity in purified enzyme preparations and in biological material.

Application of Method: See p. 814. Since the studies of *Wohlgemuth*[6] it has been known that experimental ligation of the pancreas can result in the appearance of pancreatic enzymes in blood and their excretion in urine. Thus increased amylase or lipase activities in serum and even in urine are indicators of pancreatic disease. In contrast to amylase which occurs in significant amounts in the serum of healthy subjects, lipase is either absent or present in very low activity in normal serum[2].

In the last decade due to the difficulties of the assay in serum the value of these enzymes has been limited to measurement of their activity in duodenal contents as indication of pancreatic function. After administration of secretogues like secretin and pancreozymin the duodenal contents are fractionated and the amount of secretion, bicarbonate and enzymes measured.

Principle

See p. 814. A stabilized olive oil emulsion prepared according to *Fraser*[3] is used as substrate. The free fatty acids are separated in the form of their copper salts by chloroform extraction and the copper is determined colorimetrically with diethyldithiocarbamate[4,5]. The amount of free fatty acid liberated per unit time under optimum conditions is a measure of the lipase activity.

Optimum Conditions for Measurements

The 3 fatty acid residues of a triglyceride molecule are not hydrolysed simultaneously, but rather successively in a 3-stage reaction:

$$\text{Triglyceride} + H_2O \rightarrow \text{Diglyceride} + \text{Fatty Acid}$$
$$\llcorner\!\rightarrow + H_2O \rightarrow \text{Monoglyceride} + \text{Fatty Acid}$$
$$\llcorner\!\rightarrow + H_2O \rightarrow \text{Glycerol} + \text{Fatty Acid}$$

In the absence of calcium ions the main product is diglyceride and, in their presence, monoglyceride[7]. The individual glycerides react at different rates. We measure without Ca^{2+}, so that the hydrolysis to diglycerides and free fatty acids may be considered to be the preferred reaction. Free glycerol is not formed in the reaction time used. Conjugated bile acids such as tauro- and glycocholate activate the enzyme, as does alcohol sulphonate. The pH optimum of pancreatic lipase is around 8–9 with olive oil as substrate[1,8]; in the presence of bile acids it is below 8[9].

Equipment

Thermostat equipped with shaker, spectrophotometer or spectrum-line photometer suitable for measurements at 440 or 436 nm.

Reagents

1. Gum arabic
2. Olive oil, DAB 6
3. Sodium chloride, NaCl (0.89%), A. R.
4. Sodium deoxycholate, $C_{24}H_{39}O_4Na$, for bacteriology
5. Chloroform, A. R.
6. Copper nitrate, $Cu(NO_3)_2 \cdot 3H_2O$, A. R.

7. Triethanolamine hydrochloride, cryst.
8. Sodium hydroxide, 5 N, A. R.
9. sec-Butanol, A. R.
10. Sodium diethyldithiocarbamate, $C_5H_{10}NNaS_2 \cdot 3H_2O$, A. R.
11. Stearic acid, $C_{10}H_{36}O_2$, A. R.

Preparation of Solutions

I. Olive oil suspension (prepared according to *Fraser* (58 mM):
   Blend 5 g. olive oil +5 g. gum arabic with 95 ml. 0.89% NaCl solution in a mixer for two 5 min. periods.
II. Deoxycholate (10 mM):
III. Triethanolamine buffer (1 M; pH 8.5):
   Dissolve 18.6 g. triethanolamine hydrochloride in 70 ml. distilled water, and adjust to pH 8.5 with ca. 16 ml. 5 N NaOH; dilute to 100 ml. with distilled water.
IV. Copper reagent:
   Dissolve 18.6 g. triethanolamine hydrochloride in ca. 70 ml. distilled water and 6.45 g. $Cu(NO_3)_2 \cdot 3H_2O$ in 100 ml. distilled water. Mix both solutions, adjust to pH 7.5 with ca. 18.5 ml. 5 N NaOH (pH meter) and dilute to 200 ml. with distilled water.
V. Diethyldithiocarbamate (11 mM):
   Dissolve 250 mg. sodium diethyldithiocarbamate in sec-butanol and make up to 100 ml.
VI. Stearic acid standard solution (50 μM):
   Dissolve 142.25 mg. stearic acid in 100 ml. chloroform and dilute 1 ml. of this solution to 100 ml. with chloroform.

Stability of Solutions

Store solutions I–V at 0–4 °C. Prepare the olive oil suspension (I) freshly each week. Copper reagent (IV) and sodium diethyldithiocarbamate solution (V) can be used for a month.

Procedure

Collection, Treatment and Stability of Sample

Use only fresh serum free from haemolysis, which has been obtained as soon as possible after collection of the blood. Store duodenal contents in ice and carry out the assay as soon as possible.

Stability of sample:

Serum: In a refrigerator for 24 hr. Duodenal juice: at 0 °C up to a maximum of 2 hr.; deep-frozen for 14 days. Crude pancreatic extracts (pH 8–9): at 4 °C ca. 10% loss of activity.

Assay System

Incubation temperature: 30 °C, incubation volume: 1.1 ml.
Sample Blank: inactive 0.1 ml. of the sample by heating in a water-bath at 70–90 °C for 1 min.
(Treat as sample.)
Reagent blank: 5 ml. chloroform and 2.5 ml. copper reagent (IV); proceed as described in the
protocol given below.
Photometric determination at 440 or Hg 436 nm (room temperature) against the corresponding
sample blank. Include in each series of determinations a standard which contains 5.00 ml.
standard solution (VI) instead of chloroform and read against the reagent blank.

Incubation mixture

Prepare immediately before the assay:

Olive oil suspension (I)	50 volumes
Deoxycholate solution (II)	5 volumes
Triethanolamine buffer (III)	45 volumes

Equilibrate the incubation mixture to 30 °C.

Pipette into stoppered centrifuge tubes:		Concentration in assay mixture
Incubation mixture	1.0 ml.	30 mM olive oil 0.5 mM deoxycholate 0.5 M buffer
Sample	0.1 ml.	up to ca. 1 U/l.
Incubate in a 30 °C bath equipped with shaker. After exactly 10 min. immerse the tubes in a water bath at 70–90 °C for 1 min. to stop the reaction. With a large number of samples carry out the steps at timed intervals.		
Chloroform	5.0 ml.	
Copper reagent (solution IV)	2.5 ml.	
Stopper tubes, shake for 20 min. in a shaker and centrifuge for a few minutes to separate the phases. Suck off the aqueous phase with a polyvinylchloride capillary (water pump). Pipette into a clean centrifuge tube (without carrying over traces of copper.).		
Chloroform layer	2.00 ml.	
Solution V	0.25 ml.	
Measure extinction. The colour is stable for 24 hr.		

Calculations

The following formula applies to the conditions described above. Insert the sample volume v and where
necessary the sample dilution factor F.

$$\text{Volume activity} = \frac{E_{\text{Lipase}} \times 250}{E_{\text{Standard}} \times 10 \times v} \times F \ [U/l.]$$

Precision of Method

The enzyme activity is linearly proportional to the amount of enzyme added (pancreatic cyst fluid, serum, pancreatin). Addition of increasing amounts (10–100 μl.) of a pathological serum gave a non-linear curve. To obtain linear reaction rates with serum no more than 50 μl. should be added.

The lipase activity determined at pH 8.5 with the autotitrator has been compared with the colorimetric technique. The results on 14 duodenal juice and serum samples and 14 crude enzyme preparations from pig pancreas are given in Fig. 1.

Correlation coefficient for duodenal juice and serum r = 0.978; for pancreas preparations r = 0.973. Accuracy (6 assays), pancreatin (6 weighings): mean x = 14.66 U/mg., deviation S_x = 0.6, coefficient of variation = 4.09%.

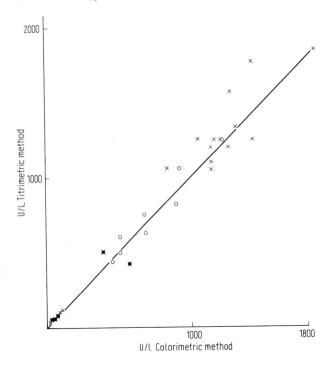

Fig. 1. Comparison of lipase activity by the colorimetric and titrimetric methods.

○ Duodenal juice
× Serum samples
+ Pancreatin

Normal Values

We found a mean activity of 146 ± 89 U/l. serum on 16 samples from healthy subjects. The normal activity in serum is < 300 U/l. allowing two standard deviations. Two serum samples from patients with chronic pancreatitis gave values of 400 U/l. and 680 U/l. Results on 104 duodenal juice samples gave a mean activity of 513 ± 301 U/l. The results on 5 duodenal juice samples from cases of pancreatic insufficiency were as follows: 123, 228, 240, 142 and 84 U/l.

Sources of Error

Haemolysed serum, icteric serum and duodenal juice with a high content of bile pigments or bile acids or samples with a high phosphatide content can give false results.

Specificity of Method

The specificity of the method depends to a large extent on the type of fatty acid residue. Low-molecular weight fatty acids, e. g. those contained in tributyrin and triacetin, are not ideal substrates. This is also true of the unnatural chromogenic substrates, e. g. β-naphthyl-laurate, indoxylactate, etc. The latter substrate is also hydrolysed by peptide-peptido-hydrolases. The method described here is specific for lipase.

References

1 *W. Rick & T. U. Hausamen*, Clin. Chem. *14*, 796 [1968].
2 *A. M. Seligman & M. M. Nachlas*, J. clin. Invest. *29*, 31 [1950].
3 *G. P. Fraser & A. D. Nicol*, Clin. Chim. Acta *13*, 552 [1966].
4 *W. G. Duncombe*, Biochem. J. *88*, 7 [1963].
5 *W. G. Duncombe*, Clin. Chim. Acta *9*, 122 [1964].
6 *I. Wohlgemuth*, Biochem. Z. *9*, 1 [1908].
7 *P. Desnuelle, M. Naudet & M. Constantin*, Biochim. & Biophys. Acta *5*, 561 [1950].
8 *I. S. Cherry & L. A. Crandall*, Amer. J. Physiol. *100*, 266 [1931].
9 *B. Borgström*, J. Lipid. Res. *5*, 523 [1964].

Postheparin Lipase

Wolf-Peter Fritsch and Wirnt Rick [+]

After intravenous injection of heparin, a factor (*clearing factor*) can be detected in human blood plasma. This factor leads to clearing of lipaemic plasma[1]. The reason for this effect is the lipolytic activity of the factor, which is also known as lipoprotein lipase[2,3]. It has been possible to concentrate the activity 16 000-fold from human plasma obtained after injection of heparin[4]; a preparation obtained in this way was found to be chromatographically and electrophoretically homogeneous[5]. Enzyme activities with similar properties have been detected in rat myocardium[6], adipose tissue of rats[7], rat liver, kidney, skeletal muscle, lung, and spleen[8], in the corresponding organs of other mammals, and in milk[9], and have been concentrated from these organs or secretions and partly characterized.

Postheparin lipase hydrolyses triglycerides of long-chain fatty acids. The following products have been isolated with triolein as the substrate[10]: diglycerides (about 9–30% of 1,3-diglycerides and 70–91% of a mixture of 1,2- and 2,3-diglycerides; the latter contains about 73–96% of 2,3-diglycerides), monoglycerides (51–87% of 1 or 3-monoglyceride, 13–49% of 2-monoglyceride), glycerol, and free fatty acids. A number of observations suggest that this sequence of hydrolytic reactions is catalysed by several enzyme proteins[11,12]. For the nomenclature of the lipids, see[13].

For the lipoprotein lipase (*clearing factor;* postheparin lipase) the systematic name Diacylglycerol acylhydrolase, EC 3.1.1.34, was defined by the Enzyme Commission of the IUB. In the following the name postheparin lipase is used instead of lipoprotein lipase according to the nomenclature of Fredrickson et al.[14]. The substrates used for the determination of postheparin lipase activity are chylomicrons[6], coconut oil that has been "activated" with serum[15], unactivated coconut oil[14], commercial triglyceride emulsions such as Intralipid* or Ediol**[16] (Intralipid exhibited properties similar to those of a suspension of chylomicrons, whereas Ediol behaved quite differently; however, different batches of Intralipid also gave substantial differences in the measured activities[17]), or very low density lipoproteins[18], the glycerol formed is then determined or the liberated fatty acids are titrated, usually after extraction. The measurement of the decrease in the extinction of a triglyceride emulsion did not give reproducible results[16]. Very sensitive test methods have been developed with glycerol [1-^{14}C]-trioleate, the liberated [^{14}C]-oleate being determined[19]; it should be noted, however, that the optimum substrate concentration cannot be achieved and that a detergent such as Triton X-100, which may inhibit the liberation of fatty acids by postheparin lipase[20], was used to emulsify the substrate. In one recently reported procedure, triolein is used on a Celite support and the liberated fatty acids are titrated[20], while another makes use of [2-^{3}H]-glyceryl triolein and involves precipitation of the unreacted substrate with trichloroacetic acid and determination of the [^{3}H]-glycerol formed[21].

In connection with the "activation" of triglyceride emulsions by serum as described by various authors, it should be noted that the serum used contains pancreatic lipase (activity in healthy human serum 60–160 U/l. at 25 °C)[22], which causes triglycerides to react during the "activation". The serum must therefore be inactivated before addition to the triglyceride used as the substrate[23]. The linear relation that exists up to high activities between the quantity of enzyme per determination and the liberated product[12,14] gives no indication of the presence of a cofactor in the serum or plasma. The inhibition by sodium chloride in high concentrations (1 M) or by protamine, which was formerly regarded as specific for the postheparin lipase in plasma and was used to differentiate it from other triglyceride-cleaving enzymes, is very variable and strongly dependent on the preparation of the substrate[24].

Application of Method: In biochemistry, in clinical chemistry.

[+] Technical assistance by Marianne Hockeborn.
  * AB Vitrum, Stockholm. Emulsion with 10% soybean oil, 1.2% phosphatides and 2.5% glycerol.
 ** Schenley Laboratories; Serva Heidelberg. Emulsion with 50% coconut oil and Tween 60 as emulsifier.

Continuous Titration of Oleic Acid Liberated from Triolein

Principle

See p. 814. The substrate is an emulsion of triolein in gum arabic solution. The liberated fatty acids or protons are titrated by continuous addition of sodium hydroxide solution, and the pH is thus kept constant, so that there is no need to add buffers.

Optimum Conditions for Measurements

The optimum pH for the hydrolysis of triolein by postheparin lipase is[12] pH 9.0. As an inert polysaccharide, gum arabic serves to give a stable triolein emulsion. Sodium chloride is used in a final concentration of 0.15 M as an activator.

Equipment

1. pH Meter and regulator (e.g. Radiometer pH Meter 26 with Titrator 11).
2. Piston burette (e.g. Radiometer Autoburette ABU 1 with burette unit B 160, corresponding to an available titration volume of 250 μl).
3. Recorder (e.g. Radiometer Titrigraph SBR 2, 25 cm. pen deflection corresponding to 250 μl. of titration solution, i.e. 100% of the stroke of the burette piston).
4. Electrodes (e.g. Radiometer Glass Electrode G 202 C or Glass Electrode G 2222 C, Calomel Electrode K 4112).
5. Burette tip (e.g. glass capillary Radiometer D 4331).
6. Plastic tip for nitrogen inlet.
7. Holder for the electrodes, the burette tip, and the plastic tip for nitrogen inlet (e.g. electrode head of the microtitration assembly Radiometer TTA 31).
8. Titration vessels:
   a) For standardization of the 0.01 N NaOH: e.g. microtitration vessel Radiometer V 521 with corresponding magnetic stirrers.
   b) For enzymatic reactions: 25 ml. beakers with tightly fitting copper temperature vessel.
9. Rubber seal for the electrode head.
10. Magnetic stirrer with magnetic rods, approx. 25 mm. long, 9 mm. in diameter.
11. Ultrathermostat.
12. Starmix or similar.

All apparatus, including the magnetic stirrer and the temperature vessel, is earthed. To avoid electrostatic interference due to plastic bench tops, the entire apparatus may be assembled on an earthed metal foil. Screening against external influences is further improved by addition of potassium nitrate (0.2%, w/v, final concentration) to the water in the thermostat.

Reagents

1. Pure triolein, > 95% triolein
   Olive oil DAB 7 may be used only if extensive comparison analyses have shown that the same activity is obtained with the batch in question as with pure triolein.

2. Gum arabic
   selected, finely powdered
3. Doubly distilled water
   free from carbon dioxide

4. Sodium hydroxide solution, 1 N, 0.1 N, and 0.01 N

Standardization of the 0.01 N NaOH: Introduce 1.0 ml. of CO_2-free dist. water into the titration vessel (8a on p. 825), which has previously been brought to 25 °C. Adjust the water to pH 7.0 by titration with 0.01 N NaOH. To protect against atmospheric carbon dioxide, pass a uniform stream of nitrogen over the liquid in the titration vessel. Introduce 20 μl. of 0.1 N oxalic acid into the titration vessel with a calibrated *Sanz* pipette or similar; record the titration curve of this acid in accordance with the procedure.

Protect 0.01 N sodium hydroxide solution in the storage vessel against atmospheric carbon dioxide by means of a soda lime tube.

5. Hydrochloric acid, 1 N
6. Oxalic acid solution, 0.1 N
7. Sodium chloride, A. R.
8. Nitrogen, free from carbon dioxide

Preparation of Solutions

Prepare all solutions with fresh doubly distilled water.

I. Gum arabic solution (10% w/v):

Mix 50 g. gum arabic and about 450 ml. water in the Starmix (stage I) until the material is completely dissolved (about 15 min.). Make up the solution to 500 ml. with water in a 500 ml. measuring cylinder. Mix well. After a few hours, a sediment is found in the measuring cylinder. Decant the slightly turbid supernatant into a polyethylene bottle.

II. Triolein or olive oil emulsion (20% v/v):

Homogenize 400 ml. 10% gum arabic solution (I) and 100 ml. triolein or olive oil in the Starmix (stage II) for 5 min., adjust to approx. pH 11 with ca. 5 ml. 1 N NaOH, homogenize for a further 2 min., and adjust to ca. pH 9 with N HCl.

III. Sodium chloride solution (2.25 M):

Dissolve 13.14 g. sodium chloride in water and make up to 100 ml.

Stability of Solutions

Store gum arabic solution (I) and substrate emulsion (II) in tightly stoppered containers in a refrigerator at 2° to 4 °C. If growth of bacteria is avoided, the gum arabic solution is stable for at least 4 weeks, and the triolein emulsion for at least 8 days. If slight phase separation occurs, homogenize again for a short time. The sodium chloride solution (III) can be kept almost indefinitely at room temperature.

Procedure

Collection and Stability of Sample

Take blood sample from fasted subject without pretreatment; inject 10 units of heparin i.v. per kg. of body weight, and take a second blood sample 10 min. later.

Obtain serum or plasma without haemolysis and use undiluted. The enzyme activity does not decrease significantly in 24 hr. at room temperature, in 8 days at 0 to 4 °C, or in 2 years at −20 °C.

Assay System

Settings on the pH meter: Temperature compensation "internal"; temperature 25 °C. Settings on the titrator: End point 9.0; selector "up scale"; proportional band 0.05. Settings on the Autoburette: Select "Speed" 1–16, depending on enzyme activity. Setting on the Titrigraph: For the paper drive, use the motor at 4 rpm and the 2.5 mm/revolution gear setting; this corresponds to a speed of the paper drive of 10 mm per min.

Adjust temperatures of substrate emulsion (II), sodium chloride solution (III), and CO_2-free water to 25 °C. Allow enzyme reaction to proceed under nitrogen purge to exclude atmospheric carbon dioxide.

Pipette into a 25 ml. beaker (in the thermostatically controlled copper vessel):			Concentration in assay mixture
Substrate emulsion	(II)	10.0 ml.	133 μl. triolein/ml.
Water (CO_2-free)		3.0 ml.	
Sodium chloride solution	(III)	1.0 ml.	150 mM
Serum or plasma		1.0 ml.	
The pH should be between 9.0 and 9.1; otherwise adjust to this range with a small volume of 0.1 N NaOH or 0.1 N HCl. Add 0.01 N NaOH uniformly from the burette, and record the consumption on the recording paper of the Titrigraph (about 5–10 min.). Determine consumption of NaOH solution V in μl./min.			

Calculations

V = 1 μl. 0.01 N sodium hydroxide solution corresponds to 0.01 μmole of liberated fatty acids. If 1 μl. 0.01 N sodium hydroxide solution is consumed per min., the enzyme activity is 10 U/l. of serum or plasma.

One obtains

$$\text{volume activity} = 10 \times V/\Delta t \text{ [U/l.]; 25 °C}$$

Δt in min.

The activity of the preheparin serum is subtracted from that of the postheparin plasma; the difference corresponds to the postheparin and triglyceride lipase liberated by heparin.

Precision of Method

With activities of about 350 U/l. a value of s = 15 U/l. was found. The coefficient of variation in this range is 4.3%.

Normal Values

A postheparin lipase activity of 200–530 U/l. is found in serum obtained 10 min. after intravenous injection of heparin.

Sources of Error

No interference due to therapeutic measures has so far been observed.

Interference in assay technique: If the surface of the test solution is not adequately protected against atmospheric carbon dioxide by a stream of nitrogen, excessively high activities are found.

If the consumption of sodium hydroxide solution is not linear with respect to time, the recording cannot be evaluated.

Disturbances in the course of recording are mostly due to contamination of the membrane of the glass electrode by triolein. The membrane must therefore be carefully cleaned with ether and ethanol after use and then soaked in water.

Specificity of Method

If the lipase activity of the serum obtained before the heparin injection is subtracted, as described, from the activity of the postheparin plasma, the method is specific for the postheparin lipase. Postheparin lipase and pancreatic lipase cannot be differentiated on the basis of inhibition of the enzyme activity by sodium chloride (final concentration about 1 M, literature data often not clear); neither enzyme is inhibited by sodium chloride (up to 1 M in the test solution). However, if the test solution contains bile acids, e.g. 1.5 mM sodium glycocholate, the activities of both enzymes are decreased to about 10% of the initial value by 1 M NaCl[12,22].

Continuous Titration of Oleic Acid Liberated from 1-Mono-olein

Principle

See pp. 814 and 825. The substrate is a micellar solution of 1-mono-olein in sodium glycocholate solution.

Optimum Conditions for Measurements

The pH optimum for the hydrolysis of 1-mono-olein by postheparin lipase is 9.0, and the optimum substrate concentration is 60 mM 1-mono-olein in micellar solution. Sodium chloride (0.2 M) increases the activity by about 40%. However, since distinct separation of the substrate solution occurs simultaneously, we do not add sodium chloride in the test.

Equipment, see p. 825, equipment 1–12.

Reagents

1. 1-Mono-olein (e.g. Calbiochem), >90% (w/w)

   If the mono-olein contains free oleic acid, dissolve the preparation in ether and wash this solution repeatedly with 2% $NaHCO_3$ solution and then repeatedly with water.
2. Diethyl ether p.a., peroxide-free
3. Doubly distilled water, CO_2-free

4. Sodium hydroxide solutions, 1 N, 0.1 N, and 0.01 N
   For standardization of the 0.01 N NaOH, see p. 826.
5. Hydrochloric acid, 1 N and 0.1 N
6. Oxalic acid solution, 0.1 N
7. Pure glycocholic acid
8. Nitrogen, CO_2-free

Preparation of Solutions

Prepare all solutions with fresh doubly distilled water.

I. Sodium glycocholate solution (75 mM):
Dissolve 1.87 g. glycocholic acid in 3.8 ml. N NaOH and about 40 ml. water (magnetic stirrer). After complete dissolution, adjust pH to about 9.0 with N NaOH. Transfer contents of the beaker quantitatively with water into a 50 ml. graduated flask, make up to 50 ml. with water, and shake. Centrifuge off any fine fibres present.

II. Substrate solution: Micellar solution of 1-mono-olein (approx. 90 mM):
Dissolve 10 g. mono-olein in approx. 30 ml. ether. Rinse the glass vessel of the mixer repeatedly with water at approx. 70 °C. Warm 300 ml. CO_2-free water to 65–70 °C and introduce into the preheated mixer. Add 6.0 ml. 75 mM sodium glycocholate solution (I) and allow to stir at stage I; during stirring, slowly add the mono-olein dissolved in ether. Rinse the beaker repeatedly with small volumes of ether. Homogenize for 5 min. at stage III. Allow the resulting opalescent solution to cool, adjust pH to ca. 11 with 1 N NaOH, then homogenize for a further 2 min. at stage III.

Stability of Solutions

The sodium glycocholate solution (II) is stable for several months at 0 to 4 °C. The unbuffered substrate solution is stable for about 4 weeks if protected from atmospheric carbon dioxide and stored at 0 to 4 °C. Phase separation and turbidity occur at pH values below 6; the solution can then no longer be used.

Procedure

Collection and Stability of Sample, see p. 826.

Since no activity towards 1-mono-olein can be detected in the sample obtained before the heparin injection, only postheparin plasma is investigated.

Assay System

For instrument settings, see p. 827. Adjust temperatures of substrate solution and of CO_2-free water to 25 °C.

Pipette into 25 ml. beaker (in the thermostatically controlled copper vessel):			Concentration in assay mixture
Substrate solution	(II)	10.0 ml.	approx. 60 mM 1-mono-olein in micellar solution
Water (CO_2-free)		4.0 ml.	
Serum or plasma		1.0 ml.	
The pH should be between 9.0 and 9.1, otherwise adjust to this range with small volumes of 0.1 N NaOH or 0.1 N HCl. Add 0.01 N NaOH uniformly from the burette and record the consumption on the recording paper of the Titrigraph (approx. 5–10 min.). Determine the consumption of sodium hydroxide solution V in μl./min.			

Calculations

$V = 1\ \mu l.$ 0.01 N sodium hydroxide solution corresponds to 0.01 μmole of liberated fatty acids. If 1 $\mu l.$ 0.01 N sodium hydroxide solution is consumed per min., the enzyme activity is 10 U/l. of serum or plasma
One obtains

$$\text{volume activity} = 10 \times V/\Delta t\ [U/l.];\ 25\ °C$$

Δt in min.

Precision of Method

For activities of about 300 U/l. it was found that $s = 9$ U/l. The coefficient of variation in this range is 3%.

Normal Values

An activity towards 1-mono-olein of 270-570 U/l. is found in serum or plasma obtained 10 min. after intravenous injection of heparin.

Sources of Error

See p. 828.

Specificity of Method

The method is specific for postheparin lipase[12,22].

References

1 *P. F. Hahn*, Science *98*, 19 [1943].
2 *N. G. Anderson & B. Fawcett*, Proc. Soc. Exp. Biol. Med. *74*, 768 [1950].
3 *R. K. Brown, E. Boyle & C. B. Anfinsen*, J. biol. Chem. *204*, 423 [1953].
4 *C. J. Fielding*, Biochim. biophys. Acta *206*, 109 [1970].
5 *P. Nilsson-Ehle, P. Belfrage & B. Borgström*, Biochim. biophys. Acta *248*, 114 [1971].
6 *E. D. Korn*, J. biol. Chem. *215*, 1 [1955].
7 *E. D. Korn & T. W. Quigley Jr.*, Biochim. biophys. Acta *18*, 143 [1955].
8 *Y. Biale, E. Gorin & E. Shafrir*, Biochim, biophys. Acta *152*, 28 [1968].
9 *E. D. Korn*, J. Lipid Res. *3*, 246 [1962].
10 *N. Morley & A. Kuksis*, J. biol. Chem. *247*, 6389 [1972].
11 *H. Greten, R. I. Levy & D. S. Fredrickson*, J. Lipid Res. *10*, 326 [1969].
12 *W.-P. Fritsch & W. Rick*, Enzymol. biol. clin. *10*, 351 [1969].
   W.-P. Fritsch, M. Hockeborn & W. Rick, Z. anal. Chem. *252*, 198 [1970].
13 The Nomenclature of Lipids, J. Lipid Res. *8*, 523 [1967].
14 *D. S. Fredrickson, K. Ono & L. L. Davis*, J. Lipid Res. *4*, 24 [1963].
15 *E. D. Korn*, J. biol. Chem. *215*, 15 [1955].
16 *J. Boberg & L. A. Carlson*, Clin. chim. Acta *10*, 420 [1964].
17 *J. Boberg*, Lipids *5*, 452 [1970].
18 *G. G. de Pury & F. D. Collins*, J. Lipid Res. *13*, 268 [1972].
19 *H. Greten, R. I. Levy & D. S. Fredrickson*, Biochim. biophys. Acta *164*, 185 [1968].
20 *I. Posner & V. Bosch*, J. Lipid Res. *12*, 768 [1971].
21 *M. C. Schotz & A. S. Garfinkel*, J. Lipid Res. *13*, 824 [1972].
22 *W. Rick*, Z. klin. Chem. u. klin. Biochem. *7*, 530 [1969].
23 *D. S. Fredrickson*, New Engl. J. Med. *286*, 601 [1972].
24 *J. C. La Rosa, R. I. Levy, H. G. Windmüller & D. S. Fredrickson*, J. Lipid Res. *13*, 356 [1972].

Cholinesterases

Wolfgang Pilz

	Page
General Information	831
Manometric Method	835
Electrometric Method	838
Photometric Methods	840
Determination of AChE activity in whole blood	843
Determination of AChE activity in erythrocytes	844
Determination of AChE activity in serum	845
Determination of PChE activity in serum	846
Determination of Dibucaine Number and Fluoride Number in Serum	846
Determination in Blood with Automated Analysers	851

General Information

Since the first edition of this book there have been a large number of new discoveries in the cholinesterase field, especially in regard to human serum. In erythrocytes too a series of new enzymes has been found which belong to the cholinesterase group. In addition, there have been new biochemical findings, e. g. the fact that the enzyme activity depends on the chemical composition of the buffer[1].

Nomenclature

These more recent findings have made a correct nomenclature more difficult to achieve. Many workers consider that acetylcholinesterase occurs only in human erythrocytes, and that the so-called cholinesterase is contained in serum. In this case the term cholinesterase is not defined more precisely. Many clinically important findings are difficult to interpret, because many workers talk of "cholinesterases" without indicating the substrate used. Officially[2,3] three enzymes have been designated cholinesterases.

Table 1. Registered cholinesterases

System Name	Trivial Name	EC Number	Reaction
Acetylcholine hydrolase	Acetylcholine esterase	3.1.1.7	Acetylcholine + H_2O = choline + acetic acid
Acylcholine acyl-hydrolase	Choline esterase	3.1.1.8	Acylcholine + H_2O = choline + corresponding acid
	Benzoylcholine esterase*		Benzoylcholine + H_2O = choline + benzoic acid

How strongly opinions differ, especially on the cholinesterase from human serum, is shown by a compilation of substrates recommended in the last 15 years (Table 2). There is no claim that it is complete. The usually accepted text book information on cholinesterases is given in Table 3[4].

---

* Eliminated according to EC recommendations 1972, since it is a side activity of EC 3.1.1.8.

Table 2. Selection of the most frequently recommended substrates for the determination of cholinesterase in human serum[4].

Butyrylcholine	*Hawkins & Mendel*[5]
Succinylcholine*	*Kalow*[6]
Benzoylcholine	*Kalow & Genest*[7]
Propionylcholine	*Sailer & Braunsteiner*[8]
Butyrylthiocholine	*Koelle & Friedenwald*[9]
Acetyl-β-methylcholine	*Adams & Whittaker*[10]
α-Naphthylbutyrate	*Goedde & Fuss*[11]
α-Naphthylacetate	*Harris, Robson, Geln-Batt & Thornton*[12]
β-Naphthylacetate	*Pinter*[13]
Phenylacetate	*Augustinsson*[14]
Phenylbutyrate	*Augustinsson*[14]
Neostigmine (prostigmine)	*Nowell, Scott & Wilson*[15]
o-Nitrophenylacetate	*Main*[16]
o-Nitrophenylbutyrate	*Main, Miles & Braid*[17]
p-Nitrophenylacetate	*Huggins & Lapides*[18]
Tributyrin	*Adams & Whittaker*[10]
Indophenylacetate	*Kramer & Gamson*[19] (at present standard US Army method)
Indoleacetate	*Augustinsson*[20]
Resorufinbutyrate	*Guilbaut & Kramer*[21]

* Synonyms: suxamethonium, succinylbischoline, diacetylcholine

Table 3. Trivial names and characteristics of cholinesterases from serum and erythrocytes.

Erythrocytes	Serum
Trivial names	
True cholinesterase	False cholinesterase
Genuine cholinesterase	Non-specific cholinesterase
Acetylcholinesterase	Pseudocholinesterase
	Aliesterase
	Butyrylcholinesterase
	Benzoylcholinesterase
	Tributyrinase
*Characteristics**	
pH-Optimum 7.2	pH Optimum 8.4–9.0
Inhibited by excess substrate	No inhibition by excess substrates
Hydrolyses only acetylcholine	Hydrolyses esters of short-chain fatty acids (mainly butyric acid esters) *and* acetylcholine; no specific substrate known.

* Details are reviewed in [22].

Benzoylcholine and butyrylcholine are considered "specific" substrates for pseudocholinesterase (EC 3.1.1.8). The enzyme should be inhibited by excess benzoylcholine (substrate excess)[23-27]. Acetyl-β-methylcholine has been found to be a specific substrate for the enzyme from erythrocytes (EC 3.1.1.7)[23,24]; inhibition by excess substrate occurs only with acetylcholine as substrate[25].

With "preparative starch-paste electrophoresis"[4,28] (where 200 ml. of serum can be added), we were able to separate the individual enzymes described here in preparative amounts[29]. This showed that human serum contains two specific acetylcholinesterases, which hydrolyse acetylcholine only and no other substrate. In addition there are a further 11 non-specific enzymes, e. g. that hydrolyse benzoylcholine, tributyrin, α-naphthylpropionate and other esters. Although the separation of the two specific acetylcholinesterases was straight-forward, the isolation of the 11 non-specific enzymes has been achieved only recently[30].

The two specific acetylcholinesterases are distinguished solely by the pH optimum (pH 7.2 and pH 8.6–8.8), while the 11 non-specific esterases have widely differing characteristics. With various α-naphthylesters as substrate each enzyme shows a different optimum chain length; in addition the pH optima of these enzymes are different (varying between pH 7.2 and 9.0). Each of these 11 enzymes also hydrolyses butyrylcholine, benzoylcholine and several other esters (for details, see[4]). It is therefore necessary when determining cholinesterases in whole serum to speak of two enzymes or a group of enzymes:

1. The sum of the two specific *acetylcholinesterases (AChE)* which hydrolyse only acetylcholine.
2. The sum of 11 non-specific enzymes, for which the term *pseudocholinesterase (PChE)*[31] is gaining acceptance.

The differentiation of PChE and AChE in serum is important because a formal genetic model has been derived from the atypical PChE[31]. A change in the nomenclature would therefore be detrimental. According to the nomenclature proposed here (trivial names) AChE would be EC 3.1.1.7 and PChE EC 3.1.1.8. We have shown that human erythrocytes which have been washed 20 times contain apart from the specific acetylcholinesterase a series of other enzymes, although their activity is lower than that in serum[32] (for details, see Table 4).

Table 4. Comparison of enzymatic activities of whole human serum with a haemolysate of 20-times washed human erythrocytes[32].

Alcohol	Chain length optima of fatty acid with pH optima	
	Whole serum	Erythrocytes washed 20-times with 10 parts 0.9% NaCl solution
Choline	Acetic acid (pH 8.6)	Acetic acid (pH 7.8—8.6)
	Benzoic acid (pH 8.6)	Benzoic acid (pH 7.0—7.2)
	Butyric acid (pH 8.6)	—
α-Naphthol	Propionic acid (pH 8.6)	Acetic acid (pH 7.0–7.5)
β-Naphthol	Propionic acid (pH 8.2–8.6)	Acetic acid (pH 7.7–8.2)
		Butyric acid (pH 7.6–8.2)
		Caproic acid (pH 8.6–9.4)

Importance in Clinical Chemistry

AChE is found in the free state mainly in brain, in nerve cells (in particular the end plates), in muscle (the amount depends on the number of nerve endings), in lung[35] and erythrocytes. Also in the animal kingdom the enzyme is highly active and widely distributed. For example, 400–500 mg. chicken brain can hydrolyse 10^{15} molecules acetylcholine in a millisecond[33]. The electric organ of the electric eel (*Torpedo vulgaris*) is one of the tissues richest in AChE[34]. The site of synthesis of AChE in the human organism is not completely settled. The usually accepted theory that AChE and PChE are formed in human liver does not agree with our findings that an homogenate from serum and erythrocyte-free liver does not hydrolyse either benzoylcholine or acetylcholine[22]. It is however probable that the enzymes are synthesized in liver and are excreted with an inhibitor protein and only become active in the receptor organ. AChE and PChE have been closely studied in rat[36+38] and dog blood[39]; the behaviour is similar to that in humans.

The assay of AChE and PChE is of diagnostic value[40], e. g. in various liver diseases[41,42,52], malignant tumours[43,44], bronchial asthma[45], pulmonary tuberculosis[46,47]. The activity of AChE and PChE in serum is altered by sex hormones[48] and certain drugs (e. g. sympathol, atropine, physostigmine, neostigmine, cocaine, muscarine, etc.)[49], while only the muscle activity of AChE is affected by testosterone and insulin[50].

Particularly important is the fact that AChE and PChE are inhibited to a different extent by the muscle relaxant succinylcholine[51].

In the determination of PChE (e. g. whole serum) a single pH optimum, pH 8.6 has been found for the 11 enzymes[4]. However, in the serum of arteriosclerotic patients and hyperlipaemic patients there are several pH optima[29]. *In vitro* loading of serum from healthy humans with maize oil results in a time-dependent appearance of more pH optima; simultaneously the dibucaine number decreases[53]. Thus there is a probable connection between PChE and fat metabolism, but so far no further results have been reported[54].

In cases of anaesthetic complications after succinylcholine (prolonged apnoea) atypical forms of PChE have recently been found. Atypical forms can be detected by assay of PChE activity on addition of dibucaine or sodium fluoride[55,56]. In the first case the dibucaine number (DN) and in the second the fluoride number (FN) is determined. With the fluoride and dibucaine numbers it is possible to determine two different atypical forms of PChE[57-59]. For a detailed scheme of the genetic model, see [31,54,60a].

All genetic theories stem from the assumption that succinylcholine is hydrolysed *in vivo* by PChE and that an atypical enzyme does not have this hydrolytic capacity. In the meantime we have established that lung is the site of succinylcholine degradation. Succinylcholine is degraded in the lung to succinylmono-choline[35]; this compound has only about one-tenth of the relaxing activity of succinylcholine. Thus the theory depending on presence of the atypical PChE is limited to "genetically-determined atypical PChE". In addition a series of drugs, in particular Endoxan (cyclophosphamide), affect both the activity of PChE and the magnitude of the FN[60]. A critical survey of the literature shows that at least the FN is doubtful and the related genetic model cannot be accepted without some reservations (see also [61]). Moreover, in cases with decreased DN and FN there was no prolonged apnoea after succinylcholine; this is the first known case[62]. We were able to show in 2 cases with greatly increased duration of narcosis after administration of a new short-acting narcotic (not the muscle relaxant succinylcholine) normal DN and normal FN, but a 50% lower absolute activity of PChE and AChE[63]. Although in most cases of prolonged apnoea after succinylcholine a decreased DN has been found. *Kalow* showed in Canada in 1962–65 that of 104 cases of prolonged apnoea 39 had normal DN (reviewed in [22]).

This puts the anaesthetist in a difficult situation, because a lowering of the PChE and a lowering of DN and FN makes the likelihood of anaesthetic complication after succinylcholine and short acting narcotics greater, but by no means certain. Other enzymes apart from AChE and PChE are changed in cases of prolonged apnoea after succinylcholine[63]. The same applies to the picture with myotonia[64,65].

Although no exact evidence for the biochemical connection between decreased PChE, lower DN or FN and an anaesthetic complication can be put forward[66], in all cases PChE, DN and FN should be determined; according to present evidence the probability of a complication after succinylcholine (prolonged apnoea) can then be predicted with greater chance of success. A systematic study of DN and FN before administration of succinylcholine would add more safety and make a correct prediction more likely. In all cases of decreased PChE and lowered DN and FN organophosphorus poisoning must be excluded clinically, because in this situation all three parameters (as well as the serum and erythrocyte AChE) are greatly decreased. Recently a case of this type has been observed[67].

Assay Methods

The most important methods for the determination of activity depend on the following principles: manometric measurements[68-71]; electrometric measurement of the change in pH due to formation of acetic acid[72-74] (in a simplified assay this pH change can be measured with an indicator[75]). This method has also been used as a test paper method to determine PChE in serum[76] (according to[77,78] it gives values which agree with the spectrophotometric methods). Older methods are, for example, the titration of the acetic acid liberated from acetylcholine[79], the photometric measurement of the acetic acid as the ferri-acetate complex[80]. Other possible substrates for PChE are the α-naphthyl esters. Of all the α-naphthyl esters, α-naphthylpropionate is best hydrolysed by whole serum at pH 8.6[4]. As a routine method for the clinical laboratory the determination of the α-naphthol liberated from α-naphthylpropionate has proved popular[81].

The most universal method is the photometric determination of the residual choline esters[82,83,86], because according to the choice of substrate both AChE and PChE can be measured very accurately. The method has been treated as a pure analytical problem before its introduction into enzymatic analysis and the earlier errors contained in similar methods have been corrected[84,85]. The manometric method, the electrometric method (ΔpH), the photometric method and the determination of DN and FN are desribed here. All other useful methods have been mentioned above.

Manometric Method*

Application of Method: In biochemistry and clinical chemistry for the determination of AChE in erythrocytes.

Principle

(1) $(CH_3)_3N-CH_2-CH_2O-CO-CH_3 + H_2O \xrightarrow{\text{AChE}} (CH_3)_3N-CH_2-CH_2OH + CH_3COOH$

The acetic acid formed per unit time is quantitatively measured by the liberation of an equimolar amount of CO_2 from a Ringer bicarbonate buffer.

Optimum Conditions for Measurements

The reproducibility for the analysis of serum is only moderate because it is not possible to work at the pH or substrate optimum. The methods of *Ammon*[70] and *Wirth*[71] are most suitable for the assay of activity in erythrocytes.

To ensure the necessary excess of substrate, the assay system contains 41 μmole acetylcholine chloride. This concentration is sufficient to yield ca. 925 μl. CO_2, which is more than five times the amount of CO_2 actually released. Under the conditions of method (30 min. incubation at 37°C) there is a linear relationship between the amount of CO_2 formed and the time.

Equipment

Warburg apparatus, calibrated *Warburg* flasks (15 ml.) with side arm.

Reagents

1. Sodium chloride
2. Potassium chloride
3. Calcium chloride, anhydrous
4. Sodium hydrogen carbonate

5. Acetylcholine hydrochloride,
   e.g. from Merck, Darmstadt, Germany
6. CO_2 gas
7. CO_2/N_2 gas, 5 vol. % CO_2 in N_2

---

* The section on the manometric method and the electrometric method was compiled by *A. Eben*.

Preparation of Solutions

I. Ringer bicarbonate buffer (pH 7.4):
   a) 96.0 ml. physiological NaCl solution (0.155 M; 9.0 g. NaCl in 1000 ml. distilled water) +2.0 ml. 0.155 M KCl solution (11.5 g. KCl in 1000 ml. distilled water) +2.0 ml. 0.11 M CaCl$_2$ solution (12.22 g. CaCl$_2$ in 1000 ml. distilled water).
   b) 0.155 M NaHCO$_3$ solution (13.0 g. NaHCO$_3$ in 1000 ml. distilled water), immediately before use mix 100 ml. solution a) with 30 ml. solution b) and gas with CO$_2$ for 10 min.

II. Acetylcholine (82 mM; pH 7.2):
   Dissolve 200 mg. acetylcholine chloride just before use in 13.4 ml. Ringer bicarbonate buffer (I).

Stability of Solutions

The NaCl, KCl and CaCl$_2$ solutions are stable for several weeks at 0–4 °C. The Ringer bicarbonate and the acetylcholine chloride solution must be prepared freshly just before use.

Procedure

Collection, Treatment and Stability of Sample

Collection of sample:

Allow the blood collected from the finger tip to flow into a heparinized capillary tube[74]. For this use a melting point tube (100 mm., 1.5–1.8 mm. wide) which has been dipped in heparin solution (1 g. Na heparin in 100 ml. distilled water). Fill the capillary 3/4 full with blood, and melt the empty end in a Bunsen flame and centrifuge for 1 hr. at ca. 3000 g. With an ampoule file cut off the part of the capillary containing the plasma. It is not necessary to wash the erythrocytes with physiological saline. Always collect blood cells from the cell-plasma interphase.

Stability of enzyme in sample:

After centrifugation the samples can be stored for several days at 4 °C without measurable loss of activity.

Assay System

Temperature: 37 °C; total volume: 2.02 ml.; gas phase 5% CO$_2$-95% N$_2$; shaking speed: 90/min.; amplitude: 5 ± 2.5 cm.
To control the endogenous hydrolysis of acetylcholine and to allow for the effects of pressure changes prepare 2 flasks with 1.5 ml. Ringer bicarbonate buffer but without erythrocytes and tip in acetylcholine from the side-arm.

Pipette into the main compartment:			Concentration in assay mixture
Ringer-bicarbonate buffer	(I)	1.50 ml.	85 mM NaCl
			1.77 mM KCl
			1.26 mM $CaCl_2$
Erythrocytes		0.02 ml.	26.6 mM $NaHCO_3$
Pipette into the side-arm:			
Acetylcholine chloride solution	(II)	0.50 ml.	20.3 mM
Place the vessels on the manometers, gas for 3 min. with CO_2 (150 mm. pressure). then immediately gas with 5% CO_2/95% N_2 for 2 min.; equilibrate for 5 min. with open taps. Then close taps and after exactly 30 min. read the manometers.			

Calculations

Convert the pressure readings into volume changes with the vessel constants. Subtract the endogenous hydrolysis of acetylcholine. $\Delta V = 22.4 \,\mu l.$ corresponds to 1 μmole substrate reacting, therefore under the above conditions:

$$\text{Volume activity} = \frac{\Delta V}{22.4} \times \frac{2.02 \times 1000}{30 \times 0.02} = \Delta V \times 150 \; [\text{U/l.}]; 37\,°\text{C}$$

Precision of Method

With values around 80 μl. CO_2 the accuracy is 2.5 μl. CO_2. The coefficient of variation is 5%.

Normal Values

The activity is still given in the literature in "μl. CO_2/30 min."; for conversion to mU/ml., see the above formula.
According to *Hecht* and *Stillger*[86] the normal values for AChE activity in erythrocytes of males are 88.61 $\pm$ 11.04 μl. CO_2/30 min. and of females are 79.3 $\pm$ 7.2 μl. CO_2/30 min. (37 °C). *Callway*, et al.[87] found for males values of 109.6 $\pm$ 16.4 μl. CO_2/30 min. and for females 107.7 $\pm$ 12.8 μl. CO_2/30 min. (37 °C).

Sources of Error

Effects of drugs and other therapeutic measures: See p. 833–834.

Interference in the assay technique: If strict attention is paid to the method and the conditions for the *Warburg* technique (e. g. working in a room without draughts) most of the errors are eliminated.

Specificity of Method

With acetylcholine as substrate the method is specific.

Electrometric Method

Application of Method: In biochemistry and clinical chemistry for the determination of AChE activity in erythrocytes, especially in cases of poisoning with organophosphorus compounds.

Principle

Reaction formula, see p. 835. The acetic acid liberated causes a decrease in pH in a standard buffer solution, which is measured electrometrically over a given time period. The measure of AChE activity is the decrease of pH which occurs in 1 hr. at 25 °C. (Δ pH/hr.).

Optimum Conditions for Measurements

Reproducible results are given by the method of *Michel*[72] which has been slightly modified by *Hamblin* and *Marchand*[73] and by *Wolfsie* and *Winter*[74].
The substrate must always be present in excess, a suitable concentration is 9.9 mM. The final pH value should be read exactly one hour after addition of substrate. The pH decreases linearly between 1 and 120 min. The best incubation temperature is 25 °C.

Equipment

pH Meter (e. g. Type 62, Knick Electronische Meßgeräte, Berlin); glass electrode (e. g. Type X, Metrohm A. G., Herisau, Switzerland); water bath (25 °C); stoppered test tubes (10 ml.).

Reagents

1. Sodium veronal (sodium barbital)
2. Potassium dihydrogen phosphate, KH_2PO_4
3. Potassium chloride, KCl

4. Hydrochloric acid, 1 N
5. Saponin album
6. Acetylcholine chloride
   e. g. from Merck, Darmstadt, Germany.

Preparation of Solutions

Use only doubly distilled water.
  I. Veronal buffer (20 mM; pH 8.1):
     Dissolve 4.1236 g. sodium veronal +0.5446 g. KH_2PO_4 + 44.73 g. KCl in 900 ml. distilled water, add 28 ml. 0.1 N HCl and dilute to 1 000 ml. with distilled water.
 II. Substrate solution (110 mM):
     Dissolve 2.0 g. acetylcholine chloride in 100 ml. distilled water.
III. Saponin (0.01% w/v):
     Dissolve 10 mg. saponin in distilled water and make up to 100 ml.

Stability of Solutions

Add a few drops of toluene to solutions I and II; they are stable for up to 2–3 weeks at 4 °C.

Procedure

Collection, Treatment and Stability of Sample

The collection of the blood and erythrocytes as well as the stability of the sample are as described on p. 836.

Assay System

Final volume: 2.22 ml.; 25 °C (constant temperature water bath); incubation period: 1 hr. Always prepare duplicate determinations. For each series of measurements prepare a blank containing physiological saline instead of sample to measure the non-enzymatic hydrolysis.

Pipette into 10 ml. test tubes			Concentration in assay mixture
Saponin solution (III)		1.00 ml.	45 μg./ml.
Sample (erythrocytes)		0.02 ml.	
Mix thoroughly to give complete haemolysis.			
Buffer solution (I)		1.00 ml.	9 mM veronal
			1.82 mM phosphate
			270 mM KCl
Equilibrate for 10 min. and determine pH (pH$_1$).			
Acetylcholine chloride solution (II)		0.20 ml.	9.9 mM
Shake thoroughly, note time. After exactly 1 hr. read pH (pH$_2$). ΔpH = pH$_1$ — pH$_2$ is used for the calculations. For the blank ΔpH = b (correction factor).			

The initial pH is generally between 7.97 and 8.03. b = correction factor for non-enzymatic hydrolysis.

Calculations

$$\Delta pH/hr. = \Delta pH - b$$

The ΔpH/hr. cannot be directly converted to mU/ml. If pH$_2$ lies between pH 7.3 and 6.9, the correction factor b is a maximum of 0.01 pH units and can be neglected. If pH$_2$ values between 7.5 and 7.9 are found (strong to total inhibition) b has a value of 0.02 to 0.03.

As the rate of the enzymatic hydrolysis varies slightly with changes in pH$_2$, the calculations can be made with the following formula[72]:

$$\Delta pH = \frac{pH_1 - pH_2}{t_2 - t_1} \times f$$

Here is correction factor for the change of the ΔpH/hr. with the pH. The values for f are 1.01 (at pH$_2$ 6.6) or 0.99 (at pH$_2$ 7.9).

Precision of Method

With a ΔpH/hr. of ca. 0.80 a precision of 0.02 to 0.03 ΔpH/hr. was found. The coefficient of variation is 3%.

Normal Values

In human erythrocytes of healthy probands the following values have been found (ΔpH/hr.; 25 °C):

Reference	Men	Women
Michel[72]	0.753	
Wolfsie & Winter[74]	0.861 $\pm$ 0.091	
Grobb et al.[89]	0.809 $\pm$ 0.097	
Rider et al.[90]	0.766 $\pm$ 0.081	0.750 $\pm$ 0.082
Ganelin et al.[91]	0.760 $\pm$ 0.106	
Hecht & Stillger[86]	0.84 $\pm$ 0.11	0.75 $\pm$ 0.07

Sources of Error

Effects of drugs and other therapeutic measures: As described on p. 833–834.

Interference in the assay technique: Possibly by changes in the buffer capacity. Interference can arise due to deterioration of the electrode.

Photometric Methods

The photometric method is universally applicable. The methods described here can be taken as examples. All other esters (chain length of the fatty acid up to C_5[85] or benzoic acid ester) can be used as substrate. Under different reaction conditions esters of the long-chain fatty acids can be used as substrates[92,93]. The considerable non-enzymatic hydrolysis, for example, of choline esters[94], does not affect the calculations.

Application of Method: In biochemistry, in clinical chemistry, in toxicology and in anaesthesia.

Principle

$$
\begin{array}{l}
CH_2OCOR \\
| \\
CH_2 \\
| \\
(1) \quad HCl \cdot N\text{—}(CH_3)_3 + H_2O \xrightarrow{Enzyme} HCl \cdot N\text{—}(CH_3)_3 + RCOOH \\
| \\
OH
\end{array}
\qquad
\begin{array}{l}
CH_2OH \\
| \\
CH_2 \\
| \\
\\
| \\
OH
\end{array}
$$

The removal of acetylcholine per unit time is measured by comparison of the initial concentration in a reference tube (minus the non-enzymatic hydrolysis) with the final concentration in the experimental tube. The acetylcholine is converted with hydroxylamine to the corresponding acylhydroxamic acid, which forms a strongly coloured ferric hydroxamate with ferric salts. The colour is read at 490 nm.

Optimum Conditions for Measurements

For the methods described here the following apply: pH optimum at pH 8.6; incubation time between 30 and 60 min.[83] Measurements at different temperatures may require different measuring conditions (cf. p. 127). Nevertheless, results obtained under the same measuring conditions but at different temperatures were formerly compared with each other ("conversion factors" were determined). Such conversion factors may be correct if determined with a relatively large proband collective; however, they cannot be applied generally to the individual case (cf. p. 129). The value of the following relative reaction rates thus lies in being able to appraise the temperature dependence of the reaction and at the most to compare qualitatively values up to the limit of normal.

°C	18	20	25	30	*37*	42
	1.3	1.2	1.15	1.1	*1.0*	ca. 1.7 (start of enzyme decomposition)

Equipment

Constant temperature incubator; mixer; filter photometer with a filter for 490 nm., e. g. Zeiss-Elko with filter S 49.

Reagents

1. Sodium veronal (sodium barbital)
2. Sodium acetate, crystalline
3. Acetylcholine chloride
   e. g. from Merck, Darmstadt, Germany.
4. Benzoylcholine chloride
5. Sodium hydroxide

6. Hydroxylammonium chloride, hydroxyl-amine
7. Ammonium ferric sulphate, $Fe(NH_4)(SO_4)_2 \cdot 12 H_2O$
8. Potassium nitrate
9. Citric acid, monohydrate
10. Hydrochloric acid, 1 N

Preparation of Solutions

  I. Veronal buffer (0.1 M; pH 8.6):
     Dissolve 49.2 g. sodium veronal and 32.4 g. sodium acetate in about 3000 ml. distilled water, add 30 ml. 1 N HCl and dilute to 5000 ml. with distilled water.
 II. Benzoylcholine stock solution (200 mM):
     Add. 2.4374 g. benzoylcholine chloride* to a 50 ml. volumetric flask, dissolve in distilled water and make up to 50 ml. Store at 4 °C.
III. Acetylcholine stock solution (200 mM):
     Add 1.8167 g. acetylcholine chloride* to a 50 ml. volumetric flask, dissolve in distilled water and make up to volume.
 IV. Substrate benzoylcholine (1.33 mM):
     Mix 150 ml. veronal buffer (I) and 1 ml. benzoylcholine stock solution (II) in a mixer.
  V. Substrate acetylcholine (1.33 mM):
     Mix 150 ml. veronal buffer (I) and 1 ml. acetylcholine stock solution (III) thoroughly in a mixer.
 VI. Sodium hydroxide (2.5 N):
     Dissolve 100 g. NaOH in distilled water and make up to 1000 ml.
VII. Hydroxylamine (1 N):
     Dissolve 70 g. hydroxylammoniumchloride in distilled water and make up to 1000 ml. Store the solution in well-stoppered polyethylene flasks in a refrigerator.

---

* Acetylcholine chloride and benzoylcholine chloride are hygroscopic. It is therefore recommended to determine the purity of the preparations before weighing[84].

VIII. Alkaline hydroxylamine solution:
    Mix equal volumes of solutions (VI) and (VII).
  IX. Iron solution (0.7 M):
    Dissolve 337.5 g. $Fe(NH_4)(SO_4)_2 \cdot 12 H_2O$ in ca. 700 ml. distilled water with gentle warming. Add 25 g. potassium nitrate (dissolved in a little distilled water), transfer to a 1 000 ml. volumetric flask and dilute to the mark.
   X. Citrate buffer (1 M; pH 1.4):
    Dissolve 10.5 g. citric acid +4.0 g. NaOH in the minimum distilled water in a 500 ml. volumetric flask, add 445 ml. 1 N HCl and dilute to the mark with distilled water. Check: dilute 10 ml. of this solution in a volumetric flask to 100 ml.; the pH of this solution must be between pH 1.4 and 1.2.

Stability of Solutions

With the exception of substrate solutions IV and V all the solutions are stable for several months under the stated conditions.

Procedure

The following procedure is common to all methods, so that by appropriate variation of the substrate, samples and incubation time all methods can be described.
In the reference tube the initial concentration of the substrate is measured and in the test the final concentration. Incubation temperature: 37 °C; incubation volume: 27 ml. Colorimetric measurements at 490 nm; light path: 1 cm. Read against a blank cuvette.

Pipette into a 50 ml. volumetric flask:	Reference	Test	Blank	Concentration in assay mixture.
Sample	—	2 ml.	—	
Substrate solution (IV or V)	25 ml.	25 ml.	—	1.23 mM
Mix and incubate.				
Alkaline hydroxylamine solution (VIII)	5 ml.	5 ml.	5 ml.	0.125 N NaOH 50 mM NH_2OH
Sample	2 ml.	—	—	
Citrate buffer (X)	5 ml.	5 ml.	5 ml.	0.10 M
Ferric solution (IX)	10 ml.	10 ml.	10 ml.	0.14 M

Allow the ferric solution to run slowly down the walls of the flask. Dilute to the mark with distilled water, shake thoroughly and allow to stand for 20 min. at room temperature. Filter the solutions through a double folded filter paper* and discard the first portion of filtrate. Measure the extinction of the filtrates. The extinction difference ΔE between E_R (reference) and E_T (test) is used for the calculations.

---

* e. g. Schleicher & Schuell No. 602 h 1/2.

Photometric Determination of AChE Activity in Whole Blood

Collection, Treatment and Stability of Sample

Collection of sample:

Collect 0.2 ml. blood from a well-cleaned finger tip and transfer to 5 ml. distilled water (rinse the pipette several times). Use the haemolysate for the assay.

Stability of sample:

The haemolysate can be stored for a maximum of 24 hr. at 4 °C. Storage for longer periods results in loss of activity.

Assay System

As for the general procedure (see above). Substrate: acetylcholine (solution V); incubation time: 30 min.

Calculations

For measurements at 490 nm the extinction of the dye is 0.961 cm.^{2}/μmole. Therefore according to the equation (2) on p. 312 the amount of dye formed from the non-hydrolysed acetylcholine in 50 ml.:

$$c = \frac{\Delta E \times 50}{0.961 \times 1.0} \; [\mu\text{mole}/50 \text{ ml.}]$$

The AChE activity in whole blood is given by:

$$\text{Volume activity} = \frac{\Delta E \times 50}{0.961 \times 1.0} \times \frac{1}{0.08 \times 30} \times 1000 = \Delta E \times 21667 \; [\text{U/l.}]$$

Precision of Method

For a mean value of 6300 U/l. (37 °C) a standard deviation of 13.42 U/l. was found. The coefficient of variation is 0.213%.

Normal Values

6300 ± 1500 U/l. whole blood.

Sources of Error

Effects of drugs and other therapeutic measures: The enzyme activity is strongly inhibited in cases of poisoning with organophosphorus compounds (alkyl phosphates, insecticides[95]). Inhibition also occurs with eserine[96], neostigmine (prostigmine)[97] and Endoxan (cyclophosphamide)[60]. The determination of AChE in whole blood is of importance when there is a question of possible poisoning with organophosphorus compounds. A temporary decrease in activity occurs after administration of oestrogens, cortisone, and drugs, such as quinine, atropine, hyoscyamine, morphine, codeine, caffeine, theobromine, theophylline, barbiturates, antipyrine, sulphanilamide, quaternary ammonium salts, antimalarial preparations, atoxyl, chloroform, amidone, anti-histamines, reserpine, lysergic acid and derivatives, etc.[98].

Interference in the assay technique: With pH values above 1.7 the formation of hydroxamate is no longer reproducible. The occasional practice of correcting the veronal buffer (I) with NaOH and a glass electrode, results in large errors in the results (too low values), because iron hydroxide is precipitated and the iron concentration is no longer sufficient to form the complex.

Specificity of Method

With acetylcholine as substrate the sum of the two specific serum acetylcholine esterases and the whole blood acetylcholinesterase is determined. The method is therefore specific.

Details for Measurements in Tissues

Acetylcholinesterase occurs in many tissues. It is not known if this is always a single protein. This, however, has no effect on the assay technique because a specific substrate is always used.

Photometric Determination of AChE Activity in Erythrocytes

Collection, Treatment and Stability of Sample

Collect 0.2 ml. blood from a well-cleaned finger tip or ear lobe and transfer to ca. 10 ml. physiological saline (rinse pipette several times). In the usual way wash three times with 10 ml. physiological NaCl each time and centrifuge (it is best to draw off the supernatant fluid with a syringe and long needle). Free the erythrocytes as well as possible from the NaCl solution, pipette on them 5.0 ml. distilled water and mix thoroughly; haemolysis occurs immediately.

Stability of sample:

The suspension of erythrocytes in physiological NaCl is stable for several days at 4 °C without loss of activity. The haemolysate should be analysed as rapidly as possible (at least within 4 hr.).

Assay System

As for the general procedure. Substrate: acetylcholine; incubation time: 30 min.

Calculations

For extinction coefficient, see p. 843. The AChE activity in whole blood is given by:

$$\text{Volume activity} = \Delta E \times 21\,667 \; [\text{U/l.}]$$

Note

The determination can be carried out with greater accuracy if the haemoglobin content of the haemolysate is determined[98a] and the enzyme activity is expressed in mU/mg. Hb.

Precision of Method

A mean of 4000 U/l. whole blood was found in erythrocytes with a standard deviation of 8.74 U/l. whole blood. The coefficient of variation is 0.219%.

Normal Values

4000 ± 1000 U/l. whole blood.

Sources of Error, see p. 843.

Specificity of Method

As the acetylcholinesterase of erythrocytes only hydrolyses acetylcholine, the method is specific.

Determination of AChE Activity in Serum

Collection, Treatment and Stability of Sample

Collection of sample:

Collect blood from the cubital vein, allow to coagulate at room temperature and centrifuge at ca. 3000 g. Do not use haemolysed serum. Add 0.2 ml. serum to 5.0 ml. distilled water.

Stability of sample:

Undiluted serum is stable for several days at 4 °C. Diluted serum is not stable for longer than 4–6 hr.

Assay System

As for the general procedure. Substrate: acetylcholine; incubation time: 60 min.

Calculations

For extinction coefficient, see p. 843. The AChE activity in serum is given by:

$$\text{Volume activity} = \Delta E \times 10833 \text{ [U/l.]}$$

Precision of Method

For a mean value 2500 U/l. serum a standard deviation of 4.91 U/l. was found. The coefficient of variation is 0.196%.

Normal Values

2500 ± 625 U/l. serum.

Sources of Error, see p. 843.

Specificity of Method

As serum contains 2 specific acetylcholinesterases, which only hydrolyse acetylcholine and no other substrate[4], the method is specific.

Determination of PChE Activity in Serum

Assay System

As for the general procedure. Substrate: benzoylcholine; incubation time: 60 min.

Calculations

For extinction coefficient, see p. 843. The PChE activity in serum is given by:

$$\text{Volume activity} = \varDelta E \times 10833 \text{ [U/l.]}$$

Precision of Method

For a mean value of 2000 U/l. serum a standard deviation of $\pm$ 3.625 U/l. was found. The coefficient of variation is 0.207%.

Sources of Error, see p. 843.

Normal Values

2000 $\pm$ 500 U/l. in Serum.

Specificity of Method

There are 11 enzymes contained in human serum, which hydrolyse benzoylcholine and many other esters at different rates. The above method determines the sum of the activity of the 11 enzymes against a non-specific substrate. The pH-optimum of the sum of the 11 enzymes (whole serum) is pH 8.6. Strongly lipaemic sera may have several pH optima[53].

Determination of Dibucaine Number (DN) and Fluoride Number (FN) in Serum

As the two terms DN and FN, are in agreement with the extensive literature and a formal genetic model only under certain well-defined conditions (not optimum reaction conditions, e. g. substrate concentration, chemical composition of the buffer[1]), it is best to use the reaction conditions first reported by *Kalow* et al. [102], and later adopted throughout the world. Under these conditions PChE can also be measured in serum[77], but they do not permit conversion to International units (spectrophotometric assay of *Kalow* et al.[77], for details, see[78]).

A variation of the assay, which consists of increasing the time of incubation (giving higher $\varDelta E$ values) and results in better reproducibility, can be used, even near the limits, without the risk of interfering with the connection between known data and the genetic model[99].

While the original method of *Kalow* et al.[101] required an incubation time of 3 min. (see also *Goedde* et al.[100] and *Schmiedinger* and *Doenicke*[78]) the incubation time was extended to 10 min.[31]. By a further extension to 20 min.[99] the method can be better controlled and now allows more accurate differentiation which should lead to an extension of the genetic model.

In only a small proportion of the published methods (e. g.[31]) is a blank used. In our modification a blank is required because measurements against air at 240 nm can, in certain circumstances, lead to large errors.

Application of Method: In anaesthesia and in genetics.

Principle

Fluoride and dibucaine inhibit pseudocholinesterase; the ratio between the PChE activities in the inhibited and non-inhibited reactions gives the dibucaine or fluoride numbers. Benzoylcholine has a stronger absorption at 240 nm than the hydrolysis products, benzoic acid and choline. The decrease in extinction is linear with time for 20 min. (20 °C).

Optimum Conditions for Measurements

The assay conditions have been chosen[99] so that the results will be consistent with the existing work (formal genetic model, etc.) but will also guarantee far greater reliability and accuracy than the methods published so far. Conditions: 66.7 mM phosphate buffer, pH 7.4; substrate: 200 μM benzoylcholine; 40 μM dibucainehydrochloride; 200 μM sodium fluoride; reaction time: 20 min. at 20 °C.

Equipment

Spectrophotometer with UV attachment and constant temperature cuvette holder.

Reagents

1. Disodium hydrogen phosphate, $Na_2HPO_4 \cdot 2H_2O$
2. Potassium dihydrogen phosphate, KH_2PO_4
3. Benzoylcholine chloride*
4. Sodium fluoride
5. Dibucaine (cinchocaine HCl = nupercaine = percaine) (mol. wt. 379.92)

Preparation of Solutions

  I. Phosphate buffer (66.7 mM; pH 7.4):
     Dissolve 47.213 g. $Na_2HPO_4 \cdot 2H_2O$ and 9.078 g. KH_2PO_4 in 5000 ml. distilled water.
 II. Benzoylcholine stock solution (20 mM):
     Dissolve 487 mg. benzoylcholine chloride in distilled water and make up to 100 ml. (stable for several weeks at 4 °C).
III. Substrate benzoylcholine (200 μM):
     Dilute 1 ml. solution II to 100 ml. with solution I (stable for about 6−8 hr.).
 IV. Sodium fluoride stock solution (20 mM):
     Dissolve 84 mg. sodium fluoride in distilled water and make up to 100 ml. (not stable for longer than 24 hr.).

---

* Benzoylcholine chloride is hygroscopic. It is recommended that the purity is determined[84] before weighing.

V. Sodium fluoride inhibitor solution (200 μM):
   Dilute 1 ml. solution IV to 100 ml. with solution I.
VI. Dibucaine stock solution (3 mM):
   Dissolve 151.9 mg. dibucaine in distilled water and make up to 100 ml. (not stable for longer than 24 hr.).
VII. Dibucaine inhibitor solution (40 μM):
   Dilute 1 ml. solution VI to 100 ml. with solution I (not stable for more than 24 hr.).

Stability of Solutions

With the exception of the phosphate buffer (solution I), all solutions should be prepared freshly.

Procedure

Collection, Treatment and Stability of Sample

Collect blood from a cubital vein with the minimum of stasis, allow to coagulate and centrifuge at ca. 3000 g. Dilute 0.5 ml. serum with phosphate buffer (solution I) to 100 ml. Only use fresh non-haemolysed serum. Dilute serum is not stable for more than 6–8 hr. Undiluted serum can be stored for several days at 4 °C.

DN Assay System

Wavelength: 240 nm; light path: 1 cm. quartz cuvettes; final volume: 4 ml.; temperature: 20 °C (constant temperature cuvette holder); read against blank.
Prepare a blank for both the inhibited and non-inhibited reactions, containing 2 ml. buffer (solution I) +2 ml. dilute serum.

FN Assay System

Conditions analogous to the DN assay system; instead of dibucaine inhibitor solution (VIII) add sodium fluoride inhibitor solution (V).

Pipette into the cuvettes:	Non-inhibited reaction	Inhibited reaction	Concentration in assay mixture
Buffer (I)	1 ml.	—	66.7 mM phosphate
Sample (dilute serum)	2 ml.	2 ml.	
Dibucaine inhibitor solution (VII)	—	1 ml.	10 μM dibucaine
Substrate solution (III)	1 ml.	2 ml.	50 μM benzoylcholine
Mix, after 1 min. read extinction E_1 and after exactly a further 20 min. read extinction E_2. The value $\Delta E = E_1 - E_2$ is used for the calculations.			

Calculations

According to *Kalow* et al.[102] the dibucaine number and according to *Goedde*[100] the fluoride number is calculated by the following formula:

$$DN\,(FN) = 100 \times \left(1 - \frac{\Delta E_{inhibited\ reaction}}{\Delta E_{non-inhibited\ reaction}}\right)$$

To simplify the calculations the formula can be changed:

$$DN\,(FN) = 100 \times \left(\frac{\Delta E_{non-inhibited\ reaction} - \Delta E_{inhibited\ reaction}}{\Delta E_{non-inhibited\ reaction}}\right)$$

Precision of Method

With a mean value for DN of 82 a standard deviation of 0.365 and a coefficient of variation of 0.445% were found.
The corresponding values for FN were a mean of 57, a standard deviation of 0.374 and a coefficient of variation of 0.655%.

Normal Values

In general anaesthetic practice the following values are accepted[103,104]:

	Normal	Intermediate	Atypical
DN	70—86	below 60	below 30
FN	55—60	40—55	20—28

In the most recent literature different values for DN have been found resulting in four groups.[78]

Sources of Error

Effects of drugs and other therapeutic measures: Cytotoxic drugs and organophosphorus esters (even in therapeutic doses, e. g. Endoxan[60]) can affect the fluoride number.

Interference in the assay technique: No interference occurs if the method is followed.

References

1 *W. Pilz & A. T. Boo,* Z. Klin. Chem. Klin. Biochem., *5,* 173 [1967].
2 Enzyme Nomenclature, Recommendations 1964 (Paper back edition), Elsevier Publ. Co., Amsterdam 1965.
3 *M. Florkin & E. H. Stotz:* Comprehensive Biochemistry, Vol. 13,2. Edn., Elsevier Publ. Co., Amsterdam 1965.
4 *W. Pilz,* in 6th International Congress of Clinical Chemistry, Ed. by O. Wieland, Vol. 2, p. 121, 1968.
5 *R. D. Hawkins & B. Mendel,* Brit. J. Pharmacol., *2,* 173 [1947].
6 *W. Kalow,* Anästhesiology, *20,* 505 [1959].
7 *W. Kalow & K. Genest,* Canad. J. biochem. Physiol., *35,* 339 [1957].
8 *S. Sailer & H. Braunsteiner,* Klin. Wschr., *37,* 986 [1959].
9 *G. B. Koelle & J. B. Friedenwald,* Proc. Soc. exp. Biol., N. Y., *70,* 617 [1949].
10 *D. H. Adams & V. P. Whittaker,* Biochem. Biophys. Acta *3,* 358 [1948].
11 *H. W. Goedde & W. Fuss,* Klin. Wschr. *42,* 286 [1964].
12 *H. Harris, E. B. Robson, A. M. Glen-Batt & I. A. Thornton,* Nature, London, *220,* 1185 [1963].

13 *L. Pinter*, Acta physiol. Acad. Sci. hung., *11*, 39 [1957].
14 *K. B. Augustinsson*, Nature, London, *181*, 1786 [1958].
15 *P. T. Novell*, Brit. J. Pharmacol., *19*, 498 [1962].
16 *A. R. Main*, Biochem. J., *79*, 246 [1961].
17 *A. R. Main, K. E. Miles & P. E. Braid*, Biochem. J., *78*, 769 [1961].
18 *Ch. Huggins & J. Lapides*, J. biol. Chem. *170*, 467 [1947].
19 *D. N. Kramer & R. M. Gamson*, Analyt. Chem., *30*, 251 [1958].
20 *K. B. Augustinsson*, Acta Chem. scand., *13*, 571 [1959].
21 *G. G. Guilbaut & D. N. Kramer*, Analyt. Chem., *37*, 120 [1965].
22 *W. Pilz*, Z. Klin. Chem. Klin. Biochem., *5*, 1 [1967].
23 *B. Mendel, D. B. Bundel & H. Rudney*, Biochem. J., *37* 473 [1943].
24 *B. Mendel & H. Rudney*, Biochem. J., *37*, 59 [1943].
25 *K. B. Augustinsson & D. Nachmannsohn*, Science *110*, 98 [1949]; see *W. Pilz*, Z. ges. exp. Med., *132*, 310 [1959].
26 *W. K. Berry*, Biochem. Biophys. Acta, *39*, 346 [1960].
27 *W. Kalow, G. Genest & N. Staron*, Canad. J. Biochem., *34*, 637 [1956]; see *W. Pilz*, Z. ges. exp. Med., *132*, 310 [1959].
28 *W. Pilz*, Z. analyt. Chem., *243*, 587 [1968].
29 *W. Pilz*, Hoppe-Seylers Z. physiol. Chem., *345*, 80 [1966].
30 *W. Pilz*, 1973, in preparation.
31 *H. W. Goedde, A. Doenicke & K. Altland*, Pseudocholinesterasen, Springer Verlag, 1967.
32 *W. Pilz & I. Johann*, Biochim. Biophys. Acta 1973, in press.
33 *D. Nachmannsohn*, C. R. Seances Soc. Biol. Filiales Associes, *127*, 670 [1938].
34 *D. Nachmannsohn & N. Lederer*, C. R. Seances Soc. Biol. Filiales Associes, *130*, 321 [1939].
35 *W. Pilz & H. Hörlein*, Hoppe-Seylers Z. physiol. Chem., *348*, 65 [1967]; *W. Pilz & I. Johann*, Hoppe-Seylers Z. physiol. Chem., *348*, 73 [1967].
36 *W. Pilz & A. Eben*, Hoppe-Seylers Z. physiol. Chem., *348*, 625 [1967].
37 *A. Eben & W. Pilz*, Arch. Toxikol., *23*, 27 [1967].
38 *W. Pilz & A. Eben*, Arch. Toxikol., *23*, 17 [1967].
39 *W. Pilz & A. Eben*, unpublished.
40 *L. J. Vorhaus & R. M. Kark*, Amer. J. Med., *14*, 707 [1953].
41 *L. J. Vorhaus, H. S. Scudamore & R. M. Kark*, Amer. J. med. Sci., *221*, 140 [1951].
42 *F. Zinnitz & H. Enzinger*, Münchener med. Wschr., 1950, 1170,
43 *W. Pilz & H. Hörlein*, Europ. J. Biochem., in preparation.
44 *H. J. Wetstone, R. V. LaMotta, A. Belluci, R. Nennant & B. V. White*, Ann. intern. Med., *52*, 102 [1960].
45 *H. H. Scudamore, L. J. Vorhaus & R. M. Kark*, J. Lab. clin. Med. *37*, 860 [1951].
46 *H. Münch & E. Auenmüller*, Beitr. Klin. Tuberkul., *109*, 482 [1953].
47 *H. Hörlein*, Tuberkulosearzt, *4*, 512 [1950].
48 *K. Habbe & W. Pförtner*, Dtsch. med. Wschr., *76*, 269 [1951].
49 *K. Çeeser*, Klin. Wschr., *17*, 1811 [1938].
50 *A. N. Granitsas, N. Dede & A. J. Philippu*, Nature London, *185*, 320 [1960].
51 *W. Pilz, A. T. Boo & E. Stelzl*, Z. Klin. Chem. Klin. Biochem., *5*, 134 [1967].
52 *W. Pilz & U. Korallus*, Der Anästhesist 1973, in press
53 *W. Pilz & E. Stelzl*, Z. Klin. Chem. Klin. Biochem. *6*, 30 [1968].
54 *G. S. Robertson*, Brit. J. Anästh., *38*, 355 [1966].
55 *W. Kalow & K. Genest*, Canad. J. Biochem., *35*, 339 [1957].
56 *H. Harris*, Brit. med. Publ., *17*, 217 [1961].
57 *H. Harris & M. Whittaker*, Nature, London, *191*, 496 [1961].
58 *H. Lehmann, J. Liddell, B. Blackwell, D. S. O'Connor & A. V. Paws*, Brit. med. J., 1963 I, 1116.
59 *H. Harris, E. B. Robson & M. Whittaker*, Ann. hum. Genet., *27*, 53 [1963].
59a *W. Kalow*, Anästhesist, *15*, 13 [1966].
60 *A. Priesching, Helga Seidl & K. Steinbereithner*, Wiener klin. Wschr., *79*, 238 [1967].
60a *K. Steinbereithner*, Wiener med. Wschr., *76*, 785 [1964].
61 *K. Steinbereithner*, personal communication
62 *H. Garritzmann & W. Pilz*, J. Anestysiol. 1973, in press.
63 *W. Pilz, H. von Beeck & E. Scherz*, J. Anestysiol. 1973, in press.
64 *W. Pilz*, Z. Klin. Chem., *3*, 89 [1965].
65 *H. Hutschenreuter, W. Pilz & U. Herz*, J. Anestysiol. 1973, in press.
66 *W. Pilz & H. Hörlein*, Hoppe-Seylers Z. physiol. Chem., *339*, 157 [1964].
67 *R. Seybold & K. H. Bräutigam*, Dtsch. Med. Wschr., *93*, 1405 [1968].
68 *K. B. Augustinsson*, Acta physiol. scand., *15*, Suppl. *52*, 1 [1948].
69 *K. B. Augustinsson*, Acta physiol. scand., *35*, 40 [1955].

70 R. Ammon, Pflügers Arch. Physiol., 233, 486 [1934].
71 W. Wirth, Arch. exper. Path. Pharmak., 217, 144 [1953].
72 H. O. Michel, J. Lab. clin. Med., 34, 1 564 [1949].
73 D. O. Hamblin & H. F. Marchand, N. Y. American Cyanid Company, March 1951 cited in Arch. Indust. Hyg., 6, 43 [1952].
74 J. H. Wolfsie & G. D. Winter, A. M. A. Arch. Indust. Hyg., 6, 43 [1952].
75 J. Gregoire, J. Gregoire & N. Limozin, Bull. soc. Chim. biol., 37, 66, 81 [1955].
76 R. Richterich, Schweiz. Med. Wschr., 92, 263 [1962].
77 W. Kalow & H. A. Lindsay, Canad. J. Biochem. physiol., 33, 568 [1955].
78 St. Schmiedinger & A. Doenicke, Z. Klin. Chem., 4, 273 [1966].
79 O. G. Cesaire, Ann. Biol. clin. (Paris), 10, 84 [1952].
80 N. O. Abdon & B. Monäs, Scand. Arch. Physiol., 76, 1 [1937].
81 W. Pilz & I. Johann, Z. analyt. Chem., 210, 113 [1965].
82 W. Pilz, Z. ges. exper. Med., 132, 310 [1959].
83 W. Pilz, I. Johann & E. Stelzl, Klin. Wschr., 43, 1 227 [1965].
84 W. Pilz, Z. analyt. Chem., 162, 81 [1958].
85 W. Pilz, Z. analyt. Chem., 166, 190 [1959].
86 H. Hecht & E. Stillger, Z. Klin. Chem. Klin. Biochem., 5, 156 [1967].
87 S. Calaway, D. R. Davies & J. Rutland, Brit. Med. J., 2, 812 [1951].
88 E. Stillger, Inaugural-Dissertation, Med. Fakultät, Univ. Köln, 1966.
89 D. Grob, W. L. Garlick & A. M. Harvey, Bull. Johns Hopkins Hosp., 87, 106 [1950].
90 J. A. Rider, J. L. Hodges Jr., J. Swader & A. D. Wiggins, J. Lab. Clin. Med., 50, 376 [1957].
91 R. S. Ganelin, C. Cueto Jr., & G. A. Mail, J. A. M. A., 188, 807 [1964].
92 W. Pilz, Z. analyt. Chem., 193, 338 [1963].
93 W. Pilz & I. Johann, Z. analyt. Chem., 218, 426 [1966].
94 W. Pilz & I. Johann, Z. Klin. Chem., 4, 215 [1966].
95 G. Schrader: Die Entwicklung neuer Insektizide auf Grundlage organischer Fluor- und Phosphor-verbindungen, Verlag Chemie, Weinheim/Bergstraße, 1952.
96 L. Loewi & N. Navratil, Pflügers Arch. ges. Physiol. Menschen Tiere, 214, 678 [1926].
97 R. Ammon, Zbl. Inn. Med. 63, 114 [1942].
98 R. Abderhalden: Klinische Enzymologie, Verlag Georg Thieme, Stuttgart 1958.
98a W. Pilz, I. Johann & E. Stelzl, Z. analyt. Chem., 215, 260 [1966].
99 W. Pilz, unpublished.
100 H. W. Goedde, D. Gehring & R. Hofman, Z. analyt. Chem., 212, 248 [1965].
101 W. Kalow, K. Genest & N. Staron, Canad. J. Biochem., Physiol., 34, 637 [1956].
102 W. Kalow & K. Genest, Canad. J. Biochem. Physiol., 35, 339 [1957].
103 K. Steinbereithner, personal communication.
104 J. C. Thompson & M. Whittaker, Acta genet. (Basel), 16, 209 [1966].

Determination in Blood with Automated Analysers

Jacob B. Levine

We use acetylthiocholine as substrate and measure the thiocholine formed with 5 : 5-dithiobis-(2-nitroben-zoic acid). *Ellman*[1] was first to use DTNB as a sensitive indicator for SH-groups. He used this compound on the basis of the work of *Koelle*[2] to follow the enzymatic hydrolysis of thiocholine esters. *Garry*[3] developed a suitable routine method for the clinical chemistry laboratory. The automated method[4-6] that follows is based on this method[3].

Application of Method: Cholinesterases are inhibited by organophosphorus insecticides and carbamates. The automated micro-method described here is used for toxicity testing in small laboratory animals and in screening people who handle insecticides.

Principle

(1)   Acetylthiocholine $+ H_2O \xrightarrow{\text{ChE}}$ Thiocholine $+$ Acetic acid

Thiocholine reacts with 5:5-dithiobis-(2-nitrobenzoic acid), DTNB, to give a yellow derivative 5-thio-2-nitrobenzoic acid, which can be measured at 420 nm.

The reaction product diffuses by dialysis into the recipient stream which contains DTNB. As interfering pigments from haemolysed blood and lipaemic sera are non-dialysable a blank is unnecessary.

Optimum Conditions for Measurements

For human acetylcholinesterase we found 1 : 10 diluted blood cells and 2.8 mM acetylthiocholine optimum; for human plasma a 1 : 4 dilution and 5.3 mM acetylthiocholine. These dilutions give about the same extinctions with normal samples. Higher concentrations of substrate inhibit the erythrocyte enzyme by about 10%.

Equipment

The Autoanalyzer®* system consists of sampler II, proportioning pump, manifold system, dialyser with type C membrane, 37 °C heating bath with two 12 metre heating coils, recorder colorimeter with filter for 420 nm and 15 nm flow-through cuvette. Flow diagram, see Fig. 1.

Reagents

1. Tris-hydroxymethyl-aminomethane, tris
2. Acetylthiocholine iodide
3. 5 : 5-Dithiobis-(2-nitrobenzoic acid), DTNB
4. Thiocholine iodide
5. Sodium chloride, NaCl
6. Hydrochloric acid, 1 N
7. Brij 35*
8. Triton X-100**

Preparation of Solutions

Use only fresh distilled water.
  I. Tris buffer (50 mM; pH 7.4):
     Dissolve 6.1 g. tris in 850 ml. distilled water, add 6.64 g. NaCl and 35 ml. 1 N HCl and adjust to pH 7.4 at 37 °C with 1 N HCl. Dilute with distilled water to 1 000 ml. Before use add 0.5 ml. Brij 35 per litre.
 II. Acetylthiocholine iodide:
     For measurements in plasma and serum (38 mM): dissolve 1.094 g. acetylthiocholine iodide in 100 ml. distilled water.
     For measurements in erythrocytes (20 mM): dissolve 576 mg. acetylthiocholine iodide in 100 ml. distilled water.

---

  * Technicon Instruments Corporation, Tarrytown N. Y., USA.
 ** Rohm and Haas Company, Philadelphia, USA.

III. DNTB (2.5 mM):
   Dissolve 99 mg. DTNB in 1 000 ml. tris buffer (solution I) .
IV. Thiocholine iodide (100 mM stock solution):
   Dissolve 289 mg. thiocholine iodide in distilled water and make up to 100 ml.; prepare
   the following standards by dilution of this solution with distilled water: 1, 3, 5, 7, and
   10 mM.

Stability of Solutions

Prepare the substrate solution freshly each day. The buffer is stable at room temperature. The DTNB
solution is stable for 1 week in the refrigerator. The thiocholine iodide stock solution is stable for 3 months
at -20 °C; the standard solutions prepared from it are stable for at least 3 weeks at 5 °C.

Procedure

Collection, Treatment and Stability of Sample

Serum, plasma and erythrocytes can be analysed with this method. Separate the samples as
quickly as possible into plasma and erythrocytes and store at 0–5 °C until analysed. Collect
blood from finger tips with heparinized capillaries, $7.5 \times 1.4 - 1.6$ mm. (Aloe Scientific
No. V 23922 C). Fill the capillaries within 10–15 mm. of the upper end, stopper with *Adams
Weisston* (plastic clay) and centrifuge for 4 min. in a micro-capillary centrifuge (IEC, Model
M. B.).
Determine the haematocrit in the usual way with a suitable IEC apparatus. File the tubes and
break at the interface. Transfer 50 μl. centrifuged cells to a micro-sample cup with 950 μl. 5%
Triton X-100 in 0.9% NaCl. This gives a dilution of 1 : 20.
Stopper the cups and mix. Store at 0–5 °C until the assay. Immediately before the assay warm
to room temperature. Samples of 400 μl. 1 : 20 dilution (equivalent to 20 μl. centrifuged cells)
are put through in cycles of 40/hr.
Collect plasma samples from the other half of the haematocrit tube and dilute 1 : 4 with 0.9%
NaCl.

Stability of sample:

If possible store the samples at 0–5 °C, because they lose activity at room temperature. Diluted
plasma and haemolysed cells are stable for several hours at 0–5 °C. Frozen samples keep for
several months.

Assay System

See Fig. 1. Forty samples can be analysed per hour. The diluted samples are mixed in the single
mixing coil with substrate and warmed in the 37 °C water bath for ca. 4 min. They are then
incubated in the dialyzer for a further minute. The liberated thiocholine diffuses into the
recipient stream with buffer and DTNB. The thiocholine-DTNB mixture flows from the

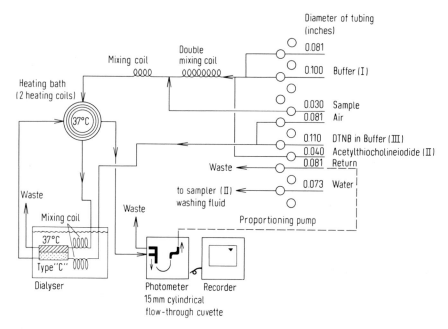

Fig. 1.

dialyser to the second 12 metre coil of the 37 °C heating bath, where the colour develops. From there the mixture flows to the colorimeter for the measurements.

Pump solutions in the manifold system:		Tubing diameter	ml./min.	Concentration in assay mixture
Buffer solution	(I)	0.100″	3.40	35 mM tris
Substrate solution	(II)	0.040″	0.60	2.8 mM with erythrocytes; 5.3 mM with plasma
Substrate and buffer are mixed and sample added. After ca. 5 min. incubation at 37 °C the substrate is dialysed into the recipient stream.				
DTNB solution	(III)	0.110″	3.90	2.5 mM
Colour development during ca. 4 min. at 37 °C; read in a 15 mm. flow-through cuvette at 420 nm.				

For standardization analyse a series of standards of increasing concentrations containing 1, 3, 5, 7 and 10 mM thiocholine iodide (solution IV).

Calculations

Calculate the results by means of standard curves.

Sources of Error

Blood samples after carbamate inhibition should be measured immediately after dilution[6], because otherwise the inhibition might be partially reversed. It is especially important to ensure careful separation of erythrocytes and plasma. The centrifuged cells contain ca. 4% plasma as shown by addition of iodine-labelled serum albumin to erythrocytes. This adhering plasma can be washed away, but this is time-consuming. As the enzyme activity of erythrocytes is about 2.5 times that of plasma, the error is about 2%.

Specificity of Method

Plasma and haemolysed cells to which eserine, a strong inhibitor of cholinesterase has been added, give no reaction with DTNB. This indicates that the substrate is not hydrolysed by non-specific esterases and that there is no reaction with SH groups contained in the sample.

References

1 *G. L. Ellman, D. K. Courtney, V. Andres jr & R. M. Featherstone,* Biochem. Pharmacol. *7,* 88 [1961].
2 *G. B. Koelle,* J. Pharmacol. Exp. Therap. *100,* 158 [1958].
3 *P. J. Garry & J. I. Routh,* Clin. Chem. *11,* 91 [1965].
4 *J. B. Levine, R. A. Scheidt & D. A. Nelson,* Automation in Analytical Chemistry, Technicon Symposia 1965, Mediad, Inc., N. Y., 1966, p. 582–585.
5 *C. G. Humiston & G. J. Wright,* Clin. Chem. *11,* 802 [1965].
6 *P. R. Fowler & J. M. McKenzie,* Automation in Analytical Chemistry, Technicon Symposia 1966, vol. I, White Plains, New York 1967, p. 155–159.

Phosphatases

Phosphatases catalyse the hydrolytic cleavage of phosphoric acid esters. They are designated either "acid" or "alkaline" phosphatases according to their pH optima.

Alkaline phosphatases (Orthophosphoric monoester phosphohydrolase, alkaline optimum, EC 3.1.3.1) occur in practically all animal and human tissues. Bile and osteoblasts have particularly high activity. Several isoenzymes can be demonstrated in serum and tissue extracts[1]. Raised values in human serum are nearly always due to diseases accompanied by increased osteoblast activity or involvement of the liver or bile ducts[2].

Acid phosphatases (Orthophosphoric monoester phosphohydrolase, acid optimum, EC 3.1.3.2) are also found in nearly all human and animal cells. High activity is found in erythrocytes and particularly in prostatic tissue. By means of electrophoresis 3 active fractions have been separated in serum[3] and up to 17 fractions in various tissue extracts[4]. The acid phosphatases of human erythrocytes are inhibited by formaldehyde[5], while those of normal serum are selectively inhibited by fluoride ions[6-8]. Prostatic phosphatase is inhibited by 20 mM tartrate[9,10] so that it is possible to determine prostatic phosphatase separately. In clinical chemistry the measurement of acid phosphatase is used almost exclusively in the diagnosis and control of therapy of prostatic carcinoma.

The older methods of assay use the amount of phosphate liberated from a substrate as an index of phosphatase activity[11].

There has been a great improvement in the technique by use of substrates, e.g. phenolphthalein diphosphate ester[12,13], the phosphate-free residue of which can be determined by direct colorimetry after making the reaction mixture alkaline without the need for deproteinization. The substrate phenolphthalein monophosphate is especially suitable for automated methods[14], because the bilirubin content of the serum does not affect the results and therefore the difficulty of allowing for serum blanks in the flow system can be avoided. Prostatic phosphatase reacts more specifically with α-naphthyl phosphate than with any other substrate[15]. 4-Nitrophenylphosphate whose hydrolysis product, 4-nitrophenol, gives an intense yellow colour in alkaline solution, is without doubt the most widely used substrate[16-19].

Acid and Alkaline Phosphatase in Serum
(Two-point method)

Klaus Walter and Christian Schütt

Principle

(1) $O_2N\!-\!\langle\ \rangle\!-\!O\text{-}PO_3H_2 + H_2O \longrightarrow O_2N\!-\!\langle\ \rangle\!-\!OH + H_3PO_4$

The amount of 4-nitrophenol liberated per unit time, as determined in alkaline solution at 400–420 nm, is a measure of the phosphatase activity.

The reaction is stopped by the addition of NaOH. In the determination of acid phosphatase the alkali results in the formation of a yellow colour due to the 4-nitrophenol liberated. Acid phosphatase of prostatic origin can be distinguished by the enzyme activity in the presence and absence of tartrate.

Optimum Conditions for Measurements

Acid phosphatases:

The acid phosphatases in normal men and women have the highest activity with a broad optimum between pH 5.5 and 6.1 (50 mM citrate buffer, 50 mM 4-nitrophenyl phosphate).

On the other hand the prostatic phosphatase has a relatively high activity at pH 4.8[20,21]. As the clinical interest is mainly in the increase in activity due to the prostate-specific phosphatase the measurement of activity at pH 4.8 is most suitable. This applies in particular to the assay system with and without tartrate. Measurements at different temperatures may require different measuring conditions (cf. p. 127). Nevertheless, results obtained under the same measuring conditions but at different temperatures were formerly compared with each other ("conversion factors" were determined). Such conversion factors may be correct if determined with a relatively large proband collective; however, they cannot be applied generally to the individual case (cf. p. 129). The value of the following relative reaction rates thus lies in being able to appraise the temperature dependence of the reaction and at the most to compare qualitatively values up to the limit of normal.

°C	18	19	20	21	22	23	24	25	26	27
	1.92	1.69	1.54	1.35	1.25	1.15	1.07	*1.00*	0.92	0.83
°C	28	29	30	31	32	33	34	35	36	37
	0.77	0.71	0.67	0.63	0.60	0.57	0.55	0.52	0.50	0.48

Alkaline phosphatases:

Optimum reaction conditions are not suitable for the assay of alkaline phosphatase activity in serum by the method described here. The amounts of normal undiluted serum which can be pipetted with sufficient accuracy result in too high a conversion of substrate under optimum conditions during a reasonable reaction time. We therefore use suboptimum substrate concentrations.

Studies of *Rick* et al,[22,23] have shown that the usual glycine buffer concentration of 50 mM has too low a buffering capacity. With higher glycine concentrations the enzyme activity is strongly inhibited[20,23]. In the method given here 0.1 M diethanolamine has good buffering capacity against serum and atmospheric-CO_2. Activity measurements at different temperatures yield the following relative reaction rates:

°C	18	19	20	21	22	23	24	25	26	27
	1.38	1.32	1.25	1.20	1.14	1.09	1.04	*1.00*	0.96	0.93
°C	28	29	30	31	32	33	34	35	36	37
	0.90	0.87	0.84	0.81	0.79	0.77	0.74	0.72	0.70	0.69

Equipment

Spectrophotometer or spectrum-line photometer or filter photometer for measurements at 405 nm (400–420 nm); 25 °C water bath; stopwatch.

Reagents*

1. Citric acid, $C_6H_8O_7 \cdot H_2O$
2. Sodium citrate, $C_6H_5Na_3O_7 \cdot 5H_2O$
3. Sodium tartrate, $C_4H_4Na_2O_6 \cdot 2H_2O$, A.R.
4. Diethanolamine, $C_4H_{11}NO_2$

5. 4-Nitrophenylphosphate
   disodium salt, $C_6H_4NNa_2O_6P \cdot 6H_2O$, A.R.
6. Sodium hydroxide, 0.05 N and 0.1 N
7. Hydrochloric acid, 0.1 N

Purity of Reagents

The water content of nitrophenylphosphate is not constant in the commercial preparations and therefore should be checked.

---

* Complete reagent kits are commercially available, see p. 558.

Preparation of Solutions

I. Acid buffer/substrate solution (50 mM citrate buffer, pH 4.8; 5.5 mM 4-nitrophenyl-phosphate):
   Dissolve 0.41 g. citric acid +1.125 g. sodium citrate +0.203 g. 4-nitrophenylphosphate in doubly distilled water to 100 ml. Check pH with a glass electrode.
II. Alkaline buffer/substrate solution (0.1 M diethanolamine, pH 9.8; 1.25 mM 4-nitro-phenylphosphate):
   Dissolve 1.052 g. diethanolamine +8.0 ml. 0.1 N HCl + 46.4 mg. 4-nitrophenylphos-phate in 85 ml. doubly distilled water, adjust to pH 9.8 by addition of 0.1 N HCl (glass electrode) dilute to 100 ml. with distilled water.
III. Tartrate (0.4 M):
   Dissolve 9.2 g. sodium tartrate in distilled water and make up to 100 ml.

Stability of Solutions

Store the buffer/substrate solutions at 0–4 °C; they are stable for 1 week. The tartrate solution is stable for 1 year.

Procedure

Collection, Treatment and Stability of Sample

Collection of sample:

Allow blood to flow from the vein through a cannula (No. 1 or larger) into a centrifuge tube. Centrifuge for 10 min. at ca. 3000 g to obtain serum. Use only non-haemolysed, fresh serum, especially for the assay of acid phosphatase.

Stability of enzyme in sample:

The stability of acid phosphatase is very dependent on the pH of the serum[20]. Although the enzyme is stable for two weeks in serum at pH 5–6 at room temperature, the activity decreases to 50% after 7 days in non-acidified serum. According to *Rosenmund*[24] addition of 5 mg. sodium hydrogen sulphate (NaHSO$_4$·H$_2$O) to 1 ml. serum stabilizes it sufficiently for dispatch by post.
The alkaline phosphatases in serum are stable for at least 1 week at room temperature provi-ding that bacterial contamination is excluded.

Assay System

Wavelength: Hg 405 nm (400–420 nm); light path: 1 cm.; 25 °C. Incubation volume: 1.25 ml.; final volume: 3.25 ml. Read against blank (without tartrate) to which the sample is added *after* the NaOH. Bring the buffer/substrate solution to 25 °C before the start of the assay.

Acid phosphatases:

Pipette into 12 ml. test tubes:		Sample A	Sample B	Concentration in assay mixture
Buffer/substrate solution, pH 4.8	(I)	1.0 ml.	1.0 ml.	41.6 mM citrate 4.58 mM 4-nitro-phenylphosphate 16 mM tartrate
Tartrate solution	(III)	—	0.05 ml.	
Serum		0.2 ml.	0.2 ml.	
Mix and incubate for exactly 30 min. in a water bath.				
0.1 N NaOH		2.0 ml.	2.0 ml.	0.062 N NaOH
Measure extinctions. The increase in extinction ΔE over the blank is used for the calculations. The yellow colour is stable for several hours.				

Calculations

The calculation formula (8) on p. 313 applies. The extinction coefficient of 4-nitrophenol in alkaline solution is 18.5 cm.^{2}/μmole at 405 nm. Therefore under the above conditions:

$$\text{Volume activity} = \frac{\Delta E \times 3.2 \times 1\,000}{30 \times 18.5 \times 0.2} = \Delta E \times 28.8 \quad [\text{U/l.}]$$

The activity of prostatic phosphatase is obtained by the difference between the activities of sample A and B (the total acid phosphatase activity is measured in A). If prostatic phosphatase only is to be determined, prepare reaction mixtures A and B and read A against B.
The volume of the reaction mixture in B is 50 μl larger than in A, but this difference can be neglected in the calculations. If the measurements cannot be made at 405 nm, it is necessary to prepare a standard curve.

Alkaline phosphatases:

Read against blank to which the sample is added *after* the NaOH. Incubation volume: 2.05 ml.; final volume: 12.05 ml.

Pipette into test tubes:		Concentration in assay mixture
Buffer/substrate solution, pH 9.8 (II)	2.0 ml.	97.5 mM diethanolamine 1.21 mM 4-nitrophenyl-phosphate
Serum	0.05 ml.	
Mix and incubate for exactly 30 min.		
0.05 N NaOH	10.0 ml.	0.041 N NaOH
Read extinction. The increase in extinction ΔE above the blank is used for the calculations. The yellow colour is stable for several hours.		

With extinctions above 0.800 dilute 0.1 ml. serum with 0.9 ml. physiological NaCl solution and assay again. Make the calculations with the help of standard curve.

Calculations

$$\text{Volume activity} = \frac{\Delta E \times 12.05 \times 1\,000}{30 \times 18.5 \times 0.05} = \Delta E \times 434 \quad [\text{U/l.}]$$

Precision of Method

Acid phosphatase: with values around 4 U/l. (25 °C) the coefficient of variation in a series of assays was 1.9%. Alkaline phosphatase: with values around 40 U/l. (25 °C) the coefficient of variation was 2.1%.

Normal Values

Total acid phosphatase in serum: up to 5.5 U/l. (25 °C); prostatic phosphatase: up to 2 U/l. (25 °C). Alkaline phosphatase in serum: 18–63 U/l. (25 °C) (normal adults 18–85 years). The upper normal limit of alkaline phosphatase in serum of children is 150 U/l. (25 °C).

Sources of Error

Effects of drugs and other therapeutic measures: None known.

Interference in the assay technique: If the instructions are adhered to there should be no interference. A falsely high acid phosphatase activity due to slight haemolysis is eliminated by the tartrate technique described here.

Alkaline Phosphatase in Serum (Continuous Assay)

Klaus Walter and Christian Schütt

The assay of phosphatase activity by continuous measurements[22,23,25–29] has the advantage that only one pipetting is necessary and the measurements can be carried out rapidly. A disadvantage is the greater expenditure of time with a series of assays in the routine laboratory.

Principle

See p. 856. The amount of 4-nitrophenol liberated is measured continuously at 405 nm. The extinction increase per min. is linearly proportional to the enzyme activity.

Optimum Conditions for Measurements

Serum alkaline phosphatase is most active in 2 M diethanolamine buffer, pH 9.8 with 25 mM nitrophenyl-phosphate[21]. Under these conditions magnesium ions do not have an activating effect. With 1 M diethanol-amine (pH 9.8) and 15 mM nitrophenylphosphate the activity is 14% lower[21]. The former "optimum" buffer/substrate solution has a relatively strong yellow colour (at 405 nm and 1 cm. light path the extinction is 0.800). There is a rapid spontaneous hydrolysis of the substrate (increase in extinction of ca. 0.500 in 7 days). Therefore it is better for a routine method to work with 1 M diethanolamine. The higher activity in diethanolamine buffer compared to other buffers (glycine, piperazine) is not due to a change in the molar extinction coefficient of nitrophenol in this buffer.

Alterations in temperature give considerable variations in the extinctions (possibly due to differences in substrate dissociation). Above 30 °C there is considerable spontaneous hydrolysis of the substrate Relative reaction rates at activity determinations between 18 °C and 30 °C (see p. 857):

°C	18	19	20	21	22	23	24	25	26
	1.34	1.27	1.22	1.17	1.12	1.07	1.03	*1.00*	0.98
°C	27	28	29	30					
	0.95	0.93	0.91	0.89					

Equipment

Spectrophotometer, spectrum-line photometer or filter photometer suitable for measurements at 405 (400–420) nm; constant temperature cuvette holder, stopwatch; preferably extinction recorder.

Reagents*

1. Diethanolamine, $C_4H_{11}NO_2$
2. Hydrochloric acid, 1.0 N

3. 4-Nitrophenylphosphate
   disodium salt, $C_6H_4NNa_2O_6P \cdot 6H_2O$
4. Sodium hydroxide, 0.1 N

Preparations of Solutions (for ca. 50 assays)

I. Buffer/substrate solution (1.0 M diethanolamine buffer, pH 9.8; 15 mM 4-nitrophenyl-phosphate):
   Dissolve 10.514 g. diethanolamine +0.557 g. 4-nitrophenylphosphate +9.0 ml. 1.0 N HCl in 80 ml. doubly distilled water, adjust to pH 9.8 with 1.0 N HCl and dilute to 100 ml. with doubly distilled water.

II. 4-Nitrophenol standard solution (50 μM):
   Dissolve 696 mg. 4-nitrophenol in 0.1 N NaOH and make up to 1 000 ml., dilute 10 ml. of this solution to 1 000 ml. with 0.1 N NaOH.

Stability of Solutions

The buffer/substrate solution is stable for 8 days at 0–4 °C, Prepare the nitrophenol standard solution immediately before preparation of the standard curve.

---

* Complete reagents kits are available commercially, see p. 558.

Procedure

Collection, Treatment and Stability of Sample, see p. 858.

Assay System

Wavelength: Hg 405 nm; light path: 1 cm.; final volume: 2.02 ml.; temperature: 25 °C (constant temperature cuvette holder). A blank is not necessary. Bring the buffer/substrate solution and serum to 25 °C before the start of the assay.

Pipette into cuvettes:			Concentration in assay mixture
Buffer/substrate solution	(I)	2.00 ml.	0.99 M diethanolamine 14.85 mM nitro-phenylphosphate
Wait until the temperature of the cuvette contents is constant (1–2 min.) and then note the temperature.			
Serum		0.02 ml.	
Mix and after ca. 1 min. start stopwatch, measure the extinctions at 2 min. intervals (preferably use a recorder). Determine ΔE/min.			

If ΔE/min. > 0.200/min. dilute 0.1 ml. serum with 0.4 ml. physiological NaCl, assay again and multiply the results by 5.

Calculations

The calculation formula (8) on p. 313 applies. The extinction coefficient of 4-nitrophenol in alkaline solution is 18.5 cm.^{2}/μmole. Under the above conditions the

$$\text{Volume activity (25 °C)} = 5460 \times \Delta E/\text{min.} \quad [\text{U/l.}]$$

The following conversion factors apply for comparison of measurements of phosphatase activity with different methods:

For conversion of units (definition and method) according to	to mU according to the methods described here	
	A (two-point method)	B (continuous method) multiply by
Alkaline phosphatase		
Bodansky	9.3	34.2
King & Armstrong	4.6	16.9
Huggins & Talalay	5.3	19.4
Bessey & Lowry [nmole/hr., 38 °C]	18.0	66.0
Bessey & Lowry [mU; 37 °C]	1.08	3.96
Acid phosphatase		
Bessey & Lowry [nmole/hr.,38 °C]	8.3	—
Bessey & Lowry [mU, 37 °C]	0.48	—

Standard Curve

If the measurements cannot be made at 405 nm, a standard curve must be prepared.
Pipette into test tubes:

Nitrophenol standard solution	ml.	1.0	2.0	4.0	6.0	8.0
	nmole	50	100	200	300	400
0.1 N NaOH	ml.	11.05	10.05	8.05	6.05	4.05

Mix and read extinctions at the chosen wavelength (400–420) nm. Plot the extinction (ordinate) against the nmole (abscissa).

The measured extinctions correspond in
method A (two-point method)

alkaline phosphatase U/l.	33.3	66.6	133.2	199.8	266.4
acid phosphatase U/l.	2.2	4.4	8.8	13.2	17.6
in method B (continuous method)					
alkaline phosphatase U/l.	420	840	1680	2520	3360

Precision of Method

With values around 300 U/l. the coefficient of variation in series of assays was 3.9%.

Normal Values

According to our studies the normal range for adults of 18–85 years is 66–230 U/l. (25 °C). The upper limit for normal in children is 550 U/l. (25 °C) Other normal values: 61–171 U/l. (25 °C)[23]; 76–190 U/l. (25 °C)[30]; for men 63–160 U/l. (25 °C) and for women 41–154 U/l. (25 °C)[31]. The differences between normal ranges reported by the different groups is at least to some extent due to the fact selected groups of subjects (e. g. blood donors) were studied.

Details for Measurements in other Biological Fluids, Cell Suspensions and Tissue Homogenates

The above methods can be used for the determination of phosphatase activity in urine and semen. To determine alkaline phosphatase activity in leucocyte suspensions (of importance for the differential diagnosis of haematological diseases)[32,33] the leucocytes are isolated from freshly collected blood, repeatedly washed and suspended in physiological NaCl (5000–10000 cells/ml.). It is recommended that during the incubation period for method A the mixture of leucocytes, buffer and substrate is shaken mechanically in a water bath. Before the assay centrifuge at high speed. The colour of the cell-free supernatant fluid is measured.

The phosphatase activity in tissue homogenates has usually been measured with glycerophosphate as substrate. Depending on the type of tissue the pH of the buffer/substrate solution must be adjusted to the optimum pH[34]. Method A is in principle also suitable for the assay of activity in tissue homogenates. Whole homogenate[34,35] or autolysate[34,36] is used. There is an extensive literature on studies of serum and tissue phosphatase after electrophoretic separation on starch-gel, acrylamide and Sephadex. For a review of recent work, see[1].

References

1 *A. L. Latner & A. W. Skillen:* Isoenzymes in Biology and Medicine. Academic Press London and New York 1968.
2 *R. Schoen & H. Südhof:* Biochemische Befunde in der Differentialdiagnose innerer Krankheiten. Thieme, Stuttgart, 1965.
3 *C. A. Dubbs, C. Vironia & J. M. Hilburn,* Science *131,* 1 529 [1960].
4 *L. G. Lundin & A. C. Allison,* Biochim. biophys. Acta *127,* 527 [1966].
5 *B. Estborn,* Z. Klin. Chem. *2,* 53 [1964].
6 *M. A. M. Abul-Fadl & E. J. King,* Biochem. J. *45,* 51 [1949].
7 *G. E. Delory, T. H. Sweetser jr., & T. A. White,* J. Urol. *66,* 724 [1951].
8 *E. P. Kintner,* J. Lab. a. clin. Med. *37,* 637 [1951].
9 *M. A. M. Abul-Fadl & E. J. King,* Biochem. J. *42,* 28 [1948].
10 *W. H. Fishman & F. Lerner,* J. biol Chem. *200,* 89 [1953].
11 *W. Bodansky,* J. biol. Chem. *101,* 93 [1933].
12 *H. Huggins & P. Talalay,* J. biol Chem. *159,* 399 [1945].
13 *K. Linhard & K. Walter,* Hoppe-Seylers Z. Physiol. Chem. *289,* 245 [1952].
14 *B. Klein & J. H. Kaufmann,* Clin. Chem. *13,* 290 [1967].
15 *A. L. Babson & P. A. Read,* Am. J. Clin. Pathol. *32,* 88 [1959].
16 *O. A. Bessey, O. H. Lowry & M. J. Brock,* J. biol. Chem. *164,* 321 [1946].
17 *M. A. Andersch & A. J. Scypinski,* Am. J. Pathol. *17,* 571 [1947].
18 *N. Brock, H. J. Hohorst, B. Schneider & G. Siems,* Arzneimittelforschg. *14,* 757 [1964].
19 *N. Brock, H. J. Hohorst, B. Schneider & H. Wilmanns,* Arzneimittelforschg. *14,* 762 [1964].
20 *N. Brock & H. Wilmanns,* Ärztl. Lab. *5,* 33 [1959].
21 *K. Walter & Ch. Schütt,* unpublished experiments.
22 *W. Rick & T. U. Hausamen,* Ergeb. Labor. Med. *3,* 86 [1967].
23 *T. U. Hausamen, R. Helger, W. Rick. & W. Gross,* Clin. Chim. Acta *15,* 241 [1967].
24 *H. Rosenmund,* Habilitationsschrift, Med. Fakultät, Universität Zürich [1953].
25 *E. Amador, T. S. Zimmermann & W. E. C. Wacker,* J. Am. Med. Assoc. *185,* 953 [1963].
26 *G. N. Bowers jr. & R. B. McComb,* Clin. Chem. *10,* 636 [1964].
27 *W. J. Frajola, R. D. Williams & R. A. Anstad,* Am. J. Clin. Pathol. *43,* 261 [1965].
28 *A. Garen & C. Levinthal,* Biochim. Biophys. Acta *38,* 470 [1960].
29 *F. Melani & A. Guerritore,* Experentia *20,* 464 [1964].
30 *H. Büttner,* cited in [33].
31 *G. Szasz,* cited in [33].
32 *A. G. Meislin, S. Lee & L. R. Wassermann,* Cancer *12,* 760 [1959].
33 *H. Merker & L. Heilmeyer,* Schweiz. Med. Wschr. *89,* 1 051 [1959].
34 *J. Roche* in *J. B. Summer & K. Myrbäck:* The Enzymes, Academic Press, New York 1950, vol. I, p. 473.
35 *K. Walter & H. Achternich* in *H. Nowakowski:* Die endokrine Behandlung des Mamma- und Prostatacarcinoms; Endokrine Regulationen des Kohlenhydratstoffwechsels, Springer, Berlin, Göttingen, Heidelberg 1961, p. 241.
36 *C. D. Kochakian,* Am. J. Physiol. *46,* 118 [1945].

Alkaline Phosphatase in Serum
Determination with Automatic Analysers

Hans Ulrich Bergmeyer, Erich Bernt & Rudolf Lachenicht

With the method described here phosphatase activities of from 60–300 U/l. can be determined with optimum conditions for measurements.

Application of Method: In routine clinical chemistry.

Principle

(1)   p-Nitrophenylphosphate $\xrightarrow{\text{phosphatases}}$ p-Nitrophenol + Phosphate

p-Nitrophenylphosphate is hydrolysed by phosphatases to phosphate and p-nitrophenol. The amount of p-nitrophenol liberated in a given time is proportional to the phosphatase activity and can be determined as the yellow colour at 420 nm. This is also the basis of the *Sterling*[1] and *Morgenstern*[2] assay methods for use with automatic analysers.

Equipment

AutoAnalyzer®system* consisting of sampler II; proportioning pump; heating bath with a 12 m. long heating spiral (internal diameter 1.6 mm.), 37 °C; dialyser with dialysis membrane, type C; photometer with 15 mm. cylindrical flow-through cuvette, 420 nm filter and recorder with a chart speed of 18″ (ca. 45 cm.) per hr.

Reagents

1. Diethanolamine
2. Magnesium chloride, $MgCl_2 \cdot 6 H_2O$
3. Hydrochloric acid, 1 N
4. p-Nitrophenylphosphate
   disodium salt $\cdot 6 H_2O$ (<0.01% free p-nitro-phenol)

5. Sodium azide
6. Bovine serum albumin, purest available
7. Control serum with above-normal activity ca. 300 U alkaline phosphatase/l.
8. Triton X-405

Preparation of Solutions**

Prepare all solutions with fresh, doubly distilled water.

  I. Diethanolamine buffer (1.0 M; pH 9.8; 0.5 mM $MgCl_2$):
     Dissolve 105 g. diethanolamine and 0.107 g. magnesium chloride·$6 H_2O$ in 700 ml. distilled water and adjust to pH 9.8 with about 170 ml. 1 N HCl. Dilute to 1 000 ml. with distilled water.

 II. Buffer/substrate solution (10 mM p-nitrophenylphosphate):
     Dissolve 1.938 g. p-nitrophenylphosphate-$Na_2 \cdot 6 H_2O$ in 500 ml. solution I. Check pH is 9.8.

III. Serum albumin (5.0% serum albumin; 0.1% sodium azide):
     Dissolve 5.0 g. serum albumin and 100 mg. sodium azide in 100 ml. distilled water.

 IV. Control sera:
     Prepare a series of dilutions of the commercially available high activity serum (ca. 300 U/l.) with solution III.

---

 * Technicon Corporation, Tarrytown, N. Y., USA.
** Complete reagent kits are available commercially, see p. 558.

e. g.   0.25 ml. control serum + 2.25 ml. solution III
               0.50 ml. control serum + 2.00 ml. solution III
               1.00 ml. control serum + 2.00 ml. solution III
               1.00 ml. control serum + 1.00 ml. solution III
               2.00 ml. control serum + 1.00 ml. solution III
                         control serum undiluted.

Prepare the dilutions very accurately. Check the activity by manual methods.

Stability of Solutions

Solution I is stable for a year at room temperature. Store solutions II, III and IV at ca. 4 °C. Solution II
is stable for 3 days. A precipitate which forms in the cold disappears on warming. The stability of solution III
is 3 weeks. The activity of the alkaline phosphatase in control sera IV is constant for ca. 10 hr.

Procedure

Only use fresh serum free from haemolysis.
Prepare the manifold system as shown in Fig. 1. Use Tygon tubing for connections.
The assays are carried out with cam set at 40–1/2, i.e. at the rate of 40 assays per hr. and
a ratio of sample to washing fluid of 1 : 2.
The sample collector tube is then immersed for 30 sec. in the sample and 60 sec. in the washing
fluid.
In the H3 fitting (see Fig. 1.) the sample is mixed with buffer/ substrate solution and then
follows ca. 20 min. incubation in the 37 °C heating bath, where the p-nitrophenylphosphate
is hydrolysed. After dialysis the p-nitrophenol solution is diluted with water and measured.

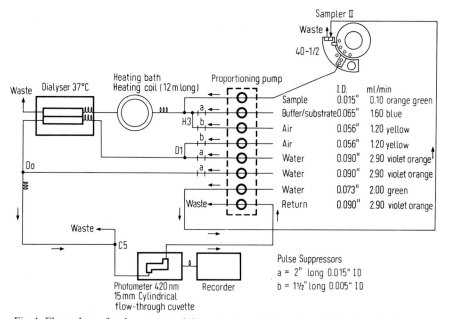

Fig. 1. Flow scheme for the automated determination of the activity of alkaline phosphatase.

Calculations

Read off the enzyme activity in the samples (serum) in U/l. from the standard curve (Fig. 3.).
Fig. 2. shows a trace with different dilutions of the control serum and from this the standard curve is
constructed (Fig. 3.)

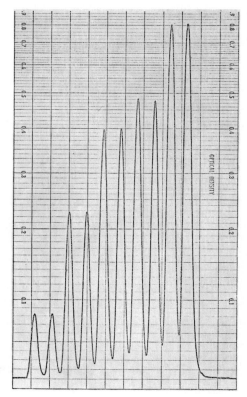

Fig. 2. Tracing of assays of control sera with
increasing activity of alkaline phosphatase (30, 88,
151, 184 and 300 U/l.).

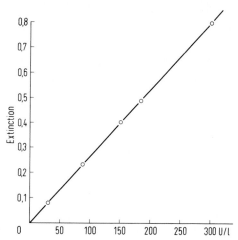

Fig. 3. Standard curve from the values of Fig. 2.

Precision of Method

The variance coefficient for the automated assay of alkaline phosphatase is 1.2% at ca. 80 U/l. Fig. 4. shows the reproducibility of the method.

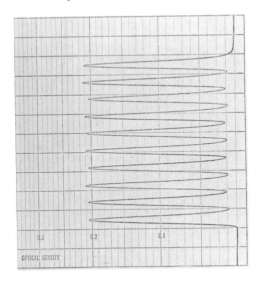

Fig. 4. Reproducibility of the assays (10 determinations).

References

1 *R. E. Sterling, A. A. Wilcox, A. G. Ware & M. R. Umehara,* Clin. Chem. *10,* 1112 [1964].
2 *S. Morgenstern, G. Kessler, J. Auerbach, R. O. Flor & B. Klein,* Clin. Chem. *11,* 876 [1965].

Alkaline Phosphatase in Milk

Erich Bernt

The assay of phosphatase activity in milk serves to control efficiency of the pasteurization process. Because fat interferes the samples must first be centrifuged to remove most of the cream. The method with phenolphthalein phosphate[1] can also be used to determine the activity.

Application of Method: In foodstuff chemistry.

Principle

p-Nitrophenylphosphate is used as substrate (see p. 856). After incubation for an hour NaOH is added and the yellow colour of the liberated p-nitrophenol is measured at 405 nm.

Equipment

Spectrophotometer, spectrum-line photometer or filter photometer suitable for measurements at Hg 405 nm (400–420 nm); water bath (37 °C); laboratory centrifuge; blue band filter.

Reagents*

1. Glycine
2. Magnesium chloride, A. R., MgCl$_2$ · 6 H$_2$O
3. Sodium hydroxide, 2 N and 0.02 N
4. p-Nitrophenylphosphate, disodium salt · 6 H$_2$O

Purity of Reagents

The water content of the commercial preparations of nitrophenylphosphate is not constant and should should therefore be checked.

Preparation of Solutions

I. Buffer/substrate solution (50 mM glycine, pH 10.5; 0.5 mM MgCl$_2$; 5.5 mM p-nitrophenyl-phosphate):
   Dissolve 0.375 g. glycine, 10 mg. MgCl$_2$·6 H$_2$O and 0.204 g. p-nitrophenylphosphate, disodium salt·6 H$_2$O, in 80 ml. doubly distilled water, adjust to pH 10.5 with 2 N NaOH and dilute to 100 ml. with doubly distilled water.

Stability of Solutions

Solution I is stable for one week at ca. 4 °C.

Procedure

Collection and Stability of Sample

Centrifuge 2 ml. milk for 10 min. at 3000 g, penetrate the layer of fat with a pipette and take off the milk free from cream. Filter the skimmed milk through a small, moist blue band filter. Add 0.1 ml. of the filtrate to the assay. The activity of alkaline phosphatase is stable in milk for ca. one week[2].

Assay System

Wavelength: Hg 405 nm (400–420 nm); light path: 1 cm.; temperature: 37 °C; incubation volume: 1.10 ml.; final volume: 6.10 ml.; read against blank.

---

* Complete reagent kits are available commercially, see p. 558.

Pipette into test tubes	Blank	Sample	Concentration in assay mixture
Buffer/substrate solution (I)	1.00 ml.	1.00 ml.	45 mM glycine 5 mM p-nitrophenylphosphate 0.45 mM MgCl$_2$
Sample	—	0.10 ml.	
Mix, stopper test tubes and incubate for 1 hr. at 37 °C.			
NaOH 0.02 N Sample	5.00 ml. 0.10 ml.	5.00 ml. —	16.4 mM NaOH
Mix, pour into cuvettes and measure extinction of sample against blank; ΔE is used for the calculations.			

Calculations

The formula (8) on p. 313 applies. The extinction coefficient of p-nitrophenol at Hg 405 nm is 18.5 cm^2./ μmole. Under the above assay conditions:

$$\text{Volume activity} = \Delta E \times 55 \quad [\text{U/l.}], 37 \,^{\circ}\text{C}$$

If the measurements cannot be made at Hg 405 nm a standard curve is necessary (see p. 863).

Normal Values

Wuethrich[2] found 160 U/l. alkaline phosphatase in fresh milk. He could not detect phosphatase in pasteurized and sterilized milk. However, it can happen that after heat treatment of milk the phosphatase is reactivated. The presence of reactivators has been considered[3]. *Agarwal* et al[4] consider that phosphatase-producing aerobic spore-forming bacteria are responsible for the occurrence of phosphatases in pasteurized milk.

Sources of Error

If the method is followed closely no error should occur. According to *Morton*[5,6] only 70% of the actual phosphatase activity is determined, the residual 30% is bound to lipoproteins.

References

1 *H. Janecke & W. Diemair*, Z. analyt. Chemie *130*, 56 [1949].
2 *S. Wuethrich, R. Richterich & H. Hostettler*, Z. Lebensm.-Untersuch.-Forsch. *124*, 336 [1964].
3 *K. Schormüller:* Lehrbuch der Lebensmittelchemie, 1th. ed., Springer Berlin 1961.
4 *M. L. Agarwal, R. A. Srinivasan & A. T. Dudani*, Indian J. Dairy Sci. *20*, 113 [1967].
5 *R. K. Morton*, Biochem. J. *55*, 786 [1953].
6 *R. K. Morton*, Biochem. J. *57*, 231 [1954].

5'-Nucleotidase

Ulrich Gerlach and Walter Hiby

5'-Nucleotidase (5'-Ribonucleotide phosphohydrolase, EC 3.1.3.5.) was discovered by *Reis*[1] in 1934. The enzyme specifically catalyses the dephosphorylation of nucleoside phosphates having phosphate groups attached at the C_5 position of the ribose ring. It is found together with other isodynamic and non-specific phosphomonoesterases in various human, animal and plant tissues[2,3,4]. *Heppel* and *Hilmoe*[5] isolated 5'-nucleotidase from bull semen in 1951. Since then several methods of preparation have been described[6,7,8]. Present work suggests that 5'-nucleotidase is located in the microsomal fraction[9,10,11], but the enzyme is also used as a marker enzyme for cell membranes in cell fractionation[12]. A definite histochemical location of 5'-nucleotidase in a definite cell organelle has so far proved difficult because 5'-nucleotidase is difficult to distinguish from other non-specific phosphatases in histological preparations[13].

Moss and *Campbell*[14] determined the molecular weight of 5'-nucleotidase to be over 200000. The pH optima and the *Michaelis-Menten* constants of 5'-nucleotidase depend on the source of the enzyme[5,7,15]. For the enzyme from human serum the K_M for adenosine-5'-monophosphate is 0.2 mM. *Levin* and *Bodansky*[16] found two pH optima for the 5'-nucleotidase from bull semen, namely pH 8.5 and pH 9.1–9.3. The pH optimum of 5'-nucleotidase in human serum is pH 7.5[17,18].

5'-Nucleotidase is inhibited by anions (fluoride, borate, arsenate) and by metal ions (zinc, cobalt, copper, nickel, etc.)[13,19]. A true end-product inhibition is caused by the dephosphorylated nucleosides[19,20]. The other product, orthophosphate, inhibits only at very high concentration[20]. Magnesium, calcium, iron, barium and cobalt ions activate[13,17,19,20].

Colorimetric methods are usually used for the determination of 5'-nucleotidase activity[11,15,18,21].

Application of Method: In clinical chemistry and biochemistry.

Because of its substrate specificity 5'-nucleotidase is of importance in nucleic acid analysis[8]. Several publications[25-30] describe the clinical differential diagnostic value of the assay of 5'-nucleotidase activity in addition to the assay of non-specific phosphatases in serum of patients: total serum alkaline phosphatase is raised in patients with osteoplastic skeletal diseases, cholestatic liver diseases, biliary inflammation and biliary obstruction. Where an increase in alkaline total phosphatase is found in serum the additional measurement of 5'-nucleotidase activity allows a decision as to the source of the alkaline phosphatase: in diseases of the hepato-biliary system both the alkaline phosphatase and the 5'-nucleotidase activity are significantly raised in serum, whereas the 5'-nucleotidase activity in serum is normal or only slightly raised when the alkaline phosphatase is increased due to bone disease.

Principle

(1) Adenosine-5'-monophosphate $+ H_2O \xrightarrow{5'-nucleotidase}$ Adenosine $+ H_3PO_4$

The dephosphorylation of the C_5 position of the ribose ring by isodynamic phosphomonoesterases in the same pH range must be taken into account. The various phosphatases can be distinguished by testing their behaviour to various substrates (β-glycerophosphate[22], phenylphosphate[9,19]). These substrates react with non-specific phosphatases, but not with 5'-nucleotidase. As these methods are liable to unpredictable errors[19] it is recommended to measure the 5'-nucleotidase activity by the selective complete inhibition of the enzyme by nickel ions[19]. The assay is carried out in the presence and absence of nickel ions[18]: in their presence the activity of non-specific phosphatase is determined, while in their absence the sum of the activities of non-specific phosphatases and 5'-nucleotidase is measured. The difference in the amount of phosphate ion liberated per unit time in the two assays, as determined by the *Fiske* and *Subbarrow* method[23] is a measure of 5'-nucleotidase activity. The method of *Campbell*[18] was modified for the automated assay in the AutoAnalyzer® by *Hill* and *Sammons*[24].

Optimum Conditions for Measurements

The different pH optima of 5'-nucleotidases from different sources must be taken into account[5,7,15-18]. *Campbell*[18], *Dixon* and *Purdon*[25] and *Young*[17] found the pH optimum in human serum to be pH 7.5. Adenosine-5'-monophosphate had the highest rate of hydrolysis of the 5'-nucleotides tested[13].

Measurements at different temperatures may require different measuring conditions (cf. p. 127). Nevertheless, results obtained under the same measuring conditions but at different temperatures were formerly compared with each other ("conversion factors" were determined). Such conversion factors may be correct if determined with a relatively large proband collective; however, they cannot be applied generally to the individual case (cf. p. 129). The value of the following relative reaction rates thus lies in being able to appraise the temperature dependence of the reaction and at the most to compare qualitatively values to the limit of normal.

°C	25	30	37	40
	0.44	0.73	1.00	1.21

The measured enzyme activity and the amount of enzyme added are proportional up to about 50 mU/ml, therefore it is essential not to exceed this value.

Equipment

Spectrophotometer or spectrum-line photometer suitable for measurements at 578 nm. Glass cuvettes 2 cm. light path; water bath (37 °C); stopwatch; centrifuge.

Reagents

1. Manganese sulphate, $MnSO_4$
2. Sodium-5,5-diethylbarbituric acid sodium veronal, $C_8H_{11}O_3N_2Na$
3. Hydrochloric acid, 2 N
4. Adenosine-5'-monophosphate crystalline disodium salt, $C_{10}H_{12}O_7N_5PNa_2 \cdot 6H_2O$
5. Trichloroacetic acid, CCl_3COOH

6. Nickel chloride, $NiCl_2 \cdot 6H_2O$
7. Ammonium molybdate, $(NH_4)_6Mo_7O_{24} \cdot 4H_2O$
8. 4-Methylaminophenol sulphate, $C_{14}H_{20}N_2O_6S$
9. Sodium acetate, $CH_3COONa \cdot 3H_2O$
10. Sulphuric acid, 96% (sp. gr. 1.84)
11. Potassium bisulphite, $K_2S_2O_5$

Preparation of Solutions

Prepare all solutions with doubly distilled water.

    I. Manganese sulphate (20 mM):
    Dissolve 3.38 g. $MnSO_4$ in distilled water and make up to 1 000 ml.

  II. Veronal buffer (40 mM; pH 7.5):
  Dissolve 8.25 g. sodium barbiturate in 700 ml. distilled water, adjust to pH 7.5 with 2 N HCl and dilute to 1 000 ml. with distilled water.

 III. Nickel chloride (0.1 M):
 Dissolve 23.77 g. $NiCl_2 \cdot 6H_2O$ in distilled water and make up to 1 000 ml.

IV. Adenosine-5'-monophosphate, AMP (10 mM):
Dissolve 0.0499 g. AMP-Na_2 in 10 ml. distilled water.

V. Trichloroacetic acid (0.68 M):
Dissolve 111.11 g. CCl_3COOH in distilled water and make up to 1000 ml.

VI. Ammonium molybdate (40 mM):
Stir 40.5 ml. conc. H_2SO_4 into 109 ml. distilled water (ice bath, protective goggles). Dissolve 12.5 g. ammonium molybdate in 100 ml. distilled water and stir into 125 ml. of the dilute H_2SO_4. Dilute to 250 ml. with distilled water.

VII. Reducing solution:
Dissolve 25 g. potassium bisulphite in 60 ml. distilled water; dissolve 0.2 g. methylaminophenol sulphate in 10 ml. distilled water, mix the two solutions and dilute to 100 ml. with distilled water. Filter the mixture.

VIII. Sodium acetate (2.5 M):
Dissolve 85 g $CH_3COONa \cdot 3H_2O$ in distilled water and make up to 250 ml.

Stability of Solutions

The reducing reagent (VII) is light sensitive; it is stable in a dark bottle for several days. The nucleotide solution (IV) is stable for long periods in the frozen state. All other solutions can be stored at room temperature and are stable indefinitely.

Procedure

Collection, Treatment and Stability of Sample

Collect blood by venous or arterial puncture. Avoid addition of anticoagulants. After clot has formed centrifuge and suck off serum. Use only serum free from haemolysis. The loss of 5'-nucleotidase activity in haemolysis-free serum after storage for 20 hr. at 4 °C is about 4% and at −20 °C about 1.5%. Storage of serum at room temperature for 20 hr. may result in an increase in activity of ca. 4%[26].

Assay System (Method of *Campbell*[18])

Three tubes are required: I without Ni^{2+}, II with Ni^{2+}, III phosphate blank of the sample. Incubation at 37 °C; incubation volume: 2 ml. Phosphate determination: wavelength 578 nm; light path 2 cm.; room temperature; read against air.

Pipette successively into 15 ml. centrifuge tubes:		I.	II.	III.	Concentration in assay mixture
Veronal buffer	(II)	1.5 ml.	1.3 ml.	1.5 ml.	ca. 30 mM
Manganese sulphate solution	(I)	0.1 ml.	0.1 ml.	0.1 ml.	1 mM
Nickel chloride solution	(III)	—	0.2 ml.	—	10 mM
Sample (serum)		0.2 ml.	0.2 ml.	0.2 ml.	
Distilled water		—	—	0.2 ml.	
AMP solution	(IV)	0.2 ml.	0.2 ml.	—	1 mM
Mix and incubate for 30 min. at 37 °C (water bath).					
Trichloroacetic acid	(V)	2.0 ml.	2.0 ml.	2.0 ml.	
The enzyme reaction is stopped. Centrifuge for 5 min. at 3000 g. Discard the precipitate.					
Pipette successively into test tubes:					
Supernatant fluid		2.5 ml.	2.5 ml.	2.5 ml.	
Distilled water		7.5 ml.	7.5 ml.	7.5 ml.	
Molybdate solution	(VI)	2.0 ml.	2.0 ml.	2.0 ml.	4 mM
Reducing reagent	(VII)	1.0 ml.	1.0 ml.	1.0 ml.	
Mix and allow to stand for 10 min.					
Acetate solution	(VIII)	4.0 ml.	4.0 ml.	4.0 ml.	0.5 M
Distilled water		3.0 ml.	3.0 ml.	3.0 ml.	
Mix, allow to stand for 5 min. and measure extinctions.					

Calculations

The difference $E_I - E_{II} = \Delta E$ after subtraction of the value E_{III} represents the amount phosphate ion liberated by 5′-nucleotidase (the *Lambert-Beer* law is obeyed up to a concentration of 0.04 mg. phosphorus/reaction mixture). To express the 5′-nucleotidase activity in U/l. sample multiply the extinction difference by 441.

Precision of Method

With values around 13 U/l. serum the standard deviation was 0.4 U/l. The coefficient of variation is 2.86%.

Normal Values

The normal 5′-nucleotidase activity in human serum is up to 8.5 U/l. *Hobbs, Campbell* and *Scheuer*[27]. Enzyme activity in tissues:
Using the normal methods for tissue extraction *Hobbs, Campbell* and *Scheuer*[27] measured 5′-nucleotidase activity in various organs (total activities):

Liver	(human)	12000 U	Brain	(human)	12000 U
Kidney	(human)	1250 U	Pancreas	(human)	70 U
Lung	(human)	1500 U	Thyroid	(human)	300 U
Spleen	(human)	750 U	Testicle	(human)	450 U
Aorta	(human)	800 U	Muscle	(calf)	7000 U

Source of Error

Errors may occur due to contamination by phosphate or metal ions.

Specificity of Method

It should be remembered that 5'-nucleotidase reacts not only with 5'-ribonucleotides but also with 5'-deoxyribonucleotides, nucleoside-5'-diphosphates and nucleoside-5'-triphosphates[13]. In spite of some reactive impurities in the substrate, the assay is relatively specific for 5'-nucleotidase activity[19], because nickel ions only inhibit the activity of 5'-nucleotidase.

References

1 *J. Reis*, Bull. Soc. Chim. biol. *16*, 385 [1934].
2 *J. M. Gulland & E. M. Jackson*, Biochem. J. *32*, 597 [1938].
3 *L. A. Heppel* in *Boyer-Lardy-Myrbäck:* The Enzymes, vol. I, Acad. Press, New York/London, p. 956 et seq.
4 *L. Shuster & N. O. Kaplan*, J. biol. Chem. *201*, 535 [1953].
5 *L. A. Heppel & R. J. Hilmoe*, J. biol. Chem. *188*, 665 [1951].
6 *R. O. Hurst & G. C. Butler*, J. biol. Chem. *193*, 91 [1951].
7 *E. Sulkowski, W. Björk & M. Laskowski* sen., J. biol. Chem. *238*, 2477 [1963].
8 *A. Kornberg & W. E. Pricer* jr., J. biol. Chem. *186*, 557 [1950].
9 *Z. Ahmed & E. J. King*, Biochim. biophys. Acta *34*, 313 [1959].
10 *A. B. Novikoff, E. Podber, J. Ryan & E. Noe*, J. Histochem., Cytochem. *1*, 27 [1953].
11 *H. L. Segal & B. M. Breuner*, J. biol. Chem. *235*, 471 [1960].
12 *H. Börnig, J. Štěpán, A. Born & R. Guertler*, Hoppe-Seyler's Z. Physiol. Chem. *348*, 1311 [1967].
13 *G. Siebert* in *Hoppe-Seyler/Thierfelder:* Handbuch der physiologisch- und pathologisch-chemischen Analyse, 10. Edition, vol. VI B, Springer-Verlag, Berlin/Heidelberg/NewYork 1966, p. 1049 et seq.
14 *D. W. Moss, D. M. Campbell, E. Anagnoston-Kakara & E. J. King*, Pure appl. Chem. *3*, 397 [1961].
15 *L. A. Heppel & R. J. Hilmoe* in *Colowick-Kaplan:* Methods in Enzymology vol. II, Academic Press, New York/London 1963, p. 546 et seq.
16 *S. J. Levin & O. Bodansky*, J. biol. Chem. *241*, 51 [1966].
17 *I. I. Young*, Ann. N. Y. Acad. Sci. *75*, 357 [1958].
18 *D. M. Campbell*, Biochem. J. *82*, 34 [1962].
19 *Z. Ahmed & J. L. Reis*, Biochem. J. *69*, 386 [1958].
20 *H. L. Segal & B. M. Breuner*, J. biol. Chem. *235*, 471 [1960].
21 *P. L. Ipata*, Analyt. Biochem. *20*, 30 [1967].
22 *D. Y. Wang*, Biochem. J. *83*, 633 [1962].
23 *C. H. Fiske & Y. Subbarow*, J. biol. Chem. *66*, 375 [1925].
24 *P. G. Hill & H. G. Sammons*, Clin. chim. Acta *13*, 739 [1966].
25 *T. F. Dixon & M. Purdom*, J. clin. Path. *7*, 341 [1954].
26 *H. Bartels*, Inaugural-Dissertation, Münster 1968.
27 *J. R. Hobbs, D. M. Campbell & P. J. Scheuer:* 6th Intern. Congr. Clin. Chem., Munich 1966, vol. 2, Clinical Enzymology, Karger Verlag, Basel/New York 1968, p. 106 et seq.
29 *U. Gerlach*, Enzymaktivität im Serum bei Krankheiten der Leber und Gallenwege: Praktische Enzymologie, Huber Verlag, Bern 1968, p. 165 et seq.
29 *G. C. Secchi, A. Rezzonico & N. Gervasini*, Enzym. biol. clin. *8*, 42 [1967].
30 *A. J. van Triet* jr. & *M. Frenkel*, Ned. T. Geneesk. *107*, 1598 [1963].

Glucose-6-phosphatase

Eugene S. Baginski, Piero P. Foà and Bennie Zak

Glucose-6-phosphatase, G6Pase (D-Glucose-6-phosphate phosphohydrolase, EC 3.1.3.9) was first described by *Fantl* et al[1,2]. The enzyme occurs mainly in liver and kidney, and is located in the microsomes[3]. It is considered that G6Pase is a key enzyme in carbohydrate metabolism[4]; its activity increases in starvation and in alloxan-diabetes[5,6]. The importance of the enzyme in histochemistry, embryogenesis, biochemistry and physiology, for synthesis of glycogen in the liver, in diabetes and hypoglycaemia of the neonate has been recently reviewed[7-9].

Numerous attempts have been made to determine G6Pase activity in blood and so relate its activity to liver damage[10,11]. However, it is doubtful whether, even in severe liver damage, this enzyme ever appears in the circulating blood[12]. Several characteristics of G6Pase have been described in a review by *Ashmore* and *Weber*[13]; purification of the enzyme was not possible, and the published values for the kinetic constants are contradictory. Probably the problem is the instability of G6Pase and the assay methods used at present. The activity is usually determined by measurement of the inorganic phosphate liberated from glucose-6-phosphate by the method of *Fiske* and *SubbaRow*[14]. This method, however, is not sufficiently sensitive to detect slight changes in activity[15]. In addition nucleotides interfere because they also react with molybdate[16]. The method described here is sensitive and apparently free from the inadequacies of other methods, and is well-suited to the determination of phosphate in biological material[17-20].

Application of Method: In biochemistry and clinical chemistry.

Principle

$$(1) \qquad \text{G-6-P} + H_2O \xrightarrow{\text{G6Pase}} \text{Glucose} + P_i$$

The inorganic phosphate liberated is determined with ammonium molybdate; ascorbic acid is used as the reducing agent. Excess molybdate is bound with an arsenite-citrate solution, so that it can no longer react with other phosphate esters or with P_i formed by acid hydrolysis of the substrate. Arsenite-citrate stabilizes the system.

The amount of phosphate liberated per unit time, determined as the blue phosphomolybdous complex at 700 or 840 nm, is a measure of the G6Pase activity.

G6Pase may also catalyse reactions (2) and (3)[21,22]:

$$(2) \qquad PP_i + H_2O \rightarrow 2P_i$$

$$(3) \qquad \text{Glucose} + PP_i \rightarrow \text{G-6-P} + P_i$$

Therefore with the method described here reactions (1) — (3) are determined. It is known however that reaction (2) can also be catalysed by inorganic pyrophosphatase (EC 3.6.1.1) and reaction (3) by pyrophosphate-glucose phosphotransferase.

Optimum Conditions for Measurements

The optimum pH for the enzyme reaction lies between 6.2 and 6.5[19]. Published K_M values vary greatly. Optimum activity is obtained with 20–50 μmole G-6-P in 0.4 ml. reaction mixture[19], i. e. 50–125 mM G-6-P. The reaction obeys zero order kinetics; the relationship between the amount of enzyme added and the measured activity is linear. Molybdate has a higher affinity for G-6-P than for P_i[15], (the complex is colourless) and therefore too high a concentration of G-6-P can interfere with the determination of P_i.

This occurs when attempts are made to determine the optimum substrate concentration by the stepwise increase in the G-6-P concentration. With the method described here[19] this source of error is avoided. Measurement of the colour at 840 nm gives a considerably higher extinction than at 700 nm.

Equipment

Spectrophotometer for measurements at 700 or 840 nm; 37 °C water bath; centrifuge (capable of at least 3000 rpm.); blade homogenizer and glass Teflon homogenizer; high-speed refrigerated centrifuge.

Reagents

1. Ammonium molybdate, $(NH_4)_6Mo_7O_{24} \cdot 4H_2O$, A.R.
2. Ethylenediaminetetra-acetate tetrasodium salt, EDTA-Na$_4$
3. Ascorbic acid, A.R.
4. Acetic acid, A.R.
5. Glucose-6-phosphate disodium salt, commercial preparation, see p. 538.
6. Hydrochloric acid, 0.1 N
7. Potassium dihydrogen phosphate, KH_2PO_4, A.R.
8. Sodium arsenite, anhydrous, A.R.
9. Sodium citrate, $C_6H_5O_7Na_3 \cdot 2H_2O$, A.R.
10. Sodium hydroxide, 0.1 N
11. Cacodylic acid, $(CH_3)_2AsO \cdot OH$
12. Sucrose, A.R.
13. Trichloroacetic acid.

Preparation of Solutions

Use only doubly distilled water.

 I. Sucrose (0.25 M):
   Dissolve 85.6 g. sucrose in distilled water and make up to 1000 ml.
 II. Sucrose/EDTA (0.25 M/1 mM):
   Dissolve 0.380 g. EDTA-Na$_4$ in sucrose solution (I), adjust to pH 7 with 0.1 N HCl and dilute to 1000 ml. with sucrose solution (I).
 III. Glucose-6-phosphate (0.1 M):
   Dissolve 0.336 g. G-6-P-Na$_2$ in distilled water and make up to 10 ml.
 IV. Cacodylate buffer (0.1 M; pH 6.5):
   Dissolve 0.138 g. cacodylic acid in distilled water, adjust to pH 6.5 with 0.1 N NaOH and dilute to 10 ml. with distilled water.
 V. Phosphate standard solution (1.5 mM):
   Dissolve 2.041 g. KH_2PO_4 in distilled water and make up to 100 ml. Dilute 1 ml. of this solution to 100 ml. with sucrose solution (I).
 VI. Ascorbic acid/trichloroacetic acid (2%/10% w/v):
   Dissolve 50 g. trichloroacetic acid in distilled water and make up to 500 ml.; dissolve in this solution 10 g. ascorbic acid.
 VII. Ammonium molybdate (1.0% w/v):
   Dissolve 10 g. ammonium molybdate in distilled water and make up to 1000 ml.
VIII. Arsenite/citrate (each 2% w/v):
   Dissolve 20 g. sodium citrate and 20 g. sodium arsenite in distilled water. Add 20 ml. acetic acid and dilute with distilled water to 1000 ml.

Stability of Solutions

Store the sucrose, G-6-P solution and the cacodylate buffer (I–IV) at 0–4 °C; solutions III and IV are stable for at least 1 week, solution I and the phosphate standard V are stable indefinitely providing bacterial contamination does not occur. The ascorbate/trichloroacetic acid solution (VI) is stable for at least 1 month in a dark bottle. The solution yellows with age, but this does not interfere. All other solutions are stable indefinitely at room temperature.

Procedure

Collection, Treatment and Stability of Sample

Homogenize freshly obtained tissue first in a pre-cooled blender and then in glass-Teflon homogenizer with ice-cold sucrose solution (I). Centrifuge the homogenate for 30 min. at 11 000 g in a refrigerated centrifuge. Discard the precipitate. Centrifuge the supernatant fluid for 1 hr. at 105 000 g and discard the supernatant fluid. Suspend the solid precipitate (microsomes) in ice-cold sucrose/EDTA solution (II), homogenize in a glass-Teflon homogenizer, divide into small portions and store at − 35 °C. For use thaw in ice and dilute with sucrose/EDTA solution (II). As the enzyme activity depends on the tissue and the species the dilutions must be prepared after a preliminary assay of the activity.

Stability of sample:

The enzyme is stable for several months at − 35 °C in the absence of EDTA[23]. After thawing the stability even at 0 °C is limited. EDTA increases the stability slightly[24].

Assay System

Incubation temperature: 37 °C; incubation volume: 0.4 ml.; final volume 2.5 ml.; wavelength: 700 or 840 nm; light path: 1 cm. Read against reagent blank.

Prepare a control containing sample, a standard and a reagent blank for each series of measurements. All tubes as for the experimental, but in the reagent blank add sucrose/EDTA solution (II) instead of sample; in the standard 0.1 ml. phosphate solution (V) instead of sample; in the control add the microsomal suspension after the ascorbic acid/trichloroacetic acid solution (VI). The colour is stable for several hours. The extinction of the experimental tube should not exceed 0.900, corresponding to ca. 4 µg. phosphate, at 700 nm; otherwise incubate for a shorter period or dilute the sample.

Pipette into small test tubes:			Concentration in assay mixture
Sucrose/EDTA solution	(II)	0.1 ml.	62.5 mM sucrose
			0.25 mM EDTA
G-6-P solution	(III)	0.1 ml.	25 mM G-6-P
Buffer solution	(IV)	0.1 ml.	25 mM
Mix and equilibrate.			
Sample		0.1 ml.	
Mix, and according to the activity incubate for 5–10 min.			
Ascorbic acid/trichloroacetic acid solution	(VI)	2.0 ml.	
Mix, centrifuge for 3 min. at 3 000 g. Use clear supernatant fluid. Pipette into clean test tubes:			
Supernatant fluid		1.0 ml.	
Molybdate solution	(VII)	0.5 ml.	0.2%
Mix			
Arsenite-citrate solution	(VIII)	1.0 ml.	0.8% arsenite
			0.8% citrate
Mix, allow to stand for 15 min. and read extinctions.			

Calculations

The amount of phosphate liberated by the enzyme from G-6-P is calculated by reference to the standard (0.15 μmole P_i in the assay):

$$c = \frac{E_{sample} - E_{control}}{E_{standard}} \times 0.15 \text{ } [\mu\text{mole/assay mixture}]$$

With 0.1 ml. sample and an incubation time of t min. the

$$\text{Volume activity} = \frac{E_{sample} - E_{control}}{E_{standard}} \times \frac{1\,500}{t} \text{ } [\text{U/l.}] \text{ } 37 \text{ }°C$$

Sources of Error

The instability of the enzyme causes serious errors, it is therefore necessary to assay the suspensions immediately after thawing. The order of addition of the reagents is very important for the phosphate determination; mix carefully after each addition.

Specificity of Method

The enzyme is very specific for G-6-P, although other phosphate esters can be hydrolysed[3]. As lysosomes contain non-specific phosphatases contamination of the microsomes with lysosomes is to be avoided.

References

1 *P. Fantl, M. N. Rome & J. F. Nelson*, Austrl. J. Exp. Biol *20*, 121 [1942].
2 *P. Fantl & M. N. Rome*, Austrl. J. Exp. Biol. *23*, 21 [1945].
3 *C. de Duve, J. Berthet, H. G. Hers & L. Dupret*, Bull. Soc. Chim. Biol. *31*, 1942 [1949].
4 *G. Weber, M. A. Lea, E. A. Fisher & N. B. Stamm*, Enzym. Biol. Clin. *7*, 11 [1966].
5 *G. Weber & A. Cantero*, Science *120*, 851 [1954].
6 *J. Ashmore, A. B. Hastings & F. B. Nesbett*, Proc. Nat. Acad. Sci. *40*, 673 [1954].
7 *P. P. Foà*, Handb. exp. Pharmakol. *16*, Teil 15, 1 [1966].
8 *T. A. I. Grillo & P. P. Foà*, Handb. exp. Pharmakol. *16*, Teil 15, 107 [1966].
9 *P. P. Foà*, Erg. Physiol. *60*, 142 [1968].
10 *H. Koide & T. Oda*, Clin. Chim. Acta *4*, 554 [1959].
11 *G. A. Dosta & Yu. M. Ostrovskii*, Veprosy Med. Khim. *8*, 477 [1962].
12 *M. Foz*, Clin. Chim. Acta *17*, 13 [1967].
13 *J. Ashmore & G. Weber*, Vitamins and Hormones *17*, 91 [1959].
14 *C. A. Fiske & Y. SubbaRow*, J. biol. Chem. *66*, 375 [1925].
15 *J. Imsande & B. Ephrussi*, Science *144*, 854 [1964].
16 *B. B. Marsh*, Biochim. Biophys. Acta *32*, 357 [1959].
17 *E. S. Baginski, P. P. Foà & B. Zak*, Clin. Chim. Acta *15*, 155 [1967].
18 *E. S. Baginski, P. P. Foà & B. Zak*, Clin. Chem. *13*, 326 [1967].
19 *E. S. Baginski, P. P. Foà & B. Zak*, Anal. Biochem. *21*, 201 [1967].
20 *E. S. Baginski, P. P. Foà, L. M. Weiner & B. Zak*, Microchem. J. *13*, 115 [1968].
21 *M. R. Stetten & H. L. Taft*, J. biol. Chem. *239*, 4041 [1964].
22 *R. C. Nordlie & W. J. Arion*, J. biol. Chem. *240*, 2155 [1965].
23 *M. A. Swanson*, J. biol. Chem. *184*, 647 [1950].
24 *H. Beaufay, H. G. Hers, J. Berthet & C. de Duve*, Bull. Soc. Chim. Biol. *36*, 1539 [1954].

Alkaline C_1-Fructose-1,6-diphosphatase

Erwin Latzko and Martin Gibbs

C_1-Fructose-1,6-diphosphatase, FDPase (D-Fructose-1,6-bisphosphate 1-phosphohydrolase, EC 3.1.3.11) was discovered by *Gomori*[1] in rabbit muscle. Crystalline preparations from the same organ[2] hydrolyse fructose-1,6-diphosphate (F-1,6-P_2) to F-6-P and sedoheptulose-1,7-diphosphate (S-1,7-P_2) to S-7-P; the ratio of FDPase to SDPase activity is 1,6.

Plant FDPase was first purified from spinach leaves by *Racker* and *Schröder*[3]. This enzyme is specific for F-1,6-P_2 (K_M = 0.3 mM) and is almost entirely located in the chloroplasts[4,5]. In contrast, non-photosynthetic cells and tissues contain an enzyme complex which has approximately the same affinity for F-1,6-P_2 and F-6-P, so that F-1,6-P_2 is hydrolysed to fructose[3,5].

Plant and animal FDPases are activated by Mg^{2+} and Mn^{2+}. Although both the liver and yeast enzymes are inhibited allosterically by adenosine-5'-monophosphate[6], there is no control of the photosynthetic FDPase by either adenosine or guanosine phosphates, or by inorganic pyrophosphate or orthophosphate[7]. In plant and animal cells FDPase is a key enzyme of carbohydrate synthesis[5,8,9]. Isolated chloroplasts synthesize carbohydrate at a rapid rate only if the activity of FDPase appreciably exceeds the rate of CO_2 fixation[5,9,10]. Allosteric regulation of the photosynthetic enzyme has been proposed[5], and recently demonstrated experimentally[11,12].

Application of Method: In biochemistry, microbiology, medicine and plant physiology.

Principle

(1)
$$F\text{-}1,6\text{-}P_2 \xrightarrow[Mg^{2+},\, Mn^{2+}]{\text{FDPase}} F\text{-}6\text{-}P + P_i$$

(2)
$$F\text{-}6\text{-}P \xrightarrow{\text{PGI}^*} G\text{-}6\text{-}P$$

(3)
$$G\text{-}6\text{-}P + NADP^+ \xrightarrow{\text{G6P-DH}^{**}} 6\text{-}P\text{-Gluconate} + NADPH + H^+$$

The formation of NADPH per unit time, as determined by the increase of extinction at 340 (334, 365) nm, is a measure of the FDPase activity.

Optimum Conditions for Measurements

The photosynthetic FDPase has a pH optimum >8.5 and requires EDTA. FDPase in animal tissue extracts has a sharp optimum[6] at pH 7.5, while the optimum for the crystalline preparation[2] is pH 9.0. Concentrations of F-1,6-P_2 above 1 mM inhibit[2,6].

Equipment

Spectrophotometer or spectrum-line photometer; tissue homogenizer (e.g. Sorvall Omnimixer); centrifuge.

---

* Phosphoglucose isomerase, hexose phosphate isomerase (D-Glucose-6-phosphate ketol-isomerase, EC 5.3.1.9).
** Glucose-6-phosphate dehydrogenase (D-Glucose-6-phosphate: NADP 1-oxidoreductase, EC 1.1.1.49).

Reagents

1. Tris-hydroxymethyl-aminomethane, tris
2. Magnesium chloride, $MgCl_2 \cdot 6 H_2O$
3. Nicotinamide-adenine dinucleotide phosphate, NADP
   disodium salt, NADP-Na$_2$H; commercial preparation, see p. 546.
4. Fructose-1,6-diphosphate
   crystalline trisodium salt F-1,6-P$_2$-Na$_3 \cdot 8 H_2O$; commercial preparation, see p. 534.

Additional for photosynthetic FDPase:
7. Ethylenediaminetetra-acetate, EDTA
   disodium salt, EDTA-Na$_2$H$_2 \cdot 2 H_2O$

5. Phosphoglucose isomerase, PGI
   from yeast, crystalline suspension in 3.2 M ammonium sulphate solution, $\geqq 350$ U/mg. (25 °C); commercial preparation, see p. 501.
6. Glucose-6-phosphate dehydrogenase, G6P-DH
   from yeast, suspension in 3.2 M ammonium sulphate solution, $\geqq 140$ U/mg. (25 °C); commercial preparation, see p. 458.

Additional for animal FDPase:
8. 2-Mercaptoethanol
9. Hydrochloric acid, A. R., 5 N

Purity of Reagents

Fructose-1,6-P$_2$ must be free from hexose monophosphates. Phosphoglucose isomerase must be free from 6-phosphogluconate dehydrogenase and FDP-aldolase.

Preparation of Solutions

Use only fresh distilled water.
For photosynthetic FDPase:
   I. Tris buffer (1 M; pH 8.8):
      Dissolve 12.1 g. tris in 70 ml. distilled water, adjust to pH 8.8 with 5 N HCl (glass electrode) and dilute with distilled water to 100 ml.
   II. Tris buffer (1 M; pH 7.5):
      Dissolve 12.1 g. tris in 70 ml. distilled water, adjust to pH 7.5 with 5 N HCl (glass electrode) and dilute to 100 ml. with distilled water.
   III. Magnesium chloride (0.5 M):
      Dissolve 1.02 g. $MgCl_2 \cdot 6 H_2O$ in distilled water and make up to 10 ml.
   IV. Ethylenediaminetetra-acetate, EDTA (20 mM):
      Dissolve 0.745 g. EDTA-Na$_2$H$_2 \cdot 2 H_2O$ in distilled water and make up to 100 ml.
   V. Nicotinamide-adenine dinucleotide phosphate, NADP (10 mM):
      Dissolve 8.5 mg. NADP-Na$_2$H in 1 ml. distilled water.
   VI. Fructose-1,6-diphosphate (50 mM):
      Dissolve 27.9 mg. F-1,6-P$_2$-Na$_3 \cdot 8 H_2O$ in 1.0 ml. distilled water.
   VII. Phosphoglucose isomerase, PGI (1 mg. protein/ml.):
      Dilute the crystalline suspension accordingly with distilled water.
   VIII. Glucose-6-phosphate dehydrogenase, G6P-DH (0.5 mg. protein/ml.):
      Dilute the suspension accordingly with distilled water.
For FDPase from yeast and animal cells and tissues:
Solutions I to III, V to VIII as above, substitute solution IX for solution IV.
   IX. 2-Mercaptoethanol (0.2 M):
      Dissolve 15.6 mg. 2-mercaptoethanol in 1 ml. distilled water.

Stability of Solutions

Solutions I–IV are stable indefinitely, V and VI are stable for more than a month at -20 °C. Solutions VII, VIII and IX should be prepared freshly each day.

Procedure

Collection, Treatment and Stability of Sample

Plant tissues: Homogenize 5 g. of the experimental material in 25 ml. tris buffer (solution II) containing 0.1 mM EDTA for 1–2 min. in a mixer. Centrifuge the homogenate for 5 min. at 5000 g and use the supernatant fluid for the assay. The activity in the extract reaches a maximum 3 to 4 hr. after extraction.

Animal cells and tissues: Homogenize 10 g. tissue with tris buffer (solution II) in the ratio 1 : 20 for ca. 2 min., keeping the homogenate cool. Centrifuge the homogenate for 5 min. at ca. 7000 g. and use the supernatant fluid for the assay.

Assay System

Wavelength: 340 (Hg 334, Hg 365) nm; light path: 1 cm.; final volume: 1 ml.; 25 °C. Read against air.

Pipette into cuvettes:		Assay of tissue extracts	Assay of plant extracts	Concentration in assay mixture
Tris buffer	(I)	—	0.10 ml.	0.1 M
Tris buffer	(II)	0.10 ml.	—	0.1 M
Mg^{2+} solution	(III)	0.02 ml.	0.04 ml.	10 or 20 mM
NADP solution	(V)	0.05 ml.	0.05 ml.	0.5 mM
Mercaptoethanol	(IX)	0.12 ml.	—	5 mM
EDTA solution	(IV)	—	0.12 ml.	2.4 mM
PGI solution	(VII)	0.02 ml.	0.02 ml.	10 μg./ml. $\triangleq$ 3.5 U/ml.
G6P-DH solution	(VIII)	0.02 ml.	0.02 ml.	5 μg./ml. $\triangleq$ 0.7 U/ml.
Sample + water		0.61 ml.	0.61 ml.	
F-1,6-P$_2$ solution	(VI)	0.006 ml.	0.01 ml.	0.6 or 1 mM

Mix, read the extinction every minute for 5 min. ΔE/min. is used for the calculations; it should not be greater than 0.100/min. otherwise take less sample.

Calculations

The calculation formula (8) on p. 313 applies.

Wavelength:

$$\text{334 nm} \qquad \text{340 nm} \qquad \text{365 nm}$$

$$\text{Volume activity} = \frac{163.9}{v} \times \Delta E/\text{min.} \qquad \frac{160.77}{v} \times \Delta E/\text{min.} \qquad \frac{289.86}{v} \times \Delta E/\text{min.} \quad [\text{U/l.}]$$

v = volume of sample.

Precision of Method

We found in spinach leaves a conversion of 87 μmole of substrate per mg. chlorophyll per hr., i. e. 1.45 U/mg.[5]. Standard deviation = 3.5 μmole/mg./hr. or 0.06 U/mg. Coefficient of variation = 4%.

Normal Values

The ratio of photosynthetic CO_2 fixation to FDPase activity in spinach chloroplasts is 2.5; in *Chlorella vulgaris* (photoautotroph) 3.5; in *Euglena gracilis* (photoautotroph) 2.2; in *Tolypothrix tenuis* 1.3 and in *Chromatium* 0.09[13]. *Heinz*[14] gives a value of 8.3 U/g. for rat kidney and 6.5 U/g. fresh wt. for rat liver; the activity increases ca. 400% in liver of alloxan-diabetic rats[15].

Sources of Error

High activity of 6-phosphogluconate dehydrogenase, which is generally present in animal tissues, can lead to erroneously high values. This source of error is only observed after ca. 5 min. in the above assay system. The presence of NADPH oxidase in plant tissues must be corrected for by a suitable control. In non-photosynthetic plant tissues an increased activity of F-6-Pase may be observed, but this can be eliminated by working above pH 8.8.

Specificity of Method

Plant C_1-FDPase is specific for F-1,6-P_2; it does not hydrolyse F-6-P, G-6-P or S-1,7-P_2.

References

1 *G. Gomori*, J. biol. Chem. *148*, 139 [1943].
2 *S. Pontremoli, S. Traniello, B. Luppis & W. A. Wood*, J. biol. Chem. *240*, 3459 [1965].
3 *E. Racker & E. A. R. Schröder*, Arch. Biochem. Biophys. *74*, 326 [1958].
4 *R. Smillie*, Nature *187*, 1024 [1960].
5 *E. Latzko & M. Gibbs*, Z. Pflanzenphysiol. *59*, 184 [1968].
6 *K. Takeda & B. M. Pogell*, J. biol. Chem. *240*, 651 [1965].
7 *E. Latzko & R. v. Garnier*, unpublished experiments.
8 *H. A. Krebs*, Bull. Johns Hopkins Hosp. *95*, 19 [1954].
9 *G. H. Krause & A. Bassham*, Biochim. Biophys. Acta *172*, 553 [1969].
10 *B. B. Buchanan, P. D. Kalberer & D. J. Arndt*, Fed. Proc. *27*, 344 [1968].
11 *R. v. Garnier & E. Latzko*, IInd. Int. Congr. Photosynth. Junk, Thettague [1972], p. 1839.
12 *B. B. Buchanan, P. Schürmann & P. D. Kalberer*, J. biol. Chem. *246*, 5952 [1971].
13 *E. Latzko & M. Gibbs*, Plant. Physiol. *44*, 295 [1969].
14 *F. Heinz*, Hoppe-Seyler's Z. f. Physiol. Chem. *349*, 399 [1968].
15 *P. Ritter, E. Jenny, A. Hicklin & F. Leuthardt*, Helv. Physiol. Pharmacol. Acta *19*, 234 [1961].

α-Amylase

Measurement of Reducing Groups

Wirnt Rick and Hans Peter Stegbauer

α-Amylase (1,4-α-D-Glucan glucanohydrolase, EC 3.2.1.1) hydrolyses α-1→4-glucan bonds in polysaccharides, such as starch, amylopectin and glycogen, and their degradation products with a chain length of at
least 3 D-glucose residues. The enzyme is found in micro-organisms, in plants and in particularly high
activity in germinating cereals. In the animal organism it is found especially in the secretory granules
of the cells of the salivary glands and the pancreas, and also in the secretions of these organs. Slight activity
is found in blood, serum and urine of normal subjects. The enzymes from pig pancreas[1], human saliva[2],
human pancreas[3] and rat pancreas[4] have been crystallized.

Damage to the α-amylase synthesizing tissues, in particular the pancreas, results in leakage of the enzyme
from the parenchymal cells and its appearance in the serum. Due to its relatively low molecular weight
(about 50 000) the protein is filtered by glomeruli and is excreted in the urine. The concentration gradient
between pancreatic secretion and urine in normal subjects is 500 : 1.

The present findings[5] suggest that the hydrolysis of the polysaccharide chain occurs via the principle of
"multiple attack": once the enzyme-substrate complex is formed, the enzyme can hydrolyse several
bonds of the polymer successively before the enzyme is again liberated in the free form. Under optimum
conditions the number of such hydrolytic reactions on the *same* polysaccharide chain[5] is about 6 for
pig pancreatic amylase and about 3 for the enzyme from human saliva.

The amylase activity can be measured[6] by means of the decrease in viscosity of a starch solution, the
decrease in turbidity of a starch suspension, the decrease in the intensity of the starch-iodine reaction
and the increase in the number of reducing groups. Methods of the latter group fulfil the requirements
of the Enzyme Commission of the IUB; with the other methods conversion to International Units must
be made on the basis of assays of activity of standard enzyme preparations or standard sera. Newer
methods, see p. 890 and 894.

On the basis of the starch-iodine reaction it was concluded that iso-amylases occurred in all 5 serum
fractions as separated by electrophoresis[7]. As the sum of the separate activities amounted to about 4-fold
that of the starting serum, the possibility of the removal of an amylase inhibitor was suggested[7]. However, only the apparent activity zone in the area of γ-globulin is due to enzyme activity; the decolorization
of the starch-iodine complex by the other fractions is caused by the presence of protein alone[8]. Amylases
from salivary gland and pancreas which migrate with the γ-globulin can be separated by electrophoresis
of serum in polyacrylamide gel[9].

Application of Method: In biochemistry, in clinical chemistry and in pharmacy.

Principle

Starch is hydrolysed by α-amylase to fragments whose reducing hemiacetal groups can be determined
with 3,5-dinitrosalicylic acid[10]. The concentration of the nitroaminosalicylic acid formed[11] is measured
colorimetrically; it corresponds to the concentration of newly formed terminal groups and therefore
directly to the enzyme activity.

Optimum Conditions for Measurements

Of the various starch preparations, soluble starch, A. R., *Zulkowsky's* soluble starch and *Lintner's* starch
are equally suitable. The activity of crystalline pancreatic amylase with Dr. *Schoch's* "Waxy Maize Starch"
is only 70% of that measured with *Zulkowsky* starch, while the activity with glycogen is only 50%[12].

The optimum substrate concentration with *Zulkowsky* starch is 10 mg./ml. assay mixture and the optimum
pH is 6.9. Chloride ions in a final concentration of 10 mM are added to activate the amylase.
Calcium (1 gram atom per molecule) is bound so tightly to the enzyme molecule that it can be removed
only by dialysis against EDTA or electrodialysis[13]. Addition of calcium ions results in no further increase
in activity.

Equipment

Spectrum-line or filter photometer suitable for measurements at 546, 550 nm; water baths
(25 °C; 100 °C); stopwatch or timer.

Reagents

1. Disodium hydrogen phosphate,
   $Na_2HPO_4 \cdot 2H_2O$, A. R.
2. Potassium dihydrogen phosphate,
   KH_2PO_4, A. R.
3. Sodium chloride, 0.9% (w/v)

4. Sodium hydroxide, 0.1 N, 1.0 N
5. Starch, soluble, *Zulkowsky*, A. R.
6. 3,5-Dinitrosalicylic acid
7. Potassium-sodium tartrate, A. R.
8. D(+)-Maltose

Preparation of Solutions

I. Phosphate buffer (20 mM, pH 6.9; 10 mM NaCl):
   Dissolve 1.97 g. $Na_2HPO_4 \cdot 2H_2O$ + 1.23 g. KH_2PO_4 in ca. 800 ml. doubly distilled
   water, add 65 ml. 0.9% NaCl solution, adjust to pH 6.9 with 0.1 N NaOH and dilute to
   1 000 ml. with doubly distilled water.

II. Starch solution (1% w/v):
   Dissolve 1.0 g. starch in phosphate buffer (solution I) and make up to 100 ml.

III. Dinitrosalicylic acid reagent (1% (w/v) 3,5-dinitrosalicylic acid, 30% (w/v) potassium-
   sodium tartrate):
   Dissolve with warming 10 g. 3,5-dinitrosalicylic acid in ca. 300 ml. doubly distilled water
   and 400 ml. 1 N NaOH, add 300 g. potassium-sodium tartrate and dilute to 1 000 ml. with
   doubly distilled water.

IV. Maltose standard solution:
   Determine the water content of D(+)-maltose. Dissolve 100.0 mg. maltose in doubly
   distilled water and make up to 100 ml. Calculate the concentration (ca. 2.5 mM) after
   taking into account the moisture content of the maltose.

Stability of Solutions

The phosphate buffer is stable for at least 1 year at 0–4 °C if bacterial contamination is avoided. The
substrate solution can be used for 1 week. The dinitrosalicylic acid reagent is stable for 6 months if stored
in a brown bottle protected from atmospheric CO_2.

Procedure

Collection, Treatment and Stability of Sample

Collection of sample:

Collect urine without an additive. If the amylase excretion is expressed in terms of unit time[14], the total urine must be collected for an exact period of time (e. g. 1 hr., 2 hr., 12 hr.). For the collection of duodenal contents, see under "Trypsin", p. 1015.

Stability of enzyme in sample:

The amylase activity in urine samples remains constant at room temperature for at least 8 days, and at 0–4 °C for at least 4 weeks[15]. The enzyme is stable in duodenal contents for at least 2 hr. at 37 °C[16], 24 hr. at 0–4 °C[17] and months at −20 °C[16]. This remarkable stability of amylase is explained by the complete resistance of undenatured amylase to proteases such as trypsin[18].

Assay System

Wavelength: Hg 546 nm; light path: 1 cm.; volume of incubation mixture: 2.05 ml.; incubation temperature: 25 °C; final volume: 4.05 ml. Read against water. Equilibrate the substrate solution to 25 °C before the start of the assay.

Assay in Urine:

Pipette into 12 ml. centrifuge tubes (in 25 °C water bath):	Test	Blank	Concentration in assay mixture
Buffer (I)	1.0 ml.	1.0 ml.	10 mM phosphate
Urine or enzyme solution	0.05 ml.	—	0.05–0.3 μg. protein/ml.
Substrate solution (III)	1.0 ml.	1.0 ml.	5 mg. starch/ml.
Mix, start a stopwatch and incubate for exactly 10 min.			
Dinitrosalicylic acid reagent (III)	2.0 ml.	2.0 ml.	
Urine or enzyme solution	—	0.05 ml.	
Mix, stopper tubes with glass marbles and heat for 5 min. in a 100 °C water bath. Cool in cold water and after 20–60 min. read the extinctions.			

With extinction differences of more than 1.5 dilute the urine 1:10 with buffer (I) and repeat the assay.

Maltose – Standard Curve: In 12 ml. centrifuge tubes dilute 0.2–1.0 ml. maltose standard solution (IV) with doubly distilled water to 1.05 ml. and prepare a blank with 1.05 ml. distilled water only. To all tubes add 1.0 ml. substrate (II) and 2.0 ml. dinitrosalicylic acid reagent (III). Mix thoroughly, stopper tubes with glass marbles and place in a 100 °C water bath for 5 min. Finally cool in cold water and read the extinctions against doubly distilled water after 20–60 min. Plot the extinctions against the μmole maltose per reaction mixture.

Calculations

Subtract the blanks from the corresponding test values to give ΔE. With the conditions described here (wavelength 546 nm) the

$$\text{volume activity} = 4950 \times \Delta E \ [\text{U/l.}]$$

The amylase excretion per unit time is

$$[\text{U/min.}] = [\text{U/l.}] \times [\text{l./min.}]$$

Precision of Method

With activities around 1.2 U/l. the standard deviation was 0.04 U/l. The coefficient of variation is 3.3%.

Normal Values

The amylase activities in urine of normal subjects have a logarithmic-normal distribution. The following normal ranges have been determined[12]:

Amylase activity: U/l.	$\bar{x} - 2s$	$\bar{x}$	$\bar{x} + 2s$
Men (n = 50)	220	650	1980
Women (n = 50)	240	890	3250

Amylase excretion: U/min.	$\bar{x} - 2s$	$\bar{x}$	$\bar{x} + 2s$
Men (n = 50)	0.103	0.42	1.71
Women (n = 50)	0.073	0.31	1.36

Normal values determined by other workers with other methods show a similar range[19].

Details for Measurements in Duodenal Juice

Duodenal contents are diluted 1 : 200 with 0.9% NaCl for the assay. The calculation is as follows:

$$\text{Volume activity} = 992 \times \Delta E \ [\text{U/l.}]$$

Dilute duodenal contents with low amylase activity [$\Delta E < 0.100$] correspondingly less.

Normal Values

For information on the enzyme secretion of the pancreas and the stimulation of the organ see under "Trypsin", p. 1023. After injection of pancreozymin at a dose of 1 U/kg. body wt. i. v. the following normal range of enzyme secretion rates is found[20]:

$$\bar{x} - 2s = 400 \text{ U/min.} \qquad \bar{x} = 850 \text{ U/min.} \qquad \bar{x} + 2s = 1\,780 \text{ U/min.}$$

Sources of Error

Effects of drugs and other therapeutic measures: No effect is known with urine analysis. Administration of pancreatic enzyme preparations should be discontinued before the collection of duodenal contents.

Interference in the assay technique: If the maltose standards are prepared with *pure* maltose solutions without the addition of starch, the standard curve is non-linear in the initial range. The reason for this is that a constant portion of the maltose is oxidized by dissolved oxygen. This source of error can be eliminated by passing a stream of nitrogen through the sample or addition of starch[16]. If the liberated reducing groups[21] are measured by the reduction of Cu^{2+} false values may occur with glucose concentrations in the sample of over 150 mg. %[22]. With the method described here there is no effect on the apparent enzyme activity up to a final concentration of 1 mg. glucose/2 ml. reaction mixture, i. e. up to a glucose concentration of 2000 mg./100 ml. sample[12]; the extinctions of the test and blank increase in parallel.

Specificity of Method

In human beings β-amylase (1,4-α-D-Glucan maltohydrolase, EC 3.2.1.2) and glucoamylase (1,4-α-D-Glucan glucohydrolase, EC 3.2.1.3) are not present[23] so that interference from these enzymes does not occur. Two amylolytic enzymes from urine have been separated on Sephadex G-100[24]; the further characterization of these enzymes and their association with certain organs has not yet been carried out.

Details for Measurements in Tissues

If tissues, such as pancreas, are homogenized under optimum conditions (e. g. with an Ultra-Turrax) the total amylase activity of the cells is liberated.

Amylase Clearance

The renal clearance for amylase in human is 2.4 ±0.94 ml./min.[25]; it is increased in pancreatic diseases[25]. By agar gel electrophoresis two amylases can be detected in serum and urine which originate from salivary glands and pancreas[26]. The clearance for the salivary gland enzyme has been determined to be 1.84 ± 0.38 ml./min., and that for the pancreatic enzyme 4.2 ± 1.6 ml./min.[26].

References

1 *K. H. Meyer, E. H. Fischer & P. Bernfeld,* Helv. chim. Acta *30,* 64 [1947].
2 *K. H. Meyer, E. H. Fischer, A. Staub & P. Bernfeld,* Helv. chim. Acta *31,* 2158 [1948].
3 *E. H. Fischer, F. Duckert & P. Bernfeld,* Helv. chim. Acta *33,* 1060 [1950].
4 *N. G. Heatley,* Nature *181,* 1069 [1958].
5 *J. F. Robyt & D. French,* Arch. Biochem. Biophysics *122,* 8 [1967].
6 *R. L. Searcy, P. Wilding & J. E. Berk,* Clin. chim. Acta *15,* 189 [1967].
7 *D. A. Dreiling, H. D. Janowitz & L. J. Josephberg,* Ann. Int. Med. *58,* 235 [1963].
8 *P. Wilding,* Clin. chim. Acta *8,* 918 [1963];
   J. E. Berk & R. L. Searcy, Gastroenterology *48,* 651 [1965].
9 *J. E. Berk, S. Hayashi, R. L. Searcy & N. C. Hightower jr.,* Amer. J. digest. Dis. *2,* 695 [1966].
10 *J. B. Sumner,* J. biol. Chem. *47,* 5 [1921];
   P. Bernfeld in *S. P. Colowick & N. O. Kaplan:* Methods in Enzymology. Academic Press, New York 1955; Vol. I, p. 149.
11 *F. Hostettler, E. Borel & H. Deuel,* Helv. chim. Acta *34,* 2132 [1951].
12 *W. Rick & H. Stegbauer,* Z. anal. Chem. *243,* 415 [1968].
13 *E. A. Stein, J. Hsiu & E. H. Fischer,* Biochemistry *3,* 56 [1964]; *J. Hsiu, E. H. Fischer & E. A. Stein,* Biochemistry *3,* 61 [1964].

14 *K. Heinkel,* Klin. Wschr. *34,* 155 [1956]; *E. I. Saxon, W. C. Hinkley, W. C. Vogel & L. Zieve,* Arch. int. Med. *99,* 607 [1957]; *E. E. Gambill & H. L. Mason,* J. Lab. clin. Med. *63,* 173 [1964].

15 *E. I. Saxon, W. C. Hinkley, W. C. Vogel & L. Zieve,* Arch. int. Med. *99,* 607 [1957]; *J. J. Budd, K. E. Walter, M. L. Harris & W. A. Knight,* Gastroenterology *36,* 333 [1959].

16 *A. Dahlqvist,* Scand. J. Clin. Lab. Invest. *14,* 145 [1962].

17 *W. Rick,* unpublished results.

18 *E. A. Stein & E. H. Fischer,* J. biol. Chem. *232,* 867 [1958].

19 *E. E. Gambill & H. L. Mason,* J. Lab. clin. Med. *63,* 173 [1964]; *W. G. Calkins,* Amer. J. Gastroenterology *46,* 407 [1966].

20 *W. Rick,* Acta gastroent. bèlg. *28,* 389 [1965]; Chirurg *39,* 301 [1968]; *H. Goebell, H.-D. Horn & Ch. Bode,* Verh. Dtsch. Ges. Inn. Med. *73,* 1094 [1967].

21 *M. Somogyi,* J. biol. Chem. *125,* 399 [1938].

22 *H. V. Street,* Clin. chim. Acta *3,* 501 [1958].

23 *J. R. Turvey* in *K. Lang & E. Lehnartz:* Handbuch der physiologisch- und pathologisch-chemischen Analyse. 10th. Edn. Springer Verlag, Berlin 1966, Vol. VI B, p. 1123.

24 *C. Franzini & P. A. Bonini,* Clin chim. Acta *17,* 505 [1967].

25 *A. Delcourt & P. Wettendorff,* Acta clin. belg. *19,* 265 [1964].

26 *J. Kamarýt,* Z. klin. Chem. and klin. Biochem. *7,* 51 [1969].

Determination of the Degradation Products Maltose and Glucose

Elli Rauscher

The degradation of starch by α-amylase leads to maltose as well as fragments with higher and lower molecular weights. The maltose can be determined by a UV method[1,2]. A continuous measurement has not so far been achieved. The method described was developed for serum and urine.

Principle

(1) $\text{Starch} + n\ H_2O \xrightarrow{\alpha-\text{amylase}*} (n + 1 - x)\ \text{Fragments} + x\ \text{Maltose}$

(2) $\text{Maltose} + H_2O \xrightarrow{\alpha-\text{glucosidase}**} 2\ \text{Glucose}$

(3) $2\ \text{Glucose} + 2\ \text{ATP} \xrightarrow{\text{hexokinase}\dagger} 2\ \text{Glucose-6-P} + 2\ \text{ADP}$

(4) $2\ \text{Glucose-6-P} + 2\ \text{NADP}^+ \xrightarrow{\text{G6P-DH}\dagger\dagger} 2\ \text{Gluconate-6-P} + 2\ \text{NADPH} + 2\ H^+$

After a fixed incubation time, reactions (1) and (2) stopped with perchloric acid. The amount of maltose formed in this time is determined in the supernatant of the deproteinized solution (reactions (3) and (4)). The glucose already present in the substrate or formed from the substrate by the action of α-glucosidase is determined in a blank.

---

* 1,4-α-D-Glucan glucanohydrolase, EC 3.2.1.1
** α-D-Glucoside glucohydrolase, EC 3.2.1.20
† ATP:D-hexose 6-phosphotransferase, EC 2.7.1.1
†† D-Glucose-6-phosphate:NADP 1-oxidoreductase, EC 1.1.1.49

Optimum Conditions for Measurements

The optimum substrate concentration is 30–60 mg. of starch per ml. of incubation solution. The optimum pH value is 6.9–7.0 in 20 mM phosphate buffer. Chloride ions are added to a final concentration of 50 mM for activation.

After a fixed reaction time, the enzymes are inactivated with perchloric acid and the reaction is stopped. This prevents the 6-PGDH present as a contaminating activity in α-glucosidase preparations from converting gluconate-6-phosphate further into ribulose-5-phosphate with formation of NADPH.

Since large fragments are initially formed from starch, and a uniform degradation to maltose takes place only then, an preliminary incubation phase of about 20 min. is necessary for the α-amylase reaction. The maltose concentration is therefore determined after 20 min. and after 60 min. The α-amylase activity is found from the difference between the two values in the linear region of the reaction.

Under the conditions described here (incubation at 25 °C, measurement at Hg 365 nm), measurements are possible up to an α-amylase activity of about 700 U/l.(25 °C) if the glucose concentration of the sample is in the normal range.

Equipment

Spectrum-line photometer or filter photometer for measurement at 340 nm (Hg 334 nm; Hg 365 nm); water bath or heating block 25 °C; laboratory centrifuge; stop clock.

Reagents

1. Dipotassium hydrogen phosphate, K_2HPO_4, A.R.
2. Potassium dihydrogen phosphate, KH_2PO_4, A.R.
3. Sodium chloride, A.R.
4. Starch, soluble
   acc. to Zulkowsky
5. α-Glucosidase
   from yeast, crystalline suspension in 3.2 M ammonium sulphate solution, approx. 50 U/mg. (25 °C); commercial preparation, see p. 459.
6. Perchloric acid, 70% (w/w), sp. gr. 1.67, A.R.
7. Triethanolamine hydrochloride
8. Sodium hydroxide solution, 0.1 N, approx. 5 N

9. Magnesium sulphate, $MgSO_4 \cdot 7H_2O$, A.R.
10. Nicotinamide adenine dinucleotide phosphate, NADP
    disodium salt NADP-Na_2H; commercial preparation, see p. 546.
11. Adenosine-5'-triphosphate, ATP
    disodium salt ATP-$Na_2H_2 \cdot 3H_2O$; commercial preparation, see p. 527.
12. Hexokinase
    from yeast, crystalline suspension in 3.2 M ammonium sulphate solution, approx. 140 U/mg. (25 °C); commercial preparations, see p. 473.
13. Glucose-6-phosphate dehydrogenase
    from yeast, crystalline suspension in 3.2 M ammonium sulphate solution, approx. 140 U/mg. (25 °C); commercial preparations, see p. 458.

Preparation of Solutions

Prepare all solutions with freshly distilled water.
  I. Phosphate buffer (22 mM; pH 7.0; 55 mM NaCl):
     Dissolve 3.06 g. K_2HPO_4 + 1.17 g. KH_2PO_4 + 3.22 g. NaCl in approx. 900 ml. water, check pH with the glass electrode and adjust with 0.1 N NaOH if necessary, and make up to 1 000 ml. with water.

II. Starch solution (4.4% w/v):
    Dissolve 1.10 g. starch in phosphate buffer (I) and make up to 25 ml.

III. Amylase reagent (22 mM phosphate; pH 7.0; 55 mM chloride; 4.4% (w/v) starch, approx. 250 U α-glucosidase/ml.):
    Depending on the number of assay mixtures to be prepared, centrifuge at high speed a certain volume of the commercial crystalline suspension of α-glucosidase (5 mg./ml.), discard supernatant, dissolve precipitate in starch solution (II), and make up to the original volume.

IV. Perchloric acid (0.6 N):
    Dilute 5.2 ml. 70% perchloric acid to 100 ml. with water.

V. Triethanolamine buffer (0.3 M; pH 7.5; 4 mM $MgSO_4$):
    Dissolve 5.6 g. triethanolamine hydrochloride+100 mg. $MgSO_4 \cdot 7H_2O$ in approx. 80 ml. water, adjust the pH by the glass electrode with 5 N NaOH, and make up to 100 ml. with water.

VI. Nicotinamide-adenine dinucleotide phosphate (23 mM NADP):
    Dissolve 20 mg. NADP-Na_2H in 1 ml. water.

VII. Adenosine-5'-triphosphate (0.16 M ATP):
    Dissolve 100 mg. ATP-$Na_2H_2 \cdot 3H_2O$ in 1 ml. 0.1 N NaOH.

VIII. Glucose reagent: (0.27 M triethanolamine; pH 7.5; 1.0 mM NADP; 7.2 mM ATP; 3.6 mM $MgSO_4$; 2.5 U hexokinase/ml.; 1.2 U G6P-DH/ml.):
    Mix 20 ml. triethanolamine buffer (IV) with 1.0 ml. NADP solution (V)+1.0 ml. ATP solution (VI)+0.20 ml. hexokinase crystalline suspension (2 mg./ml.)+0.20 ml. G6P-DH crystalline suspension (1 mg./ml.).

Stability of Solutions

Prepare starch solution (II), amylase reagent (III), and glucose reagent (VIII) freshly every day. Keep all solutions at 4 °C.

Procedure

Collection, Treatment and Stability of Sample

Obtain serum and urine without additives. The samples can be stored for several weeks at 4 °C without loss of activity.

Assay System

Wavelength: 340 nm (Hg 334 nm; Hg 365 nm); light path: 1 cm.; incubation volume: 0.55 ml. (V_1); incubation temperature: 25 °C; deproteinization volume: 0.30 ml. (V_2); final volume: 2.20 ml. (V_3); read at room temperature against air.
For each series of measurements, make up a blank with water instead of sample.

Incubation Mixture

Pipette into centrifuge tubes:	Sample	Blank	Concentration in assay mixture
Amylase reagent (III)	0.50 ml.	0.50 ml.	20 mM phosphate 50 mM chloride 40 mg. starch/ml. 250 U α-glucosidase/ml.
Keep at 25 °C for 5 min.			
Sample Water	0.05 ml. —	— 0.05 ml.	
Mix, incubate at 25 °C, take a 0.2 ml. portion after exactly 20 min. and after exactly 60 min. and pipette immediately into 0.1 ml. of perchloric acid (IV) (centrifuge tube). Centrifuge for 5 min. at 3000 rpm. Use supernatants.			

Glucose Determination

Pipette into cuvettes	Sample	Blank	Concentration in assay mixture
Glucose reagent (VIII)	2.00 ml.	2.00 ml.	0.24 M triethanolamine 3.2 mM MgSO$_4$ 0.9 mM NADP 6.5 mM ATP 2.2 U HK/ml. 1.1 U G6P-DH/ml.
Supernatants	0.20 ml.	0.20 ml.	
Mix; after reaction stops (20 to 30 min.), read extinctions E_1 (20 min.) and E_2 (60 min.).			

If the extinction difference is greater than 1.5 at 365 nm, dilute sample 1+9 with phosphate buffer (I) and repeat determination.

Calculations

The value ΔE determined between the 20th and 60th min. is used in the calculation.

$$\Delta E = \Delta E_S - \Delta E_B$$
where $\Delta E_S = E_{S_1} - E_{S_2}$
$$\Delta E_B = E_{B_1} - E_{B_2}$$

Formula (8) on p. 313 is valid.

$$\text{Volume activity} = \frac{1\,000 \times V_1 \times V_2 \times V_3}{\varepsilon \times d \times v_1 \times v_2 \times v_3 \times 2} \, \Delta E / \Delta t \quad [\text{U/l.}]$$

$\Delta t = 40$ min.; $V_1 = 0.55$ ml.; $V_2 = 0.30$ ml.; $V_3 = 2.20$ ml.; $v_1 = 0.05$ ml.; $v_2 = 0.20$ ml.; $v_3 = 0.20$ ml. The following relationships are therefore valid for the above procedure:

Wavelength:	334 nm	340 nm	365 nm
Volume activity =	$378 \times \Delta E$	$365 \times \Delta E$	$688 \times \Delta E$ [U/l.]

Precision of Method

A standard deviation of 2.5 U was found with values around 50 U/l. of serum. The coefficient of variation is 5%.

Sources of Error

Serum amylase is inhibited by chloride concentrations above 100 mM.
Since saliva and sweat contain α-amylase, the solutions should not be pipetted orally, and the parts of the reaction vessels that come into contact with incubation solution should not be touched with the hands. It is therefore advisable to carry out all pipetting with automatic measuring devices.
Starch may contain low molecular weight impurities that are transformed by α-glucosidase, and this leads to excessively high results. It may be assumed, however, that this occurs to an equal degree in the assay and in the blank.
In the case of samples with very high glucose contents, correspondingly high blanks are obtained. In such cases, glucose can be removed by dialysis or gel filtration.

Specificity of Method

The method is specific for α-amylase.

References

1 H.-W. Schiwara, Z. klin. Chem. u. klin. Biochem. 10, 12 [1972].
2 H.-W. Schiwara, Ärztl. Lab. 17, 340 [1971].

Determination with Coloured Insoluble Substrates

August Wilhelm Wahlefeld

In 1967, H. Rinderknecht et al.[1] described an entirely novel substrate for the determination of the activity of α-amylase. Insoluble starch was stained under alkaline conditions with the reactive dye Remazol Brilliant Blue R (manufacturer: Farbwerke Hoechst AG). The result is a covalently labelled, insoluble substrate for the determination of α- or β-amylase activities. After incubation under defined conditions, the cleavage of the coloured substrate is stopped with the aid of a suitable precipitant, with simultaneous precipitation of the insoluble and excess components of the substrate. The coloured cleavage products are determined photometrically in the supernatant.

The determination is simple to carry out. The method for the determination of α-amylase has found widespread use in clinical laboratories.

Various coloured substrates are commercially available at present:

1. Amylose-Azure® (Calbiochem, USA)

   Hall[2]: Use of this substrate.

2. Lyosine Red® substrate (Reliable Reagents, USA)

   Sax[3]: Preparation of Procion Brilliant Red M-2 BS-amylopectin.

   The dye is a product of ICI America, USA.

3. Amylochrome® substrate (Hofmann-La Roche, Switzerland)

   Klein[4]: Staining of insoluble amylose with Cibachron Blue F3G-A (manufacturer: Ciba AG, Switzerland)

4. DyAmyl® substrate (General Diagnostics, USA)

   Babson[5]: Amylopectin is stained with Reaktone Red 2 B (manufacturer: Geigy, Switzerland).

5. Phadebas® substrate (Pharmacia, Sweden)

   Ceska[6,7,8]: Soluble starch is stained with Cibachron Blue F3G-A (manufacturer: Ciba AG, Switzerland) and made insoluble by crosslinking with 1,4-butanediol glycide ether.

   Ceska's method[6,7,8] is described below.

Application of Method: In clinical biochemistry and in food chemistry.

Principle

$$x \cdot H_2O + [\text{dye}]_n \xrightarrow{\alpha\text{-amylase}} [\text{dye}]_q + [\text{dye}]_y$$

m ≫ n   p ≫ q   x ≫ y

insoluble   insoluble   soluble

Coloured starch that is insoluble as a result of crosslinking, but that is capable of swelling, is hydrolysed by α-amylase. The resulting soluble coloured cleavage products are determined photometrically in the supernatant after the reaction has been stopped. The reaction is irreversible; the α-amylase activity is determined by comparison with a standard.

Optimum Conditions for Measurements

Substrate saturation of the α-amylase of serum is reached above 30 mg. of Blue Starch Polymer per ml. For practical reasons, a substrate concentration of 10 mg. of Blue Starch Polymer per ml. is used. One thus measures α-amylase activities of up to 4500 U/l. practically at substrate saturation.

The pH optimum is relatively sharp at 7.0; the dependence on the concentrations of phosphate and of sodium chloride is less pronounced, and 0.02 M phosphate buffer with 0.05 M sodium chloride is suitable. The mixture should be incubated for not more than 30 min. at 25 °C; 10 min. gives good results. At intermediate activities, the reaction rate frequently increases with long test times, since the substrate reacts more rapidly with decreasing chain length.

Equipment

Spectrophotometer or spectrum-line photometer capable of measurement at 620 nm or at Hg 623 nm or Hg 578 nm; laboratory centrifuge; incubation bath (27 °C); filter funnel; paper filter, e. g. Schleicher and Schüll No. 595, diameter 5.5 cm. Vortex mixer*.

Reagents

1. Blue Starch Polymer (Pharmacia, Sweden) or Phadebas® tablets.
2. Sodium dihydrogen phosphate, NaH_2PO_4, A. R.
3. Disodium hydrogen phosphate, Na_2HPO_4, A. R.
4. Sodium chloride, NaCl, A. R.
5. Sodium hydroxide, NaOH, A. R.
6. Sodium azide, NaN_3, A. R.
7. Bovine serum albumin, pure
8. α-Amylase
   from hog pancreas, crystalline; suspension in 3.2 M ammonium sulphate solution; approx. 1 000 U/mg. (25 °C); commercial preparation, see p. 432.

Preparation of Solutions

Make up all solutions with freshly prepared doubly distilled water.

   I. Phosphate buffer (0.02 M phosphate, pH 7.0; 0.05 M NaCl; 0.02% of NaN_3):
      Dissolve 3.58 g. $Na_2HPO_4·12H_2O$ in 500 ml. water. Adjust the pH accurately to 7.0 with a solution of 1.38 g. $NaH_2PO_4·H_2O$ in 500 ml. water. Add 292.2 mg. sodium chloride and (for preservation) 20 mg. NaN_3 per 100 ml. buffer.
  II. Substrate/buffer (10 mg. Blue Starch Polymer/ml. of buffer I):
      Shortly before use, suspend 100 mg. Blue Starch Polymer in 10 ml. buffer (I). On pipetting, stir well.
 III. Sodium hydroxide solution (0.5 N NaOH):
      Dissolve 20 g. sodium hydroxide in water and make up to 1 litre.
  IV. α-Amylase standard (approx. 1 000 U/l.):
      Dissolve 1 mg. α-amylase in 10 ml. of a solution of 6 g. bovine serum albumin in 100 ml. phosphate buffer (I) (stock solution; stable for at least 4 weeks at 4 °C). Using this stock solution, make up a dilution of 1:100 with the same 6% bovine serum albumin solution as required (concentration approx. 1 μg. α-amylase per ml., corresponding to approx. 1 000 U/l.). Determine the exact α-amylase activity in this solution by the reducing group method (cf. p. 885).

Stability of Solutions

Solutions I and III keep indefinitely. Prepare fresh solution II daily. Solution IV is stable for at least 1 week at 4 °C.

---

* Manufacturer: Fisons Scientific App. Ltd., England.

Procedure

Collection, Treatment and Stability of Sample

Collection and preliminary treatment of sample: Obtain serum and urine without additives. At excessively high activities, $\geqslant 4\,500$ U/l., dilute serum with buffer (I). Denaturation of the α-amylase can occur in urine samples[10]; it is therefore advisable to dilute with solutions containing albumin, e.g. 20 mg. bovine serum albumin/ml. buffer (I).

Stability of sample: α-Amylase in serum samples is stable for at least 1 week at 20–25 °C, and for 2 weeks at 4 °C. In urine samples, cf. p. 887.

Assay System*

Wavelength: 620 nm, Hg 623 nm; Hg 578 nm; light path 1 cm.; final volume: 4.2 ml.; incubation temperature: 25 °C; measurement against reagent blank with water instead of sample. Use 1 reagent blank and 1 standard for each series of measurements.

Pipette into test tubes:		Sample or standard	Blank	Concentration in assay mixture
Substrate/buffer	(II)	4.0 ml.	4.0 ml.	20 mM phosphate 50 mM NaCl 0.2 mg. NaN$_3$/ml.
Maintain at 25 °C for 10 min.				
Sample (standard) Water		0.2 ml. —	— 0.2 ml.	
Mix (vortex mixer), incubate for 10 min at 25 °C.				
0.5 N NaOH		1.0 ml.	1.0 ml.	98 mM NaOH
Mix quickly (vortex mixer; reaction is stopped). Centrifuge sharply, filter supernatant, and measure extinction of the sample (E$_S$) and of the standard (E$_{Std}$) in the filtrate against the blank.				

Calculations

1 U denotes the formation of one reducing group per minute at 25 °C (reducing group method). The formula used is

$$(\text{volume activity})_{\text{sample}} = \frac{E_S}{E_{Std}} \times (\text{volume activity})_{Std} \; [U/l.]$$

Normal Values

Normal values have been determined in urine at 25 °C[11], cf. p. 888. The following normal values were found by *Ceska*[7] with Blue Starch Polymer at 37 °C.

---

* For determination with the commercial reagent kits, see the instructions included.

Serum	males	88– 282 (U/l.)
	females	86– 226 (U/l.)
Urine	males	125–1590 (U/l.)
	females	192–1310 (U/l.)

The values obtained by this and by other methods are not directly comparable.

Accuracy and Precision

With an α-amylase activity in serum at the upper limit of normal values, a coefficient of variation of 1% is found in the series; day-to-day coefficient of variation is not greater than 5%.

Sources of Error

Effects of drugs and other therapeutic measures: see p. 889.

Interference in assay technique: If the precipitate is not centrifuged off very efficiently, coloured particles are transferred into the cuvette with the supernatant, with the result that excessively high extinction values are found; additional filtration is therefore recommended. Incorrect results are readily caused by contamination with α-amylase from saliva and/or sweat from the hands.
Detergents can interfere, as can citrate or EDTA-treated plasma. No significant interference was found with the addition of heparin (0.2 mg./ml.).

Specificity of Method

The substrate is specific for amylases. A differentiation between endo(α-)- and exo(β-)-amylases should be possible with the crosslinked substrate. However, no precise experimental details are known as yet.

References

1 *H. Rinderknecht, P. Wilding & B. J. Haverback*, Experientia *23*, 805 [1967].
2 *F. F. Hall, T. W. Culp, E. Hayakawa, C. R. Ratcliff & N. C. Hightower*, Amer. J. Clin. Path. *53*, 627 [1970].
3 *S. M. Sax, A. B. Bridgewater & J. J. Moore*, Clin. Chem. *17*, 311 [1971].
4 *B. Klein, J. A. Foremann & R. L. Searcy*, Anal. Biochem. *31*, 412 [1971].
5 *A. L. Babson, S. A. Tenney & R. E. Megraw*, Clin. Chem. *16*, 39 [1970].
6 *M. Ceska, E. Hultman & B. G. A. Ingelman*, Experientia *25*, 555 [1969].
7 *M. Ceska, B. Brown & K. Birath*, Clin. Chem. Acta *26*, 445 [1969].
8 *M. Ceska, K. Birath & B. Brown*, Clin. Chem. Acta *26*, 437 [1969].
9 *G. Gerhardt*, personal communication [1971].
10 *K. Soininen, M. Harkonen & M. Ceska*, Scand. J. Clin. Lab. Invest. *30*, 291 [1972].
11 *W. Rick & H. Stegbauer*, Z. anal. Chem. *243*, 415 [1968].

Measurement of the Starch-Iodine Complex

Harold V. Street*

Amylases are found in almost all plants, animals and micro-organisms. Especially large amounts of amylase occur in the pancreas of higher animals, and in the saliva of man, ape, pig, rat, guinea pig, mouse

---

* Edited by *Karlfried Gawehn* (1969).

and squirrel[1]. Smaller amounts are found in serum, urine, liver and muscle. The saliva of carnivorous animals contains no amylase.

Animal amylase is mainly α-amylase (1,4-α-D-Glucan glucanohydrolase, EC 3.2.1.1); in plants β-amylase predominates. β-Amylase (1,4-α-D-Glucan maltohydrolase, EC 3.2.1.2) attacks starch at the non-reducing ends and splits off β-maltose. It hydrolyses starch to limit dextrins and its action is thought to be arrested by the 1,6-cross-linkages. α-Amylase attacks 1,4-linkages which lie within the starch molecule, liberating first dextrin and then a mixture of reducing sugars, especially α-maltose.

There are four main types of method for the determination of amylase activity:

1. Determination of the residual substrate by precipitation with ethanol/water. This method is not readily applicable to serum because proteins are also precipitated.
2. Measurement of the decrease of viscosity of the substrate. This method depends to a large extent on the type of substrate and the reproducibility is poor.
3. Measurement of the amount of reducing sugar liberated by the amylase[2-5]. This method depends on ratio of amylose to amylopectin in the substrate. It can also give misleading results when the blood sugar concentration is above 150 mg./100 ml.[6]
4. Measurement of the changes in the iodine colour of the assay mixture[7-12]. The method of *Street* and *Close*[12] is described here.

There is also a turbidimetric method[13,14] and one which depends on the absorption of congo red on starch[15].

Application of Method: In clinical chemistry, in biochemistry and in foodstuff chemistry.

Principle

The solution to be examined is allowed to act on amylose for 15 min. and then the blue colour formed on addition of an iodine-iodide solution is compared with the colour of an amylase-free control.

Optimum Conditions for Measurements

The pH activity curve is relatively flat between pH 6.9 and 7.1; pH 7.0 is most suitable. Animal amylase is activated by chloride ions. In the method described here maximum activity is obtained when the chloride concentration in the assay mixture is >0.01 N. A chloride content of up to 0.9% does not interfere. Plant amylase is not activated by chloride ions.

A linear relationship between the amylase activity and the colour of the iodine reaction is obtained up to an amylase content in the sample of 5000 U/l. (60 *Street-Close* units*/100 ml.) under the conditions described here (15 min. incubation at 37 °C). With higher concentrations of amylase the colour produced by the iodine is no longer blue, but instead may be violet, red or yellow[12].

Equipment

Spectrophotometer or spectrum-line photometer suitable for measurements at 578 nm.; laboratory centrifuge.

---

* 1 *Street-Close* unit corresponds to about 8.2 U.

Reagents

1. Amylose
   obtained from starch (see Appendix, p. 902) or
   commercial preparation (e. g. British Drug
   Houses Ltd., Dorset, England).
2. Potassium dihydrogen phosphate,
   KH_2PO_4
3. Disodium hydrogen phosphate, Na_2HPO_4

4. Hydrochloric acid, A. R., 0.01 N
5. Iodine, sublimed
6. Potassium iodide, A. R.
7. Sodium chloride, A. R., 0.1 N
8. Sodium hydroxide, A. R., 0.1 N
9. Ethanol

Preparation of Solutions

Prepare all solutions with fresh, doubly distilled water. To avoid the growth of micro-organisms sterilize the containers.

I. Amylose
   a) Stock solution (1% w/v):
      Heat 80 ml. 0.1 N NaOH to 90 °C in a 250 ml. beaker, and into this solution pour a suspension of 1.0 g. amylose in 5 ml. ethanol. Rinse traces of amylose from the container and stirring rod with two 1 ml. portions of ethanol and add washings to the hot NaOH (wear protective goggles). Most of the ethanol boils off immediately. Cool the solution, transfer to a volumetric flask with 0.1 NaOH and dilute to 100 ml. Mix well and store at room temperature.
   b) Dilute solution (0.1% w/v):
      Dilute 10 ml. stock solution in a volumetric flask to 100 ml. with distilled water. Store at room temperature. (If it is necessary to filter the amylose solution, use a sintered glass filter; paper absorbs amylose).

II. Phosphate buffer (20 mM; pH 7.0):
    Dissolve 1.735 g. Na_2HPO_4 + 1.06 g. KH_2PO_4 in distilled water and make up to 1 000 ml.

III. Iodine/potassium iodide
   a) Stock solution (0.1 N iodine):
      Dissolve 30 g. KI in 250 ml. distilled water. Dissolve in this solution 13 g. iodine and dilute to 1 000 ml. with distilled water. Store in the dark.
   b) Dilute solution (0.01 N iodine):
      Dilute 10 ml. stock solution to 100 ml. with distilled water. Store in dark.

Stability of Solutions

Solutions I to III are stable for several months at room temperature.

Procedure

The method described here is suitable for the assay of amylase activity in serum. If the pH optimum of plant and bacterial amylases is known and the buffer is modified accordingly, this method can also be used for the estimation of these enzymes.

Collection, Treatment and Stability of Sample

Collection of sample and treatment:

Dilute serum samples 1 : 10 with 0.1 N NaCl solution (0.2 ml. serum + 1.8 ml. 0.1 N NaCl) and 1 : 40 (0.2 ml. serum + 7.8 ml. 0.1 N NaCl).

Stability of sample:

Amylase in serum is stable for at least 1 week at room temperature[16].

Assay System

Wavelength: Hg 578 nm; light path: 1 cm.; incubation volume: 10 ml.; final volume: 100 ml.; temperature: 37 °C; read against water.

Pipette successively into 100 ml. volumetric flasks:		Dilution 1 : 10	Dilution 1 : 40	Reference	Concentration in assay mixture
Phosphate buffer	(II)	5 ml.	5 ml.	5 ml.	10 mM
Amylose solution	(I b)	2 ml.	2 ml.	2 ml.	0.2 mg./ml.
0.01 N HCl		2 ml.	2 ml.	2 ml.	0.002 N
Place for 3 min. in 37 °C water bath.					
1 : 10 Diluted serum		1 ml.	—	—	
1 : 40 Diluted serum		—	1 ml.	—	
Mix and incubate for exactly 15 min. in 37 °C water bath.					
Distilled water		70 ml.	70 ml.	70 ml.	
Iodine solution	(III b)	4 ml.	4 ml.	4 ml.	
Dilute with distilled water to 100 ml., mix thoroughly and read extinctions E_{10}, E_{40}, E_0.					

Calculations

The amylase units are calculated from the number of glucosidic linkages which are hydrolysed per min. under the assay conditions[17].

$$\text{Volume activity} = \frac{E_0 - E_{10(40)}}{E_0} \times A \times \frac{1}{t} \times \frac{1}{v} \times 1\,000 \; [\text{U/l.}]; \quad 37\,°C$$

where

E_0	extinction of reference, corresponds to t = 0 min.
E_{10}, E_{40}	extinction of test with 1 : 10 or 1 : 40 diluted serum after t = 15 min.
A	12.35 μmole amylose in assay mixture (calculated as glucose units $C_6H_{10}O_5$; mol. wt. 162)
v	volume of sample in assay

The 1 : 10 dilution of serum allows the determination of 0 to 3000 mU/ml. serum. If, after addition of the iodine solution, the contents of the flask "Dilution 1 : 10" are not blue-green, but violet, reddish or yellow, use the extinction of the "Dilution 1 : 40" flask. If this dilution is also not blue-green, repeat the assay with a greater dilution of serum (1 : 100 or 1 : 200).

The amylase activity of the serum is calculated according to the above formula for the 1 : 10 dilution:

$$\text{Volume activity} = \frac{E_0 - E_{10}}{E_0} \times 12.35 \times 0.667 \times 1\,000 = \frac{\Delta E}{E_0} \times 8\,237 \text{ [U/l.]}; \quad 37\,°C$$

for the 1 : 40 dilution:

$$\text{Volume activity} = \frac{E_0 - E_{40}}{E_0} \times 12.35 \times 2.67 \times 1\,000 = \frac{\Delta E}{E_0} \times 32\,950 \text{ [U/l.]}; \quad 37\,°C$$

Normal Values

The normal amylase content of serum was found to be between 500 and 2 700 U/l. serum[18,19].

Sources of Error

Inhibitors and activators: According to *Vallee* et al.[20], certain α-amylases (e. g. from human saliva) contain at least 1 g. atom Ca/molecule enzyme. Incubation with EDTA inhibits these enzymes. Serum amylase is inhibited by citrate and activated by borate, while fluoride ions have no effect[21].

Interference in the assay technique: It is recommended that the assay is carried out in duplicate, because contamination by saliva (pipettes, speech or sneezing) occasionally gives abnormally high results.

Determination in Foodstuff Chemistry

Methods for the determination of amylase activity in honey, flour, meal, malt and milk are very complex and must be adapted to fit the situation. A survey of about 150 methods has been prepared by *Wildner*[22].

Appendix

Preparation of Amylose

Stir 30 g. of potato starch into a cream with 150 ml. water and pour this into 1 500 ml. boiling 2% (w/v) NaCl solution. Stir the hot mixture mechanically until it is homogeneous and filter through muslin whilst hot. To the cooled filtrate add 4.5 g. powdered thymol crystals (p-isopropyl-m-cresol) and stir for 48 hr. Decant and discard the supernatant fluid which contains amylopectin. Separate the precipitate of the amylose-thymol complex from the residual fluid by centrifugation, wash the precipitate six times with thymol-saturated water and four times with absolute ethanol. Spread out the residue on a glass plate and dry for 6 hr. at 37 °C with occasional grinding in a mortar. Yield: 3.6 g. amylose. Store the white powder at room temperature in a tightly stoppered, brown bottle.

References

1 *E. W. Cohn* & *M. H. Brookes*, J. biol. Chem. *115*, 139 [1937].
2 *V. C. Myers* & *J. A. Kilian*, J. biol. Chem. *29*, 179 [1917].
3 *M. Somogyi*, J. biol. Chem. *125*, 399 [1938].
4 *H. Sobers* & *S. M. Myers*, J. Lab. clin. Med. *41*, 655 [1953].
5 *Hidet Sugu Fuwa*, J. Biochem. [Tokyo] *41*, 583 [1954].
6 *H. V. Street*, Clin. chim. Acta *3*, 501 [1958].
7 *J. Wohlgemuth*, Biochem. Z. *9*, 1 [1908].

8 C. Huggins & P. S. Russell, Ann. Surg. *128*, 668 [1948].
9 B. W. Smith & J. H. Roe, J. biol. Chem. *179*, 53 [1949].
10 J. D. Teller, J. biol. Chemistry *185*, 701 [1950].
11 E. J. van Loon, M. R. Likins & A. J. Seger, Amer. J. clin. Pathol. *22*, 1134 [1952].
12 H. V. Street & J. R. Close, Clin. chim. Acta *1*, 256 [1956].
13 G. Peralta & J. G. Reinhold, Clin. Chemistry *1*, 157 [1955].
14 T. A. Scott & E. H. Melvin, Analytic Chem. *25*, 1656 [1953].
15 B. Carroll & J. W. van Dyk, Science *116*, 168 [1952].
16 H. V. Street, unpublished results.
17 R. Richterich, Klin. Chemie, Akad. Verlagsgesellschaft, Frankfurt/M., 2nd. Edn., 1968., p. 408.
18 J. R. Close & H. V. Street, Clin. chim. Acta *3*, 476 [1958].
19 H. V. Street & J. R. Close, Nature [London] *179*, 164 [1957].
20 B. L. Vallee, E. A. Stein, W. N. Sumerwell & E. H. Fischer, J. biol. Chem. *234*, 2901 [1959].
21 H. V. Street, Biochem. J. *76*, 10 [1960].
22 H. Wildner: Methoden zur Messung der enzymatischen Amylolyse. Verlag Hans Carl, Nürnberg 1959.

Measurement by End-point Determination on Paper

Günther Hillmann

The occurrence of α-amylase (1,4-α-D-Glucan glucanohydrolase, EC 3.2.1.1) in biological fluids and tissues is subject to considerable variation. The usual modern routine methods depend on the discontinuous colorimetric measurement of the extinction decrease of the starch-iodine complex[1]. There is a linear relationship between amylase activity and the colour reaction only in the initial phase of the hydrolytic degradation of 1,4-glucopolysaccharides[2]. This necessitates the preparation of numerous dilutions of samples containing high activity and therefore limits the rationalization of the method with large series of samples, especially for the assay of α-amylase activity in urine.

The starch-iodine reaction which is the basis of all the amyloclastic methods depends on the formation of blue iodine inclusion compounds with amylose. Because of the great variability in the amylose content of starch preparations amylose itself must be used for the amylase assays in comparative studies between different laboratories[3]. *Merck* amylose has proved to be a suitable standard preparation. A suitable synthetic substrate which could be used for the direct measurement of α-amylase does not exist.

The usual amylase units (International Units, *Street-Close* units, *Somogyi* units) as determined by the iodine binding or reduction method are defined as a time unit assuming proportionality between enzyme concentration, time and substrate reaction (zero order reaction). However, the reaction of α-amylase with high polymer polysaccharides is not a zero order reaction, because hydrolytic products with different enzyme affinity are formed. The degradation of the amount of starch expressed as amylase units is therefore an approximation.

The end-point method of *Somogyi*[4] (time taken for a colour change from blue to light brown) which is rarely used as a routine method, gives an assay of α-amylase activity which is kinetically sound in principle, because the proportionality between enzyme concentration and the reciprocal of the time is independent of the progress of the time-reaction curve.

The usual method, however, requires frequent sampling for the starch-iodine reaction. In addition, the accuracy is limited by the difficulty in deciding the colour change. The modification described here allows a simple kinetic assay without the use of a photometer[5]. It is a combination of the methods of *Somogyi* and *Street* and *Close*.

Application of Method: In clinical chemistry and biochemistry for differential diagnosis of pancreatic diseases.

Principle

(1)

Maltose

Amylose

3 or more α-1,4-glucosyl units

In contrast to starch and amylose, the reaction products maltotriose, maltotetrose, etc., do not form blue iodine inclusion compounds. The activity of α-amylase is determined by the time taken for the colour to change from blue (starch-iodine) to yellowish-brown (iodine blank). This is observed by spotting on acid-soaked filter paper. The results are expressed in amylase units (mU/ml.) by factor/time calculation in comparison with parallel determinations on standard preparations whose activity has been determined by the method of *Street* and *Close*.

Optimum Conditions for Measurements

The pH activity curve has a flat maximum between pH 6.9 and 7.1; the latter pH is used here. α-Amylase from mammalian tissues is activated by chloride ions. Maximum activation is achieved with > 10 mM chloride in the assay mixture. This method requires standard conditions with regard to substrate concentration; as in the method of *Street* and *Close* a concentration of 0.2 g. amylose/litre is chosen. Data on the optimum substrate concentration is not possible at present because of the difficulty in defining the enzyme-substrate affinity of the hydrolysis products formed by amylase. In the automated method it is necessary to add Dextran 2000 to the buffer/substrate solution, which reduces the rate of drop formation. This allows a more accurate determination of the end-point.

Equipment

For the manual method: 5 ml. Record syringe, needle 20×1; support with clamp.
For automated method: use the same type of syringe and the amylase assay apparatus of *Vitatron, Dieren*, Netherlands.

Reagents

1. Amylose
   Commercial preparation (e.g. Calbiochem. Los Angeles 54, California, USA; British Drug Houses Ltd., Poole, Dorset, England; Merck, Darmstadt, Germany).
2. Disodium hydrogen phosphate, Na_2HPO_4
3. Potassium dihydrogen phosphate, KH_2PO_4
4. Potassium iodide, A.R.
5. Potassium iodate, A.R.
6. Sodium chloride, A.R.
7. Sodium hydroxide, A.R., 0.1 N
8. Ethanol

9. Citric acid
10. Amylase
    from pancreas; ca. 350 U/mg. (37 °C);
    commercial preparation, see p. 432.
11. Dextran 2000 (Pharmacia, Sweden)

12. Chromatography paper
    Schleicher & Schull No. 2668 or Marcherey &
    Nagel No. 866. Acid-soaked filter paper:
    dissolve 192 g. citric acid in distilled water and
    make up to 1000 ml. (1 M). Soak the chromato-
    graphy paper in strips 2 cm. × 40 cm. with citric
    acid solution by immersing or spraying. Remove
    excess solution by allowing to drip off or by
    blotting.

Preparation of Solutions

Prepare all solutions with doubly distilled water and store in polyethylene flasks.

I. Amylose
   Stock solution* (1% w/v similar to the description of *Street* and *Close*):
   Suspend 1.0 g. amylose in 5 ml. ethanol, and stir into 80 ml. 0.1 N NaOH warmed to ca.
   90 °C. Wash in with two 1 ml. portions of ethanol, then cool and dilute to 100 ml. with
   0.1 N NaOH in a volumetric flask. If necessary, filter through a sintered glass filter.

II. Phosphate buffer (20 mM; pH 7.1):
    Dissolve 2.38 g. Na_2HPO_4 + 0.898 g. KH_2PO_4 in distilled water and make up to 500 ml.

III. Iodide-iodate solution:
     Dissolve 1.162 g. KI and 0.15 g. KIO_3 in distilled water and make up to 100 ml.

IV. Working solution:
    a) Mix 20 ml. amylose stock solution (I) with 500 ml. phosphate buffer (solution II) and
       100 ml. iodide-iodate solution (III). Dilute to 1000 ml. with distilled water.
    b) If the test pack "Amylase-Merck" is used mix the iodide-iodate solution (without
       inclusion of HCl contained in the test kit) with the buffer substrate mixture and dilute
       to 1000 ml.
    c) With the automated micro-method add 10 g. Dextran 2000 to 1000 ml. substrate-buffer
       mixture and warm on a water bath to complete solution. The hydrolysis of amylose is
       not affected by the addition of Dextran 2000. The rate of drop formation of the enzyme-
       substrate buffer from the glass syringe is decreased due to the higher viscosity. This
       results in a bead-like succession of coloured spots and allows the end-point to be seen
       more clearly.

V. Amylase standard solution (100 mU/ml.):
   Dissolve 5 mg. amylase in 500 ml. 0.9% NaCl (stock solution; stable for ca. 4 weeks at
   0–4 °C). Dilute the stock solution 1 : 10 with 0.9% NaCl. Measure the enzyme activity by
   the method of *Street* and *Close*. Dilute with 0.9% NaCl to 100 mU/ml. (e. g. measured
   activity 330 U/l.; dilute 10 ml. of this solution to 23 ml. with 0.9% NaCl).

Stability of Solutions

The stability of the working solution IV is dependent on the absence of bacterial contamination. The average
stability without taking strict sterile precautions is about 14 days in a refrigerator. Assess the stability by
the iodometric determination of the amylose concentration.

---

* With the commercially available reagent kits it is not necessary to prepare a separate amylose stock
  solution.

Procedure

Collection, Treatment and Stability of Sample

Collection of sample:

Collect blood without venestasis. Do not add anti-coagulants. Obtain serum by centrifugation for 10 min. at ca. 3000 g. Use only fresh serum free from haemolysis.
Urine: Use freshly voided urine collected in a clean receiver. Bile/duodenal juice: carefully clean the duodenal probe; avoid contamination with saliva.

Stability of enzyme in sample:

Amylase in serum is stable for ca. 8 days at room temperature without loss of activity. The stability of amylase in urine, bile and duodenal juice depends on the sterility of the sample. This is not easy to ensure.

Assay System (manual method)

Measurements at room temperature; final volume 4.1 ml. with urine; 4.5 ml. with serum and duodenal juice. Spray or soak filter paper with citric acid solution.

Pipette into test tubes:			Concentration in assay mixture
Sample*		0.5 ml.	
Reagent mixture	(IVa)	4.0 ml.	18 mM buffer 0.018% amylose 6 mM KI 0.63 mM KIO_3
Mix, start stopwatch and immediately fill the mixture into a Record syringe. Hold the syringe tightly in a clamp. Collect the separate drops on acid-moistened filter paper. Stop the timer when the colour changes. The time t (min.) required is used for the calculations.			

* 0.1 ml. for urine analysis.

If the colour change occurs in <1 min. repeat the assay with a 1 : 10 dilution of sample. At the site of the drop a blue spot is formed due to the starch-iodine reaction; it is more easily visible on moist paper than on acidified paper which has been subsequently dried. According to the amylose content of the assay mixture the blue colour changes through dark-brown to the iodine blank colour of the end-point.

Assay System (automated method)

The reaction conditions and mixture are as for the manual method, but use reagent mixture IVc, instead of IVa.

Lay an acid-soaked sheet of chromatography paper, 35 cm. × 40 cm. on the flat surface of the amylase assay apparatus. Place 12 Record syringes in the holes of a plastic bridge. This bridge transports the syringe at a constant speed over the whole surface of the paper. The speed is set so that 400 mm. is covered in 24 min. (16.7 mm./min.). The time is measured by reading off the distance travelled in cm. By use of a standardized scale the enzyme units can be read off directly.

Assay System Rapid Method (Screening Test)

Rapidly mix 1 ml. urine (or serum) in a Record syringe with a needle (or dropping bottle) with 4 ml. reagent mixture (IVa) and start stopwatch. Continually allow the assay mixture to drop on the acid-soaked paper. Stop the timer when the colour turns to yellowish-brown. If the end-point occurs in less than 15 sec. repeat the measurements with 0.1 ml. urine (or serum). Icteric serum cannot be used; lipaemia does not interfere. Oral pipetting is not permissible; the use of *Marburg** or *Zip*-pipettes** is recommended. Use 1 ml. amylase standard solution in a similar assay as a check.

Calculations

To express the activity in International Units (U or mU) it must be related to the micro-equivalents of reducing groups formed per minute under standard conditions[6]. The number of terminal groups formed cannot, however, be directly calculated from relative decrease in the iodine-amylose colour (*Street-Close* units). A standard must therefore be prepared by comparative assays with a reduction method (*Somogyi* units). There is no general agreement in the literature on a conversion factor for the expression of results in International Units (U)[7,8] (1 *Somogyi* unit/100 ml. = 1.85 mU/ml. or 2.07 mU/ml.).
The following conversion factors relate to the more usual incubation temperature of 37 °C: 1 *Street-Close* unit/100 ml. = 3.1 *Somogyi* units/100 ml. = 5.7 mU/ml. The calculation of the amylase activity in the present assay at room temperature requires the determination of a factor by comparison with standard enzyme solutions whose activity (expressed in mU/ml. or *Street-Close* or *Somogyi* units) has been determined by the *Street-Close* or *Somogyi* assays at 37 °C. For the comparison add 0.1 ml. amylase standard solution instead of the sample to the assay mixture. In the sample

$$\text{Volume activity} = \frac{[\text{U/l.} \times \text{t}]_{\text{Standard}}}{\text{t}_{\text{Sample}}} \ [\text{U/l.}]$$

The product of the measured time and the enzyme units determined in parallel remains constant in the kinetic assay and therefore can be used as a factor if the above conditions are adhered to.
With rounded off conversion factors resulting from our comparative assays by the method of *Street* and *Close*, the following relationships apply:

0.1 ml. sample (e. g. urine) in the manual and automated assay.

$$\text{Volume activity} = \frac{7000 \times \text{F}}{\text{t (min.)}} \ [\text{U/l.}]$$

---

* Manufacturer: Eppendorf Gerätebau, 2 Hamburg 63, Germany.
** Manufacturer: QuickfitLaborglas GmbH, 62 Wiesbaden-Schierstein, Germany.

$$\text{Volume activity} = \frac{1\,200 \times F}{t\,(\text{min.})} \; [\textit{Street-Close} \text{ units}/100 \text{ ml.}]$$

$$\text{Volume activity} = \frac{3\,600 \times F}{t\,(\text{min.})} [\textit{Somogyi} \text{ units}/100 \text{ ml.}]$$

If 0.5 ml. sample (serum) is added the factors must be divided by 5.
1 ml. sample (screening test)

$$\text{Volume activity} = \frac{41\,000 \times F}{t\,(\text{sec.})} \; [\text{U/l.}]$$

$$\text{Volume activity} = \frac{7\,200 \times F}{t\,(\text{sec.})} \; [\textit{Street-Close} \text{ units}/100 \text{ ml.}]$$

$$\text{Volume activity} = \frac{21\,600 \times F}{t\,(\text{sec.})} \; [\textit{Somogyi} \text{ units}/100 \text{ ml.})$$

Precision of Method

Manual and automated method:

Blind experiment in series (N = 20), $\overline{X}$ = 12.0 min.
Standard deviation (s) = $\pm$ 0.6 min.
Coefficient of variation = $\pm$ 5%
Sensitivity (2s) = $\pm$ 1.2 min.

Screening Test:

Blind experiment in series (N = 20), $\overline{X}$ = 107 sec.
Standard deviation (s) = $\pm$ 6 sec.
Coefficient of variation (s) = $\pm$ 5.6%
Sensitivity (2s) = $\pm$ 12 sec.

Normal Values

Normal values in serum: 34–188 U/l.[9]
Normal values in urine: 105–1184 U/l.[10]

Data on normal values in duodenal juice and bile are not available.

Sources of Error

The amylase activity present in biological fluids is inhibited by chelating agents (e.g. citrate, EDTA). Chloride and borate ions activate[11,12].
A serum bilirubin content of more than 7 mg.% interferes because of the yellow colour. Lipaemia does not interfere.

Specificity of Method

The specificity of the method is that of the established colorimetric methods.

References

1 *B. W. Smith & J. H. Roe*, J. biol. Chem. *179*, 53 [1949].
   W. T. Caraway & J. Amer, J. Clin. Path. *32*, 97 [1959].
   R. Richterich & R. & J. B. Colombo, Ärztl. Laborat. *8*, 33 [1962].
2 *H. V. Street & J. R. Close*, Clin. Chim. Acta *1*, 256, [1956], *3*, 476 [1958].
3 *G. Müller*, Z. klin. Chem. & klin. Biochem. *2*, 181 [1964].
4 *M. Somogyi*, J. biol. Chemistry *125*, 399 [1938]; Clin. Chem. (New York) *6*, 23 [1960].
5 *G. Hillmann, G. Berger & R. Steger*, Z. klin. Chem. u. klin. Biochem. *5*, 128 [1967].
6 Report of the Commission on Enzymes of the International Union of Biochemistry in *M. Florkin &
   E. H. Stotz*: Comprehensive Biochemistry, Elsivier Publ. Comp., New York *13*, 5 [1964].
7 *R. Richterich & J. P. Colombo*, Ärztl. Laborat. *8*, 33 [1962].
8 *R. Helger & H. Lang*, Ärztl. Laborat. *11*, 120 [1956].
9 *H. V. Street & J. R. Close*, Clin. Chim. Acta *1*, 256, [1956].
10 *R. D. Henry & N. Chiamori*, Clin. Chem. *6*, 434 [1960].
11 *B. L. Vallee, E. A. Stein, W. N. Summerwell & E. H. Fischer*, J. biol. Chem. *234*, 2901 [1959].
12 *H. V. Street*, Biochem. J. *76*, 10 [1960].

Measurement after Electrophoretic Separation

John R. Hobbs and Swee E. Aw

Electrophoretic separation of human α-amylase (1,4-α-D-Glucan glucanohydrolase, EC 3.2.1.1) has been carried out on paper[1,2], agar[3,4], polyacrylamide[5,6] and cellulose acetate[7]. The isoenzyme distribution in urine is the same as that in serum[8,9], because all the isoenzymes mentioned below (with the exception of 02) have a molecular weight of ca. 48000 and are excreted by the normal kidney. In severe renal failure or in macroamylasaemia[10] the distribution in urine does not necessarily correspond to that in serum. Due to diurnal variation and the changes in the secretory activity of individual organs a 24 hr. urine specimen is a more homogeneous sample than a single serum sample[11]. Agar is the best medium for electrophoresis. After electrophoresis the isoamylases are best detected by an iodometric method. Methods depending on measurement of reducing power cannot be used because body fluids also contain glycoproteins which react with 3,5-dinitrosalicylic acid. If the amylase is coupled with maltase, glucose oxidase and peroxidase, then maltose, glucose and α-glucoside react in the same assay system. However, the indicator reaction is so far removed from the reaction to be measured that it becomes unreliable[8]. Similarly, it is not safe to rely only on the decrease in the starch-iodine colour, because high concentration of proteins, such as albumin, can also cause decolorization as bands. The method described below makes the hydrolysis of the starch directly visible and therefore it is certain that the decrease in starch-iodine colour is due to amylase activity.

Application of Method: In clinical chemistry. The assay of isoamylases in urine is of importance in the diagnosis of chronic pancreatitis[12]. Analysis of isoamylases is also of value to determine the origin of a tumour or a tissue fluid[8]; in certain cases it shows genetic polymorphism[6,8,11,13].

Principle

The electrophoretic separation is carried out on a slide covered with a layer of agar, which is then laid on a translucent starch substrate. The isoamylases react with the starch; at the end of the incubation the slide is removed, the starch is stained with iodine and examined for hollows in the surface due to hydrolysis of the starch. The decrease in the starch-iodine colour can be measured with a scanning apparatus.

Optimum Conditions for Measurements

Optimum α-amylase activity is measured at 20 mM Ca^{2+} and 140 mM Cl^-; absence of phosphate prevents phosphorolytic degradation of starch. The pH optimum is 6.9 (veronal buffer). The ideal substrate for amylase assays has not yet been found, but batches of hydrolysed starch yield solutions which remain translucent for several hours and give reliable results. High concentrations of possible inhibitors such as glucose are removed from the sample by dialysis.

Equipment

1. Millipore®-Filter, 1.2 μ pore diameter (cat. no. RAWP 01300), 0.2 μ pore diameter (cat. no. GSWP 01300) in Swinnex filter holders (cat. no. SXOO 01300) which fit Luer syringes.

2. Collodion bags (Sartorius, cat. no. 13200), which hang in glass holders connected to a water vacuum pump.

3. Electrophoresis apparatus: any apparatus which is suitable for agar slides can be used; the apparatus of *Wieme* (Vitatron Ltd., Amsterdam) is recommended.

4. Chromoscan double-beam integration densitometer (Joyce Loebl, London) for negative scanning. A tungsten lamp, no filter, a 6 $\times$ 1 mm slit and the gain set at the lowest sensitivity are used. The grey wedge neutral density filter is inverted from its normal position, so that the dense end as seen from the observer is on the right. If one begins with the uniform purple-stained background of undegraded starch, decolourized zones are indicated by deflection of the recorder to the right and the integration can be read off as usual.

Reagents

1. Ion agar no. 2 (Oxoid Ltd., London, S.E.1., England)
2. Veronal
   5,5-diethylbarbituric acid, barbital
3. Veronal
   sodium salt
4. Sodium acetate, CH_3COONa, A.R.
5. Hydrochloric acid, 0.1 N, A.R.
6. Calcium chloride
   dried, 70–75% $CaCl_2$, A. R.
7. Sodium chloride, A.R.
8. Hydrolysed starch
   (e. g. Batch 227–1 of Connaught Med. Res. Lab., Toronto, Canada or similar quality.)
9. Iodine solution, 0.1 N
10. Ethanol, absolute

Preparation of Solutions

I. Electrophoresis buffer (50 mM, pH 8.6):
   Dissolve 9.09 g. veronal, sodium salt, and 1.30 g. veronal in distilled water and make up to 1 000 ml.

II. Substrate buffer (pH 6.9):
   Dissolve 590 mg. sodium acetate, 1.47 g. veronal, sodium salt, 1.4 g. NaCl and 780 mg. $CaCl_2$ in distilled water. Add 62 ml. 0.1 N HCl and dilute to 250 ml. with distilled water.

III. Iodine solution for development:
   Dilute 45 ml. 0.1 N iodine solution with 55 ml. absolute ethanol.

Stability of Solutions

Solution II is not very stable.

Preparation of Plates

I. *Electrophoresis plates:*

Bring 100 ml. buffer solution I to the boil, sprinkle in 1 g. ion agar. Pour 25 ml. of this solution into a Petri dish (14 cm. diameter), allow to cool so that an even surface forms. Without disturbing the surface lay four clear slides on the agar and pour on a further 33 ml. of molten agar. After cooling store for a maximum of 6 weeks at 4 °C. Before use cut out the slides with a scalpel.

II. *Substrate plates:*

Bring 50 ml. buffer solution II to the boil, sprinkle in 500 mg. ion agar. Pour 25 ml. of this solution into a Petri dish (14 cm. diameter), allow to cool so that an even surface is formed and lay 4 slides on this. Bring a further 50 ml. buffer solution II to the boil, sprinkle in 5 g. hydrolysed starch. As soon as a clear solution is formed, deaerate with a vacuum pump, pour 33 ml. over the plates and allow to cool. The slides should be covered with a uniform 1.8 mm. thick layer of starch solution; this remains translucent for several hours. The plates are best used and studied *in situ*. As the starch layer slowly becomes opalescent, only freshly prepared plates can be used for the optical scanning. After the development they can be cut up and placed in the scanning apparatus.

Procedure

Collection, Treatment and Stability of Sample

Collection of sample:

Collect the whole 24 hr. urine in a glass bottle containing 1 ml. toluene.

Preliminary treatment:

Sterilize urine by passing first through a 1.2 μ Millipore® filter and then through a 0.12 μ filter. Concentrate 3 ml. filtrate to 0.1 ml. in a collodion bag *in vacuo* (see "Equipment").

Stability of enzyme in sample:

Under toluene the isoamylases are stable for weeks at 4 °C. Repeated freezing and thawing as well as bacterial contamination causes rapid destruction of the amylase in the concentrate. Storage at −20 °C can alter the distribution of the isoamylases, so that often extra bands appear such as P3, S3 and O1. It is therefore best to use relatively fresh material and to store reference enzymes in small portions that can be thawed out and then discarded next day.

Electrophoresis

Insert vertically two rectangular strips of filter paper (Whatman no. 1) 6 mm wide immediately adjacent to one another in the agar on the slides, 1 cm. from the middle line on the anode side. As soon as the buffer has risen 4 mm., remove the strips. This gives two identical slots which have a volume of ca. 2 μl. Fill one of these up to the rim with the unknown sample and the other with the reference sample using a Pasteur pipette drawn out to a fine tip. Either purified isoamylases[13] or a known normal urine (P2 + S1) can be used as reference samples. Allow to run for 1 hr. at 150–200 V and 20 mA per plate in the apparatus of *Wieme* with petroleum ether cooling. Albumin and more rapidly migrating proteins travel to the anode end of the plate; the run is therefore carried out only in one direction. Change the agar and buffer (I) in the electrophoresis tank after 12 runs.

Incubation

After the electrophoresis either remove the agar from the slide and carefully lay on a substrate plate (15 min. at 36 °C) or use a cellulose acetate carrier. For this lay a dry strip of cellulose acetate foil on the agar; it assumes an exact impression of the separation. Remove the strip, carefully lay on the starch plate and incubate for 1 hr. at 37 °C. A second cellulose acetate carrier can be stained for protein; for further enzyme studies dextran reference samples [14] can be used for the measurement of the relative mobility.

Development

Remove agar or cellulose acetate strips and pour the iodine solution (III) over the Petri dish. When the background is uniformly stained a translucent purple pour off the iodine solution. Decolourization occurs in open dishes due to the sublimation of the iodine; the colour reappears on further addition of iodine solution. The alcohol contained in the solution fixes the starch so that the slide can be cut up when required.

Examination

There must be depressions (Fig. 3 and 4) in areas in the starch surface where decolourized zones occur: excess protein (e. g. in nephrotic urine) can also bind iodine. Decolourization after starch hydrolysis by human α-isoamylases has been detected in 8 positions: their relative mobilities (albumin = 1.00) are P1 = 0.08; P2 = 0.14; P3 = 0.18; S1 = 0.22; S2 = 0.30; S3 = 0.36; O1 = 0.39 and O2 = 0.50 (see Fig. 1.). In normal urine the zones P2 and S1 predominate (Fig. 2.). Even with other distribution patterns it is possible to measure the whole area of the P or S isoamylases. In urine from adults P originates mainly from the pancreas and S from the salivary glands[8]. During lactation and immediately before menstruation other sources of the enzyme can play a role. Some ovarian cysts contain O1 and O2 bands, but only O1 has been found in urine.

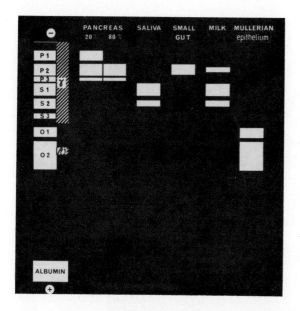

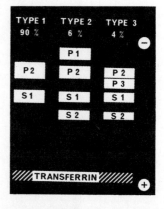

Fig. 1. Human isoamylases.
Eight human isoamylases can by identified by their electrophoretic mobility relative to transferrin (β_1 0.47) or albumin
(1.00). The main components are the same in extracts and
secretions of the five known sources: pancreas, salivary
glands, intestinal mucosa, mammary gland and Müller
epithelium of ovary and testes.

Fig. 2. Isoamylases in normal urine.
Normal 24 hr. urine samples from adults
show three different patterns of distribution, presumably due to genetic polymorphism. In all types it is possible to
determine P relative to S.

Evaluation

With the Chromoscan (see "Equipment") the decolourized zones can be measured as a percentage of the
whole decolourized area. With a little practice a P < S distribution can be decided by eye (Fig. 3 and 4).

Fig. 3. Depression of the starch surface after hydrolysis of the starch by α-amylases.

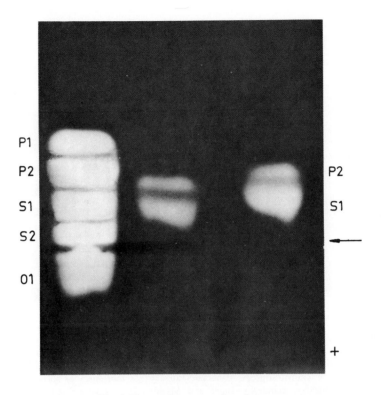

Fig. 4. Electropherogram of amylases.
The loss of starch-iodine colour corresponds to visible areas of starch hydrolysis in Fig. 3. The two samples on the right are from 24 hr. urines of patients with chronic pancreatitis, they show a significant loss of P relative to the reference isoamylases on the left.

Precision of Method

With a sufficiently large number of integration impulses (> 100) a known amount of P- or S-isoamylase can be recovered with an accuracy of $\geqq 5\%$.

Normal Values

Assuming that 1 Somogyi unit = 20.6 U/l.[15] total amylase concentrations of 1 000–8 250 U/l. were found in 24 hr. urine of adults, the mean was 3 400 U/l. Of this 720–5 150 (mean 2 150) U/l. was in the P zone and 310 to 3 450 (mean 1 250) U/l. in the S zone. The ratio P : S varied[12] between 0.9 and 3.4. Only in the first years of life is it normal that P is lower than S[16].

Sources of Error

Influence of drugs and other therapeutic measures: After oral administration of Pancrexforte (a pig pancreas extract) several patients showed slight rise of the P fraction but not to the extent that their abnormal P < S is returned to normal. Acute deterioration in pancreatitis may cause a transient increase in P (duration of 2 days to 6 weeks), which gives a false impression that chronic pancreatitis may not be present. Samples are therefore best collected at periods when the patient is free from pain.

Specificity of Method

If the hydrolysis of the starch is observed by eye the method is specific for α-amylases.

Details for Measurements in Tissues

Thin slices of freshly frozen tissue can be placed directly in the troughs in the agar and their amylase content determined by electrophoresis. Otherwise the tissue can be thoroughly homogenized in isotonic physiological saline or tris buffer and the supernatant fluid used for the assay. If pancreas or intestine (jejunum) is extracted soya bean inhibitors can be added to protect the extract from autodigestion.

References

1 R. L. McGeachin & P. Lewis, J. biol. Chem. 234, 795 [1959].
2 D. A. Dreiling, H. D. Janowitz & J. J. Lazar, Ann. intern. Med. 58, 235 [1959].
3 C. Poort & W. J. W. van Venrooy, Nature 204, 684 [1964].
4 S. Norby, Exp. Cell. Res. 36, 663 [1964].
5 J. Muus & J. M. Vnenchak, Nature 204, 283 [1964].
6 R. O. Wolf & L. L. Taylor, Nature 213, 1128 [1967].
7 S. E. Aw, Nature 209, 298 [1966].
8 J. R. Hobbs & S. E. Aw in U. C. Dubach: Enzymes in urine and kidney. Hans Huber, Berne 1968, p. 281.
9 A. Oger & L. Bischops, Clin. chim. Acta 13, 670 [1966].
10 J. E. Berk, H. Kizu, P. Wilding & R. L. Searcy, New Eng. J. Med. 277, 941 [1967].
11 R. J. Wieme in U. C. Dubach: Enzymes in urine and kidney. Hans Huber, Berne 1968, p. 293.
12 S. E. Aw, J. R. Hobbs & I. D. P. Wootton, Gut 8, 402 [1967].
13 S. E. Aw & J. R. Hobbs, Biochem. J. 99, 16 P, [1966].
14 J. R. Hobbs, Nature 207, 292 [1965].
15 K. S. Henley, E. Schmidt & F. W. Schmidt: Enzymes in Serum, Thomas, Springfield 1966, p. 16.
16 H. D. Janowitz & D. A. Dreiling, Amer. J. Med. 27, 924 [1959].

Disaccharidases

Arne Dahlqvist

Extracts of intestinal mucosa hydrolyse various disaccharides and heteroglycosides. The following enzyme activities have been detected: α-glucosidase (α-D-Glucoside glucohydrolase, EC 3.2.1.20), β-glucosidase (β-D-Glucoside glucohydrolase, EC 3.2.1.21) and β-galactosidase (β-D-Galactoside galactohydrolase, EC 3.2.1.23). This nomenclature is based on the specificity of the glucosidases with respect to the glycone* part of the substrate[1]. It is known however that with few exceptions the glucosidases (disaccharidases) from the intestine[2] and other sources have, apart from their absolute specificity for the glycone, a definite specificity for the aglycone. Several different enzymes carry out each one of the above listed activities. It is therefore considered more satisfactory to name the activity studied after the particular substrate used, where its specificity is not definitely established. However, even if the activity is named after the substrate, several enzymes are included under one name, because many substrates are hydrolysed by more than one enzyme.

Disaccharides are used as substrates in most studies on intestinal glucosidases. This is logical because disaccharides are the most important glycosides from the standpoint of nutritional physiology. The method that follows is for the measurement of the hydrolysis of disaccharides. In the last decade the determination of the activity of disaccharidases in the intestine has become of considerable interest in clinical medicine, with the discovery of the existence of diseases involving hereditary and acquired disaccharidase deficiency (for reviews, see [3-11]).

The original method [12] required two separate steps: incubation followed by determination of glucose. The glucose determination was carried out in tris buffer, which inhibits disaccharidases present as contaminants of the glucose oxidase preparations[13]. When glucose oxidase preparations with lower disaccharidase activity became available we described a coupled method[14], which is particularly suitable as an ultra-micro method. This method has, however, several disadvantages, e.g. lower apparent maltase activity (maltose in high concentration is a substrate for glucose oxidase), a marked lag phase which necessitates a 15 min. blank instead of a zero time blank, and technical difficulties with the sulphuric acid required to stop the reaction. Consequently, a modified two-step method has been developed, which has the advantages of the original method and at the same time can be used as a micro-method[15]. In this modification tris is added after the incubation with the substrate to inhibit the hydrolysis of the disaccharide. The micro modification of the method is described here.

Application of Method: In biochemistry and clinical chemistry.

Principle

(1) Disaccharide + H_2O $\xrightarrow{\text{disaccharidase}}$ Glucose + Monosaccharide

(2) Glucose + O_2 $\xrightarrow{\text{glucose oxidase**}}$ Gluconic acid + H_2O_2

(3) $H_2O_2 + DH_2$ $\xrightarrow{\text{peroxidase ***}}$ $2 H_2O$ + D

DH_2 = hydrogen donor, e.g. o-dianisidine
D = dye

---

* A glycoside can be written Gl-0-Agl, where Gl is the glycone and Agl the aglycone. The glycone is for example the sugar moiety of heteroglycosides; in disaccharides and oligosaccharides it is the sugar molecule which is bound by its reducing carbon atom to the rest of the molecule.
** β-D-Glucose: oxygen 1-oxidoreductase, EC 1.1.3.4.
*** Donor: hydrogen-peroxide oxidoreductase, EC 1.11.1.7.

The amount of glucose formed per unit time, as determined by the brown colour at 420–480 nm, is a measure of the disaccharidase activity.

Optimum Conditions for Measurements

The relatively wide pH optimum varies slightly with the different enzymes; in most cases, however, it is around pH 6 (Fig. 1). In a few cases a lower pH optimum has been found for intestinal disaccharidases. Human duodenum contains a maltase[16] with a pH optimum about 3, and a β-galactosidase from rat intestinal lysosomes has a pH optimum at 3 to 4[17-20]. Only once has a pH optimum >6 been found; two maltases in intestinal mucosa of pigs have a relatively broad pH optimum between 6.5 and 7.5[21]. Influence of the incubation temperature has not been systematically studied; we measure activity at 37 °C; a few experiments at 25 °C gave about half the activity. We use a substrate concentration of 28 mM so that the disaccharidases are more than 50% saturated. Higher substrate concentrations result in "substrate inhibition"[22], in part due to the occurrence of transglycosidation reactions instead of hydrolysis. Sodium ions activate several disaccharidases of the intestine[23,24]. Other monovalent cations are less potent activators or even inhibit. The sodium maleate buffer used in this method contains sufficient sodium ions for activation.

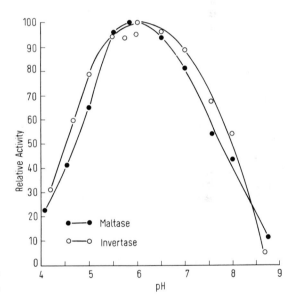

Fig. 1. pH-Optimum for maltase and invertase from human duodenal mucosa[12].

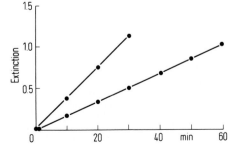

Fig. 2. Invertase of duodenal homogenate; progress curve with two concentrations.
Enzyme incubation for various times, usual colour development[15].

Under the conditions described here the reaction is a first order one until 12% of the substrate has been hydrolysed; the amount of glucose liberated per unit time is proportional to the enzyme activity (Fig. 2, 3).

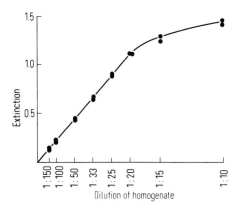

Fig. 3. Proportionality between amount of enzyme and glucose liberated (60 min.).
Sucrose as substrate, 1 : 5 homogenate of human mucosa containing 40 mg. protein/ml. Final volume: 320 μl., light path: 0.6 cm.; read against a reagent blank. The relationship is linear up to E = 1.100, equivalent to 12 μg. glucose (12% hydrolysis of the substrate)[15].

Equipment

Spectrophotometer or spectrum-line photometer or filter photometer with micro cuvettes (200 μl volume) suitable for measurements at 450 nm (420–480) nm; Carlsberg constriction pipettes; small conical test tubes, 63 mm long, 8 mm internal diameter; 37 °C water bath (constant temperature).
If no micro equipment is available add ten times the amounts of sample and reagents.

Reagents

1. Maleic acid
2. Sodium hydroxide, 1 N
3. Tris-hydroxymethyl-aminothane, tris
4. Hydrochloric acid, 5 N
5. Disaccharides*: maltose, sucrose, trehalose, lactose, cellobiose, isomaltose.
6. Glucose
7. o-Dianisidine
8. Triton X-100

9. Ethanol, 95%
10. Peroxidase, POD
    from horse radish, dry powder; ca. 36 U/mg. (measured with guaiacol; 25 °C) corresponding to a Reinheitszahl ca. 0.6; commercial preparation, see p. 494.
11. Glucose oxidase, GOD
    from moulds, dry powder ca. 90 U/mg. (25 °C); commercial preparation, see p. 457.

---

* The purest commercial preparations can be used without further purification; if they contain free glucose they should be discarded or purified (see isomaltose). Commercial maltose usually contains several higher oligosaccharides as well as glucose. Test: mix 20 μl. 1% maltose solution with 300 μl. glucose reagent (solution VII); mix 20 μl. water with 300 μl. glucose reagent as a blank; incubate for 1 hr. at 37 °C and then read extinction at 420 nm (1 cm. light path). An extinction difference of > 0.100 indicates that the substrate must be purified. We prepare isomaltose by enzymatic hydrolysis of dextran[25], followed by fractionation on Celite or Sephadex G-15 columns[25–27]. Isomaltose is now commercially available, but we have had no experience with these preparations.

Preparation of Solutions

Prepare all solutions with fresh distilled water.

I. Maleate buffer (0.1 M; pH 6.0):
   Dissolve 1.16 g. maleic acid in 15.3 ml. 1 N NaOH, and dilute with distilled water to 100 ml.; if necessary, adjust the pH to 6.0.

II. Disaccharide solution (56 mM):
   Dissolve 200 mg. maltose monohydrate (or 210 mg. trehalose dihydrate; 200 mg. lactose monohydrate; 190 mg. sucrose, isomaltose or cellobiose) in maleate buffer (I) and make up to 10 ml.

III. Tris buffer (0.5 M; pH 7.0):
   Dissolve 61.0 g. tris in 85 ml. 5 N HCl and dilute with distilled water to 1 000 ml. If necessary, adjust pH to 7.0.

IV. Peroxidase (1 mg./ml.):
   Dissolve 10 mg. peroxidase powder in 10 ml. distilled water.

V. Detergent
   Dissolve 20 g. Triton X-100 in 80 g. ethanol.

VI. o-Dianisidine (10 mg./ml.):
   Dissolve 100 mg. dianisidine in 10 ml. ethanol.

VII. Glucose reagent:
   Dissolve 2 mg. glucose oxidase in 100 ml. tris buffer (III), add 1 ml. o-dianisidine solution (VI), 1 ml. wetting agent (solution V) and 0.5 ml. peroxidase solution (IV) and mix.

VIII. Glucose standard solutions (100 μg./ml., 300 μg./ml., 500 μg./ml.):
   Dissolve 500 mg. anhydrous glucose in distilled water and make up to 1 000 ml. (solution c); dilute 300 ml. of this solution to 500 ml. with distilled water (solution b); dilute 100 ml. solution b to 300 ml. with distilled water (solution a).

Stability of Solutions

Store the disaccharide, glucose and peroxidase solutions in small portions at $-20°C$; in this state they are stable for a year; mix thoroughly on thawing. Store the o-dianisidine solution in the dark at 4 °C; fresh solutions are light-brown, but darken due to oxidation; they should then be discarded. The glucose reagent (VII) is stable for several days in the dark at 4 °C.

Procedure

Collection, Treatment and Stability of Sample

If large pieces of intestine are available, e. g. from laboratory animals or intestine removed at surgery, scrape off the mucosa with a microscope slide and homogenize in an Ultra-Turrax with four parts of distilled water. Keep in an ice bath during the homogenization. Disaccharidases are particulate enzymes, but most of the cell debris can be removed by centrifugation (10 min. at 2 000 to 4 000 g). This results in only slight loss of disaccharidase activity. The enzymes can be solubilized[28,29], but this is not necessary for the assay of activity.

Homogenize smaller mucosal samples (e. g. human jejunal mucosa obtained by peroral biopsy) in a *Potter-Elvehjem*[30] all-glass homogenizer. We use conical 10 ml. tubes and 10–20 mg. mucosa in 0.5 ml. distilled water. Pre-cool the homogenizer and contents and keep in ice bath during homogenization (1 to 2 min. at 200 to 300 rpm.). Faster motor speeds or insufficient cooling leads to loss of activity. Do not centrifuge homogenates prepared in this way even at low g, otherwise a considerable amount of activity is lost (instructions to the contrary[31],[32] are superseded).

Stability of sample: Intestinal mucosa can be stored at −20 °C for several months without loss of activity.

Assay System

Incubation temperature: 37 °C; final volume of incubation mixture: 20 μl.; wavelength: 450 (420–480) nm; light path: 1 cm.; final volume: 320 μl.; read against reagent blank containing 20 μl. distilled water and 300 μl. glucose reagent (VII) after 60 min. at 37 °C.

For each assay prepare a blank with sample, but in which the disaccharide solution (II) is added *after* the glucose reagent. The first 60 min. incubation is omitted.

Glucose standards: pipette into three test tubes 20 μl. of glucose standard solutions (VIIIa, b, c) equivalent to 2, 6 and 10 μg. glucose, add to each 300 μl. glucose reagent (VII) and incubate for 60 min.

Pipette into conical test tubes (8 mm × 63 mm)			Concentration in assay mixture
Mucosal homogenate		10 μl.	
Disaccharide solution	(II)	10 μl.	28 mM
Mix and incubate for 60 min.			
Glucose reagent	(VII)	300 μl.	470 mM tris 170 mU POD/ml. 1700 mU GOD/ml. 94 μg. o-dianisidine/ml.
Mix, the disaccharidase reaction is stopped. Allow to stand for 60 min. at 37 °C and read extinctions.			

If a sample gives a higher extinction than that of the 10 μg. glucose standard, repeat the assay with diluted homogenate.

Calculations

Average the extinctions of glucose standards; the mean value is equivalent to 6 μg. glucose. For the samples:

$$\mu g. \text{ Glucose} = 6 \times \frac{E_{sample}}{E_{standard}}$$

This amount of glucose has been formed in 60 min. by 10 μl. (0.01 ml.) of a homogenate diluted by factor F from disaccharides with n glucose units (n = 1 for sucrose and lactose, n = 2 for maltose, isomaltose, trehalose and cellobiose).

The disaccharidase activity in the homogenate is given by

$$\text{Volume activity} = 6 \times \frac{E_{sam.}}{E_{std.}} \times \frac{1\,000 \times F}{60 \times 0.01 \times n \times 180}$$

$$= \frac{E_{sam.}}{E_{std.}} \times 55.6 \times \frac{F}{n} \quad [U/l.]; 37\,°C$$

(180 = molecular weight of glucose)

For the analysis of biopsy material the activity is expressed in U/g. protein.

Normal Values

We found the following values for jejunal mucosa (taken from below *Treitz's* angle = duodeno-jejunal flexure) in 22 adults[33]:

Activity	Mean	U/g. protein range	S.D.
Maltase	266	111–420	±70
Isomaltase	97	25–183	±30
Invertase	87	26–138	±29
Lactase	44	9– 98	±22

Protein determination:

We determine protein in the homogenate by the method of *Lowry* et al.[34]; but use citrate instead of tartrate in reagent B[35]. Standard curve prepared with freshly dissolved human serum albumin. Measurements are made in a spectrophotometer. We use 50 μl. homogenate in a final volume of 6.5 ml.

All attempts to increase the sensitivity of the protein estimation by a 20 times reduction of all volumes have failed with mucosal protein although excellent standard curves were obtained with serum albumin.

Specificity of Method

Intestinal mucosa contains a mixture of glycosidases (also disaccharidases) and in many cases a substrate is hydrolysed by several enzymes. There are certain differences between different species with regard to the individual specificity of the relevant enzymes, but on the whole the number of glycosidases appears to be the same. The specificity of the human enzymes, as examined by heat inactivation[36], column chromatography[37,38] and ultracentrifugation[39], is as follows:

Enzyme	Substrate	Relative contribution for the hydrolysis in crude homogenates
Isomaltase = Maltase Ia	Isomaltose / Maltose	> 99% / ~ 50%
Invertase = Maltase Ib	Sucrose / Maltose	100% / ~ 25%
Maltase II / Maltase III	Maltose / Isomaltase	~ 25% / < 1%
Trehalase	Trehalose	100%
Lactase	Lactose / Hetero-β-galactosides	100% / < 50%

Sucrose, isomaltose and trehalose are hydrolysed by separate enzymes. Maltose reacts with four enzymes, one of which is identical with isomaltase and another with invertase.

Lactose appears to be hydrolysed by only one enzyme, but in addition there is a lysosomal β-galactosidase which is most active with synthetic substrates[38].

Earlier reports of the fractionation of human invertase (maltase Ib) and lactase into two components by Sephadex chromatography[40,41], appears to be explained by the exchange between isomaltase and the Sephadex gel[37,38,42]; it is therefore not proved that there is more than one enzyme for each of these substrates.

References

1 R. Weidenhagen, Ergebn. Enzymforsch. 1, 168 [1932].
2 A. Dahlqvist, Dissertation: Hog Intestinal α-Glucosidases. Solubilization, Separation and Character-ization. Lund [1960].
3 A. Dahlqvist, Gastroenterology 43, 694 [1962].
4 P. Durand: Disorders due to Intestinal Defective Carbohydrate Digestion and Absorption, Il Pensiero Scientifico, Rome [1964].
5 A. Littman & J. Hammond, Gastroenterology 48, 237 [1965].
6 A. Prader & S. Auricchio, Ann. Rev. Med. 16, 345 [1965].
7 C. M. Anderson, V. Burke, M. Messer & K. R. Kerry, Lancet 1, 1322 [1966].
8 A. Dahlqvist, J. Amer. Med. Assoc. 196, 225 [1966].
9 A. Dahlqvist, Bull. Soc. Chim. Biol. 49, 1635 [1967].
10 A. Dahlqvist, Ann. Biol. Clin. 26, 3 [1968].
11 J. Rey & J. Frézal, Arch. Franç. Ped. 24, 65 [1967] & 26, 3 [1968].
12 A. Dahlqvist, Analyt. Biochem. 7, 18 [1964].
13 A. Dahlqvist, Biochem. J. 80, 547 [1961].
14 M. Messer & A. Dahlqvist, Analyt. Biochem. 14, 376 [1966].
15 A. Dahlqvist, Analyt. Biochem. 22, 99 [1968].
16 S. Auricchio, personal communication.
17 R. G. Doell & N. Kretschmer, Biochim. Biophys. Acta 62, 353 [1962].
18 A. Dahlqvist & N. G. Asp, Biochem. J. 103, 86 [1967].
19 N. G. Asp & A. Dahlqvist, Biochem. J. 106, 841 [1968].
20 N. G. Asp, A. Dahlqvist & O. Koldovsky, Biochem. J. 114, 351 [1969].
21 A. Dahlqvist, Acta Chem. Scand. 14, 1 [1960].
22 A. Dahlqvist, Acta Chem. Scand. 14, 1797 [1960].
23 G. Semenza, R. Tosi & M. C. Delachaux, Helvet. Chim. Acta 46, 1765 [1963].
24 G. Semenza, R. Tosi, M. C. Vallotton-Delachaux & E. Mülhaupt, Biochim. Biophys. Acta 89, 109 [1964].
25 A. Jeanes, C. A. Wilham, R. W. Jones, H. M. Tsuchiya & C. E. Rist, J. Amer. Chem. Soc. 75, 5911 [1953].
26 A. Dahlqvist, Acta Chem. Scand. 14, 72 [1960].
27 A. Dahlqvist & H. B. McMichael, in preparation.
28 A. Dahlqvist in S. P. Colowick & N. O. Kaplan: Methods in Enzymology, Vol. III; & in E. F. Neufeld & V. Ginsburg: Complex Carbohydrates, Academic Press, New York/London 1966.
29 S. Auricchio, A. Dahlqvist & G. Semenza, Biochim. Biophys. Acta 73, 582 [1963].
30 U. R. Potter & C. A. Elvehjem, J. biol. Chem. 114, 495 [1936].
31 W. W. Peternel, Gastroenterology 48, 299 [1965].
32 H. B. McMichael, J. Webb & A. M. Dawson, Brit. Med. J. 2, 1037 [1966].
33 J. V. Dunphy, A. Littman, J. B. Hammond, G. Forstner, A. Dahlqvist & R. K. Crane, Gastroenterology 49, 12 [1965].
34 O. H. Lowry, N. J. Rosebrough, A. L. Farr & R. J. Randall, J. biol. Chem. 193, 265 [1951].
35 M. Eggstein & F. H. Kreutz, Klin. Wochschr. 33, 879 [1955].
36 A. Dahlqvist, J. Clin. Invest. 41, 463 [1962].
37 A. Dahlqvist & U. Telenius, Biochem. J. 111, 839 [1969].
38 N. G. Asp, O. Koldowsky & A. Dahlqvist, Gastroenterology 58, 591 [1970].
39 E. Eggermont, personal communication.
40 G. Semenza & S. Auricchio, Biochim. Biophys. Acta 65, 173 [1962].
41 G. Semenza, S. Auricchio & A. Rubino, Biochim. Biophys. Acta 96, 487 [1965].
42 J. Kolinska & G. Semenza, Biochim. Biophys. Acta 146, 181 [1967].

Invertase

Hans-Dieter Ohlenbusch and Peter Vögele

Invertase (β-D-Fructofuranoside fructohydrolase, EC 3.2.1.26) was extracted by *Berthelot* in 1860 from yeast[1]. Invertase activity has been demonstrated in bacteria, moulds, higher plants and in intestine of several animals, including humans[2]; but yeast is the preferred material for its isolation. The major part of the enzyme activity in the yeast cell is located on the cell wall[3-5]. So far it has not proved possible to prepare the active enzyme as a pure protein. Practically all preparations contain considerable amounts of polysaccharides (mannan)[6-8].

In the classical assay of invertase activity the change in optical activity on inversion of sucrose is measured. In other methods the reducing monosaccharides liberated on hydrolysis of the crude sugar are measured. A method is described here in which the hydrolysis product, glucose, is measured enzymatically[9].

Application of Method: In biochemistry, microbiology, foodstuff chemistry and agricultural chemistry.

Principle

(1)
$$\text{Sucrose} \xrightarrow{\text{invertase}} \text{Glucose} + \text{Fructose}$$

(2)
$$\beta\text{-D-Glucose} + H_2O + O_2 \xrightarrow[\text{oxidase}]{\text{glucose}} \text{D-Gluconic acid} + H_2O_2$$

(3)
$$H_2O_2 + DH_2 \xrightarrow{\text{Peroxidase}} 2H_2O + D$$

The amount of dye D formed can be measured optically (absorption maximum 460 nm).

The glucose component of the sucrose is liberated in reaction (1) as α-D-glucose[10]. The specific substrate of glucose oxidase is however β-D-glucose. Contrary to the findings of *Keilin* and *Hartree*[11] the glucose oxidase preparation used by us contains no mutarotase activity[12]. Because of this the assay must be carried out in 2 parts. The hydrolysis of the sucrose according to reaction (1) is stopped by the addition of Na_2CO_3. This accelerates the mutarotation of the glucose so that under these conditions the equilibrium of the two optical isomers is attained.

In the second part of the assay the amount of β-D-glucose present is determined with glucose oxidase. This is proportional to the total amount of glucose. For the glucose determination a kinetic method is used instead of the more usual end-point method (see p. 1196)[9]. The glucose concentrations occurring in the assay system are considerably lower than the Michaelis constant of the glucose oxidase[13], so that the rate of oxidation of glucose is proportional to its concentration. The proportionality factor is determined with a glucose standard.

The amount of glucose liberated per unit time is a measure of the invertase activity. This corresponds to the rate of oxidation of the hydrogen donor measured by the increase in extinction per unit time.

Optimum Conditions for Measurements

The pH optimum of invertase lies between 4.7 and 4.9[14,15]; the Michaelis constant was found to be 25 mM[12] in agreement with *von Euler* and *Laurin*[16]. *Michaelis* and *Menten* give 16.7 mM as the K_M.

Measurements at different temperatures may require different measuring conditions (cf. p. 127). Nevertheless, results obtained under the same measuring conditions but at different temperatures were formerly compared with each other ("conversion factors" were determined). Such conversion factors may be correct if determined with a relatively large proband collective; however, they cannot be applied generally to the individual case (cf. p. 129). The value of the following relative rates[18] thus lies in being able to appraise the temperature dependence of the reaction and at the most to compare qualitatively values up to the limit of normal.

°C	20	25	30	37
	1.905	1.333	1.000	0.719

Equipment

Colorimeter suitable for precise measurements at 436 nm with constant temperature cuvette holder; water bath; stopwatch.

Reagents

1. Triethanolamine hydrochloride, TRA-HCl
2. Citric acid, $C_6H_8O_7 \cdot H_2O$
3. Sodium chloride, A.R., NaCl
4. D(+)-Sucrose, pure
5. Glucose oxidase, GOD
   from moulds; salt-free lyophilisate; ca. 140 U/mg. (25 °C); commercial preparation, see p. 457.

6. Peroxidase, POD
   from horse radish; lyophilisate; ca. 36 U/mg. (25 °C); commercial preparation, see p. 494.
7. o-Dianisidine hydrochloride
8. Sodium carbonate, A.R., Na_2CO_3, anhydrous
9. D(+)-Glucose, anhydrous*
10. Hydrochloric acid, conc., A.R.
11. Acetone
12. Benzoic acid

Purity of Enzyme Preparations

The GOD should contain <0.01% amylase and invertase, <15 U/mg. catalase. The peroxidase should have a Reinheitszahl of 0.3.

Preparation of Solutions (for ca. 40 determinations)

Prepare all solutions with doubly distilled water.
   I. Triethanolamine-citrate buffer (20 mM TRA, 6.67 mM citrate; pH 4.8):
      Dissolve 3.713 g. TRA-HCl + 1.401 g. citric acid. H_2O in distilled water, adjust to pH 4.8 with conc. HCl and dilute to 1 000 ml. with distilled water.
  II. Triethanolamine-citrate buffer (145 mM TRA, 48.3 mM citrate; pH 5.4):
      Dissolve 26.921 g. TRA-HCl + 10.152 g. citric acid. H_2O, adjust to pH 5.4 with conc. HCl and dilute to 1 000 ml. with distilled water.
 III. Sucrose solution (50 mM):
      Dissolve 17.115 g. sucrose in solution I and make up to 1 000 ml.

---

* e. g. from EGA-Chemie KG, Steinheim, Germany.

IV. Glucose reagent:

Dissolve 3.75 mg. GOD + 3 mg. POD in ca. 96 ml. solution II. Dissolve 7.5 mg. o-dianisi-dine hydrochloride in 1 ml. acetone and stir this into the solution. Dilute to 100 ml. with solution II.

V. Na_2CO_3 (1.0 M):

Dissolve 106 g. Na_2CO_3 (anhydrous) in distilled water and make up to 1 000 ml.

VI. Glucose solution:

a) Stock solution (50 mM):

Dissolve 9.008 g. glucose (anhydrous) in benzoic acid-saturated water and make up to 1 000 ml.

b) Standard solution (0.5 mM):

Dilute 10 ml. stock solution I to 1 000 ml.

Stability of Solutions

Store all solutions at 4 °C. The sucrose solution (III) is stable for 1 week. Prepare the glucose reagent IV freshly each day as the dye is oxidized by atmospheric oxygen. The glucose stock solution VIa is stable indefinitely; always prepare standard solution VIb freshly.

Procedure

Collection, Treatment and Stability of Sample

The protocol for the assay system given below is valid for purified enzyme preparations. For the determination of invertase activity in biological material the assay must be modified as follows:

Determination in honey: Dissolve 30 g. honey in a little distilled water and dialyse for 2 days against running water until glucose is no longer detectable. The volume after dialysis is about 220 ml.

Modify the assay as follows: sample volume 0.1 ml. (instead of 0.01 ml.); incubation time for the hydrolysis 10 min. (instead of 1 min.); adjust the pH of solution I to pH 6, as the pH optimum of honey invertase is from pH 5.5–6.2[19].

Stability of enzyme in sample:

Purified, dried preparations of yeast invertase are stable for at least 1 year. In buffer solutions over the pH range 4–6 no loss of activity was observed in 50 days at 4 °C. At pH 3 the activity decreases by 30% during this period. Even at 37 °C there is no detectable loss of activity at pH 4.8 within 2 days[18].

Assay System

Wavelength: Hg 436 nm; light path: 1 cm.; final volume for hydrolysis: 1 ml.; final volume for assay: 3.1 ml.; 30 °C (constant temperature cuvette holder). Read against water. Bring solution to 30 °C before start of determination. To determine the glucose content of the sample (sample blank) prepare a cuvette containing distilled water instead of sucrose solution III. For each series of measurements at least 1 reagent blank without sample and 1 glucose standard containing glucose standard solution (VIb) instead of sucrose solution (III) are required.

Pipette successively into cuvettes:			Concentration in	
			Hydrolysis mixture	Assay mixture
Sucrose solution (III)		1 ml.	49.5 mM	
Sample		0.01 ml.		
Mix and start stopwatch; after exactly 1 min. add				
Na$_2$CO$_3$ solution (V)		0.1 ml.	90.1 mM	32.2 mM
Mix and after 3 min. add				
Glucose reagent (IV)		2 ml.		3.2 U GOD/ml. 0.7 U POD/ml. 48.2 μg. o-dianisidine/ml.
Mix and read extinctions exactly 30 sec. and 90 sec. after addition of glucose reagent (IV).				

The values for ΔE/min. should not exceed 0.300/min. and not be less than 0.030/min. With higher values dilute the sample, with lower prolong the hydrolysis incubation time.

Calculations

The following formula holds:

$$\text{Volume activity} = \frac{1\,000}{0.01} \times 0.5 \times \frac{\Delta E_{\text{sample}} - \Delta E_{\text{reagent blank}} - \Delta E_{\text{sample blank}}}{\Delta E_{\text{standard}}} \; [\text{U/l.}]; 30 \, °C.$$

where
1000 = conversion factor for ml. to l.
0.5 = concentration in glucose standard (0.5 mM)
0.01 = volume of sample taken

Conversion to other units

a) *Fischer* and *Kothès* units[20]

   1 A = amount of enzyme which liberates 1 mg. reducing sugar in 3 min. from a 5% sucrose solution.
   1 A (20 °C) = 1.182 U (20 °C)

b) *Willstätter* and *Kuhn*[20] sucrose units

1 sucrose unit $= \dfrac{1}{t}$

t = time required for 50 mg. enzyme at 15.5 °C to bring the optical rotation of 25 ml. of a 16% sucrose solution to 0°

1 sucrose unit (15.5 °C) $= 122.4 \dfrac{U}{mg.}$ (15.5 °C)

c) *Weidenhagen* fructosidase units[21]

1 fructosidase unit $= \dfrac{1}{t}$

t = time required for 1 g. enzyme to produce 50% hydrolysis of 4.75 g. sucrose in 50 ml. at 30 °C.

1 fructosidase unit $= 5.127 \dfrac{U}{mg.}$ (30 °C)

In these conversions the change of reaction rate with decrease of substrate concentration has been allowed for[22]. A value of 25 mM has been used for the K_M.

Precision of Method

The standard deviation in 14 parallel determinations of the same sample with a mean of 38.80 U/l. (30 °C) was 0.94 (2.5%). The activity of an invertase solution was measured 4 times with freshly prepared reagents and gave a mean value of 69.85 U/l. (30 °C) with a standard deviation of 3.37 (5%).

Normal Values

In purified preparations a specific activity of 1 000 – 3 000 U/mg. protein at 25 °C[6, 7, 18, 23, 24] has been found. In extracts of acetone-dried and ground bakers' yeast we found an activity of 30 – 40 U/mg. (30 °C). For honey 2 U/mg. (30 °C) were found with the modified method described above.

Sources of Error

Heavy metal ions such as Cu^{2+}, Hg^{2+}, Ag^+ reversibly inhibit invertase[5]. There appears to be no inhibition by the hydrolysis products at the usual physiological concentrations[1].

Specificity of Method

The method described here will determine the following activities:

β-D-Fructofuranoside fructohydrolase	EC 3.2.1.26
α-D-Glucoside glucohydrolase	EC 3.2.1.20
1,4-α-D-Glucan glucohydrolase	EC 3.2.1.3[25]

2,1-β-D-Fructan fructanohydrolase EC 3.2.1.7 does not appear to attack sucrose[26].

References

1 *M. Berthelot*, Compt. rend. acad. sci. *50*, 980 [1860].
2 *K. Myrbäck*, The Enzymes Vol. *4*, p. 379 [1960].

3 *J. W. Preiss,* Arch. Biochem. Biophys. *75*, 186 [1958].
4 *D. D. Sutton & J. O. Lampen,* Biochim. Biophys. Acta *56*, 303 [1962].
5 *K. Myrbäck & E. Willstaedt,* Arkiv Kemi *8*, 367 [1955].
6. *H. Fischer & L. Kothès,* Helv. Chim. Acta *34*, 1123 [1951].
7 *N. P. Neumann & J. O. Lampen,* Biochemistry *6*, 468 [1967].
8 *B. Berggren,* Arkiv Kemi *25*, 555 [1966].
9 *H. U. Bergmeyer & E. Bernt* in *H. U. Bergmeyer:* Methoden der enzymatischen Analyse, Verlag Chemie,
   Weinheim, 1962, p. 123
10 *D. E. Koshland* jr., Biol. Revs. *28*, 416 [1953].
11 *D. Keilin & E. F. Hartree,* Biochem. J. *50*, 341 [1952].
12 *E. Fauth,* Dissertation Kiel [1966].
13 *H. U. Bergmeyer:* Methoden der enzymatischen Analyse, Verlag Chemie, Weinheim, 1962, p. 973.
14 *J. Nelson & G. Bloomfield,* J. Amer. Chem. Soc. *46*, 1025 [1924].
15. *E. Hofmann,* Biochem. Z. *275*, 320 [1935].
16 *H. v. Euler & I. Laurin,* Z. physiol. Chemie *110*, 55 [1920].
17 *L. Michaelis & M. L. Menten,* Biochem. Z. *49*, 333 [1913].
18 *P. Vögele & H. D. Ohlenbusch,* unpublished results.
19 *J. M. Nelson & D. J. Cohn,* J. biol. Chem. *61*, 193 [1924].
20 *R. Willstätter u. R. Kuhn,* Ber. dtsch. chem. Ges. *56*, 509 [1923].
21 *R. Weidenhagen,* Erg. Enzymforsch. *1*, 201 [1932].
22 *H. D. Ohlenbusch,* Z. physiol. Chemie *342*, 174 [1965].
23 *B. Andersen,* Acta chem. scand. *14*, 1849 [1960].
24 *K. Myrbäck & W. Schilling,* Enzymologia *29*, 306 [1965].
25 *D. French & D. Knapp,* J. biol. Chem. *187*, 463 [1950].
26 *J. Edelman & J. S. D. Bacon,* Biochem. J. *47*, lii [1950].

β-Glucuronidase

William H. Fishman

The activity of β-glucuronidase (β-D-Glucuronide glucuronosohydrolase, EC 3.2.1.31) has been measured in tissue extracts of mammals and other vertebrates[1-3], digestive juice of snails (*Helix pomatia*)[4], molluscs (*Patella vulgata*)[5], locusts[6], bacteria[7] and plants[8].

The enzyme catalyses the hydrolysis of β-glucuronides and also the transfer of glucuronyl radicals to acceptor alcohols[9-12].

Like acid phosphatase β-glucuronidase has been measured as a typical lysosomal enzyme during studies of subcellular fractionation[13-15]. According to *Fishman*[16] β-glucuronidase is a structural protein of the endoplasmic reticulum and its occurrence in the lysosomes is due to changes in the endoplasmic reticulum[17].

The classical substrates of the enzyme are β-D-glucopyranosiduronic acids containing a simple aglycone from one of the following groups: drugs or exogenous chemicals (menthol, β-naphthol, phenolphthalein, p-nitrophenol, 8-hydroxyquinoline), steroids (oestriol, oestradiol, testosterone, pregnanediol, corticosteroids and their tetrahydro derivatives) and endogenous non-steroid metabolites (bilirubin and thyroxine). For a complete list of conjugates hydrolysed by β-glucuronidase, see *Marsh*[18]. The enzyme also hydrolyses β-D-galacturonides, but not α-D-glucuronides[19].

Newer substrates for the enzyme are androstendione-enol-β-D-glucuronide[20], glucuronic acid-1-phosphate[3,21], NO-β-D-glucuronide[22], glucofuranosido-uronic acids[23] and (naphthol AS-BI-D-glucuronide[24]. Three substrates are widely used: the glucuronides of phenolphthalein, of p-nitrophenol and of 8-hydroxyquinoline. Fluorimetric measurements can be carried out with 1-naphthol-β-D-glucuronide as substrate[25]. If the aglycone cannot be measured satisfactorily, the liberated glucuronic acid may be determined by the method of *Fishman & Green*[26].

The method using phenolphthalein glucuronide is described here for serum, tissue, urine, cerebrospinal fluid, bile, vaginal secretion and gastric juice. The assay conditions for the substrates p-nitrophenol glucuronide, 8-hydroxyquinoline glucuronide and 1-naphthyl-β-D-glucuronide are briefly described.

Application of Method: In biochemistry and clinical chemistry.

Principle

(1)

Glucuronide   Glucuronic Acid

R = aglycone = phenolphthalein, p-nitrophenol, 8-hydroxyquinoline

The amount of aglycone liberated per unit time under standard conditions (substrate concentration, pH and temperature) is a measure of the β-glucuronidase activity. If the reaction mixture is made alkaline after a definite time, the solution becomes red (phenolphthalein), yellow (p-nitrophenol) or orange (8-hydroxyquinoline); in the latter case it is also necessary to add 4-aminoantipyrine and ferricyanide[27] for chromogen formation.

The increase in extinction due to the colour formed is converted to amount of substrate hydrolysed by means of a standard curve.

Optimum Conditions for Measurements

The optimum conditions for the enzyme in serum are described in detail by *Fishman* et al.[28]; they should be carefully observed because higher substrate concentrations are used than in earlier work. The optimum conditions for the tissue enzyme are described in[3]. The capacity of the acetate buffer must be sufficient to maintain the serum or other type of sample safely at pH 4.5, but on the other hand must allow the assay mixture to be made alkaline at the end of the reaction.

The pH optimum of the enzyme from *E. coli* or other bacteria is pH 7.0.

Equipment

Spectrophotometer or simple colorimeter suitable for measurements at 540 nm.

Measurements in Serum

Phenolphthalein-β-D-glucuronide as Substrate

With higher substrate concentrations the rate of hydrolysis is faster and therefore the incubation time is shorter than in earlier methods (now 4 hr. instead of 5 to 17 hr.). By the use of detergents the deproteinization step with its accompanying loss of phenolphthalein can be omitted.

Reagents

1. Phenolphthalein glucuronide.
   This substance is available commercially as the cinchonidine salt with 1.5 molecules of methyl alcohol of crystallization (e.g. Sigma). The glucuronide is obtained as described in the Appendix, p. 942.
2. Hydrochloric acid, A.R., 2 N
3. Ethyl acetate
4. Sodium hydroxide, A.R., 0.1 N, 0.5 N and conc.
5. Sodium acetate, $CH_3COONa \cdot 3H_2O$, A.R.
6. Acetic acid, A.R.
7. Glycine, A.R.
8. Sodium lauryl sulphate, Duponal e.g. from E. I. DuPont de Nemours & Co., Inc., Wilmington, Del., U.S.A.
9. Phenolphthalein, pure
10. Ethanol, 95% (w/v)

Preparation of Solutions

I. Phenolphthalein glucuronide (30 mM; pH 4.5–5.0):
   For preparation, see Appendix, p. 942.
II. Acetate buffer (1.0 M; pH 4.5):
   Dissolve 57.9 g. $CH_3COONa \cdot 3H_3O$ and 336 ml. acetic acid in distilled water and dilute to 1 000 ml.
III. Glycine-Duponal (0.2 M glycine, 0.2% Duponal w/v; pH 11.7):
   Dissolve 15.01 g. glycine in 900 ml. distilled water, adjust to pH 11.7 with 50% NaOH, add 2 g. Duponal and dilute with distilled water to 100 ml.
IV. Phenolphthalein standard solution (100 μg./ml.; 0.315 mM):
   Dissolve 10 mg. phenolphthalein in 50 ml. 95% ethanol and dilute to 100 ml. with distilled water.

Stability of Solutions

All solutions are stable. Store substrate solution (I) in a refrigerator.

Procedure

Collection, Treatment and Stability of Sample

Preferably use fresh serum free from haemolysis.

Assay System

Wavelength: 540 nm; light path: 1 cm.; incubation volume: 1.00 ml.; 38 °C (constant temperature water bath); final volume for colour reaction: 6.0 ml. Read at room temperature against a blank containing distilled water instead of buffer (II) and substrate solution (I).

Pipette into test tubes:			Concentration in assay mixture
Substrate solution	(I)	0.2 ml.	6 mM
Acetate buffer	(II)	0.2 ml.	200 mM
Distilled water		0.4 ml.	
Serum		0.2 ml.	
Mix by gentle shaking, stopper tubes and incubate for 4 hr.			
Glycine-Duponal solution	(III)	2.0 ml.	67 mM glycine 0.066% Duponal
Distilled water		3.0 ml.	
Mix thoroughly and measure extinction after 10 min.*			

Analyse standards containing 0.01 to 0.20 ml. standard solution IV (1–20 μg. corresponding to 3.15 to 63 nmole) and prepare a standard curve. Ordinate: ΔE, abscissa: nmole phenolphthalein.

Calculations

Read off the phenolphthalein concentration corresponding to the ΔE from the standard curve. Under the above conditions the following relationships apply:

$$\text{Volume activity} = \frac{\text{nmole phenolphthalein}}{t \times 60 \times 0.2} \quad [\text{U/l.}]$$

t = time of incubation in hours.

---

* The intensity of the phenolphthalein colour depends on the pH. Therefore occasionally check that the final pH after dilution to 6 ml. is 10.2–10.45.

Fishman units are also still used. These are defined as the enzyme activity which liberates 1 μg. phenolphthalein in 1 hr. at pH 4.5 (0.1 M acetate buffer) from a 1 mM solution of phenolphthalein glucuronide. Accordingly this gives the following conversion factor:

$$\frac{Fishman \text{ units}}{318 \times 60} = [U] \ (38 \ ^\circ C)$$

It should however be noted that *Fishman* units are often related to other volumes (e. g. 100 ml.).

Precision of Method

In recovery experiments in which phenolphthalein was added to the enzyme assay mixtures a mean of 103.5% $\pm$ 6.1% was found. The coefficient of variation with 10 parallel determinations on sera with low activity was 6.5%, with normal activity 2.5% and with high activity only 1.4%.

Normal Values in Serum

Group	Men U/l. (38 $^\circ$C)	Women U/l. (38 $^\circ$C)
Normal adults	0.525 $\pm$ 0.142 (20)	0.392 $\pm$ 0.123 (22)
Children	0.495 $\pm$ 0.224 (26)	0.571 $\pm$ 0.302 (11)
Cancer patients	0.489 $\pm$ 0.168 (18)	0.457 $\pm$ 0.268 (43)
Diabetics	0.621 $\pm$ 0.345 (21)	0.750 $\pm$ 0.420 (23)
Cirrhosis patients	0.742 $\pm$ 0.160 (37)	0.654 $\pm$ 0.392 (32)
Pregnancy (1st trimester)		0.495 $\pm$ 0.246 (39)
(2nd trimester)		0.658 $\pm$ 0.281 (37)
(3rd trimester)		1.042 $\pm$ 0.461 (52)

The number of subjects is given in parentheses.

Sources of Error

Injection of dyes can give abnormally high blanks at alkaline pH and so interfere with the determination of phenolphthalein. On administration of glucuronolactone, a strong inhibitor of β-glucuronidase, saccharolactone is formed. In these cases at least 4 hr. should elapse before collecting the serum; by this time the metabolic products of glucuronolactone are no longer present in the blood. Chemicals which form glucuronides, such as menthol, affect the β-glucuronidase level; 12 hr. should elapse before collection of the serum.

Alternative Methods for Serum

p-Nitrophenyl-β- D-glucuronide[36] as Substrate

Reagents

See p. 930, No. 4–8, in addition:

11. p-Nitrophenyl-β-D-glucuronide   12. p-Nitrophenol
    e. g. from Calbiochem

Preparation of Solutions

See p. 930, acetate buffer (II), but adjust to pH 4.0 instead of pH 4.5, and solution III.
In addition:

V. p-Nitrophenol-*β*-D-glucuronide (40 mM):
   Dissolve 1.5 g. p-nitrophenol-*β*-D-glucuronide in distilled water and make up to 100 ml.
VI. p-Nitrophenol (0.119 mM):
   Dissolve 0.1 g. p-nitrophenol in 0.1 ml. 1 N NaOH and dilute to 100 ml.

Assay System

Wavelength: 420 nm; light path: 1 cm.; incubation volume: 1.00 ml.; 38 °C (constant temperature water bath); final volume for colour reaction: 6.00 ml. Read at room temperature against
a blank containing distilled water instead of substrate solution (V).

Pipette into test tubes			Concentration in assay mixture
p-Nitrophenyl-*β*-D-glucuronide solution	(V)	0.2 ml.	8 mM
Acetate buffer, pH 4.0	(II)	0.4 ml.	400 mM
Distilled water		0.2 ml.	
Serum		0.2 ml.	
Mix, stopper tubes and incubate for 2 hr.			
Glycine-Duponal solution	(III)	4.0 ml.	1.33 mM glycine 0.133% Duponal
Distilled water		1.0 ml.	
Mix and read extinctions after 10 min.			

The final pH should be 10.2.
Analyse standards containing 0.02–0.20 ml. standard solution VI (2–20 *μ*g. corresponding
to 14.4 to 144 nmole) and prepare a standard curve. Ordinate: ΔE; abscissa: p-nitrophenol.
Calculations as above.

8-Hydroxyquinoline-β-D-glucuronide[26] as Substrate

Reagents

See p. 930, No. 4, 5, 6, 8; in addition.

13. 8-Hydroxyquinoline-*β*-D-glucuronide · 3 H_2O
    e.g. from Calbiochem.
14. Sodium carbonate, Na_2CO_3, A.R.
15. Sodium hydrogen carbonate, $NaHCO_3$, A.R.

16. 4-Aminoantipyrine
    1-Phenyl-2,3-dimethyl-4-aminopyrazolone (5), A.R.
17. Potassium ferricyanide, $K_3[Fe(CN)_6]$, A.R.

Preparation of Solutions

See p. 930, acetate buffer (II) but adjust to pH 3.8 instead of 4.5.
In addition:
  VII. 8-Hydroxyquinoline-β-D-glucuronide (40 mM):
      Dissolve 1.501 g. hydroxyquinoline glucuronide in distilled water and make up to 100 ml.
  VIII. Carbonate-Duponal (ca. 0.34 M carbonate, 0.2% w/v Duponal):
      Dissolve 36.0 g. Na_2CO_3 and 8.4 g. $NaHCO_3$ in ca. 500 ml. distilled water, adjust pH
      to 11.7 with conc. NaOH, dilute to 1000 ml. and dissolve 2 g. Duponal in this solution.
  IX. 8-Hydroxyquinoline (0.689 mM):
      Dissolve 0.1 g. 8-hydroxyquinoline in 0.1 ml. 1 N NaOH and make up to 100 ml.
  X. 4-Aminoantipyrine (0.85% w/v; ca. 42 mM):
      Dissolve 0.85 g. 4-aminoantipyrine in distilled water and make up to 100 ml.
  XI. Potassium ferricyanide (2.4% w/v; ca. 73 mM):
      Dissolve 2.4 g. $K_3[Fe(CN)_6]$ in distilled water and make up to 100 ml.

Assay System

Wavelength: 515 nm; light path: 1 cm.; incubation volume: 1.00 ml.; 38 °C (constant temperature water bath); final volume for colour reaction: 6.00 ml. Read at room temperature against
a blank (containing water instead of 8-hydroxyquinoline-β-D-glucuronide solution VII).

Pipette into test tubes:			Concentration in assay mixture
8-Hydroxyquinoline-β-D-			
glucuronide solution	(VII)	0.2 ml.	8 mM
Acetate buffer, pH 3.8	(II)	0.5 ml.	0.5 mM
Distilled water		0.1 ml.	
Serum		0.2 ml.	
Mix, stopper tubes and incubate for 4 hr.			
Carbonate-Duponal solution	(VIII)	3.0 ml.	0.17 mM carbonate
			0.1% Duponal
4-Aminoantipyrine solution	(X)	1.0 ml.	7 mM
$K_3[Fe(CN)_6]$ solution	(XI)	1.0 ml.	12 mM
Mix and read extinctions after 10 min.			

The final pH should be 10.3.
Analyse standards containing 0.02–0.2 ml. standard solution IX (2–20 μg., corresponding to
13.8–138 nmole) and prepare standard curve. Ordinate: ΔE, abscissa: nmole 8-hydroxyquino-
line.
Calculations as above.

Measurements in Tissue

The assay with the phenolphthalein method which is used most widely is described in full here. The methods
with p-nitrophenyl-β-D-glucuronide and 8-hydroxyquinoline-β-D-glucuronide (see serum p. 932, 933 and[3])
and the fluorimetric method with 1-naphthyl-β-D-glucuronide are briefly described as alternative methods.

β-Glucuronidase assays are important in the quantitative determination of several hormone activities. Mouse kidneys, for example, react quantitatively to the amount of testosterone circulating in the blood, which is produced endogenously by gonadotrophin or by androgen injection[29]. The preputial glands of the rat likewise react to the action of several androgenic compounds[30]. *Woodbury* et al.[31] tested the sebotrophic activity of the hypophysis by the rise in *β*-glucuronidase activity in the preputial glands.

Phenolphthalein-β-D-glucuronide as Substrate

Reagents

1. Phenolphthalein glucuronide
   This substance is available as the cinchonidine salt with 1.5 molecules of methyl alcohol of crystallization (e. g. Sigma) The glucuronide is obtained as described in the Appendix, p. 942.
2. Hydrochloric acid, A. R., 2 N
3. Ethyl acetate
4. Sodium acetate, $CH_3COONa \cdot 3 H_2O$

5. Acetic acid
6. Glycine, A. R.
7. Sodium chloride, A. R.
8. Sodium hydroxide, A. R.; 0.1 N, 0.5 N and 50% (w/v)
9. Phenolphthalein, pure
10. Ethanol, 95% (w/v)
11. Trichloroacetic acid, A. R.; 5% (w/v), ca. 0.3 M

Preparation of Solutions

I. Phenolphthalein glucuronide (5 mM):
   Preparation, see Appendix, p. 942.
II. Acetate buffer (0.1 M, pH 4.5):
   Dissolve 5.79 g. $CH_3COONa \cdot 3 H_2O$ in 3.36 ml. acetic acid and dilute to 1000 ml. with distilled water.
III. Glycine (0.22 M glycine; 0.22 M NaCl):
   Dissolve 16.30 g. glycine and 12.65 g. NaCl in ca. 500 ml. distilled water, add 10.9 ml. 50% (w/v) NaOH and dilute to 1000 ml.
IV. Phenolphthalein standard solution (0.1 mg./ml.; 0.315 mM):
   Dissolve 5 mg. phenolphthalein in 25 ml. 95% ethanol and dilute to 50 ml. with distilled water.

Stability of Solutions

All solutions are stable. Store substrate solution (I) in a refrigerator.

Procedure

Collection, Treatment and Stability of Sample

The enzyme activity can either be measured in homogeneous solution or as a 1% homogenate in distilled water or acetate buffer (II). Only in such dilute solutions is the total enzyme activity determined. Standard method[29] (e. g. mouse kidneys): homogenize 100–200 mg. tissue in 2 ml. 0.1 M acetate buffer (II) in a *Potter-Elvehjem* homogenizer with a Teflon pestle for 1–2 min. Transfer the homogenate to a measuring cylinder and rinse in with acetate buffer. Dilute to 10 ml. with acetate buffer, mix thoroughly and take two 0.1 ml. samples for the assay.

Assay System

Wavelength: 540 nm; light path: 1 cm.; incubation volume: 1.0 ml.; 38 °C (constant temperature water bath); final volume for colour reaction: 6.0 ml.; Read at room temperature against
blank containing buffer (II) instead of substrate solution (I).

Samples

Pipette into test tubes:				Concentration in assay mixture
Substrate solution	(I)	0.1 ml.		0.5 mM
Acetate buffer	(II)	0.8 ml.		80 mM
Homogenate		0.1 ml.		
Mix, stopper tube and incubate for 1 hr. (longer with lower activity). Stop reaction by immersing tubes in boiling water (1 min.)				
Distilled water		1.5 ml.		
Centrifuge for 10 min. at 2000 rpm. Use the supernatant fluid.				
Glycine solution	(III)	2.5 ml.		91 mM glycine
				91 mM NaCl
Trichloroacetic acid, 5%		1.0 ml.		50 mM
Distilled water		0.5 ml.		
Supernatant fluid		2.0 ml.		
Mix and read extinctions after 10 min.				

Standards

Pipette into test tubes:			Concentration in assay mixture
Acetate buffer	(II)	0.2 ml.	3.33 mM
Phenolphthalein standard		up to	2–20 µg./tube;
solution	(IV)	1.0 ml.	6.3–63 nmole/tube
Glycine solution	(III)	2.0 ml.	73 mM
Distilled water		2.8 ml.	
Mix and after 10 min. read extinctions against water.			

Prepare a standard curve with the results. Ordinate: ΔE, abscissa: nmole phenolphthalein.

Calculations

Read off the phenolphthalein concentration (nmole) corresponding to the ΔE value from the standard
curve. Under the conditions described above the following relationships hold for tissue:

$$\text{Specific activity} = \frac{\text{nmole phenolphthalein} \times 2.5 \times (2 + g)}{t \times 60 \times 2 \times 0.1 \times g} \text{ [mU/g.]; 38 °C}$$

where
t = incubation time in hours,
g = gram tissue in homogenate
For conversion to *Fishman* units, see p. 932.

Alternative Methods for Tissue

p-Nitrophenyl-β-D-glucuronide as Substrate

The method is essentially that of *Kato* et al.[36]. It is similar to that described under "Measurements in Serum" (p.932) with the following changes:

a) 0.3 ml. acetate buffer (0.1 M; pH 4.0) and 0.4 ml. distilled water are added
b) The glycine-Duponal contains only 0.1% Duponal
c) In the blank 0.1 ml. homogenate is added after the glycine-Duponal solution.

8-Hydroxyquinoline-β-D-glucuronide as Substrate

The method is similar to that described under "Measurement in Serum" (p.933) but with the following modifications:

a) 0.1 ml. acetate buffer (1.0 M; pH 4.0) and 0.5 ml. distilled water are added.
b) Incubation time 3 hr.
c) 0.2 ml. of 1% tissue homogenate is added (allow for this in the calculations).

1-Naphthyl-β-D-glucuronide[25] as Substrate

Fluorimetric Method

Equipment

Fluorimeter with silica cuvettes; primary wavelength: 345 nm; secondary wavelength: 455 nm, e.g. Farrand spectrofluorimeter with 150 W xenon lamp, Corning filters 9863 (primary), Corning 3389 (secondary).

Reagents

1. 1-Naphthyl-*β*-D-glucuronide
2. N, N'-Dimethylformamide
3. Sodium acetate, $CH_3COONa \cdot 3H_2O$, A.R.
4. Acetic acid, A.R.
5. Sodium hydroxide, A.R., 0.5 N
6. 1-Naphthol
7. Potassium chloride, A.R.

Preparation of Solutions

I. 1-Naphthyl-*β*-D-glucuronide (40 mM):
Extract naphthyl-glucuronide with ether to remove any 1-naphthol which may be present. Dissolve 0.64 g. of the glucuronide in several drops N, N' dimethylformamide and dilute with distilled water to 50 ml.
II. Acetate buffer (0.1 M; pH 4.5):
Dissolve 5.79 g. $CH_3COONa \cdot 3H_2O$ and 11.18 g. KCl in distilled water, add 3.36 ml. acetic acid and dilute to 1000 ml. with distilled water.
III. 1-Naphthol (10 μM):
Dissolve 1.44 mg. naphthol in 20% methanol and make up to 1000 ml.

Stability of Solutions

All solutions are stable. Store the substrate solution (I) in a refrigerator.

Assay System

Primary wavelength: 345 nm; secondary wavelength: 455 nm; incubation volume: 0.65 ml.; 38 °C (constant temperature water bath); final volume: 2.65 ml. Read at room temperature against blank (add the homogenate after the NaOH).

Analyse standards containing 0.01–0.05 ml. standard solution III (corresponding to 14.4– 72.1 μg. or 100–500 nmole 1-naphthol). Ordinate = ΔF, abscissa, nmole 1-naphthol.

Pipette into test tubes:			Concentration in assay mixture
Acetate buffer	(II)	0.55 ml.	85 mM
Substrate solution	(I)	0.05 ml.	3.1 mM
Homogenate		0.05 ml.	
Mix, incubate at 38 °C for 10 min. and cool in ice water.			
NaOH, 0.5 N		2.00 ml.	0.38 M
Mix and read fluorescence against blank.			

Calculations

Read off the 1-naphthol concentration corresponding to the ΔF value from the standard curve. Under the conditions described above the following relationship holds for tissue measured at 38 °C:

$$\text{Specific activity} = \frac{\text{nmole 1-naphthol} \times (2 + g)}{t \times 0.05 \times g} \ [mU/g.]$$

where
t = incubation time in min.; g. = gram tissue in homogenate.

Measurements in Urine

The phenolphthalein glucuronide method is similar to that for tissue (p. 934). A higher substrate concentration is necessary because of the lower activity, and at the same time this reduces the competitive inhibition by low-molecular compounds contained in urine.

Reagents, see p. 935.

Preparation of Solutions

I. Phenolphthalein glucuronide (25 mM):
   For preparation, see Appendix, p. 942.

II. Acetate buffer (1.0 M; pH 5.4):
Dissolve 57.9 g. $CH_3COONa \cdot 3 H_2O$ in distilled water, add ca. 35.0 ml. acetic acid and dilute to 1000 ml.

III. Glycine (0.22 M glycine; 0.22 M NaCl):
Dissolve 16.30 g. glycine and 12.65 g. NaCl in ca. 500 ml. distilled water, add 10.9 ml. 50% NaOH and dilute to 1000 ml. with distilled water.

IV. Phenolphthalein standard solution (0.1 mg./ml.; 0.315 mM):
Dissolve 5.0 mg. phenolphthalein in 25 ml. 95% alcohol and dilute to 50 ml. with distilled water.

Procedure

Assay System

Wavelength: 540 nm; light path: 1 cm.; incubation volume: 1.00 ml.; 38 °C (constant temperature water bath); final volume of colour reaction: 6.0 ml. Read at room temperature against a blank containing substrate solution (I).

Pipette into test tubes:			Concentration in assay mixture
Acetate buffer	(II)	0.1 ml.	0.1 M
Substrate solution	(I)	0.2 ml.	5 mM
Urine		0.2 ml.	
Distilled water		0.5 ml.	
Mix, stopper tubes and incubate for 6 hr.			
Glycine solution	(III)	2.5 ml.	90 mM glycine
			90 mM NaCl
5% Trichloroacetic acid		1.0 ml.	50 mM
Distilled water		1.5 ml.	
Mix and after ca. 10 min. read extinctions.			

The calculations are analogous to those for serum, p. 931. Generally the results are expressed per 24 hr. urine.

Values of 0–300 mU/l. urine have been found.

Measurements in Cerebrospinal Fluid

There is normally only low β-glucuronidase activity in cerebrospinal fluid, and therefore a long period of incubation is required. The incubation mixture is as above for urine, except that acetate buffer, pH 5.2 and 20 mM substrate solution are used. The incubation takes 18 hr. For the colour development 1 ml. 0.2 M glycine solution (adjusted to pH 11.7 with NaOH) and 1 ml. distilled water are used. The measurements are made by the micro-method of *Reilly* and *Crawford*[32] (see this reference for details) against the reagent blank (without cerebrospinal fluid). Phenolphthalein solutions containing 0–3.0 μg./ml. in acetate buffer (20 mM; pH 5.2) are used as standards. The extinction of a tube containing cerebrospinal fluid but without substrate solution (I) must be subtracted from the extinction for the experimental tube. Values of 0–0.3 U/l. cerebrospinal fluid have been found.

Measurements in Bile[33]

The phenolphthalein glucuronide method is similar to that for tissue (see p. 934), but with some modification. It is necessary to have a long incubation time and a slightly higher substrate concentration because of the low activity.

Reagents

See p. 935.
In addition:

12. Activated charcoal
13. Toluene

Preparation of Solutions

   I. Phenolphthalein glucuronide (10 mM):
      Preparation, see Appendix, p. 942.
  II. Acetate buffer (0.2 M; pH 4.5):
      Dissolve 11.58 g. $CH_3COONa \cdot 3H_2O$ in distilled water, add 6.72 ml. acetic acid and dilute with distilled water to 1000 ml.
 III. Glycine (0.22 M; pH 10.55):
      Dissolve 16.3 g. glycine and 12.65 g. NaCl in ca. 500 ml. distilled water, adjust to pH 10.55 with 50% NaOH and dilute to 1000 ml. with distilled water.
 IV. Phenolphthalein standard solution (0.1 mg./ml. 0.315 mM):
      Dissolve 5.0 mg. phenolphthalein in 25 ml. 95% alcohol and dilute to 50 ml. with distilled water.

Procedure

Assay System

Wavelength: 540 nm; light path: 1 cm.; incubation volume: 1.00 ml.; 38 °C (constant temperature water bath); final volume for colour reaction: 6.0 ml. Read at room temperature against blank containing distilled water instead of substrate solution (I).

Pipette into small test tubes:			Concentration in assay mixture
Acetate buffer	(II)	0.8 ml.	0.16 M
Bile, undiluted		0.1 ml.	
Toluene		2–3 drops	
Substrate solution	(I)	0.1 ml.	1 mM
Mix, stopper tubes and incubate for 48 hr. (or more).			
Ethanol, 98%		0.3 ml.	
Activated charcoal		ca. 0.1 mg.	
Mix, centrifuge for 5–10 min. at 3000 rpm, and suck supernatant through sintered glass into a test tube with mark at 6.0 ml. Stir up the precipitate with two 0.3 ml. portions of ethanol, centrifuge and filter supernatant. Combine supernatant fluids and use for next stage.			15% ethanol
Glycine solution	(III)	2.0 ml.	73 mM
Wash filter with distilled water and dilute contents of test tube to 6.0 ml. with these washings. Mix and after ca. 10 min. read extinction.			

The calculations are analogous to those for serum, p. 931 (note the difference in the volume of sample).

The *Fishman* units are related to 100 ml. bile, which must be taken into account in the conversion.

Measurements in Vaginal Fluid

For measurements with the macro-assay the sample is weighed into a Potter homogenizer, diluted to 3.0 ml. with acetate buffer (0.1 M; pH 4.5) and homogenized. The procedure is the same as that for tissue samples (p. 934), except that the substrate concentration is 1 mM. Incubation for 18 hr.

The micro-method has the advantage that samples as low as 1 mg. can be easily analysed. The method has been described by *Watkins* and *Lawson*[34].

Measurements in Duodenal Juice[35]

The assay is essentially the same as for tissues, except for the following differences:

a) The phenolphthalein-β-D-glucuronic acid solution is 10 mM.

b) The incubation is between 1 and 24 hr. depending on the activity.

c) The reaction is stopped by the addition of 5.0 ml. glycine buffer (0.2 M, pH 10.4).

The calculations are analogous to those for serum, p. 931. (note the different volume of sample).

Appendix

Preparation of Phenolphthalein Glucuronide

Method with ethyl acetate: Mix 0.80 g. cinchonidine salt of phenolphthalein glucuronide in 100 ml. beaker with 20 ml. 2 N HCl, add 20 ml. ethyl acetate and stir until fully dissolved. Transfer the mixture quantitatively to a 250 ml. separating funnel (rinse in with five 6 ml. portions of ethyl acetate). Shake in the separating funnel ca. 100 times, stand for 5 min. to allow the phases to separate, run off the aqueous phase and decant the organic phase through a cotton wool plug in a funnel into a 500 ml. round-bottomed flask. Extract the aqueous phase five times with 6 ml. ethyl acetate and decant the organic phase each time as described above. Rinse the separating funnel with 20 ml. ethyl acetate, combine the extracts and evaporate to dryness in a rotary evaporator. The gum-like, colourless residue is free phenolphthalein glucuronide. Dissolve in 30 ml. hot water, adjust to pH 4.5 with 0.1 N NaOH (indicator paper). Transfer the mixture quantitatively to a 100 ml. measuring flask (rinse several times with distilled water) dilute to the mark and mix thoroughly. If the solution is turbid, stir in a little activated charcoal and filter.

This solution is 10 mM with respect to phenolphthalein glucuronide. To obtain higher concentrations use less water: e.g. for measurements in serum only dilute to 33.3 ml. (30 mM).

Method with NaOH: Dissolve 0.80 g. chinchonidine salt of phenolphthalein with 25 ml. 0.5 N NaOH with stirring. After 30 min. filter off the chinchonidine, wash the precipitate with 5 ml. 0.5 N NaOH. Adjust the filtrate to pH 4.5–5.0 with 2 N HCl and dilute to 100 ml. (10 mM) or less with distilled water.

References

1 *W. H. Fishman*, Advances in Enzymology, Academic Press, New York 1955, Vol. *16*, p. 361.
2 *G. A. Levvy & C. A. Marsh*, Advances in Carbohydrate Chemistry, Academic Press New York 1959, Vol. *14*, p. 381.
3 *W. H. Fishman* in *D. Glick,* Methods of Biochemical Analysis, John Wiley-Interscience, London-New York-Sidney, 1967, Vol. *15,* p. 77.
4 *P. Jarrige & R. Henry*, Bull. soc. chim. biol. *34*, 872 [1952].
5 *K. S. Dodgson, J. I. M. Lewis & B. Spencer*, Biochem. J. *55*, 253 [1953].
6 *D. Robinson, J. N. Smith & R. T. Williams*, Biochem. J. *53*, 125 [1953].
7 *H. J. Bühler, P. A. Katzman & E. A. Doisy*, Proc. Soc. exptl. Biol. Med. *76*, 672 [1951].
8 *T. Miwa*, Acta Phytochim. Japan *9*, 89 [1936].
9 *W. H. Fishman & S. Green*, J. Amer. chem. Soc. *78*, 880 [1956].
10 *W. H. Fishman & S. Green*, J. biol. Chem. *225*, 435 [1957].
11 *K. Kato & H. Tsukamoto*, Chem. Pharm. Bull. (Tokio) *12*, 656 [1964].
12 *B. Weissmann*, J. biol. Chemistry *216*, 783 [1955].
13 *C. DeDuve, B. C. Pressman, R. Gianetto, R. Wattiaux & F. Appelmans*, Biochem. J. *60*, 604 [1955].
14 *W. Straus*, J. Cell. Biol. *21*, 295 [1964].
15 *J. L. Van Lanker*, Fed. Proc. *23*, 1 050 [1964].
16 *W. H. Fishman, S. S. Goldman & R. DeLellis*, Nature *213*, 457 [1967].
17 *H. Ide & W. H. Fishman*, J. Cell. Biol. *35*, 60 A [1967].
18 *C. A. Marsh* in *J. F. Dutton*, Glucuronic Acid, Academic Press, New York 1967.
19 *J. Conchie, G. A. Levvy & C. A. Marsh*, Biochem. J. *62*, 24 P [1956].
20 *M. Wakabayashi, H. H. Wotiz & W. H. Fishman*, Biochim. biophys. Acta *48*, 198 [1961].
21 *G. A. Levvy & C. A. Marsh*, Biochem. J. *52*, 690 [1952].
22 *H. Ide, S. Green, K. Kato & W. H. Fishman*, Biochem. J. *106*, 431 [1968].
23 *K. Kato, K. Yoshida & H. Tsukamoto*, Chem. Pharm. Bull. (Tokio) *12*, 670 [1964].
24 *W. H. Fishman, Y. Nakajima, C. Anstiss & S. Green*, J. Histochem. and Cytochem. *12*, 298 [1964].

25 M. A. Verity, R. Caper & W. J. Brown, Arch. Biochem. Biophys. *106*, 386 [1964].
26 W. H. Fishman & S. Green, J. biol. Chem. *215*, 527 [1955].
27 M. E. A. Powel & M. J. H. Smith, J. clin. Pathol. *7*, 245 [1954].
28 W. H. Fishman, K. Kato, C. L. Anstiss & S. Green, Clin. Chim. Acta *15*, 435 [1967].
29 W. H. Fishman, Methods in Hormone Research *4*, 273 [1965].
30 J. F. Patterson, M. Cheney & W. H. Fishman, Endocrinology *75*, 273 [1964].
31 L. P. Woodbury, A. J. Lorinez & P. Ortega, J. Invest. Dermatol. *45*, 362 [1965].
32 C. N. Reilley & C. M. Crawford, Anal. Chem. *27*, 716 [1955].
33 T. Sato, Tohoku J. exptl. Med. *77*, 23 [1962].
34 D. K. Watkins & J. G. Lawson, Clin. Chim. Acta *8*, 646 [1963].
35 Y. S. Kim & A. G. Plaut, Gastroenterology *49*, 50 [1965].
36 K. Kato, K. Yoshida, H. Tsukamoto, M. Nobunaga, T. Masuya & T. Sawada, Chem. Pharm. Bull. (Tokio) *8*, 239 [1960].
37 J. T. Park & M. S. Johnson, J. biol. Chem. *181*, 149 [1949].
38 H. Yuki & W. H. Fishman, Biochim. biophys. Acta *74*, 302 [1963].

Hyaluronidase

Alfred Linker

The term hyaluronidase (Hyaluronate glycanohydrolase, EC 3.2.1.36) refers here to an enzyme which acts on hyaluronic acid, irrespective of activity with other substrates. Hyaluronidase was first isolated from micro-organisms[1], later from mammalian testis; this is now the main source. With one exception, all these enzymes are endohexosaminidases. It has been shown that the bacterial enzyme is not a hydrolase, but acts as eliminase[2], while the hyaluronidase from testis, although a hydrolase, also has transglycosylase activity[3]. Enzymes having similar properties to the testis hyaluronidase have been obtained from tadpoles[4], snake venom[5], bee venom[6], numerous animal tissues[7], human serum[8] and other sources. The tissue enzyme most probably originates from the lysosomes[9,10].

The method described here is mainly suitable for tissue hyaluronidase and similar enzymes. Bacterial enzymes can be determined with this method, but better methods have been described[11]. The enzyme from leeches, which is an endoglucuronidase[12], cannot be determined by this method.

Application of Method: In biochemistry and physiology. Under certain conditions it can be used to differentiate mucopolysaccharides[13].

Principle

For the reaction formula see the chapter "Hyaluronic Acid", p. 1157. Hyaluronidases are endohexosaminidases and catalyse the degradation of hyaluronic acid with the liberation of acetylglucosamine terminal groups which can be measured in a colorimetric assay[14].

In the assay the anhydro sugar is first formed from N-acetylglucosamine in alkaline solution, then this is converted in acid solution to the furan derivative, which reacts with p-dimethylaminobenzaldehyde to form a coloured complex[15]. The amount of acetylglucosamine liberated per unit time is a measure of the hyaluronidase activity.

Optimum Conditions for Measurements

The pH optimum varies with the source of the enzyme. The enzyme from testis has a wide pH optimum between pH 4.0 and 6.0 (dependent on the buffer used). The optimum for the majority of the bacterial enzymes is around pH 5.0. Serum hyaluronidase has a rather sharp optimum at pH 4.0 and the lysosomal enzyme a sharp optimum at pH 3.5. As a compromise we use pH 4.0. If accurate measurements are required, particularly in the case of enzymes of unknown origin, the pH optimum must be determined specially. It is preferable to assay hyaluronidases at 37 °C.

Equipment

Spectrophotometer of suitable accuracy: 37 °C water bath; boiling water bath.

Reagents

1. Acetic acid, 0.1 M
2. Sodium acetate, $CH_3COOONa \cdot 3H_2O$

3. Acetic acid
4. Sodium chloride

5. Hyaluronic acid
   free acid, sodium or potassium salt; commercial
   preparation, see p. 543.
6. N-Acetyl-D-glucosamine
   commercial preparation, see p. 524.

7. Potassium tetraborate, $K_2B_4O_7 \cdot 4H_2O$
8. Potassium hydroxide, ca. 5 M
9. p-Dimethylaminobenzaldehyde
10. Hydrochloric acid, 10 N

Purity of Reagents

Only reagents of A. R. grade should be used. p-Dimethylaminobenzaldehyde must be recrystallized if the commercial preparation is not of sufficient purity. Good commercial preparations of hyaluronic acid are available; they should contain at least 30% uronic acid as measured by the carbazole reaction[16]. A preparation of good quality can be prepared from umbilical cords[9].

Preparation of Solutions (for ca. 15 determinations)

Use only doubly distilled water.
  I. Acetate buffer (50 mM acetate; pH 4.0; 0.15 M NaCl):
     a) dilute 5.78 ml. acetic acid to 1 000 ml. with distilled water (0.1 M);
     b) dissolve 13.6 g. $CH_3COONa \cdot 3 H_2O$ in distilled water and make up to 1 000 ml. (0.1 M); add 41.0 ml. solution a) to 9.0 ml. solution b) and, if necessary, adjust the pH of the mixture to pH 4.0. Add. 0.875 g. NaCl and dilute to 100 ml. with distilled water.
 II. Hyaluronate (1.25 mg./ml.):
     Dissolve 62.5 mg. hyaluronic acid in 50 ml. acetate buffer (I). The compound is not easily soluble; it is best to prepare the solution the day before.
III. N-Acetylglucosamine standard solution:
     Dissolve 10 mg. N-acetylglucosamine in 10 ml. acetate buffer (I); dilute a) 1 ml. to 50 ml. with acetate buffer (I) (20 μg./ml.) and b) 1 ml. to 100 ml. (10 μg./ml.)
 IV. Tetraborate (0.8 M; pH 9.1):
     Dissolve 24.44 g. $K_2B_4O_7 \cdot 4H_2O$ in distilled water and make up to 100 ml. Adjust to pH 9.1 with 5 N KOH
  V. Dimethylaminobenzaldehyde reagent:
     Dissolve 10 g. p-dimethylaminobenzaldehyde in 100 ml. acetic acid (containing 12.5% v/v 10 M HCl). Just before use dilute with 9 vol acetic acid.

Stability of Solutions

Store all solutions at 0–4 °C. The buffer solution is stable providing that there is no growth of bacteria or moulds. Prepare the hyaluronate and acetylglucosamine solutions freshly each week. The dimethylaminobenzaldehyde stock solution is stable for a month.

Procedure

Collection, Treatment and Stability of Sample

Collect and prepare the samples just before the assay; take up in acetate buffer (I). They can be stored for a limited time at 0–4 °C. With the exception of highly purified hyaluronidase preparations the enzyme is very stable in a dry state at low temperature.

Assay System

Enzyme reaction

Carry out all assays in duplicate
Incubation temperature: 37 °C; incubation volume: 1.0 ml. Prepare a blank for each series of
measurements: 0.2 ml. tetraborate solution (IV) + 0.8 ml. hyaluronate solution (II) + 0.2 ml.
sample. Take 0.6 ml. of this mixture for the colour reaction.

Pipette into test tubes (10 mm. × 70 mm.):			Concentration in assay mixture
Hyaluronate solution	(II)	0.8 ml.	1 mg./ml.
Pre-incubate for 15 min.			
Sample (buffered)		0.2 ml.	
Mix and incubate for exactly 10 min. Then add immediately 0.5 ml. to the colour reaction.			

Spectrophotometric measurements

Also carry out duplicate determinations.
Wavelength: 585 nm; light path: 1 cm.; final volume: 3.6 ml. Read against blank (tube 1).

Pipette into text tubes (10 mm × 100 mm):		1	2	3	4	5
Tetraborate solution	(IV)	0.1 ml.	0.1 ml.	0.1 ml.	0.1 ml.	—
Acetate buffer	(I)	0.5 ml.	—	—	—	—
10 μg. Standard	(III)	—	0.5 ml.	—	—	—
20 μg. Standard	(III)	—	—	0.5 ml.	—	—
Incubation solution		—	—	—	0.5 ml.	—
Blank + sample		—	—	—	—	0.6 ml.

Heat for 3 min. in boiling water bath and the cool with running tap water.

Dimethylaminobenz-aldehyde reagent	(V)	each 3.0 ml.

Mix, incubate for 20 min. in a 37°C water bath and cool with running tap water. If necessary,
centrifuge the solutions to clear, pour into cuvettes and immediately measure the extinctions.

Calculations

The enzyme activity is expressed as μmole N-acetylglucosamine liberated per min. Refer to the standards
to calculate the amount of acetylglucosamine liberated in 10 min. incubation time. The extinctions of both
standards must have the relationship 1:2, otherwise the assay is not functioning correctly. The 10 μg.
standard is taken for the calculations.

Thus

E_{St} = extinction of 10 μg. standard
E_{Sam} = extinction of sample
$E_{Blk+Sam}$ = extinction of blank containing sample

In the sample $c = \dfrac{E_{Sam} - E_{Blk+Sam}}{E_{St}} \times 2 \, [\mu g./ml.]$

Volume activity $= \dfrac{E_{Sam} - E_{Blk+Sam}}{E_{St}} \times \dfrac{2}{0.2} \times \dfrac{F}{221.2} \times 1\,000 = \dfrac{E_{Sam} - E_{Blk+Sam}}{E_{St}} \times 45 \times F \, [U/l.]; 37 \,^{\circ}C$

where

0.2 = volume of sample in enzymatic reaction

221.2 = molecular weight of N-acetylglucosamine

F = dilution factor of sample during pretreatment

The measured activity can be compared with commercially available hyaluronidase preparations of known activity from testis (National Formulary units, N. F. Units). Standard preparations can also be obtained from National Formulary, Office of the Director of Revision, 2215 Constitution Ave., N. W., Washington, D. C. 20037.

Precision of Method

With values of 20 mU/mg. protein a standard deviation of 1 mU/mg. was found.
The sensitivity of the method is better than 2 mU (equivalent to 15 N. F. Units) per mg. protein. For the assay of lower activities the reaction time can be prolonged, but this reduces the accuracy.

Sources of Error

Effects of drugs and other therapeutic measures: Heparin inhibits the enzyme.

Interference in the assay system: Heavy metals and strong polyanions inhibit hyaluronidases. Variation of the ionic strength of the buffer, the pH or the amount of sample can alter the final pH of the colour test for acetylglucosamine which functions only in alkaline solution. If modifications are made the incubation mixture must be neutralized before the colour reaction. The blank + sample are important as a time blank and therefore should not be prepared too long before the heating step, because even in alkaline solution low enzyme activity can be present. In the analysis of crude enzyme preparations or extracts turbidity is a source of error; it should be removed by centrifugation before the extinction measurements. Hyaluronic acid is not very soluble, it is inclined to swell; the solution must be thoroughly mixed.

Specificity of Method

Chondroitin-6-sulphate can serve as substrate instead of hyaluronic acid, whereas chondroitin-4-sulphate cannot.

Other Methods of Assay

A series of methods with advantages and disadvantages have been described. Measurement of turbidity[13] which is a standard method for purified hyaluronidases is not applicable to crude extracts, although it is specific, sensitive and accurate. It requires a particularly pure substrate, a standard enzyme as reference and the method must be carried out carefully. The viscosimetric method[17] is very sensitive, the results depend on the purity of the substrate and on the molecular weight; decrease of viscosity due to non-enzymatic reactions is a serious problem.

The measurement of the reducing groups liberated[18] is not very specific, unless the appropriate control values are measured; too high values are found with crude extracts. The method described here, although it is less sensitive and less accurate than those described above, has the advantage of simplicity, high specificity and applicability to virtually all crude enzyme preparations and tissue extracts. If the samples contain β-glucuronidase and β-acetylglucosaminidases too high values are obtained.

References

1 K. Meyer, R. Dubos & E. M. Smyth, J. biol. Chem. 163, 723 [1937].
2 A. Linker, K. Meyer & P. Hoffmann, J. biol. Chem. 219, 13 [1956].
3 B. Weissmann, K. Meyer, P. Sampson & A. Linker, J. biol. Chem. 208, 417 [1954].
4 J. E. Silbert, Y. Nagai & J. Gross, J. biol. Chem. 240, 1509 [1965].
5 B. Weissmann, J. biol. Chem. 216, 783 [1955].
6 S. A. Barker, S. J. Bayyuk, J. S. Brimacombe & D. J. Palmer, Nature 199, 693 [1963].
7 A. J. Bollet, W. M. Bonner jr. & J. L. Nance, J. biol. Chem. 238, 3522 [1963].
8 W. M. Bonner & E. Y. Cantey, Clin. chim. Acta 13, 746 [1966].
9 N. N. Aronson jr. & E. A. Davidson, J. biol. Chem. 242, 437 [1967].
10 G. Vaes, Biochem. J. 103, 802 [1967].
11 A. Linker in S. P. Colowick & N. O. Kaplan: Methods in Enzymology. Academic Press, New York 1966, vol. VIII, p. 650.
12 A. Linker, K. Meyer & P. Hoffmann, J. biol. Chem. 235, 924 [1960].
13 M. B. Mathews in S. P. Colowick & N. O. Kaplan: Methods in Enzymology. Academic Press, New York 1966, vol. VIII, p. 654.
14 J. L. Reissig, J. L. Strominger & L. F. Leloir, J. biol. Chem. 217, 959 [1955].
15 D. H. Leaback & P. G. Walker, Biochim. biophys. Acta 74, 297 [1963].
16 Z. Dische, J. biol. Chem. 167, 189 [1947].
17 H. E. Alburn & R. W. Whitley, J. biol. Chem. 192, 379 [1951].
18 M. M. Rapport, K. Meyer & A. Linker, J. biol. Chem. 196, 615 [1950].

Peptidases

Walter Appel

	Page
Review	949

Aminopeptidases and Amino Acid Arylamidases
General Information	950
Leucine Aminopeptidase	954
Amino Acid Arylamidases ("Leucine nitroanilidase")	958
Angiotensinase	964
Oxytocinase (L-Cystine-di-β-naphthylamide as substrate).	967
Oxytocinase (S-Benzyl-L-cysteine p-nitroanilide as substrate	971

Di- and Polypeptidases
| General Information . . . . | 978 |
| Glycylglycine Dipeptidase . . . . | 982 |

Carboxypeptidases
General Information	986
Carboxypeptidase A (Determination with N-carbobenzoxy-glycyl-L-phenylalanine)	989
Carboxypeptidase A (Determination with N-carbo-β-naphthoxy-DL-phenylalanine) . . .	993
Carboxypeptidase B (Determination with hippuryl-L-arginine)	996

Review[1−5, 158−160]

Peptidases (Peptidyl hydrolases) in the broadest sense hydrolyse peptides bonds in peptides and proteins: equivalent amounts of amino (or imino-) and carboxyl groups are liberated. Peptidases, which cleave consecutive COOH or NH₂- (or NH-) terminal amino acids from the end of the chain, are termed *exopeptidases,* and these are further subdivided into *carboxypeptidases* and *aminopeptidases.* These enzymes usually require only two points of attachment on the substrate for their activity: the sensitive peptide bond and a free NH₂- or COOH-group. A third group is composed of peptidases which attack dipeptides and tripeptides: the *dipeptidases* and *tripeptidases.* They require *three* points of attachment: a sensitive peptide bond (or bonds) and both terminal amino acids.

Enzymes which hydrolyse a specific peptide bond without regard for its position in the polypeptide or protein molecule are termed *endopeptidases* or more commonly *proteinases.* (See p. 1000).

A further classification of peptidases can be made on the basis of their specificity towards synthetic substrates, although according to current concepts this is no longer strictly practicable. Apart from preference for certain *amino acids* in the bonds to be hydrolysed, there also exists a preference for the type of bond, e. g. peptide, acid ester and acid amide bonds. The difficulties of classification on this basis hold in particular for the so-called (tissue) *cathepsins.*

If an isolated peptidase which has been sufficiently characterized is being studied, it usually has a more or less specific substrate specificity, on the other hand it cannot be assumed on the basis of the observation of the enzymatic hydrolysis of a "specific" substrate by a tissue (homogenate or crude extract) that a single enzyme or class of enzymes is responsible. Histochemical findings require particularly careful interpretation in this respect.

The activity of peptidases is determined according to accepted rules. In the majority of cases the amount of residual substrate is determined, rather than the reaction product.

The following methods have proved themselves in practice:

1. *Titrimetric methods*
   Formol titration[6,7]
   Alkalimetric titration in alcoholic solution[8,9]
   Acidimetric titration in acetone solution[10,11]
   Titration of ammonia after diffusion[12,13]

2. *Manometric methods*
   Determination of amino-N *(van Slyke)*[14]
   Determination of the O_2 consumption on oxidation by D-amino acid oxidase[15] or L-amino acid oxidase[16,118] of the amino acids formed.
   Determination of the CO_2 production on decarboxylation with L-amino acid decarboxylases[17] of the amino acids formed.

3. *Colorimetric Methods*
   Determination of amino acids with ninhydrin[18].

4. *Spectrophotometric methods*
   For special purposes, e.g. kinetic measurements[19,20].

5. *Chromatographic methods*
   Paper chromatographic determination of the amino acids[1,21].

6. *Methods with chromogenic substrates*
   Colorimetric[22-24] and kinetic methods [25,26,119,121,125].

Expression of enzyme activities. Frequently the "proteolytic coefficient C" is used as a measure of activity:

$$C = \frac{K}{E} \times \log \frac{100}{100-\alpha}; \qquad K = \frac{1}{t}$$

$\alpha = \%$ hydrolysis of the substrate (usually 50 mM), t = incubation time in min., E = enzyme concentration, e.g. mg. protein/ml. assay mixture. We recommend that even with peptidases the activity should be expressed in units (U), the formation of reaction product is a measure of the activity. It must be established that the product is not converted further and that it reacts completely in the estimation; in addition the degree of hydrolysis α should be calculated. With certain reservations this system of reference is also suitable for the hydrolysis of natural substrates of high molecular weight.

Nomenclature: In the following text the usual rules for nomenclature and abbreviations apply. "Z" stands for "Cbz" (N_{α}-carbobenzoxy).

Aminopeptidases and Amino Acid Arylamidases
"Leucine aminopeptidase", Oxytocinase, Angiotensinase
General Information

Walter Appel

With the aminopeptidases (α-Aminoacylpeptide hydrolases, EC 3.4.11.1 to 3.4.11.4) the overlapping of the specificity is most marked. Only a few representatives have so far been prepared in a homogeneous state, characterized and assigned an EC number. In the last years many papers have been published on new peptidases: aminopeptidases from *Aspergilli*[161,162] (aminopeptidase M), *Bac. subtilis*[163] and *E. coli* [164,165], peptidases from leucocytes [166-168] and granulocytes [169] and lysosomal peptidases from different tissues, especially skin [170-175].

Leucine aminopeptidase (LAP) is the term for an aminopeptidase which has a preference for leucine. The activity of this enzyme however is not limited to N-terminal leucine and also does not always show a preferential hydrolysis of L-leucylpeptides, for example in comparison to its activity with L-alanylpeptides; in addition amino acid amides and arylamides are hydrolysed. Typical substrates of LAP are L-leucyl-glycine, L-leucyl-glycyl-glycine and L-leucinamide[3,4,36-40,118]. The lysosomal cathepsins are still under intensive investigation [176-180]. Whereas cathepsin A [17] and B [181-183] seem to be acid and basic proteinases respectively, cathepsin D appears to be a typical neutral proteinase [184-200] and cathepsin C now has been identified as a "Dipeptidylaminopeptidase" (dipeptidylarylamidase) (see next chapter).

Amino acid arylamidases have for several years been included in the aminopeptidase group of enzymes[22-30,49-61,70-79]. They hydrolyse preferentially or exclusively "chromogenic" substrates, like naphthylamides or anilides[25] of amino acids. These substrates are also partially hydrolysed by the aminopeptidases, so that here again demonstration of hydrolysis of a particular substrate does not allow the classification of the enzyme. Several representatives of this group of enzymes have been purified and sufficiently characterized to indicate that they exhibit a marked preference for arylamides. More recently subgroups have been distinguished: a) arylamidases* with a preference for aminodicarboxylic acid arylamides ("aminopeptidase A")[29]; b) arylamidases* with broad unspecificity, but perhaps with a preference for L-leucine or L-alanine[25,26,30,52-61,70-79,109,110]; c) arylamidases with a preference for diaminocarboxylic acid arylamides ("arylamidase B")[78,79,108,210-216]. Very probably the hydrolysis of glycyl-L-prolylarylamides[111,217] and L-cystine arylamides (oxytocinases), possibly also the hydrolysis of L-aspartic acid arylamides (angiotensinase) is due to distinct arylamidases. (See also the dipeptidyl arylamidases I, II, III[112-114]). The chymotryptic cathepsin C [201-204] has been isolated and characterized as an dipeptidylarylamidase [205], now designated as dipeptidylaminopeptidase [206-209].

Typical substrates are the β-naphthylamide and p-nitroanilide of L-glutamic acid, L-leucine or L-alanine, L-lysine or L-arginine, glycyl-L-proline and L-cystine. Whether the hydrolysis of both arylamides proceeds in parallel has not yet been established[24,38,75,126-131]; for L-valine and L-methionine, see[156].

Oxytocinase is the collective term for a group of enzymes which inactivate oxytocin by hydrolysis of the peptide bond between the half cysteine in position 1 and tyrosine[31,32]. Although the tissue enzymes are probably aminopeptidases and/or amino acid arylamidases, two forms have been demonstrated in serum during pregnancy and retroplacental serum[25,32] and have been purified and characterized[32,33,65,93-95]. The main component is a L-cysteine aminopeptidase with the above mentioned specificity, and, apart from oxytocin[32,94-98], the following substrates are used for its determination: L-cystine-di-β-naphthylamide[33,65,100, 75,99-101,132,133], L-cystine-di-p-nitroanilide[25] and S-benzyl-L-cysteine-β-naphthylamide[102]. These arylamides, however, are hydrolysed by other arylamidases or aminopeptidases[75], so that in the analysis of impure enzyme preparations the hydrolysis of oxytocin should be checked. More recent work, see[218-227].

The term *Angiotensinase* represents a group of peptidases which hydrolyse angiotensins** and destroy their biological activity (hypertensive effects)[34,35,62,63]. The inactivation of angiotensin II is initiated by cleavage of the N-terminal asparagine, which represents the rate-limiting step[35,62]. The peptidases

---

* The terms "aminopeptidase" and "arylamidase" are often interchanged in the literature. If arylamides are used as substrates the term "arylamidase" should only be used, especially in the assay of homogenates, sera, urine or other biological material.
** "Angiotensin" is synonymous with the terms "angiotonin" and "hypertensin" used in the earlier literature.

Table 1. Classification, occurrence, purification, substrates and activity optima of aminopeptidases.

Enzyme	Occurrence	Purification from	Substrate	Optimum pH	Effectors		
					Activators	Inhibitors	Inactive
Leucine aminopeptidase EC 3.4.11.1	Intestine (pig, rat, chicken, trout); kidney (pig); liver, lung, lens of eye (beef); muscle, heart (rat, rabbits humans); malt; cabbage; spinach; serum of many species including humans	Pig kidneys[36-40]; lens of eye[41]; spleen[42] (beef)	L-Leucinamide; L-Leu-Gly	8.5–10.0 according to source, substrate activator	Mn^{2+}, Mg^{2+}, Pre-incubate crude preparations for 3 hr.	Cd^{2+}, Cu^{2+}, Hg^{2+}, Pb^{2+}, Fe^{3+}, EDTA, citrate; weak: Ni^{2+}, Zn^{2+}, Fe^{2+}, $P_2O_7^-$, SH^-, CN^-	Ca^{2+}, Co^{2+}, glutathione, iodoacetate, DFP, p-chloro mercuribenzoate
Aminopeptidases (aminopolypeptidases) EC 3.4.11.2	Ubiquitous, e.g. intestinal mucosa, juice, spleen, kidney, liver, serum, leucocytes, erythrocytes, urine, bile; many species, including humans, plants and micro-organisms[43,44]	Intestinal mucosa, kidney and spleen of pig[45]; brewers' yeast[48]; ox brain[61]	Various peptides	7.2–8.0 (7.8–8.0) (6.1–7.9) according to source	Mn^{2+}, Mg^{2+}, weak, according to source; Zn^{2+}, Co^{2+}, Cl^-	Hg^{2+}, SH^-, CN^-	Mn^{2+}, Mg^{2+} according to source
Aminotripeptidase EC 3.4.11.4	Intestine (pig); liver, kidney, muscle (rat); thymus (calf); skin, lung, serum (rabbit); erythrocytes (horse); brain, erythrocytes, leucocytes, serum (human); micro-organisms[43,44]	Calf thymus[49]; erythrocytes of humans[50]; of horse[51]; ox brain[61]	Gly-Gly-Gly	7.5–7.9 (7.0) (7.9) according to source		Cd^{2+} (Mn^{2+}) Cysteine according to source	Mn^{2+}, Co^{2+}, Zn^{2+}, Mg^{2+}, Ca^{2+}, Cu^{2+}, Ni^{3+}, Al^{3+}, CN^-, SH^-, Citrate, DFP

Table 1. Classification, occurrence, purification, substrates and activity optima of aminopeptidases (continued).

Enzyme	Occurrence	Purification from	Substrate	Optimum pH	Activators	Effectors Inhibitors	Inactive
Amino acid arylamidases EC 3.4.11.2	Usually together with LAP. Spleen, heart, kidney, liver, hypophysis (rat); spleen, liver (beef); liver, kidney, colon, heart, mammary gland, muscle, bladder, intestine, lymph nodes, placenta, erythrocytes (human); mainze[82], bakers' yeast[83]	Mouse ascites[52]; pig kidneys[53,71]; human liver[54]; plasma and erythrocytes[55]; bovine spleen[42]; bovine hypo- and kidneys[78]	Naphthylamide and p-nitro-anilides of L-Leu, L-Ala, L-Glu, L-Arg; L-Lys, L-Cys, Gly-L-Pro Gly-L-Pro	5.0–9.0 according to source, substrate, activators	Mn^{2+} Mg^{2+} Co^{2+} Cu^{2+} Zn^{2+} Mg^{2+}	Mn^{2+} Mg^{2+} Co^{2+} Cd^{2+} Cu^{2+} Ni^{2+} Ni^{2+} acids[71,76]; L-leucylpeptide[76]; puromycin derivatives[79]	Mn^{2+} Mg^{2+} CMP[78]* EDTA[56] Citrate Mn^{2+}
Angiotensinase EC 3.4.99.3	Kidney, liver, intestinal mucosa, serum erythrocytes of many species; yeast, snake venom, Aspergillus and Streptomyces, human serum	—	Angiotensin α-L-Gluna	4.0–9.0 according to source	—	—	—
Oxytocinase EC 3.4.11.3	Liver, pancreas, kidney, uterus, ovaries placenta, mammary glands, human erythrocytes. Pregnant serum and retroplacental serum	Retroplancental serum[65], pregnant serum	Oxytocin L-Cysna L-Cyspa	7.0–7.7 according to substrate	—	Zn^{2+}, Pb^{2+}, Ni^{2+}, Mn^{2+}, Fe^{2+}, Cu^{2+}, Co^{2+}, 8-hydroxy-quinoline, EDTA Cysteine, S-benzyl-cysteine, -containing peptides, HCO_3	Ca^{2+}, Mg^{2+}, (Co^{2+}), Citrate Oxalate, $P_2O_7^{4-}$ Iodoacetamide DFP, SH^-

* Lysosomes from rat kidney and liver   ** Microsomes from rat kidney   *** Microsomes from rat kidney and liver

*** Microsomes and supernatant rat liver

of this group show a certain substrate and stereospecificity for angiotensin II and are designated as angio-tensinase A[62]. The further degradation of the resulting heptapeptide occurs with amino- and carboxypep-tidases, probably also endopeptidases (proteinases) *in vitro* and *in vivo*. Peptidases with angiotensinase activity show a group specificity, which can be demonstrated and quantitatively determined by means of the chromogenic substrates α-L-glutamyl-β-naphthylamide and p-nitroanilide[64]. This establishes a relationship with the amino acid arylamidases, especially to the subgroup of aminodicarboxylic acid arylamidases ("aminopeptidase A"). Angiotensinases can be determined by various methods: a) incubation of the enzyme preparation with angiotensin II, followed by determination of the residual biological activity[34,63,64,108], chromatographic examination of the hydrolysis products[35,64] or a very elegant method, the determination in a NADH-dependent assay of the aspartic acid liberated from the N-terminal asparagine with aspara-ginase[107]. b) hydrolysis of chromogenic substrates[62]. For other references, see[134–157,228–234].

Vasopressinase[103] is an enzyme mixture which inactivates vasopressin and probably does not contain an enzyme specific for vasopressin. This is also true of the so-called "insulinase" and the various "kininases". A review on the occurrence, suitable starting material, purification or isolation, activators, inhibitors and pH optima is given in Table 1.
The clinical importance of arylamidases is due to the group which is determined for diagnostic purposes in serum as "LAP". The hope that determination of oxytocinase would be of diagnostic value in pregnancy[96] has so far not been fulfilled[33]; the same is true of the determination of "angiotensinase" activity in connect-ion with hypertonia.

Transpeptidases: can also be determined with arylamides[120–125]. One member of this family, glutamyl-transpeptidase is of considerable value[235–238]. Further enzymes are still under investigation: bradykininase [239–244], proliniminopeptidase[245–247], pyrrolidonylpeptidase[248], insulinase[249–250], proinsulinase[251] and aspartate aminopeptidase[252].

References, p. 973.

Leucine Aminopeptidase

Walter Appel

Determination with L-Leucinamide as Substrate[1, 26]

Under this designation "leucine nitroanilidase", an amino acid arylamidase, is measured in clinical chemistry (see p. 952). For classification see, p. 958.

Application of Method: In biochemistry.

Principle

$$\text{L-Leucinamide} + H_2O \xrightarrow[\text{peptidase}]{\text{leucine amino-}} \text{Leucine} + NH_3$$

The ammonia which arises by hydrolysis is liberated in a *Conway* diffusion cell by addition of K_2CO_3 solution and diffused into a borate solution; the latter is then back-titrated with acid.

Optimum Conditions for Measurements

The enzyme solution must contain 1 mM Mn^{2+} or 4 mM Mg^{2+} at pH 7.9–8.0, and be pre-incubated at 37–40 °C. The pre-incubation time with highly purified enzyme preparations should be 10–15 min., with sera, crude extracts or homogenates up to 120 min. The substrate concentration is usually 50 mM; at 0.1 M there is only a slight increase in enzyme activity[42]. The pH optimum of the enzyme reaction is 8.6; for simplicity the enzyme reaction can be carried out at the same pH as the pre-incubation (pH 8.0). The reaction time is between 20 and 120 min., and under certain conditions up to 4 hr., and should be chosen so that in 15– 30 min. 15–30% hydrolysis occurs. The kinetics are linear in this range (zero order reaction), but then become first order. Measurements at different temperatures may require different measuring conditions (cf. p. 127). Nevertheless, results obtained under the same measuring conditions but at different temperatures were formerly compared with each other ("conversion factors" were determined). Such conversion factors may be correct if determined with a relatively large proband collective; however, they cannot be applied generally to the individual case (cf. p. 129). The value of the following relative reaction rates[42] thus lies in being able to appraise the temperature dependence of the reaction and at the most to compare qualitatively values up to the limit of normal.

C°	20	25	30	37	40	45
	1.62	1.00	0.85	0.73	0.68	(0.83)

Equipment

Water bath (37 °C), cold bath (4 °C); stopwatch or laboratory alarm clock; 2–5 ml. burette with "Schellbach"-stripe. Conway diffusion dishes, e. g. 90 mm. external diameter, 35 mm. internal diameter, 20 mm. high for normal assays (see also[69]) or 20 mm. external, 7 mm. internal and 14 mm. high* for micro methods.

Reagents

1. Tris-hydroxymethyl-aminomethane, tris
2. Hydrochloric acid, 1.0 N and 0.1 N
3. L-Leucinamide hydrochloride
4. Manganese chloride, $MnCl_2 \cdot 4H_2O$
5. Boric acid, H_3BO_3, cryst.
6. Methyl red
7. Bromocresolgreen
8. Ethanol, A. R.
9. Potassium carbonate, K_2CO_3

Preparation of Solutions (for ca. 20 normal or 200 micro-assays)

Only use doubly distilled water
   I. Tris buffer (0.2 M; pH 8.0):
      Dissolve 1.21 g. tris in 25 ml. distilled water; add 6.1 ml. 1.0 N HCl and dilute to 50 ml. with distilled water; check pH with glass electrode.
   II. L-Leucinamide (125 mM):
      Dissolve 520 mg. L-leucinamide hydrochloride in 25 ml. distilled water.
   III. Manganese chloride (10 mM):
      Dissolve 50 mg. $MnCl_2 \cdot 4H_2O$ in 25 ml. distilled water.

---

* Manufactured according to the details of [42] by Gefa, Mannheim, Germany.

IV. Boric acid – indicator mixture:
  a) Boric acid: dissolve 1.25 g. boric acid in 50 ml. ethanol.
  b) Indicator: dissolve ca. 2 mg. bromocresolgreen + ca. 3 mg. methyl red in 5 ml. ethanol.
  Mixture: Dilute 50 ml. boric acid solution + 2.5 ml. indicator solution up to 250 ml. with distilled water. The solution should not be green; if necessary, adjust with 1 drop 0.01 N HCl.
 V. Potassium carbonate (saturated):
  Dissolve 30 g. K_2CO_3 in 25 ml. distilled water, heat to boiling, filter and allow to cool overnight at room temperature.

Stability of Solutions

Substrate solution II is stable for several days at 4 °C, but should be prepared freshly each week. The boric acid-indicator mixture IV should be prepared immediately before use. The other solutions are stable for months at room temperature.

Procedure

Collection, Treatment and Stability of Sample

Collection and treatment of sample:

Use fresh as possible serum or plasma, free from haemolysis. Addition of citrate, oxalate, fluoride, cyanide, cysteine or EDTA interferes. Use heparin (0.2 mg./ml.) for plasma. Centrifuge for 10 min. at ca. 3000 g to obtain serum or plasma. Prepare animal blood in the same way; in the case of rat and dog blood centrifuge immediately. Use duodenal juice directly. Use homogenates, extracts and cell fractions of tissues after suitable dilution.

Stability of enzyme in sample:

Store serum, organ extracts and solutions of pure enzyme for not more than 24 hr. at 4 °C. These samples are stable for a week at −20 °C, while purified bovine organ preparations are stable for at least 1 month.

Assay System

Reaction temperature: 37 °C; incubation volume: 2.50 ml. (normal); 0.250 ml. (micro-method). Several values, or values at different times of reaction, can be obtained from the same incubation mixture.

Blank (t_0) from the test mixture: immediately after addition of the substrate solution (II) take 0.5 ml. sample and treat as for the test mixtures. Control (to determine the spontaneous hydrolysis of the substrate): as for the test mixture, but with 0.5 ml. physiological saline instead of sample.

The extent of NH_3 diffusion must be tested once in each individual diffusion dish with 25 mM $(NH_4)_2SO_4$ before the start of the experiments; the NH_3 diffusion amounts to 85–98% depending on the length of diffusion and on the type of diffusion dish. Enzyme samples can also give NH_3.

Pipette into test tubes:			Concentration in assay mixture
Buffer solution	(I)	0.50 ml.	40.0 mM
$MnCl_2$ solution	(III)	0.50 ml.	2.0 mM
Sample (serum, homogenate, etc.)		0.50 ml.	
Mix thoroughly and pre-incubate for 15 min. (2 hr.) at 37 °C.			
Leucinamide solution	(II)	1.0 ml.	50.0 mM
Mix thoroughly and start stopwatch. Immediately pipette (t_0) and after 2 hr. (t_x) into previously prepared diffusion dishes:			
Outer ring:			
Boric acid- indicator mixture	(IV)	4.0 ml.	
Inner ring:			
K_2CO_3 solution	(V)	0.50 ml.	
Incubation mixture		0.50 ml.	
Immediately seal with a well-greased lid and allow to stand for at least 2 hr., preferably 3 hr. at room temperature. Back-titrate the contents of the outer ring with 0.1 N HCl to the turning point of the boric acid-indicator mixture (from green to the first appearance of red).			

Calculations

1 ml. 0.1 N HCl corresponds to 0.1 mmole substrate hydrolysed (do not forget the titration correction of the HCl). The amount of HCl required with the t_0 samples is V_0 and the amount of HCl required with the t_x samples is V_x. Calculate the difference $\Delta V = V_x - V_0$; convert to the whole incubation mixture (times 5), to 1.0 ml. sample solution (times 2), and to 1 min. (divide by 120).

With the inclusion of factor F to allow for any dilution the following formula is obtained for calculation of enzyme activity in U/l.:

Normal method Volume activity $= \Delta V_{(ml.)} \times 8340 \times F$ [U/l.]

Micro-method Volume activity $= \Delta V_{(\mu l.)} \times 83.4 \times F$ [U/l.]

Precision of Method

It is recommended in each series of measurements to include a control sample (pure enzyme or pooled sample) as a check on the value x ± 2 s range.

The coefficient of variation is 2.8% with 20 assays of an enzyme sample (precision) and 8.3% with 76 assays of 38 different enzyme samples (rat liver homogenate).

Normal Values

Reliable values are not available. With a small group of human sera values of 1.2–5.4 U/l.[26], and even 80–130 U/l.[42] have been published; for 11 children x ± 2 s = 105 ± 113 U/l.[92]. In the rat the following values were found: serum 15–25 U/l., heart 3–5 U/g. and liver 1–5 U/g.; these values are only an indication of the range (all at 37 °C).

Sources of Error

Effects of drugs and other therapeutic measures: None known.

Interference in the assay technique: No interference is expected in the enzyme incubation. The tightness of the seal on the diffusion dish and the yield in the diffusion must be determined previously by addition of 2.0 ml. 20 mM $(NH_4)_2SO_4$ solution instead of sample. L-Leucinamide must be free from NH_3 (autohydrolysis). The distilled water for the boric acid-indicator mixture IV must be fresh. The ethanol used must be A. R. grade.

Specificity of Method

Choice of L-leucinamide instead of the frequently used L-leucylglycine or L-leucyl-glycylglycine virtually excludes the determination of other peptidases, or proteinases. A differentiation from amino acid arylamidases must be undertaken in individual cases.

Details for Measurements in Tissues[42]

0.25 M aqueous sucrose solution + 0.1 % (v/v) Triton X-100 are recommended as homogenization media (1:5 w/v), because other media, especially sucrose, dextran or glycerol, with or without the addition of other components (deoxycholate) give lower activity. Cell fractions can also be studied in the same way. Highly active homogenates of several organs (e.g. rat liver) must be diluted 1:3 and 1:10; most can usually be used undiluted[42].

Other Assay Method

The determination with L-leucine-β-naphthylamide is described by[5], while that with L-leucine-p-nitroanilide is described below. An enzymatic assay of the NH_3 liberated has been described by [26]. The assay with L-leucylglycine can be carried out analogously to the determination of leucylglycine dipeptidase (p. 981).

Micro-Assay

The method described above is so arranged that a 1 : 10 reduction of all volumes is possible without further changes. It is recommended to take 100 μl. instead of 200 μl. of the sample mixture for the NH_3 determination. For the micro-method 30 μl. of a 1 : 50 (w/v) homogenate equivalent to 0.5 mg. rat liver is required[42]. We have had considerable experience with the Beckman-Spinco and Eppendorf micro-systems.

References p. 973.

Amino Acid Arylamidases ("Leucine-nitroanilidase")

Walter Appel

Determination with L-Leucine-p-nitroanilide as Substrate[26, 70-73]

In clinical chemistry this enzyme is determined under the term "leucine aminopeptidase". For classification, p. 952–953.

Application of Method: In clinical chemistry and general biochemistry.

Principle

(1)   L-Leucine-p-nitroanilide + H_2O $\xrightarrow[\text{nitroanilidase}]{\text{leucine}}$ p-Nitroaniline + L-Leucine

(2)   p-Nitroaniline $\xrightarrow[\text{napthylethylenediamine}]{HNO_2/HCl}$ Azo dye

The p-nitroaniline liberated on enzymatic hydrolysis is either determined directly in the cuvette by measurement of the increase in extinction at 405 nm (continuous method) or by diazotization and coupling converted to an azo dye (equation 2), whose concentration can be measured at 546 nm (discontinuous method). The latter method is recommended when low enzyme activity or high blanks occur or when a spectro- or spectrum-line photometer is not available and it is the method of choice with impure extracts from organs.

Optimum Conditions for Measurements

The individual representatives of the group of arylamidases differ in their properties which explains the many conflicting data in the literature. The optimum conditions of measurements and kinetic constants depend in particular on the type and concentration of the substrates and activators, as well as the source of the enzyme preparation and are preferably determined for each individual case. The pH-optimum for serum and erythrocytes is between pH 6.8–7.6 [54,56,57,70–77], for organ enzymes between pH 8.0 and 8.6[25,70,79], but in the case of lysosomes the optimum pH can be between 6.0 and 8.0[78] and in addition is in part dependent on the type of buffer and the substrate concentration[71]. The optimum substrate concentration is 0.8 mM[26,70] (0.5 mM[80]), the optimum temperature for measurements with a pig kidney preparation is 60 °C[71], but usually it is lower[42]. So far no definite activators of serum arylamidases have been described, so that the present method contains no activation or pre-incubation step. In the case of organ enzymes a pre-incubation for about 1 hr. with 1 mM Mn^{2+} salt is necessary; for full details see Table 1 or the original literature. Measurements at different temperatures may require different measuring conditions (cf. p. 127). Nevertheless, results obtained under the same measuring conditions but at different temperatures were formerly compared with each other ("conversion factors" were determined). Such conversion factors may be correct if determined with a relatively large proband collective; however, they cannot be applied generally to the individual case (cf. p. 129). The value of the following relative reaction rates[70],[71] thus lies in being able to appraise the temperature dependence of the reaction and at the most to compare qualitatively values up to the limit of normal.

C°	25	30	35	37	40	45	50	55	60
	1.00	0.65	0.43	0.38	0.30	0.21	0.17	0.14	0.12

Equipment

Spectrophotometer or filter photometer, preferably with constant temperature cuvette holder; water bath (37 °C); cold bath (4 °C); stopwatch or laboratory alarm clock; darkened chamber or dark room with red light.

Reagents*

1. Tris-hydroxymethyl-aminomethane, tris
2. Hydrochloric acid, 0.1 N
3. N-Dimethylformamide
4. L-Leucine-p-nitroanilide
   For the discontinuous method the following are
   also required:

5. Perchloric acid, 70% (w/w), sp. gr. 1.67
6. Sodium nitrite, crystalline
7. Ammonium sulphamate
8. N,N'-(1-naphthyl)ethylenediamine·2 HCl
9. p-Nitroaniline
10. Methanol.

---

* Complete reagent kits are available commercially, see p. 558.

Preparation of Solutions (for ca. 50 normal assays or 500 micro-assays)

Use only doubly distilled water

I. Tris buffer (50 mM; pH 7.2):
   Dissolve 1.21 g. tris in 50 ml. distilled water, add 90 ml. 0.1 N HCl and dilute to 200 ml.
   with distilled water; check pH with glass electrode.

II. L-Leucine-p-nitroanilide (1.2 mM):
   Dissolve 30.2 mg. L-leucine-p-nitroanilide in 100 ml. of buffer solution I or stock solution
   for micro-assay: dissolve 30.2 mg. L-leucine-p-nitroanilide in 5.0 ml. dimethylformamide,
   just before use dilute 0.5 ml. of this stock solution to 10.0 ml. with buffer I.
   Additional for the discontinuous method:

III. a) Perchloric acid (20% w/w):
        Dilute 17.5 ml. perchloric acid to 100 ml. with distilled water
     b) Perchloric acid (5% w/w):
        Dilute 4.4 ml. perchloric acid to 100 ml. with distilled water.

IV. Sodium nitrite (0.2%):
    Dissolve 200 mg. sodium nitrite in 100 ml. distilled water.

V. Ammonium sulphamate (0.5%):
   Dissolve 500 mg. ammonium sulphamate in 100 ml. distilled water.

VI. Naphthylethylenediamine, chromogen (0.05%):
    Dissolve 100 mg. N,N'-(-1-naphthyl)-ethylenediamine dihydrochloride in 100 ml. methanol.

Stability of Solutions

The stock solutions and solutions III a and b are stable for months at 4 °C. Solution VI is stable for ca. 3
weeks in a dark bottle. Solution II and dilutions of this solution, as well as solutions IV and V must be
prepared freshly each day and stored in a cold bath.

Procedure

Collection, Treatment and Stability of Sample

Collection and treatment:

Use fresh as possible serum or plasma free from haemolysis. Addition of citrate (1 mg./ml.),
fluoride or heparin (0.2 mg./ml.) has no harmful effect. If EDTA is used controls are recommended. Centrifuge for 10 min. at ca. 3000 g to obtain serum or plasma. Other body fluids
should be used directly or if necessary after centrifugation.
Serum is diluted 1 : 20 or 1 : 40 with 0.9% NaCl solution, buffer I or with 1.2% bovine serum
albumin solution[76]. Use homogenates, extracts and cell fractions of tissues directly for the assay
after suitable dilution (see last section) (for human tissues, see[54,81]) likewise extracts of wheat
germ[82] or bakers' yeast[83].

Stability of enzyme in sample:

Serum is stable for at least 24 hr. at 4 °C.; after 3 days' storage at 4 °C there is a ca. 10–30% loss of activity. In the frozen state (−20 °C) or as a lyophilized powder or pure enzyme preparations (also from tissues) the activity remains unchanged for months. However, repeated freezing and thawing is to be avoided[42].

Assay System

Continuous method: Wavelength: Hg 405 nm; light path: 1 cm.; reaction temperature: 37 °C; final volume: 3.0 ml. Read against a reference cuvette (as for test but containing 1 ml. physiological saline instead of sample) whose extinction is set to zero. Control (to determine the spontaneous hydrolysis of the substrate): reference cuvette measured against water.

Discontinuous method: Wavelength: Hg 546 nm; light path: 1 cm.; reaction temperature: 37 °C; final volume: 3.00 ml. (normal), 0.300 ml. (micro-assay). Read against doubly distilled water. Blank (E_o), parallel to the test assays: immediately after addition of enzyme stop the reaction by addition of perchloric acid solution IIIa, then treat as for the test assays. Control (to determine the spontaneous hydrolysis of substrate): as for test but containing 1.0 ml. physiological saline instead of sample.

Pipette successively into cuvettes or centrifuge tubes:		Concentration in assay mixture
L-Leucine-p-nitroanilide solution (II) Sample (serum dilution, extracts, etc.)	2.00 ml. 1.00 ml.	0.8 mM; 33 mM tris
Mix thoroughly. In the continuous method read extinction E_o immediately. Incubate for 30 min. and read extinction E_x. In the discontinuous method incubate for 2 hr.		
Perchloric acid solution (IIIa)	1.00 ml.	
Centrifuge for 10 min. at 3000 rpm and pipette into test tubes:		
Supernatant fluid Nitrite solution, pre-cooled (IV)	2.00 ml. 2.00 ml.	
Allow to stand for 10 min. at 4 °C to diazotize.		
Ammonium sulphamate solution (V)	2.00 ml.	
Allow to stand for ca. 2–5 min. to destroy the excess nitrite.		
Chromogen solution (VI)	4.00 ml.	
Stand in the dark for 30 min. at 37 °C and then read extinction E_o (blank) or E_x (test).		

Calculations

Continuous method: The calculations are based on the molar extinction coefficient of p-nitroaniline $\varepsilon = 9.62$ cm.^{2}/μmole[26,71,72,79]. Subtract the increase in extinction in the control (spontaneous hydrolysis of substrate) from E_x. $\Delta E = E_{x(corr.)} - E_o$ is used for the calculations. With allowance for the volume of the assay mixture and any dilution of the sample with the factor F the activity is calculated as follows:

$$\text{Volume activity} = \Delta E/\text{min.} \times 311.9 \times F \text{ [U/l.]}$$

Discontinuous method: First prepare standard curve to check the apparatus and reagents. For this dissolve 138.1 mg. p-nitroaniline ($= 1$ mmole) in 100 ml. perchloric acid solution IIIb (stock solution). Dilute 10 ml. of this solution to 100 ml. with $HClO_4$ solution (IIIb) and again dilute 10 ml. of this solution to 100 ml. Total dilution 1 : 100, the concentration in the standard solution is 0.1 mM. Dilute 0.05–2.0 ml. (0.005– 0.2 μmole) of this standard solution to 2.0 ml. with $HClO_4$ solution (IIIb) and carry out the diazotization and coupling as described above. Prepare a blank without p-nitroaniline and measure. Plot the extinction differences (ordinate) against the "μmole p-nitroaniline" (abscissa).

Convert the extinction differences $\Delta E = E_x - E_o$ obtained for the samples into μmole p-nitroaniline with the help of the standard curve. The spontaneous hydrolysis in the control is calculated in the same way and the value is subtracted from the sample values (μmole$_{corr.}$). With allowance for the aliquot taken (times 2), the reaction time (divide by 120) and any dilution of sample with the factor F the activity is calculated from the following formula:

Normal assay: $\text{Volume activity} = \mu\text{mole}_{corr.} \times 16.6 \times F \text{ [U/l.]}$
Micro assay: $\text{Volume activity} = \text{nmole}_{corr.} \times 0.166 \times F \text{ [U/l.]}$

Precision of Method

The coefficient of variation is 3.1% for 25 determinations on a single enzyme sample (precision) and 9.8% on 100 determinations on 40 different rat liver homogenates[42] or 14.8% with 48 determinations on 24 different human sera[91]. For other data, see[76,85 85,88,90].

Normal Values

For human serum (37 °C) the published normal values are 8–22[72], 14.5–28.1[91] and in children x $\pm$ 2 s (n = 91) 20.2 $\pm$ 8.6[92] U/l.; the largest numerical sample (n = 692) gives 15.6 $\pm$ 5 U/l.[70]. In dog serum values of 461 $\pm$ 31 U/l. have been found, in rat serum (n = 75) 98.2 $\pm$ 16.7 U/l., in liver 110–345, up to 4000, in heart 90–240, up to 1800 U/g. fresh wt.[42]; these values are only an indication of the range. For other values using L-leucine-β-naphthylamide as substrate: human serum[5,55,70,76,84–86], human serum and human urine[85,87,88,90], duodenal juice[89].

Sources of Error

Effects of drugs and other therapeutic measures: Administration of 40 mg. prednisone orally in patients with obstructive jaundice increases the serum level[86]; infusion of 500–1000 ml. dextran solution (10%) has no effect[42].

Interference in the assay technique: If the method is adhered to no interference is to be expected. The diazotization should be carried out in the cold and the development of the colour in the dark.

Specificity of Method

According to the definition the method is specific for all amino acid arylamidases. Exceptions: arginyl-p-nitroanilidase does not react[79], and leucine aminopeptidase and oxytocinase[26] only partially react.

Details for Measurements in Tissues

Aqueous sucrose solution, 0.25 M + 0.1% (v/v) Triton X-100 is recommended as the homogenization medium (1 : 5, w/v); cell fractions can also be studied in this medium. Highly active homogenates of organs (e. g. liver, spleen, lung or intestine of rat) must be diluted 1 : 10, while kidney extracts must be diluted 1 : 50[42].

Other Assay Methods

For another colorimetric method, see[5] for a rapid spectrophotometric method, see[62].
The continuous method is recommended for serum (1 : 10 dilution), while the colorimetric method is recommended for all other samples, especially those with high blanks or low activity (tissues).

Micro-assay

The discontinuous method described here is so arranged that a 1 : 10 reduction in all volumes iş possible. The same solutions are used for the standardization; standard curves for the normal method are identical with those obtained with one-tenth of the concentration on the abscissa. In this method, for example, 10 μl of a 1 : 250 (w/v) homogenate of rat kidney equivalent to 0.05 mg. are required[42]. We have had considerable experience with the Beckman-Spinco and Eppendorf micro-systems.

References p. 973.

Angiotensinase
Determination with α-L-Angiotensin-II-amide as Substrate[115-117]

Walter Appel

Application of Method: In clinical chemistry.

Principle

Angiotensinase liberates asparagine from the octapeptide α-L-angiotensin-II-amide and the asparagine is then determined in the following series of reactions:

(1)   Asparagine + H_2O $\xrightarrow{\text{asparaginase}^*}$ L-Aspartate + NH_3

(2)   L-Aspartate + 2-Oxoglutarate $\xrightleftharpoons{\text{GOT}^{**}}$ L-Glutamate + Oxaloacetate

(3)   Oxaloacetate + NADH + H^+ $\xrightleftharpoons{\text{MDH}^{***}}$ L-Malate + NAD^+

The oxidation of NADH is the measure of the activity and is determined by means of its absorption at 334, 340 or 365 nm.

Optimum Conditions for Measurements

Tris or phosphate buffers have proved suitable[115-117]. The optimum substrate concentration is 2 mM and the optimum pH of the reaction is between 7.0 and 7.5[115].

Equipment

Spectrophotometer or spectrum-line photometer suitable for accurate measurements at 340, 334, or 365 nm, preferably with constant temperature cuvette holder; water bath (37 °C and boiling); stopwatch.

Reagents

1. Potassium dihydrogen phosphate, KH_2PO_4
2. Dipotassium hydrogen phosphate, K_2HPO_4
3. Tris-hydroxymethyl-aminomethane, tris
4. α-L-Angiotensin-II-amide
   e.g. Hypotensin from Ciba, Basel, Switzerland
5. Reduced nicotinamide-adenine dinucleotide, β-NADH
   disodium salt, NADH-Na_2. Commercial preparation, see p. 545.

6. Malate dehydrogenase, MDH
   from pig heart, suspension in 3.2 M ammonium sulphate solution; ≥ 1100 U/mg. (25 °C). Commercial preparation, see p. 485.
7. Glutamate-oxaloacetate transaminase, GOT
   from pig heart, suspension in 3.2 M ammonium sulphate solution, containing 2.5 mM oxoglutarate and 50 mM maleate; ≥ 180 U/ml. (25 °C); commercial preparation, see p. 462.
8. Asparaginase
   from *E. coli,* solution in 50% glycerol, ≥ 80 U/mg. (25 °C); commercial preparation, see p. 435.

---

* Asparaginase (L-Asparagine amidohydrolase, EC 3.5.1.1).
** Glutamate-oxaloacetate transaminase, GOT (L-Aspartate: 2-oxoglutarate aminotransferase, EC 2.6.1.1).
*** Malate dehydrogenase, MDH (L-Malate: NAD oxidoreductase, EC 1.1.1.37).

9. 2-Oxoglutaric acid
   commercial preparation, see p. 548.
10. Acetic acid, conc., A. R.

11. Hydrochloric acid, 2 N
12. Sodium hydroxide, 0.1 N
13. Sodium bicarbonate, $NaHCO_3$

Purity of Reagents

L-α-Angiotensin should not contain more than 0.5% asparagine and aspartate.
GOT, asparaginase and MDH must not contain more than 0.01% of GlDH, LDH and not more than 0.05% GPT and oxaloacetate decarboxylase (relative to the respective specific activity). The enzymes should be free from angiotensinase. The asparaginase must not contain more than 0.01% of L-glutaminase and L-arginase.

Preparation of Solutions (for ca. 25 determinations)

Prepare all solutions with fresh doubly distilled water.
   I. Tris buffer (0.25 M; pH 7.5):
      Dissolve 1.51 g. tris in 25 ml. distilled water, add ca. 5.0 ml. 2 N HCl and dilute with distilled water to 50 ml. (check pH).
   II. Angiotensin (4.8 mM):
      Dissolve 31.1 mg. α-L-angiotensin-II-amide in 5.0 ml. solution I.
   III. Acetic acid (16.7 mM):
      Dilute 0.10 ml. acetic acid in 100 ml. distilled water.
   IV. Phosphate/oxoglutarate (0.1 M phosphate, pH 7.2; 5 mM oxoglutarate):
      Dissolve 0.2 g. KH_2PO_4 + 1.5 g. K_2HPO_4 + 73.1 mg. oxoglutaric acid in 50 ml. distilled water, adjust to pH 7.2 with 0.1 N NaOH and dilute to 100 ml. with distilled water.
   V. Reduced nicotinamide-adenine dinucleotide (10 mM β-NADH):
      Dissolve 20 mg. NADH-Na_2 and 25 mg. $NaHCO_3$ in 2.5 ml. distilled water.
   VI. Malate dehydrogenase/glutamate-oxaloacetate transaminase (2.5 mg. MDH/ml.; 5 mg. GOT/ml.):
      Dilute stock suspensions with 3.2 M ammonium sulphate solution and mix accordingly.
   VII. Asparaginase (1 mg. protein/ml.):
      Dilute the stock solution with 50% glycerol accordingly.

Stability of Solutions

Store all solutions at 0–4 °C. Solutions II, IV and V are stable for ca. 4 weeks at 4 °C, solutions VI and VII for ca. 1 year and solutions I and III are stable indefinitely.

Procedure

Collection, Treatment and Stability of Sample

Use fresh serum or plasma, free from haemolysis. Additions of citrate (1 mg./ml.), fluoride or heparin (0.2 mg./ml.) do not interfere; in the case of EDTA control experiments are recommended. To obtain plasma or serum centrifuge at ca. 3000 g for 10 min.; centrifuge rat or dog blood immediately. Other body fluids can be used directly, if necessary, after centrifugation.
No other information on the stability of the enzyme in serum is available.

Assay System

Wavelength: 340 (Hg 334, Hg 365) nm; light path: 1 cm.; incubation volume: 0.50 ml.; reaction temperature: 37 °C; blank: as for test but with tris buffer (I) instead of substrate solution (II). Final volume for asparagine assay: 2.59 ml.; read against air at room temperature.

Pipette successively into a centrifuge tube:			Concentration in assay mixture
Tris buffer	(I)	0.20 ml.	100 mM
Serum		0.10 ml.	
Angiotensin solution	(II)	0.20 ml.	1.94 mM
Mix and incubate for exactly 30 min. at 37 °C.			
Acetic acid	(III)	1.50 ml.	
Mix and immediately place in a boiling water bath (5 min.). Centrifuge for 5 min. at ca. 3000 rpm. Use the supernatant fluid. Pipette into cuvettes:			
Supernatant fluid		1.00 ml.	
Phosphate/oxoglutarate solution	(IV)	1.50 ml.	60 mM phosphate; 3 mM oxoglutarate
NADH solution	(V)	0.05 ml.	0.4 mM β-NADH
MDH/GOT suspension	(VI)	0.02 ml.	19 μg. MDH $\geqq$ 21 U/ml. 32 μg. GOT $\geqq$ 7 U/ml.
Mix and after 10 min. read extinction E_1			
Asparaginase suspension	(VII)	0.02 ml.	7.7 μg. asparaginase $\geqq$ 0.6 U/ml.
Mix, wait for the completion of the reaction ca. 10 min.), otherwise make 5 further readings at 2 min. intervals and extrapolate the extinction E_2 to the time of asparaginase addition. $\Delta E = (E_1\text{-}E_2)_{sample} - (E_1\text{-}E_2)_{blank}$			

The ΔE values should not exceed 0.400 at 365 nm, otherwise dilute the serum 10 times with physiological saline.

Calculations

The calculation formula (8) on p. 313 applies and therefore for this method with a 30 min. reaction time the following relationships hold:

Wavelength:	334 nm.	340 nm.	365 nm.
Volume activity =	$283.1 \times \Delta E$	$277.6 \times \Delta E$	$507.8 \times \Delta E$ [U/l.]

Precision of Method

With a mean value of 10 U/l. serum the coefficient of variation is ca. 5%.

Normal Values

The normal range in human serum is around 8–18 U/l. (25 °C)[115].

Sources of Error

Effects of drugs and other therapeutic measures: None known.

Interference in the assay technique: Insufficient purity of the reagents, especially the angiotensin, leads to false values. If angiotensin contains L-asparagine this should be corrected for by a blank.

Specificity of Method

Angiotensinase reacts preferentially with α-L-angiotensin-II-amide. α-L-Angiotensin-II is hydrolysed at a considerably lower rate and β-L-angiotensin is not attacked.

References p. 973.

Oxytocinase

Determination with L-Cystine-di-β-naphthylamide as Substrate[33, 65, 75, 99–101]

Walter Appel

Application of Method: In clinical chemistry, histochemistry, gynaecology and general biochemistry.

Principle

(1) $\text{L-Cystine-di-}\beta\text{-naphthylamide} + H_2O \xrightarrow{\text{oxytocinase}} 2\text{-}\beta\text{-Naphthylamine} + \text{L-Cystine}$

(2) $\beta\text{-Naphthylamine} \xrightarrow[\text{naphthylethylenediamine}]{\text{HNO}_2/\text{HCl}} \text{Azo dye}$

After diazotization and coupling the β-naphthylamine is converted to an azo dye, which is measured at 578 nm.

Optimum Conditions for Measurements[65, 104]

The pH optimum is between pH 7.4 and 7.8, the optimum substrate concentration between 0.5 and 0.7 mM. Addition of 0.05–0.25 ml. of serum from a pregnant subject gives practically direct proportionality to the rate of hydrolysis, while this is not quite the case for incubation times of from 1 to 6 hr. Measurements at different temperatures may require different measuring conditions (cf. p. 127). Nevertheless, results obtained under the same measuring conditions but at different temperatures were formerly compared with each other ("conversion factors" were determined). Such conversion factors may be correct if determined with a relatively large proband collective; however, they cannot be applied generally to the individual case (cf. p. 129). The value of the following relative reaction rates[65] thus lies in being able to appraise the temperature dependence of the reaction and at the most to compare qualitatively values up to the limit of normal.

C°	17	20	25	30	37
	1.12	1.04	*1.00*	0.95	0.91

Equipment

Filter photometer; water bath (37 °C); cold bath (4 °C); stop-watch or laboratory alarm clock; darkened chamber or dark room with red light.

Reagents

1. Tris-hydroxymethyl-aminomethane, tris
2. Hydrochloric acid, 0.2 N and 0.005 N
3. Perchloric acid, 70% (w/w)
4. Sodium nitrite, crystalline
5. Ammonium sulphamate

6. N,N'-(1-naphthyl)ethylenediamine·2HCl
7. L-Cystine-di-β-naphthylamide
8. β-Naphthylamine
9. Methanol.

Preparation of Solutions (for ca. 50 normal assays or 500 micro-assays)

Only use doubly distilled water

I. Tris buffer (0.1 M; pH 7.4)

Dissolve 1.21 g tris in 25 ml. distilled water, add 44 ml. 0.2 N HCl and dilute to 100 ml. with distilled water, check the pH with a glass electrode.

II. L-Cystine-di-β-naphthylamide (2 mM):

Dissolve 98.0 mg. L-cystine-di-β-naphthylamide in 100 ml. 0.005 N HCl, with slight warming if necessary.

For the micro-assay: dissolve 98.0 mg. L-cystine-di-β-naphthylamide in 5.0 ml. dimethylformamide (stock solution); just before use dilute 0.5 ml. to 10 ml. with 0.005 N HCl.

III. a) Perchloric acid (20%, w/w):

Dilute 17.5 ml. perchloric acid to 100 ml. with distilled water

b) Perchloric acid (5%, w/w):

Dilute 4.4 ml. perchloric acid to 100 ml. with distilled water

IV. Sodium nitrite (0.2%):

Dissolve 200 mg. sodium nitrite in 100 ml. distilled water.

V. Ammonium sulphamate (0.5%):

Dissolve 500 mg. ammonium sulphamate in 100 ml. distilled water

VI. Naphthylethylenediamine, chromogen (0.10%):

Dissolve 100 mg. N,N'-(1-naphthyl)ethylenediamine dihydrochloride in 100 ml. methanol.

Stability of Solutions

The stock solution and solutions III a & b are stable for months at 4 °C, while solution VI is stable in a dark bottle for ca. 3 weeks. Solution II or its dilutions, and solutions IV and V should be prepared freshly each day and stored in a cold box.

Procedure

Collection, Treatment and Stability of Sample

Collection and treatment of sample: Use fresh serum completely free from haemolysis. Maximum activity is shown by serum in the 36 th to 40 th week of pregnancy or by placenta fluid free from amniotic fluid; obtain the latter within 30 min and the former as usual after centrifugation for 10 min. at ca. 3000 g. Addition of citrate (1mg./ml.), oxalate (1mg./ml.) or heparin (0.2 mg./ml.) is not harmful; EDTA interferes. Dilute serum 1 : 2 or 1 : 5 with 0.9% NaCl solution before use. Add ca. 2% gum arabic to the buffer in the case of retroplacental serum[65]. Use homogenates, extracts and cell fractions directly after suitable dilution.

Stability of enzyme in sample: The enzyme is stable in serum for at least 24 hr. (4 °C); purified enzyme solutions dissolved in buffer are stable for several weeks at 4 °C[65].

Assay System

Wavelength: Hg 578 nm; light path: 1 cm.; reaction temperature: 37 °C; final volume: 3.0 ml. (normal); 0.300 ml. (micro-assay). Read against reference cuvette containing distilled water; blank (E_0): as for test, but immediately after addition of enzyme pipette perchloric acid solution (IIIa) and then treat as for test; control (to determine spontaneous hydrolysis of the substrate): as for test, but containing 1 ml. physiological saline instead of sample.
Pre-cool nitrite solution (IV) to ca. 4 °C.

Pipette into centrifuge tubes:			Concentration in assay mixture
Buffer solution	(I)	1.00 ml.	33 mM
L-Cystine-di-β-naphthylamide solution	(II)	1.00 ml.	0.66 mM
Sample (serum dilution, extract etc.)		1.00 ml.	
Mix thoroughly and incubate for 2 hr. (4 hr. with low activities)			
Perchloric acid solution	(IIIa)	1.00 ml.	
Centrifuge for 10 min. at 3000 rpm; pipette into a test tube:			
Supernatant fluid		2.00 ml.	
Nitrite solution, pre-cooled	(IV)	2.00 ml.	
For diazotization allow to stand for 10 min. at 4 °C			
Ammonium sulphamate solution	(V)	2.00 ml.	
To destroy excess nitrite allow to stand ca. 2–5 min.			
Chromogen solution	(VI)	4.00 ml.	
For development of colour allow to stand for 30 min. in dark at 37 °C and then read extinctions E_0 (blank) or E_x (test).			

Calculations

Standard curve: Dissolve 143.0 mg. β-naphthylamine (1 mmole) in 100 ml. perchloric acid solution (II b) (the compound is not very soluble; complete solution is only obtained after prolonged stirring). Dilute 10 ml. to 100 ml. with distilled water; of this dilute 10 ml. to 100 ml.; total dilution 1 : 100. This standard solution is 0.1 mM. Dilute 0.05–2.0 ml. (0.005–0.2 μmole) of this solution to 2.0 ml. with 5% $HClO_4$ (solution IIIb) and then carry through the diazotization and the coupling procedure. Read against blank (as for standards, but without β-naphthylamine). Plot the extinction differences (ordinate) against μmole β-naphthylamine (abscissa).

Convert the extinction differences $\Delta E = E_x - E_o$ for the enzyme assays into μmole β-naphthylamine from the standard curve. Proceed in the same way for the control to determine the spontaneous hydrolysis and subtract this value (μmole$_{corr.}$).

The activity is calculated taking into account the aliquot taken (times 2), the reaction time (divide by 120) and any dilution of the sample by factor F:

Normal assay: Volume activity $= \mu$mole$_{corr} \times 16.6 \times$ F [U/l.]

Micro-assay: Volume activity $= \mu$mole$_{corr} \times 0.166 \times$ F [U/l.]

Precision of Method

The coefficient of variation was 8.0% for 20 assays on an enzyme sample (precision) and 8.6% for 58 assays on 30 different sample (rat liver homogenate)[42], or 1–5%[99] and 6.9% (n = 44)[101] on different human sera.

Normal Values

According to[99] 1 ml. serum in the 1st month of pregnancy liberates (27 °C; 4 hr) 1.4–6.0 μg. (mean 4.4 $\pm$ 1.3) free β-naphthylamine, and 123.5 μg. in the 9th month, i.e. 0.13 U/l. and 3.5 U/l. respectively. Serum from non-pregnant subjects contains 0.5 U/l., while serum in the 10th lunar month of pregnancy contains 6.6 U/l.[104] or 1.5–3.5 U/l.[42]. Values of x $\pm$ 2s = 0.30 $\pm$ 0.31 U/l. have been found in serum from 26 children[26,42]. The activity can rise on physical work from 0.8 U/l. to 1.3 U/l.[132].

Sources of Error

Effects of drugs and other therapeutic measures: Allyloestrenol, 5 $\times$ 5 mg. orally, or 17-α-hydroxyprogesterone, 250 mg. per week increases the activity in serum in pregnant women[105]. Operative trauma (between the 2nd and 10th day), as well as jaundice also cause high values[99].

Interference in the assay technique: If the described conditions are adhered to no interference should occur. The diazotization should be carried out in the cold and the development of the colour in the dark.

Specificity of Method

See "General Information", p. 950.

Details for Measurements in Tissues

Aqueous sucrose solution, 0.25 M + 0.1% (v/v) Triton X-100 is recommended as homogenization medium (1 : 5 w/v). This medium can also be used for cell fractions. Homogenates of liver, spleen, kidney and lung of rat can be diluted 1 : 10–1 : 50[42].

Other Assay Methods

The same reaction is also described for L-cystine-p-nitroanilide[25] and it allows kinetic measurements with high enzyme activities.

Micro-Assay Methods

The present method is so arranged that a 1 : 10 reduction of all volumes can be made. The same solution is used for standardization, and the standard curves with 10 times smaller amounts of standards on the abscissa are identical with those obtained by the normal assay. For this micro-assay, for example 30 μl. of pregnant serum is required[42]. We have had considerable experience with the Beckman-Spinco and Eppendorf micro-systems.

Determination with S-Benzyl-L-cysteine p-nitroanilide as Substrate[253]

Antonius P. M. van Oudheusden

Application of Method: In clinical chemistry.

Principle

(1)   S-Benzyl-L-cysteine p-nitroanilide $+ H_2O$ $\xrightarrow{\text{oxytocinase}}$ p-Nitroaniline $+$ S-Benzyl-L-cysteine

p-Nitroaniline has an absorption at about 410 nm, whereas the substrate does not absorb at this wavelength. The oxytocinase activity is directly proportional to the quantity of p-nitroaniline liberated per unit time.

Optimum Conditions for Measurements

The pH optimum is 7.5, and the optimum substrate concentration is 0.48 mM. With 0.1 ml. of various mixtures of pregnant serum with non-pregnant serum, proportionality exists with the hydrolysis rate. The time-conversion curve is linear over a measuring period of five to ten min., depending on the activity. Measurements at different temperatures may require different measuring conditions (cf. p. 127). Nevertheless, results obtained under the same measuring conditions but at different temperatures were formerly compared with each other ("conversion factors" were determined). Such conversion factors may be correct if determined with a relatively large proband collective; however, they cannot be applied generally to the individual case (cf. p. 129). The value of the following relative reaction rates thus lies in being able to appraise the temperature dependence of the reaction and at the most to compare qualitatively values up to the limit of normal.

°C	20	25	30	35	40	45	50
	0.71	*1.00*	1.45	1.81	2.57	2.93	3.17

Equipment

Filter photometer capable of measurement between 405 and 410 nm, preferably with automatic cuvette changer (thermostatically controlled cuvette holder and recording device), water bath (25 °C), stop clock.

Reagents

1. S-Benzyl-L-cysteine p-nitroanilide (Boehringer Mannheim)
2. 2-Methoxyethanol, A. R.

3. Potassium dihydrogen phosphate,
   KH_2PO_4
4. Disodium hydrogen phosphate,
   $Na_2HPO_4 \cdot 2H_2O$, A. R.

Preparation of Solutions (for about 75 determinations)

Use only doubly distilled water.

I. Phosphate buffer (0.1 M; pH 7.5):
   Dissolve 20.4 g. KH_2PO_4 in water and make up to 150 ml.
   Dissolve 2.68 g. $Na_2HPO_4 \cdot 2H_2O$ in water and make up to 150 ml. Add KH_2PO_4 solution
   to the Na_2HPO_4 solution until pH 7.5.
II. S-Benzyl-L-cysteine p-nitroanilide (3.5 mM):
   Dissolve 29 mg. S-benzyl-L-cysteine p-nitroanilide in 2-methoxyethanol and make up to
   25 ml.

Stability of Solutions

Solution I keeps indefinitely at room temperature if micro-organisms are excluded. Solution II is stable for
about 2 months at 4 °C in a dark bottle.

Procedure

Collection, Treatment and Stability of Sample

Collection of sample: Use only haemoglobin-free pregnant serum (24th to 40th week of
pregnancy).

Stability of sample: The enzyme in the pregnant serum is stable for at least two days at 4 °C
and for at least three months at -20 °C.

Assay System

Wavelength: 405–410 nm; light path: 1 cm.; final volume 2.2 ml.; reaction temperature: 25 °C
(in constant-temperature cell holder). Read against water. No control is necessary for determination of the non-enzymatic hydrolysis of the substrate. Adjust temperature of solutions
to 25 °C before start of test.

Pipette into cuvettes:			Concentration in assay mixture
Phosphate buffer	(I)	1.8 ml.	0.08 M
Serum		0.1 ml.	
Substrate	(II)	0.3 ml.	0.48 mM
Mix, start stop clock, and read extinction every 30 sec for 5–10 min.			

Calculations

The calculation is based on the molar extinction coefficient of p-nitroaniline ($\varepsilon_{405 \text{ nm}} = 10.82$; $\varepsilon_{410 \text{ nm}} = 9.48$; $\varepsilon_{411 \text{ nm}} = 9.18$ [cm²/μmole].
Formula (8) on p. 313 is valid. The following relationships are therefore hold for the activity in the serum in this procedure:

Wavelength:	405 nm	410 nm	411 nm
Volume activity =	$2201 \times \Delta E/\text{min.}$	$2321 \times \Delta E/\text{min.}$	$2397 \times \Delta E/\text{min.}$ [U/l.]

Precision of Method

For 6 serum samples in the course of 13 days, $\bar{x} = 104$ mU/ml. The coefficient of variation is 3.8%.

Normal Values

The oxytocinase activity increases exponentially during pregnancy. We followed the course of this activity in sera from 11 normal pregnant women (longitudinal, n = 121). Statistical evaluation of these values gave: log y = 0.2104 + 0.0497 x; $s_{res} = 0.354$; (y = oxytocinase activity in U/l.; x = week of pregnancy). The activities found in sera of non-pregnant females and of males were

$\bar{x} = 2.8$ U/l. s = 1.3 U/l.(n = 27) and
$\bar{x} = 3.9$ U/l. s = 1.2 U/l.(n = 21) respectively.

Sources of Error

Effects of drugs and other therapeutic measures: None known at present.

Interference in assay technique: No interference is to be expected if the indicated conditions are observed.

Specificity of Method

This substrate is also hydrolysed by other arylamidases, e.g. the activities of the amino acid arylamidase (EC 3.4.1.2) with S-benzyl-L-cysteine p-nitroanilide and leucine p-nitroanilide occur in the ratio 1:8.4.

Other Methods of Determination

The same kinetic assay is also possible with L-cysteine p-nitroanilide[254].
The linear regression of the values for this method is x = 0.151 x + 1.22; r = 0.93; p < 0.001; n = 180.

References

1 *H. Hanson* in Hoppe-Seyler-Thierfelder: Handb. d. physiol. & path.-chem. Analyse, Springer Verlag, Berlin – Heidelberg – New York, 10th edn., 1966, Vol. *VI*, part C, p. 2 (Reviews cited.)
2 *M. Bergmann*, Advances in Enzymology *2*, 49 [1942] and in *S. P. Colowick & N. O. Kaplan:* Methods in Enzymology, New York–London, 1956, Vol. II, p. 83.
3 *E. L. Smith*, Advances in Enzymology *12*, 191 [1951].
4 *E. L. Smith, H. Neurath, R. L. Fruton & M. R. Pollock* in: Boyer-Lardy-Myrbäck; The Enzymes, Academic Press, New York – London, 2nd edn., 1960, Vol. *IV*, p. 1 ff.

5 *H. Wüst* in *H. U. Bergmeyer:* Methoden der enzymatischen Analyse, Verlag Chemie, Weinheim 1962, 1st edn., 824 ff. see also *H.-J. Lee, J. N. La Rue & J. B. Wilson,* Analyt. Biochem. *41,* 397 [1971].
6 *S. P. L. Sörensen,* Biochem. Z. *7,* 45 [1908].
7 *J. H. Northrop,* J. gen. Physiol. *9,* 767 [1926].
8 *R. Willstätter & E. Waldschmidt-Leitz,* Ber. Dtsch. Chem. Ges. *54,* 2988 [1928].
9 *W. Grassmann & W. Heyde,* Hoppe-Seylers Z. physiol. Chem. *183,* 32 [1929].
10 *K. Linderström-Lang,* Hoppe-Seylers Z. physiol. Chem. *173,* 32 [1928].
11 *K. Linderström-Lang & H. Holter,* Hoppe-Seylers Z. physiol. Chem. *201,* 9 [1931].
12 *E. I. Conway & E. O'Malley,* Biochem. J. *36,* 655 [1942].
13 *G. W. Schwert, H. Neurath, S. Kaufmann & J. E. Snoke,* J. biol. Chem. *172,* 221 [1948].
14 *A. B. Kendrick & M. E. Hanke,* J. biol. Chem. *117,* 161 [1937].
15 *H. Herken & R. Merten,* Hoppe-Seylers Z. physiol. Chem. *270,* 201 [1941].
   H. Herken, Hoppe-Seylers Z. physiol. Chem. *283,* 277 [1948].
16 *E. A. Zeller & A. Maritz,* Helv. physiol. Acta *3,* C 6, C 48 [1945].
17 *P. C. Zameenik & M. L. Stephenson,* J. biol. Chem. *169,* 349 [1947].
18 *A. T. Matheson & B. L. Tattrie,* Canad. J. Biochem. *42,* 95 [1964].
19 *F. Binkley & C. Torres,* Arch. Biochem. Biophys. *86,* 201 [1960].
20 *A. Schmitt & G. Siebert,* Biochem. Z. *334,* 96 [1961].
21 *H. Hanson & R. I. Haschen,* Hoppe-Seylers Z. physiol. Chem. *310,* 213 & 221 [1958].
22 *H. A. Ravin & A. M. Seligman,* J. biol. Chem. *190,* 391 1951]
23 *I. A. Goldbard, E. P. Pineda & A. M. Rutenburg,* Amer. J. clin. Pathol. *32,* 571 [1959].
24 *M. Rybák, M. Petáková & E. Simonianová,* Collect. Czechoslov. Chem. Commun. *32,* 1051 [1967].
25 *H. Tuppy, U. Wiesbauer & E. Wintersberger,* Hoppe-Seylers Z. physiol. Chem. *329,* 278 [1962].
26 *W. Nagel, F. Willig & F. H. Schmidt,* Klin. Wschr. *42,* 447 [1964].
27 *B. Sylvén & O. Snellmann,* Histochemie *3,* 484 [1964].
28 *W. Appel,* 1. FEBS Meeting London 1964.
29 *G. G. Glenner, P. I. McMillan & J. E. Folk,* Nature *149,* 867 [1962].
30 *N. Marks, R. K. Datta & A. Lajhta,* J. biol. Chem. *243,* 2882 [1968].
31 *E. Werle,* 5. FEBS Meeting Prague 1968.
32 *H. Tuppy* in: Schachter, Polypeptides, Pergamon Press, London 1960, p. 49.
33 *S. Melander,* Acta endocrinol. *48,* Suppl. 96, 9 [1965].
34 *H. Brunner & D. Regoli,* Experientia, *18,* 504 [1962].
35 *D. Klaus, H. Kaffernik & H. Pfeil,* Klin Wschr. *41,* 376 & 380 [1963].
36 *D. H. Spackman, E. L. Smith & D. L. Brown,* J.biol. Chem. *212,* 255 [1955].
37 *R. L. Hill & E. L. Smith,* J. biol. Chem. *228,* 577 [1957], see also 1 p. 156 ff.
38 *H. Fasold, P. Linhart & F. Turba,* Biochem. Z. *336,* 182 [1962], see also 1, p. 159 ff.
39 *G. Pfleiderer & P. G. Celliers,* Biochem. Z. *339,* 186 [1963].
40 *S. R. Himmelhoch & E. A. Peterson,* Biochem. 7, 2085 [1968].
41 *D. Glässer & H. Hanson,* Hoppe-Seylers Z. physiol. Chem. *329,* 249 [1962]; Naturwiss. *51,* 110 [1964]; see also 1, p. 160 ff.
42 *W. Appel,* unpublished.
43 *E. Maschmann,* Ergebn. Enzymforsch. *9,* 155 [1943].
44 *I. Mandl, L. T. Ferguson & S. F. Zaffuto,* Arch. Biochem. *69,* 565 [1957].
45 *E. Waldschmidt-Leitz & A. Schäffner,* Hoppe-Seyler's Z. physiol. Chem. *151,* 31 [1926].
46 *A. K. Balls & F. Köhler,* Hoppe-Seylers, Z. physiol. Chem. *219,* 128 [1933]; see also 1, p. 51 & 149.
47 *E. Waldschmidt-Leitz & L. Keller,* Hoppe-Seyler's Z. physiol. Chem. *309,* 228 [1958].
48 *W. Grassmann, L. Emden & H. Schneller,* Biochem. Z. *271,* 216 [1934]; see also 1, p. 147 ff.
49 *D. Ellis & J. S. Fruton,* J. biol. Chem. *191,* 153 [1951].
50 *K. K. Tsubio, Z. J. Penefski & P. B. Hudson,* Arch. Biochem. *68,* 54 [1957].
51 *E. Adams, N. C. Davis & E. L. Smith,* J. biol. Chem. *199,* 845 [1952].
52 *E. K. Patterson, S. H. Hsiao, A. Keppel & S. Sorof,* J. biol. Chem. *240,* 710 [1965].
53 *G. Pfleiderer, P. G. Celliers, M. Stannlovic, E. D. Wachsmuth, H. Determann & G. Braunitzer,* Biochem. Z. *340,* 552 [1964].
54 *E. E. Smith, I. T. Kaufmann & A. M. Rutenburg,* J. biol. Chem. *240,* 1718 [1965].
55 *F. J. Behal, R. D. Hamilton, Ch. B. Kavanagl & E. C. Kelly,* Arch. Biochem. Biophys. *100,* 308 [1963].
56 *J. E. Folk & M. S. Burstone,* Proc. Soc. exp. Biol. Med. *89,* 473 [1955].
57 *M. M. Nachlas, T. P. Goldstein & A. M. Seligman,* Arch. Biochem. Biophys. *97,* 223 [1962].
58 *W. Nagel & F. Willig,* Naturwiss. *51,* 115 [1964].
59 *H. H. Hanson, P. Bohley & H. G. Mannsfeldt,* Clin, Chim. Acta *8,* 555 [1963].
60 *R. Keller,* Schweiz. Med. Wschr. *93,* 1504 [1963].
61 *A. S. Brecher & R. E. Sobel,* Biochem. J. *105,* 641 [1967].
62 *P. A. Khairalla, F. M. Bumpus, I. H. Page & R. R. Smeby,* Science *140,* 672 [1963].

63 *I. Nagutsu, L. Gillespie, I. M. George, J. E. Folk & G. G. Glenner*, Biochem. Pharmacol. *14*, 853 [1965].
64 *R. Hess*, Biochim. Biophys. Acta *99*, 316 [1965].
65 *H. Tuppy & E. Wintersberger*, Mh. Chem. *91*, 1001 [1960].
66 *G. de la Haba, P. S. Cammarata & S. N. Timasheff*, J. biol. Chem. *234*, 316 [1959].
67 *E. M. Press, R. R. Porter & J. Cebra*, Biochem. J. *74*, 501 [1960].
68 *C. Lapresle & T. Webb*, Biochem. J. *76*, 538 [1960].
69 *Hoppe-Seyler-Thierfelder*, Handb. d. physiol.- & pathol.-chem. Analyse, 10th. edn., 1955, Vol. *III/1*, p. 17; see also 1, p. 20 ff.
70 *F. Willig, I. Greiner, H. Stork & F. H. Schmidt*, Klin. Wschr. *5*, 474 [1967].
71 *E. D. Wachsmuth, I. Fritze & G. Pfleiderer*, Biochemistry, *5*, 169 and 175 [1966].
72 *G. Brunner, J. Sommer & R. Kattermann*, Klin. Wschr. *46*, 541 [1968].
73 *E. D. Wachsmuth*, Biochem. Z. *344*, 361 [1966].
74 *E. Bernhammer & K. Krisch*, Z. Klin. Chem. *4*, 49 [1966].
75 *E. Wintersberger & K. P. Chatterje*, Mh. Chem. *93*, 1268 [1962].
76 *G. A. Fleisher, M. Pankow & C. Warmka*, Clin. Chim. Acta *9*, 259 [1964].
77 *S. Nakagawa & H. Tsuji*, Clin. Chim. Acta *13*, 155 [1966].
78 *S. Mahadevan & A. L. Tappel*, J. biol. Chem. *242*, 2369 [1967].
79 *St. Ellis & M. Perry*, J. biol. Chem. *241*, 3679 [1966].
80 *F. Dienstl, S Sailer, F. Sandhofer & H. Braunsteiner*, Klin. Wschr. *42*, 794 [1964].
81 a *D. K. Panveliwalla & D. W. Moss*, Biochem. J. *96*, 73 P [1965], b ditto *95*, 31 P [1965].
82 *I. Hasegawa*, J. Histochem. Cystochem. *11*, 474 [1963].
83 *A. Tjeder*, Acta Chem. Scand. *20*, 1442 [1966].
84 *H. Weber*, Clin. Chim. Acta *10*, 521 [1964].
85 *M. Roth*, Clin. Chim. Acta *9*, 448 [1964].
86 *W. Pruzanski & J. Fischl*, Amer. J. Med. Sci. *248*, 581 [1964].
87 *W. Raab & E. Kaiser*, Experientia *21*, 720 [1965].
88 *R. G. Martinek, L. Berger & D. Broida*, Clin. Chem. *10*, 1087 [1964].
89 *B. Schobel, N. Steffenelli, F. Wewalka & J. H. Holzner*, Klin. Wschr. *43*, 628 [1964].
90 *N. K. Mottet*, Amer. J. Pathol. *39*, 17 [1961].
91 *W. Appel, V. Wirmer & St. Ebenezer*, Anästhesist *17*, 96 [1968].
92 *W. Appel, E. Huth & H. Hermann*, Z. klin. chem. klin. Biochem. *7*, 576 [1969].
93 *M. Cihar, Z. Beránková, I. Rychlik & F. Sorm*, Collect. Czechoslov. Chem. Commun. *26*, 2632 [1961].
94 *T. Barth, V. Pliska, I. Rychlik & F. Sorm*, Collect. Czechoslov. Chem. Commun. *32*, 2327 [1967].
95 *I. Sjöholm*, Acta Chem. Scand. *18*, 899 [1964].
96 *E. Werle & K. Semm*, Arch. Gynäk. *187*, 449 [1956].
97 *K. C. Hooper*, Biochem. J. *90*, 584 [1964].
98 *K. Semm*, Drug research, *12*, 252 [1962].
99 *R. Klimek & M. Pietrzycka*, Clin. Chim. Acta *6*, 326 [1961].
100 *S. M. Hardy & J. M. Ritchie*, Nature *209*, 76 [1966].
101 *E. Suska-Brzezinska & A. Slebodzinski*, Experientia *24*, 437 [1968].
102 *E. Wintersberger, W. Müller-Hartburg & H. Tuppy*, Clin. Chim. Acta *14*, 786 [1966].
103 *A. C. Barnes & J. B. Sawyer*, Amer. J. Obstetr. Gynec. *79*, 1053 [1960].
104 *H. Tuppy & H. Nesvadba*, Mh. Chem. *88*, 977 [1957].
105 *K. Semm*, Geburtsh. Frauenheilk. *25*, 149 [1965].
106 *D. Reguli, B. Riniker & H. Brunner*, Biochem. Pharmacol. *12*, 637 [1963].
107 *W. Oelkers & I. U. v. Goddacker*, Klin. Wrschr. *45*, 649 [1967].
108 *L. Berrens*, Nature *217*, 664 [1968], Clin. Chim. Acta *20*, 170 [1968].
109 *H. Hanson, H.-J. Hütter, H.-G. Mannsfeldt, K. Kretschmer & Ch. Sohr*, Hoppe-Seylers Z. physiol. Chem. *348*, 680 [1967].
110 *H. Hanson, D. Glässer, M. Ludewig, H.-G. Mannsfeldt, M. John & H. Nesvadba*, Hoppe-Seylers Z. physiol. Chem. *348*, 689 [1967].
111 *V. K. Hopsu-Havu & S. R. Sarimo*, Hoppe-Seylers Z. physiol. Chem. *348*, 1540 [1967].
112 *J. K. McDonald, S. Ellis & T. J. Reilly*, J. biol. Chem. *241*, 1494 [1966].
113 *S. Ellis & J. M. Nuenke*, J. biol. Chem. *242*, 4623 [1967].
114 *J. K. McDonald, F. H. Leibach, R. E. Grindeland & S. Ellis*, J. biol. Chem. *243*, 4143 [1968].
115 *H. U. Bergmeyer & E. Bernt*, personal communication.
116 *D. Klaus, H. Kaffarnik & H. Pfeil*, Klin. Wschr. *41*, 380 [1963].
117 *W. Oelkers & I. U. v. Goldacker*, Klin. Wschr. *45*, 649 [1967].
118 *G. Schwabe*, Biochem. *8*, 771, 783 & 795 [1969].
119 *J. A. Knight & D. T. Hunter*, Clin. Chem. *14*, 555 [1968].
120 *G. G. Glenner & J. E. Folk*, Nature *192*, 338 [1961].

121 *J. Swinnen*, Clin. Chim. Acta, *17*, 255 [1967].
122 *M. Orlowski & A. Meister*, Abstr. Pap. Am. Chem. Soc. Nr. 156, Biol. 154 [1968].
123 *D. M. Dimor*, Clin. Chim. Acta, *21*, 427 [1968].
124 *F. H. Leibach & F. Binkley*, Arch. Biochem. Biophys. *127*, 292 [1968].
125 *T. Laursen & K. Jacyszyn*, Clin. Chim. Acta *21*, 497 [1968].
126 *N. Rehfeld, J. E. Peters, H. Giesecke & R. J. Haschen*, Acta Biol. Med. Germ. *19* [6], 819 [1967].
127 *F. J. Behal, G. H. Little & R. A. Klein*, Biochim. Biophys. Acta *178*, 118 [1969].
128 *F. J. Behal & G. H. Little*, Clin. Chim. Acta *21*, 347 [1968].
129 *I. Nagatsu, T. Nagatsu & T. Yamamoto*, Experientia *24*, 347 [1968].
130 *J. B. Suszkiw & A. S. Brecher*, Am. Chem. Soc. Nr. 156, Biol. 159 [1968].
131 *S. Mattila*, Scand. J. Clin. Lab. Invest. *21*, Suppl. 101, 36 [1968].
132 *V. S. Mathur & J. M. Walker*, Brit. Med. J. *1968*, 96.
133 *E. Suska-Brzezinska & A. Slebodzinski*, Experientia *24*, 437 [1968].
134 *R. B. Hickler, D. P. Lauler & G. W. Thorn*, J. Clin. Invest. *42*, 635 [1963].
135 *D. Regoli, B. Riniker & H. Brunner*, Biochem. Pharmacol. *12*, 637 [1963].
136 *D. Klaus & P. Biron*, Nature *204*, 381 [1964].
137 *C. A. Saravis & R. B. Huckler*, Proc. Soc. Exp. Biol. Med. *117*, 499 [1964].
138 *P. Biron & W. P. Baldus*, Proc. Soc. Exp. Biol. Med. *116*, 1074 [1964].
139 *P. Biron, R. Landesman & J. C. Hunt*, Nature *204*, 1096 [1964].
140 *D. Klaus, A. Heizmann & H. Vehleke*, Arch. Exp. Pathol. Pharmacol. *250*, 264 [1965].
141 *M. G. Myers, P. R. Robinson, R. E. Morris & J. Hopkins*, Clin. Res. *13*, 215 [1965].
142 *Y. Yamamura*, Clin. Chim. Acta, *12*, 484 [1965] & *14*, 410 [1966].
143 *E. Haas, H. Goldblatt, E. C. Gipson & L. Lewis*, Circul. Res. *19*, 739 [1966].
144 *M. P. Sambhi & J. D. Barrett*, Clin. Res. *14*, 149 [1966].
145 *T. Kokubu, E. Ueda, S. Fujimoto, K. Hiwaga, H. Sanga & Y. Yamamura*, Clin. Chim. Acta *13*, 13 [1966].
146 *G. D. Lubash*, Clin. Res. *15*, 363 [1967].
147 *H. D. Itskovitz, S. J. Dudrick, J. Dyrda & J. J. Murphy*, Arch. Internal Med. *119*, 341 [1967].
148 *G. D. Lubash, E. C. Hammel & R. J. Mearles*, Ann. Intern. Med. *66*, 1031 [1967].
149 *G. Morandini, D. Dimich, P. Manca & M. Spanedda*, Minerva Med. *58*, 1876 [1967].
150 *M. Berger & J. Langhans*, Am. J. Obstet. Gynecol. *98*, 215 [1967].
151 *O. E. Talledo, K. Rhodes & E. Livingston*, Am. J. Obstet. Gynecol. *97*, 571 [1967].
152 *H. Y. T. Yang, E. G. Erdös & T. S. Chiang*, Nature *218*, 1224 [1968].
153 *K. K. F. Ng & J. R. Vane*, Nature *218*, 144 [1968].
154 *G. D. Lubash*, Clin. Res. *16*, 390 [1968].
155 *A. B. Kurtz & E. D. Wachsmuth*, Nature *221*, 92 [1969].
156 *P. L. Mäkinen & J. Raekallio*, Acta Chem. Scand. *22*, 3111 [1968].
157 *D. C. Johnson & J. W. Ryan*, Biochim. Biophys. Acta *160*, 196 [1968].
158 *G. E. Perlmann & L. Lorand* in *S. P. Colowick & N. O. Kaplan:* Methods in Enzymology, Vol. XIX "Proteolytic Enzymes", New York–London [1970].
159 *E. G. Erdös*, First Internat. Pharmacol. Meeting, cit. in: Biochem. Biophys. Res. Comm. *6*, 159 [1962].
160 *A. Williams*, Quarterly Reviews *23*, 1 [1969].
161 *K. Lehmann & H. Uhlig*, Hoppe-Seyler's Z. physiol. Chem. *350*, 99 [1969].
162 *U. Femfert & G. Pfleiderer*, FEBS Letters *4*, 262 [1969].
163 *N. Minamiura, Y. Matsumara, T. Yamamotu & J. Fukumoto*, Agric. Biol. Chem. *33*, 653 [1969].
164 *A. Yaron & D. Mlynar*, Biochim. Biophys. Res. Comm. *32*, 658 [1968].
165 *S. Simmonds*, Biochemistry *9*, 1 [1970].
166 *A. Janoff & J. Blondin*, Proc. Soc. Exptl. Biol. Med. *135*, 302 [1970].
167 *K. Ohlsson*, Clin. Chim. Acta *32*, 399 [1971].
168 *Ph. Davies, K. Krakauer & G. Weissmann*, Analyt. Biochem. *45*, 428 [1972].
169 *J. Prokopowicz*, Thromb. Diath. Haemorrhag. *19*, 84 [1968].
170 *J. C. Houck, Y. M. Patel & J. Gladner*, Biochem. Pharmacol. *16*, 1099 [1967].
171 *K. Adachi & S. Yamasawa*, J. Invest. Dermat., *50*, 360 [1968].
172 *W. Domschke & H. G. Weber*, Drug Res. *20*, 269 [1970].
173 *G. P. Lewis, J. Peters & A. M. White*, Brit. J. Pharmacol. *42*, 437 [1971].
174 *J. Raekallio & P. L. Mäkinen*, Experientia *27*, 1276 [1971].
175 *J. E. Fräki & V. K. Hopsu-Havu*, Arch. Derm. Forsch. *242*, 329 [1972].
176 *V. Patel & A. L. Tappel*, Biochim. Biophys. Acta, *208*, 163 [1970].
177 *W. Goettlich-Riemann, J. O. Young & A. L. Tappel*, Biochim. Biophys. Acta, *243*, 137 [1971].
178 *I. L. Mego*, Biochem. J. *122*, 445 [1971].
179 *H. Ikezawa, T. Aoyagi, T. Takeuchi & H. Umezawa*, J. Antibiotics *24*, 488 [1971].
180 *U. Stein, H. Heissmeyer, G. Wangemann, R. Lesch, W. Reutter & D. Keppler*, Klin. Wschr. *49*, 550 [1971].
181 *O. Snellman*, Biochem. J. *114*, 673 [1969].

182 J. Ken McDonald, B. B. Zeitman & S. Ellis, Nature 225, 1048 [1970].
183 H. Keilová & J. Turková, FEBS Letters, 11, 287 [1970].
184 A. Suzuki & M. Fujimaki, Agric. Biol. Med. 32, 975 [1968].
185 M. S. Pollack & J. W. C. Bird, Am. J. Physiol. 215, 716 [1968].
186 F. H. Schneider, Biochem. Pharmacol. 19, 819 [1970].
187 D. Hegner & R. Leurs, Intern. Z. Vitaminforsch. 40, 9 [1970].
188 A. I. Sapolsky, Dissertation Abstr. Intern. 30, 3486 B [1970].
189 J. C. Guckian, B. F. Morrey & H. B. Kirby, J. Infec. Dis. 122, 290 [1970].
190 T. L. Zaetz, Biochem. Biophys. Res. Comm. 40, 356 [1970].
191 A. J. Barrett, Biochem. J. 117, 601 [1970].
192 M. B. Hille, A. J. Barrett, J. T. Dingle & H. B. Fell, Exp. Cell. Res. 61, 470 [1970].
193 H. Keilová, FEBS Letters 6, 312 [1970].
194 J. T. Dingle, A. J. Barrett & P. D. Weston, Biochem. J. 123, 1 [1971].
195 J. F. Woessner jr. & R. J. Shamberger jr., J. biol. Chem. 246, 1951 [1971].
196 V. Ghetie & C. Motas, Immunochemistry 8, 89 [1971].
197 S. Bazin & A. Delauney, Ann. Inst. Pasteur 120, 50 [1971].
198 N. Allegretti, I. Andreis, M. Kopitar & D. Lebez, Nature New Biol. 229, 180 [1971].
199 U. Stein, H. Heissmeyer, W. Zimmermann & R. Lesch, Klin. Wschr. 49, 1271 [1971].
200 A. I. Sapolsky & J. F. Woessner jr., J. biol. Chem. 247, 2069 [1972].
201 W. Rothe, G. Pfleiderer & R. Zwilling, 351, 629 [1970].
202 W. H. Vensel, J. Komender & E. A. Barnard, Biochim. Biophys. Acta 250, 395 [1971].
203 R. J. Planta & M. Gruber, Biochim. Biophys. Acta, 89, 503 [1964].
204 J. K. McDonald, T. J. Reilly, B. B. Zeitman & St. Ellis, Biochem. Biophys. Res. Comm. 24, 771 [1966].
205 J. K. McDonald, St. Ellis & T. R. Reilly, J. biol. Chem. 241, 1494 [1966].
206 J. K. McDonald, P. X. Callahan, B. B. Zeitman & St. Ellis, J. biol. Chem. 244, 6199 [1969].
207 J. K. McDonald, B. B. Zeitman, T. J. Reilly & St. Ellis, J. biol. Chem. 244, 2693 [1969].
208 J. Gorter & M. Gruber, Biochim. Biophys. Acta, 198, 546 [1970].
209 F. L. Huang & A. L. Tappel, Biochim. Biophys. Acta, 236, 739 [1971].
210 K. K. Mäkinen & V. K. Hopsu-Havu, Enzymologia, 32, 333 [1967].
211 K. K. Mäkinen & V. K. Hopsu-Havu, Enzymologia, 32, 347 [1967].
212 V. K. Hopsu-Havu, K. K. Mäkinen & G. G. Glenner, Acta Chem. Scand. 20, 1231 [1966].
213 V. K. Hopsu-Havu, K. K. Mäkinen & G. G. Glenner, Arch. Biochem. Biophys. 114, 567 [1966].
214 V. K. Hopsu-Havu, P. Rintola & G. G. Glenner, Acta Chem. Scand. 22, 299 [1968].
215 K. K. Mäkinen, Arch. Biochem. Biophys. 126, 803 [1968].
216 K. K. Mäkinen & K. U. Paunio, Acta Chem. Scand. 24, 1103 [1970].
217 P. Dehm & A. Nordwig, FEBS Letters 9, 225 [1970].
218 H. P. Selig, Klin. Wschr., 48, 567 [1970].
219 H. Droszdz, Clin. Chim. Acta, 28, 141 [1970].
220 W. R. Shlank, J. D. Glass, I. L. Schwartz & T. D. Kerenyi, Science 173, 827 [1971].
221 T. Barth, I. Rychlik & H. G. Mannsfeldt, Collect. Czechoslow. Chem. Commun. 36, 2540 [1971].
222 H. D. Taubert, H. Bickel & H. Huhl, Acta Endocrin. 67, 27 [1971].
223 H. P. Seelig & E. Lassen, Z. Ges. Exp. Med. Exp. Chir. 154, 265 [1971].
224 H. Heil, V. Meltzer, H. Kuhl, R. Abraham & H. D. Taubert, Fert. Ster. 22, 181 [1971].
225 L. A. Branda & B. M. Ferrier, Am. J. Obstet. Gynec. 109, 943 [1971].
226 A. P. M. can Oudheusden, Clin. Chim. Acta, 32, 140 [1971].
227 M. Koida, J. D. Glass, I. L. Schwartz & R. Walter, Endocrinology 88, 633 [1971].
228 I. v. Goldacker & W. Oelkers, Z. klin. Chem. klin. Biochem. 7, 250 [1969].
229 I. Nagatsu, T. Nagatsu, T. Yamamoto, G. G. Glenner & J. W. Mehl, Biochim. Biophys. Acta, 198, 255 [1970].
230 H. Y. T. Yang, E. G. Erdös, T. S. Chiang, T. A. Jenssen & J. G. Rodgers, Biochem. Pharmacol. 19, 1201 [1970].
231 M. Matsunaga & G. M. C. Masson, Experientia 26, 1297 [1970].
232 D. Regoli, W. K. Park & M. C. Carrara, Clin. Res. 19, 761 [1971].
233 L. Abrash, R. Walter & N. Marks, Experientia, 27, 1352 [1971].
234 G. D. Lubash, G. E. Muiesan, C. L. Alicandri, D. J. Garfinkel, E. C. Siekierski & C. K. McConnaughey, Experientia 27, 68 [1971].
235 J. Swinnen, Z. klin. Chem. klin. Biochem. 8, 557 [1970].
236 G. Szasz, Z. klin. Chem. klin. Biochem. 8, 1 [1970].
237 L. de Soldati, H. Cammarota & F. Chalbaud, Cardiovasc. Res. VI World Congr. Cardiol. 121 [1970].
238 S. Fiala & E. S. Fiala, Naturwiss. 58, 330 [1971].
239 J. B. Suszkiw & A. S. Brecher, Biochemistry 9, 4008 [1970].
240 T. Shikimi, S. Houki & H. Iwata, Jap. J. Pharmacol. 20, 169 [1970].

241 *H. Iwata, T. Shikimi, M. Iida & H. Miichi*, Jap, J. Pharmacol. *20*, 80 [1970].
242 *J. Lonovics, L. Szekeres & A. Gecse*, Acta Phys. Acad. Sci. Hung. *37*, 405 [1970].
243 *T. Shikimi & H. Iwata*, Biochem. Pharmacol. *19*, 1399 [1970].
244 *A. Gecse, J. Lonovics, E. Zsilinsky & Szekeres*, J. Med. Exptl. Clin. *2*, 129 [1971].
245 *V. K. Hopsu-Havu, C. T. Jansen & M. Jarvinen*, Clin. Chim. Acta *28*, 25 [1970].
246 *K. K. Mäkinen*, FEBS Letters, *2*, 101 [1968].
247 *P. Dehm & A. Nordwig*, Europ. J. Biochem. *17*, 364 [1970].
248 *A. Szewczuk & J. Kwiatkowska*, Europ. J. Biochem. *15*, 92 [1970].
249 *G. A. Burghen, J. S. Brush, S. S. Solomon, J. N. Etteldorf & A. E. Kitabchi*, Diabetes *20*, Suppl. *1*, 342 [1971].
250 *A. E. Kitabchi, F. B. Stentz, W. C. Duckworth & M. Heinemann*, Clin. Res. *19*, 477 [1971].
251 *C. C. Yip*, Proc. Natl. Acad. Sci. *68*, 1312 [1971].
252 *H. S. Cheung & D. W. Cushman*, Biochim. Biophys. Acta, *242*, 190 [1971].
253 *A. P. M. van Oudheusden*, Z. Klin. Chem. & Klin. Biochem. *10*, 345 [1972].
254 *A. P. M. van Oudheusden*, Clin. Chim. Acta *32*, 140 [1971].

Di- and Polypeptidases

Walter Appel

General Information*

Dipeptidases hydrolyse only dipeptides. If a single dipeptide is hydrolysed the existence of a certain dipeptidase can only be assumed; if several dipeptides are hydrolysed, they must be structurally related and the ratio of the rates of hydrolysis must remain constant during purification. Further requirements are: both amino acids of the dipeptide must have the L-configuration, must have a free H in the α or α' position as well as free NH_2 and COOH groups (the NH_2 group must not be monoalkylated). Apart from these highly specific dipeptidases there is a group of less specific enzymes which is included under the heading of dipeptidases, and which hydrolyse dipeptides consisting of different amino acids. In the case of the hydrolysis of L-leucyl-glycine there is the possiblity of confusion with leucine aminopeptidase, EC 3.4.11.1.

Tripeptidases hydrolyse tripeptides; some show marked specificity. They often hydrolyse N-terminal amino acids and therefore have the characteristics of an aminopeptidase, EC 3.4.11.4 [47-49].

Polypeptidases is a loose term for several peptidases which cannot be included in the above groups of peptidases. In part they have the non-specific character of an amino(poly)peptidase, EC 3.4.11.2, and in part their specificity overlaps with that of the endopeptidases. This term should only be used in a limited way or preferably avoided. Even in the case of the dipeptidases a classification and characterization is only possible when a homogeneous or at least highly purified enzyme is under study. For a new peptidase, see[45,46,52].

The following Table 1. gives a survey. For the determination of the activity of dipeptidases, see the "Review" on p. 950.

Titrimetric methods are generally applicable and are usually used when different substrates are studied. In addition, there are special methods which depend on the decrease of UV-extinction

---

* See p. 949, cited by[1].

Table 1. Classification, occurrence, purification, substrate and activity optima of dipeptidases.

Enzyme	Substrate	Occurrence	Purification from*	Optimum pH	Activators	Effectors Inhibitors	Inactive
Glycylglycine dipeptidase EC 3.4.13.1	Gly-Gly	Intestinal mucosa, liver kidney, muscle, uterus, serum (pig, rabbit, guinea pig, human); liver, kidney (rat); yeasts; erythrocytes, thrombocytes, leucocytes (human); cod muscle.	Rat skeletal muscle[1], human uterus[1], pig intestinal mucosa[2], kidneys[3,28], bakers' yeast[4,13].	7.6	Co^{2+}, (Mn^{2+})	Zn^{2+}	Mg^{2+}, Zn^{2+}
Glycyl-L-leucyl dipeptidase EC 3.4.13.2	Gly-L-Leu	As above; placenta, milk (human); erythrocytes (human); serum (human);	Pig intestinal mucosa[1] human uterus[1], human milk[42,51,52].	7.8–8.0 (9.2)	Mn^{2+}, Co^{2+} (Zn^{2+})*	Zn^{2+}, Ca^{2+}, cysteine, CN^-, $P_2O_7^{4-}$, EDTA, o-phenanthroline, (according to the source (Mn^{2+}, Co^{2+})**).	Mg^{2+}, Zn^{2+}
Carnosinase EC 3.4.13.3	Carnosine	Kidney (pig, rat); liver, spleen (rat); muscle (cod); yeast; serum (human).	Pig kidney[5,6]	7.4–7.5 ($+Zn^{2+}$: 7.8–7.9; $+Mn^{2+}$: 8.0–8.4); 7.65 in tris buffer	Mn^{2+}, Zn^{2+}	S^-, CN^-, EDTA, cysteine, (N_3^-, F^-); veronal; Ca^{2+}; phosphate (only after Mn^{2+} activation)	Mg^{2+}, Cd^{2+}, Fe^{2+}, Co^{2+}, Ca^{2+}
Anserinase EC 3.4.13.5	Anserine	Kidney (pig); muscle (cod, pike, rabbit); yeast	Pig kidney[7]; cod muscle[8];	7.3–7.5	Zn^{2+}, (Co^{2+})	Pb^{2+}, Ag^+, Fe^{2+}, Mn^{2+}, cysteine, CN, (F^-)	K^+, Mg^{2+}
Iminodipeptidase (prolinase) EC 3.4.13.8	L-Pro-Gly	Intestinal mucosa, liver, lung, kidney, spleen, kidney (pig); muscle, lens, plasma (bovine)	Pig kidney[11]	8.0 (–9.2)	Mn^{2+}, Cd^{2+}, (Zn^{2+}), Fe^{2+}, Co^{2+})	Ag^+ (PO_4^{3-}), $P_2O_7^{4-}$, S^-, F^- citrate, after activation	Mg^{2+}, Hg^{2+}, Ba^{2+}

* See also p. 949.
** With homogenates or crude preparations (glycerol extraction), erythrocytes.

Table 1. Classification, occurrence, purification, substrates and activity optima of dipeptidases, (continued).

Enzyme	Substrate	Occurrence	Purification from*	Optimum pH	Activators	Effectors Inhibitors	Inactive
Imidodipeptidase (prolidase) EC 3.4.13.9	Gly-L-Pro	Muscle, uterus, intestinal mucosa, serum (rabbit, rat); adrenals (pig); erythrocytes (horse)	Pig intestine[12]; pig kidneys[13]; horse erythrocytes[14]	7.8–8.0	Mn^{2+}	Fe^{2+}, Co^{2+}, Ni^{2+}, Cu^{2+}, Zn^{2+}, Cd^{2+}, Ag^+, Hg^{2+}, Pb^{2+}, Pt^{4+}, $P_2O_7^{4-}$, F^-, EDTA, citrate, p-mercuribenzoate, iodoacetamide	Mg^{2+}, Fe^{3+}
L-Cysteinyl-glycine dipeptidase EC 3.4.13.6	L-Cys-Gly	Kidney, liver, muscle (pig, rat)	Pig kidney[9,10]	8.0–8.5	Mn^{2+}, Fe^{2+} Co^{2+}	Mg^{2+}, Ca^{2+}, Pb^{2+}, PO_4^{3-}, PO_3^-	(Mg^{2+}, Ca^{2+}, Pb^{2+})***
Dipeptidases (with lower specificity) partly identical with EC 3.4.11.1 and EC 3.4.11.2[17]	See Table 2	Brewers' and bakers' yeast; kidney and intestinal mucosa, pancreas, spleen, brain (mouse); bacteria; E. coli; various human tumors; human milk; cod muscle; fibroblasts (bovine)[46].	Brewers' yeast[15]; bakers' yeast[16]; pig intestinal mucosa[17] kidneys[17–19]; pancreas[17]; bacteria[20]; cod muscle[43]; E. coli[44]; ascites cells[45]	7.8 7.5–8.0 7.8–8.0 7.6 8.0–8.5 7.5 8.2	Mn^{2+} Mg^{2+}*** hexametaphosphate (Mn^{2+}, Co^{2+})** — —	Co^{2+}, Mn^{2+}*; *** cysteine; SH^-, CN^-, $P_2O_7^{4-}$, EDTA, p-chloromercuribenzoate — EDTA, o-phenanthroline	Puromycin
Tripeptidases EC 3.4.11.4	Gly-Gly-Gly	see p. 952, Table under "Aminotripeptidases" and [44].					Mn^{2+}, Co^{2+}, Ca^{2+}, Mg^{2+}, Zn^{2+}, SH^-

* According to substrate.
** Probably not an activation of the enzyme, but a reaction with the substrates[14].
*** According to source.

Table 2. Optimum conditions for measurements.

Enzyme	Substrate	mM*	Activator	mM*	Buffer	mM*+	pH	Incubation Preliminary (hr.)	Incubation Main (hr.)++	Incubation Temperature*** (°C)	References
Glycylglycine dipeptidase	Gly-Gly	50	CoSO4	1	Tris	30	7.8	0.2	0.5–2	37	25–28, 32
Glycyl-L-leucine dipeptidase	Gly-L-Leu	50	CoSO4	1	Phosphate**	30	7.8	1	1–3	37	1, 27
Carnosinase	Carnosine	50	MnCl2	2	Tris	80	8.0	1–3	1–4	37	4
Anserinase	Anserine	0.5	ZnSO4	0.1	Veronal	40	7.5	1–2	1–6	15	7, 8
L-Cysteinyl-glycine dipeptidase	L-Cys-Gly	20	MnCl2	1	Tris	30	8.3	15	15	37	28
Prolinase	L-Hypro-Gly	50	MnSO4	1	Tris	100	8.0	0	0.5–2	40	11, 29, 30
Prolidase	Gly-L-Pro	50	MnCl2	20	Tris	40	7.8	1	1	40	12–14, 16
Unspecific dipeptidases	L-Leu-Gly	50	—	—	without	—	7.8	—	1–4	40	16–19, 31
from yeast	Gly-Gly	30	MnSO4	1	without	—	7.8	1	23	30	
intestine	L-Ala-Gly	30	MnSO4	1	without	—	7.8	1	0.5	30	
pancreas	L-Val-Gly	25	MnSO4	1.5	without	—	7.8	1	0.5–2	30	
kidney	L-Asp-Gly	10	—	—	without	—	7.8	—	0.2	30	
uterus	Gly-L-Tyr	—	—	—	Phosphate	20	7.0	—	—	37	32
kidney	L-Leu-L-Asp	20	—	—	—	—	—	—	—	—	
serum	L-Ala-Gly	0.05	MgSO4	6	Phosphate	30	7.8	—	1	40	33
	Gly-dehydro-L-Phe	—	—	—	—	—	—	—	—	—	
Leucyl-glycine dipeptidase***	L-Leu-Gly	5	MnCl2	2	Tris (barbital)	33	8.4	—	4	37	19, 47
Tripeptidase*****	Gly-Gly-Gly	25	CoCl2	50	Phosphate	50	7.8	—	1	37	34, 35
	(Leu-Gly-Gly)										36, 17, 27, 30–32
Tripeptidase******	L-Pro-Gly-Gly	50	—	—	Tris	40	7.9	—	4	40	37, 40
Tripeptidase	Gly-Pro-L-Hyp	—	—	—	—	—	—	—	—	—	41

* Concentrations in incubation mixture
** Tris-HCl is recommended instead.
*** 37 °C is recommended.
**** Probably identical with leucine aminopeptidase, EC 3.4.11.1
***** Probably identical with aminopeptidase, EC 3.4.11.4, or at least closely related.
****** Probably identical with proline iminopeptidase, EC 3.4.11.5.

+ 50 mM is recommended.
++ 15–60 min. is recommended, even up to 4 hr., but only in exceptional cases up to 17 hr.

at 225–235 nm with increase in hydrolysis of the peptide bond of dipeptides[18–20] or the decrease of colour intensity of the copper complex with tripeptides at 555 nm[21].

A generally applicable titrimetric method is described below which determines the free amino acids liberated on hydrolysis of di- or tripeptides. It is used to measure glycyl-glycine dipeptidase activity in serum; the optimum conditions for other dipeptidases are given in Table 2.

References, p. 985.

Glycyl-glycine Dipeptidase

Determination with Glycyl-glycine as Substrate[22, 25–28]

Application of Method: In biochemistry and clinical chemistry[45,53].

Principle

(1) $\text{Glycyl-glycine} + H_2O \xrightarrow[\text{dipeptidase}]{\text{glycyl-glycine}} 2 \text{ Glycine}$

The amino acid is quantitatively determined by the formol titration method of *Sörensen*.

Optimum Conditions for Measurements

See section on "General Information", p. 978. No conversion factors for measurements at different temperatures are available.

Equipment

Water bath (37 °C); stopwatch or alarm clock; 2–5 ml. burette with "Schellbach"-stripe; cold bath (4 °C).

Reagents

1. Tris-hydroxymethyl-aminomethane, tris
2. Hydrochloric acid, 1.0 N
3. Glycyl-glycine
4. Cobalt sulphate, $CoSO_4 \cdot 7H_2O$

5. Formol, 18%
6. Thymol blue
7. Phenolphthalein
8. Sodium hydroxide, 0.1 N

Preparation of Solutions (for ca. 20 normal or 200 micro-assays)

Use only doubly distilled water
  I. Tris buffer (0.2 M; pH 8.0):
     Dissolve 1.21 g. tris in 25 ml. distilled water, add 6.1 ml. 1.0 N HCl and dilute to 50 ml. with distilled water; check pH with a glass electrode.
 II. Glycyl-glycine (125 mM):
     Dissolve 412 mg. glycyl-glycine in 25 ml. distilled water.
III. Cobalt sulphate (10 mM):
     Dissolve 70.2 mg. $CoSO_4 \cdot 7H_2O$ in 25 ml. distilled water.
 IV. Indicator mixture:
     Dissolve 5 mg. phenolphthalein + 5 mg. thymol blue in 50 ml. formol solution and filter.

Stability of Solutions

The substrate solution is stable for about 1 week at 4 °C, but it is preferable to prepare it freshly each day and to store it in a cold bath. The indicator mixture and the other solutions are stable for months at 4 °C.

Procedure

Collection, Treatment and Stability of Sample

Collection and treatment: Use fresh serum completely free from haemolysis. No interference due to addition of citrate (1 mg./ml.), oxalate (1 mg./ml.) or heparin (0.2 mg./ml.) is known. Centrifuge for 10 min. at ca. 3000 g to obtain serum of plasma. Solubilize suspensions of erythrocytes by haemolysis (dilute 1 : 2, v/v with distilled water) and suspensions of thrombocytes by ultrasonic treatment. Use homogenates, extracts or cell fractions after suitable dilution (according to the source).

Stability of enzyme in sample: Store serum and organ extracts for preferably not more than 24 hr. at 4 °C. The stability of purified preparations depends on the source, the method and degree of purification, and therefore must be determined individually. This applies in particular to other dipeptidases.

Assay System

Reaction temperature: 37 °C; final volume: 2.50 ml. (normal), 0.250 ml. (micro-assay).
Several values or values at different times of reaction can be taken for titration from the same incubation mixture.
Blank (t_0) from the test mixture: immediately after addition of substrate solution (II), take 0.5 ml. sample and treat as for test; control (to determine the spontaneous hydrolysis of the substrate): as for test, but containing 0.5 ml. physiological saline instead of sample.

Pipette into a test tube:			Concentration in assay mixture
Tris buffer	(I)	0.50 ml.	40 mM*
CoSO$_4$ solution	(III)	0.50 ml.	2 mM*
Sample (serum, homogenate, etc)		0.50 ml.	
Mix, pre-incubate for 10 min.			
Glycyl-glycine solution	(II)	1.00 ml.	50 mM
Mix. Immediately (0 min.) and after 4 hr. pipette into titration flask:			
Indicator mixture	(IV)	1.00 ml.	
Incubation solution		0.50 ml.	
Titrate with 0.1 NaOH to a light blue-purple colour. With homogenate samples titrate until the faded greyish-yellow colour of the indicator turns greyish-blue.			

* 67 or 13.3 mM respectively in the pre-incubation.

Calculations

1 ml. 0.1 N NaOH corresponds to 0.1 mmole hydrolysed substrate (do not forget titration correction of the NaOH). The amount of NaOH required in t_o samples is V_o and that required in the t_x samples is V_x. Calculate the difference $\Delta V = V_x - V_o$ and convert to the total incubation mixture (times 5), to 1.0 ml. sample volume (times 2) and to 1 min. (divide by 240). Calculate the activity in the sample, taking into account any dilution of the sample with factor F, from the following formula:

Normal assay: Volume activity $= \Delta V_{(ml.)} \times 4170 \times F$ [U/l.]

Micro-assay: Volume activity $= \Delta V_{(\mu l)} \times 41.7 \times F$ [U/l.]

Precision of Method

The coefficient of variation is 5.8% with 50 determinations on a single enzyme sample (precision) and 25% with 20 determinations on 20 different samples (rat liver homogenate)[33]. Another value of ca. 0.5% has been published[26] for multiple determinations on the same sample.

Normal Values

No data are available for a large collective. Human serum contains $x \pm s = 240 \pm 130$ U/l. (n = 24)[39], serum of children 160 ± 120 U/l.[38] (37 °C). With L-alanyl-alanine, values of 366 U/l.[33] (mouse plasma) have been found, while for L-leucyl-glycine values of 11.5 ± 0.5 U/l.[34], or 8.2 ± 9.0 ($\female$) and 14.9 ± 11.2 ($\male$) U/l. have been reported (all at 37 °C)[35]. With carnosine as substrate, values of 11.9 ± 5.2 U/l. (children) and 20.3 ± 8.6 U/l. (adults) have been published[48].

Sources of Error

Effects of drugs and other therapeutic measures: None known.

Interference in the assay technique: If the method is adhered to there should be no interference.

Specificity of Method, see "General Information", p. 978.

Details of Measurements in Tissues[42]

See p. 958, p. 963, p. 970. For other details, see original references, and Table 1 and 2 of this chapter. It is recommended to use 0.25 M sucrose $+ 0.1\%$ (v/v) Triton X-100 as homogenization medium (1 : 5, w/v). The same medium can be used for cell fractions[38].

Other Assay Methods

The determination of the enzymatically liberated amino acids can also be made with the ninhydrin reaction[35].

Micro-method

The method described here is so arranged that a 1 : 10 reduction of all volumes can be made. For micro-assay for example, 20–50 μl. of human serum are required. We have had considerable experience with the Beckman-Spinco and Eppendorf micro-systems[38].

References

1 *E. L. Smith* in *S. P. Colowick* & *N. O. Kaplan:* Methods in Enzymol., Academic Press, New York–London 1965, Vol. *II*, p. 93.
2 *E. L. Smith*, J. biol. Chem. *176*, 9 & 21 [1948].
3 *D. S. Robinson, S. M. Birnbaum* & *J. P. Greenstein*, J. biol. Chem. *202*, 1 [1953].
4 *A. Nishi*, J. Biochem. *45*, 991 [1958].
5 *H. T. Hanson* & *E. L. Smith*, J. biol. Chem. *179*, 789 [1949].
6 *A. Rosenberg*, Arch. Biochem. *88*, 83 [1960].
7 *N. R. Jones*, Biochem. J. *64*, 20 P [1956].
8 *N. R. Jones*, Biochem. J. *60*, 81 [1955].
9 *F. Binkley, V. Alexander, F. E. Bell* & *C. Lea*, J. biol. Chem. *228*, 559 [1957].
10 *G. Semenza*, Biochim. Biophys. Acta *24*, 401 [1957].
11 *N. C. Davis* & *E. L. Smith*, J. biol. Chem. *200*, 373 [1953].
12 *E. .L. Smith* & *M. Bergmann*, J. biol. Chem. *153*, 627 [1944].
13 *N. C. Davis* & *E. L. Smith*, J. biol. Chem. *224*, 261 [1957].
14 *E. Adams* & *E. L. Smith*, J. biol. Chem. *198*, 671 [1952].
15 *F. Schneider*, Biochem. Z. *307*, 427 [1940/41].
16 *R. Cordonnier*, Bull. Soc. Chim. Biol. *43*, 1155 [1961] and Compt. Rend. Acad. sci. Paris, *253*, 748 [1961].
17 *E. Waldschmidt-Leitz* & *L. Keller*, Hoppe-Seylers Z. physiol. Chem. *309*, 228 [1958].
18 *S. Traniello* & *A. Vescia*, Arch. Biochem. Biophysics, *105*, 465 [1964].
19 *B. J. Campbell, Y. Ch. Lin, R. V. Davis* & *E. Ballew*, Biochim. Biophys. Acta *118*, 371 [1966].
20 *F. J. Behal, J. D. Folds*, Biochem. Biophys. Res. Comm. *27*, 344 [1967].
21 *F. Binkley* & *C. Torres*, Arch. Biochem. Biophysics, *86*, 201 [1960].
22 *A. Schmitt* & *G. Siebert*, Biochem. Z. *334*, 96 [1961].
23 *L. Josefsson* & *T. Lindberg*, Biochim. Biophys. Acta *105*, 149 [1965].
24 *Z. Placer* & *J. Horky*, Clin. Chim. Acta 7, 190 [1962].
25 *H. Wüst* in *H. U. Bergmeyer:* Methoden der enzymatischen Analyse, Verlag Chemie, Weinheim 1962, 1st. edn., p. 824 ff.
26 *W. Rademaker* & *J. B. J. Scons*, Biochim. Biophys. Acta *24*, 209 [1957].
27 *W. Kocholaty*, Thromb. Diath. Häm. 7, 295 [1962].
28 *F. Binkley, V. Alexander, F. E. Bell* & *Ch. Lea*, J. biol. Chem. *228*, 559 [1957].
29 *S. Sarid, A. Berger* & *E. Katchalski*, J. biol. Chem. *237*, 2207 [1962].
30 *B. Sylvén* & *I. Bois*, Histochem. *3*, 65 [1962].
31 *M. Messer, Ch. M. Anderson* & *R. R. W. Townley*, Clin. Chim. Acta *6*, 768 [1961].
32 *H. J. Albers, J. M. Bedford* & *M. C. Chang*, Amer. J. Physiol. *201*, 554 [1961].
33 *R. Ottoson* & *B. Sylvén*, Arch. Biochem. Biophysics 87, 41 [1960].
34 *G. A. Fleisher, M. Pankow* & *C. Warmka*, Clin. Chim. Acta 9, 259 [1964].
35 *G. Brunner, J. Sommer* & *R. Kattermann*, Klin. Wschr. *46*, 541 [1968].
36 *R. Noack, O. Koldovsky, M. Friedrich, A. Heringova, V. Jirsova* & *G. Schenk*, Biochem. J. *100*, 775 [1966].
37 *E. Adams, N. C. Davis* & *E. L. Smith*, J. biol. Chem. *199*, 845 [1952].
38 *W. Appel*, unpublished results.
39 *W. Appel, V. Wirmer* & *St. Ebenezer*, Anästhesist. *17*, 95 [1968].
40 *H. Kirschke*, Abstr. 5th. FEBS-Meeting, Prague, 43 [1968].
41 *A. Nordwig*, Abstr. 5th. FEBS-Meeting, Prague, 83 [1968].
42 *Ch. A. Gründig, F. Felicetti* & *W. Rumler*, Hoppe-Seylers Z. physiol. Chem. *348*, 51 [1967].
43 *A. Schmitt* & *G. Siebert*, Hoppe-Seylers Z. physiol. Chem. *348*, 1009 [1967].
44 *N. O. Berg, A. Dahlqvist, T. Lindberg* & *A. Norden*, Gastroenterology *59*, 575 [1970].
45 *A. Dillon, J. Duffy, J. O. Dolly* & *P. F. Fottrell*, Biochem. J., *119*, 7P [1970].
46 *A. P. Douglas* & *T. J. Peters*, Gut, *11*, 15 [1970].
47 *T. J. Peters*, Biochem. J. *120*, 196 [1970].
48 *D. Felicetti* & *H. Hanson*, Hoppe-Seyler's Z. Physiol. Chem. *351*, 1253 [1970].
49 *D. Felicetti* & *H. Hanson*, Hoppe-Seyler's Z. Physiol. Chem. *351*, 1260 [1970].
50 *K. T. Kossmann* & *U. Kühner*, Klin. Wschrft. *48*, 297 [1970].
51 *W. J. Williams, F. A. Pitlick, Y. Nemerson, A. J. Gottlieb* & *R. G. Gordon*, Biochemistry, *10*, 2650 [1971].
52 *J. O. Dolly, A. Dillon, M. J. Duffy* & *P. F. Fottrell*, Clin. Chim. A. *31*, 55 [1971].
53 *F. Sadikali*, Gut, *12*, 276 [1971].

Carboxypeptidases

Walter Appel

General Information*

Carboxypeptidases (EC 3.4.12.–) hydrolyse peptides with a free COOH group on the adjacent peptide or ester bond; an additional free NH_2-group is not necessary and can even inhibit the hydrolysis.

Carboxypeptidase A, EC 3.4.12.2, (pancreatic carboxypeptidase) is one of the longest known and most studied peptidases; its properties, structure and active site are known[1-6]. It acts on many proteins and peptides but C-terminal proline and basic amino acids are not hydrolysed. Different types of carboxypeptidase A_1, A_2 and A_3[7,36] or A_α, $_\beta$ and A_γ[5,8] are formed from procarboxypeptidase[41-44].

Carboxypeptidase B, EC 3.4.12.3 (protaminase) is also an homogeneous form which can be isolated from pancreas[9]. It hydrolyses particularly rapidly C-terminal basic amino acids like L-arginine, L-lysine or L-ornithine from natural or synthetic peptides or proteins. For a new peptidase, see[45].

Yeast carboxypeptidase, EC 3.4.12.8, has only been obtained in partially purified form[10]. It resembles carboxypeptidase A in its substrate specificity, but it hydrolyses C-terminal glycine and L-leucine more rapidly, and L-phenylalanine more slowly.

Carboxypeptidases occur in many organs and are generally termed catheptic carboxypeptidases[11,12]. This also includes cathepsin IV[13] and -A[14,15]. A new group is the acid carboxypeptidases[16,17,40,46], which differ from all other carboxypeptidases. In blood serum an enzyme distinct from carboxypeptidase B has been found; it hydrolyses in particular C-terminal basic amino acids and bradykinin[18-21]. This carboxypeptidase N is related to the kininases, but is not identical with them[37]. Recently carboxytripeptidases have been described[22,23,47]. In bacteria, moulds and plants carboxypeptidases have been found[48-50]; a bacterial carboxypeptidase G^{24} and a carboxypeptidase C from citrus fruits have been described in more detail[38,39]. For the sake of completeness information is given on enzyme groups related to the carboxypeptidases, namely amino acid acylases and γ-glutamylcarboxypeptidases (conjugases)[1]. Other enzymes are still under investigation: carboxypeptidase I from *E. coli*[51], D-alanine-carboxypeptidase from *B. subtilis*[52,53], D-Ala-D-Ala-carboxypeptidase from *Streptomyces* strains[54], carboxypeptidase G_1 from *Pseudomonas* strains[55,56] and the very interesting group of dipeptidylcarboxypeptidases from higher animals, the so called "Kininase II" or "Angiotensin-I-converting enzyme". For diagnostic applications, see [57-62].

Two methods for the determination of carboxypeptidase A and one for carboxypeptidase B are described here. Of these the colorimetric method is particularly suited for assays of tissue homogenates, because it gives very low blanks. Catheptic carboxypeptidases can also be determined by these two methods, but in this case cysteine is used instead of Co^{2+} in the pre-incubation; the pH is 4.0[15].

References, see p. 998.

---

* See p. 949.

Table 1. Classification, occurrence, purification and activity optima of carboxypeptidases.

Enzyme	Occurrence	Purification from	Optimum Substrate	pH	Activators	Effectors Inhibitors	Inactive
Carboxypeptidase A EC 3.4.12.2	Pancreas and pancreatic juice; intestine of many mammals and humans	Bovine pancreas[1-8]	Z-Gly-L-Phe; Z-L-Ala-L-Phe; Carbonaphthoxy-L-Phe	7.5–7.8 $\mu = 0.3$ (NaCl, LiCl)	Zn^{2+}, Mn^{2+}, Fe^{2+}, Co^{2+}, Ni^{2+}, Cd^{2+}, Hg^{2+} (apoenzyme)	Cu^{2+}, Pb^{2+}, Fe^{2+}, EDTA, citrate, oxalate, PO_3^{-}, $P_2O_7^{4-}$, cysteine, CN^{-}, SH^{-}, o-phenanthroline, L-Phe*	Zn^{2+}, Ni^{2+}, Fe^{2+}, Mn^{2+} **, Co^{2+}, Mg^{2+}, Ca^{2+}, (holoenzyme); F^{-}, N_3^{-}
Carboxypeptidase B EC 3.4.12.3	Pancreas	Pig pancreas[9]; bovine pancreas[25,26] (via procarboxy-peptidase)	Hipp-L-Arg; Hipp-L-Lys	7.6–8.0 according to the substrate	Zn^{2+}, Co^{2+}, Ca^{2+}, (only n-butanol)	Cd^{2+} (peptidase); o-phenanthroline; α, α'-dipyridyl	EDTA DFP Hippuric acid Arginine
Yeast carboxypeptidase EC 3.4.12.8	Brewers' yeast, bakers' yeast	Brewers' yeast[10]	DNP-Gly-Gly; Z-Gly-L-Leu	6.0	—	Hg^{2+}	Co^{2+}, Mn^{2+}, Ca^{2+}, Mg^{2+}, Ba^{2+}
Catheptic carboxypeptidase EC 3.4.12.12	Many organs of many mammals; bacteria; moulds; plants	Rat liver, rat kidneys[11], pig liver, pig spleen[12]; pig kidney[25]; ox kidneys and spleen[13,15]; *Phymototrichum omnivorum*[26]	Z-Gly-L-Phe; Z-Gly-L-Tyr	5.0–5.1 3.4–4.0[15]	SH^{-}, CN^{-}, glutathione, cysteine, 2-mercapto-ethylamine	ZN^{2+}, monoiodoacetic acid, phenylhydrazine	Co^{2+}, Ascorbic acid

* Also hydrolysis products of other substrates or substrate analogues.
** According to the source; the data in the literature is not in agreement.

Table 1. Classification, occurrence, purification and activity optima of carboxypeptidases (continued).

Enzyme	Occurrence	Purification from	Optimum Substrate	pH	Activators	Effectors Inhibitors	Inactive
Acid carboxypeptidase EC 3.4.12.-	Bovine aorta; bovine spleen	Bovine spleen[17]	L-Ser-L-Ser-L-leu	5.0	—	Hg^{2+}, Ca^{2+}, Mn^{2+}, Co^{2+}, Zn^{2+}, Mg^{2+}, Al^{2+}, Fe^{2+}, Fe^{2+}, CN^-, cysteine, p-CMB, glutathione, EDTA, iodoacetamide, aminocaproic acid, O-phenanthroline	—
Carboxypeptidase N EC 3.4.12.7	Serum and plasma of many mammals; birds and amphibia; lymph, urine, and thrombocytes of human	Human plasma[18] rabbit serum[27]	Hipp-L-Lys; Hipp-L-Arg; bradykinin	7.4 (7.6)	Co^{2+}, Ni^{2+} n-butanol	Hg^{2+}, Zn^{2+}, Cd^{2+}, EDTA, mercaptoethanol	—
Carboxypeptidase EC 3.4.12.11	Pituitary	Anterior pituitary[22]; pig kidneys[23]	L-Ala-L-Ala -L-Ala; Z-Gly-L-Pro-L-Ala	4.5 (7.8)	(Mn^{2+})	Hg^{2+}	EDTA SH-reagents

Carboxypeptidase A

Determination with N-Carbobenzoxy-glycyl-L-phenylalanine as Substrate[1, 28]

Application of Method: In biochemistry

Principle

(1)   N-Carbobenzoxy-glycyl-L-phenylalanine + H_2O $\xrightarrow[\text{peptidase}]{\text{carboxy}-}$

N-Carbobenzoxy-glycine + Phenylalanine

The second acid amide bond which disappears on enzymatic hydrolysis causes a decrease in the extinction at 232 nm which can be measured quantitatively. The amino acid formed can be determined with the ninhydrin method (colorimetric method). The latter method is recommended when the enzyme activity is low or the blanks are high or no spectrophotometer is available, and is certainly the method of choice with impure preparations from organs.

Optimum Conditions for Measurements

The pH optimum is between 7.5 and 7.8. Phosphate buffer is to be avoided and should be replaced by tris. The activity is maximal with a salt concentration of 0.1 M to 0.3 M and is independent of the type of cation or anion; therefore LiCl used in earlier work is replaced by NaCl. The substrate concentration must not exceed 50 mM and is best between 10–20 mM. According to[28] the activity increases by 100% after 15 min. pre-incubation in 10 mM Co^{2+} solution. Addition of 1 mM Ca^{2+} to the incubation mixture has been suggested[29,30], which is not justified on theoretical grounds and in general the requirement has not been confirmed experimentally. With pure enzymes and high activity the pre-incubation can be omitted. Measurements at different temperatures may require different measuring conditions (cf. p. 127). Nevertheless, results obtained under the same measuring conditions but at different temperatures were formerly compared with each other ("conversion factors" were determined). Such conversion factors may be correct if determined with a relatively large proband collective; however, they cannot be applied generally to the individual case (cf. p. 129). The value of the following relative reaction rates[33] thus lies in being able to appraise the temperature dependence of the reaction and at the most to compare qualitatively values.

°C	20	*25*	30	35	40	40	45
	1.22	*1.00*	0.85	0.63	0.59	0.53	0.46

Equipment

Spectrophotometer or filter photometer, preferably with constant temperature cuvette holder; water baths (37 °C and boiling); cold bath (4 °C); stopwatch or laboratory alarm clock; 1 cm. quartz cuvettes.

Reagents

1. Tris-hydroxymethyl-aminomethane, tris
2. Hydrochloric acid, 1.0 N
3. Sodium chloride, NaCl

4. Cobalt chloride, $CoCl_2 \cdot 6\,H_2O$
5. N-Carbobenzoxy-glycyl-L-phenyl-alanine

6. Sodium cyanide, NaCN
7. Sodium acetate, $CH_3COONa \cdot 3H_2O$
8. Acetic acid
9. Ninhydrin
10. Ethyleneglycolmonomethylether

11. Ethanol
12. Sodium hydroxide, 1 N
13. Phenylalanine
14. N-Carbobenzoxy-glycine

Preparation of Solutions (for ca. 20 normal or 200 micro-assays).

Use only doubly distilled water.

I. Tris buffer (0.15 M; pH 7.6):
   Dissolve 0.91 g. tris in ca. 25 ml. distilled water, add 5.5 ml. 1.0 N HCl and dilute with distilled water to 50 ml.; check the pH with a glass electrode.

II* Cobalt chloride (40 mM) in sodium chloride (600 mM):
   Dissolve 0.24 g. $CoCl_2 \cdot 6H_2O$ and 0.88 g. NaCl in 25 ml. distilled water.

III. N-Carbobenzoxy-glycyl-L-phenylalanine (30 mM):
   Suspend 0.225 g. in 15-20 ml. distilled water, adjust to pH 7-8 with ca. 0.6 ml. 1 N NaOH and dilute to 25 ml. with distilled water.

IV. Acetate-cyanide reagent:
   Dilute 0.360 g. sodium acetate, 0.01 g. NaCN and 67 ml. acetic acid to 1 000 ml. with distilled water. It is recommended to prepare this amount because the buffer must stand for at least one week at 4 °C, otherwise high blank values are obtained.

V. Ninhydrin reagent:
   Dissolve 0.750 g. ninhydrin in 25 ml. ethyleneglycolmonomethylether.

VI. Ethanol, ca. 50%:
   Mix 50 ml. ethanol with 50 ml. distilled water.

Stability of Solutions

The substrate solution must be prepared freshly each day and stored in a cold bath. The other solutions are stable for months at 4 °C. The ninhydrin reagent should be protected from ammonia.

Procedure

Collection, Treatment and Stability of Sample

No information is available for serum. If necessary, filter duodenal juice and dilute 1 : 3–1 : 10. Use homogenates, extracts or cell fractions of tissues directly after suitable dilution (according to source). Crystalline, commercially available carboxypeptidase A.

Assay System

UV Method: Wavelength: 232 nm; light path: 1 cm.; reaction temperature: 37 °C; final volume: 3.0 ml.; read against a reference cuvette: as for test but containing 1 ml. physiological saline

---

* Solution II also without $CoCl_2$ (see section on Optimum Conditions for Measurements, p. 989).

instead of sample; set the extinction at E = 1.0; control (to determine the spontaneous hydrolysis of the substrate): measure reference cuvette against water.

Colorimetric method: Wavelength: 570 nm; light path: 1 cm.; reaction temperature: 37 °C; final volume: 3.00 ml. (normal), 0.300 ml. (micro-assay); read against reference cuvette containing solution VI; blank (E_0): immediately after addition of the substrate solution (III) to the test remove samples and treat as for test; control (to determine the spontaneous hydrolysis of the substrate); as for test but containing 1.0 ml. physiological saline instead of sample.

Pipette into quartz cuvettes (UV method) or test tubes (colorimetric method):			Concentration in assay mixture
Tris buffer	(I)	0.50 ml.	25 mM*
CoCl$_2$ - NaCl solution	(II)	0.50 ml.	6.6 mM Co^{2+}
Sample (duodenal juice, homogenate, etc.)		1.00 ml.	100 mM Na$^+$
Mix with a plastic spatula and preincubate for 15 min.			
Z-Gly-Phe-solution	(III)	1.00 ml.	10 mM
Mix and start stopwatch. *UV method:* Read extinction E_x at 1–2 min. intervals. *Colorimetric method:* Take a sample immediately (t_o) and then again after 30 min. incubation (t_x) and pipette into stoppered test tube (placed in a cold bath):			
Distilled water		0.90 ml.	
Acetate-cyanide reagent	(IV)	0.50 ml.	
Incubation solution		0.10 ml.	
Place for 2 min. in a boiling water bath.			
Ninhydrin reagent	(V)	0.50 ml.	
Place for exactly 15 min. in a boiling water bath and cool under running water and place in a cold bath			
Ethanol	(Solution VI)	3.00 ml.	
Add, mix thoroughly and measure the extinctions E_o or E_x			

* Concentrations in pre-incubation 38 mM tris, 10 mM Co^{2+}, 600 mM Na$^+$.

Calculations

UV Method:

Under the above conditions an extinction increase of $\Delta E = 0.85$ corresponds to 100% hydrolysis of the substrate. After allowing for the assay volume, for any dilution with the factor F and correction for spontaneous hydrolysis, the activity is calculated as follows:

$$\text{Volume activity} = 35200 \times F \times \Delta E_{corr.}/\text{min. [U/l.]}$$

Colorimetric Method:

Standard curve: Dissolve 10.33 mg. phenylalanine (62.5 μmole) in 50 ml. tris buffer (I). The concentration of the standard solution is 1.25 mM. Dilute 0.05–0.50 ml. (0.063–0.625 μmole) to 1.0 ml. with distilled water, add 0.50 ml. acetate-cyanide reagent (IV) and treat as described above. Blank as for standards but without phenylalanine. Plot the extinction differences (ordinate) against the μmole phenylalanine (abscissa). Convert the extinction differences $\Delta E = E_x - E_o$ for the enzyme assays into "μmole phenylalanine" by reading off from the standard curve. The controls to determine the spontaneous hydrolysis of substrate are calculated in the same way and this value is subtracted from the test to give the "μmole$_{corr.}$". After allowing for the aliquot taken (times 30), the reaction time (divide by 30) and any dilution of the sample by factor F the activity is calculated as follows:

Normal assay: Volume activity $= \mu$mole$_{corr.} \times$ F [U/l.]

Micro-assay: Volume activity $=$ nmole$_{corr.} \times 0.01 \times$ F [U/l.]

Precision of Method

The coefficient of variation is 9.8% (UV method) and 8.6% (colorimetric micro-assay) respectively with 30 assays on a single enzyme sample (precision) and 18.3% (colorimetric micro-assay) on 20 different enzyme samples (rat liver homogenate).

Normal Values

In serum of 51 children an activity of $\bar{x} \pm 2 s = 103 \pm 106$ U/l. (37 °C) was found[33]. In rat liver values of 10–1300 U/g. fresh wt. (37 °C) and in rat heart of 10–770 U/g. fresh wt. (37 °C) have been obtained; these values are only to give an indication of the range[35].

Sources of Error

No interference is to be expected if the method is adhered to.

Specificity of Method

The method is specific for caboxypeptidase A.

Details for Measurements in Tissues

It is recommended to use 0.25 M aqueous sucrose $+$ 0.1% (v/v) Triton X-100 as medium for homogenization (1 : 5 w/v). The same medium can be used for the study of cell fractions[33].

Micro-assay

The above method is so arranged that a 1 : 10 or 1 : 20 reduction in all volumes can be made. For the standardization the same solutions are used, the standard curves are identical with those for the normal assay (but have 10 times smaller values on the abscissa). For this method, for example, 20 mg. rat liver are required. We have had considerable experience with the Beckman-Spinco and Eppendorf micro-systems.

References, p. 998.

Carboxypeptidase A

Determination with N-(Carbo-β-naphthoxy)-DL-phenylalanine as Substrate[1, 29-32]

Application of Method: In biochemistry and clinical chemistry

Principle

(1)   N-(Carbo-β-naphthoxy)-DL-phenylalanine $+ H_2O \xrightarrow[\text{peptidase A}]{\text{carboxy}}$

Carbonic acid-β-naphthylester $+$ DL-Phenylalanine

(2)   Carbonic acid-β-naphthylester $\longrightarrow$ β-Naphthol $+ CO_2$

(3)   β-Naphthol $\xrightarrow[\text{di - o - anisidine}]{\text{tetrazotized}}$ Azo dye

The carbonic acid-β-naphthylester formed during the enzymatic hydrolysis decomposes spontaneously to give CO_2 and β-naphthol; the latter forms an insoluble azo dye with tetrazotized di-o-anisidine. This is extracted with ethyl acetate and the concentration is measured at 546 nm. It is the method of choice for weakly active or impure samples because of the low blanks.

Optimum Conditions for Measurements

The pH optimum is between 7.4–7.8. As there is no linearity between the amount of enzyme and the substrate hydrolysed[28,29] at a substrate concentration of 0.16 mM[31], this is increased to 0.6 mM[29]. For information on the question of activation, see p. 989. Co^{2+} causes high blanks[33] (catalysis of the spontaneous hydrolysis of the substrate?) and is therefore replaced here by Ca^{2+} [29,30]. The blanks can increase considerably with assays at temperatures above 37 °C. The suggested reaction times are 25 min. for duodenal juice and 120 min. for serum. Relative reaction rates[33] according to p. 989.

C°	20	25	30	35	37	40	45
	1.22	1.00	0.85	0.63	0.59	0.53	0.46

Equipment

Filter photometer, water bath (37 °C), cold bath (4 °C); stopwatch or laboratory alarm clock; test tubes (20–25 ml.) with ground-glass stoppers.

Reagents

1. Tris-hydroxymethyl-aminomethane, tris
2. Hydrochloric acid, 0.1 N
3. Calcium chloride, $CaCl_2 \cdot 2H_2O$
4. N-(Carbo-β-naphthoxy)-DL-phenyl-alanine
5. True blue salt B (tetrazotized di-o-anisidine)

6. Perchloric acid, ca. 70% (w/w), sp. gr. 1.67
7. Ethyl acetate
8. Sodium sulphate, Na_2SO_4, anhydrous
9. Methanol
10. β-Naphthol

Preparation of Solutions (for ca. 20 normal or 200 micro-assays)

Use only doubly distilled water.
I. Tris buffer (50 mM; pH 7.8):
   Dissolve 1.21 g. tris in ca. 50 ml. distilled water, add 68.4 ml. 0.1 N HCl and dilute to 200 ml.
   with distilled water; check pH with glass electrode.
II. Calcium chloride (250 mM):
   Dissolve 1.84 g. $CaCl_2 \cdot 2H_2O$ in 50 ml. distilled water.
III. N-(Carbo-β-naphthoxy)-DL-phenylalanine (6 mM L-isomer):
   Dissolve 80 mg. DL-form in 20 ml. methanol.
IV. Tetrazotized di-o-anisidine, chromogen (0.4%):
   Dissolve 200 mg. true blue salt B in 50 ml. distilled water.

Stability of Solutions

Prepare the true blue salt solution (IV) immediately before use, the substrate solution (III) freshly each day;
the other solutions are stable for months.

Procedure

Collection, Treatment and Stability of Sample

See p. 990. Dilute duodenal juice 1 : 20 (v/v)

Assay System

Wavelength: Hg 546 nm; light path: 1 cm.; reaction temperature: 37 °C; final volume: 5.0 ml.
(normal), 0.50 ml. (micro-assay); read against reference cuvette containing ethyl acetate.
Blank (E_0) parallel to the tests: immediately after addition of substrate solution (III) add the
chromogen solution (IV)(or inactivate the enzyme before addition by heating for 5 min. in a
boiling water bath) then treat as described for the test; control (to determine the spontaneous
hydrolysis of the substrate); as for the test but containing 0.4 ml. physiological saline instead
of sample.

Pipette into a test tube:			Concentration in assay mixture
Tris buffer	(I)	4.00 ml.	40 mM*
CaCl$_2$ solution	(II)	0.10 ml.	5 mM*
Sample (duodenal juice, homogenate)		0.40 ml.	
Mix thoroughly and pre-incubate for about 10 min.			
N-Carbo-β-naphthoxy-Phe- solution	(III)	0.50 ml.	0.6 mM
Mix thoroughly and incubate for exactly 25 min. (or 120 min.).			
Chromogen solution	(IV)	1.00 ml.	
After exactly 1 min. add			
70% Perchloric acid		1.00 ml.	
Ethyl acetate**		10.00 ml.	
Extract by frequent back-and-forth movement (do not shake). Allow the phases to separate, transfer 7–9 ml. of the clear upper phase (without any of the inter-phase) to a dry test tube containing a spatula tip of Na$_2$SO$_4$ and read the extinction E$_0$ or E$_x$			

* Concentrations in the pre-incubation: 45 mM tris and 11 mM Ca^{2+}.
** It is recommended to use double the equivalent volume, i.e. 2.0 ml. in the micro-assay.

Calculations

Standard Curve:

Dissolve 72.1 mg. β-naphthol (0.5 mmole) in ca. 100 ml. methanol and dilute to 1 000 ml. with distilled water (0.5 mM). Dilute 0.05–0.80 ml. of this standard solution (0.025–0.40 μmole) with tris buffer (I) to 5.0 ml. and then treat as described above. Blank as for standard but without β-naphthol. Plot the extinction differences (ordinate) against "μmole β-naphthol" (abscissa).
Convert the extinction differences $\Delta E = E_x - E_0$ for the enzyme assays into "μmole β-naphthol" by reading off from the standard curve. The control values are calculated in the same way and then subtracted from the test; this gives the "μmole$_{corr.}$". With allowance for the amount of sample taken (times 2.5), the reaction time (divide by 25) and any dilution of the sample with the factor F, the activity is calculated as follows:

Normal assay: Volume activity $= \mu$mole$_{corr.} \times 100 \times$ F [U/l.]

Micro assay: Volume activity $=$ nmole$_{corr.} \times$ F [U/l.]

Precision of Method

The coefficient of variation was 10.2% with 23 assays on a single sample (precision) and 8.6% on 21 different human sera.

Normal Values

In serum of 21 children a value of $\bar{x} \pm 2s = 2.5 \pm 0.6$ U/l. (37 °C) was obtained[33]. For duodenal juice a hydrolysis of 10–25 mg. substrate[29] or 2.1–51.0 μmole β-naphthol/min./ml. has been published, this corresponds to 15–327 U/l.[30]. Duodenal juice contains 80–240 U[32] carboxypeptidase A per litre (n = 100).

Sources of Error

No interference should occur if the conditions described above are adhered to. EDTA interferes with the diazotization. If the true blue salt does not dissolve to give a clear solution, the reagent should be obtained from another manufacturer. Variation of the ethyl acetate volume is hardly possible, because otherwise two phases are not formed. The substrate solution shows considerable spontaneous hydrolysis, so therefore always prepare freshly[33].

Specificity of Method

The method is specific for carboxypeptidases. There are however indications that as with the aminopeptidases, the catheptic carboxypeptidases of animal tissues include enzymes with a preference for amino acid amides, which may hydrolyse N-(carbo-β-naphthoxy)-L-phenylalanine[33].

Details for Measurements in Tissues

It is recommended to use 0.25 M aqueous sucrose solution + 0.1% (v/v) Triton X-100 as the medium for homogenization (1 : 5, w/v). This medium can also be used for cell fractions[33].

Micro-assay

The method described here is so arranged that a 1 : 10 and 1 : 20 reduction of all volumes can be made; for example, 10 mg. rat liver are then required. We have had considerable experience with the Beckman-Spinco and Eppendorf micro-systems.

References, p. 998.

Carboxypeptidase B

Determination with Hippuryl-L-arginine as Substrate[9, 28, 34]

Application of Method: In biochemistry

Principle

(1)   N-Benzoyl-glycyl-L-arginine + H_2O $\xrightarrow[\text{peptidase B}]{\text{carboxy} -}$ N-Benzoyl-glycine + L-Arginine
(Hippuric acid)

The hippuric acid formed in the enzymatic hydrolysis has a higher absorption at 254 nm than the original peptide, and this allows the enzyme activity to be followed.

Optimum Conditions for Measurements

As described below. Relative reaction rates[35] according to p. 989:

C°	20	25	30	35	37	40
	1.50	1.00	0.76	0.61	0.56	(0.56)

Equipment

Spectrophotometer, preferably with constant temperature cuvette holder; water bath (37 °C); cold bath (4 °C); stopwatch; 1 cm. quartz cuvettes.

Reagents

1. Tris-hydroxymethyl-aminomethane, tris
2. Hydrochloric acid, 0.1 N
3. Sodium chloride, NaCl
4. N-Benzoyl-glycyl-L-arginine (hippuryl-L-arginine)
5. N-Benzoyl-glycine (hippuric acid)

Preparation of Solutions (for ca. 30 normal assays)

 I. Tris buffer (27.5 mM, pH 7.6; containing 0.11 M NaCl):
Dissolve 0.33 g. tris and 0.64 g. NaCl in ca. 25 ml. distilled water, add 22.5 ml. 0.1 N HCl and dilute to 100 ml. with distilled water; check pH with glass electrode.
 II. Hippuryl-L-arginine (1.1 mM):
Dissolve 39 mg. hippuryl-L-arginine in 100 ml. tris buffer (I).

Stability of Solutions

Prepare the substrate solution II freshly each day.

Procedure

Collection, Treatment and Stability of Sample

The conditions must be studied in each case, because no general rules can be given.

Assay System

Wavelength: 254 nm; light path: 1 cm.; reaction temperature: 37 °C; final volume: 3.00 ml. Read against reference cuvette: as for test cuvette, but containing 0.3 ml. distilled water instead of sample; the extinction is set to E = 0. Control cuvette (to determine the spontaneous hydrolysis of the substrate): read reference cuvette against distilled water.

Pipette into quartz cuvettes:			Concentration in assay mixture
Hippuryl-L-arginine solution (II)	2.7 ml.		1 mM
Sample (duodenal juice,			25 mM tris
homogenate, etc.)	0.3 ml.		100 mM NaCl
Mix thoroughly with a plastic spatula and read the extinction at 1–2 min. intervals.			

Calculations

Under the conditions chosen an increase in extinction of $\Delta E = 0.34$ corresponds to a 100% hydrolysis of the substrate. With allowance for the amount of sample taken (times 3.33), the assay volume (times 3.0) and any dilution with the factor F and after correction of spontaneous hydrolysis, the activity is given by the following formula:

$$\text{Volume activity} = 29\,400 \times F \times \Delta E_{corr.}/\text{min. [U/l.]}$$

Precision of Method

The coefficient of variation is 10.8% with 12 assays on a single sample (precision).

Normal Values

No normal values are available. A mean of 770 U/l. was found with hippuryl-L-lysine as substrate on sera 50 healthy blood donors[19].

Sources of Error

No interference should occur if the method is adhered to.

Specificity of Method

The method is specific for carboxypeptidase B.

References

1 *H. Hanson* in Hoppe-Seyler-Thierfelder: Handb. d. physiol.- a. path.-chem. Analyse, Springer Verlag, Berlin–Heidelberg–New York, 10th. edn., 1966, Vol. IV, Part C, p. 84.
2 *H. Neurath* in *S. P. Colowick* & *N. O. Kaplan:* Methods in Enzymol., Academic Press, New York–London, 1956, Vol. *II*, p. 77.
3 *P. D. Boyer, H. Lardy* & *K. Myrbäck:* The Enzymes, Academic Press, New York–London, 1960, Vol. *IV*.
4 *B. J. Allan, P. J. Keller* & *H. Neurath,* Biochem. *3,* 40 [1964].
5 *D. J. Cox, F. C. Bovard, J. P. Bargetzi, K. A. Walsh* & *H. Neurath,* Biochem. *3,* 44 [1964].

6 *M. Ebata & K. Miyazaki,* Experientia *23,* 1007 [1967].
7 *J. E. Folk & E. W. Schirmer,* Fed. Proc. *23,* 594 [1963].
8 *K. S. V. S. Kumar, K. A. Walsh, J. P. Bargetzi & H. Neurath,* Biochem. *2,* 1475 [1963].
9 *J. E. Folk, K. A. Piez, W. R. Carroll & J. A. Gladner,* J. biol. Chem. *235,* 2272 [1960].
10 *F. Félix & J. Labouesse-Mercouroff,* Biochim. Biophys. Acta *21,* 303 [1956].
11 *H. Hanson, W. Blech, P. Hermann & R. Kleine,* Hoppe-Seylers Z. physiol. Chem. *315,* 181 [1959].
12 *E. Waldschmidt-Leitz, A. Schäffner, I. J. Bek & E. Blum,* Hoppe-Seylers Z. physiol. Chem. *188,* 17 [1930].
13 *H. H. Tallan, M. E. Jones & J. S. Fruton,* J. biol. Chem. *194,* 793 [1952].
14 *A. A. Jodice,* Arch. Biochem. Biophysics *121,* 241 [1967].
15 *L. M. Greenbaum & R. Sherman,* J. biol. Chem. *237,* 1082 [1962].
16 *E. Buddecke, G. Reich & U. Stein,* Hoppe-Seylers Z. physiol. Chem. *347,* 192 [1966].
17 *U. Stein, U. Weber & E. Buddecke,* Hoppe-Seylers Z. physiol. Chem. *349,* 472 [1968].
18 *E. G. Erdös, E. M. Sloane & I. M. Wohler,* Biochem. Pharmacol. *13,* 893 [1964].
19 *E. G. Erdös, I. M. Wohler & M. I. Levine,* Clin. Chim. Acta *11,* 39 [1965].
20 *T. S. Paskhina & S. S. Trapesnikova,* Biokhimiya *32,* 527 [1967].
21 *H. E. Rugstad,* Brit. J. Pharmacol. Chemotherapie *30,* 425 [1967].
22 *F. H. Leibach & S. Ellis,* Abstr. Pap. Amer. Chem. Soc. 169 C [1966].
23 *A. Nordwig,* Abstr. 5th. FEBS-Meeting, Prague, 83 [1968], Hoppe-Seylers Z. physiol. Chem. *349,* 1353 [1968].
24 *C. C. Levy & P. Goldman,* J. biol. Chem. *243,* 3507 [1968].
25 *M. Bergmann,* Adv. Enzymology *2,* 49 [1942].
26 *J. D. Boston & J. M. Prescott,* Abstr. Pap. Amer. Chem. Soc. 170 C [1966].
27 *T. S. Paskhina, V. M. Gurtovenko, V. P. Zykova, V. Ph. Narticova, S. S. Trapesnikova,* Abstr. 5th. FEBS-Meeting Prague, 662 [1968].
28 *J. E. Folk & J. A. Gladner,* J. biol. Chem. *235,* 60 [1960].
29 *H. Schön, B. Rässler & N. Henning,* Klin. Wschr. *39,* 217 [1961].
30 *H. Wüst* in *H. U. Bergmeyer:* Methoden der enzymatischen Analyse, Verlag Chemie, Weinheim 1962, 1st. edn., p. 828 ff.
31 *H. A. Ravin & A. M. Seligman,* J. biol. Chem. *190,* 391 [1951].
32 *W. Rick,* Klin. Wschr. *38,* 408 [1960].
33 *W. Appel, E. Huth & H. Hermann,* Z. klin. Chem. klin. Biochem. *7,* 576 [1969].
34 *E. C. Wolff, E. W. Schirmer & J. E. Folk,* J. biol. Chem. *237,* 3094 [1962].
35 *W. Appel,* unpublished results.
36 *B. Hadorn & V. L. Silberberg,* Biochim. Biophys. Acta *151,* 702 [1968].
37 *S. S. Trapesnikova & T. S. Paskhina,* Biokhimiya *33,* 1012 [1968].
38 *K. Isaki & J. L. Strominger,* J. biol. Chem. *243,* 3193 [1968].
39 *H. Zuber,* Hoppe-Seylers Z. physiol. Chem. *349,* 1337 [1968].
40 *U. Stein & D. Platt,* Klin. Wschr. *46,* 1145 [1968].
41 *M. J. Pitout & W. Nel,* Biochem. Pharmacol. *18,* 1837 [1969].
42 *P. H. Pétra & H. Neurath,* Biochemistry *8,* 2466 [1969].
43 *A. S. Narayanan & R. A. Anwar,* Canad. J. Biochem. *48,* 7 [1970].
44 *D. S. Auld & B. L. Vallee,* Biochemistry *9,* 602 [1970].
45 *A. Kumon, Y. Matsuoka, Y. Kakimoto, T. Nakajima & I. Sano,* Biochim, Biophys. Acta, *200,* 466 [1970].
46 *D. Keppler, U. Stein, H. Heissmeyer, H. Wangemann, R. Lesch & W. Reutter,* Klin. Wochschr. *49,* 550 [1971].
47 *P. Dehm & A. Nordwig,* Europ. J. Biochem. *17,* 372 [1970].
48 *K. Visuri, J. Mikola & T. M. Enari,* Europ. J. Biochem. *7,* 193 [1969].
49 *J. D. Boston & J. M. Prescott,* Arch. Biochem. Biophys. *128,* 88 [1969].
50 *B. Sprössler, H.-D. Heilmann, E. Grampp & H. Uhlig,* Hoppe-Seyler's Z. Physiol. Chem. *352,* 1524 [1971].
51 *D. Bogdanovsky, E. Bricas & P. Dezelee,* Compt. Rend. Ser. D. *269,* 390 [1969]:
52 *P. M. Blumberg & J. L. Strominger,* Proc. Natl. Acad. sci. *68,* 2814 [1971].
53 *J. L. Strominger, K. Izaki & P. L. Lawrence,* Abstr. Pap. Am. Chem. Soc. 1969 No. 158 BIOL 3
54 *M. Leyh Bouille, J. Coyette, J. M. Ghuysen, J. Idczak, H. R. Perkins & M. Nieto,* Biochemistry *10,* 2163 [1971].
55 *B. A. Chabner, J. L. McCullough & J. R. Bertino,* Proc. Am. Assoc. Cancer Res. *12,* 88 [1971].
56 *J. L. McCullough, B. A. Chabner & J. R. Bertino,* J. biol. Chem. *246,* 7207 [1971].
57 *H. Y. T. Yang, E. G. Erdös & Y. Levin,* J. Pharmacol. Exp. Ther. *177,* 291 [1971].
58 *D. W. Cushman & H. S. Cheung,* Biochim. Biophys. Acta *250,* 261 [1971].
59 *L. P. Alexeenko, Y. E. Elisseeva, V. N. Orekhovich & L. V. Pavlikhina,* Clin. Chim. Acta, *31,* 413 [1971].
60 *J. J. Summary & H. A. Lillevik,* Abstr. Papers Am. Chem. Soc. 1971, No. 162 BIOL 184.
61 *E. G. Erdös, R. Igic & H. S. J. Yeh,* Pharmacologist *13,* 214 [1971].
62 *M. J. Pitout,* Biochem. Pharmacol. *18,* 1829 [1969].

Proteinases

Method for Automatic Analysers

George G. Hazen

The control of the production of proteinases by fermentation is an example of where manual analytical methods are too time-consuming and expensive and the required reproducibility even in the hands of highly qualified workers is lacking. An automated method for proteinase assay was described by *Hazen, Hause* and *Hubicki*[1] in 1965 (a modification of the azocasein method of *Charney* and *Tomarelli*[2].). *Berman, Lowenthal, Webster, Altieri* and *Gochenour*[3] had already improved the manual method and used it for the assay of proteinase in *Clostridium histolyticum*. The automated method has been used for the assay of keratinase in broth and concentrates of *Streptomyces fradiae*. The method of *Kunitz*[4] with casein was automated by *Reisner* and *Uhlig*[5] in 1966. Both methods use the AutoAnalyzer® with continuous filter; this allows the analysis of even gelatinous precipitates.

Application of Method: In research and industrial laboratories.

Principle

Azocasein hydrolysed by proteinases to form trichloroacetic acid-soluble chromophore compounds. The residual azocasein is precipitated by trichloroacetic acid and the precipitate is removed by a continuous filter. The filtrate develops a colour with NaOH which is measured at 420 nm. The samples are automatically taken up, exactly divided into aliquots and distributed by the continuous flow system which contains the substrate azocasein.

Optimum Conditions for Measurements

The proteinase activity is read off from a standard curve, which during continuous operation is checked every three to four hours with a sample of known proteinase activity. Exactly the same conditions must be used for the samples and the standards.

The azocasein concentration is chosen so that even with the highest measurable enzyme activity a visible precipitate forms in the presence of trichloroacetic acid. However, the substrate concentration should not be so high that clots form in the absence of enzyme. The highest standard should give an extinction of at least 0.200 at 420 nm. The assay is most accurate when the dilute samples are just below the highest standard. Optimum pH values, temperature and buffer vary with the enzyme added and must be determined afresh for each new enzyme. As standard and samples are measured under exactly the same conditions a certain range of variation is permissible.

Equipment

AutoAnalyzer* consisting of sampler, proportioning pump, 37 °C heating bath; continuous filter, 6 mm. flow-through cuvette (No. 105–1457), photometer and recorder, see Fig. 1 and 2. The heating bath has a coil double the standard length and diameter; two standard mixing coils are required. Acid resistant tubing (acid flex) is used for the trichloroacetic acid solution; Tygon is suitable for the other solutions. For the diameter of the tubing, see Fig. 2. Filter paper: $1'' \times 100'$ rolls (ca. 25 mm. × 30 m.), SS No. 2043 FF.

---

* AutoAnalyzer System from Technicon Controls Inc., Chauncey, New York, U.S.A.

Reagents

1. Potassium dihydrogen phosphate,
   KH_2PO_4
2. Dipotassium hydrogen phosphate,
   K_2HPO_4
3. Trichloroacetic acid
4. Sodium hydroxide, 0.5 N; 1 N; 1.5 N; 5 N
5. *Hammersten* casein, powdered*
6. Sodium acetate

7. Sulphanilamide
8. Sodium nitrite
9. Hydrochloric acid, 1 N; 5 N
10. Supercel**
11. Acetone
12. Tween 20***
13. Azocasein
    Preparation, see Appendix, p. 1005.
14. Protease standard preparation****

Preparation of Solutions (for ca. 2000 determinations)

Use only distilled water
   I. Phosphate buffer (0.1 M; pH 7.5):
      Dissolve 156.6 g. K_2HPO_4 in 9000 ml. distilled water. Dissolve 20.42 g. KH_2PO_4 in 1500 ml. distilled water. Adjust the first solution to pH 7.5 with the second.
  II. Trichloroacetic acid (6% w/v):
      Dissolve 1.2 kg. trichloroacetic acid in 18.8 l. distilled water.
 III. Azocasein:
      Thaw out the frozen azocasein preparation, dilute with phosphate buffer (solution I) and cool to 5 °C. The exact amount of diluent (between 1.75 and 3.75 vol.) depends on the azocasein preparation. The dilution should be such that when the highest standard is used there is visible precipitation with trichloroacetic acid in the AutoAnalyzer®. If the azocasein concentration is too high clots are formed when it comes into contact with trichloroacetic acid. The accurately diluted substrate should give an extinction of at least 0.200 at 420 nm with the highest standard.
  IV. Enzyme standard solutions:
      Dilute a protease preparation of known activity with phosphate buffer (solution I) so that extinctions of 0.05, 0.100, 0.150 and 0.200 are obtained at 420 nm (see Fig. 3, A).

Procedure

Collection, Treatment and Stability of Sample

Filter sample or centrifuge, dilute with phosphate buffer (solution I) so that the activity falls within the range of the standards. Store samples frozen; keratinase from *Streptomyces fradiae* broths is stable for several weeks at −20 °C. Other enzymes show different stability.

---

   * e.g. from Mann Research Laboratories, 136 Liberty St., New York 10006, U.S.A.
  ** Product of John-Mansville Prod. Corp., 22 E 40th St., New York 10006, U.S.A.
 *** Product of Atlas Chem. Ind., Wilmington, De. 19899, U.S.A.
**** One of the many commercial enzyme preparations of which the activity is determined manually (e. g. trypsin activity according to p. 1013. The units determined automatically are then the same as those measured manually.

Assay System

For flow scheme, see Fig. 2. For cleaning and setting the zero of instrument rinse all manifolds with distilled water (containing a few drops of Tween 20 per litre). Pump for at least 10 min. (with new tubing increase the time to 1 hr.). During this time set the recorder and photometer to 100% transmission or null.

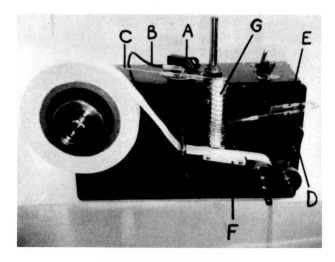

Fig. 1. Continuous Filter.

A Rate control	E Connection to pump
B Tube for trichloroacetic acid	F Teflon filter holder
C Tube for 37 °C heating bath	G Mixing coil
D Air tube	

The "h" glass tube which connects tubing B and C with the mixing coil G must fit well or be completely joined to the coil. Any unevenness of flow at this point leads to the deposition of azocasein and the blocking of the system.

Prepare the sampler for 40 samples/hr., fill the odd numbered vessels with phosphate buffer (solution I) for washing. Fill every tenth vessel with 1.5 N NaOH; this prevents the deposition of azocasein in the system. Sixteen vessels are left empty, fill the first 12 with 3 series of standards and the others with samples. Fill the 16 vessels with samples in the succeeding runs. Position the table so that NaOH is sucked up first.

Set the alarm disc at the phosphate buffer cup which precedes the first caustic wash.

The sample is sucked up from sampler, mixed with azocasein solution and separated with air. Air, phosphate buffer, and samples are sucked up successively and so guarantee constant bubble size and sufficient washing between samples. The mixture is pumped through a horizontal standard mixing coil and then goes for 30 min. into the coil of the 37 °C heating bath. Subsequently a continuous stream of trichloroacetic acid (solution II) flows through, which precipitates unreacted protein (2nd. mixing coil); the suspension drops onto the continuous filter. Speed of the filter paper: 8–9 feet/hr. (ca. 2.5 m/hr.).

The filtrate must immediately be segmented with air and pumped through the manifold,

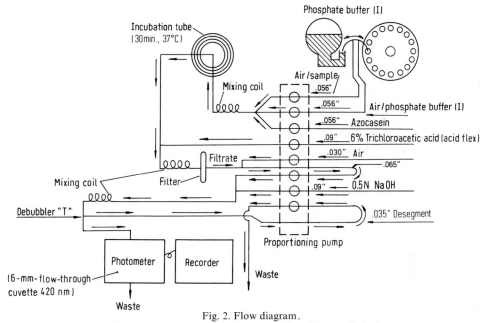

Fig. 2. Flow diagram.
The values for the internal diameter of the tubing are in inches.

where it is mixed with a continuous stream of 0.5 N NaOH. In the next mixing coil the sample is desegmented and flows into the flow-through cuvette of the photometer.

The azocasein solution is kept at 5 °C during the analysis. Connect the tubes with reagent solutions and after pumping for 10 min. set the sampler in motion. Do not wait too long otherwise azocasein will be deposited in the system. This length of time is also sufficient to record the zero value which is usually at E = 0.010. About 35 min. after start of operations the result of the first assay is recorded. Discard the first standard curve, it is usually too high because the equilibrium has not been attained. Correct the mean of the next two standard curves for the reagent blank. Plot the extinctions against the concentration on linear graph paper. A straight line is obtained. Repeat the standard curve every three to four hours. Slight deviations can be ignored.

If the filter paper should tear in the alkaline wash, reduce the speed or wash with a more dilute NaOH.

Calculations

Calculate the protease activity by means of a standard curve; take into account the dilution factors.

Precision of Method

For samples with ca. 50000 K units/ml. the standard deviation was 1000 K units*/ml.; the coefficient of variation is 2%.

---

* K-Units are arbitrary units defined by *Nickerson*[6]. Crystalline keratinase has a specific activity of 4380 K-units/mg.[7].

Sources of Error

Occasionally the base line drifts; possible reasons are: decrease of the activity of the standard, over-extended manifolds or deposition of precipitates in the flowthrough cuvette.

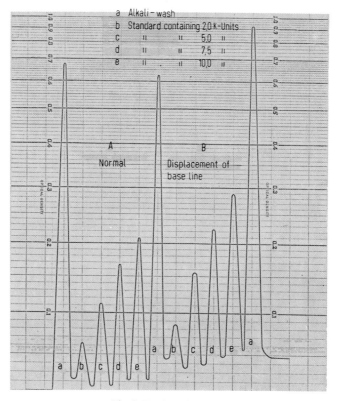

Fig. 3. Tracing of Assays.

Note the difference between run A and run B. Careful washing of the cuvette with a pipe cleaner during the wash process with alkali corrects the last-mentioned error.

Specificity of Method

The total activity of proteases which degrade azocasein is measured.

Example

A keratinase concentrate obtained from the culture medium of *Streptomyces fradiae* by concentration and filtration has been studied. A purified keratinase with a specific activity of 527 K units/mg. served as a standard. Portions (40 ml.) of a standard solution containing 100 K units/ml. were frozen, and after thawing dilutions in phosphate buffer (solution I) containing 2.5, 5.0, 7.5 and 10 K units/ml. were prepared. The standard curve was obtained by triplicate analysis of these standards. The mean extinctions were 0.095,

0.168, 0.221 and 0.259. Two 1 ml. samples were diluted to 1000 ml. with distilled water, and 1 ml. of the diluted samples was diluted to 10 ml. with phosphate buffer (solution I). In the assay duplicate determinations gave the following extinctions 0.173, 0.177 and 0.180, 0.173, that is 51000, 53000 and 55500, 51500 K units/ml. As crystalline keratinase has a specific acitivity of 4380 K units/mg. the "apparent" keratinase concentrations in the samples are 11.8, 12.1, 12.7 and 11.8 mg./ml.

Appendix

Preparation of Azocasein[3]

The preparation is critical; slight deviations from this method result in an unsuitable reagent; commercial azocasein gives lower extinctions and therefore insufficient accuracy in the method.

Add 50 g. powdered *Hammersten* casein with vigorous stirring to a solution of 10 g. sodium acetate in 1000 ml. distilled water. The casein must be evenly distributed. Place a glass electrode of a pH-meter in the mixture and slowly add 1 N NaOH until pH 7.0 is reached. On addition of NaOH the pH rises somewhat, and then slowly falls; add more NaOH to maintain the pH at 7.0. After about 2 hr. the pH no longer changes; all the casein is in solution although it is a little turbid. Continue stirring at 25 °C.

Dissolve 5 g. sulphanilamide in 200 ml. distilled water, add 6 ml. 5 N NaOH and then 2.2 g. $NaNO_2$ with stirring at 25 °C. Start a stopwatch, immediately add 18 ml. 5 N HCl, stir for exactly 2 min. and then add 18 ml. 5 N NaOH. Keep at 25 °C.

Add this diazotized solution to the stirred casein solution, adjust the pH to 8.5 with 1 N HCl or 1 N NaOH and stir for a further 2 hr.

Add 1500 ml. distilled water to the deep-red solution and filter through a sintered glass filter precoated with Supercel. Adjust the pH of the filtrate to pH 4.5 with 1 N HCl; a yellow, curdy precipitate is obtained. Filter off through a coarse sintered glass funnel, wash twice with 1000 ml. water, twice with 1000 ml. acetone and again with two 1000 ml. portions of water. At this stage the moist product can be left overnight in the cold. Suspend the azocasein in 2 l. distilled water at 25 °C with vigorous stirring and adjust to pH 7.0 with 1 N NaOH. As the azocasein dissolves the pH falls and it must therefore be re-adjusted. At the beginning the NaOH can be added rapidly (maximum pH 7.3), but only as long as the pH rapidly returns to pH 7.0. The azocasein is usually completely dissolved in 5 hr. If necessary clarify the solution by filtration through Supercel. The yield is 2300 ml. of a 2% solution; divide into appropriate portions and freeze (stock solution). Preferably the largest possible batch of azocasein is prepared, or several smaller batches are carefully mixed before freezing. In this way the time expended on an exact dilution is decreased.

References

1 *G. G. Hazen, J. A. Hause & J. A. Hubicki*, Ann. N. Y. Acad. Sci. *130*, 761–768 [1965].
2 *J. Charney & R. M. Tomarelli*, J. biol. Chem. *177*, 501–505 [1947].
3 *S. Bergman, J. P. Lowenthal, M. E. Webster, P. L. Altieri & R. B. Gochenour*, Proc. Exptl. Biol. Med. *107*, 79–83 [1961].
4 *M. Kunitz*, J. Gen. Physiol. *30*, 291 [1947].
5 *W. Reisner & H. Uhlig*, Z. Anal. Chem. *215*, 190–196 [1966].
6 *W. Nicherson, J. Noval & R. Robison*, Biochem. Biophys. Acta *77*, 75 [1963].
7 *W. Nickerson & S. Durand*, Biochem. Biophys. Acta *77*, 91 [1963].

Chymotrypsin

Wirnt Rick

In addition to trypsinogen, chymotrypsinogen occurs in the pancreas and in pancreatic secretion as the inactive precursor of another endopeptidase, chymotrypsin. Two zymogens, chymotrypsinogen A and chymotrypsinogen B, have been isolated from bovine pancreas[1]. The amino acid sequence of chymotrypsinogen A has been elucidated[2]. The activation by trypsin and other autocatalytic interconversions are shown in Fig. 1[3]. α-Chymotrypsin (EC 3.4.21.1) is formed from chymotrypsinogen A by cleavage of the peptides Ser-14-Arg-15 and Thr-147-Asn-148. The different forms can be distinguished by their electrophoretic mobility, their chromatographic behaviour on resins, and their crystalline forms, etc. α-Chymotrypsin and chymotrypsin B (EC 3.4.21.1) have the same substrate specificity, but hydrolyse various synthetic substrates at different rates. All enzymes of this group hydrolyse esters and amides of aromatic amino acids[1,4] as well as proteins and peptides. In the case of proteins, peptide bonds involving the carboxyl groups of aromatic amino acids such as phenylalanine and tyrosine are readily hydrolysed. The hydrolytic reactivity increases in the following order: proteins < amides < esters (especially N-substituted tyrosine esters). Esters of tryptophan, methionine, norvaline, norleucine, and also N-benzoyl-L-arginine methyl ester are hydrolysed at much slower rates. Chymotrypsin also causes clotting of casein in milk. The stability of α-chymotrypsin can be increased by calcium ions, so that in systems where addition of calcium ions does not lead to precipitation of the substrate, higher activity is measured[1].

Suitable substrates for the determination of the activity are proteins (haemoglobin, casein[1]) and synthetic substrates such as N-acetyl-L-tyrosine ethyl ester (I)[5], N-benzoyl-L-tyrosine ethyl ester (II)[6], N-carbobenzoxy-L-tyrosine-p-nitrophenyl ester[7], N-acetyl-phenyl-alanine-p-nitroanilide[8], N-succinyl-L-phenyl-

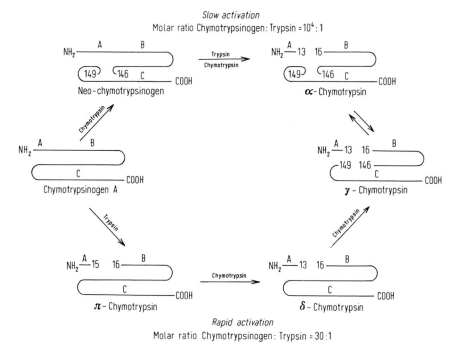

Fig. 1. Formation of various forms of chymotrypsin on activation of chymotrypsinogen A by trypsin[3]

alanine-p-nitroanilide (III)[9] and glutaryl-L-phenylalanine-p-nitroanilide[10]. The hydrolysis of I can be followed spectrophotometrically or titrimetrically, that of II spectrophotometrically whilst the hydrolysis of III can be measured by photometry in the visible range. The activity of purified chymotrypsin solutions, e.g. during the purification of the enzyme, can be determined with haemoglobin as substrate (see under Trypsin, p. 1 013). A method[11] for the direct determination of the concentration of enzymatically active chymotrypsin depends on the reaction of the protein with 2-nitro-4-carboxyphenyl-N,N-diphenyl-carbamate; this gives inactive diphenylcarbamylchymotrypsin and a stoichiometric amount of 3-nitro-4-hydroxybenzoic acid, whose concentration can be measured by its yellow colour. For other suitable reagents, see[12].

Chymotrypsin A from pig pancreas differs from chymotrypsin A from bovine pancreas in its activity to various synthetic substrates[13].

In the purification of procarboxypeptidase A from pig pancreas a zymogen was obtained which was designated chymotrypsinogen C[13]. Activation with trypsin gave chymotrypsin C[13] (EC 3.4.21.2) which, in contrast to bovine chymotrypsins and to pig chymotrypsin A, shows a high activity with N-benzoyl-L-leucine ethyl ester. The pentapeptide Ser-His-Leu-Val-Glu is hydrolysed only by chymotrypsin C and not by chymotrypsin A or B. The action of chymotrypsin C on carboxymethylated, reduced ribonuclease gives a completely different peptide map to that obtained after incubation with chymotrypsin A or B; the same is true for glucagon[13].

Measurements with Casein as Substrate

Application of Method: In biochemistry, in clinical chemistry and in pharmacy.

Principle

Casein is hydrolysed by chymotrypsin with the formation of hydrolysis products whose tyrosine and tryptophan content can be measured spectrophotometrically at 280 nm after precipitation of the residual substrate.

Optimum Conditions for Measurements

The pH optimum for the hydrolysis of casein by chymotrypsin is pH 8.0[1]. A final concentration of 0.4% is the optimum substrate concentration. The addition of calcium chloride (5 mM) to the substrate solution increases the activity of crystalline α-chymotrypsin by 10–12%[14]; this concentration is optimum.

Equipment

Spectrophotometer for measurements at 280 nm; constant temperature water bath (35 °C); stopwatch or timer; laboratory centrifuge.

Reagents

1. Casein according to *Hammarsten*
2. Boric acid, crystalline, A.R.
3. Sodium hydroxide, A.R., 1 N
4. Hydrochloric acid, A.R., 1 N; 0.1 N; 1 mN
5. Calcium chloride, 5% (w/v)
6. Trichloroacetic acid, 5% (w/v)

Preparation of Solutions

I. Borate stock solution (0.8 M):
Suspend 49.5 g. boric acid in doubly distilled water, dissolve by the addition of 400 ml. 1 N NaOH and dilute to 1 000 ml. with doubly distilled water.

II. Borate buffer (0.1 M; pH 8.0):
Add 130 ml. doubly distilled water to 25 ml. borate solution (I), adjust to pH 8.0 $\pm$ 0.05 with 1 N and 0.1 N HCl (glass electrode) and dilute to 200 ml. with doubly distilled water.

III. Substrate solution:
Suspend 1 g. casein in 95 ml. 0.1 M borate buffer (solution II), heat mixture in a boiling water bath (about 10 min.) until the casein has dissolved, add 1.1 ml. 5% $CaCl_2$ solution and dilute to 100 ml. with buffer (solution II).

Stability of Solutions

The borate buffer is stable about 1 year in a refrigerator; the substrate solution for about 1 week.

Procedure

Collection, treatment and stablity of sample, see under "Trypsin", p. 1013.

Assay System

Wavelength: 280 nm; silica cuvettes, light path: 1 cm.; incubation temperature: 35 °C; incubation volume: 2 ml. Read against water. Equilibrate the substrate solution for at least 5 min. at 35 °C. Incubate several tubes with different amounts of sample (2–50 µg. chymotrypsin).

Pipette into 12 ml. centrifuge tubes (in 35 °C water bath):	Test	Blank	Concentration in assay mixture
Sample (2–50 µg. chymotrypsin in 1 mN HCl) + borate buffer (II)	1.0 ml.	—	50–100 mM borate
Prewarmed substrate solution (III)	1.0 ml.	1.0 ml.	5 mg. casein/ml.
Mix, start stopwatch and incubate for exactly 20 min.			
5% Trichloroacetic acid	3.0 ml.	3.0 ml.	3%
Sample + borate buffer (II)	—	1.0 ml.	
Mix, allow to stand for 30 min. at room temperature and then centrifuge for 20 min. at 3 000 g. Measure the extinction of the supernatant fluids at 280 nm.			

Calculations

A unit of activity analogous to that defined by *Kunitz*[15] can be used. Fig. 2. (taken from[16]) shows the relationship between the extinctions and the amounts of α-chymotrypsin and chymotrypsin B added. Under the conditions described here α-chymotrypsin is more active than chymotrypsin B. For example, from Fig. 2 a

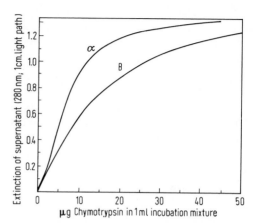

Fig. 2. Standard curves for the hydrolysis of casein by α-chymotrypsin and chymotrypsin B (according to [16]). Volume of incubation mixture: 2 ml.; casein concentration: 0.5%; incubation: 20 min. at 35 °C; volume after addition of trichloroacetic acid: 5 ml.; final concentration of trichloroacetic acid: 3%.

concentration of 6 μg. α-chymotrypsin per ml. assay mixture gives an extinction of 0.600; the number of units (for measurements with casein as substrate) is therefore:

$$\frac{0.60}{0.006 \times 20} = 5 \ [\text{units}^{\text{Cas}}/\text{mg. protein}]$$

The protein concentration of the enzyme solution is determined with the optical factor, i. e. from the reciprocal of the extinction of a solution of 1 mg. protein/ml. at 280 nm and 1 cm. light path, which is 0.500[1] for α-chymotrypsin.

Precision of Method, Normal Values, Sources of Error, Specificity of Method and Details for Measurements in Tissues, see under "Trypsin", p. 1013.

Measurements with N-Benzoyl-L-Tyrosine Ethyl Ester as Substrate

Application of Method: In biochemistry, in clinical chemistry and in pharmacy.

Principle

(1)   N-Benzoyl-L-tyrosine Ethyl Ester + H₂O $\xrightarrow{\text{chymotrypsin}}$ N-Benzoyl-L-tyrosine + Ethanol

N-Benzoyl-L-tyrosine with an undissociated carboxyl group absorbs less between 250 and 260 nm than N-benzoyl-L-tyrosine with a dissociated carboxyl group. N-Benzoyl-L-tyrosine ethyl ester behaves like undissociated N-benzoyl-L-tyrosine, so that hydrolysis of the ester can be followed by measurements of the extinction changes. By plotting the extinction against time a reaction curve is obtained from which it is easy to determine the initial rate of the reaction (see p. 309). Trypsin does not hydrolyse N-benzoyl-L-tyrosine ethyl ester, so that in studies on enzyme mixtures the method is specific for chymotrypsin.

Optimum Conditions for Measurements

The optimum substrate concentration is 0.5 mM and the pH optimum of the reaction is pH 7.8[6]. The hydrolysis of the ester is linear until about 30% of the substrate has reacted[6]. As α-chymotrypsin is stabilized by calcium ions the assay mixture contains 50 mM Ca^{2+}.

Equipment

Spectrophotometer for measurements at 256 nm, preferably with constant temperature cuvette holder; constant temperature water bath (25 °C); stopwatch, refrigerated centrifuge. The accuracy of the determination is greatly increased if the extinction changes are registered on a recorder connected to the spectrophotometer.

Reagents

1. Tris-hydroxymethyl-aminomethane, tris
2. Calcium chloride, 5% (w/v) solution
3. Hydrochloric acid, A.R., 1 N
4. Methanol, A.R.
5. N-Benzoyl-L-tyrosine ethyl ester

Preparation of Solutions

I. Tris buffer (80 mM, pH 7.8; 0.1 M $CaCl_2$):
   Dissolve 4.84 g. tris in ca. 300 ml. doubly distilled water, add 110 ml. 5% (w/v) $CaCl_2$ solution, adjust to pH 7.8 with HCl and dilute to 500 ml. with doubly distilled water.

II. 50% (w/w) Methanol:
   Mix 50 ml. doubly distilled water with 63 ml. methanol, A.R.

III. N-Benzoyl-L-tyrosine ethyl ester (1.07 mM):
   Dissolve 16.8 mg. N-benzoyl-L-tyrosine ethyl ester in 50 ml. 50% methanol.

Stability of Solutions

Store the buffer and substrate solution, stoppered, in a refrigerator at 0–4 °C. If bacterial contamination is prevented the buffer is stable for at least 1 year and the substrate solution for 4 weeks.

Procedure

Collection, Treatment and Stability of Sample, see under "Trypsin", p. 1015.

Assay System

Wavelength: 256 nm; silica cuvettes, light path: 1 cm.; final volume: 3.0 ml.; temperature: 25 °C (constant temperature cuvette holder). Read against air. A blank is not required. Equilibrate the solutions to 25 °C in a water bath.

Spectrophotometry

The difference spectrum of N-benzoyl-L-tyrosine ethyl ester and N-benzoyl-L-tyrosine has a sharp maximum at 256 nm[6]. As the absorption on either side of the maximum decreases steeply it is important to work with a small half band width. If the Zeiss spectrophotometer PMQ II is used the extinction of the ester solution can be set at with a 0.2 mm. slit width and an amplification of I/10/1. The half bandwidth at 256 nm is then about 0.8 nm. Because of the narrow maximum of the difference spectrum, slight errors in the wavelength setting can cause considerable deviations in the molar extinction coefficient and therefore errors in the calculations. It is therefore advisable to check the wavelength scale with a mercury lamp. The mercury lines 244.6; 246.4; 248.2; 257.6; 260.3; 264.0 and 265.2 nm are used as standards.

Pipette into cuvettes:			Concentration in assay mixture
Tris buffer	(I)	1.5 ml.	40 mM Tris
			50 mM Ca^{2+}
Substrate solution	(III)	1.4 ml.	0.5 mM
Sample (duodenal juice, etc.)		0.1 ml.	
Mix, set the extinction to 0 and start a stopwatch. After exactly 1, 2 and 3 min. read the extinction again. When using a recorder calculate $\Delta E/min.$ from the slope of the tracing.			

If $\Delta E/min.$ is larger than 0.100 dilute the enzyme solution 5–10 fold with buffer (I).

Calculations

The calculation formula (8) on p. 313 applies. $\varepsilon_{256\ nm} = 0.964\ cm^2./\mu mole$. Therefore for the sample and assay volumes used here:

$$\text{Volume activity} = 31\,100 \times \Delta E/min.\ [U/l.]$$

Precision of Method

With activities around 17000 U/l. duodenal juice a standard deviation of 450 U/l. was found. The coefficient of variation for this range is 2.7%.

Normal Values

For the basal and stimulated enzyme secretion of the pancreas, see under "Trypsin", p. 1023. After administration of pancreozymin at a dose of 1 U/kg. body weight i. v. the rate of enzyme secretion in normal subjects showed a log normal distribution:

$$\bar{x} - 2\,s = 28\ U/min., \bar{x} = 66\ U/min., \bar{x} + 2\,s = 154\ U/min.$$

Sources of Error, see under "Trypsin", p. 1017.

Specificity of Method

The method is specific for chymotrypsin.

Details for Measurements in Tissues, see p. 1018.

References

1 *M. Laskowski sr., B. Kassell, R. J. Peanasky & M. Laskowski jr.,* in *K. Lang & E. Lehnartz:* Handbuch der physiologisch- und pathologisch-chemischen Analyse. 10th. Edn. Springer, Berlin 1966, Vol. VI C, p. 229.
2 *B. S. Hartley,* Nature *201,* 1284 [1964].
3 *H. T. Wright, J. Kraut & P. E. Wilcox,* J. Mol. Biol. *37,* 363 [1968].
4 *H. Neurath & G. W. Schwert,* Chem. Revs. *46,* 69 [1950].
   G. L. Neil, C. Niemann & G. E. Hein, Nature *210,* 903 [1966].
5 *G. W. Schwert & Y. Takenaka,* Biochim. biophys. Acta *16,* 570 [1955].
6 *B. C. W. Hummel,* Can. J. Biochem. Physiol. *37,* 1393 [1959].
7 *C. J. Martin, J. Golubow & A. E. Axelrod,* J. biol. Chem. *234,* 294 [1959].
8 *H. Tuppy, V. Wiesbauer & E. Wintersberger,* Hoppe-Seylers Z. physiol. Chem. *329,* 278 [1962].
9 *W. Nagel, F. Willig, W. Peschke & F. H. Schmidt,* Hoppe-Seylers Z. physiol. Chem. *340,* 1 [1965].
10 *B. F. Erlanger, F. Edel & A. G. Cooper,* Arch. Biochem. Biophys. *115;* 206 [1966].
11 *B. F. Erlanger & F. Edel,* Biochemistry *3,* 346 [1964].
12 *M. L. Bender* et al., J. Amer. chem. Soc. *88,* 5890 [1966]; *F. J. Kézdy & Kaiser* in *G. E. Perlmann & L. Lorand:* Methods in Enzymology. Academic Press, New York 1970, Vol. 19, p. 3.
13 *J. E. Folk & E. W. Schirmer,* J. biol.Chem. *240,* 181 [1965].
14 *N. M. Green, J. A. Gladner, L. W. Cunningham jr. & H. Neurath,* J. Amer. chem. Soc. *74,* 2122 [1952].
15 *M. Kunitz,* J. gen. Physiol. *30,* 291 [1947].
16 *F. C. Wu & M. Laskowski,* J. biol. Chem. *213,* 609 [1955].

Trypsin

Wirnt Rick

Trypsin[1] (EC 3.4.21.4) is a proteolytic enzyme, whose inactive precursor trypsinogen (molecular weight of trypsinogen from bovine pancreas is 24433, and of the corresponding trypsin is 23746[2]) is formed in the exocrine cells of the pancreas and is secreted into the lumen of the intestine. The proenzyme is converted to the active enzyme by enterokinase and also autocatalytically by the action of the trypsin formed. Enterokinase, which is secreted by the cells of the mucus membrane of the small intestine, acts by splitting a hexapeptide, H_2N-Val-Asp$_4$-Lys-COOH from trypsinogen[3]. The pH optimum for the activation is between pH 7.0 and 9.0 for bovine trypsinogen[1]. Trypsin is most stable at pH ca. 2.3[4]. An inert protein is also formed during the activation process[5]. This inactive protein sediments slower than the native trypsin in the ultracentrifuge and has therefore been considered to be a polymer of the monomeric enzyme[6]. The formation of the inert protein can be inhibited by Ca^{2+} ions[7-9], which prevent the aggregation of the trypsin molecule[6]. Magnesium ions are inactive in this process. Owing to the increased stability of trypsin in the presence of calcium ions, a higher activity of the enzyme is found in most assay systems when Ca^{2+} is added. The hydrolysis of protamines and the activation of α-chymotrypsinogen are, however, independent of Ca^{2+} [10].

The enzyme hydrolyses bonds in proteins and peptides involving the carboxyl group of lysine or arginine[11]. Amides and esters of these amino acids are also hydrolysed and the reactivity increases in the following order peptides < amides < esters. Proteins which are not denatured are attacked only slowly. The ester of m-hydroxybenzoic acid[12] and fatty acid esters[1] are also hydrolysed by trypsin.

If the activity of pure trypsin or the total proteolytic activity of protease mixtures is to be measured, denatured proteins (haemoglobin[13], casein[14]) are suitable substrates for the assay. To determine trypsin specifically in the absence of thrombin and plasmin, e.g. in duodenal juice, the amides or esters of arginine or lysine (e.g. N_α-p-toluene-sulfonyl-L-arginine methyl ester (I)[15], N_α-benzoyl-DL-arginine-β-naphthylamide (II)[16], N_α-benzoyl-DL-arginine-p-nitroanilide (III)[17]) are used. The hydrolysis of the substrate can be followed spectrophotometrically[15], or titrimetrically[1] in the case of I, photometrically after coupling to an azo dye[16] or fluorimetrically (highly sensitive)[18] with II and photometrically with III. Compounds have been described which are suitable for the direct titration of the active centres of hydrolytic enzymes[19]; p-nitrophenyl-N^2-benzyloxycarbonyl-L-lysinate is used for trypsin.

Autocatalytic hydrolysis of bovine trypsin at the peptide bond Lys$_{176}$-Asn$_{177}$ yields pseudotrypsin, which has a much lower affinity for N_α-benzoyl-L-arginine ethyl ester and for benzamidine than trypsin[19a].

Trypsin cannot be detected in serum[19b] because the capacity of trypsin inhibitors in serum is sufficient to inhibit about 1 mg. trypsin per ml. serum.

The trypsinogen secreted by the pancreas into the duodenum is extremely rapidly activated by the enterokinase of the intestinal mucosa and the trypsin already present, so that samples of duodenal contents contain no inactive zymogen but only active trypsin.

Measurement with Haemoglobin as Substrate

The method of *Anson*[13] for the measurement of trypsin activity in pure solution is described below.

Application of Method: In biochemistry, clinical chemistry and pharmacy.

Principle

Haemoglobin is denatured with alkaline urea solution. Trypsin hydrolyses compounds from the denatured protein which are soluble in trichloroacetic acid and whose tyrosine and tryptophan content can be determined by the method of *Folin* and *Ciocalteu*[20].

Optimum Conditions for Measurements

The pH optimum for the proteolytic action of trypsin is between 7.0 and 8.0. The optimum substrate concentration is around 6.7 mg. haemoglobin/ml. reaction mixture. Higher concentrations of haemoglobin do not alter the rate of the reaction. The addition of 20 mM calcium ions prevents the formation of enzymatically inert protein (see above).

Equipment

Filter photometer, spectrum-line photometer or spectrophotometer; water bath (25 °C); stopwatch or timer.

Reagents

1. Bovine haemoglobin*
2. Sodium hydroxide, A.R., 1 N and 0.5 N
3. Urea, pure crystalline
4. Boric acid, crystalline, A.R.
5. Sodium chloride, A.R.
6. Calcium chloride solution, 5% (w/v)
7. Hydrochloric acid, A.R., 0.001 N; 0.2 N and ca. 1 N

8. Trichloroacetic acid, 5% (w/v)
9. *Folin* and *Ciocalteu* phenol reagent** available ready-made, e.g. from E. Merck, Darmstadt, Germany
10. L-(−)-Tyrosine, chromatographically pure

Preparation of Solutions

I. Boric acid (1 M):
   Dissolve 6.184 g. boric acid and 0.292 g. NaCl in doubly distilled water and make up to 100 ml.
II. Substrate solution:
   Suspend 2.0 g. haemoglobin with about 50 ml. doubly distilled water in a 100 ml. volumetric flask, add 36 g. urea, 8 ml. 1 N NaOH and dilute with doubly distilled water to about 80 ml. To denature the haemoglobin allow to stand for 30–60 min. at room temperature, then add 10 ml. boric acid solution (I) and after thorough shaking add 4.4 ml. 5% CaCl₂ solution. Adjust to pH 7.5 with 1 N HCl (glass electrode) and dilute to 100 ml. with doubly distilled water. Centrifuge off any erythrocyte stroma (15 min., 4000 g).

---

* e.g. from Behringwerke, Marburg, Germany; Armour, Kankakee, USA: Serva, Heidelberg, Germany.
** J. biol. Chem. *73*, 627 (1929); see also *P. B. Hawk, B. L. Oser* & *W. H. Summerson:* Practical Phys. Chem. The Blakiston Comp., Philadelphia, 1947, p. 879.

III. Phenol reagent:
    a) The commercially available stock solution contains: 10 g. $Na_2WO_4 \cdot 2H_2O$; 2.5 g. $Na_2MoO_4 \cdot 2H_2O$; 15 g. Li_2SO_4 and 5 ml. 85% H_3PO_4 in 100 ml. ca. 1 N HCl.
    b) Dilute solution: dilute the stock solution three-fold with doubly distilled water.
IV. Tyrosine standard solution (1 mM tyrosine):
    Dissolve 181.19 mg. L-($-$)-tyrosine in 0.2 N HCl and make up to 1 000 ml.

Stability of Solutions

Store the substrate and tyrosine standard solution in a refrigerator at 0–4 °C. To prevent the growth of micro-organisms add 2.5 mg. merthiolate* (Lilly) per 100 ml. substrate solution, and before diluting the tyrosine solution to 1 000 ml. add 14.3 ml. 35% formaldehyde (A. R.).

Procedure

Collection, Treatment and Stability of Sample

Obtain duodenal contents free from contamination (e. g. gastric juice) and cool in ice water. To remove any interfering turbidity centrifuge for 20 min. at 10 000–15 000 g and 0–4 °C. If the duodenal contents are collected as above the trypsin content remains constant for up to 7 hr. after collection[21].

Tyrosine Standard Curve

Pipette into 50 ml. Erlenmeyer flasks 0.2–1.0 ml. tyrosine standard solution (IV), 4.8–4.0 ml. 0.2 N HCl and 10.0 ml. 0.5 N NaOH. Add with continuous shaking 3.0 ml. dilute phenol reagent (solution IIIb). Read the extinction against a blank containing 0.2 N HCl instead of tyrosine standard solution (as described under "Assay System, Colour Reaction") and plot values against the μmole tyrosine/reaction mixture.

---

* Sodium salt of o-(ethylmercurythio)benzoic acid.

Assay System

Enzymatic reaction

Incubation temperature: 25 °C; incubation volume: 6 ml. Equilibrate the substrate solution to exactly 25 °C before the assay.

Pipette into 20 ml. centrifuge tubes (in 25 °C water bath):			Concentration in assay mixture
Substrate solution (II)		5.0 ml.	16.7 mg. haemoglobin/ml.
Samples (2–20 µg. enzyme in 0.001 N HCl)		1.0 ml.	0.3–3 µg. protein/ml.
Mix and incubate for exactly 10 min.			
5% Trichloroacetic acid		10.0 ml.	3.1%
Shake, allow to stand for 30 min. at room temperature and filter or centrifuge for 20 min. at 4000 g.			

Prepare a blank for each assay in which the haemoglobin is first precipitated with trichloroacetic acid and then the trypsin solution (sample) is added.

Colour reaction

Wavelength: 578, 691 or 750 nm; light path: 1 cm.; final volume: 18 ml.; room temperature. Read against water.

Pipette into 50 ml. Erlenmeyer flasks:	
Filtrate	5.0 ml.
0.5 N NaOH	10.0 ml.

With continuous shaking add 3.0 ml. phenol reagent (dilute solution IIIb); centrifuge off any slight precipitate (5 min., 4000 g). Between 5 and 10 min. after addition of the phenol reagent measure the extinction of the solution.

Calculations

The "trypsin unit" (TU^{Hb}) proposed by *Anson*[13] is similar to the pepsin unit: 1 trypsin unit (TU^{Hb}) is defined as the amount of enzyme, which under the standard conditions of *Anson* (6 ml. final volume containing 0.1 g. haemoglobin, temperature: 35.5 °C), hydrolyses haemoglobin at such an initial rate that the amount of hydrolysis products formed per minute has the same extinction on reaction with the phenol reagent as 1 mmole tyrosine.

The specific activity is defined as the number of trypsin units (TU^{Hb}) per mg. protein nitrogen.

At 25 °C the trypsin activity is 1.78 times lower than at 35.5 °C, so that results obtained at 25 °C must be multiplied by this factor. As in the case of pepsin, there is no linear relationship between the trypsin activity and the amount of hydrolysis products formed. The trypsin activity must therefore be extrapolated to the origin or a standard curve must be used. The extrapolation method is employed for the assay of the activity of purified enzyme preparations: different and sufficiently small amounts of trypsin are incubated with substrate as described above. After determination of the hydrolysis products (corrected for the blank) the μmole tyrosine (obtained from the tyrosine standard curve) are plotted against the amounts of trypsin and a tangent is drawn to the curve through the origin. The amount of enzyme which liberates 1 μmole tyrosine is read off from the tangent. This amount of enzyme is multiplied by $1000 \times (5/16) \times 10 \times (1/1.78)$ to obtain the amount of enzyme corresponding to a trypsin unit TU^{Hb}. The multiplication factors are derived as follows:

$1000 =$ conversion of μmole to mmole
$5/16 =$ conversion from colour reaction to enzymatic reaction
$10 =$ conversion from 10 min. to 1 min.
$1/1.78 =$ conversion from 25 °C to 35.5 °C.

For routine work *Anson*[13] modified the method of calculation and gave an empirical standard curve (Fig. 1). The extinction read on the photometer is converted to mmole tyrosine by means of the tyrosine standard curve and the trypsin units (TU^{Hb}) corresponding to this amount are read off from the abscissa of Fig. 1. To obtain the units per ml. sample it is necessary to divide by the volume of sample taken for assay.

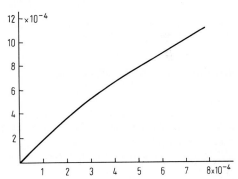

Fig. 1. Dependence of the hydrolysis of haemo-globin by trypsin on the amount of enzyme (according to *Anson*[13]).

Ordinate: Tyrosine equivalent (mmole) of the hydrolysis products in 5 ml. filtrate (see text under "Assay System"). Enzymatic reaction: 10 min. at 25 °C.
Abscissa: Trypsin units (TU^{Hb}) according to *Anson*[13].

Precision of Method

In the range of 2×10^{-4} TU^{Hb} per assay (see Fig. 1) the standard deviation is 0.07×10^{-4} TU^{Hb}, and the coefficient of variation 3.5%.

Normal Values

Values of $8-50$ $TU^{Hb}/l.$ were found in duodenal juice of subjects without pancreatic disease.

Sources of Error

Effects of drugs and other therapeutic measures: Discontinue administration of pancreatic enzyme preparations to patients before commencing the studies.

Interference in the assay technique: None known.

Specificity of Method

If a mixture of proteases, e.g. trypsin and chymotrypsin is analysed, all the different enzymes liberate trichloroacetic acid soluble peptides and therefore only the total proteolytic activity can be determined. The result can be expressed in TU^{Hb}, but it must be noted that this gives no information on the proportion of the various enzymes.

Details for Measurements in Tissues

As active trypsin is not present in fresh pancreas and is only present in small amounts in pancreatin, the zymogen must first be activated before this type of sample is analysed. For the method, see[22].

Measurement with Casein as Substrate

Application of Method: In biochemistry, in clinical chemistry and pharmacy.

Principle

During the hydrolysis of casein by trypsin, products soluble in trichloroacetic acid are formed, and the tyrosine and tryptophan content of these is determined by measurement of the extinction at 280 nm.

Optimum Conditions for Measurements

The pH optimum of the reaction lies between 7.0 and 8.0. As described above, calcium ions stabilize trypsin by preventing the formation of enzymatically inactive protein during the assay. However, if calcium chloride is added to a 1% casein solution in 0.2 M borate buffer (pH 7.6)[1] to give a final concentration of 5 mM, a slight opalescence occurs due to the formation of insoluble salts of casein[23]. In this case the enzymatic hydrolysis is reduced by about 10% as compared to reaction mixtures without calcium ions[24] and therefore calcium is omitted from this assay.

Equipment

Spectrophotometer for measurements of extinction at 280 nm; water bath (35 °C); stopwatch or timer; centrifuge.

Reagents

1. Casein according to *Hammarsten**
2. Potassium dihydrogen phosphate, KH_2PO_4
3. Disodium hydrogen phosphate, $Na_2HPO_4 \cdot 2H_2O$
4. Trichloroacetic acid, 5% (w/v)
5. Hydrochloric acid, A.R., 1 mN

Preparation of Solutions

I. Phosphate buffer (0.1 M; pH 7.6):
Dissolve 0.157 g. KH_2PO_4 and 1.575 g. $Na_2HPO_4 \cdot 2H_2O$ in about 90 ml. doubly distilled water, adjust to pH 7.6 (glass electrode) and dilute to 100 ml. with doubly distilled water.

---

* e.g. from E. Merck, Darmstadt, Germany.

II. Substrate solution:

Suspend 1 g. casein in 100 ml. phosphate buffer (solution I), heat for about 15 min. in a boiling water bath until all the casein has dissolved and then dilute to 100 ml. with doubly distilled water.

Stability of Solutions

Store the buffer and substrate solution, stoppered, in a refrigerator at 0–4 °C. If bacterial contamination does not occur the buffer solution is stable at this temperature for about 1 year and the casein solution for at least 1 week.

Procedure

Collection, Treatment and Stability of Sample, see p. 1015.

Assay System

Wavelength: 280 nm; silica cuvettes; light path: 1 cm.; incubation temperature: 35 °C; incubation volume: 2.0 ml.; read against water. Equilibrate the substrate solution for at least 5 min. at 35 °C. Incubate several tubes with different amounts of sample (1–25 μg. trypsin).

Pipette into 12 ml. centrifuge tubes (in 35 °C water bath)	Test	Blank	Concentration in assay mixture
Sample (1–25 μg. trypsin in 1 mN HCl) + phosphate buffer (I)	1.0 ml.	—	50–100 mM phosphate 5 mg. casein/ml.
Substrate solution prewarmed (II)	1.0 ml.	1.0 ml.	
Mix and start a stopwatch. Incubate for exactly 20 min.			
5% Trichloroacetic acid	3.0 ml.	3.0 ml.	3%
Sample + phosphate buffer	—	1.0 ml.	
Mix thoroughly, allow to stand for at least 30 min. at room temperature and centrifuge for 20 min. at 3000 g. Measure extinction of supernatant fluid at 280 nm.			

If several determinations are to be carried out, pipette the substrate into the test tubes in the 35 °C water bath at timed intervals, for example, every 30 sec. Exactly 20 min. after the start of the incubation of the first tube add 3 ml. trichloroacetic acid to each tube in the same order and after the same time interval.

Calculations

The extinction of the experimental tube after subtraction of the blank extinction is used to calculate the enzyme activity. As the extinction of the casein hydrolysis products is not proportional to the amount of enzyme (compare determination with haemoglobin), the initial rate of the reaction must be obtained by extrapolation. For this, several tubes containing different amounts of sample (1–25 μg. trypsin) are incubated. Plot the extinctions against the μg. enzyme/ml. incubation mixture (for a 2 ml. incubation mixture divide the amount of trypsin per tube by 2) (Fig. 2). Draw a tangent to the initial part of the curve; the slope of this is a measure of the specific activity of the preparation. According to *Kunitz*[14] a unit (TU^{Cas}) is the amount of trypsin which under defined conditions (20 min. incubation at 35 °C, final volume of the incubation mixture: 2.0 ml.; after addition of trichloroacetic acid: 5 ml.) liberates sufficient trichloroacetic acid soluble hydrolysis products so that the extinction at 280 nm increases by 1.00 in 1 min. Specific activity: TU^{Cas}/mg. protein.

According to Fig. 2:

$$\text{TU}^{Cas}/\mu\text{g. Trypsin} = \frac{0.25}{2.1 \times 20} = 6 \times 10^{-3}, \text{ i.e. 1 mg. crystalline trypsin contains 6 TU}^{Cas},$$

where

0.25 = ΔE_{280}/20 min.

2.1 = μg. trypsin/ml.

20   = conversion of ΔE/20 min. to ΔE/min.

The upper abscissa of Fig. 2 gives the TU^{Cas} corresponding to the ordinate (ΔE_{280}/20 min.). This scale is independent of the purity of the enzyme preparation. The activity of unknown samples can be read directly from the curve (Fig. 2) in TU^{Cas}.

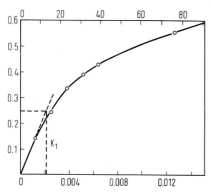

Fig. 2. Standard curve for the hydrolysis of casein by trypsin (according to *Kunitz*[14].)

Volume of incubation mixture: 2 ml.; casein concentration: 0.5%; 20 min. incubation at 35 °C; volume after addition of trichloroacetic acid: 5 ml.; final concentration of trichloroacetic acid: 3%.

Lower abscissa: μg. trypsin in 1 ml. incubation mixture.

Ordinate: extinction at 280 nm of the hydrolysis products liberated from casein in 20 min. by the action of trypsin (1 cm. light path; 5 ml. final volume).

Upper abscissa: 10^{-3} TU^{Cas} in 1 ml. incubation mixture.

The optical factor (i.e. the reciprocal of the extinction of a solution of 1 mg. protein/ml. at 280 nm and 1 cm. light path for crystalline trypsin) is 0.585[14].

Precision of Method

With activities around 7 TU^{Cas}/ml. duodenal juice a standard deviation of 0.4 TU^{Cas} was found. The coefficient of variation for this range is therefore 6%.

Normal Values

The normal range for 55 subjects without pancreatic disease was between 2400 and 12000 TU^{Cas}/l. duodenal juice.

Sources of Error

Effects of drugs and other therapeutic measures: Discontinue all pancreatic preparations before the start of the study.

Interference in the assay technique: None known.

Specificity of Method, see above p. 1017.

Details for Measurements in Tissues

Although trypsin and chymotrypsin are not detectable in fresh pancreas, a proteolytic enzyme with a pH optimum of 7.5 with casein as substrate can be purified from rat pancreas and characterized by inhibitor studies[25]. See also above p. 1018.

Measurement with N_α-p-Toluenesulfonyl-L-arginine Methyl Ester as Substrate

Principle

The absorption of N_α-p-toluenesulfonyl-L-arginine methyl ester at 247 nm is much weaker than that of toluenesulfonyl-L-arginine[15], so the hydrolysis of the ester can be followed spectrophotometrically.

Optimum Conditions for Measurements

The pH optimum of the reaction is around pH 8.1[15] and the optimum substrate concentration is 1 mM. Calcium ions at a final concentration of 10 mM are added to stabilize the enzyme.

Equipment

Spectrophotometer suitable for measurements at 247 nm, preferably with constant temperature cuvette holder. Constant temperature water bath (25 °C); stopwatch; refrigerated centrifuge.

The assay is more elegant and accurate if the extinction is recorded with a recorder directly connected to the spectrophotometer.

Reagents

1. Tris-hydroxymethyl-aminomethane, tris
2. Calcium chloride solution, 5% (w/v)
3. Hydrochloric acid, 1 N
4. N_α-p-Toluenesulfonyl-L-arginine methyl ester hydrochloride

Preparation of Solutions

I. Tris buffer (46 mM; pH 8.1; 11.5 mM $CaCl_2$):
   Dissolve 2.78 g. tris in ca. 400 ml. doubly distilled water, add 12.8 ml. 5% (w/v) calcium chloride solution, adjust to pH 8.1 with 1 N HCl, and dilute to 500 ml. with doubly distilled water.
II. N_α-p-Toluenesulfonyl-L-arginine methyl ester (10 mM):
   Dissolve 37.9 mg. N_α-p-toluenesulfonyl-L-arginine methyl ester in 10 ml. doubly distilled water.

Stability of Solutions

The buffer solution (I) is stable, stoppered, in a refrigerator at 0–4 °C for at least 1 year if bacterial contamination is avoided. The substrate solution (II) is stable for at least 2 weeks under these conditions.

Procedure

Collection, Treatment and Stability of Sample, see p. 1015.

Assay System

Wavelength: 247 nm; silica cuvettes, light path: 1 cm.; final volume: 3.0 ml.; temperature: 25 °C (constant temperature cuvette holder). Read against air; there is no need for a blank. Equilibrate the solutions in a water bath to 25 °C.

Spectrophotometry

The difference spectrum of N_α-p-toluenesulphonyl-L-arginine methyl ester and N_α-p-toluene-L-arginine has a sharp maximum at 247 nm. As the absorption rapidly decreases on either side of this maximum it is important to use a small bandwidth for the measurements. If the Zeiss spectrophotometer PMQ II is used it is possible with the amplifier I/10/1 and a slit width of 0.2 mm. to set the ester solution at an extinction of 0. The appropriate half band width of the 247 nm wavelength is then about 0.8 nm. Because of the sharp extinction maximum small errors in the wavelength adjustment can cause considerable variation in the molar extinction coefficient and therefore in the calculations. The wavelength scale should therefore be checked with a mercury lamp; the mercury lines 244.6, 246.4, 248.2, 257.6, 260.3, 264.0, and 265.2 nm are used as standards.

Pipette into cuvettes:			Concentration in assay mixture
Tris buffer	(I)	2.6 ml.	40 mM tris 10 mM Ca^{2+}
Substrate solution	(II)	0.3 ml.	1 mM
Sample (duodenal juice, etc.)		0.1 ml.	
Mix, set the extinction at about 0 and start a stop-watch. After exactly 1, 2 and 3 min. read the extinction again. Using a recorder the $\Delta E/min.$ can be calculated from the slope of the tracing.			

If $\Delta E/min.$ exceeds 0.100, dilute the sample 5–10-fold with buffer (I).

Calculations

The calculation formula (8) from p. 313 applies. $\varepsilon_{247\ nm} = 0.540\ cm.^2/\mu mole$. Therefore for the sample and assay volumes used here:

$$\text{Volume activity} = 55600 \times \Delta E/min.\ [U/l.]$$

Precision of Method

With activities around 30000 U/l. duodenal juice a standard deviation of ± 900 U/l. was found. The co-efficient of variation in this range is $\pm 3.0\%$.

Normal Values

As duodenal juice does not consist of pure pancreatic secretion, but contains other secretions such as intestinal juice and bile (especially after contraction of the gall bladder) expression of results as a concentration is not meaningful; the secretion of the enzyme is expressed as a rate (U/min.), so that dilution effects play no role[26]. The activities of duodenal juice which have been collected without stimulation of the pancreas vary greatly. The function of the exocrine pancreas is therefore tested after stimulation of the organ with pancreozymin-cholecystokinin which give the greatest stimulus to enzyme secretion. After administration of this hormone i. v. in a dose of 1 U/kg. body weight a log normal distribution was obtained with normal subjects:

$$\bar{x} - 2s = 55.5 \text{ U/min.}, \bar{x} = 136 \text{ U/min.}, \bar{x} + 2s = 335 \text{ U/min.}$$

Sources of Error

See above p. 1020. Gastrografin, which is occasionally given in the radiographic control of the position of probes, absorbs strongly in the UV and therefore interferes. This effect is only found in the first fractions before stimulation.

Specificity of Method

In the absence of thrombin and plasmin the method is specific for trypsin. For the separation of trypsin/plasmin, see [27].

Details for Measurements in Tissues, see p. 1018, 1021.

References

1 *M. Laskowski sr., B. Kassell, R. J. Peanasky & M. Laskowski jr.,* in *K. Lang & E. Lehnartz:* Handbuch der physiologisch- und pathologisch-chemischen Analyse. 10th. Edn., Springer, Berlin 1966, Vol. VI C, p. 229.
2 *C. M. Kay, L. B. Smillie & F. A. Hilderman,* J. biol. Chem. *236*, 118 [1961].
3 *H. Neurath & G. H. Dixon,* Fed. Proc. *16*, 791 [1957]; *F. Turba & W. Zillig* in Ergebnisse der medizinischen Grundlagenforschung. Thieme, Stuttgart 1960, Vol. III, p. 253.
4 *M. Kunitz & J. H. Northrop,* J. gen. Physiol. *17*, 591 [1934].
5 *M. Kunitz,* J. gen. Physiol. *22*, 293 [1939].
6 *M. Bier, L. Terminiello & F. F. Nord,* Arch. Biochem. Biophys. *41*, 238 [1952].
7 *M. R. McDonald & M. Kunitz,* J. gen. Physiol. *25*, 53 [1941].
8 *M. R. McDonald & M. Kunitz,* J. gen. Physiol. *29*, 155 [1946].
9 *M. Bier & F. F. Nord,* Arch. Biochem. Biophys. *33*, 320 [1951]; *L. Gorini,* Biochim. biophys. Acta *7*, 318 [1951].
10 *N. M. Green & H. Neurath,* J. biol. Chem. *204*, 379 [1953].
11 *H. Neurath & G. W. Schwert,* Chem. Rev. *46*, 69 [1950]; *M. Dixon & E. C. Webb:* Enzymes 2nd. Edn.; Longmans, Green & Co., London 1964.
12 *B. H. J. Hofstee,* Biochim. biophys. Acta *24*, 211 [1957].
13 *M. L. Anson,* J. gen. Physiol. *22*, 79 [1939]; *M. L. Anson & A. E. Mirsky,* J. gen. Physiol. *17*, 151 [1933].
14 *M. Kunitz,* J. gen. Physiol. *30*, 291 [1947].
15 *B. C. W. Hummel,* Canad. J. Biochem. Physiol. *37*, 1393 [1959].

16 *A. Riedel & E. Wünsch*, Hoppe-Seylers Z. physiol. Chem. *316*, 61 [1959].
17 *B. F. Erlanger, N. Kokowsky & W. Cohen,* Arch. Biochem. Biophysics *95*, 271 [1961]; *W. Nagel, F. Willig, W. Peschke & F. H. Schmidt,* Hoppe-Seylers Z. physiol. Chem. *340*, 1 [1965].
18 *M. Roth,* Clin. chim. Acta *8*, 574 [1963].
19 *M. L. Bender* et al., J. Amer. chem. Soc. *88*, 5890 [1966].
19a *R. L. Smith & E. Shaw,* J. biol. Chem. *244*, 4704 [1969].
19b *I. Trautschold* in *E. G. Erdös, N. Bach & F. Sicuteri:* Hypotensive Peptides. Springer-Verlag, Berlin 1966, p. 472.
20 *O. Folin & V. Ciocalteu,* J. biol. Chem. *73*, 627 [1927].
21 *G. Lundh,* Scand. J. clin. Lab. Invest. *9*, 229 [1957].
22 *P. Desnuelle, J. P. Reboud & A. Ben Abdeljlil* in *A. V. S. de Reuck & M. P. Cameron:* CIBA Found. Symp. on The Exocrine Pancreas, Churchill, London 1962, p. 94.
23 *G. Schmidt* in *K. Lang & E. Lehnartz:* Handbuch der physiologisch- und pathologisch-chemischen Analyse. 10th. Edn., Springer, Berlin 1960, Vol. IV, p. 627.
24 *W. Rick* in *H. U. Bergmeyer:* Methoden der enzymatischen Analyse, 1st Edn. Verlag Chemie, Weinheim 1962, p. 812.
25 *W. Rick, W. Bernard, W. Gross & T.-U. Hausamen* in *O. Wieland,* Adv. in Clinico-Biochemical Research, Karger; Basel 1968, Vol. 4, p. 86.
26 *W. Rick,* Acta gastro-ent. belg. *28*, 389 [1965]; Chirurg *39*, 301 [1968].
27 *U. Nissen,* Anal. Biochem. *14*, 480 [1966].

Thromboplastin Time [Prothrombin Time]

Heinrich Südhof[†]

Blood plasma contains 300–400 mg.% fibrinogen and during coagulation of blood this is converted to insoluble fibrin by thrombin (EC 3.4.21.5). The highly active enzyme thrombin is formed from an inactive precursor, prothrombin. A prerequisite for this conversion of prothrombin to thrombin is the presence of conversion factor. The classical scheme of blood coagulation[1] assumes the presence of a pre-formed cell constituent, the prothrombin converting factor (thrombokinase) which is liberated on cell or tissue damage.

(1)

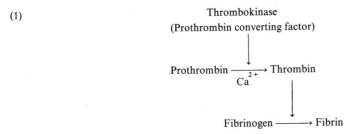

Studies during the last two decades have shown that the prothrombin converting factor is not present in an active form, but is formed by the combined action of plasma proteins with a tissue factor or blood cell factor. Therefore reference is made to either a blood thrombokinase or tissue thrombokinase[2–4]. The series of reactions (2) gives a simplified scheme of the formation of thrombokinase by two pathways (in italics: coagulation factors whose synthesis is blocked by dicoumarol analogues).

The formation of thrombin depends therefore on the one hand on the available prothrombin, and on the other on the formation, amount and activity of the factors which convert prothrombin (blood thrombokinase, tissue thrombokinase, etc).

In the method described by *Quick* in 1934[5,6] for the determination of prothrombin, the tissue extract (prepared in accordance with the knowledge at that time), which contains thromboplastin* and Ca^{2+}, is added to oxalated-blood or plasma. The coagulation time measured in this way is termed the prothrombin time. However, according to the above scheme (reaction 2) on addition of this tissue extract, plasma factors VI, VII and X are still required for the formation of the so-called tissue thrombokinase; only then does the conversion of prothrombin to thrombin occur. Therefore the *Quick* "Prothrombin time" includes factors V, VII and X, as well as prothrombin.

Disorders of clotting (hypercoagulaemia, hypocoagulaemia) can be further "localized" by coagulation studies. It is assumed that under certain conditions the clotting activity can be obtained from the clotting time, if the activity of normal plasma is set at 100% and the clotting time of a certain blood sample is related to it.

Providing that all except one of the factors are kept constant in parallel assays (other factors added in excess), the range of differences in coagulation time depend on the difference in activity of the factor which is varied. In this way several complicated reaction mixtures can be built up in which the reaction time can be measured directly (so-called one stage methods) or the activity can be tested on normal plasma (so-called two stage methods).

Application of Method: In clinical chemistry. The clinical importance of thromboplastin time determination lies in the necessity to control or regulate[7] hypocoagulaemia induced with dicoumarol analogues (inhibition of synthesis of coagulation factors II, VII, IX and X).

[†] deceased in 1973.
* Synonym for thrombokinase.

The determination of thromboplastin time is also used to control the coagulation characteristics of patients treated with anti-coagulants (e.g. in myocardial infarct and thrombosis). In addition it is used in the diagnosis of haemorrhagic diathesis (bleeding disorders).

Principle

Reaction scheme, see reaction (2) below.
The reaction time required for the first fibrin threads to form in the presence of excess Ca^{2+} and thromboplastin is termed the thromboplastin time and the corresponding activity as a percentage of normal (the Quick* value). This gives no information on the plasma content of individual coagulation factors, but only the coagulation activity as a percentage of normal, i.e. how far normal plasma must be diluted so as to have the same reaction time (thromboplastin time) as the patient's plasma. The reaction times of different dilutions of a normal plasma are determined for each thromboplastin preparation or for each batch of commercial thromboplastin preparation (standard curve, see below).

(2)

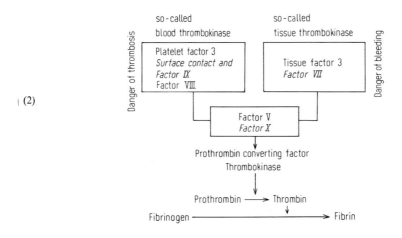

Optimum Conditions for Measurements

pH 7.0; temperature 37 °C. The fibrinogen content of the reaction mixture should not exceed 100 mg. %. Use an active thrombokinase which gives a thromboplastin time with normal plasma of 11–16 sec.

Equipment

Test tubes (length 8–10 cm., diameter 0.9–1.3 cm.); heated and cooled platinum loop; 37 °C water bath.

---

* In medical literature many other terms are used for thromboplastin time, e.g. one stage coagulation index, coagulation power, coagulation index, Quick coagulation time, prothrombin content, prothrombin index, prothrombin level, prothrombin time, Percentage Quick. In general, expression of results as percentage activity (Quick value) has gained favour.

Original Quick Method[5,8,9]

Reagents

1. Thromboplastin
2. Sodium oxalate

3. Calcium chloride, anhydrous
4. Sodium chloride, 0.85% (w/v)

Some Commercially Available Thromboplastin Preparations

Calcium thromboplastin, lyophilized, "Behringwerke": extract from human placenta very strongly factor X-sensitive, obtainable in bottles, the contents of which are dissolved in 2 ml. or 8 ml. distilled water. Calcium thromboplastin, lyophilized, "Boehringer Mannheim": extract from monkey brain, factor II, V, VII, X sensitive.

Thrombokinase "Geigy": thrombokinase from lung extracts, factor II or X-sensitive. Thrombokinase-$CaCl_2$ mixture in tablet form. Place 1 tablet on a folded paper and grind to a powder by rolling a bottle over it; shake the powder into a test tube, taking care that very little of the substance is lost. Stir the powder with 2 drops of distilled water to give a fine paste and then suspend in 2.5 ml. distilled water. Incubate this suspension in a water bath at 37 °C for 15 min.

Thromboplastin solution "Roche": extracts from rabbit lung, which are factor VII-sensitive. Standardized to 11.5 ± 1 sec. Ampoules containing 1 and 5 ml. Gelatine is added to the solution. The contents coagulate when stored in a refrigerator. Before use carefully liquefy the gel at room temperature or in a water bath at 37 °C.

The thrombokinases are type specific and are most active in autologous systems. Therefore for studies on human plasma human thrombokinases are most suitable, although rabbit thrombokinases can be used instead.

Preparation of Solutions

I. Thromboplastin solution:
As described above for the commercial preparations.
II. Sodium oxalate (0.1 M):
Dissolve 1.34 g. sodium oxalate in distilled water and make up to 100 ml.
III. Calcium chloride (25 mM):
Dissolve 0.275 g. $CaCl_2$ in 100 ml. distilled water: 10 ml. of this solution should be equivalent to 5 ml. 0.1 N $HgNO_3$ solution (indicator: potassium chromate).
IV. Sodium chloride (0.85% w/v):
Dissolve 0.85 g. NaCl in distilled water and make up to 100 ml.

Stability of Solutions

Thrombokinase is stable in stoppered ampoules for several months; the prepared thrombokinase suspensions keep for several hours in a refrigerator.

Procedure

Collection, Treatment and Stability of Sample

Draw up 0.2 ml. Na citrate solution (II) with a 2 ml. syringe. With light pressure on the upper arm puncture the cubital vein and withdraw 1.8 ml. blood. Mix the contents of the syringe carefully by withdrawing the plunger somewhat further and tilting the syringe back and forth. Transfer the blood to a centrifuge tube and centrifuge for 5 min. 1 500 rpm. Carefully take off the plasma and store at room temperature until ready for the determination (no later than 2 hr. after collection of the blood).

Assay System

Preferably carry out duplicate determinations; incubation temperature: 37 °C; final volume: 0.3 ml. Equilibrate the thromboplastin and calcium chloride solution to 37 °C (water bath).

Pipette into test tubes:			Concentration in assay mixture
Plasma		0.1 ml.	
Thromboplastin solution	(I)	0.1 ml.	
CaCl$_2$ solution	(III)	0.1 ml.	8.3 mM
Mix, start stopwatch, draw platinum loop through the solution once or twice every sec. As soon as the first fibrin threads hang on loop stop the stopwatch*.			

Calculations

Convert the thromboplastin time to % activity of normal by means of a standard curve.

Standard curve: Obtain mixed plasma from 3 normal plasma (clinically and metabolically healthy subjects) as described above** and dilute with 0.85% NaCl solution (IV) in volume ratio of 20 : 100; 40 : 100; 60 : 100 and 80 : 100. (For research purposes prepare the plasma dilutions with fibrinogen solution or better still with barium absorptive plasma instead of with NaCl solution).
Determine the thromboplastin times for these dilutions and for the undiluted plasma. Plot the measured coagulation times (ordinate) against % by volume of plasma in the dilute solution (abscissa). On linear graph paper increasing dilutions give a steeply rising curve (Fig. 1a), while on double logarithmic paper it gives a straight line (Fig. 1b). It is recommended to use double logarithmic paper, because 3 or 4 points on the line are sufficient. If these points do not lie on a line, it suggests an error in the method.

---

 * The following methods can be used to detect the onset of clotting:
   1. Observation of a small glass bead in the reaction mixture which is rotated in a test tube. At the onset of coagulation the glass bead, which previously lay at the deepest point in the tube, rises up.
   2. Test of the fluidity of the blood by tipping through about 180 °C. The moment when the surface of the blood or plasma no longer returns to the horizontal is recorded as the start of coagulation and the end is when on tipping the tube through 180 °C the liquid no longer flows.
   3. Recording of the rate of flow or dropping from a tube (cannula) of known gauge.
   4. Formation of fibrin results in decrease of the translucency due to the increase of turbidity, before this can be detected by one of the methods (1–3) described above. The more regular and similar the movement of the coagulation reaction mixture the lower the range of error.

** The plasma for the standard curve must be obtained under the same conditions as for the routine determination; the same applies to the determination of the thromboplastin times for the standard curve: if for example, blood samples are routinely dealt with only 1hr. after reception in the laboratory, or if the determination can only be carried out 2 hr. later, the plasma for the standard curve must be treated in exactly the same way.

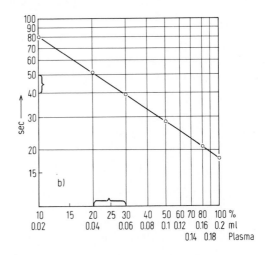

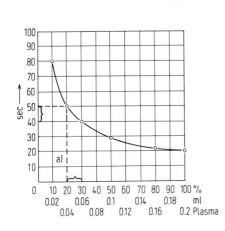

Fig. 1.

a) Standard curve on linear graph paper.   b) The same curve on double logarithmic paper.

In the interpretation of the *Quick* value[16] the half-lives of the coagulation factors (II 50–60 hr.; VII 5 hr.; X 50 hr.; IX 50–60 hr.) must be taken into account because of the particular sensitivity of the thrombokinase used. A value of 25% *Quick* obtained with thrombokinase "Geigy" and thromboplastin solution "Roche" from the respective standard curves, may not be equivalent at a given time, especially during the first 3 days of treatment with dicoumarol analogues (e. g. Marcumar). Factor VII sensitive thrombokinases give lower *Quick* values earlier than factor II or X-sensitive ones.

Precision of Method

The range of error increases with dilution of the plasma. The error is 5% of the measured reaction time.

Normal Values

Depending on the thromboplastin preparation: 11–16 sec.

Sources of Error

The results are affected by apparatus which is not thoroughly clean, e. g. by unclean cannulae (traces of thrombin) during the collection of the blood.
Abnormally low concentrations of fibrinogen in the reaction mixture or the presence of thrombokinase inhibitors are important sources of error[8,9].

Quick Method using Citrated Blood[8,9]

As citrated blood can be stored longer, without losing activity (factor V), the use of sodium citrate in place of sodium oxalate is now preferred.

Reagents

1. Thromboplastin
   commercial preparation, see p. × ×.
2. Trisodium citrate, $C_6H_5O_7Na_3 \cdot 5^1/_2 H_2O$

3. Calcium chloride, A. R., $CaCl_2 \cdot 6 H_2O$
4. Sodium chloride
5. Phenol solution, 5% (w/v)

Preparation of Solutions

I. Thromboplastin solution:
   Prepare as described for the particular commercial preparation.
II. Sodium citrate (3.8% w/v):
   Dissolve 3.8 g. trisodium citrate in 5% phenol solution and make up to 100 ml. Sterilization of this solution is not necessary.
III. Sodium chloride (0.85% w/v):
   Dissolve 0.85 g. NaCl in distilled water and make up to 100 ml.
IV. Calcium chloride (ca. 18.3 mM and 2.5 mM):
   a) Dissolve 4.0 g. $CaCl_2 \cdot 6 H_2O$ in NaCl solution (III) and make up to 1 000 ml.
   b) Dissolve 0.55 g. $CaCl_2 \cdot 6 H_2O$ in distilled water and make up to 1 000 ml.

Procedure as for the original method.

Other Methods

Apart from the methods described here there are a number of well-tried modifications[10-13], including the so-called bedside method which enables the thromboplastin time to be determined directly at the bedside of the patient, e.g. the methods of *Marbet & Winterstein*[14] and *Hartert*[15].

References

1 *P. Morawitz*, Erg. Physiol. *4*, 307 [1905].
2 *F. Leuthardt,* Lehrbuch der physiol. Chemie, 15th. Edn., W. de Gruyter, Berlin, 1963.
3 *E. Deutsch* in: Die thromboembolischen Erkrankungen, 2nd. Edn., F. K. Schattauer, Stuttgart, 1960, p. 73.
4 *M, Verstraete, K. Irsigler* in: Suppl. 13 ad Thromb. Diathes. hämorrh. (Stuttgart), p. 429, 433.
5 *A. J. Quick, M. Stanley-Brown & Bancroft,* Amer. J. med. Sci. *190,* 501 [1935].
6 *A. J. Quick,* Amer. J. Physiol. 118, 260 [1937]; Amer. J. Physiol. *123,* 712 [1938].
7 *P. Matis* in: Die thromboembolischen Erkrankungen, 2nd. Edn., F. K. Schattauer, Stuttgart, 1960, p. 371.
8 *F. K. Beller* in: Die thromboembolischen Erkrankungen, 2nd. Edn., F. K. Schattauer, Stuttgart, 1960, p. 404.
9 *J. Jürgens & F. K. Beller:* Klinische Methoden der Blutgerinnungsanalyse. Thieme. Stuttgart, 1958.
10 *P. A. Owren* & K. Aas, Scand. J. clin. Lab. Invest. *3,* 201 [1951].
11 *C. Montigel,* Therap. Umschau *9,* 17 [1952].
12 *H. E. Schultze & G. Schwick,* Laboratoriumsblätter der Behring-Werke, Heft 2, October 1953.
13 *N. Fiechter,* Schweiz. med. Wschr. *21,* 259 [1940].
14 *R. Marbert & A. Winterstein,* Die Medizinische 1954, 877.
15 *H. Hartert,* Suppl. 9 ad Thrombos. Diathes. hämorrh. (Stuttg.), p. 181.
16 *W. Matis, W. Mayer & W. Nagel,* Med. Welt 1961, 1891.
17 *Th. Nägeli, P. Matis, R. Gross, H. Runge & H. W. Sachs:* Die thromboembolischen Erkrankungen, 2nd. Edn., F. K. Schattauer, Stuttgart, 1960.

Kallikrein

Ivar Trautschold, Eugen Werle and Gertraud Schweitzer

The enzyme kallikrein (EC 3.4.21.8) belongs to the group of peptidylpeptide hydrolases, but in contrast to most of the enzymes in this class it is characterized by a high substrate specificity. It liberates the extraordinarily active kinins* from kininogen, a glycoprotein which occurs in the globulin fraction of serum, by hydrolysis of two peptide bonds[1].

Humans and mammals contain kallikrein (also called kininogenase from its hydrolytic action on kininogen) in urine and in salivary glands, together with an inactive precursor, prekallikrein in pancreas and serum[4]. The kallikreins from urine, salivary glands and pancreas, which can be isolated as extensively purified enzyme preparations[4], differ in many of their properties[5,6], but can be considered isoenzymes because the decapeptide kallidin is the common physiological reaction product. In contrast, the kallikrein from serum, which can only be partially purified, yields unstable preparations, and, like trypsin liberates the nonapeptide bradykinin from kininogen. In addition it has a slight non-specific proteolytic activity.

$$R_1 \ldots \text{Met-Lys-Arg-Pro-Pro-Gly-Phe-Ser-Pro-Phe-Arg-Ser-Val-GluNH}_2\text{-Val-R}_2$$

$$\uparrow \quad \uparrow \qquad\qquad\qquad\qquad\qquad\qquad \uparrow$$

$$1 \quad\ 2 \qquad\qquad\qquad\qquad\qquad\quad\ \ 1 \text{ and } 2$$

Points of attack of kallikrein on the kininogen molecule:

1. Kallikrein from pancreas, salivary glands and urine (the hydrolysis product is the decapeptide kallidin);
2. Kallikrein from serum or trypsin (hydrolysis product is the nonapeptide bradykinin).

All kallikreins also have esterolytic activity, which is predominantly against the esters of arginine and parallels the kinin-forming activity[7].

Kallikrein activity can be quantitatively determined[4] by means of its hypotensive effect in experimental animals in comparison to a standard preparation**. A further biological method consists of determining the amount of kinin liberated by measurements of its uterus- or intestine-contracting activity, again using a standard reference preparation[4].

However, a simpler and more accurate method is measurement of the activity by means of the ester hydrolysing activity of kallikrein[5,8]. The preferred substrate for measurement of the esterolytic activity of kallikrein is benzoyl-L-arginine ethyl ester (BAEE).

The determination of kallikrein activity is important because of the increased kinin formation in various pathological conditions (e.g. infection, shock) due to an elevation in kininogenase activity. In addition, changes in the activity of kallikrein, especially in urine and in serum are directly related to diseases, e.g. of the kidney, and allow an early sign of organ failure in kidney transplantation[4].

Application of Method: In clinical chemistry and clinical biochemistry.

Principle

(1) $\qquad$ Benzoyl-L-arginine ethyl ester $\xrightarrow{\text{Kallikrein}}$ Benzoyl-L-arginine + Ethanol

(2) $\qquad\qquad$ Ethanol + NAD$^+$ $\xrightarrow{\text{ADH}}$ Acetaldehyde + NADH + H$^+$

---

* Kinins are polypeptides which in ng. quantities lower blood pressure, increase capillary permeability, excite contractions of smooth muscle such as intestine and uterus[2,3] and cause pain.

** Padutin® (Bayer, Leverkusen) standardized kallikrein from pig pancreas.

The equilibrium of reaction (1) lies on the side of the hydrolysis products. The hydrolysis of BAEE gives 5 possibilities for the assay of kallikrein activity (see "Other Methods", p. 1039). The most reliable and sensitive is the enzymatic determination of the ethanol liberated in a coupled reaction.

The amount of ethanol reacting per unit time, as measured by the increase in extinction at 340, 334 or 365 nm due to the formation of NADH, is a measure of the kallikrein activity.

The determination of prekallikrein, e. g. from pancreas, can be carried out in the same way. After activation of the proteolytically and esterolytically inactive prekallikrein (kallikreinogen) by trypsin, the latter is selectively inhibited by addition of soya bean inhibitor. The activated pancreatic kallikrein, which is not affected by the soya bean inhibitor, can be quantitatively determined in this way.

Manual Method (UV-Assay)

Optimum Conditions for Measurements

A BAEE concentration of 1 mM is sufficient at 25 °C. The hydrolysis of BAEE has a wide maximum at pH 8.5. This pH range is similar to the pH optimum of 8.7 required for the determination of ethanol. The non-enzymatic hydrolysis of BAEE which is measureable at this pH must be taken into account.

The temperature dependence of the hydrolysis reaction is approximately the same for different kallikreins. A reaction rate at a given temperature can be converted to other temperatures between 10 °C and 40 °C:

$$\log \frac{k_2}{k_1} = \frac{0.219 \times E \times (T_2 - T_1)}{T_1 \times T_2}$$

where the activation energy $E = 11\,700$ cal./mole; T is the absolute temperature; k_1 or k_2 is the reaction rate constant at the respective temperatures.

Equipment

Spectrophotometer, spectrum-line photometer suitable for accurate measurements at 340, 334, 365 nm, with constant temperature cuvette holder; water bath with circulating pump; stopwatch.

Reagents

1. Sodium pyrophosphate, $Na_4P_2O_7 \cdot 10\,H_2O$
2. Semicarbazide
3. Glycine
4. Sodium hydroxide, 2 N
5. Nicotinamide-adenine dinucleotide, NAD
   free acid, commercial preparation, see p. 545.

6. Benzoyl-L-arginine ethyl ester
   as hydrochloride
7. Alcohol dehydrogenase, ADH
   from yeast crystalline suspension in 2.4 M ammonium sulphate; $\geqq 200$ U/mg. (25 °C; commercial preparation, see p. 428.

Preparation of Solutions (for ca. 25 determinations)

I. Pyrophosphate-semicarbazide-glycine buffer (pH 8.7):
   Dissolve 8.9 g. $Na_4P_2O_7 \cdot 10\,H_2O$ + 2.2 g. semicarbazide + 0.4 g. glycine in doubly distilled water, adjust to pH 8.7 with 2 N NaOH and dilute to 100 ml. with doubly distilled water.

II. Nicotinamide-adenine dinucleotide (ca. 30 mM NAD):
   Dissolve 60 mg. NAD in 3 ml. doubly distilled water.
III. Benzoyl-L-arginine ethyl ester (6 mM):
   Dissolve 34.8 mg. BAEE (L-isomer) in 15 ml. doubly distilled water.
IV. Alcohol dehydrogenase, ADH (30 mg. protein/ml.):
   If necessary, dilute the stock solution with 2.4 M ammonium sulphate solution.

Stability of Solutions

Solution I and II are stable for 1 week at 0–4 °C and solution III is stable for 1–2 days. The ADH suspension is stable for several months.

Procedure

Collection, Treatment and Stability of Sample

Suitable samples are kallikrein-containing solutions in the form of tissue extracts, duodenal juice, urine or serum. During the purification of enzymes in absence or after separation of other BAEE-hydrolysing enzymes the assay of activity can be carried out directly. When the activity of impure enzyme solutions is determined, the conditions given under "Specificity of Method" (p. 1034) must be adhered to. With the exception of purified kallikrein solutions from serum, neutral sample solutions are stable for weeks in the cold.

Assay System

Wavelength: 340 (Hg 334, Hg 365) nm; light path: 1 cm.; final volume: 3.0 ml.; temperature: 25 °C. Read against a blank containing buffer (solution I) instead of sample. Equilibrate solutions to 25 °C before the assay.
The increase in extinction ΔE/min. at 365 nm should not exceed 0.030/min., otherwise the sample must be diluted.

Pipette into cuvettes:			Concentration in assay mixture
Buffer solution	(I)	2.30 ml.	154 mM phosphate
			154 mM semicarbazide
			40 mM glycine
NAD solution	(II)	0.10 ml.	1 mM
ADH suspension	(IV)	0.02 ml.	200 μg./ml. $\cong$ 40 U/ml.
BAEE solution	(III)	0.50 ml.	1 mM
Mix and allow to stand for 5 min.			
Sample		0.10 ml.	
Mix, read extinction E_1 against blank and start stop-watch. After exactly 5 min. or 10 min. read extinction E_2. $\Delta E = E_2 - E_1$; calculate ΔE/min.			

Calculations

The activity of kallikrein has so far been given in biological units, where 1 kallikrein unit (KU) is defined as the amount of kallikrein which, on intravenous injection into a dog, has the same effect on the carotid blood pressure curve as 5 ml. of human urine, which has been taken from a 50 l. sample and has been dialysed for 24 hr. against running tap water. The kallikrein preparation Padutin ® can be used for standardization (see footnote on p. 1031).

According to the definition of the international unit, it is possible with the above method to express the activity of kallikrein in international units without the use of a standard preparation.

With a final volume in the cuvette of 3.0 ml. 1 mU of kallikrein activity corresponds to an extinction change of 0.0021 ΔE/min., i.e. the conversion of 1 nmole substrate/min.

The calculation formula (8) on p. 313 applies and therefore with this method the enzyme activity is calculated as follows:

Wavelength:	*334 nm*	*340 nm*	*365 nm*
Volume activity =	4918 × ΔE/min.	4823 × ΔE/min.	8824 × ΔE/min. [U/l.]

Conversion to Other Units

The large range of error in the determination of activity with biological assay methods (contraction of smooth muscle, blood pressure lowering effects) allows only an approximate comparison of the biological unit (KU) with the international unit (U), which can determined exactly. 1 Biological unit KU = 0.1–0.3 U. In the method described above the lower limit of the assay is 5 mU.

Specificity of Method

There are a number of hydrolases (e. g. trypsin, plasmin, esterases) which can hydrolyse BAEE, therefore the specificity of this method for the determination of kallikrein activity is uncertain with impure enzyme samples. The specificity of the method can be improved by use of specific inhibitors for the other enzymes which hydrolyse BAEE. For more information see the chapter "Protease Inhibitors", p. 1064.

Determination of Kallikrein and Prekallikrein with Automatic Analysers

The determination of kallikrein activity with the method of *Fiedler* and *Werle*[9] is possible in the range of 0.5–20 biological units (KU)/ml. (for definition, see above).

Principle

The method is based on the same principle as that for the manual method (p. 1031).

Equipment

Technicon AutoAnalyzer ® (sampler I, proportioning pump, heating bath, dialyser, photometer and recorder).

Reagents

See p. 1032; in addition:

8. Triethanolamine hydrochloride
9. Triton X-100
10. Trypsin
   from pancreas, salt-free preparation; $\geq$ 1 U/mg.
   (25 °C); commercial preparation, see p. 515.

11. Trypsin inhibitor
   from soya beans, ca. 1 IU/mg. (25 °C); commercial preparation, see p. 517.
12. Hydrochloric acid, 1 mN
13. Standard preparation from pancreas*

Preparation of Solutions

  I. Pyrophosphate-semicarbazide-glycine buffer (pH 8.7):
     as p. 1032, but add 0.1 ml. Triton X-100.
 II. Triethanolamine buffer (50 mM; pH 7.8):
     Dissolve 4.65 g. triethanolamine hydrochloride in ca. 200 ml. distilled water, adjust to
     pH 7.8 with 2 N NaOH, add 0.1 ml. Triton X-100 and dilute to 500 ml. with distilled
     water.
III. Benzoyl-L-arginine ethyl ester (17.6 mM):
     Dissolve 680 mg. BAEE in distilled water and make up to 100 ml.
 IV. Nicotinamide-adenine dinucleotide (ca. 2 mM):
     Dissolve 150 mg. NAD in 100 ml. distilled water.
  V. Alcohol dehydrogenase, ADH (150 μg. protein/ml.):
     Dissolve 15 mg. protein in distilled water and make up to 100 ml.
 VI. Trypsin (500 μg. protein/ml.):
     Dissolve 50 mg. crystalline trypsin in 1 mN HCl and make up to 100 ml. (keep cold).
VII. Soya bean inhibitor, SBI (5 mg. protein/ml.):
     Dissolve 500 mg. SBI in solution II and make up to 100 ml.; centrifuge before use.
VIII. Kallikrein standard (0.5–20 biological units (KU/ml.):
     Dissolve the lyophilysate in distilled water according to the instructions of the manufacturer.

Stability of Solutions

Store all solutions at 0–4 °C. Solutions I, VI–VIII are stable for a week, solution III for 1–2 days and solution II for several months.

Procedure

Wavelength: 340 nm; cylindrical flow-through cuvette: 15 mm. The sample solutions like the standards can have a kallikrein content of 0.5–20 biological units (KU)/ml. Carry out the measurements according to the flow scheme (Fig. 1).

Even without the use of a "scale expander" the highest sample concentrations give a deflection of about 0.25 extinction units (ca. 40% of the range of a non-linear recorder).

The automated determination of pancreatic prekallikrein (kallikreinogen) is as for the manual

---

* e. g. Standard Padutin® (Bayer, Leverkusen, Germany).

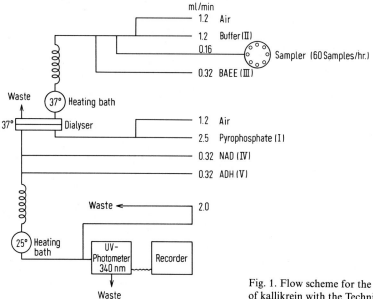

Fig. 1. Flow scheme for the determination of kallikrein with the Technicon AutoAnalyzer®.

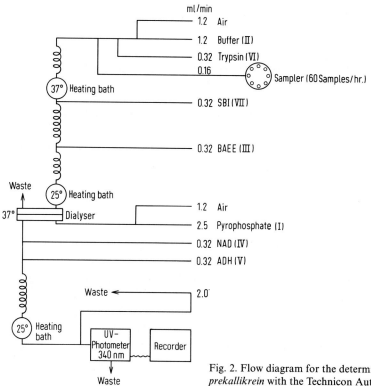

Fig. 2. Flow diagram for the determination of pancreatic *prekallikrein* with the Technicon AutoAnalyzer®.

method, p. 1032: the enzyme is first activated with trypsin and then the excess trypsin is selectively inhibited with trypsin inhibitor. The kallikrein formed is determined as described. The tubing system is shown in Fig. 2. By interchange of a few connections it is possible to convert it to the system for the determination of kallikrein. If the same system is used for the determination of the two compounds, after some time the lines for the kallikrein assay become contaminated with trypsin and this results in a high and non-constant baseline. This effect can be overcome by occasional repeated rinsing of the tubing (without dialyser) with dilute NaOH.

Calculations

The measurement of enzyme kinetics in the continual flow method is still a problem. The method described above has an accurary of $\pm 10\%$ if kallikrein standard solutions are used at the stated concentrations. The evaluation of activity of sample solutions is always made relative to the standard curve in the above stated range.

Fluorimetric Method

With this method as little as 0.01 mU per assay mixture can be measured accurately. It is therefore 500 times more sensitive than the UV method described above.

Principle

The NADH formed per unit time according to the reaction schemes (1) & (2), p, is converted to a fluorescent product by treatment with strong alkali after destruction of the excess NAD[10]. The increase of fluorescence per unit time is a measure of the kallikrein activity.

Equipment

Eppendorf microlitre system (thermostat, shaker, pipettes); fluorimeter (Farrand or Zeiss) with primary filter 365 nm, secondary filter 460 nm.

Reagents

See p. 1032. Additional:
8. Sodium hydrogen carbonate, $NaHCO_3$, 1% (w/v)
9. Sodium hydroxide, 1 N and 10 N

10. Reduced nicotinamide-adenine dinucleotide, NADH disodium salt NADH-Na_2; commercial preparation, see p. 545.
11. Hydrogen peroxide, 0.2% (w/v).

Preparation of Solutions

To maintain exact pH values in the alkaline destruction of NAD, a less concentrated pyrophosphate-semicarbazide-glycine buffer is used. Prepare all solutions with doubly distilled water.

I. Pyrophosphate-semicarbazide-glycine buffer (pH 8.7):
   Dissolve 15.2 g. $Na_4P_2O_7 \cdot 10H_2O$ (68 mM) $+4.1$ g. semicarbazide (74 mM) $+0.9$ g.
   glycine (24 mM) in about 400 ml. distilled water, adjust to pH 8.7 with 2 N NaOH and
   dilute to 500 ml. with distilled water.
II. Nicotinamide-adenine dinucleotide (ca. 12 mM NAD):
   Dissolve 9 mg. NAD in 1 ml. distilled water.
III. Benzoyl-L-arginine ethyl ester (18 mM):
   Dissolve 7 mg. BAEE (L-isomer) in 1 ml. distilled water.
IV. ADH suspension, see p. 1033.
V. Kallikrein standard, Padutin®, see p. 1031.
VI. NADH standard solution (10 mM):
   Dissolve 8.3 mg. NADH-Na_2 in 1.0 ml. 1% $NaHCO_3$ solution. Dilute 1 : 100 with 1%
   $NaHCO_3$ for the assay.
VII. NaOH/H_2O_2 solution:
   Mix 10 ml. 10 N NaOH and 0.1 ml. 2% H_2O_2

Stability of Solutions

See p. 1033. Solution VI as for solution II; prepare solution VII freshly.

Procedure

Collection, Treatment and Stability of Sample, see p. 1033.

Assay System

Prepare the required amount of reagent mixture depending on the number of determinations:

Buffer solution	(I)	0.79 Vol.
NAD solution	(II)	0.10 Vol.
BAEE solution	(III)	0.10 Vol.
ADH suspension	(IV)	0.01 Vol.
		1.00 Vol.

Primary wavelength: 365 nm; secondary wavelength: 460 nm; light path: 1 cm.; incubation
volume: 200 μl.; final volume: 520 μl.; 25 °C. Read against blank containing distilled water
instead of sample.
Analyse a standard with each series of measurements. For this add 10 μl. 1 : 100 diluted NADH
standard solution (corresponding to 1 nmole NADH) instead of sample.

Pipette into reaction vessel:		Concentration in assay mixture
Reagent mixture	100 μl.	27 mM pyrophosphate 29 mM semicarbazide 9.5 mM glycine 0.6 mM NAD 0.9 mM BAEE 150 μg. ADH/ml. ≙ 30 U/ml.
Distilled water (varies with different sample volumes)	90 μl.	
Equilibrate tube to 25 °C.		
Sample (kallikrein solution) (V)	10 μl.	
Shake and incubate for exactly 15 min. at 25 °C.		
1 N NaOH	20 μl.	91 mM NaOH
Reaction is stopped; excess of NAD is destroyed by 15 min. incubation at 56 °C.		
NaOH/H_2O_2 (VII)	300 μl.	6 N NaOH, 0.01% H_2O_2
To form the fluorescent product of NADH incubate for 30 min. at 37 °C; dilute with distilled water 1 : 10 and measure the fluorescence.		

Calculations

For the calculations the measured fluorescence is related to the fluorescence of a NADH standard solution. With 1 nmole (10 μl. diluted standard solution) a fluorescence is obtained which under the given conditions corresponds to an enzyme activity of 0.066 mU kallikrein in the assay system. Therefore with 10 μl. samples:

$$\text{Volume activity} = \frac{F_{Sample}}{F_{Standard}} \times 6.6 \text{ [U/l.]}; 25 \text{ °C}$$

Other Methods for the Determination of Kallikrein Activity

Apart from the previously mentioned biological-pharmacological methods (see p.1031) the activity can be determined by following the esterolytic hydrolysis of BAEE:
1. Direct measurement of extinction increase at 253 nm[5,11].
2. Continual automated micro-titration of the liberated carboxyl groups[5,6].
3. Volumetric determination of carboxyl groups with hydrogen carbonate/CO_2 buffer[5,6].
4. Determination of ester bond in a colorimetric assay[12].

References

1 *M. E. Webster:* Report of the committee on nomenclature for hypotensive peptides, in *E. G. Erdös, N. Back & F. Sicureti:* Hypotensive peptides, Springer Verlag, N. Y. 1966 and Bradykinin and kalli-krein, *E. G. Erdös:* Handbuch der experimentellen Pharmakologie, Springer Verlag, New York 1970.
2 *I. Trautschold & G. Rüdel,* Klin. Wschr. *41*, 297 [1963].

3 *E. Werle*, Dtsch. med. Wschr. *92*, 1 573 [1967].

4 *E. K. Frey, H. Kraut, E. Werle, R. Vogel, G. Zickgraf-Rüdel & I. Trautschold:* Das Kallikrein-Kinin-System und seine Inhibitoren, Enke Verlag, Stuttgart [1968].

5 *I. Trautschold & E. Werle*, Hoppe Seylers Z. physiol. Chem. *325*, 48 [1961].

6 *I. Trautschold*, Habilitationsschrift, Medizinische Fakultät der Universität München 1965.

7 *E. Werle & B. Kaufmann-Bötsch*, Naturwissenschaften *46*, 559 [1959]; *E. Habermann*, Naunyn Schmiedeberg's Arch. exp. Pathol. Pharmakol. *236*, 492 [1959]; *E. Werle & B. Kaufmann-Bötsch*, Hoppe Seylers Z. physiol. Chem. *319*, 52 [1960]

8 *E. Werle & I. Trautschold* in Hoppe-Seyler-Thierfelder: Handbuch der physiologischen und pathologisch-chemischen Analyse, Springer-Verlag, Vol. VI C, 745 [1967].

9 *F. Fiedler & E. Werle*, Hoppe Seylers Z. physiol. Chem. *348*, 1 087 [1967].

10 *O. H. Lowry, N. R. Roberts & J. I. Kapphahn*, J. biol. Chem. *224*, 1 047 [1957].

11 *I, Trautschold & E. Werle* in H. U. *Bergmeyer:* Methoden der enzymatischen Analyse, Verlag Chemie Weinheim 1962, 1st. Edn., p. 880.

12 *S. Hestrin*, J. biol. Chem. *180*, 249 [1949].

Elastase

General Information[1,2]

Walter Appel

Elastase, EC 3.4.21.11 was discovered in 1950 by *Balo* and *Banga*[3] and is characterized by its ability to hydrolyse the elastin fibres of the aorta. Native collagen and keratin are not hydrolysed, but haemoglobin, casein or fibrin are. Elastase occurs mainly in the pancreas and pancreatic juice of many mammals and birds, as well as in human serum[4-7], granulocytes[36] and erythrocytes[8] (but not leucocytes[9]), in *Flavobact. elastolyticum*[11], *Clostrid. histolyticum*[10,32] and *Staph. epidermis*[34]. In pig pancreas it occurs as proelastase which is activated by trypsin[11,37-39]. For preparative purposes the usual starting material is crude pancreatin or trypsin from pig or beef[2,12-14,33,46]. Crystalline preparations are not homogeneous, on the contrary they can be separated by electrophoretic or chromatographic methods to give an elastomucoproteinase[15] and a non-specific proteinase[16-18]. The purest preparations still contain a small percentage of proteolytic, non-elastolytic activity, which has led to discussion on the possibility of a bifunctional enzyme[12,18,19]. The structure[20] and enzymatic specificity (esterase activity[11,21,40]) of elastase resemble those of trypsin and chymotrypsin.

No activators are known, while high salt concentrations are inhibitory: $50-70$ mM NaCl, KCl or $(NH_4)_2SO_4$ causes a 50% inhibition, 166 mM gives 75% inhibition. 1 mM Ca^{2+}, Mg^{2+}, Zn^{2+}, Co^{2+}, Mn^{2+} and cysteine have no effect; 20 mM EDTA[31] and 0.01 mM Cu^{2+} give 50% inhibition (see also [42,43]). The inhibition by ovomucoid, pancreas or ascarides trypsin inhibitor are probably due to contamination of the enzyme, while inhibition by kallikrein trypsin inhibitor from beef lung and parotid gland (Trasylol®) is due to binding of the inhibitor to the substrate. Sera of various mammals and humans contain highly active inhibitors of elastase which are proteins[2,5,6,22,41]. All quantitative methods for the determination of elastase activity are based on the degradation (proteolytic + mucolytic) of elastin. The older gravimetric methods[1] are not recommended. The modern methods use an insoluble elastin which is coupled with a dye. The amount of soluble dye formed during the hydrolysis is a measure of the elastase activity. Suitable dyes include congo red[4,8,18,23], orcein[5,24-28], dimethylaminonaphthalenesulphonic acid[7], and more recently fluorescein[29]. The orcein method is described here because so far there has been little experience with the more sensitive fluorescein-elastin methods.

The physiological and pathophysiological importance of elastase is still not clear. It has been discussed in connection with pancreatitis[7,30,35] and atherosclerosis[27,44,45].

Determination with Orcein-elastin

Application of Method: In biochemistry and clinical chemistry.

Principle

(1) $$\text{Orcein-elastin} \xrightarrow{\text{elastase}} \text{Orcein} + \text{Hydrolysis Products}$$

The mucoprotein fraction of isoluble orcein-elastin is degraded by the enzyme to soluble hydrolysis products; the amount of dye liberated into solution per unit time is a measure of the enzyme activity.

Optimum Conditions for Measurements

The pH optimum is 8.7–9.2 and depends in part on the of buffer used. The substrate (insoluble) is present in large excess. Activation or pre-incubation is not possible or necessary. The reaction is first order up to about 35% hydrolysis.

Measurements at different temperatures may require different measuring conditions (cf. p. 127). Nevertheless, results obtained under the same measuring conditions but at different temperatures were formerly compared with each other ("conversion factors" were determined). Such conversion factors may be correct if determined with a relatively large proband collective; however, they cannot be applied generally to the individual case (cf. p. 129). The value of the following relative reaction rates[31] thus lies in being able to appraise the temperature dependence of the reaction and at the most to compare qualitatively values up to the limit of normal.

°C	20	25	30	35	37	40
	1.35	1.00	0.83	0.70	0.67	0.64

Equipment

Spectro- or filterphotometer; water bath (37 °C); cold bath (4 °C); stopwatch or laboratory alarm clock; centrifuge.

Reagents

1. Tris-hydroxymethyl-aminomethane, tris
2. Hydrochloric acid; 0.1 N and 1 N
3. Sodium hydroxide, 0.1 N
4. Disodium hydrogen phosphate, $Na_2HPO_4 \cdot 2H_2O$
5. Potassium dihydrogen phosphate, KH_2PO_4
6. Orcein-elastin
   e.g. from Worthington
7. Orcein
   e.g. from Merck

Preparation of Solutions (for ca. 20 normal assays and 200 micro-assays)

Use only doubly distilled water

I. Tris buffer (0.1 M; pH 8.8):
   Dissolve 1.21 g. tris in ca. 25 ml. distilled water, add 19 ml. 0.1 N HCl and dilute with distilled water to 100 ml.; check pH with glass electrode.

II. Phosphate buffer (0.7 M; pH 6.0):
   Dissolve 6.23 g. disodium hydrogen phosphate in 50 ml. distilled water and add to this 100 ml. of a solution of 9.52 g. potassium dihydrogen phosphate in 100 ml. distilled water; check the pH.

III. Orcein standard solution (0.4 mM):
   Dissolve 72.4 mg. orcein in a 500 ml. volumetric flask with 20.0 ml. 0.1 N NaOH, add 6.05 g. tris and ca. 400 ml. distilled water. Adjust to pH 8.8 with 11.5 ml. 1 N HCl and dilute to 500 ml. distilled water; check the pH.

Stability of Solutions

The solutions are stable for months at 4 °C.

Procedure

Collection, Treatment and Stability of Sample

No special precautions are required. Store the enzyme solutions frozen and prepare dilutions freshly each day.

Assay System

Wavelength: Hg 578 nm; light path: 1 cm.; reaction temperature: 37 °C; final volume: 3.0 ml. (normal assay), 0.300 ml. (micro-assay); read against a reference cuvette containing buffer solution (I).

Blank (E_0) parallel to the test: immediately after addition of sample stop the reaction by addition of 2 ml. phosphate buffer (solution II), then treat as for the test; control (to determine the spontaneous hydrolysis of the substrate): as for test but containing 1 ml. physiological saline instead of sample.

Weigh or pipette into a centrifuge tube:		Concentration in assay mixture
Orcein-elastin	20 mg.	6.6 mg./ml.
Tris buffer (solution I)	2.00 ml.	66 mM
Sample (serum, homogenate, etc.)	1.00 ml.	
Add immediately to (E_0) and after 30 min. incubation, preferably with horizontal shaking or magnetic stirring.		
Phosphate buffer (solution II)	2.00 ml.	
Centrifuge and measure extinction E_x of the supernatant fluid. $\Delta E = E_x - E_0$ is used for the calculations.		

Calculations

Direct expression of the enzyme activity in units (U) according to the recommendations of the IUB is not possible because the substrate is not sufficiently well-defined and the reaction occurs in a heterogeneous medium. As a first approximation[*] the enzyme activity is expressed in μmole of hydrolysis products, where the molar extinction of orcein is considered to equal the extinction of the orcein derivatives that go into solution on degradation of elastin.

To check equipment and different batches of reagents prepare a standard curve as follows: dilute 0.05–1.0 ml. (20–400 nmole) orcein standard solution III to 2.0 ml. with solution I, then treat as described above. Prepare also a blank as for the standards but without orcein. Plot the extinction differences (ordinate) against the "μmole orcein" (abscissa). Read off the "μmole orcein" corresponding to the extinction differ-

---

[*] The calculation of the standard curve is based on a molecular weight for orcein of 362. Orcein is a mixture of dyes, which consist of 8 main components of similar molecular weight (α, β and γ-amino-orcein $C_{21}H_{18}O_4N_2$, mol. wt. = 362; α, β and γ -amino-orceinimine, mol. wt. = 360).

A further simplification is that the ratio of orcein: elastin in the substrate remains constant within certain limits and the orceinelastopeptides which may be formed during the hydrolysis of the protein have the same or similar extinctions to that of the free dye.

ences obtained for the samples from this standard curve. The control to determine the spontaneous hydrolysis of the substrate is treated in the same way and then subtracted from the test; this gives "$\mu\text{mole}_{\text{corr.}}$". After correction for the reaction time (divide by 30) and for any dilution of the sample with the factor F the activity is calculated as follows:

Normal assay: volume activity $= \mu\text{mole}_{\text{corr.}} \times 33.3 \quad \times \text{F} \quad [\text{mU/ml.}]$

Micro-assay: volume activity $= \text{nmole}_{\text{corr.}} \times 0.333 \times \text{F} \quad [\text{mU/ml.}]$

Precision of Method

The coefficient of variation is 5.6% for 20 determinations on a single sample (precision).

Normal Values

Normal values have been omitted here because of the varying conditions of the measurements and definition of units in the literature.

Sources of Error

According to [28] plasma albumin and other plasma proteins cause faulty results, likewise trypsin and chymotrypsin present in tissue extracts. With low enzyme activity the incubation time can be increased to several hours.

Specificity of Method

The method described here is considered by most authors to be specific for elastase.

Micro-Assay

The method described here is so arranged that a 1 : 10 reduction in all volumes can be easily made. It is then recommended to add double the amount of substrate, i. e. 4 mg. We have had experience with the "Beckman-Spinco" and "Eppendorf" micro-assay systems.

Other Assay Methods

The previously mentioned method with fluorescein-elastin as substrate[7] has several advantages over the method described here; in particular, it is possible to express the measured enzyme activities in U. However, the method has not yet been sufficiently proved and the substrate is not readily available.

References

1 *H. Hanson* in *Hoppe-Seyler-Thierfelder:* Handb. d. physiol.- u. path.-chem. Analyse, Springer-Verlag, Berlin-Heidelberg-New York, 10. Edition 1966, Vol. IV, part C, p. 297.
2 *J. Mandl* in *S. P. Colowick & N. O. Kaplan:* Methods in Enzymology, Academic Press, New York-London, 1962, Vol. V, p. 665.
3 *J. Balo & J. Banga,* Biochem. J. *78,* 156 [1961].
4 *D. A. Hall,* Biochem. J. *101,* 29 [1966].
5 *S. Chao, J. J. Sciarra & G. J. Vosburgh,* Proc. Soc. Expl. Biol. Med. *109,* 342 [1962].
6 *J. S. Baumstark,* Arch. Biochem. Biophysics *118,* 619 [1967].

7 *H. Rinderknecht, M. C. Geokas, P. Silverman & B. J. Haverback*, Clin. Chim. Acta *19*, 89 [1968].
    21, 197 [1968] und Clin. Res. *16*, 291 [1968].
8 *J. Schönemann*, Klin. Wschr. *45*, 847 [1967].
9 *G. Chotiner, J. G. Jr. Smith & T. Rosett*, J. Invest. Derm. *49*, 333 [1967].
10 *J. Mandl & B. B. Cohen*, Arch. Biochem. *97*, 122 [1962].
11 *F. Lamy & St. Tauber*, J. biol. Chem. *238*, 939 [1963].
12 *U. J. Lewis, D. E. Williams & N. G. Brink*, J. biol. Chem. *222*, 705 [1956].
13 *M. A. Naughton & F. Sanger*, Biochem. J. *78*, 156 [1961].
14 *D. A. Hall & J. W. Czerkawski*, Biochem. J. *73*, 359 [1959].
15 *J. Banga*, Structure and Funktion of Elastin and Kollagen, Akadémiai kiado Budapest 1966.
16 *F. Lamy, C. P. Craigh & S. Tauber*, J. biol. Chem. *236*, 86 [1961].
17 *V. Ling & R. A. Anwar*, Biochem. Biophys. Res. Commun. *24*, 593 [1966].
18 *R. L. Walford & B. Kickhöfen*, Arch. Biochem. Biophys. *98*, 191 [1962].
19 *D. A. Hall*, Arch. Biochem. Biophys. *1*, 239 [1963].
20 *J. R. Brown, D. L. Kauffmann & B. S. Hartley*, Biochem. J. *103*, 497 [1967].
21 *M. L. Bender & T. H. Marshall*, Amer. Chem. Soc. *90*, 201 [1968].
22 *N. Heimburger & H. Haupt*, Klin. Wschr. *44*, 1196 [1966].
23 *M. A. Naughton & F. Sanger*, Biochem. J. *70*, 4 P [1958].
24 *L. A. Sacher, K. K. Winter, N. Sicher & S. Fraukel*, Proc. Soc. Expl. Biol. Med. *90*, 323 [1955]·
25 *V. Scarselli*, Nature *183*, 1739 [1959].
26 *G. Rancati, P. Marrama, C. Ferreri & B. Bonati*, Ital. J. Biochem. *8*, 71 [1959].
27 *U. Butturini & M. Langer*, Klin. Wschr. *40*, 472 [1962].
28 *K. Morihara, H. Tsuzuki, T. Oka, H. Inove & M. Ebata*, J. biol. Chem. *240*, 3295 [1965].
29 *H. Rinderknecht, M. C. Geokas, P. Silverman & Y. Lillard*, Clin. Chim. Acta *19*, 327 [1968].
30 *M. C. Geokas & J. Haverback*, Clin. Res. *15*, 129 [1967].
31 *W. Appel*, unpublished results.
32 *V. D. Hospelhorn*, Abstr. Pap. Amer. Chem. Soc. *148*, 60 C [1964].
33 *W. Ardelt, S. Ksiežny, J. N. Namyslowska*, 5. FEBS-Meeting, Prague, [1968}.
34 *D. P. Varadi & A. C. Saqueton*, Clin. Res. *16*, 260 [1968].
35 *M. C. Geokas, H. Rinderknecht, V. Swanson, B. P. Citron & B. J. Haverback*, Clin. Res. *16*, 285 [1968].
36 *A. Janoff*, Biochem. Pharmacol. *19*, 626 [1970].
37 *F. Lamy & M. Uram*, 6th. FEBS-Meeting, Madrid [1969].
38 *A. Gertler & Y. Birk*, 6th. FEBS-Meeting, Madrid [1969].
39 *A. Hercz*, J. biol. Chem., *244*, 5556 [1969].
40 *Th. H. Marshall, J. R. Whitaker & M. L. Bender*, Biochemistry *8*, 4665 [1969] and *8*, 4671 [1969].
41 *G. M. Turino, R. M. Senior, B. D. Garg, S. Keller, M. M. Levi & J. Mandl*, Science *165*, 709 [1969].
42 *W. E. Brown & F. Wold*, Science *174*, 608 [1971].
43 *L. Visser, D. S. Sigman & E. R. Blout*, Biochemistry, *10*, 735 [1971].
44 *A. Tax & L. Korngold*, J. Immunol. *107*, 1189 [1971].
45 *W. A. Loeven*, J. Endocrinol. *48*, 401 [1970].
46 *D. M. Shotton* in: *S. P. Colowick & N. O. Kaplan*, Methods in Enzymology, *19*, 613, Academic Press
    New York, London, 1970.

Pepsin

(Pepsin, Gastricsin, Pepsinogen, Uropepsinogen)

Wirnt Rick and Wolf-Peter Fritsch

The proteolytic enzyme pepsin[1] (EC 3.4.23.1) occurs in the gastric juice of all mammals. The chief cells of the gastric mucosa secrete the inactive precursor pepsinogen (the molecular weight of pepsinogen from pig stomach[2] is 38 944), which is converted into proteolytically active pepsin (molecular weight 34 163)[2] by cleavage of a peptide (molecular weight 3 242)[3] which acts as inhibitor of pepsin and other peptides. The activation at pH 5.0 is an autocatalytic process[3]. Pepsin is an endopeptidase which shows low substrate specificity[1]. Peptide bonds between aromatic amino acids are attacked particularly readily by pepsin. In insulin the enzyme hydrolyses the bonds between: -Glu·NH$_2$-His, -Leu-Val-, -Glu-Ala-, -Ala-Leu-, -Glu-Glu·NH$_2$-, Val-CySO$_3$H-, -Glu·NH$_2$-Leu-, -Leu-Glu-, etc.[1,4].

Pepsin also acts as an esterase: (β-phenyl)-L-lactic acid is split from the substrate benzyloxycarbonyl-L-histidyl-p-nitrophenyl-alanyl-(β-phenyl)-L-methyl lactate[5]. However, amides of amino acids are not hydrolysed.

Methods of assay:[6]

Measurement of viscosity on protein solutions; determination of the nitrogen in the trichloroacetic acid-soluble products liberated or formol titration of the amino groups liberated after action of the enzyme on gelatine, casein, edestin, milk proteins, etc[7]; determination of the tyrosine and tryptophan content of the hydrolysis products[8,9] with the phenol reagent of *Folin* and *Ciocalteu*[10] or direct measurement of the UV absorption[11] of the peptides formed after action of the enzyme on haemoglobin; determination of the rennet activity of the enzyme[12,13] or the use of isotopically labelled serum albumin as substrate[14]. With several synthetic substrates the reaction can be followed directly by spectrophotometry[5,15]. The most suitable synthetic substrates are N-acetyl-L-phenylalanyl-L-phenylalanine[16] and N-acetyl-L-phenylalanyl-L-3,5-di-iodotyrosine[16,17].

Application of Method: In biochemistry, in clinical chemistry and in pharmacy.

Measurements with Haemoglobin as Substrate

Principle

Pepsin splits off products from haemoglobin which are soluble in trichloroacetic acid[9]. The tyrosine and tryptophan content of these compounds can be determined by the method of *Folin* and *Ciocalteu*[10] or by measurement of the extinction at 280 nm.

Optimum Conditions for Measurements

The pH optimum for the proteolytic activity is pH 1.8–2.0[18,19]. According to *Ohlenbusch*[19] the pH activity curve of pepsin is contributed to by the change in activity with pH below pH 2 and the change in activity due to the substrate above pH 2. With denatured haemoglobin the pH optimum is pH 3.1. At pH 4 not more than 50% of the maximum activity is measured (denaturation of the haemoglobin in 40% alkaline urea solution, enzyme reaction in 10% urea solution). The optimum substrate concentration is 1.6 mg. haemoglobin/ml. and the rate of hydrolysis is constant between 1.6 and 16 mg. substrate/ml.

1. Assay with Phenol Reagent of Folin and Ciocalteu

Equipment

Spectrophotometer of filter-photometer suitable for measurements at 578, 691 or 750 nm; water bath (25 °C); stopwatch or laboratory timer.

Reagents

1. Hydrochloric acid, conc., 36% (w/w)*
2. Hydrochloric acid, A. R., 0.2 N
3. Hydrochloric acid, A. R., 0.06 N
4. Hydrochloric acid, A. R., 0.01 N
5. Sodium hydroxide, A. R., 0.5 N
6. Trichloroacetic acid
7. Sodium tungstate, $Na_2WO_4 \cdot 2H_2O$*
8. Sodium molybdate, $Na_2MoO_4 \cdot 2H_2O$*
9. Lithium sulphate, Li_2SO_4*
10. Orthophosphoric acid, conc., 85% (w/w)*
11. Bovine haemoglobin**
12. L-(−)-Tyrosine chromatographically pure.

Preparation of Solutions

I. Substrate solution:
    Dissolve 2 g. haemoglobin in 0.06 N HCl and make up to 100 ml. (pH ca. 1.8). Centrifuge off any stromata which may be present at 4000 g for 15 min.

II. Phenol reagent[20]:
    Dissolve 10 g. $Na_2WO_4 \cdot 2H_2O$ + 2.5 g. $Na_2MoO_4 \cdot 2H_2O$ + 15 g. Li_2SO_4 + 10 ml. conc. HCl + 5 ml. conc. H_3PO_4 and make up to 100 ml. with distilled water. Before use dilute 1 part of this solution with 2 parts doubly distilled water.

III. Tyrosine standard solution (1 mM tyrosine):
    Dissolve 181.19 mg. L-(−)-tyrosine in 0.2 N HCl and make up to 1000 ml.

IV. Trichloroacetic acid (5% w/v):
    Dissolve 5 g. trichloroacetic acid in distilled water and make up to 100 ml.

Stability of Solutions

Store the substrate and tyrosine solution in a refrigerator at 0−4 °C. To prevent bacterial contamination 2.5 mg. merthiolate*** (Lilly) can be added per 100 ml. substrate solution and formaldehyde (0.5% final concentration) to the tyrosine solution.

Procedure

Collection, Treatment and Stability of Sample

Collection:

Dissolve enzyme in 10 mM HCl. Obtain gastric juice as free as possible from contamination (e. g. bile), and centrifuge for 15 min. at 10−15 000 g and 0−4 °C.

---

* Reagents 1, 7, 8, 9 and 10 are constituents of the *Folin* and *Ciocalteu*[10] phenol reagent. This reagent can be obtained commercially, e. g. from E. Merck, Darmstadt, Germany.
** e. g. from Behringwerke, Marburg, Germany; Armour, Kanakee, Ill. USA: Serva, Heidelberg, Germany.
*** Na-salt of o-(ethylmercurythio) benzoic acid.

Stability of enzyme in sample:

Pepsin solutions are stable for about 8 days at 4 °C. The proteolytic activity of gastric juice initially increases after collection, reaches a maximum at about 9 hr ($+15\%$) and then slowly falls. The initial value is reached after about 24 hr. and the further decrease in activity is about 2% in 24 hr.[21].

Tyrosine Standard Curve

Pipette into 50 ml. Erlenmeyer flasks:
> 0.2–1.0 ml. tyrosine standard solution (III) (0.2–1.0 μmole tyrosine)
> 4.8–4.0 ml. 0.2 N HCl
> 10.0 ml. 0.5 N NaOH

add with continual shaking
> 3.0 ml. dilute phenol reagent (solution II).

Measure the extinction against a blank containing 0.2 N HCl instead of tyrosine standard as described under "Assay System" and plot the results against the μmole tyrosine.

Assay System

Wavelength: 578, 691 or 750 nm; light path: 1 cm.; volume of incubation mixture: 6.0 ml.; incubation temperature: 25 °C; volume for colour reaction: 18 ml. Read against water. Bring substrate solution to 25 °C before assay.

Enzymatic Reaction

Pipette into 20 ml. centrifuge tubes:			Concentration in assay mixture
Substrate solution (I)		5.0 ml.	16.7 mg. haemoglobin/ml. ca. 0.05 N HCl
Equilibrate to 25 °C.			
Undiluted gastric juice 0.01 N HCl or enzyme solution		0.01-0.04 ml. 0.99-0.96 ml. 1.0 ml.	ca. 1–3 μg. cryst. pepsin/ml.
Mix and incubate for exactly 10 min.			
Trichloroacetic acid solution (IV)		10.0 ml.	
Shake, filter or centrifuge off precipitate (20 min. at 4000 g).			

Colorimetric Reaction

Pipette into 50 ml. Erlenmeyer flasks:		
Filtrate or supernatant fluid 0.5 N NaOH	5.0 ml. 10.0 ml.	0.278 N
Add with constant shaking:		
Dilute phenol reagent (soln. II)	3.0 ml.	
Measure the extinction 5 to 10 min. after the addition of the phenol reagent.		

Prepare a blank for every assay: Add 10 ml. trichloroacetic acid solution (IV) to substrate solution (I), then add enzyme, mix and filter or centrifuge off precipitate. Take filtrate or supernatant fluid for the colorimetric reaction.

Calculations

The "Pepsin Unit" (PU^Hb) defined by *Anson*[9] is the amount of enzyme which hydrolyses haemoglobin at such an initial rate under standard conditions (total volume 6 ml. containing 0.1 g. haemoglobin; temperature 35.5 °C), that the amount of trichloroacetic acid-soluble hydrolysis products formed per minute gives the same extinction with the phenol reagent as 1 mmole tyrosine. If the incubation is carried out at 25 °C instead of 35.5 °C, the activity of the enzyme is 1.82 times lower.

There is however no linearity between the pepsin activity and the amount of hydrolysis products formed. Therefore the pepsin activity must be extrapolated to zero or a standard curve can be used.

The extrapolation method is used for the determination of the activity of purified enzymes: different, sufficiently small amounts of enzyme are incubated with substrate as described above. After determination of the hydrolysis products (corrected for the blank) the μmole tyrosine are plotted against the amounts of enzymes and then a tangent to the curve is drawn through the origin. From the tangent the amount of enzyme which corresponds to 1 μmole tyrosine is read off. This amount of enzyme is multiplied by:

$$10 \times 1\,000 \times \frac{5}{16} \times \frac{1}{1.82} = 1\,717$$

to give the amount of enzyme corresponding to one pepsin unit (PU^Hb). The factors are derived as follows:

10　　= conversion from 10 min. to 1 min.
1 000　= conversion from μmole to mmole
5/16　 = conversion from colorimetric reaction to enzymatic reaction mixture
1/1.82 = conversion from 25 °C to 35.5 °C.

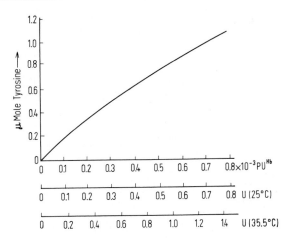

Fig. 1. Dependence of hydrolysis of haemoglobin by pepsin on amount of enzyme (modification of method of *Anson*[9]).
Upper abscissa scale: pepsin units according to *Anson*[9], PU^Hb. – Middle abscissa scale: International units, 25 °C. – Lower abscissa scale: International units, 35.5 °C. – Ordinate: Tyrosine equivalent (μmole) of the hydrolysis products in 5 ml. filtrate (see text under "Enzymatic reaction"). Enzymatic reaction: 10 min. at 25 °C.

For studies on gastric juice and other biological fluids *Anson*[9] has published a standard curve obtained by use of a modified assay (Fig. 1).

The extinction read on the spectrophotometer is converted to μmole tyrosine by means of the tyrosine standard curve and the pepsin units corresponding to this amount of tyrosine are read off from the abscissa of Fig. 1. For conversion to units per ml. sample the results must be divided by the volume of sample taken.

Conversion to International Units:

As different peptide bonds of haemoglobin are hydrolysed at different rates by pepsin, it is necessary to use a wider definition of International Unit. Instead of 1 μmole substrate, 1 μmole of the group involved is substituted, i. e. 1 μmole of tyrosine equivalent in acid soluble products of the enzymatic hydrolysis. Therefore 1 PU^{Hb} corresponds to 1000 U (35.5 °C). As the enzyme activity at 25 °C is 1.82 times lower than at 35.5 °C, the conversion factor for this temperature is 1 PU^{Hb} = 549 U (25 °C).

2. Assay at 280 nm[11]

Equipment

Spectrophotometer for measurements at 280 nm; water bath (35.5 °C); stopwatch; laboratory centrifuge.

Reagents, Preparation of Solutions and Stability of Solutions

See above under 1, p. 1047. The phenol reagent and tyrosine standard solution are not required.

Procedure

Collection, Treatment and Stability of Sample, see above, p. 1047–1048.

Assay System

Wavelength: 280 nm; light path: 1 cm.; volume of incubation mixture: 6 ml.; incubation temperature: 35.5 °C. Read against blank. Bring substrate solution to 35.5 °C before start of assay.

Prepare a blank for each assay: 2.5 ml. substrate solution (I) +5.0 ml. trichloroacetic acid solution (IV) +0.5 ml. enzyme solution (sample). After a few minutes filter or centrifuge off the precipitate.

Pipette into 10 ml. centrifuge tubes:			Concentration in assay mixture
Substrate solution (I)	2.5 ml.		16.7 mg. haemoglobin/ml. ca. 0.05 N HCl
Equilibrate to 35.5 °C.			
Pre-warmed enzyme solution (sample)	0.5 ml.		
Mix and incubate for exactly 10 min.			
Trichloroacetic acid (IV)	5.0 ml.		
Allow to stand for several minutes at 35.5 °C, centrifuge or filter. Pour the supernatant fluid or filtrate into cuvettes and measure extinction.			

Calculations

Read off the pepsin activity in PU[Hb] from Fig. 2[11]. For conversion to U, see p. 1050.

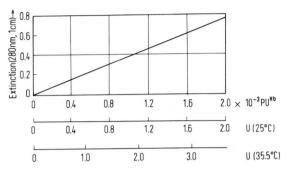

Fig. 2. Dependence of hydrolysis of haemoglobin by pepsin on the amount of enzyme (modification of method of *Northrop*[11] from [1]).
Upper abscissa scale: pepsin units of *Anson*[9], PU[Hb], 35.5 °C. – Middle abscissa scale: International units, 25 °C. – Lower abscissa scale: International units, 35.5 °C. – Ordinate: extinction of supernatant fluid or filtrate at 280 nm, 1 cm. light path.

Precision of Method

In the range around 1.5 U (25 °C) per assay the standard deviation was 0.07 U (25 °C). The coefficient of variation is 4.7%.

Normal Values in Gastric Juice

Pepsin activity in gastric juice

As results of assays of pepsin activity in healthy subjects without stimulation of the gastric mucosa vary greatly, the gastric secretion should be stimulated[21] (e. g. with Betazol, 50 mg. s. c. or 1.7 mg./kg. body wt. s.c., or with pentagastrin, 6 μg./kg. body weight, s.c.).

Pepsin activity, U/l. (25 °C):

	$\bar{x}$	s	Range
Basal secretion	0.054	0.030	0.006–0.123
Secretion after Betazol	0.063	0.019	0.027–0.092

Pepsinogen secretion per unit time

The normal range can be more accurately determined, especially after stimulation, if the secretion is quantitatively collected at different time intervals and not the volume activity, but *the secretion per unit time*, is considered.

Pepsinogen excretion, expressed as pepsin, U (25 °C) per min.:

	$\bar{x}$	s	Range
Basal secretion	73	43	9.5–169
Secretion after Betazol	164	52	79–254

Sources of Error

Effects of drugs and other therapeutic measures: Treatment of patients with gastric enzyme preparations should be discontinued before the test.

Interference in the assay technique: None known.

Specificity of Method

With proteins as substrate the activity of gastricin[1,22] in the gastric juice is also measured.

Details for Measurements in Serum

A smaller fragment of the pepsinogen formed in the gastric mucosa is secreted into the blood. The proteolytic activity contained in serum has two optima in the acid range at pH 2.0 and 3.5[23]. Normal values in serum: in healthy subjects the pepsin activity was found to be 1.72 ± 0.91 U/l. (37 °C)[24].

Details for Measurements in Tissues

Pepsinogen (see p.1046) is found in the central or chief cells of the gastric mucosa as an inactive precursor of pepsin.

Measurements with N-Acetyl-L-phenylalanyl-L-3,5-di-iodotyrosine as Substrate

Principle

N-Acetyl-L-phenylalanyl-L-3,5-di-iodotyrosine + H_2O $\xrightarrow{\text{pepsin}}$ N-Acetyl-L-phenylalanine +

+ L-3,5-di-iodotyrosine

The L-3,5-di-iodotyrosine formed is determined with ninhydrin[25]. The amount of substrate reacting per minute is a measure of the enzyme activity. Of all the low molecular weight substrates N-acetylphenyl-alanyl-L-3,5-di-iodotyrosine is attacked most rapidly by pepsin.

Optimum Conditions for Measurements

The pH optimum of the hydrolysis of the substrate is around pH 2.0[17]. The Michaelis constant, Km at this pH value is 0.075 mM; as the maximum concentration of substrate obtainable at this pH is 0.16 mM, this concentration is used in the assay.

Equipment

Filter or spectrum-line photometer suitable for measurements at 570–578 nm; water bath (25 °C; 100 °C); stopwatch or laboratory timer.

Reagents

1. N-Acetyl-L-phenylalanyl-L-3,5-di-iodotyrosine
2. Sodium hydroxide, 0.1 N
3. Hydrochloric acid, 0.1 N; 0.01 N
4. Ninhydrin, A. R.
5. Hydrindantin
6. Ethyleneglycolmonomethylether (methylcellosolve)
7. Sodium acetate · $3H_2O$, A. R.
8. Acetic acid, A. R., 96%
9. Ethanol, 50% (v/v)
10. L-3,5-di-iodotyrosine

Preparation of Solutions

I. Substrate solution (0.16 mM):
Dissolve 9.94 mg. N-acetyl-L-phenylalanyl-L-3,5-di-iodotyrosine in 1 ml. 0.1 N NaOH, dilute with 80 ml. doubly distilled water, adjust to pH 2.0 with 0.1 N HCl and dilute the solution to 100 ml. with 0.01 N HCl.

II. Acetate buffer (4 N; pH 5.5):
Dissolve 272 g. sodium acetate · $3H_2O$ with warming and stirring in ca. 200 ml. doubly distilled water. Allow to cool, add 50 ml. acetic acid and dilute to 500 ml. with doubly distilled water. Check the pH.

III. Ninhydrin reagent:
Dissolve 20 g. ninhydrin and 3 g. hydrindantin in 750 ml. peroxide-free ethyleneglycolmonomethylether, add 250 ml. buffer (II) and immediately pour into a dark bottle. Store under N_2.

IV. L-3,5-Di-iodotyrosine standard solution (0.1 mM):
Dissolve 43.39 mg. L-3,5-di-iodotyrosine in doubly distilled water and make up to 1 000 ml.

Stability of Solutions

The substrate solution keeps for about 2 weeks at room temperature and the buffer for at least a year at 0−4 °C. The ninhydrin reagent is stable for about 4 weeks in a dark bottle under nitrogen at room temperature[25].

Procedure

Collection, Treatment and Stability of Sample, see p. 1047−1048.

Assay System

Wavelength: 570–578 nm; light path: 1 cm.; volume of incubation mixture: 1.1 ml.; incubation temperature: 37 °C; volume of colorimetric reaction: 2.6 ml. Read against water.

Pipette into 12 ml. centrifuge tubes (in 37 °C water bath)		Test	Blank	Concentration in assay mixture
Pre-warmed substrate solution	(I)	1.0 ml.	1.0 ml.	0.15 mM substrate 0.01 N HCl
Gastric juice or pepsin solution		0.1 ml.	—	ca. 10–100 μg. enzyme protein/ml.
Mix, start a stopwatch at the same time, and incubate for exactly 10 min.				
Ninhydrin reagent	(III)	0.5 ml.	0.5 ml.	
Gastric juice or pepsin solution		—	0.1 ml.	
Mix, stopper tubes with glass marbles and place in 100 °C water bath for 15 min. Then cool in cold water.				
Ethanol, 50%		1.0 ml.	1.0 ml.	19.3%
Mix and measure the extinctions within the next 60 min.				

With extinction differences of more than 0.500 dilute the gastric juice 1 : 10 with 0.01 N HCl and repeat the assay.

Di-iodotyrosine Standard Curve

In 12 ml. centrifuge tubes dilute 0.2–1.0 ml. L-3,5-di-iodotyrosine standard solution (IV) to 1.1 ml. with doubly distilled water (blank containing 1.1 ml. distilled water). Add 0.5 ml. ninhydrin reagent (III), stopper tubes with a glass marble and place for 15 min. in a water bath at 100 °C. Cool in cold water, dilute with 1.0 ml. 50% ethanol and read extinctions as above. Plot the extinctions against μmole di-iodotyrosine per assay.

Calculations

Subtract the extinctions of the blanks from those of the appropriate experimental values. For the sample under the conditions described here and for the wavelength 578 nm and 37 °C:

$$\text{Volume activity} = 194 \times \Delta E \text{ [U/l.]}$$

The pepsin secretion per unit time is calculated as follows:

$$\text{[U/min]} = \text{[U/l.]} \times \text{[l./min]}$$

Precision of Method

With activities around 50 U/l. (37 °C) the standard deviation was 3 U/l. (37 °C). The coefficient of variation is 6%.

Normal Values

On stimulation, see p. 1051.
Pepsin activity in gastric juice, U/l. (37 °C)

	$\bar{x}$	s	Range
Basal secretion	45	29	5–108
Secretion after Betazol	53	15	23– 81

Pepsinogen secretion per unit time
For calculations, see p. 1051.
Pepsinogen secretion, expressed as pepsin, U/l. (37 °C)

	$\bar{x}$	s	Range
Basal secretion	61	41	8–148
Secretion after Betazol	136	40	66–220

Sources of Error

Effects of drugs and other therapeutic measures: See, p. 1052.

Interference in the assay technique: None known.

Specificity of Method

As N-acetyl-L-phenylalanyl-L-3,5-di-iodotyrosine is not hydrolysed by gastricin[22,26] the method is specific for pepsin.

Details for Measurements in Tissues, see p. 1052.

Automated Method, see[27].

Gastricsin, Pepsinogen, Uropepsinogen, Isoenzymes

Gastricsin

A second protease has been crystallized from human gastric juice, and this has been named gastricsin[22] (EC 3.4.23.3). Pepsin and gastricsin can be obtained by activation of a common zymogen[28].
The pH optimum of the hydrolysis of haemoglobin by gastricsin is pH 3.0; the activity at pH 2.0 is 80% of that at pH 3.0[22]. If the proteolytic activity of gastric juice is measured with haemoglobin as substrate, both pepsin and gastricsin are determined. Most of the synthetic substrates react with pepsin and gastricsin, although at different rates[26]. However, gastricsin cannot hydrolyse N-acetyl-L-phenylalanyl-L-3,5-di-iodotyrosine, so that this substrate is specific for pepsin. From the difference in the measurements of the total activity and of pepsin, the activity of gastricsin can be calculated[26]. Pepsin and gastricsin can be separated by ion exchange chromatography on Amberlite IRC-50 XE 64[22]. In human gastric juice from healthy subjects 5–10% of the total proteolytic activity is gastricsin[21].

Pepsinogen

Pepsin is inactivated at pH $> 6^1$. Pepsinogen is stable at this pH and therefore it can be determined in the presence of pepsin if the solution containing the enzyme and the proenzyme is adjusted with NaOH to pH 8 and then acidified to pH 2–3 with HCl to convert pepsinogen to pepsin. Then proceed as for pepsin.

Uropepsinogen

The pepsinogen secreted in the blood is excreted via the urine as uropepsinogen[29]. To convert uropepsinogen to pepsin acidify the urine to pH 2.5–3 with HCl and incubate for 1 hr. at 37 °C[13,30]. Then proceed as for pepsin.

Normal values: excretion of pepsinogen in urine in healthy subjects in μg./hr., relative to crystalline pepsin[30]: $\bar{x} = 77.5$; range 29.5–189.

Isoenzymes of Pepsinogen and Pepsin

Three pepsinogens have been isolated from human gastric muscosa, pepsinogen I–III. Activation gives pepsin I from pepsinogen I and pepsin III from pepsinogen III, while pepsinogen II is converted to two different, active proteases, pepsin IIA and IIB[31].

References

1 *M. Laskowski sr., B. Kassell, R. J. Peanasky & M. Laskowski jr.* in *K. Lang & E. Lehnartz:* Handbuch der physiologisch- und pathologisch-chemischen Analyse 10th. edn., Springer, Berlin 1966, vol. VI C, p. 229; *J. Tang,* Nature *199*, 1094 [1963].
2 *T. G. Rajagopalan, S. Moore & W. H. Stein,* J. biol. Chem. *241*, 4940 [1966].
3 *R. M. Herriott,* J. Gen. Physiol. *45*, Suppl. [1962], p. 57.
4 *F. Sanger & E. O. P. Thompson,* Biochem. J. *53*, 366 [1953].
5 *K. Inouye & J. S. Fruton,* Biochemistry *6*, 1765 [1967].
6 *N. C. Davis & E. L. Smith* in *D. Glick:* Methods in Biochemical Analysis. Interscience Publ. New York 1955, vol. *2*, p. 215.
7 *J. H. Northrop,* J. gen. Physiol. *16*, 41 [1933].
8 *M. L. Anson & A. E. Mirsky,* J. gen. Physiol. *16*, 59 [1933].
9 *M. L. Anson,* J. gen. Physiol. *22*, 79 [1939].
10 *O. Folin & V. Ciocalteu,* J. biol. Chem. *73*, 627 [1927]; see also *P. B. Hawk, B. L. Oser & W. H. Summerson:* Practical Physiological Chemistry. The Blakiston Comp., Philadelphia 1947, p. 879.
11 *J. H. Northrop, M. Kunitz & R. M. Herriott:* Crystalline Enzymes. 2nd edn., Columbia Univ. Press, New York 1948.
12 *P. M. West, F. W. Ellis & B. L. Scott,* J. Lab. clin. Med. *39*, 159 [1952].
13 *B. Kickhöfen, F. E. Struwe, B. Bramesfeld & O. Westphal,* Biochem. Z. *330*, 467 [1958].
14 *M. K. Loken, K. D. Terrill, J. F. Marvin & D. G. Mosser,* J. gen. Physiol. *42*, 251 [1958].
15 *J. Lenard, S. L. Johnson, R. W. Hyman & G. P. Hess,* Anal. Biochem. *11*, 30 [1965].
16 *L. E. Baker,* J. biol. Chem. *193*, 809 [1951].
17 *W. T. Jackson, M. Schlamowitz & A. Shaw,* Biochemistry *4*, 1537 [1965].
18 *R. M. Herriott* in *S. P. Colowick & N. O. Kaplan:* Methods in Enzymology. Academic Press, New York 1955, vol. *II*, p. 6.
19. *H. D. Ohlenbusch,* Vortr. Tagung franz., schweiz. und dtsch. Ges. physiol. Chemie, Zürich 1960.
20 *E. Layne* in *S. P. Colowick & N. O. Kaplan:* Methods in Enzymology. Academic Press, New York 1957, vol. *III*, p. 448.
21 *W. P. Fritsch,* M. D. Thesis, Med. Faculty, University of Düsseldorf. 1969.
22 *J. Tang, S. Wolf, R. Caputto & R. E. Trucco,* J. biol. Chem. *234*, 1174 [1959].
23 *M. Borch Jørgensen:* Pepsinogen in blood and urine. Munksgaard, Copenhagen 1961.
24 *B. I. Hirschowitz,* J. Lab. clin. Med. *46*, 568 [1955].
25 *S. Moore & W. H. Stein,* J. biol. Chem. *211*, 907 [1954].
26 *J. Tang, J. Mills, L. Chiang & L. de Chiang,* Ann. N. Y. Acad. Sci. *140*, 688 [1967]; *W. Y. Huang & J. Tang,* J. biol. Chem. *244*, 1085 [1969].

27 *A. J. Cornish-Bowden & J. R. Knowles*, Biochem. J. *95*, 71 P [1965];
    J. Lenard, S. L. Johnson, R. W. Hyman & G. P. Hess, Anal. Biochem. *11*, 30 [1965].
28 *J. Tang & K. I. Tang*, J. biol. Chem. *238*, 606 [1963].
29 *G. R. Bucher*, Gastroenterology *8*, 627 [1947].
30 *W. P. Peak, E. Viergiver, E. J. Van Loon & G. G. Duncan*, J. Amer. med. Ass. *162*, 1441 [1956].
31 *M. D. Turner, L. L. Miller & H. L. Segal*, Gastroenterology *51*, 1097 [1966].

Collagenases

Walter Appel

General Information[1 − 4,61,62]

Collagenases, e.g. clostridopeptidase A, EC 3.4.24.3 hydrolyse native collagen under physiological conditions. The point of attack has been found to be the polar area of the collagen molecule with a sequence (Gly-Pro-y)$_n$. In earlier studies insufficient care was taken to ensure that collagen was not denatured, because when this occurs it is attacked by other proteinases. Many controversies in the literature concerning the existence of collagenases in mammalian tissues can be ascribed to this source of error.

The collagenases present in the larvae of *Muscidae* and botflies[3] have not been studied further. The most extensively studied are the bacterial collagenases; they are found, in particular, in *Clostridium histolyticum* and – *perfringens*[1,5], as well as *-capitorale* and *-welchii*[6], in *Pseudomonas aeruginosa*[7] and *Mycobacterium tuberculosis*[8]. The enzyme from tadpoles[9,10] is well studied, while that from *Fasciola hepatica*[11] is less well-known. Although the existence of collagenases in mammalian tissues (e.g. pig pancreas[12] and beef pancreas[13,14], liver[15,16], uterus[17,18], kidney[17], skin[29] and bone[20] of rat, liver of rabbit and guinea pig[15], ox dental pulp[21] and gums[22,23], in skin[24], human tissues[25] and in tumours[60]) is no longer disputed the reason for their existence is in doubt. The presence of collagenases in uterus, bones and healing wound tissue of various mammals has been thoroughly studied[26,63 − 67]; especially convincing are the findings with a new type of substrate on cultures of primary mouse fibroblasts and human HeLa cells[27,57]. Finally, a collagenase-like enzyme from *Aspergillus oryzae* has been described[29]. The most important starting material for the preparation of collagenase is *Cl. histolyticum*[30 − 43,56]; such preparations have a therapeutic value[71]. The question whether other collagenases, apart from clostridiopeptidase A[56] exist (pseudocollagenase[48]; a clostridiopeptidase B has in fact been classified, EC 3.4.22.8, but only recently has been sufficiently characterized[58]) has been extensively studied, as has the problem of the existence of isoenzymes, formation of sub-units or of dimers and tetramers[32,40,43 − 47,59]. A collagenase has been purified from pig pancreas[49]. The question of whether clostridiopeptidase A is a metalloenzyme and consequently can be activated and inhibited is still under discussion. According to[33,34] the enzyme is activated by Ca^{2+}, and inhibited by cysteine, o-phenanthroline, α,α'-dipyridyl and 8-hydroxyquinoline; EDTA, Mg^{2+} and di-isopropyl-fluorophosphate are without effect; histidine and, especially, 2,3-dimercaptoethanol inhibit (50% at 10 μM); Zn^{2+} may be the metal involved in the active site[50]. The Ca^{2+} needed for activity acts to stabilize the structure[51]. Anti-inflammatory drugs may inhibit or activate[68].

Three methods have proved suitable in practice for the determination of activity. 1. The degradation of bovine achilles heel tendons or rat tail collagen[1,2,33,40,51] and measurement of the liberated NH_2-groups with ninhydrin; the assay is carried out in suspension and has therefore all the disadvantages associated with this type of system. 2. The degradation of ichthyocol (fish bladder collagen) in aqueous solution and measurement of the decrease of viscosity[2,33]. 3. Hydrolysis of the synthetic hexapeptide Z-glycyl-L-prolyl-glycyl-glycyl-L-prolyl-L-alanine and determination of the free tripeptide Gly-L-Pro-LAla with ninhydrin[53,54]; this method has proved the method of choice and is described below. 4. The hydrolysis of the chromogenic substrate p-phenylazobenzyloxycarbonyl-L-prolyl-L-leucyl-glycyl-L-prolyl-D-arginine and colorimetric determination of the yellow p-phenyl-azobenzyloxycarbonyl-L-Pro-L-Leu[55] liberated. This method is not yet generally used, because the substrate has only recently become available commercially. Recently new peptide substrates have been used, i.e. derivatives of N-[(Azulen-4-yl)-acetyl]-L-prolyl-L-leucyl-glycyl-L-prolyl-L-arginine.

Clostridiopeptidase A

Determination with Z-Glycyl-L-prolyl-glycyl-glycyl-L-prolyl-L-alanine as substrate[53,54]

Application of Method: In biochemistry.

Principle

$$\text{Z-Gly-L-Pro-Gly-Gly-L-Pro-L-Ala} + H_2O \xrightarrow[\text{peptidase A}]{\text{Clostridio-}} \text{Z-Gly-L-Pro-Gly} + \text{Gly-L-Pro-L-Ala}$$

In the enzymatic hydrolysis of the hexapeptide, two tripeptides are formed; the tripeptide Gly-L-Pro-L-Ala is quantitatively determined with the ninhydrin reaction.

Optimum Conditions for Measurements[54]

The pH optimum is between pH 6.5 and 8.8[53]. Tris buffer has proved most suitable. The optimum Ca^{2+} concentration is 0.1 M and the optimum substrate concentration 4.3 mM. A pre-incubation of 15 min. is sufficient. As the preliminary reaction depends on the purity of the sample and of the substrate, measurements are made after 5–10 min. and this value is used for the blank, while the test is allowed to continue. Measurements at different temperatures may require different measuring conditions (cf. p. 127). Nevertheless, results obtained under the same measuring conditions but at different temperatures were formerly compared with each other ("conversion factors" were determined). Such conversion factors may be correct if determined with a relatively large collective; however, they cannot be applied generally to the individual case (cf. p. 129). The value of the following relative reaction rates thus lies in being able to appraise the temperature dependence of the reaction.

°C	20	*25*	30	35	37	40
	0.89	*1.00*	1.18	1.26	1.28	1.09

We use a substrate concentration of only 1.70 mM on the grounds of economy. The proportionality between time and enzyme concentration is still maintained, but the specific activities are about 42 % lower than with the optimum substrate concentration.

Equipment

Spectrophotometer or filter photometer; water baths (37 °C and boiling); cold bath (4 °C); stopwatch or laboratory alarm clock.

Reagents

1. Tris-hydroxymethyl-aminomethane, tris
2. Hydrochloric acid, 0.1 N
3. Calcium acetate, $(CH_3COO)_2Ca \cdot H_2O$
4. Carbobenzoxy-glycyl-L-prolyl-glycyl-glycyl-L-prolyl-L-alanine (hexapeptide)
5. Sodium cyanide, NaCN
6. Sodium acetate, $CH_3COONa \cdot 3 H_2O$
7. Acetic acid
8. Ninhydrin
9. Ethyleneglycol monomethylether
10. Ethanol
11. Sodium hydroxide, 1 N
12. Glycyl-L-prolyl-L-alanine

Preparation of Solutions (for ca. 20 normal and 200 micro-assays)

Use only doubly distilled water.

   I. Tris buffer (50 mM; pH 7.2; containing 0.1 M calcium acetate):
      Dissolve 0.60 g. tris in ca. 25 ml. distilled water, add 45 ml. 0.1 N HCl and then dissolve
      in this solution 1.58 g. calcium acetate and dilute the mixture to 100 ml.; check the pH.
  II. Z-Glycyl-L-prolyl-glycyl-glycyl-L-prolyl-L-alanine (1.7 mM):
      Dissolve 10 mg. of the hexapeptide in 10 ml. tris buffer (solution I).
 III. Sodium cyanide reagent:
      Dissolve 10 g. sodium cyanide, 72 g. sodium acetate and 13 ml. acetic acid in distilled
      water and make up to 1 000 ml. The solution must be stored for about 1 week at 4 °C
      before use.
 IV. Ninhydrin reagent:
      Dissolve 0.75 g. ninhydrin in 25 ml. ethyleneglycol monomethylether.
  V. Ethanol (50% v/v):
      Mix 50 ml. ethanol with 50 ml. distilled water.

Stability of Solutions

Prepare solutions II and IV freshly each day and keep in a cold bath until required. All other solutions are
stable for months at 4 °C.

Procedure

Collection, Treatment and Stability of Sample

So far there are no data for serum or other body fluids, because with this method the enzyme
cannot be determined with sufficient reliability. In aqueous solution impure preparations
from bacteria lose measurable activity in 3 hr. at 4 °C. The pure enzyme is thermolabile:
at pH 7.0 in the presence of 1 mM Ca^{2+} there is no loss of activity in 1 hr. at 40 °C, 50% loss
in 10 min. at 48 °C and 100% in 5 min. at 60 °C[51].

Assay System

Wavelength: 570 nm; light path: 1 cm.; reaction temperature: 37 °C; final volume 2.2 ml.
(normal assay), 0.220 ml. (micro-assay); read against reference cuvette containing solution V.
Blank (E_0) from the test mixtures: exactly 10 min. after addition of enzyme remove samples
and treat as for test; control (to determine the spontaneous hydrolysis of the substrate): as
for test, but containing 0.20 ml. distilled water instead of sample.

Pipette into a test tube:			Concentration in assay mixture
Hexapeptide	(solution II)	2.00 ml.	1.53 mM 45 mM tris 90 mM Ca^{2+}
Sample solution		0.20 ml.	
Mix thoroughly, after exactly 10 min. remove sample for blank (E_0) and incubate test for a further 20 min. Pipette into stoppered test tubes (standing in a cold bath):			
Distilled water Sodium cyanide reagent (solution III) Incubation solution		0.50 ml. 0.50 ml. 0.50 ml.	
Immediately place in a boiling water bath for 2 min.			
Ninhydrin reagent	(solution IV)	0.50 ml.	
Stopper tubes and leave for exactly 15 min. in a boiling water bath. Cool under running water and finally in a cold bath.			
Ethanol	(solution V)	3.00 ml.	
Measure extinctions			

Calculations

Standard curve:
Dissolve 15.2 mg. glycyl-L-prolyl-L-alanine (62.5 μmole) in 50 ml. tris buffer (solution I). Dilute 0.05–0.50 ml. of this 1.25 mM standard solution (0.062–0.625 μmole) to 1.0 ml. with distilled water, add 0.5 ml. sodium cyanide reagent (III) and treat as described above. Blank as for standard but without tripeptide. Plot the extinction difference (ordinate) against the "μmole Gly-L-Pro-L-Ala" (abcissa).
Convert the measured extinction differences of the samples $\Delta E = E_x - E_o$ into μmole Gly-L-Pro-L-Ala by reading off from the standard curve. Treat the control in the same way and subtract this value to give "$\mu mole_{corr.}$". After allowance for the aliquot taken ($\times$ 4.4), the amount of sample taken ($\times$ 5), the reaction time (divide by 20) and any dilution of the sample by the factor F, the activity is given by:

Normal assay: volume activity $= \mu mole_{corr.} \times 733 \times F$ [U/l.]
Micro-assay: volume activity $= nmole_{corr.} \times 7.33 \times F$ [U/l.]

Precision of Method

The coefficient of variation is 5.1% with 40 assays on a single sample (precision) and 15.0% on 10 samples of enzyme preparations from *Cl. histolyticum*[54].

Normal Values

Normal values are not available.

Sources of Error

No interference is expected if the conditions are adhered to.

Specificity of Method

The method described here is not completely specific, because it also includes the so-called "pseudo-collagenase" and "collagen peptidases".

Other Assay Methods

Clostridiopeptidase A is strictly specific with native bovine tendon or rat tail collagen as substrate, as well as with ichthyocol collagen. Recently the chromogenic substrate p-phenylazobenzyloxycarbonyl-L-Pro-L-Leu-Gly-L-Pro-D-Arg has been introduced[55] and proved suitable[57], although the specificity has yet to be critically examined (see also[63,70]).

Micro-assay

The method described here is so arranged that a 1 : 10 decrease of all volumes can be readily made. The same solution can be used for the standardization; the standard curves are identical with those for the normal method but with 10 times smaller values on the abscissa. We have had considerable experience with the "Beckman-Spinco" system.

References

1 *I. Mandl* in *F. F. Nord:* Advances in Enzymology, Interscience Publishers, Inc., New York, 1961 Vol. 23, p. 163.
2 *S. Seifter & P. M. Gallop* in *S. P. Colowick & N. O. Kaplan:* Methods in Enzymology, Academic Press, New York-London, 1962, Vol. 5, p. 659.
3 *A. Nordwig*, Leder *13*, 10 [1962].
4 *W. Grassmann*, Deidesheimer Gespräch 1967.
5 *G. A. Levdikova*, Biochimiya *31*, 821 [1966].
6 *E. Habermann*, Naunyn Schmiedebergs Arch. exp. Path. *235*, 513 [1959].
7 *G. Schölmann & E. Fisher jr.*, Biochim. Biophysica Acta *122*, 557 [1966].
8 *S. Takahashi*, J. Biochem. *61*, 258 [1967].
9 *C. Lapiere, Y. Nagai & J. Gross*, Fed. Proc. *23*, 648 [1963].
10 *A. H. Kang, Y. Nagai, K. A. Piez & J. Gross*, Biochemistry *5*, 509 [1966].
11 *R. M. Howell*, Nature 209, 713 [1966].
12 *J. C. Houck & Y. M. Patel*, Proc. Soc. Exper. Biol. Med. *116*, 382 [1964].
13 *B. S. Kasavina, A. L. Laufer, L. S. Pozarijskaja & V. O. Ryndina*, Doklady Akademii Nauk SSSR *142*, 706 [1962].
14 *A. A. Hakim*, Enzymologia acta biocatalytica *30*, 299 [1966].
15 *J. Barsky & W. L. Farrison*, Abstr. Pap. Amer. Chem. Soc. *144*, 221 [1963].
16 *C. H. Wynn & M. A. Wahid*, Biochem. J. *98*, 10 P [1966].
17 *M. C. Schaub*, Helvet. Physiol. Pharmakol. Acta *22*, [1964].
18 *M. C. Schaub*, Experimentia *20*, 675 [1964].
19 *E. R. Goldstein, Y. M. Patel & J. C. Houck*, Science *146*, 942 [1964].
20 *J. F. Woods & G. Nichols*, Nature *208*, 1 325 [1965].
21 *C. Schwabe & G. Kalnitsky*, Arch. Biochem. Biophysics *109*, 68 [1965].
22 *E. H. Beutner, C. Triftshauser & S. P. Hazen*, Proc. Soc. Exp. Biol. Med. *121*, 1 082 [1966].
23 *H. M. Fullmer & W. Gibson*, Nature *209*, 728 [1966].
24 *H. M. Fullmer, G. Lazarus, W. A. Gibson, A. C. Stam jr. & C. Link jr.*, Lancet *1*, 1007 [1966].
25 *W. B. Riley jr. & E. E. Peacock jr.*, Proc. Soc. Exp. Biol. Med. *124*, 207 [1967].

26 *J. Gross & R. A. Milch:* Structural Organisation of the Skeleton. Pefects, Orig. Series, The National Foundation March of Dimes, New York 1966. Vol. 2, p. 18.
27 *L. Strauch & H. Vencely,* Hoppe-Seylers Z. physiol. Chem. *348,* 456 [1967].
28 *J. C. Houck & V. K. Sharmo,* Science *161,* 1 361 [1968].
29 *A. Nordwig & W. F. Jahn,* Hoppe-Seylers Z. physiol. Chem. *345,* 284 [1966].
30 *A. A. Tytell & K. Hewson,* Proc. Soc. Exp. Biol. Med. *74,* 555 [1950].
31 *J. Mandl, J. D. MacLeunan & E. L. Howes,* Clin. Invest. *32,* 1 323 [1953].
32 *S. Keller & J. Mandl,* Arch. Biochem. Biophysics *101,* 81 [1963].
33 *P. M. Gallop, S. Seifter & E. Meilman,* J. biol. Chem. 227, 891 [1957].
34 *S. Seifter, P. M. Gallop, Le Roy Klein & E. Meilman,* J. biol. Chem. *234,* 285 [1959].
35 *N. H. Grant & H. E. Alburn,* Arch Biochem. Biophysics *82,* 245 [1959].
36 *K. Heyns & G. Legler,* Hoppe Seylers Z. Physiol. Chem. *321,* 184 [1960].
37 *E. V. Vlasova & N. J. Solovjeva,* Vopr. Med. Khim *8,* 424 [1962], cited in Fed. Proc. *22,* T 915 [1963]
38 *N. J. Solovjeva,* 5th. FEBS-Meeting Prague, 1968.
39 *V. D. Hospelhorn,* Abstr. Pap Amer. Chem. Soc. *148,* 60 C [1964].
40 *E. Yoshida & H. Noda,* Biochem. Biophys. Acta.'*105,* 562 [1965].
41 *A. Nordwig & L. Strauch,* Hoppe-Seylers Z. physiol. Chem. *330,* 145 [1963].
42 *W. Grassmann, L. Strauch & A. Nordwig,* Hoppe-Seylers Z. physiol. Chem. *332,* 325 [1963].
43 *L. Strauch & W. Grassmann,* Hoppe-Seylers Z. physiol. Chem. *344,* 140 [1966].
44 *E. Harper, S. Seifter & D. Hospelhorn,* Biochem. Biophysics Res. Commun. *18,* 627 [1965].
45 *I. Mandl, S. Keller & J. Manahan,* Biochemistry *3,* 1 737 [1964].
46 *G. A. Levdikova, V. N. Orekhovich, N. J. Solovjeva & V. O. Shpikiter,* Dokl. Akad. Nauk. SSSR *153,* 725 [1963], cited in Ber. ges. Physiol. exper. Pharmakol. *266,* 140 [1965].
47 *M. C. Schaub & L. Strauch,* Biochem. Res. Commun. *21,* 34 [1965].
48 *W. M. Mitchel,* Biochim. Biophysics Acta *159,* 554 [1968].
49 *A. A. Hakim & R. L. Peters,* U.S.Patent 3 267006 [1966].
50 *E. Harper & S. Seifter,* Abstr. Pap. Amer. Chem. Soc. *152,* 39 C [1966].
51 *A. Nordwig & L. Strauch,* Hoppe-Seylers Z. physiol. Chem. *330,* 153 [1963].
52 *Y. Nagai,* J. Biochemistry *50,* 486 [1961].
53 *W. Grassmann & A. Nordwig,* Hoppe-Seylers Z. physiol.-Chem. *322,* 267 [1966].
54 *W. Appel,* Deidesheimer Gespräch 1967.
55 *E. Wünsch & H. G. Heidrich,* Hoppe-Seylers Z. Chem. *333,* 149 [1963].
56 *K. Kesselring, E. Wolff & Th. Kengen-Taefi,* in: *J. Mandl,* First Interdisciplinary Symposium, Gordon and Breach, New York, 1971.
57 *L. Strauch,* Colloquium über Kollagenasen, 5th. FEBS-Meeting Prague 1968.
58 *W. M. Mitchel & W. F. Harrington,* J. biol. Chem. *243,* 4683 [1968].
59 *T. Kono,* Biochemistry, *7,* 1106 [1968] & Biochim. Biophys. Acta *178,* 397 [1969].
60 *D. M. Robertson & D. C. Williams,* Nature *221,* 259 [1969].
61 *S. Seifter & E. Harper* in: *S. P. Colowick & N. O. Kaplan,* Methods in Enzymology, Vol. 19, p. 613, Academic Press, New York, London 1970.
62 *A. Nordwig* in: *F. F. Nord,* Advances in Enzymology, Vol. 34, p. 155, Interscience Publishers, Div. John Wiley & Sons, New York, London, 1971.
63 *V. Dinnenthal & D. A. Kalbhen,* Arch. Intern. Pharmacodyn. *192,* 393 [1971].
64 *K. R. Cutroneo & G. C. Fuller,* Arch. Intern. Pharmacodyn. *188,* 67 [1970].
65 *J. J. Jeffrey, R. J. Coffey & A. Z. Eisen,* Biochim. Biophys. Acta *252,* 143 [1971].
66 *J. N. Ryan,* Dissertation Abstr. Intern. B. *32,* 797 [1971].
67 *W. M. Weinstein, D. R. Saunders, G. N. Tytgat & C. E. Rubin,* New. Engl. J. Med. *283,* 1297 [1970].
68 *J. H. Brown & S. H. Pollock,* Proc. Soc. Exp. Biol. Med. *135,* 792 [1970].
69 *E. Wuensch, E. Jaeger & G. Schoensteiner-Altmann,* Hoppe-Seylers Z. physiol. Chem. *352,* 1560 [1971].
70 *E. Wuensch, E. Jaeger & G. Schoensteiner-Altmann,* Hoppe-Seylers Z. physiol. Chem., *352,* 1568 [1971].
71 *J. Mazurek,* Med. Welt, p. 150 [1971].

Protease Inhibitors

Hans Fritz, Ivar Trautschold and Eugen Werle*

General Information

High molecular weight protease inhibitors occur surprisingly frequently and in a wide range of concentrations in plants and animals[1,2]. These inhibitors include polypeptides, proteins and glycoproteins. They form enzyme-inhibitor complexes with the proteases in question in a reaction which is usually reversible. In the complex the enzymatic activity of the enzyme towards its natural or synthetic substrates is completely or partially' blocked.

Although the determination of the inhibitory capacity of relatively pure inhibitor preparations can be easily carried out with insensitive and unspecific methods[1], the accurate determination of protease inhibitors in body fluids and tissue extracts is made difficult by various factors.

Definition of Inhibitor Unit

Usually the inhibitor unit is defined as the amount of enzyme inhibited by a unit weight of inhibitor or the amount of inhibitor which completely inhibits 1 mg. or 1 μg. of enzyme[1,2]. Therefore it is dependent on purity of the inhibitor or the enzyme preparation. To allow comparison of results from different laboratories inhibitor units should be expressed on the basis of the international enzyme unit[3,4]: 1 inhibitor unit (IU) is the amount of inhibitor which completely inhibits 1 enzyme unit (U), i.e. 1 IU decreases the enzymically catalysed hydrolysis of the substrate** by 1 μmole/min. under defined conditions. With practically all known inhibitors the inhibition is not linearly proportional to the inhibitor concentration up to the 100% value; the measurements must be made in the linear part of the inhibition curve. For practical purposes this is from 20 to 70% inhibition (see Fig. 1). Under the chosen assay conditions the enzyme should have maximal activity (see Optimum Conditions for Measurements, p. 1067).

Enzyme-Inhibitor Complex

This complex is formed relatively rapidly even when the concentration of the reaction partners is very low ($10^{-7} - 10^{-8}$ M). After mixing the enzyme and inhibitor solution (without substrate), the inhibitor equilibrium and therefore the maximum obtainable inhibition is generally reached within a few seconds (examples: trypsin inhibitors from pancreas[5-7], serum[8,9,9b], seminal vesicles[10,11] and soya beans[12]), or at least after a few minutes (example: trypsin-kallikrein inhibitor, 4 min. for the higher degrees of inhibition[13]). The rate of attainment of equilibrium is virtually independent of the temperature of incubation. By pre-incubation at different temperatures (0°, 20°, 25°, 37°) it is therefore possible to distinguish between a "true" inhibition caused by an inhibitor and enzymatic degradation processes.

The dissociation constant for the protease-inhibitor complex are in general extremely small (K_I at $10^{-9} - 10^{-12}$ M) at pH 7–9 (pH optimum of proteases)[1,14]. On displacement of the pH to the alkaline range, and more particularly in the acid range, the dissociation equilibrium is usually displaced in favour of the individual components[1,15]. As reagents which cause denaturation also favour the dissociation of protease-inhibitor complexes[16,17], the use of organic solvents for the solution of synthetic substrates[9,9c,18] should be avoided in the assay of inhibitors.

---

* With the technical assistance of Ingeborg Hüller.
** The substrates used in this work have been chosen arbitrarily on the basis of their properties and have not yet been recommended by the Enzyme Commission.

Because of the rapid formation of the complex a preliminary incubation of 1–5 min. after mixing the enzyme and inhibitor solutions is sufficient. With longer times and temperatures above 25 °C there is the danger that enzymatic activation and inactivation processes will affect the true level of inhibitor. The following are possible sources of error:

1. Activation of proenzymes in serum (e. g. plasminogen, prothrombin and prekallikrein), secretions and extracts of the pancreas (e. g. trypsinogen, chymotrypsinogen, prekallikrein),

2. Progressive inhibition ("slow-reacting inhibitors") of plasmin[19] and kallikrein[3,11,19a] and enzymatic inactivation by proteases or by autolysis (trypsin, plasmin),

3. Enzymatic inactivation of an inhibitor by the inhibited enzyme ("temporary inhibition")[7,20] or by other proteases.

In example 2 the inhibitor values found are too high, in example 3 (inhibitors from pancreas, seminal vesicles, submaxillary glands and ovomucoid, see Table 1) and example 1 (e.g. activation of trypsinogen in pancreatic extracts by the added trypsin) values found are too low.

In tissue homogenates, which contain the inhibitor and the enzyme to be inhibited in separate cell compartments, only the component which is in excess can be detected. To determine the inhibitor content in this case, the tissue extract must be obtained under conditions which do not permit complex formation, e. g. acid stable inhibitors in acid solution[1,3,5–7]. In suitable cases the enzyme is denatured with other accompanying proteins (deproteinization); occasionally it is possible to separate enzyme and inhibitor under mild conditions with the help of molecular sieves[1,5,6].

In the presence of inhibitors the enzyme activities obtained can be too low. For example, in the assay of plasminogen, prekallikrein and prothrombin levels in serum a considerable proportion of these enzymes can be trapped by serum inhibitors immediately after their activation and so are not determined. In such cases the inhibitor concentration must be determined before the activation of the proenzyme. Only in this way is it possible to decide whether an increase or decrease in the activity of the enzyme in question is due to the zymogen content of the serum or to a rise or fall in the inhibitor concentration.

Substrate for the Enzymatic Assay

Methods in which the kinetics of the enzymatic hydrolysis can be followed directly (photometry, autotitration) are most suitable. Activation or inactivation processes in the assay system are rapidly detected in this case[3,5,6]. It is recommended to use a specific substrate, a short period of incubation (not more than 15 min.) and a relatively low incubation temperature (25 °C, see above). The natural substrates casein and haemoglobin[21] are therefore not suitable. Synthetic ester substrates such as N-benzoylarginine ethyl ester (BAEE), N-tosylarginine methyl ester (TAME), N-acetyltyrosine ethyl ester (ATEE) and tyrosine ethyl ester (TEE) give a rapid assay, but have the following disadvantages:

1. They are relatively unspecific: BAEE and TAME are hydrolysed by trypsin, plasmin, thrombin, kallikrein, serum and pancreatic esterases.

2. The direct optical measurement of the hydrolysis of the ester at 253 nm (see[21]) is not possible with protein- or nucleic acid-containing samples because of the high light absorption below 350 nm[5,6].

3. The inhibition of the esterolytic activity of proteases by inhibitors is not always paralleled by the inhibition of their proteolytic or biological activity. For example, the BAEE-hydrolysing activity of plasmin is not inhibited by the high concentration of plasmin inhibitors which occur in serum[8].

To obtain reliable values with ester substrates it is necessary to titrate the alkali requirement during the hydrolysis or to determine the liberated ethanol by means of alcohol dehydrogenase in a coupled assay[22]. Differentiation of the ester hydrolysing activity of the protease added to the assay and the spontaneous esterase activity of serum and tissue extracts is possible by use of specific protease inhibitors[1] (see Table 1). A nearly ideal and universally applicable combination which fulfills the requirements of high sensitivity and specificity, is the trypsin system (EC 3.4.21.4) with the substrate N-benzoylarginine-p-nitroanilide (BAPNA)[3,5,9,9b,9c,23–25]. As known inhibitors of proteases virtually without exception inhibit trypsin[1], the trypsin inhibitor values of the individual inhibitors, independent of their purity, are directly comparable with each other.

The combination chymotrypsin (EC 3.4.21.1) with the substrate N-(3-carboxypropionyl)-phenylalanine-p-nitroanilide (CPPN)[3,6,9a-c,18] is also suitable for the determination of inhibitors. In both cases the hydrolysis of the substrates can be followed directly at 400–420 nm. The protein or nucleic acid content of the samples does not interfere. Activation or inactivation processes in the assay system can be detected immediately. In contrast, the quantitative determination of inhibitors for plasmin (EC 3.4.21.7), thrombin (EC 3.4.21.5) and for kallikrein (EC 3.4.21.8) is possible only with the aid of the ester substrates BAEE or TAME[26]. The method of choice is the titration of the alkali requirement with an autotitrator[27]. The determination of the ethanol liberated on hydrolysis of BAEE with alcohol dehydrogenase (ADH) from yeast[28] is affected by high protein and nucleic acid concentrations[6], but it permits the determination of smaller amounts of enzyme and therefore lower inhibitor concentrations than the titrimetric method and in addition can be automated for routine work[29]. The determination of inhibitors of kallikrein, plasmin and thrombin with the help of ester substrates in native fluids and extracts should be guaranteed by the use of specific assay methods. A suitable method for kallikrein is the comparative hypotensive effect on the dog[30], for plasmin the euglobulin lysis time[31] or the fibrin plate method of *Astrup* and *Müllertz*[32], and for thrombin the determination of thromboplastin time by the method of *Quick* or *Geigy*[33] (see p. 1025).

With all determinations of inhibitors using synthetic substrates it should be noted that under certain circumstances the equilibrium of the complex formation (K_I at $10^{-7} - 10^{-11}$ M) can be displaced in favour of the individual components (competitive inhibition) because of the low Michaelis constants (K_M $10^{-4} - 10^{-7}$ M). This results in lower degrees of inhibition than with protein substrates. Other sources of interference in the formation of the complex are given by *Bieth* et al.[9c].

Application of Method: In biochemistry, in clinical chemistry and in pharmacology.

Trypsin and Plasmin Inhibitors

Trypsin Inhibitors: Assay with N-Benzoylarginine-p-nitroanilide as Substrate

Principle

N-Benzoylarginine-p-nitroanilide   N-Benzoylarginine + p-Nitroaniline

The liberation of p-nitroaniline ($\varepsilon_{405} = 9.95$ cm.^{2}/μmole[3] or 9.90 cm.^{2}/μmole[18], $\varepsilon_{410} = 8.8$ cm.^{2}/μmole[23], $\varepsilon_{420} = 4.73$ cm.^{2}/μmole[9c]) from N-benzoyl-DL-arginine-p-nitroanilide (BAPNA) is followed directly by the increase in extinction at 405 nm. By diazotization of the p-nitroaniline the sensitivity of the method can be increased[9,18]

Optimum Conditions for Measurements

Under the conditions given below the Michaelis constant K_M is 4.3×10^{-4} mole/l[3,13]. Also see the general section.

With optimum activation of the trypsin (buffer solution III) the activity is about 4% higher than in Ca^{2+}-free buffer; differences in the inhibitor content of a sample are therefore within the range of error given below (refer to chymotrypsin inhibitors). The degree of inhibition and therefore the complex formation between trypsin and the inhibitors described here is not affected by the Ca^{2+} content of the assay mixture (between 0 and 0.5 M Ca^{2+})[8,9b]. The inhibitor content of a sample is independent of the proportion of the acid-denatured trypsin in solution IV, as only active trypsin is capable of forming a complex[8].

With a 5 min. period of incubation the ΔE/min. values between 0.0033 and 0.132 (1–40 mU) are linearly proportional to the amount of trypsin.

The measured trypsin activity is 1.26 times higher at 30 °C and 1.64 times higher at 37 °C.

Equipment

Spectrophotometer or spectrum-line photometer suitable for precise measurements at 405 nm.; constant temperature cuvette holder. For tissue extraction: homogenizer (Ultra-Turrax made by Janke and Kunkel, Type 18/2, 20 000 rpm); centrifuge.

Reagents*

1. Perchloric acid, 70% (w/w), sp. gr. 1.67
2. Potassium carbonate, K_2CO_3
3. Triethanolamine hydrochloride, TRA
4. Calcium chloride, $CaCl_2 \cdot 2 H_2O$
5. Sodium hydroxide, 2 N

6. Hydrochloric acid, 0.001 N
7. Trypsin
   lyophilizate; ≥ 1 U/mg. (4 °C); commercial preparation**, see p. 515.
8. N-Benzoyl-arginine-p-nitroanilide***, BAPNA

Purity of Reagents

Trypsin free from contaminating proteases (e.g. chymotrypsin); other reagents usual commercial quality.

Preparation of Solutions (for ca. 50 determinations)

Prepare all solutions with distilled water
I. Perchloric acid (6% w/v):
   Dilute 53.5 ml. 70% perchloric acid to 1 000 ml. with distilled water.
II. Potassium carbonate solution (5 M):
   Dissolve 691 g. K_2CO_3 in distilled water and make up to 1 000 ml.
III. Triethanolamine buffer (0.2 M TRA; pH 7.8; 20 mM $CaCl_2$):
   Dissolve 18.6 g. TRA and 1.47 g. $CaCl_2 \cdot 2 H_2O$ in 450 ml. distilled water, adjust to pH 7.8 with 2 N NaOH and dilute to 500 ml. with distilled water.

---

  * A combination of reagents for the assay of trypsin activity is available commercially (test pack TC 15950 from Boehringer Mannheim (GmbH), Germany. The trypsin units given in the information leaflet are not identical with those described here.
 ** We prefer Trypure-Novo ®, Ca-stabilized; Novo-Industrie, Mainz, Germany.
*** e.g. from Boehringer Mannheim or Merck, Darmstadt, Germany.

IV. Trypsin (50 μg. protein/ml.; 50 mU/ml.):
   Dissolve 500 μg. trypsin in 10 ml. 0.001 N HCl.
V. Substrate solution (2.2 mM):
   Dissolve 50 mg. BAPNA in 50 ml. distilled water by warming on a water bath (at 95 °C).

Stability of Solutions

The stability of solutions I and II is unlimited, solution III is stable for 1 month at room temperature, solution IV for 8 days at 0–4 °C and solution V for 14 days at room temperature.

Procedure

Collection, Treatment and Stability of Sample

To exclude possible errors the organ extracts and secretions which contain acid stable inhibitors should be treated with perchloric acid to remove high molecular weight proteins before the determination of the inhibitor.

Pancreatic secretion (secretion studies)[7,34]: mix 0.5 ml. secretion with 0.5 ml. 6% perchloric acid (solution I). To completely destroy the trypsinogen heat for 3 min. at 60 °C and cool. Centrifuge off the precipitate, adjust the supernatant fluid to pH 4–7 (pH paper) by dropwise addition of 5 M K_2CO_3 solution II and after allowing to stand for ca. 1 hr. in a refrigerator decant the clear supernatant fluid (inhibitor sample) from the precipitate of potassium perchlorate. The inhibitor content remains constant in a refrigerator (0–4 °C) for at least 30 days.

Native pancreatic juice: Collect pancreatic juice in a glass or polyethylene tube cooled to 0 °C. Carry out the inhibitor determination within 1 hr. or freeze samples at −20 °C. Note the danger of trypsinogen activation[5]: preliminary incubation: 1 min.; incubation with substrate: 5 min. at 25 °C, see below; use Ca^{2+}-free buffer.

Submaxillary gland secretion[35] *and seminal fluid*[10]: Preparation and stability of the inhibitor samples as for pancreatic secretion, but without heating to 60 °C.

Pancreas (e.g. inhibitor level in experimental pancreatitis[36]*):* Homogenize 1 g. tissue with 1 ml. ice-water and 2 ml. 6% perchloric acid (solution I) for 3 min. in a centrifuge tube in the cold. Heat the mixture for 3 min., at 60 °C, and centrifuge off the precipitate. Adjust the supernatant fluid to pH 4–7 with 5 M K_2CO_3 solution II. Further treatment and stability of inhibitor samples: see pancreatic secretion.

Distribution of acid stable trypsin inhibitors after i. v. injection[13,37]: For the measurement of the trypsin-kallikrein inhibitor, Trasylol®, or inhibitors from pancreas, seminal vesicles and submaxillary glands in serum, organs (e.g. liver, kidney, spleen, lung) and urine proceed as follows: homogenize 1 g. tissue with 1 ml. distilled water and 2 ml. 6% perchloric acid (solution I) in the cold. Centrifuge off the precipitate and adjust the supernatant fluid to pH 4–7 with 5 M K_2CO_3 solution II. For further treatment, see under pancreatic secretion.
Store blood at 0–4 °C. When completely clotted centrifuge, pipette off serum and add the same volume of 6% perchloric acid (solution I). Centrifuge off precipitate. Treat supernatant fluid as described for pancreatic secretion.

Store urine collections in cold with addition of chloroform (1 ml./100 ml.) and use directly for the assay; note the slight trypsin inhibitor blank in urine.

Serum: Use only sera free from haemolysis (e. g. no anticoagulants[9b]) and store in a refrigerator. The inhibitor concentration falls by ca. 5% in 24 hr. at 0–4 °C or in 10 days at −20 °C. Preliminary incubation (trypsin plus diluted serum plus buffer): between 30 and 70% inhibition of the trypsin the degree of inhibition (see Fig. 1) is independent of the temperature of the

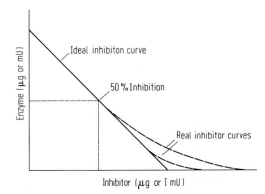

Fig. 1. Ideal and actual inhibition curves: increasing amounts of inhibitor (abscissa) were added to a fixed amount of enzyme and the residual activity (ordinate) was determined (*Fritz, Trautschold & Werle*).

preliminary incubation (between 0 and 25 °C) and of the period of the preliminary incubation between 1 and 15 min.[8]. Dilute serum for the inhibitor assay 1 : 25 with physiological saline; if the inhibition exceeds 70%, use only 0.05 ml. serum dilution or dilute serum 1 : 50.

Assay System

Wavelength: Hg 405 nm; light path: 1 cm.; final volume: 3 ml.; 25 °C (constant temperature cuvette holder). Read against air. Pre-incubate all solutions to 25 °C.

Pipette into cuvettes:		Inhibitor assay (I)	Trypsin reference assay (Tr)	Concentration in assay mixture
Trypsin solution	(IV)	0.2 ml.	0.2 ml.	ca. 3.3 μg./ml. = 3.3 mU/ml.
Buffer solution	(III)	1.7 ml.	1.8 ml.	110 mM TRA 11 mM Ca^{2+}
Sample (inhibitor)*		0.1 ml.		
Mix and incubate for 5 min.				
Substrate solution	(V)	1.0 ml.	1.0 ml.	0.77 mM
Mix, and read extinction every 5 min.; preferably use an extinction recorder.				

* up to 0.5 ml. sample; adjust buffer with solution (III) to give 1.8 ml.

Calculations[3]

1 U Trypsin corresponds to an extinction change ΔE_{405} of 3.32 per min. in a 3 ml. assay mixture. Consequently an inhibitor unit (1 IU) for trypsin inhibits the $\Delta E/min$. value by this amount. The inhibitor content of the added sample is:

$$\frac{(\Delta E/min.)_{Tr} - (\Delta E/min.)_l}{3.32} \; [\text{IU}]$$

By multiplication with the appropriate dilution factor the inhibitor concentration of the sample is obtained. For example, the inhibitor concentration in serum is calculated as follows:

$$\frac{(\Delta E/min.)_{Tr} - (\Delta E/min.)_l}{3.32} \times 250 \times 1000 \; [\text{IU}/l.]$$

Precision of Method

The range of error of the method for individual measurements after a short period of practice is below ± 5% (see[9b,c]); duplicate measurements (an inhibitor assay with half or double the amount of the normal assay) are recommended.

Normal Values

Pancreas, submaxillary glands and seminal vesicles or seminal fluid: Normal values for inhibitors in extracts and secretions can only be given approximately, because the amount of inhibitors in glands and their secretions varies greatly; it depends on the functional state of the glands and on the type of stimulation of the secretion. The amount of inhibitor (2.5–500 IU/l., according to the stimulation) in the pancreatic secretion of dogs can on average inhibit 0.5–3% of the simultaneously excreted trypsinogen after its activation[5,34]. Pancreas of dog, cat, pig and human contains 0.03–0.80 IU/g. wet weight of tissue[5−7], submaxil-

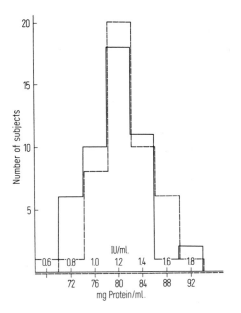

Fig. 2. Trypsin inhibitor content of sera from 46 healthy subjects (*Fritz, Trautschold & Werle*).

lary glands of dog contain up to 10 IU/g.[1,11,35], seminal vesicles and spermatozoa of various animals contain up to 5 IU/g. or ml.[1,10,11].

Urine: The trypsin inhibitor concentration is below 10 IU/l.[37].

Human sera: The frequency distribution of normal values found on 46 normal persons[8] is shown in Fig. 2.

Bieth, Métais and *Warter*[9b] gave a normal value (100 subjects) of 4.9 UTI/ml. serum with a standard deviation of $\pm$ 14%; 1 IU is equivalent to about 2.1 UTI. The normal value for the inhibitor content of the sera of ca. 2000 patients[38] was between 100–185 mg./100 ml. (relative to a trypsin inhibitor preparation from soya bean), which corresponds to 1500–2800 IU/l. serum (see frequency distribution curve in [38], under "Methods and Procedures", p. 42). Other data (see[1], p. 47, Table 11) indicate that 1 ml. normal human sera can inhibit 0.42–1.9 mg. trypsin (corresponding to 0.4–1.9 IU), or according to[39] 1.1–1.22 mg. (see Fig. 2).

The inhibitor concentration in serum increases 2–4-fold in myocardial infarction (from the 5th day), various types of hepatitis, acute inflammatory diseases of the biliary tract and obstructive jaundice, acute necrotic pancreatitis, tumours, pneumonia, kidney infarction and urinary tract infections[38,40]. The relationship of the actual inhibitor level to the different enzyme activities in serum has been used for differential diagnosis[38]. In hypo-α_1-antitrypsinaemia the inhibitor concentration in serum is reduced by ca. 50% (heterozygotes) or 90% (homozygotes)[41].

Pharmacological studies: After i.v. injection of 3000 ImU for trypsin, i.e. 5400 KIE of trypsin-kallikrein inhibitor Trasylol ®, to rats 66% of the injected inhibitor was found in the serum, liver and kidneys after 1 hr., and 87% after 4 hr., 93% of this amount was found in the kidneys[14,37].

Sources of Error

A too high or too low content of inhibitor in the inhibitor assay can be simulated by: 1. displacement of pH due to insufficient buffering capacity, 2. formation of seed crystals (BAPNA) on unclean surfaces of cuvettes, 3. occurrence of turbidity in solutions during the measurements (due to addition of inhibitor samples with too high a protein content or not sufficiently "clear" after centrifugation), in this case use Ca^{2+}-free buffer solution III.

Specificity of Method

The method described here is also suitable for the determination of the activity and inhibition of papain (EC 3.4.22.2)[3,7,25]. Plasmin also hydrolyses BAPNA, but at a very much slower rate than trypsin[5,9]. 1 Novo unit plasmin is equivalent in the BAPNA assay (50 mM L-lysine instead of calcium chloride in buffer solution III; follow the change in extinction for 10 min. instead of 5 min.) to about 4.2 mU, i.e. ΔE_{405}/10 min. = 0.140; the extinction change ΔE_{405}/10 min. increases in the range of 0.8 mU to 8.4 mU are practically proportional to the amount of plasmin added (about 0.2 to 2 Novo units). Thrombin hydrolyses BAPNA extremely slowly: 40 NIH units (thrombin assay, Behringwerke) causes an extinction change of ΔE_{405}/30 min. of 0.040 in buffer solution, pH 8.4 (after taking into account the reagent blank). No other BAPNA hydrolysing proteins are known[5,18].

Trypsin and Plasmin Inhibitors; Assay with Azocasein as Substrate

Azocasein has proved a suitable substrate for the determination of the protein-hydrolysing activity of trypsin and plasmin because it requires only a relatively short period of incubation.

Principle

The formation of trichloroacetic acid-soluble hydrolysis products is followed during the enzymatic break-down of azocasein by means of the increase in extinction at 366 nm (extinction maximum).

Equipment

Spectrophotometer or spectrum-line photometer suitable for measurements at 366 nm; constant temperature cuvette holder.

Reagents

1. Disodium hydrogen phosphate, $Na_2HPO_4 \cdot 2H_2O$
2. Potassium dihydrogen phosphate, KH_2PO_4
3. L-Lysine monohydrochloride
4. Azocasein
   e.g. from Fluka, Buchs, St. Gallen, Switzerland.

5. Trypsin
   lyophilizate; ≥ 1 U*/mg. (0–4 °C); commercial preparation, see p. 515.
6. Plasmin
   lyophilized, stabilized; ≥ 0.7 U**/mg. (0–4 °C), equivalent to 1.2 Novo units.
7. Trichloroacetic acid

Purity of Reagents

Usual commercial quality.

Preparation of Solutions

Prepare all solutions with distilled water.
  I. Phosphate buffer (0.1 M; pH 7.6):
     Dissolve 7.74 g. $Na_2HPO_4 \cdot 2H_2O$ and 0.884 g. KH_2PO_4 in distilled water and make up to 500 ml.
 II. Lysine/phosphate buffer (0.15 M L-lysine; 0.1 M phosphate; pH 7.6):
     Dissolve 6.8 g. lysine-HCl in phosphate buffer (solution I) and make up to 250 ml.
III. Substrate solution (2% azocasein):
     Dissolve 2 g. azocasein with warming (80 °C) in phosphate buffer (solution I) and make up to 100 ml.
 IV. Trypsin (50 μg. protein/ml.; 50 U/l.):
     Dissolve 500 μg. trypsin in 10 ml. 0.001 N HCl.
  V. Plasmin (8.3 mg. protein/ml.; ca. 6000 U/l.):
     Dissolve 8.3 mg. plasmin (ca. 10 Novo units) in 1 ml. 0.001 N HCl; the pH should be ca. 2.5.
 VI. Trichloroacetic acid (5% w/v):
     Dissolve 5 g. trichloroacetic acid in distilled water and make up to 100 ml.

---

 * Substrate: BAPNA
** Substrate: BAEE

Stability of Solutions

Solutions I and II are stable for one month at 0–4 °C, solutions IV and V for one week. Prepare solution III freshly each day. The trichloroacetic acid solution VI is stable indefinitely.

Procedure

Collection, Treatment and Stability of Sample, see p. 1068.

Assay System

Incubation volume: 3.0 ml.; incubation temperature: 30 °C; wavelength: Hg 365 nm; light path: 1 cm.; room temperature. Read against reagent blank (as for inhibitor assay, but without enzyme solution).

Equilibrate the buffer and substrate solution to 30 °C. Before the start of a series of measurements prepare an activity curve for the respective enzyme, determine the range of proportionality and the range of the extinction values, which depend on the azocasein used. In the trypsin assay the extinction increases from $E = 0.065$ to $E = 0.250$ are proportional to the amount of enzyme added (1–4 μg.); in the plasmin assay between $E = 0.100$ and $E = 0.700$, corresponding to 0.3–2 Novo units plasmin.

Pipette into centrifuge tubes:	Inhibitor assay	Reference assay	Concentration in assay mixture
Enzyme solution (IV) or (V)	0.1—0.2 ml.	0.1—0.2 ml.	1.67–3.3 U trypsin/l. or 200–400 U plasmin/l.
Sample (inhibitor)	0.1—0.2 ml.	—	
Buffer solution (I for trypsin, II for plasmin)	0.8—0.6 ml.	0.9—0.8 ml.	ca. 30 mM phosphate (ca. 45 mM L-lysine)
Mix and incubate for 5 min.			
Substrate solution (III)	2.0 ml.	2.0 ml.	13 mg. azocasein/ml.
Mix and incubate for 10 min.			
Trichloroacetic acid (solution V)	3.0 ml.	3.0 ml.	
Mix, allow to stand for 30 min. at room temperature and centrifuge. Pour the supernatant fluid into cuvettes and read extinctions.			

Calculations

The inhibition on addition of inhibitor is best related by means of an activity curve to the amount of inhibited enzyme (μg. trypsin) or activity (Novo units plasmin). In the assay of plasmin inhibition by serum (0.01 to 0.05 ml.) it should be noted that the inhibition is only proportional to the amount of serum up to 20% inhibition.

Precision of Method

The method described here is less accurate and more sensitive to interference than the assay of inhibitors with synthetic substrates. However, it gives information on whether results obtained with synthetic substrates are generally applicable (in the inhibition of the proteolytic activity of proteinases).

Normal Values

1 ml. Human serum inhibits ca. 8 Novo units plasmin. Note the range of proportionality (see under "Calculations").

Sources of Error

The supernatant fluids transferred to the cuvettes should not be turbid.

Specificity of Method

In principle the method is applicable to all proteinases (e.g. chymotrypsin, papain, subtilisin).

Chymotrypsin Inhibitors

Principle

N-3-(Carboxypropionyl)-L-phenylalanine-p-nitroanilide

N-3-(Carboxypropionyl)-L-phenylalanine + p-Nitroaniline

The liberation of p-nitroaniline from N-3-(carboxypropionyl)-L-phenylalanine-nitroanilide (CPPN) is measured. The substrate is also known as N-succinyl-L-phenylalanine-p-nitroanilide (SUPHEPA). For ε values, see p. 962. The sensitivity of the method can be increased by diazotization of the p-nitroaniline formed[9a,18].

Optimum Condition for Measurements

The Michaelis constant K_M is 1.05 mM (37 °C)[9a]. As the activation of chymotrypsin is not optimum even at 1.4 M $CaCl_2$[9a], an arbitrary concentration of 56 mM Ca^{2+} has been chosen. The formation of the complex and therefore the degree of inhibition is independent of the Ca^{2+} content of the assay mixture (this also applies to the serum inhibitors according to our measurements[8]). The inhibitor content of a sample increases with increasing activation of the enzyme, because the absolute extinction difference between the inhibitor assay and the chymotrypsin reference assay increases with the same degree of inhibition. If in this case the inhibition is related to the weight of enzyme added, the measured inhibitor content is independent of the degree of activation of the enzyme. According to[9b] the assay of inhibitor content of serum with chymotrypsin is only optimum with relatively high Ca^{2+} concentration (above ca. 0.5 M).

With a 30 min. period of incubation values of $\Delta E/min.$ between 0.001 and 0.008 (0.3 to 2.4 mU) are proportional to the amount of chymotrypsin.

Equipment and Reagents*

The equipment and the preparation of solutions are described on p. 1067. Instead of trypsin and its substrate the following are required:

7. Chymotrypsin
   lyophilizate, $\geq$ 50 mU/mg.; commercial preparation**, see p. 440.
8. N-3-(carboxypropionyl)-L-phenylalanine-p-nitroanilide*** (CPPN)

Purity of Reagents

Chymotrypsin should be free from trypsin; other reagents are usual commercial quality.

Preparation of Solutions (for ca. 50 determinations)

Prepare all solutions with distilled water. Prepare solutions I and II as described on p. 1067.
   I. Perchloric acid (6% w/v).
   II. Potassium carbonate solution (5 M).
   III. Triethanolamine buffer (0.2 M TRA; pH 7.8; 0.1 M $CaCl_2$):
      Dissolve 18.6 g. TRA and 7.35 g. $CaCl_2 \cdot 2H_2O$ in 450 ml. distilled water, adjust to pH 7.8 with 2 N NaOH and dilute to 500 ml. with distilled water.
   IV. Chymotrypsin solution (0.1 mg. protein/ml.; ca. 5 U/l.):
      Dissolve 1 mg. dry powder in 10 ml. 0.001 N HCl.
   V. Substrate solution (12.9 mM):
      Dissolve 250 mg. CPPN in 50 ml. buffer (solution III).

Stability of Solutions

Solutions I and II are stable indefinitely, solution III for 1 month at room temperature, solution IV 8 days at 4 °C and solution V at room temperature for 1 day.

Procedure

Collection, Treatment and Stability of Sample

Prepare extracts of organs and secretions which contain acid-stable chymotrypsin inhibitors (see Table) by the method described under "Trypsin Inhibitors" on p. 1068.

---

 * A combination test kit of reagents for the determination of chymotrypsin is available commercially (Test pack TC 15951, from Boehringer Mannheim). The units given in the information leaflet are not identical with the mU described here.
 ** We use the three times recrystallized preparation from Schuchardt. Munich. Germany.
 *** e. g. from Boehringer Mannheim, Germany.

Table 1. Inhibitor spectra, molecular weights and behaviour with 3% perchloric acid of important protease inhibitors.

Inhibitor	Trypsin	Chymotrypsin	Plasmin	Thrombin	Serum kallikrein	Pancreatic kallikrein (Pig)	Approximate molecular weight	Precipitation by acid	Notes
Soya bean inhibitor	++	+	+	−[a]	+	−	22000	+	Temporary inhibition[7,20] i.e. the inhibitor is also destroyed by the enzyme it inhibits
Pancreatic secretion (beef, human, dog, pig, cat) and pancreatic tissue	++	−	+	−[a]	−	−	6000–7000	−	
Submaxillary gland (dog, cat)	++	+	−[a]	−[a]	−	−	6500	−	
Seminal vesicles (human, guinea pig, mouse)	++	−	+[a]	−[a]	−	−	6800	−	
Bovine organs (liver, lung, pancreas, parotid glands)	+	+	+	−[a] / +[b]	+	+	6500	−	"Trasylol ®" "Kunitz inhibitor"
Human serum[43]									
α1-Antitrypsin	+++	++	−	+	−	−	60000	+	92% ⎫
α2-Macroglobulin	+++	+	+[c]	+	−	−	800000		5.5% ⎬ of the trypsin inhibition/ml. serum
Inter-α-trypsin inhibitor	+++	−	−	+	−	−	177000	+	2.2% ⎭
Antithrombin III (heparin cofactor)	−	−	+	+	−	−	8000		
α1-Antichymotrypsin	−	+	−	−	+	+	68000		
α + β-Fraction		−	−		+	+			

[a] BAEE-substrate   [b] thromboplastic activity   [c] immediate plasmin inhibitor

Assay System

Wavelength: Hg 405 nm; light path: 1 cm.; final volume: 3 ml.; 25 °C (constant temperature cuvette holder). Read against air. Equilibrate all solutions to 25 °C.

Pipette into cuvettes:		Inhibitor assay	Chymotrypsin reference assay (Ct)	Concentration in assay mixture
Chymotrypsin solution	(IV)	0.2 ml.	0.2 ml.	ca. 6.7 μg./ml. = 0.33 U/l.
Buffer solution	(III)	1.6 ml.	1.6 ml.	110 mM TRA 56 mM CaCl$_2$
Sample (inhibitor)*		0.2 ml.		
Mix and incubate for 5 min.				
Substrate solution	(V)	1.0 ml.	1.0 ml.	4.3 mM
Distilled water		—	0.2 ml.	
Mix, read the extinction at 5 min. intervals for 20–30 min. If the progress is not linear read at shorter intervals. Preferably use a recorder. Determine Δ E/min.				

* up to 0.5 ml. sample; where necessary make up to 1.8 ml. with buffer solution (III).

Calculations

Calculations are analogous to those on p. 1070. Inhibitor concentration in IU for chymotrypsin.

Precision of Method

The range of error for an individual measurement is below ± 8% (see[9b]).

Normal Values

Bieth, Métais & Warter[9b,40] found a similar relationship between the chymotrypsin inhibitor concentration in normal and pathological human serum to that for the trypsin inhibitor concentration (see p. 1071).

Specificity of Method

Trypsin, plasmin and thrombin do not hydrolyse CPPN[6,9a,18]; the CPPN-hydrolysing proteases contained in tissue homogenates (rat kidney[18], pancreatic extract[6]) have not been characterized further.

Inhibitors for Kallikrein, Plasmin and Thrombin

As the kallikrein inhibitor assay is about 100 times more sensitive than the trypsin inhibitor assay, it is particularly suited for the determination of small amounts of trypsin-kallikrein inhibitor from bovine organs (Trasylol®), e.g. pharmacological studies (see trypsin inhibitors)[4,13,37]. The inhibition of the

BAEE-hydrolysing activity of kallikrein (from pig pancreas) parallels the inhibitions of the kinin-liberating activity[30].

The plasmin-inhibiting activity is also suitable for the determination of trypsin-kallikrein inhibitor; the high molecular weight plasmin inhibitors of serum, however, do not inhibit the BAEE-hydrolysing (esterolytic) activity of plasmin[8].

Principle

Enzymatic determination of the alcohol liberated on hydrolysis of N-benzoylarginine ethyl ester (BAEE).

Optimum Conditions for Measurements, Equipment and Reagents

As for the assay of kallikrein (p. 1032).

Procedure

Treatment of Sample

For the determination of the high molecular weight serum kallikrein inhibitor ("immediate inhibitor") dilute the serum 1 : 5 with physiological saline and take 0.1 to 0.2 ml. of this dilution for the assay.

Assay System

See kallikrein determination, p. 1032.

Units for the determination of activity and inhibition of proteases in the BAEE-ADH assay[3,37]: 1 mU corresponds to an extinction change of $\Delta E_{366} = 0.0011/\text{min.}$ in a 3 ml. assay mixture.

a) *Inhibitor assay:* Incubate 0.1 ml. protease solution (ca. 0.1 U) +0.1 ml. inhibitor solution (0.02–0.07 IU) +0.8 ml. 0.1 M triethanolamine buffer (pH 7.8) for 5 min. at 25 °C. For the measurement of activity proceed as for the determination of kallikrein, but instead of kallikrein solution add 0.1 ml. of the pre-incubated inhibitor mixture.

b) *Protease reference assay:* Instead of 0.1 ml. pre-incubated inhibitor mixture (a) add 1/10 of the amount of protease added to (a) in 0.1 ml.

c) *Blank assay:* Reagent blank (spontaneous hydrolysis of BAEE). Make up the volume with buffer. In the determination of kallikrein inhibitors in serum add 0.1 ml. of an equivalent serum dilution.

Measure against blank. For period of incubation and measurement of extinction changes, see determination of kallikrein.

Calculations

1 IU for kallikrein, plasmin and thrombin corresponds to a decrease in extinction compared to the protease reference tube of $\Delta E = 1.1$ per min[3].

The inhibitor content of the sample is calculated according to the formula:

$$\frac{(\Delta E/\text{min.})_{\text{Protease}} - (\Delta E/\text{min.})_{\text{Inhibitor}}}{1.1} \times 1000 \; [\text{IU/l.}]$$

Normal Values

0.2–0.3 or 0.1–0.5 IU for kallikrein per ml. serum[3,42], i. e. ca. 2–3 or 1–5 KIU*.

Precision of Method

The range of error of the method for an individual measurement is below $\pm$ 10%, providing that the range of measurements given in Table 2 is adhered to. The inhibitor determination is preferably carried out with 50% inhibition; below 20% inhibition and above 70% the values are not reliable.

Table 2.

	Kallikrein EC 3.4.21.8	Plasmin EC 3.4.21.7	Thrombin EC 3.4.21.5
Preparation from	Pig pancreas	Novo®, Novo-Industrie	Test-Thrombin Behring-Werke
1 U is equivalent to	10 KU**	2 Novo units	170 NIH units
µg. protein equivalent to 1 U	8	550	600
Range of measurement (proportionality in assay)			
in U	0.005–0.011	0.0015–0.011	0.0015–0.0085
in ΔE_{365}/10 min.	0.055–0.120	0.016–0.120	0.016–0.094

Specificity of Method

It is possible to differentiate the BAEE-hydrolysing activities of enzyme mixtures with the help of protease inhibitors[1].

References

1 *R. Vogel, I. Trautschold & E. Werle:* Natürliche Proteinase-Inhibitoren, Georg Thieme Verlag, Stuttgart 1967.
2 *M. Laskowski & M. Laskowski jr.,* Adv. Protein Chem. *9,* 203 [1954], *M. Laskowski,* Methods in Enzymology *2,* 36 [1955].
3 *I. Trautschold,* Habilitationsschrift, Mediz. Fakultät der Univ. München, 1965; *I. Trautschold, H. Fritz & E. Werle* in Hypotensive Peptides, p. 221, Springer Verlag, New York 1966.
4 Recommendation of "International Commission for the Standardization of Pharmaceutical Enzymes, Third Report, Trypsin-Inhibitor".
5 *H. Fritz, G. Hartwich & E. Werle,* Z. physiol. Chem. *345,* 150 [1966].
6 *H. Fritz, F. Woitinas & E. Werle,* Z. physiol. Chem. *345,* 168 [1966].
7 *H. Fritz, I. Hüller, M. Wiedemann & E. Werle,* Z. physiol. Chem. *348,* 405 [1967].
8 *H. Fritz, I. Hüller & E. Werle,* unpublished results.
9 *J. Bieth, P. Métais & J. Warter,* Ann. Biol. Clin. *24,* 787 [1966]; 9a *26,* 143 [1968]; 9b Rev. franc. etudes clin. biol. *14,* 466 [1969]; 9c Clin. Chimica Acta *20,* 69 [1968].
10 *H. Haendle, H. Fritz, I. Trautschold & E. Werle,* Z. physiol. Chem. *343,* 185 [1965].
11 *H. Fritz, I. Trautschold, H. Haendle & E. Werle* Ann. N. Y. Acad. Sci. *146,* 400 [1968].
12 *N. M. Green,* Biochem. J. *66,* 407 [1957].
13 *I. Trautschold, E. Werle & H. Fritz* in: *R. Gross & G. Kroneberg:* Neue Aspekte der Trasylol-Therapie, F. K. Schattauer-Verlag, Stuttgart 1966, p. 3; see lit. cit. [12].
14 *J. Pütter,* Z. physiol. Chem. *348,* 1197 [1967].
15 *H. Fritz, I. Trautschold & E. Werle,* Z. physiol. Chem. *342,* 253 [1965].

---

 * Biological kallikrein inhibitor units[30].
** Biological kallikrein units[30].

16 *H. Fritz, H. Schult, M. Hutzel, M. Wiedemann & E. Werle,* Z. physiol. Chem. *348,* 308 [1967]; *H. Fritz, B. Brey & E. Werle,* Z. physiol. Chem. *350,* 617 [1969].
17 *K. Hochstraßer, M. Muss & E. Werle,* Z. physiol. Chem. *348,* 1337 [1967].
18 *W. Nagel, F. Willig, W. Peschke & F. H. Schmidt,* Z. physiol. Chem. *340,* 1 [1965].
19 *P. S. Norman,* Fed. Proc. *25,* 63 [1966].
19a*E. Habermann,* Ann. N. Y. Acad. Sci. *146,* 479 [1968].
20 *M. Laskowski & F. C. Wu,* J. biol. Chem. *204,* 797 [1953].
21 See *W. Rick* in *H. U. Bergmeyer:* Methoden der enzymatischen Analyse von Verlag Chemie, Weinheim 1970, 2nd. edn., p. 974.
22 *I. Trautschold & E. Werle,* Z. physiol. Chem. *325,* 48 [1961].
23 *B. F. Erlanger, N. Kokowsky & W. Cohen,* Arch. Biochem. Biophys. *95,* 271 [1961].
24 *B. J. Haverback, B. Dyce, H. Bundy & H. A. Edmondson,* Amer. J. Med. *29,* 424 [1960].
25 *H. Tuppy, U. Wiesbauer & E. Wintersberger,* Z. physiol. Chem. *329,* 278 [1962].
26 See *F. B. Ablondi & J. J. Hagan* and *D. F. Waugh, D. J. Baughman & K. D. Miller* in *P. D. Boyer, H. Lardy & K. Myrbäck:* The Enzymes Vol. 4, Academic Press, New York and London 1960, p. 175 or 215.
27 *S. Ehrenpreis & H. A. Scheraga,* J. biol. Chem. *227,* 1043 [1957]; Review of *L. W. Cunningham* in Hoppe-Seyler/Thierfelder: Handbuch der physiologisch- und pathologisch-chemischen Analyse, Springer-Verlag Berlin, New York, 1964, Vol. VI A, p. 279 f.; *F. Fiedler & E. Werle,* European J. Biochem., *7,* 27 [1968].
28 *E. Werle & I. Trautschold* in Hoppe-Seyler/Thierfelder Vol. VI C, p. 745, and this book, p. 1032.
29 *F. Fiedler & E. Werle,* Z. physiol. Chem. *348,* 1087 [1967].
30 *E. K. Frey, H. Kraut & E. Werle:* Das Kallikrein-Kinin-System und seine Inhibitoren, Ferdinand Enke Verlag, Stuttgart 1968, p. 10.
31 *H. Milstone,* J. Immunol. *42,* 109 [1941]; see *S. Witte & P. Dirnberger,* Klin. Wschr. *32,* 133 [1954].
32 *T. Astrup & S. Müllertz,* Arch. Biochem. Biophys. *40,* 346 [1952].
33 This book, p. 1025.
34 *H. Fritz, M. Hutzel, I. Hüller, M. Wiedemann, H. Stahlheber, P. Lehnert & M.-M. Forell,* Z. physiol. Chem. *348,* 1575 [1967].
35 *I. Trautschold, E. Werle, H. Haendle & H. Sebening,* Z. physiol. Chem. *332,* 328 [1963].
36 *M. Wanke:* Experimentelle Pankreatitis, Georg Thieme Verlag, Stuttgart 1968.
37 *H. Fritz, K. H. Oppitz, D. Meckl, B. Kemkes, H. Haendle, H. Schult & E. Werle,* Z. physiol. Chem. *350,* 1541 [1969].
38 *H. Weber & T. Wegmann:* Atlas der klinischen Enzymologie, Georg Thieme Verlag, Stuttgart 1968.
39 *H. G. Schwick, N. Heimburger & H. Haupt,* Zschr. inn. Med. *11,* 1 [1966].
40 *J. Warter, P. Métais & J. Bieth,* Rev. franç. études clin. biol. *14,* 466 [1969].
41 *C. B. Laurell & S. Eriksson,* Clin. chim. Acta *11,* 395 [1965].
42 *E. Werle & W. Appel,* Naturwissenschaften *45,* 60 [1958].
43 *N. Heimburger & Haupt,* Klin. Wschr. *44,* 1196 [1966].

Urease

Hans-Günter Schlegel and Heinrich Kaltwasser

Urease (Urea amidohydrolase, EC 3.5.1.5) occurs in bacteria, moulds, higher plants and in some lower animals. Humans and other mammals do not detoxify via urease; the repeated demonstration of urease in intestinal mucosa and other tissues of man and mammals is due to the presence of micro-organisms[1,2]. Urease was first studied by *Musculus*[3] and *Miquel*[4] in bacteria which decompose urine, and was obtained from plant seeds as the first crystalline enzyme by *Sumner*[5] in 1929. *Larsen* and *Kallio*[6] have purified the enzyme from *Bacillus pasteurii* to high specific activity. Urease is virtually substrate-specific; in micro-organisms it catalyses the hydrolysis of exogenous urea and is the terminal step of purine, pyrimidine and arginine degradation. In bacteria the ability to synthesize urease is used as a taxonomic characteristic; a culture medium containing a pH indicator is used to detect the enzyme[7]. In some strains of bacteria urease formation is constitutive, in others it is under regulatory control. The formation of urease in many of the strains studied is not induced by urea, but rather by nitrogen deficiency[8-10,28].

Manometric, titrimetric, colorimetric[11,12] and potentiometric[13] methods as well as a continuous spectro-photometric method using horse-radish peroxidase[14] have been described for the determination of urease activity. For a survey of the preparation and properties of urease, see[15-18]. In the method described here[19] the reaction product, ammonia, is determined in the NADH-dependent glutamate dehydrogenase (GlDH) reaction (L-glutamate: NAD oxidoreductase, deaminating, EC 1.4.1.2). The method is also suitable for the assay of threonine[20] and cytosine[27] deaminase.

Application of Method: In biochemistry, microbiology and for bacterial identification.

Principle

(1)
$$\text{Urea} + H_2O + 2H^+ \xrightarrow{\text{urease}} 2NH_4^+ + CO_2$$

(2)
$$2NH_4^+ + 2\ \text{2-Oxoglutarate} + 2NADH \xrightleftharpoons{\text{GlDH}} 2\ \text{Glutamate} + 2H_2O + 2NAD^+$$

Two moles NADH are oxidized per mole urea; the change in extinction at 340 (334, 365) nm per unit time is a measure of the urease activity.

Optimum Conditions for Measurements

The equilibrium of indicator reaction (2) lies far to the right, and therefore it is possible to measure the rate of urea hydrolysis in the coupled system by the decrease of extinction due to NADH with time. A prerequisite is that v_{max}/K_M of the GlDH indicator reaction is sufficiently large (see p. 123 et seq.).

For the assay of activity in bacterial extracts[9,10] and in commercial urease preparations the optimum urea concentration is 25 and 100 μmole/3 ml. respectively. The NADH concentration has not been varied. The optimum concentration of oxoglutarate for the indicator reaction is 2.5 μmole/3 ml. The pH optimum of the GlDH reaction in tris buffer is around pH 8.3, and that of the coupled reaction at pH 7.6. The present method is carried out at pH 8.0, because at this pH the interference from nonspecific NADH oxidase is excluded by Na_2S[9]. If Na_2S is not used the assay can be carried out at pH 7.2. The optimum amount of GlDH in the assay is 10 mg. protein. This also holds in the presence of Na_2S which inhibits the indicator reaction (see p. 1085). A decrease in the amount of indicator enzyme to between 1.5 and 0.25 mg. protein/cuvette resulted in a more prolonged lag phase with virtually the same maximal rate in the coupled reaction. With 0–14 μg. urease*/3 ml. = 0–64 mU/3 ml. the ΔE/min. is linearly proportional to the amount of enzyme added.

Measurements at different temperatures may require different measuring conditions (cf. p. 127). Nevertheless, results obtained under the same measuring conditions but at different temperatures were formerly compared with each other ("conversion factors" were determined). Such conversion factors may be correct if determined with a relatively large proband collective; however, they cannot be applied generally to the individual case (cf. p. 129). The value of the following relative reaction rates thus lies in being able to appraise the temperature dependence of the reaction and at the most to compare qualitatively values up to the limit of normal.

°C	18	19	20	21	22	23	24	25
	1.42	1.34	1.27	1.23	1.16	1.11	1.05	1.00
°C	26	27	28	29	30	31	32	33
	0.95	0.90	0.86	0.82	0.78	0.75	0.72	0.70
°C	34	35	36	37				
	0.68	0.66	0.65	0.64				

Equipment

Spectrophotometer or spectrum-line photometer suitable for exact measurements at 340, 334 or 365 nm, preferably with extinction recorder, otherwise use stop watch; water bath (25 °C).

Reagents

1. Tris-hydroxymethyl-aminomethane, tris
2. Hydrochloric acid, 0.1 N
3. 2-Oxoglutarate
   free acid; commercial preparation, see p. 548.
4. Glutamate dehydrogenase, GlDH
   free from ammonium ions, e.g. Boehringer Mannheim, GlDH-S 15324; $\geq$ 90 U/mg. (25 °C) 10 mg./ml.; other commercial preparations, see p. 461.

5. Reduced nicotinamide-adenine dinucleotide, NADH
   disodium salt, NADH-Na$_2$, commercial preparation, see p. 545.
6. Sodium hydroxide, 5 N

Purity of Reagents

All the compounds used must be free from ammonium ions.

Preparation of Solutions (for ca. 40 determinations)

Prepare all solutions with doubly distilled water.

I. Tris buffer (50 mM; pH 8.0):
   Dissolve 0.6 g. tris in 60 ml. distilled water, adjust to pH 8.0 with ca. 29 ml. 0.1 N HCl and dilute to 100 ml. with distilled water.

---

* Urease solution from the test combination for determination of urea supplied by Boehringer Mannheim; 1 mg. urease/ml.

II. 2-Oxoglutarate (0.25 M):
   Dissolve 95 mg. Na-2-oxoglutarate in 2 ml. distilled water or 73 mg. 2-oxoglutaric acid in 1.5 ml. distilled water, adjust to pH 5 with about 0.2 ml. 5 N NaOH and dilute to 2 ml.

III. Urea (0.3 M):
   Dissolve 1.8 g. urea in 100 ml. distilled water.

IV. Reduced nicotinamide-adenine dinucleotide (1.5 mM β-NADH):
   Dissolve 10 mg. NADH-Na$_2$ in 1 ml. distilled water.

V. Reagent mixture for	10	20	30	40 assays
Tris buffer (solution I)	23 ml.	46 ml.	69 ml.	92 ml.
2-Oxoglutarate (solution II)	0.1 ml.	0.2 ml.	0.3 ml.	0.4 ml.
NADH solution (IV)	0.6 ml.	1.2 ml.	1.8 ml.	2.4 ml.
Distilled water	0.3 ml.	0.6 ml.	0.9 ml.	1.2 ml.

VI. Glutamate dehydrogenase, GlDH (10 mg. protein/ml.):
   Use the stock solution undiluted.

Stability of Solutions

The 2-oxoglutarate solution is stable for several months if stored at -16 °C. Store tris buffer at 4 °C in the dark to prevent the growth of micro-organisms. Prepare the urea solution and the reagent mixture freshly each day.

Procedure

Collection, Treatment and Stability of Sample

Collection: Cell-free extracts are prepared by usual methods (see p. 401 et seq.), and in the case of bacteria by ultrasonic treatment, or with the *Hughes* or *French* presses.

Stability of enzyme in sample:

The activity of urease in phosphate buffer is not significantly decreased after 2 days at 0 °C or after 2 weeks at -16 °C.

Assay System

Wavelength: 340 (Hg 334, Hg 365) nm; light path: 1 cm.; final volume: 3.0 ml.; 25 °C (preferably constant temperature cuvette holder). Urea-free blank is required, because NH_4^+ and non-specific oxidases are frequently present. Equilibrate solutions to 25 °C before start of measurements. Read against air.

Pipette successively into cuvettes:		Experimental	Blank	Concentration in assay mixture
Reagent solution	(V)	2.4 ml.	2.4 ml.	31 mM tris
				0.81 mM oxoglutarate
				0.24 mM NADH
GlDH solution	(VI)	0.05 ml.	0.05 ml.	166 μg./ml. $\triangleq$ 15 U/ml.
Distilled water		0.35 ml.	0.45 ml.	
Urease sample		0.10 ml.	0.10 ml.	
Mix. If no interfering compounds are present the extinction remains constant.				
Urea solution	(III)	0.10 ml.	—	10 mM urea
Mix. Start stopwatch and read extinction at 3 and 6 min.; calculate ΔE/min. from these values. Preferably record extinctions alternately for 7 min.; from tangents at 5 min. determine ΔE/min.				

The ΔE/min. values should not be more than 0.1/min. at 365 nm, otherwise dilute the urease sample.

Calculations

Subtract the extinction change occurring in the blank cuvette from that in the experimental cuvette. A unit (U) of urease liberates 2 μmole NH_4^+ per minute. The calculation formula (8) on p. 313 applies and the following relationships hold.

Wavelength:	*334 nm*	*340 nm*	*365 nm*
Volume activity =	2459 × ΔE/min.	2412 × ΔE/min.	4412 × ΔE/min. [U/l.]

Precision of Method

With values around 400 U/l. the coefficient of variation is 2.8%.

Normal Values

The specific activities of crude extracts of *Bacillus pasteurii* and *Proteus* are 4000 and 1500 U/g. respectively[6,10]. In bacteria with repressed urease the activity varies between 1 and 150 U/g. For the urease content of plant and animal tissues, see[15,21].

Sources of Error

Effects of drugs and other therapeutic measures: Urease is inhibited by acetohydroxamic acid, suramin, furacin and other compounds[22-25]; hydroxyurea is a substrate and competitive inhibitor of urease[26].

Interference in the assay: Ammonium ions cause an extinction change which is independent of the urease activity, and which starts before the addition of urea. Large amounts of ammonia can be removed by dialysis, traces (< 0.8 μmole/3 ml.) can be removed by preliminary incubation with excess NADH. Avoid ammonia vapour in the laboratory and also dust which frequently contains NH_4Cl. The non-specific NADH oxidase which is located in bacterial particles can be inhibited by 1 mM Na_2S^9 or removed by centrifugation at 100000 g. NADH oxidase activity and traces of NH_4^+ are measured in the urea-free blank cuvette and are subtracted in the calculations. Deaminases only interfere if their respective substrates are present. In the assay of urease activity in compost the humic acids can inhibit GlDH.

Specificity of Method

Urease is virtually a substrate-specific enzyme, and as long as the possible sources of error are avoided the assay is specific for urease activity.

References

1 *H. L. Kornberg & R. E. Davies,* Phys. Rev. *35,* 169 [1955].
2 *S. M. Levenson, L. V. Crowley, R. E. Horowitz & O. J. Malm,* J. biol. Chem. *234,* 2061 [1959].
3 *M. Musculus,* Pflügers Arch. *12,* 214 [1876].
4 *P. Miquel,* Compt. rend. acad. sci. *111,* 397 [1890].
5 *J. B. Sumner,* J. biol. Chem. *69,* 435 [1926].
6 *A. D. Larson & R. E. Kallio,* J. Bact. *68,* 67 [1954].
7 *W. B. Christensen,* J. Bact. *52,* 461 [1946].
8 *D. J. Stewart,* J. gen. Microbiol. *41,* 169 [1965].
9 *C. König, H. Kaltwasser & H. G. Schlegel,* Arch. Mikrobiol. *53,* 231 [1966].
10 *J. Krämer, H. Kaltwasser & H. G. Schlegel,* Zentralbl. Bakteriol. *121,* 414 [1967].
11 *D. D. van Slyke & R. M. Archibald,* J. biol. Chem. *154,* 623 [1944].
12 *R. C. Dickenman, B. Crafts & B. Zak,* Amer. J. Clin. Path. *24,* 981 [1954].
13 *S. A. Katz, J. A. Cowans,* Biochim, Biophys. Acta *107,* 605 [1965].
14 *P. Stutts & I. Fridovich,* Anal. Biochem. *8,* 70 [1964].
15 *J. B. Sumner* in: *J. B. Sumner & K. Myrbäck:* The Enzymes, Academic Press, New York 1951, vol. I, part I, p. 873.
16 *J. E. Varner* in: *P. D. Boyer, H. Lardy & K. Myrbäck:* The Enzymes, Academic Press, New York 1960, vol. 4, p. 247.
17 *D. M. Greenberg* in: *Hoppe-Seyler & Thierfelder:* Handbuch der physiologisch- und pathologisch-chemischen Analyse, vol. 6, part C, p. 362, Springer Berlin, Heidelberg, New York 1966.
18 *G. Mamiya & G. Gorin,* Biochim. Biophys. Acta *105,* 382 [1965].
19 *H. Kaltwasser & H. G. Schlegel,* Anal. Biochem. *16,* 132 [1966].
20 *M. Reh,* Diss. Göttingen,1967.
21 *C. L. Prosser & F. A. Brown jr.:* Comparative animal physiology. *W. B. Saunders Comp.* Philadelphia, London 1961.
22 *W. N. Fishbein & P. P. Carbone,* J. biol. Chem. *240,* 2407 [1965].
23 *E. D. Wills & A. Wormall,* Biochem. J. *47,* 158 [1950].
24 *I. Yall & M. N. Green,* Proc. Soc. Exptl. Biol. Med. *79,* 306 [1952].
25 *G. R. Gale,* J. Bact. *91,* 499 [1966].
26 *W. N. Fishbein, T. S. Winter & J. D. Davidson,* J. biol. Chem. *240,* 2402 [1965].
27 *H. Kaltwasser & J. Krämer,* Arch. Mikrobiol. *60,* 172 [1968].
28 *C. König & H. G. Schlegel,* Biochim. Biophys. Acta *139,* 182 [1967].

Guanase

Giuseppe Giusti

Guanase (Guanine aminohydrolase, EC 3.5.4.3) occurs in many animal tissues; in rabbit the activity decreases in the order: liver, brain, intestinal mucosa and skeletal muscle *(Wakabayasi[1])*. In humans, guanase occurs mainly in liver, in kidney, in brain and in small intestine. Less or no activity has been found in heart, lung, spleen, pancreas, skeletal muscle, erythrocytes and leucocytes[2,3]. *Stern[4]* showed that guanase occurs in both the cytoplasm and nuclei of liver cells of horse and rat. After fractionation of liver homogenate by centrifugation *Bowkiewicz-Surma* and *Krawczynski[5]* found the following distribution of total guanase activity: nuclei 15.2%, mitochondria 12.3%, cytoplasm 72.5%. None or very little guanase activity is detectable in normal human serum[3,6-8], slight activity occurs in blood or serum of rabbits[1] and fowl[9] and relatively high activity in normal rat serum[5,10].

The enzyme can be purified by the method of *Kalckar[11]*; commercial preparations are available (see p. 471.) In diffuse or focal liver necrosis the enzyme occurs in serum. The guanase activity in serum in different diseases was first measured by *Hue* and *Free[6,7]*, *Knight, Whitehouse* et al.[3,12] and *Giusti* and *Galanti[8,10,13]*. The guanase activity is considerably raised in acute viral hepatitis. Normal values or slight increases occur in obstructive jaundice, liver cirrhosis, ascending cholangitis, myocardial infarction, acute pancreatitis, malignant tumors and typhoid fever. The observations of the workers mentioned above have been confirmed by others[14-18].

Methods for the determination of guanase activity include measurement of ammonia formation *(Caraway[19]*, colorimetric assay*), or the spectrophotometric method of *Roush* and *Norris[21]*, modified by *Hue* and *Free[6,7]* and *Quast* et al. [22] for clinical purposes. The most suitable method for clinical studies is the spectrophotometric method of *Kalckar[11]* as modified by *Giusti* et al.[8,10,13]. This type of method, which is described below, is more sensitive than the method of *Hue* and *Free* and allows the kinetics of the reaction to be followed.

Application of Method: In biochemistry and clinical chemistry.

Principle

(1)
$$\text{Guanine} + H_2O \xrightarrow{\text{guanase}} \text{Xanthine} + NH_3$$

(2)
$$\text{Xanthine} + O_2 + H_2O \xrightarrow{\text{xanthine oxidase}} \text{Uric acid} + H_2O_2$$

Xanthine oxidase (xanthine: oxygen oxidoreductase, EC 1.2.3.2) is the indicator enzyme. The reaction is followed by spectrophotometric measurements at 290 nm of the formation of uric acid.

Optimum Conditions for Measurements

With guanine as substrate the enzyme shows a wide pH optimum between pH 6 and 10, the flat peak is around pH 8. The K_M value for guanine in 50 mM phosphate buffer is 5 μM. In studies on human sera *Caraway[19]* and *Quast* et al.[22] observed that the rate of the reaction does not increase appreciably when the concentration of substrate is raised from 66 μM to 490 μM. Guanine at concentrations of 0.53 mM or higher, causes inhibition of enzyme activity according to *Nyssen[20]*. About 30–80 mU purified xanthine

---

* *Nyssen* and *Dorche[20]* have described a semi-automated colorimetric method for the determination of activity in serum with the Technicon Autoanalyser®.

oxidase must be added to the assay mixture. The buffered guanine solution must be saturated with oxygen. Because of the low guanase activity in normal sera the reaction should be carried out at 37 °C. According to [16] the guanase activity increases by a factor of 2.4 between 25 °C and 37 °C.

Measurements at different temperatures may require different measuring conditions (cf. p. 127). Nevertheless, results obtained under the same measuring conditions but at different temperatures were formerly compared with each other ("conversion factors" were determined). Such conversion factors may be correct if determined with a relatively large proband collective; however, they cannot be applied generally to the individual case (cf. p. 129). The value of the following relative reaction rates thus lies in being able to appraise the temperature dependence of the reaction and at the most to compare qualitatively values up to the limit of normal.

°C	25	30	37
	1	1.5	2.3

Equipment

Spectrophotometer suitable for accurate measurements at 290 nm. with secondary electronic multiplier and constant temperature cuvette holder; water bath; stopwatch.

Reagents

1. Tris-hydroxymethyl-aminomethane, tris
2. Hydrochloric acid, 0.1 N
3. Sodium hydroxide, 1 N
4. Guanine
   commercial preparation, see p. 521.

5. Xanthine oxidase, XOD
   from milk, suspension in 3.2 M ammonium sulphate solution containing 10 mM EDTA: ≧ 0.4 U/mg. (25 °C). Commercial preparation, see p. 541.

Purity of Enzyme Preparations

XOD should, relative to its activity, contain less than 0.01% guanase and uricase activity.

Preparation of Solutions

Prepare all solutions with doubly distilled water.
 I. Guanine stock solution (1.03 mM guanine):
    Dissolve 16 mg. guanine in a few ml. 1 N NaOH and dilute to 100 ml. with distilled water.
 II. Tris buffer (0.1 M; pH 8.0):
    Dissolve 6.055 g. tris in about 200 ml. distilled water, add 268 ml. 0.1 N HCl and dilute to 500 ml. with distilled water.
III. Buffered guanine solution (90 mM tris; 0.103 mM guanine):
    Dilute 1 volume guanine stock solution (I) with 9 volumes tris buffer (II). Prepare daily.
IV. Xanthine oxidase (2–2.5 mg. protein/ml.):
    Dilute the stock suspension with tris buffer (II). The activity should be between 1.0 and 1.5 U/ml. (25 °C).

Stability of Solutions

Store all solutions and suspension, stoppered, at 0–4 °C. Prepare stock solution (I) freshly each week. Prepare the guanine buffered solution (III) freshly each day. The tris buffer (II) is stable until bacterial decomposition occurs. Both the XOD stock suspension and the XOD suspension IV are stable for several months.

Procedure

Collection, Treatment and Stability of Sample

Collection and treatment of sample:

Collect blood from a vein. Addition of oxalate (1–2 mg./ml.), citrate (1–1.5 mg./ml.), fluoride (2 mg./ml.), EDTA (1–2 mg./ml.) or heparin (0.2 mg./ml.)* does not interfere. Centrifuge at ca. 3000 g to obtain plasma or serum. If necessary, store samples at 0–4 °C. Moderate haemolysis does not affect the results in human serum as human erythrocytes do not contain guanase[2,16]. In contrast, haemolysis must be avoided with rat plasma because rat erythrocytes have high guanase activity[5].

For enzyme assays in tissue preparations it is best to measure the activity in the supernatant fluid after high-speed centrifugation (15000–20000 g; 15–30 min.; 0 °C). The presence of uricase in the samples should be checked (see below). Changes in extinction during the reaction due to turbidity can be detected at 320 nm, because guanase and XOD-reaction cause no extinction change at this wavelength.

Stability of sample:

Serum can be stored for two weeks at 4 °C without any appreciable loss of activity[16]. Incubation at 56 °C for 30 min. causes only 10% loss of activity. Plasma and serum guanase are stable for months at −13 °C[3]. According to[17] there was no loss of guanase activity in serum samples stored 3 days at 4 °C or one week at −40 °C. Between 3rd and 6th day of storage at 4 °C a 15% loss of activity has been observed. According to[19] the guanase activity slowly decreases over 24 hr. at room temperature, but the enzyme is stable at 4 °C for one week and at −20 °C for at least two weeks. We use only fresh plasma or serum which has been stored for not longer than 48 hr. at 4 °C.

---

* We use Liquemin (solution of 5% heparin, 0.5% phenol, 0.7% NaCl)

Assay System

Wavelength: 290 nm; light path: 1 cm.; final volume: 3.10 ml.; temperature: 37 °C (constant temperature cuvette holder). Read against a reference cuvette (3.0 ml. tris buffer II, 0.05 ml. sample)*.

Before the assay equilibrate the guanine solution (III) to 37 °C and saturate with O_2.

Pipette into cuvettes:			Concentration in assay mixture
Buffered guanine solution	(III)	3.00 ml.	0.1 mM guanine 87 mM tris
XOD suspension	(IV)	0.05 ml.	30–40 μg./ml.
Mix and wait for 5 min.			
Sample		0.05 ml.	
Mix, read extinction and start stopwatch; after exactly 10, 20 and 30 min. read extinction again.			

The values for $\Delta E/30$ min. at 290 nm. should not exceed 0.300/30 min. (a ΔE of 0.363 indicates that half the substrate has been consumed). Dilute active serum 2 or 4-fold with isotonic saline and/or read extinctions at shorter intervals. If the activity is less than 0.001/min. it is necessary to read at 40, 50 and 60 min.

The assay can also be carried out as a semi-micro method using a semi-micro cuvette (e. g. Hellma 104 QS). The assay system then consists of 1 ml. buffered guanine solution (III), 5 μl.XOD suspension (10 mg. protein/ml.); 20 μl. serum.

Calculations

According to Kalckar[23] the specific extinction increase for the overall reaction guanine → xanthine → uric acid is $\varepsilon_{290} = 7.25$ cm.^{2}/μmole.

Therefore for the samples:

Macro assay: volume activity $= 8552 \times \Delta E/$min. [U/l.]
Micro assay: volume activity $= 7070 \times \Delta E/$min. [U/l.])

Precision of Method

Repeated determinations on the same enzyme preparation with 50 U/l.**, gave values ranging from 45 to 56 U/l. By repeating determinations nine times on each of 5 serum samples, a mean coefficient of variation of $\pm$ 6.22% was found. These assays were carried out by the analyst on sera of patients with acute viral hepatitis.

---

  * Using a Beckman-DU spectrophotometer or similar instrument with constant temperature holder for 4 cuvettes it is possible to carry out simultaneously 3 determinations against a reference cuvette.
** The assay was carried out with serum albumin solutions to which known amounts of purified guanase had been added.

Normal Values

Knights et al.[3] found with the method of *Hue* and *Free* in human serum a range of 0–3.0 U/l., with a mean value of 2.2 ± 1.1 U/l. (37 °C). *McLeod*[14] found normal values of 0–3.4 U/l. *Giusti* and *Galanti* found a range of 0–7.0 U/l. with a mean 2.1 ± 2.0 U/l. (37 °C) on more than 100 normal subjects with the method described here. *Caraway*[19] and *Nyssen & Dorsche*[20] found normal values of 0–3.0 U/l. (37 °C). *Giusti* and *Galanti* found mean values of 19.6 ± 14.9 U/l. (37 °C) and a range of 2.0–73.2 U/l. in more than 100 cases of acute viral hepatitis. In 13 cases of severe viral hepatitis with coma *Giusti* et al.[13] found a mean value of 97.23 ± 55.40 U/l. (37 °C). In 24 icteric patients *Caraway*[19] found values between 3.2 and 53.2 U/l. (37 °C); acute hepatocellular disease showing higher values than obstructive jaundice.

In obstructive jaundice, liver cirrhosis and other hepatic diseases all the above mentioned workers obtained normal or only slightly raised values (e.g. 0.0–14.5 U/l. at 37 °C)[13].

The guanase content of several organs of humans[2,3] and rat[5] have been described in the literature. For information on serum and liver guanase activity in experimental liver necrosis, see[3,5,10].

Sources of Error

Effects of drugs and other therapeutic measures: None known.

Interference in the assay technique: The presence of uricase in the sample prevents quantitative formation of uric acid in the assay mixture. To test for uricase in the sample add 10 μg. uric acid in 3 ml. tris buffer (II) and check whether a decrease in extinction occurs at 290 nm. Uricase activity has been reported in serum of mice with experimental liver necrosis[24]. In samples containing uricase activity the guanase activity can be measured with the method of *Quast* et al.[22] in which the xanthine oxidase is inhibited with borate.

The assay is not affected by the presence of xanthine oxidase in the sample.

Specificity of Method

The method is specific. The assay system can be checked if purified uricase (urate: oxygen oxidoreductase, EC 1.7.3.3) is added after the main reaction; the oxidation of the uric acid formed in the main reaction results in a decrease in extinction at 290 nm.

References

1 *Y. Wakabayasi,* J. biol. Chem. *28,* 185[1963].
2 *R. Levine, T. C. Hall & C. A. Harris,* Cancer *16,* 269 [1963].
3 *E. M. Knights, J. L. Whitehouse, A. C. Hue & C. L. Santos,* J. Lab. Clin. Med. *65,* 355 [1965].
4 *H. Stern, V. Allfrey, A. E. Mirsky & H. Saetren,* J. Gen. Physiol. *35,* 559 [1952].
5 *E. Bowkiewicz-Surma & J. Krawczynski,* Clin. chim. Acta *16,* 29 [1967].
6 *A. C. Hue & A. H. Free,* Clin. Chem. *10,* 631 [1964].
7 *A. C. Hue & A. H. Free,* Clin. Chem. *11,* 708 [1965].
8 *G. Giusti & B. Galanti,* Boll. Soc. ital. Biol. Sper. *41,* 1567 [1965].
9 *E. J. Conway & R. Cooke,* Biochem. J. *33,* 457 [1939].
10 *G. Giusti & B. Galanti,* Minerva Med. *56.II,* 4448 [1965].
11 *H. M. Kalckar,* J. biol. Chem. *167,* 461 [1947].
12 *J. L. Whitehouse, E. M. Knights, C. L. Santos & A. C. Hue,* Clin. Chem. *10,* 632 [1964].
13 *G. Giusti, B. Galanti & A. Mancini,* Enzymologia *38,* 373 [1970].
14 *S. McLeod,* Canad J. Med. Techn. *29,* 60 [1967].
15 *E. L. Coodley,* Amer. J. Gastroenterol. *50,* 55 [1968].
16 *A. Bel, R. Dietsch, R. Alary, B. Savoye, R. Levrat, J. Nesmoz & M. Nyssen,* Presse Medicale *78,* 495 [1970].

17 *E. E. Mandel, L. R. Macalincag, T. Tiongson & E. Tiongson,* Amer. J. Gastroenterol. *54,* 253 [1970].
18 *M. C. Tamarelle, A. Quinton, J. Bancons & J.-J. Dubarry,* Arch. Fr. Mal. App. Dig. *59,* 697 [1970].
19 *W. T. Caraway,* Clin. Chem. *12,* 187 [1966].
20 *M. Nyssen & J. Dorche,* Clin. Chim. Acta *22,* 363 [1968].
21 *A. Roush & E. R. Norris,* Arch. Biochem. *29,* 124 [1950].
22 *N. M. Quast, K. J. Clayson & P. E. Strandjord,* Amer. J. Med. Tech. *34,* 513 [1968].
23 *H. M. Kalckar,* J. biol. Chem. *167,* 429 [1947].
24 *B. Galanti. G. Giusti & A. Mancini,* Boll. Soc. ital. Biol. Sper. *41,* 1563 [1965].

Adenosine Deaminase

Giuseppe Giusti

Adenosine deaminase, ADA (Adenosine aminohydrolase, EC 3.5.3.3) specifically reacts with adenosine and several adenine nucleoside analogues[1-3]. The enzyme is widely distributed in animal tissues. *Conway* and *Cooke*[4,5] were first to study the distribution of ADA in various organs of the rabbit, and also showed that normal blood of humans and mammals contained activity. The highest activity is found in the caecum, intestinal mucosa and spleen, while less or no activity is found in skeletal muscle, skin and bone. The ADA content of liver is 7–10% of that of the intestine. The enzyme is present in the cytoplasmic fraction of the cell and a certain amount is located in the nucleus[6-8].

Comparative studies on the substrate specificity[2,9] show differences between the enzymes from different species. *Brady* and *O'Donovan*[10] found differences in the pH optimum, the electrophoretic mobility and the substrate specificity of ADA from many tissues of 6 mammalian species. Their findings, however, suggest that the enzyme is the same in different tissues of the same organism. According to *Chilson* et al.[11] and *Fisher* et al.[12] the ADA from liver and duodenum of chicken and frog differ in regard to their relative substrate specificity and their apparent energy of activation.

ADA can be purified from intestine by the method of *Kalckar*[13]. Commercial preparations are available (see p. 426).

The enzyme level in serum increases in patients with different types of malignant tumours, but various workers* do not agree upon the proportion of patients with leukaemia and tumours having high ADA concentrations in serum. High activity of the enzyme in serum has been found in viral hepatitis[16,18,20-24], infectious mononucleosis[16,18] and liver cirrhosis[18,21,23-25]. The ADA activity in serum is less in obstructive jaundice than in viral hepatitis[18,20,25]. The determination of ADA activity is therefore of value in the differential diagnosis of icteric patients.

Müller-Beissenhirtz and *Keller*[18] were first to report on the raised ADA values in serum of three patients with typhoid fever, *Galanti* and *Giusti*[25,26], *Galanti* et al.[27] and *Giusti* et al.[28,29] carried out extensive studies on more than 130 typhoid fever patients and found early and very considerable rises in serum ADA activity. Patients with other infectious or non-infectious diseases in which high fevers occurs showed slight or moderate increases in serum ADA activity[25-28]. The assay of ADA activity is therefore useful in the diagnosis of typhoid fever. The increase of serum ADA activity is probably due to enzyme release from the involved Peyer's patches, mesenteric lymph nodes and even the intestinal mucosa.

For biochemical purposes the ADA activity can be measured by a spectrophotometric method based on the different absorption spectra of adenosine and inosine at 265 nm. This principle is used for the spectrophotometric assay of adenosine (see p. 1919). Several workers have used this method for the determination of ADA activity in serum, but it is less suitable for clinical chemistry.

The sensitive colorimetric method of *Galanti* and *Giusti*[30] is described here. It is a modification of the method of *Martinek*[31] using much higher substrate concentration. The composition of the reagent described by *Chaney*[32] has also been slightly modified.

Application of Method: In clinical chemistry.

Principle

The equilibrium of reaction (1) is far to the right. Ammonia is determined in the *Chaney* and *Marbach*[32] modification of the *Berthelot* reaction[33]: ammonia forms an intensely blue indophenol with sodium hypo-

---

* *Straub* et al.[14] and *Letnansky* and *Seelich*[15] reported increased ADA activity in serum of 70–90% of the patients, *Köhler* and *Benz*[16] in 10–30%, *Schwarts* and *Bodansky*[17] and *Müller-Beissenhirtz* and *Keller*[18] in about 15%. *Schaedel* and *Schlenk*[19] found no increase.

(1)   Adenosine + H$_2$O $\xrightarrow{\text{ADA}}$ Inosine + NH$_3$

(2)   NH$_3$ + OCl$^-$ + 2 ⟨benzene⟩-OH $\xrightarrow[\text{Na}_2[\text{Fe(CN)}_5\text{NO}]]{\text{OH}^-}$ O=⟨⟩=N-⟨⟩-O$^-$

chlorite and phenol in alkaline solution. Sodium nitroprusside is the catalyst. The ammonia concentration is directly proportional to the extinction of the indophenol. The reaction catalysed by ADA is stopped at the end of the incubation period by the addition of the phenol-nitroprusside solution[30,31,34].

Optimum Conditions for Measurements

The optimum conditions for measurements[30,34] are 20 mM adenosine, phosphate buffer (ionic strength ca. 0.10) and a pH range between 6.2 and 6.8.

None of the other quoted methods employ optimum conditions. All the ADA activities given in the literature[14-21,23,24], are to a differing extent lower than the values of *Galanti* and *Giusti*[22,25-27]. According to recent results in our laboratory the optimum adenosine concentration for assay of ADA activity in serum is the same for normal subjects and for patients with various diseases. According to [35], the rate of the ADA reaction increases up to 64 °C, but the data are not suitable for calculation of the temperature coefficient. According to[18] the rate of the reaction at 37 °C is 2.2 times that at 25 °C.

Measurements at different temperatures may require different measuring conditions (cf. p. 127). Nevertheless, results obtained under the same measuring conditions but at different temperatures were formerly compared with each other ("conversion factors" were determined). Such conversion factors may be correct if determined with a relatively large proband collective; however, they cannot be applied generally to the individual case (cf. p. 129). The value of the following relative reaction rates[36] thus lies in being able to appraise the temperature dependence of the reaction and at the most to compare qualitatively values up to the limit of normal.

°C	25	30	37
	1.0	1.30	1.85

Equipment

Spectrophotometer, spectrum-line photometer or simple photometer (with tungsten lamp and filter) suitable for accurate measurements at wavelengths between 620 and 650 nm.; water bath (37 °C).

Reagents

1. Sodium dihydrogen phosphate, NaH$_2$PO$_4$·H$_2$O
2. Disodium hydrogen phosphate, Na$_2$HPO$_4$·12H$_2$O
3. Adenosine
   crystalline, chromatographically pure.
4. Phenol, A. R.
5. Sodium nitroprusside, Na$_2$(Fe[CN]$_5$NO)·2H$_2$O, A. R.

6. Sodium hypochlorite, NaOCl
   commercial hypocholorite bleaching agents, e. g. Clorox ® (Clorox Co., Oakland, Calif.)[37,38], White ®, West Best ®[37] are suitable as well as other usual preparations such as sodium hypochlorite solution (Merck, Darmstadt, Germany).
7. Sodium hydroxide, 1 N
8. Ammonium sulphate, (NH$_4$)$_2$SO$_4$

Preparation of Solutions

Prepare all solutions with doubly distilled, ammonia-free water. Ammonia can be removed by addition of a little H_2SO_4 and $KMnO_4$ and a second distillation from a glass apparatus. This precaution is particularly necessary if the ammonia content of the tap water is high.

  I. Phosphate buffer (50 mM; pH 6.5):
     Dissolve 4.73 g. $NaH_2PO_4 \cdot H_2O$ and 5.62 g. $Na_2HPO_4 \cdot 12\,H_2O$ in distilled water and dilute to 1 000 ml. with boiled distilled water.
 II. Buffered adenosine solution (21 mM adenosine, 50 mM phosphate, pH 6.5):
     Add ca. 15 ml. phosphate buffer (I) to 140 mg. adenosine in a 25 ml. volumetric flask, warm in a hot water bath and cool under running water. Adjust to pH 6.5 and dilute to 25 ml. with phosphate buffer (I).
III. Ammonium sulphate stock solution (15 mM):
     Dissolve 1.982 g. anhydrous ammonium sulphate in ammonia-free distilled water, make up to 1 000 ml. and mix thoroughly.
 IV. Ammonium sulphate standard solution (75 μM; 0.15 μval, NH_3/ml.):
     Dilute 0.5 ml. ammonium sulphate stock solution (III) (precision pipette) to 100 ml. with phosphate buffer (I).
  V. Phenol/nitroprusside solution (106 mM phenol; 0.17 mM sodium nitroprusside):
     Dissolve 10 g. phenol and 50 mg. sodium nitroprusside in ca. 500 ml. distilled water and dilute to 1 000 ml.
 VI. Alkaline hypochlorite solution (11 mM NaOCl; 125 mM NaOH):
     Mix 125 ml. 1 N NaOH and 16.4 ml. Clorox® (contains 5% w/v NaOCl) to 1 000 ml. with distilled water.

Note: Solution V corresponds to the dilute reagents of *Chaney* and *Marbach*[32]. Solution VI contains more hypochlorite than their dilute reagent. Both solutions are available from commercial sources, but the concentrations vary. Presumably all these solutions are suitable for the ADA assay, because according to *Kaplan* et al.[37] the concentrations of phenol, nitroprusside, NaOH and NaOCl in the reaction mixture are not critical for the formation of indophenol. We use the reagents from Boehringer Mannheim whose composition is that of solutions V and VI.

Stability of Solutions

Store all solutions at 0–4 °C. Solutions I, III, IV, V (in dark bottle) and VI are stable for at least 2 months. Adenosine crystallizes out from solution II at 4 °C; it can be brought into solution again by warming the volumetric flask, but a little ammonia is set free. We, therefore, prepare the daily requirement so as to obtain an ammonia-free adenosine solution. Solution V should be discarded if it becomes brown.

Procedure

Collection, Treatment and Stability of Sample

Collection and treatment of sample:

Use venous blood. Addition of oxalate (1 mg./ml.), citrate (1 mg./ml.) or EDTA (1 mg./ml.) does not interfere with the assay. According to [15,31,36] heparinized plasma can also be used, but we found that addition of liquemin (4 μl./ml.)* caused a slight inhibition of ADA, presumably because of the phenol content of the anticoagulant. Addition of fluoride gives unsatisfactory results. Use only serum or plasma free from haemolysis, because human erythrocytes have a high ADA content[18]. The samples should not be stored for longer than 48–72 hr. at 4 °C. For measurements of activity in tissues, prepare homogenates and centrifuge for 15–30 min. at high speed (15000 g–20000 g) and 0 °C. If the protein content of the complete reaction mixture is below 5 μg./ml. and the haemoglobin content can be neglected, deproteinization can be omitted. With higher protein content deproteinize as described for the determination of guanase activity[38] or ADA activity[36]. In this case it is necessary to change the concentrations of the *Chaney* and *Marbach*[32] reagents. A check must always be made whether, in the absence of adenosine, ammonia is liberated or bound (see under "Sources of Error").

Stability of enzyme in sample:

The information on the relatively high stability of ADA in serum varies: at least 1 day at room temperature and one week at 4 °C[16,31]; up to 1 week at room temperature without loss of activity [36]; up to 1 month at 4 °C with slight loss of activity[18]. According to our experience storage of sera for more than 5–6 days at 4 °C results in liberation of ammonia, even if bacterial contamination is avoided. This gives high blank values.

Assay System

Wavelength: 620–650 nm (optimum 628 nm[37]); light path: 1 cm.; incubation volume: 1.05 ml.; incubation temperature: 37 °C; final volume: 7.05 ml. Read against water. Also prepare a sample blank and a reagent blank.

Pipette successively in test tubes:		Reagent blank	Standard	Sample blank	Sample
Phosphate buffer	(I)	1.0 ml.	—	—	—
Buffered adenosine solution	(II)	—	—	1.0 ml.	1.0 ml.
Ammonium sulphate standard solution	(IV)	—	1.0 ml.	—	—
Sample (serum)		—	—	—	0.05 ml.
Distilled water		0.05 ml.	0.05 ml.	—	—

The addition of distilled water can be omitted without causing any appreciable error. Mix and stopper tubes with Parafilm®. Incubate for 60 min. in a 37 °C water bath.

Phenol/nitroprusside solution	(V)	3.0 ml.	3.0 ml.	3.0 ml.	3.0 ml.
Sample (serum)		—	—	0.05 ml.	—
Alkaline hypochlorite solution	(VI)	3.0 ml.	3.0 ml.	3.0 ml.	3.0 ml.

Add solution V and VI in the given order and mix the contents of the tube before pipetting into the next test tube.
Incubate for 30 min. in a 37 °C water bath. Measure extinctions against distilled water.

---

* Liquemin® is a solution of 5.0% heparin, 0.5 % phenol and 0.7% NaCl.

If any extinction value exceeds 1.000 dilute the sample 2–5 times with distilled water and measure again. With this value as a guide dilute serum accordingly with phosphate buffer (I) and repeat the assay.

Calculations

$$\text{Volume activity} = \frac{E_{Sample} - E_{Sample\ blank}}{E_{Standard} - E_{Reagent\ blank}} \times 50 \ [\text{U/l.}]; \ 37 \ ^{\circ}\text{C}$$

Alternative Method

If numerous assays have to be carried out simultaneously a different protocol is more suitable: an adenosine blank (for the whole series) is prepared instead of the sample blank described above and a corresponding number of sample blanks (one for each sample, without adenosine) are also prepared. The incubation conditions are the same.

Pipette successively into test tubes:		Reagent blank	Standard	Adenosine blank	Sample blank	Sample
Phosphate buffer	(I)	1.0 ml.	—	—	1.0 ml.	—
Buffered adenosine solution	(II)	—	—	1.0 ml.	—	1.0 ml.
Ammonium sulphate standard solution	(IV)	—	1.0 ml.	—	—	—
Sample (serum)		—	—	—	0.05 ml.	0.05 ml.
Distilled water		0.05 ml.	0.05 ml.	0.05 ml.	—	—

The addition of water can be omitted without causing any appreciable error. Mix, stopper with Parafilm® and incubate for 60 min. in a 37 °C water bath.

Phenol/nitroprusside solution	(V)	3.0 ml.	3.0 ml.	3.0 ml.	3.0 ml.	3.0 ml.
Alkaline hypochlorite solution	(VI)	3.0 ml.	3.0 ml.	3.0 ml.	3.0 ml.	3.0 ml.

Add solution V and VI in the order given and mix the contents of the tube before pipetting into the next test tube.

Incubate for 30 min. in a 37 °C water bath. Read the extinctions against water.

Solutions V and VI can be added more rapidly with this method, and less of solution II is required.

Calculations

Calculate the following differences:

$$E_{Sample} - E_{Sample\ blank} = A$$

$$E_{Adenosine\ blank} - E_{Reagent\ blank} = B$$

$$E_{Standard} - E_{Reagent\ blank} = C$$

$$\text{Volume activity} = \frac{A - B}{C} \times 50 \ [\text{U/l.}]; \ 37 \ ^{\circ}\text{C}$$

Precision of Method

By repeating the ADA assay ten times on each of 5 different serum samples the coefficients of variation ranged from 1.88% to 2.50%.

Ten simultaneous assays on a serum sample with a Beckman DU 2 spectrophotometer gave a mean value of 69.38 ± 1.46 U/l., while with a *Bausch* and *Lomb* spectrophotometer 10 assays gave a mean of 69.45 ± 1.36 U/l.

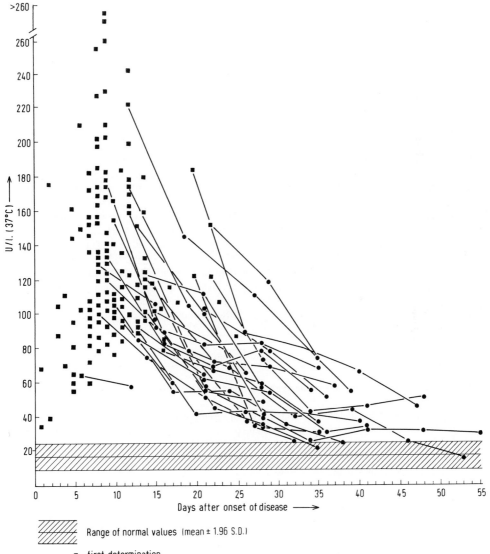

Fig. 1. ADA level in serum in typhoid fever patients (*Galanti* and *Giusti* published and unpublished results).

Normal Values

Various workers give the following normal values for human serum at 37 °C: 2.38 $\pm$ 1.43 U/l.[20]; 4.42 U/l.[24]; 5.4 $\pm$ 1.12 U/l.[18]; 5.9 — 17.6 U/l.[31]; 10.8 U/l.[16]; 12.1 U/l.[15]; 12.49 $\pm$ 2.50 U/l.[17]; 13.14 $\pm$ 4.28 U/l.[21] and 15.8 $\pm$ 3.7 U/l.[36].

With the optimum conditions of measurement described here we found[25-29] a mean value of 17.05 $\pm$ 3.75 U/l. serum (37 °C) on more than 100 normal subjects. The values measured by us on typhoid fever patients are summarized in Fig. 1. Results on various hepatic and extra-hepatic diseases with the method described here are given by *Galanti* and *Giusti*[25].

Sources of Error

Effects of drugs and other therapeutic measures: A direct effect of therapy on the serum ADA level is not known. Treatment of typhoid fever patients with antibiotics results in a slow decrease in the values.

Interference in the assay technique: With the ADA reaction liberation of ammonia from adenosine in the sample blank (or in the adenosine blank) is negligible. Neither liberation nor binding of ammonia occurs if serum and ammonia are incubated for 60 min. at 37 °C. Purified ADA[39,40] is competitively inhibited by urea and by several purine and pyrimidine compounds. The high substrate concentration used by us and the low concentration of these inhibitory compounds in serum prevents any interference.

With *Berthelot's* reaction it is essential that the reaction is carried out in a room which is free from traces of ammonia vapours. The extinction of the reagent blank measured at 630–640 nm against distilled water should be below 0.040.

The following substances which normally or occassionally occur in serum cause no significant interference in the measurement of ammonia nitrogen with the reagents of *Chaney* and *Marbach*[32]: glucosamine, citrulline, bilirubin, glutamine, haemoglobin, histidine, uracil, arginine, lysine, sulfadiazine, alanine, phenylalanine, uric acid, creatinine, salicylic acid. Further information is given by *Fawcett* and *Scott*[41] and *Fenton*[42]. If necessary, in special cases the following compounds can be added to the reaction mixture[34]: citric acid, sodium citrate, sodium chloride. On the other hand the following compounds must not be present in the assay system as they interfere with the formation of indophenol[34] under the conditions described here: glycine buffer, glycylglycine buffer, diethylbariturate-(veronal) buffer, triethanolamine buffer and, in particular, tris buffer.

Specificity of Method

Under the conditions described above the method is specific for determination of adenosine deaminase activity in serum.

As according to *Giusti* and *Galanti*[34] neither A-5-MP, nor cytidine deoxyriboside nor deoxy-CMP up to a concentration of 10 to 20 μmole/ml. in the reaction mixture interfere with the determination of ammonia nitrogen with the reagents of *Chaney* and *Marbach*[32], the method described here can be easily adapted for the assay of the activity of other deaminases. A-5-MP deaminase is raised in the serum of rodents with experimental liver necrosis, but does not change in human liver disease[22].

References

1 *N. O. Kaplan* in *S. P. Colowick & N. O. Kaplan:* Methods in Enzymology. Academic Press, New York 1951, Vol. 2, p. 473.
2 *T. G. Brady*, Biochem. J. *36*, 478 [1942].
3 *J. L. York & G. A. LePage*, Canad. J. Biochem. *44*, 331 [1966].
4 *E. J. Conway & R. Cooke*, Biochem. J. *33*, 457 [1939].
5 *E. J. Conway & R. Cooke*, Biochem. J. *33*, 479 [1939].

6 *R. M. Smillie*, Arch. Biochem. *67*, 213 [1957].
7 *H. Stern & E. Mirsky*, J. Gen. Physiol. *37*, 177 [1953].
8 *W. K. Jordan, R. March, O. B. Houchin & E. Popp*, J. Neurochem. *4*, 170 [1959].
9 *T. G. Brady & C. I. O'Donovan*, Biochem. J. *80*, 17 [1961].
10 *T. G. Brady & C. I. O'Donovan*, Comp. Biochem. Physiol. *14*, 101 [1965].
11 *O. P. Chilson & J. R. Fisher*, Arch. Biochem. Biophys. 102, 77 [1963].
12 *J. R. Fisher, P. F. Ma & O. P. Chilson*, Comp. Biochem. Physiol. *16*, 199 [1965].
13 *H. M. Kalckar*, J. biol. Chem. *167*, 445 [1947].
14 *F. B. Straub, O. Stephaneck & G. Acs*, Biochimia *22*, 118 [1957].
15 *K. Letnansky & F. Seelich*, Klin. Wschr. *36*, 826 [1958].
16 *H. Köhler & E. J. Benz*, Clin. Chem. 8, 133 [1962].
17 *M. K. Schwarts & O. Bodansky*, Proc. Soc. Exptl. Biol. Med. N. Y. *101*, 560 [1959].
18 *W. Müller-Beissenhirtz & H. Keller*, Dtsch. med. Wochenschr. *91*, 159 [1966].
19 *M. L. Schädel & F. Schlenk*, Texas Rep. Biol. Med. *6*, 176 [1948].
20 *D. M. Goldberg*, Brit. Med. J. *1*, 353 [1965].
21 *J. Krawczynski, J. Raczynska, S. Jonas, J. Wencel & K. Ilowiecka*, Clin. Chim. Acta *11*, 227 [1965].
22 *G. Giusti & B. Galanti*, Minerva Med. *56-II*, 4448 [1965].
23 *J. Raczynska, S. Jonas & J. Krawczynski*, Clin. Chim. Acta *13*, 151 [1966].
24 *G. C. Secchi, A. Rezzonico & N. Gervasini*, Enzymol. biol. clin. *8*, 67 [1967].
25 *B. Galanti & G. Giusti*, Minerva Med. *59-II*, 5867 [1968].
26 *B. Galanti & G. Giusti*, Boll. Soc. Ital. Biol. Sper. *45*, 327 [1969].
27 *B. Galanti, G. Manzillo & G. Giusti*, Giorn. Mal. Inf. Parass. *20*, 982 [1968].
28 *G. Giusti*, Pol. Arch. Med. Wewn. *44*, 524 [1970].
29 *G. Giusti, L. Castagnari, C. Gakis & B. Galanti*, Giorn. Mal. Inf. Parass. *24*, 296 [1972].
30 *B. Galanti & G. Giusti*, Boll. Soc. Ital. Biol. Sper. *42*, 1 316 [1966].
31 *R. G. Martinek*, Clin. Chem. *9*, 620 [1963].
32 *A. L. Chaney & E. P. Marbach*, Clin. Chem. *8*, 130 [1962].
33 *M. Berthelot*, Repertoire de Chimie appliqué *1*, 284 [1859].
34 *G. Giusti & B. Galanti*, Boll. Soc. Ital. Biol. Sper. *42*, 1 312 [1966].
35 *H. Karker*, Scand. J. Clin. Lab. Inv. *16*, 570 [1964].
36 *G. Giusti & C. Gakis*, Enzyme *12*, 417 [1971].
37 *A. Kaplan, A. L. Chaney, R. L. Lynch & S. Meites* in: Standard Methods of Clinical Chemistry. Academic Press, New York 1965, Vol. 5, p. 245.
38 *W. J. Caraway*, Clin. Chem. *12*, 187 [1966].
39 *G. Ronca*, Biochim. Biophys. Acta *132*, 214 [1967].
40 *G. Ronca & G. Zucchelli*, Biochim. Biophys. Acta *159*, 203 [1968].
41 *J. K. Fawcett & J. E. Scott*, J. Clin. Pat. *13*, 156 [1960].
42 *J. C. B. Fenton*, Clin. Chim. Acta *7*, 163 [1962].

Fructose-1,6-diphosphate Aldolase

UV Assay, Manuel Method

Hans Ulrich Bergmeyer and Erich Bernt

Aldolase (D-Fructose-1,6-bisphosphate D-glyceraldehyde-3-phosphate-lyase, EC 4.1.2.13) was first crystallized in 1943 by *Warburg* and *Christian*[1] from rat muscle. Yeast aldolase was purified by *Warburg*[2] in 1948 to the same specific activity as the muscle aldolase. The yeast enzyme was crystallized by *Warburg* and *Gawehn*[3] and others[4] in 1954. In contrast to aldolase from mammalian tissues, the enzymes from yeast[2,5], *Clostridium perfringens*[5] and *Aspergillus niger*[6] require divalent metal ions. Aldolase preferentially catalyses reaction (1)[7].

The enzyme is widely distributed; it is found in all cells which catabolize carbohydrate via glycolysis.

The highest aldolase activity is found in skeletal muscle (Table 1). In this tissue the enzyme accounts for ca. 10% of the total soluble protein.

Table 1. Aldolase activity in rat tissues[8] measured at 38 °C (expressed in U/g. fresh wt).

Tissue	Activity	Tissue	Activity
Skeletal muscle	55.6	Parotid gland	2.8
Brain	11.7	Stomach	2.7
Heart	11.6	Bladder	2.4
Liver	9.0	Placenta	2.2
Bone marrow	7.1	Testes	2.15
Adrenals	6.4	Lung	2.1
Kidney	5.8	Uterus	1.56
Spleen	3.6	Erythrocytes	0.67
Thyroid glands	3.6	Pancreas	0.37
Thymus	3.5	Adipose tissue	0.30
Prostate gland	3.3	Serum	0.045

The activity of the enzyme in serum is comparatively low, particularly in human serum (Table 2).

Table 2. Aldolase activity in serum[9] measured at 37 °C (expressed in U/l. serum).

Species	Activity	
	Mean	Range
Human	4.0	2.7 – 6.0
Dog	11.0	9.0 – 16.5
Horse	16.4	7.5 – 34
Hen	26.0	12.5 – 52
Ox	30.0	18 – 43
Sheep	30.0	22 – 48
Guinea pig	31.2	12.5 – 48
Rat	32.8	21 – 48
Pig	35.0	34.5 – 45
Rabbit	40.0	36 – 51
Mouse	74.5	48 – 90

Four methods are available for the assay of aldolase activity by measurements of the hydrolysis of fructose-1,6-diphosphate: determination of the alkali-labile triose phosphate formed[7]; colorimetric estimation of the triose phosphate formed by the method originally described for lactate[10]; colorimetric estimation acc. to[8,11,12]; measurement of the activity in the spectrophotometric assay of *Warburg*[13,14]. The last method is described here.

Application of Method: In biochemistry and clinical chemistry.

Principle

(1)   Fructose-1,6-diphosphate $\xrightleftharpoons{\text{aldolase}}$ Dihydroxyacetone phosphate +

D-Glyceraldehyde-3-phosphate

(2)   D-Glyceraldehyde-3-phosphate $\xrightleftharpoons{\text{TIM}^*}$ Dihydroxyacetone phosphate

(3)   Dihydroxyacetone phosphate + NADH + H$^+$ $\xrightleftharpoons{\text{GDH}^{**}}$ Glycerol-3-phosphate + NAD$^+$

The equilibrium of reaction (2) lies 96% to the right, while that of reaction (3) is completely to the right and therefore F-1,6-P$_2$ reacts quantitatively.

With an excess of TIM and GDH, reaction (1) is rate-limiting; for each mole F-1,6-P$_2$, 2 moles of NADH are oxidized. The decrease in extinction at 340, 334 or 365 nm per min. is a measure of the aldolase activity.

The pyruvate contained in the sample reacts with lactate dehydrogenase*** and NADH before the start of the assay.

Optimum Conditions for Measurements

With collidine buffer the aldolase activity of serum, blood haemolysates and muscle homogenates has a broad pH optimum between 7 and 8, while with veronal buffer it is between 8.5 and 9. Phosphate and borate inhibit the enzyme; the latter reacts with *cis*-hydroxyl groups of the substrate[15] (Fig. 1).

In the presence of cyanide crystalline aldolase from bovine liver has a pH optimum between 9.1 and 9.4 (glycylglycine-NaOH buffer) with fructose-1,6-diphosphate and between 8.1 and 8.4 with fructose-1-phosphate. With fructose-1,6-diphosphate concentrations above 5 mM the serum enzyme is saturated

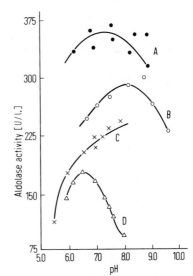

Fig. 1. pH-Activity curves for aldolase (human haemolysate 1 : 10). Final concentration of buffer: 33 mM; A) collidine buffer; B) veronal buffer; C) phosphate buffer; D) borate buffer.

---

   * Triosephosphate isomerase (D-Glyceraldehyde-3-phosphate ketol isomerase, EC 5.3.1.1).
  ** Glycerophosphate dehydrogenase (*sn*-Glycerol-3-phosphate: NAD 2-oxidoreductase, EC 1.1.1.8).
 *** Lactate dehydrogenase (L-Lactate: NAD oxidoreductase, EC 1.1.1.27).

with substrate ($K_M = 0.75$ mM). Even with greatly increased serum aldolase activity, as is found in certain pathological conditions, the rate of hydrolysis under the given assay conditions is directly proportional to time, and enzyme concentration (amount of serum). For animal sera and homogenates of liver, kidney, etc., this is only true after suitable dilution. Maximum rates are obtained with serum at 46 °C, whereas crystalline muscle aldolase is partially inactivated above 30 °C[16].

Equipment

Spectrophotometer or spectrum-line photometer suitable for precise measurements at 340, 334 or 365 nm; water bath (37 °C); stopwatch.

Reagents*

1. Collidine (2,4,6-trimethylpyridine)
   The liquid should be colourless, if not it must be redistilled; b. p. 171 °C, sp. gr. 0.917
2. Hydrochloric acid, A. R., ca. 5 N
3. Monoiodoacetic acid, pure
4. Fructose-1,6-diphosphate, F-1,6-P_2
   sodium salt, F-1,6-P_2-Na$_3$·8H$_2$O or crystalline tricyclohexylammonium salt F-1,6-P_2-($C_6H_{13}N$)$_3$·10H$_2$O. Commercial preparations, see p. 534.
5. Reduced nicotinamide-adenine dinucleotide, NADH
   disodium salt, NADH-Na$_2$. Commercial preparation, see p. 545.
6. Sodium hydrogen carbonate, A. R.
7. Glycerophosphate dehydrogenase, GDH**
   from rabbit muscle, crystalline suspension in 3.2 M ammonium sulphate solution; ≧40 U/mg. (25 °C); commercial preparation, see p. 468.
8. Triosephosphate isomerase, TIM**
   from rabbit muscle, crystalline suspension in 3.2 M ammonium sulphate solution; ≧5000 U/mg. (25 °C); commercial preparation, see p. 515.
9. Lactate dehydrogenase, LDH
   from rabbit muscle, crystalline suspension in 3.2 M ammonium sulphate solution; ≧ 550 U/mg. (25 °C); commercial preparation, see p. 481.

Purity of Reagents

The GDH, TIM and LDH preparations should contain <0.01% aldolase, relative to their respective specific activities. The F-1,6-P_2 sodium salt must contain at least 65% F-1,6-P_2, the tricyclohexylammonium salt at least 36% and they should not be contaminated with pyruvate. All other reagents should be A. R. or the purest grade available.

Preparation of Solutions

Prepare all solutions with fresh doubly distilled water.
  I. Buffer/substrate solution (4 mM F-1,6-P_2; 0.3 mM iodoacetate; 55 mM collidine buffer, pH 7.4):
     Dissolve 220 mg. F-1,6-P_2Na$_3$·8H$_2$O or 370 mg. F-1,6-P_2-tricyclohexylammonium salt ·10H$_2$O and 6.2 mg. iodoacetic acid in 90 ml. distilled water. Add 0.75 ml. collidine, mix and adjust to pH 7.4 with ca. 0.6 ml. 5 N HCl. Dilute with distilled water to 100 ml.

---

  * Complete reagent kits are available commercially, see p. 558.
 ** GDH and TIM are available commercially as a mixed crystalline suspension (*Boehringer Mannheim GmbH*), see p. 468.

II. Reduced nicotinamide-adenine dinucleotide (15 mM β-NADH):
Dissolve 25 mg. NADH-Na$_2$ and 20 mg. NaHCO$_3$ in 2 ml. distilled water.

III. Glycerophosphate dehydrogenase/triosephosphate isomerase/lactate dehydrogenase
(2 mg. GDH/ml.; 0.2 mg. TIM/ml.; 0.5 mg. LDH/ml.):
Mix the stock suspension of the enzymes and dilute accordingly with 3.2 M ammonium
sulphate solution. Protein ratio GDH : TIM : LDH ca. 10 : 1 : 2.5; activity ratio ca.
1 : 6 : 2.5.

Stability of Solutions

Store all solutions at ca. 4 °C. The buffer/substrate solution (I) and the NADH solution (II) are stable for
at least 4 weeks; the mixed enzyme suspension is stable for more than a year.

Procedure

Collection, Treatment and Stability of Sample

Collection of sample:

Collect blood without venestasis. Addition of oxalate (1 mg./ml.), citrate (1 mg./ml.), fluoride
(2 mg./ml.), heparin (0.2 mg./ml.) or EDTA (1 mg./ml.) do not affect the activity. Centrifuge
for 10 min. at 3000 g to obtain plasma or serum. Use only fresh serum or plasma free from
haemolysis.

Stability of enzyme in sample:

Aldolase is relatively thermostable in the presence of large amounts of other proteins. Blood
samples can be allowed to clot at room temperature and the serum subsequently obtained
by centrifugation. Plasma activity is identical with serum activity. The activity in serum is
stable for several hours at room temperature and for 3 to 4 days at 0 to 4 °C.

Assay System

Wavelength: 340 (Hg 334, Hg 365) nm; light path: 1 cm.; final volume: 2.76 ml.; 25 °C (constant temperature cuvette holder); read against a blank containing physiological saline instead of buffer/substrate solution (I) and without NADH solution (II) and GDH/TIM/LDH suspension (III).

Pipette into cuvettes:			Concentration in assay mixture
Buffer/substrate solution	(I)	2.50 ml.	3.6 mM F-1,6-P_2
			0.27 mM iodoacetate
			50 mM collidine
NADH solution	(II)	0.05 ml.	0.27 mM β-NADH
GDH/TIM/LDH suspension	(III)	0.01 ml.	7 μg. GDH/ml. $\geqq 0.28$ U/ml.
			0.7 μg. TIM/ml. ≥ 3.6 U/ml.
			1.8 μg. LDH/ml. ≥ 1 U/ml.
Serum		0.20 ml.	
Mix and equilibrate for 5 min. Read extinction E_1 against blank. Exactly 20 min. after the first reading measure extinction E_2 against blank. $E_1 - E_2 = \Delta E/20$ min. is used for the calculations.			

With extinction differences above 0.250 (365 nm) dilute the serum 5- to 10-fold with physiological saline.

Calculations

The calculation formula (8) on p. 313 applies. For this method the following relationships hold.

Wavelength:	*334 nm*	*340 nm*	*365 nm*
Volume activity =	56.56 $\times$ $\Delta E/20$ min.	55.47 $\times$ $\Delta E/20$ min.	101.5 $\times$ $\Delta E/20$ min. [U/l.].

Precision of Method

With values around 10 U/l. a standard deviation of 0.5 U/l. was found. The coefficient of variation is therefore ca. 5%.

Normal Values

In human serum to 6 U/l. (25 °C) according to[17]. Raised activity (over 20 U/l.) is found particularly in hepatitis[11,17], progressive muscular dystrophy[18] and myocardial infarction[19]. For a review see[20] and also p. 9 et seq.

Sources of Error

Effects of drugs and other therapeutic measures: No effects are known.

Interference in the assay: With highly active sera a large amount of the available NADH can be oxidized in the time between the addition of the serum and the first reading, with the result that insufficient NADH is available for the usual incubation period of 20 min. The reaction comes to completion before time and too low values are obtained. In this case it is necessary to read the extinction at minute intervals and to calculate the value from the linear part of the reaction curve.

Specificity of Method

Aldolase also catalyses the formation of methyltetrose phosphate, D-fructose-1-phosphate and L-sorbose-1-phosphate from dihydroxyacetone phosphate and acetaldehyde, D-glyceraldehyde or L-glyceraldehyde[21] and the formation of D-xylulose-1-phosphate and D-xylulose-1,5-diphosphate[22] from glycolaldehyde or glycolaldehyde phosphate and dihydroxyacetone phosphate. The crystalline enzyme obtained from ox liver catalyses the cleavage of fructose-1-phosphate and the synthesis of erythrulose phosphate from dihydroxyacetone phosphate to about the same extent[23], which suggest that existence of separate enzymes for these reactions[24-26] is unlikely.

Measurement of Activity in Tissues

According to[8] rat liver is simply homogenized in cold water. *Pette*[27] obtained ca. 90% of the aldolase activity in the first extract by extraction of the tissue brei from rat liver with a sucrose-triethanolamine-EDTA solution, pH 7.2.

References

1 *O. Warburg & W. Christian,* Biochem. Z. *314,* 149 [1943].
2 *O. Warburg,* Wasserstoffübertragende Fermente, p. 51, Berlin 1948.
3 *O. Warburg & K. Gawehn,* Z. Naturforsch. 9b, 206 [1954].
4 *B. S. Vanderheiden, J. O. Meinhart, R. G. Dodson & E. G. Krebs,* J. biol. Chem. *237,* 2095 [1962].
5 *R. C. Bard & I. C. Gunsalus,* J. Bacteriol. *59,* 387 [1950].
6 *V. Jagannathan & K. Singh,* Biochim. biophys. Acta *15,*138 [1954].
7 *O. Meyerhof & K. Lohmann,* Biochem. Z. *271,* 89 [1934]; *273,* 73, 413 [1934]; Naturwissenschaften *22,* 134, 220, 452 [1934].
8 *J. A. Sibley & A. L. Lehninger,* J. biol. Chem. *177,* 859 [1949].
9 *F. H. Bruns & Ch. Kirschner,* Naturwissenschaften *41,* 141 [1954].
10 *S. B. Barker & W. H. Summerson,* J. biol. Chem. *138,* 535 [1941].
11 *A. L. Dounce & G. Thannhauser-Beyer,* J. biol. Chem. *173,* 159 [1948].
12 *O. Warburg & W. Christian,* Biochem. Z. *314,* 149 [1943].
13 *G. Beisenherz, H. J. Boltze, Th. Bücher, R. Czok, K. H. Garbade, E. Meyer-Arendt & G. Pfleiderer,* Z. Naturforsch. 8b, 555 [1953].
14 *F. H. Bruns,* Biochem. Z. *325,* 156 [1954].
15 *F. H. Bruns & W. Puls,* Klin. Wschr. *32,* 656 [1954].
16 *U. S. Beck,* J. biol. Chem. *212,* 847 [1955].
17 *F. H. Bruns,* Biochem. Z. *325,* 429 [1954].
18 *A. C. Dounce & G. Thannhauser-Beyer,* J. biol. Chem. *173,* 159 [1948].
19 *O. Meyerhof, K. Lohmann & P. Schuster,* Biochem. Z. *286,* 301 [1936].
20 *W. L. Byrne & H. A. Lardy,* Biochim. biophys. Acta *14,* 495 [1954].
21 *R. J. Peanasky & H. A. Lardy,* J. biol. Chem. *233,* 365, 371 [1958].
22 *U. Kaletta-Gmünder, H. P. Wolf & F. Leuthardt,* Helv. chim. Acta *40,* 1027 [1957].
23 *F. Leuthardt, E. Testa & H. P. Wolf,* Helv. chim. Acta *36,* 227 [1952].
24 *F. C. Charalampous & G. C. Müller,* J. biol. Chem. *201,* 161 [1953].
25 *D. Pette* in: Praktische Enzymologie, Verlag Hans Huber, Bern u. Stuttgart 1968, p. 15.
26 *S. Freissli, G. Forster, G. Laudahn & I. W. Schmidt,* Klin. Wschr. *44,* 390 [1966].
27 *J. A. Sibley & A. L. Lehninger,* J. nat. Cancer Inst. *9,* 303 [1949].
28 *B. W. Volk, S. Losner & St. M. Aronson,* Amer. J. med. Sci. *232,* 38 [1956].
29 *F. H. Bruns,* Clin. chim. Acta *2,* 257 [1957].

UV Assay, Automated Method

Günter Bechtler

This method corresponds in principle to the preceding one on p. 1100, but in detail is based more on the method recommended by *Richterich*[1]. In particular the GDH/TIM concentration is increased to ensure that the linear part of the reaction curve is reached approximately 1 min. after addition of substrate.

Equipment

Eppendorf-Automat 5010 for the determination of enzyme activities by spectrophotometric assay[2].

Reagents

1. Triethanolamine hydrochloride
2. Ethylenediaminetetra-acetic acid, EDTA disodium salt, EDTA-Na$_2$H$_2$·2H$_2$O
3. Fructose-1,6-diphosphate, F-1,6-P$_2$ trisodium salt, F-1,6-P$_2$-Na$_3$·8H$_2$O; commercial preparation, see p. 534.

4. Reduced nicotinamide-adenine dinucleotide, NADH disodium salt, NADH-Na$_2$, commercial preparation, see p. 545.
5. Sodium hydroxide, A. R., 0.01 N and 1 N
6. Glycerol-3-phosphate dehydrogenase, GDH
7. Triosephosphate isomerase, TIM
8. Lactate dehydrogenase, LDH for the specification of the enzymes, see p. 1102.

Purity of Reagents, see "UV Assay", p. 1102.

Preparation of Solutions

   I. Buffer (50 mM triethanolamine, 5 mM EDTA, pH 7.5):
Dissolve 9.28 g. triethanolamine hydrochloride and 1.86 g. EDTA in ca. 800 ml. fresh, doubly distilled water, adjust to pH 7.5 with 1 N NaOH and dilute to 1000 ml. with distilled water.

  II. Reduced nicotinamide-adenine dinucleotide (3 mM β-NADH):
Dissolve 21 mg. NADH-Na$_2$ in 10 ml. 0.01 N NaOH.

 III. Glycerol-3-phosphate dehydrogenase/triose phosphate isomerase/lactate dehydrogenase:
See "UV Assay", p. 1102.

 IV. Substrate solution (30 mM F-1,6-P$_2$):
Dissolve 165 mg. of F-1,6-P$_2$-Na$_3$·8H$_2$O in 10 ml. doubly distilled water.

  V. Reagent mixture:

Number of assays	Buffer (I) ml.	NADH solution (II) ml.	GDH/TIM/LDH suspension (III) ml.
10	4.5	0.5	0.25
20	9.0	1.0	0.5
50	22.5	2.5	1.25
100	45.0	5.0	2.5

Stability of Solutions

The reagent mixture (V) can be stored for 12 hr. without any harmful effects. For other details, see p. 1103.

Procedure

Collection, Treatment and Stability of Sample, see "UV Assay", p. 1103.

Preparation of the Automat*

Programmer	Sample	Reagent dispenser	Incubator	Reagent dispenser	Photo-meter	Analogue printer
Analysis time 30 sec.	Cylinder "100" Serum 200 μl.	Cylinder "100" Reagent mixture (V) 500 μl.	15 min. 20 °C.	Cylinder "10" Substrate solution (IV) 100 μl.	Filter Hg 334 nm	Extinction 0–1 (1–2) Chart speed 1 cm./min.

Assay System

Wavelength: Hg 334 nm; light path: 1 cm.; final volume: 800 μl.; temperature: 25 °C; read against air. Reagent mixture (V) should not be brought to temperature; substrate solution (IV) should be about room temperature .

The following are automatically pipetted into reaction cuvettes:		Concentration in assay mixture
Serum Reagent mixture (V)	200 μl. 500 μl.	27 mM triethanolamine 2.7 mM EDTA; 0.2 mM NADH; 2.4 U GDH/ml.; 30 U TIM/ml.; 8 U LDH/ml.
Incubation at 25 °C (15 min.; automatic).		
F-1,6-P$_2$ solution (IV)	100 μl.	3.7 mM
Mix, 46 sec. after addition 1st reading and a total of 7 readings in 154 sec.		

If the activity is more than 40 U/l. repeat the assay with 50 μl. serum.

---

* See information leaflet B 5010 of Eppendorf Gerätebau Netheler & Hinz GmbH, Hamburg, Germany.

Calculations

The activity is determined by means of the enzyme angle[3] α (tg $\alpha = \Delta E/\Delta t$). The activity is either read off directly from the calibrated scale in U/l. or the activity of the sample is calculated from the angle on the graduated scale according the following relationships:

Sample volume:	*200 µl.*	*50 µl.*
Volume activity =	$16.7 \times$ tg α	$54.2 \times$ tg α [U/l.]

Precision of Method

The standard deviation over the normal range is ca. 0.2 U/l.

Normal Values

The data in the literature are not in agreement. According to[4] values up to 6 U/l. are normal, while according to[5] the upper limit is ca. 11 U/l. In contrast, the values of *Feissli* et al.[6] (0.5–3.1) and of *Eggstein*[7] (0.6–3.5) are in good agreement. Those of *Eggstein* were obtained with the present method.

References

1 *R. Richterich:* Klin. Chemie, Theorie und Praxis, Karger-Verlag, Basel 1965, p. 264.
2 *G. Bechtler,* Ärztl. Lab. *15,* 86 [1969].
3 *H. Weber & R. Richterich,* Klin. Wschr. *41,* 665 [1963].
4 *P. Otto, E. Schmidt & F. W. Schmidt,* Klin. Wschr. *42,* 75 [1964].
5 *E. Gautier, E. R. Gautier & R. Richterich,* Helv. päd. acta *17,* 415 [1962].
6 *S. Feissli, G. Forster, G. Laudahn, E. Schmidt & F. W. Schmidt,* Klin. Wschr. *44,* 390 [1966].
7 *M. Eggstein,* Die Ärztliche Fortbildung *3,* 185 [1969].

1-Phosphofructoaldolase

Franz Leuthardt and Hans Peter Wolf

The enzyme 1-phosphofructoaldolase, PFA (D-Fructose-1,6-bisphosphate D-glyceraldehyde-3-phosphate-lyase, EC 4.1.2.13) has so far been detected mainly in liver[1,2] and in smaller amounts in kidney and intestinal mucosa of several mammals[2,3]. At present 3 distinct separate aldolases are known, which were designated A, B, and C by *Rutter*[4]. Aldolase A is the muscle aldolase (see p. 1100), aldolase B is the liver aldolase described here. Aldolase C was mainly found in brain using immunological methods by *Rutter* and extensively purified. Aldolase A and B are distinguished by their substrate specificity. Highly purified muscle aldolase cleaves fructose-1-phosphate only slowly even at high substrate concentration; the ratio of the F-1,6-P$_2$ activity to the F-1-P activity is ca. 50:1. With the liver aldolase (aldolase B) the ratio of the activities with F-1,6-P$_2$ and F-1-P is ca. 1.5:1; with aldolase C about 10:1. A further difference between aldolases A and B is that the activity of aldolase A is reduced to about 5% on treatment with carboxypeptidase A[5], while the activity of liver aldolase under the same conditions decreases only slightly with F-1,6-P$_2$ and F-1-P[6]. PFA has been obtained in a crystalline state[6a].

All aldolases consist of 4 subunits[7]. The subunits of A and C can easily form hybrids with each other[4,8]. The relationships are similar to those with lactate dehydrogenase: for example, brain contains 5 isoenzymes of the composition a$_4$, a$_3$c, a$_2$c$_2$, ac$_3$ and c$_4$.

PFA occurs in human serum only after damage to the parenchymal cells of the liver[9-11]. Rat serum always has a certain amount of activity towards fructose-1-phosphate[2]. An enzyme with the properties of PFA has also been found in *Canavalia ensiformis*[12]. The method described here was developed by *Wolf, Forster* and *Leuthardt*[9] for measurements on serum and modified by *E. Holzer* and *Stewing*[13].

Application of Method: In clinical chemistry and in clinical biochemistry.

Principle

(1)   Fructose-1-phosphate $\xrightleftharpoons{\text{PFA}}$ Dihydroxyacetone phosphate $+$
                                                                $+$ D-Glyceraldehyde

(2)   Dihydroxyacetone phosphate $+$ NADH $+$ H$^+$ $\xrightleftharpoons{\text{GDH}^*}$ α-Glycerophosphate $+$ NAD$^+$

The equilibrium of reaction (1) lies to the left. The further conversion of dihydroxyacetone phosphate in the indicator reaction however ensures a quantitative reaction of fructose-1-phosphate. The oxidation of NADH is proportional to the amount of dihydroxyacetone phosphate formed and therefore to the PFA activity.

Optimum Conditions for Measurements

The pH optimum of the enzyme lies between pH 6.7 and 7.8[1]. The reaction is linear with time with a F-1-P concentration of 11 mM[10]. For routine determinations it is recommended to work at 25 °C; the rate of the reaction is almost doubled by increasing the temperature to 36 °C. Buffer is normally not used, but strongly icteric serum should be diluted with 50 mM triethanolamine buffer (pH 7.6).

The NADH concentration should be about 0.3 mM (this means that the photometer should be so adjusted that accurate readings are possible).

Equipment

Spectrophotometer or spectrum-line photometer suitable for measurements at 334, 340 or 365 nm.

---

* *sn*-Glycerol-3-phosphate: NAD 2-oxidoreductase, EC 1.1.1.8.

Reagents

1. Triethanolamine hydrochloride, TRA
2. Sodium hydroxide, 1 N
3. Fructose-1-phosphate, F-1-P

   disodium salt or crystalline dicyclohexyl-
   ammonium salt; commercial preparation,
   see p. 534.
4. Reduced nicotinamide-adenine dinucleotide, NADH

   sodium salt, NADH-Na$_2$; commercial
   preparation, see p. 545.

5. Sodium hydrogen carbonate, NaHCO$_3$,
   1% solution.
6. Glycerol-3-phosphate dehydrogenase,
   GDH

   crystalline suspension in ammonium sulphate
   solution; $\geqq$ 40 U/mg (25 °C); commercial
   preparation, see p. 468.

Purity of Indicator Enzyme

The GDH preparation must not contain more than the following amounts (related to the GDH activity) of contaminating enzymes: muscle aldolase $< 0.01\%$; lactate and glyceraldehyde-3-phosphate dehydrogenase $< 0.05\%$; pyruvate kinase $< 0.03\%$.

Preparation of Solutions

Prepare all solutions with quartz distilled water.
  I. Triethanolamine buffer (50 mM; pH 7.6):
     Dissolve 9.3 g. TRA in 22 ml. 1 N NaOH and dilute to 1000 ml. with distilled water.
 II. Fructose-1-phosphate (ca. 0.2 M):
     Dissolve 0.6 g. F-1-P-Na$_2$ or 0.9 g. dicyclohexylammonium salt in distilled water and make up to 10 ml.
III. Reduced nicotinamide-adenine dinucleotide (ca. 15 mM β-NADH):
     Dissolve 100 mg. NADH-Na$_2$ in 10 ml. distilled water and adjust to pH 7.6 with 1% NaHCO$_3$ solution.
 IV. Glycerol-3-phosphate dehydrogenase, GDH (2 mg. protein/ml):
     If necessary, dilute the commercially available crystalline suspension with 2 M ammonium sulphate solution.

Stability of Solutions

Store all solutions, stoppered, in a refrigerator at 0–4 °C. The GDH suspension must not be frozen. Prepare the NADH solution freshly each week; the fructose-1-phosphate solution is stable for a long period if bacterial contamination is prevented by sterilization of the bottles and removal of the solution under clean conditions. It can also be stored frozen; after thawing it must be mixed thoroughly.

Procedure

Collection, Treatment and Stability of Sample

Obtain serum in the usual way (do not allow to clot in the refrigerator). Homogenize tissue (mainly liver) in isotonic KCl (1 : 2) and use the clear supernatant fluid after centrifugation.

The samples can be stored in a refrigerator at 4 °C for at least 4 days. Serum may be stored at room temperature for at least 24 hr. without loss of activity.

Assay System

Wavelength: 340 (Hg 334, Hg 365) nm; light path: 1 cm.; final volume: 2.07 ml.; temperature: constant at 25 °C. Read against air or water.

Pipette into cuvettes		Concentration in assay mixture
Sample (serum)	1.80 ml.	0.36 mM
NADH solution (III)	0.05 ml.	
Mix and allow to stand for 15 min.; compounds contained in serum react (especially pyruvate).		
GDH suspension (IV)	0.02 ml.	ca. 10 μg./ml. $\geqq$ ca. 0.2 U/ml.
F-1-P solution (II)	0.20 ml.	ca. 20 mM
Mix; about 3 – 4 min. after the start of the reaction note the time required for an easily measurable ΔE. If the needle of a direct reading photometer has previously been adjusted to a suitable range ΔE values of 0.020 to 0.050 are satisfactory. Calculate ΔE/min.		

If the serum is very icteric, it must be diluted with triethanolamine buffer (solution I) so that $\log I_0/I = \, < 1.0$ (including the extinction of NADH). This dilution must be taken into account in the calculations.

Calculations

The PFA reaction is linear with time up to $\Delta E \approx 0.200$ at 365 nm. The calculation formula (8) on p. 313 applies. The results are obtained in mU/ml. In the assay of homogenate supernatant fluids the activity is related to mg. protein. The following relationships hold for the conditions given here:

Wavelength:	334 nm	340 nm	365 nm
Volume activity =	189 $\times$ ΔE/min.	185 $\times$ ΔE/min.	338 $\times$ ΔE/min. [U/l.]

Precision of Method

With values in the pathological range (e. g. 20 U/l.) a standard deviation of 1.36 was obtained. The coefficient of variation was 6.8%.

Normal Values

Values of 0–3 U/l. with a mean value of 1 U/l. (s = 0.9)* were found in subjects without liver damage. All values over 4 U/l. must be considered pathological.

---

* Our studies have been extended especially by *E. and F. W. Schmidt*, Medizinische Hochschule, Hannover, *E. Jenny*, Biochemisches Institut der Universität, Zürich, and *G. Forster*, Medizinische Poliklinik der Universität, Zürich. We are grateful to these authors for making their results available.

Sources of Error

No effects of drugs or other therapeutic measures are known. Interference in the assay technique is usually due to insufficient dilution of icteric serum or in the assay of homogenates to turbidity resulting from inadequate centrifugation. Too high values can be obtained if the reaction of other substrates (pyruvate) has not ceased before the start of the PFA reaction. The alcohol dehydrogenase present in liver homogenates, which can reduce the D-glyceraldehyde arising in reaction (1) with NADH to glycerol and so simulate high PFA values, may be ignored because under the above conditions insignificant amounts of D-glyceraldehyde are reduced.

If PFA activity is to be determined in protein fractions which have been obtained by ammonium sulphate fractionation[14], it is necessary to dialyse the fractions against quartz distilled water because PFA is inhibited by high concentrations of ammonium sulphate[15].

Specificity of Method

1-Phosphofructoaldolase (liver aldolase) is specifically determined; the 2% additional cleavage of substrate in the presence of an equal amount of muscle aldolase is insignificant.

References

1 *F. Leuthardt, E. Testa & H. P. Wolf*, Helv. chim. Acta *36*, 227 [1953].
2 *F. Schapira*, C. R. hebd. Séances Acad. Sci. *247*, 157 [1958].
3 *H. P. Wolf & F. Leuthardt*, Helv. chim. Acta *40*, 1033 [1957].
4 *E. Penhoet, T. V. Rajkumar & W. I. Rutter*, Proc. Natl. Acad. Sci (USA) *56*, 1275 [1966].
5 *E. Drechsler*, Fed. Proc. *16*, 174 [1957].
6 *W. S. Rutter, O. C. Richards & B. M. Woodfin*, J. biol. Chem. *236*, 3193 [1961].
   M. Mehler, J. biol. Chem. *238*,100 [1963].
6a *R. I. Peanasky & H. A. Lardy*, J. biol. Chem. *233*, 315 [1958].
   M. Göschke & F. Leuthardt, Helv. chim. Acta *46*, 1791 [1963].
7 *K. Kavahava & C. Tanford*, Biochemistry *5*, 1578 [1966].
8 *U. Rensing, A. Schmid, Ph. Christen & F. Leuthardt*, Zuschr. physiol. Chem. *348*, 1001 [1967].
9 *H. P. Wolf, G. Forster & F. Leuthardt*, a) Gastroenterologia *87*, 172 [1957]; b) Helv. physiol. Acta *15*, C 44 [1957].
10 *E. Jenny*, Dissertation, Universität Zürich, 1958.
11 *W. Rick & H. Oesterle*, Verh. dtsch. Ges. inn. Med. 1959, 692
12 *E. C. Cardini*, Enzymologia *15*, 503 [1952].
13 *E. Holzer & Ch. Stewing*, unpublished results.
14 *U. Kaletta-Gmünder, H. P. Wolf & F. Leuthardt*, Helv. chim. Acta *40*, 1027 [1957].
15 *H. P. Wolf & F. Leuthardt*, Helv. chim. Acta *40*, 237 [1957].

Glucosephosphate Isomerase

John King

Glucosephosphate isomerase, phosphoglucose isomerase or phosphohexose isomerase, PGI (D-Glucose-6-phosphate ketol-isomerase, EC 5.3.1.9) was first discovered by *Lohmann*[1] in animal tissues and yeast extracts. As an enzyme of glycolysis and pentose metabolism, PGI is widely distributed in the cytoplasmic compartment of the cell. Normally it occurs in measurable amounts in human serum[2,3] and cerebrospinal fluid[4]. Liver, muscle, bone, brain, lung and erythrocytes are rich in PGI[5]. *Bodansky*[5-10] and *Bruns*[4,11-13] were the first of many authors[14-37] to study the enzyme in various diseases.

The PGI activity is usually determined by the colorimetric assay of the fructose-6-phosphate formed from the aldose ester[2,3,38,39]. A method with glucose-6-phosphate dehydrogenase as indicator enzyme, which measures the initial rate of the reaction in the reverse direction, has been described[40-42]. The presence of glucose-6-phosphate in most fructose-6-phosphate preparations necessitates a preliminary incubation, before the addition of the sample. In addition, the reaction product of the indicator reaction (6-phosphogluconate) is an inhibitor of PGI[43].

Information on isoenzymes of human PGI has been recently published[43a,b]; heterogeneity of PGI from mouse erythrocytes and from yeast has been described[44,45].

Application of Method: In biochemistry and in clinical chemistry.

Principle

(1) $\qquad\qquad$ D-Glucose-6-phosphate $\xrightleftharpoons[\text{isomerase}]{\text{glucosephosphate}}$ D-Fructose-6-phosphate

The reaction proceeds at the same rate in either direction. The equilibrium is 60–70% to the left[1,2]. If the ketose is selectively bound as a complex with 0.1 M borate the reaction proceeds completely to the right[45]. Under optimum conditions the reaction is linear with time and amount of enzyme up to 10% isomerization of the glucose-6-phosphate. The fructose-6-phosphate is determined colorimetrically with resorcinol[47,48]. The absorption maxima occur at 405 nm and 520 nm. Fructose[38] which is obtainable in high purity, can be used as standard because fructose and its 6-phosphate ester give the same colour[40,42].

Optimum Conditions for Measurements

The activity of the back reaction (1) is only slightly dependent on the pH in the range pH 7.2 to 8.4; it is maximum in borate buffer. Under these conditions the maximum activity is given with 8 mM glucose-6-phosphate ($K_M = 0.8$ mM). The serum enzyme is stable below 45 °C. As the equilibrium concentration of glucose-6-phosphate decreases with increasing temperature[40], it is best to carry out the assay at 37 °C. Assays at 25 °C, 30 °C and 37 °C give activity ratios of 1 : 1.4 : 2.

Equipment

Spectrophotometer or photometer, preferably with monochromatic light at 405 nm or 520 nm; water bath (37 °C and 75 °C).

Reagents

1. Boric acid, A. R., H_3BO_3
2. Potassium chloride, A. R.
3. Sodium hydroxide, A. R., 0.1 N
4. D-Glucose-6-phosphate

   disodium salt, G-6-P-Na_2; commercial preparation, see p. 538.

5. Hydrochloric acid, ca. 10 N
6. Resorcinol, A. R.
7. Thiourea
8. Acetic acid, A. R.
9. D(−)-Fructose
10. Benzoic acid, A. R.

Preparation of Solutions

Prepare all solutions with doubly distilled water.

   I. Borate buffer (0.1 M; pH 7.8):

   Dissolve 6.184 g. H_3BO_3 and 7.456 g. KCl in 53 ml. 0.1 N NaOH, and dilute with distilled water to 1 000 ml.

   II. Buffer/substrate solution (ca. 7.5 mM G-6-P):

   Dissolve 3 mg. G-6-P-Na_2 in 1 ml. buffer (I).

   III. Resorcinol/thiourea solution (9 mM resorcinol; 33 mM thiourea):

   Dissolve 100 mg. resorcinol and 250 mg. thiourea in 100 ml. acetic acid.

   IV. Colour reagent:

   Dilute 50 ml. resorcinol/thiourea solution (III) with 50 ml. distilled water and 350 ml. 10 N HCl.

   V. Fructose standard solution (0.3 mM):

   Dissolve 54 mg. fructose in 1 000 ml. 0.25% benzoic acid solution.

Stability of Solutions

Store all solutions at 4 °C. The borate buffer and fructose standard are stable virtually indefinitely. The resorcinol/thiourea solution is stable for a long period in a dark bottle; it should be discarded when discolorization occurs. The buffer/substrate solution can be stored for several weeks, but it is better prepared freshly just before use. The colour reagent must be prepared freshly each day.

Procedure

Collection, Treatment and Stability of Sample

Collect blood without venestasis. Obtain serum as soon as possible; haemolysis gives high values. Varying activity is obtained with plasma[27,39]. According to [2] the enzyme in serum is stable for 24 hr. at room temperature, about 3 weeks at 4 °C and several months at −10 °C.

Assay System

Wavelength: 405 nm; light path: 1 cm.; incubation volume: 1.1 ml.; 37 °C; volume for colorimetric measurements: 10.1 ml.; read against water.

Analyse a standard containing 1.0 ml. standard solution V instead of incubation solution for each series of assays. Read this against the blank (containing distilled water instead of standard solution).

The extinction at 405 nm changes by $< 5\%$ within one hour after cooling.

Equilibrate the buffer/substrate solution to 37 °C before the assay.

Pipette into test tubes:		Test	Blank	Concentration in assay mixture
Buffer/substrate solution (II)		1.0 ml.	1.0 ml.	ca. 7 mM G-6-P
Sample (serum)		0.1 ml.	—	
Mix, incubate for exactly 30 min. in a water bath.				
Sample (serum)		—	0.1 ml.	
Colour reagent (IV)		9.0 ml.	9.0 ml.	
Mix, heat for exactly 15 min. at 75 °C (water bath) and cool under running tap water. Read extinctions. Calculate the difference between test and blank.				

With extinction differences > 0.600 repeat the assay with more dilute sample.

Standard Curve

As the development of the colour is greatly dependent on both the time and incubation temperature, a standard curve is omitted and a standard is analysed with each series of measurements.

Calculations

1 ml. Fructose standard solution contains 300 nmole fructose. If the extinction of 1 ml. standard solution is produced by 0.1 ml. serum in 30 min., this corresponds to $300 \times (1/0.1) \times (1/30) = 100$ nmole/min. per ml. $= 100$ mU/ml. $= 100$ U/l. Therefore

$$\text{Volume activity} = \frac{E_{Test} - E_{Blank}}{E_{Standard} - E_{Blank}} \times 100 \ [\text{U/l.}]; 37 \ °C$$

Precision of Method

With values around 120 U/l. $\pm$ 12.5 U/l. the coefficient of variation was 5.25%.

Normal Values

In human serum from adults 13–80 U/l. (37 °C). Higher values are found immediately after birth. Serum from cord blood contains 45–170 U/l. Cerebrospinal fluid of healthy subjects contains low but measurable activity (0.3–6.2 U/l.)[39]. Normal values in vaginal fluid have been determined by *Muir* and *Valteris*[37].

Sources of Error

Effects of drugs and other therapeutic agents: None is known.

Interference in the assay technique: Slight opalescence is corrected for by the blank and does not interfere in the assay.

Specificity of Method

Spontaneous or enzymatic hydrolysis of the substrate and product have an insignificant effect on the equilibrium of the reaction and no effect on the specificity.

Details for Measurements in Tissues

Prepare homogenates as a 10% dilution in ice-cold isotonic 0.15 M KCl solution. Dialyse overnight at 4 °C against the extraction medium. Centrifuge 1 hr. at 4 °C and 6000 g[38,50]. Store the supernatant fluid, which is used for the assay, at −15 °C. According to *Muir* and *Valteris*[37] freeze-drying causes loss of activity.

References

1   *K. Lohmann*, Biochem. Z. *262*, 137 [1933].
2   *O. Bodansky*, J. biol. Chem. *202*, 829 [1953].
3   *F. H. Bruns & K. Hinsberg*, Biochem. Z. *325*, 532 [1954].
4   *F. H. Bruns, W. Jacob & F. Weverinck*, Clin. Chim. Acta *1*, 63 [1956].
5   *O. Bodansky*, Cancer *7*, 1191 [1954].
6   *O. Bodansky*, Cancer *7*, 1200 [1954].
7   *O. Bodansky*, Cancer *8*, 1087 [1955].
8   *O. Bodansky*, Cancer *10*, 856 [1957].
9   *O. Bodansky, S. Krugman, R. Ward, M. K. Schwartz, J. P. Giles & A. M. Jacobs*, Amer. J. Dis. Child. *98*, 166 [1959].
10 *W. P. Myers & O. Bodansky*, Amer. J. Med. *23*, 804 [1957].
11 *F. H. Bruns & W. Jacob*, Klin. Wschr. *32*, 1041 [1954].
12 *F. H. Bruns*, Clin. Chim. Acta *2*, 257 [1957].
13 *F. H. Bruns, E. Dünwald & E. Noltmann*, Biochem. Z. *330*, 497 [1958].
14 *G. Schapira, J.-C. Dreyfus, F. Schapira & J. Kruh*, Amer. J. Phys. Med. *34*, 313 [1955].
15 *J.-C. Dreyfus, G. Schapira, F. Schapira & J. Demos*, Clin. Chim. Acta *1*, 434 [1956].
16 *J.-C. Dreyfus, G. Schapira & F. Schapira*, Ann. N. Y. Acad. Sci. *75*, 235 [1958].
17 *A. Siegel & R. J. Bing*, Proc. Soc. exptl. Biol. Med. *91*, 604 [1956].
18 *R. J. Bing, A. Castellanos & A. Siegel*, J. Amer. med. Ass. *164*, 647 [1957].
19 *L. P. White*, New Eng. J. Med. *255*, 984 [1956].
20 *L. P. White*, J. Nat. Cancer Inst. *21*, 671 [1958].
21 *L. White*, California Med. *90*, 1 [1959].
22 *M. C. Blanchaer, P. T. Green, J. P. MacLean & M. J. Hollenberg*, Blood *13*, 245 [1958].
23 *L. J. Israels & G. E. Delory*, Brit. J. Cancer *10*, 318 [1956].
24 *L. J. Israels, G. E. Delory, L. Hnatiuk & E. Friesen*, Blood *13*, 78 [1958].
25 *H. G. Thompson, E. Hirschberg, M. Osnos & A. Gellhorn*, Neurology *9*, 545 [1959].
26 *C. M. Pearson, W. S. Beck & W. H. Blahd*, Arch. Internal Med. *99*, 376 [1957].
27 *P. Heller, H. G. Weinstein, M. West & H. J. Zimmermann*, J. Lab. clin. Med. *55*, 425 [1960].
28 *H. Kalk, E. Schmidt, F. W. Schmidt & E. Wildhirt*, Klin. Wschr. *38*, 421 [1960].
29 *C. Gronvall*, Scand. J. clin. Lab. Invest. *13*, 29 [1961].
30 *R. Merten & H. G. Solbach*, Klin. Wschr. *39*, 222 [1961].
31 *M. West, D. Gelb, C. G. Pilz & H. J. Zimmermann*, J. Amer. med. Sci. *241*, 350 [1961].
32 *K. A. Jegatheesan & G. E. Joplin*, Brit. med. J. *1*, 831 [1962].
33 *G. E. Joplin & K. A. Jegatheesan*, Brit. med. J. *1*, 827 [1962].
34 *M. A. Schwartz, E. Greenberg & O. Bodansky*, Cancer *16*, 583 [1963].
35 *K. Hulanicka, R. Arend & M. Orlowski*, Arch. Neurol. *8*, 194 [1963].

36   *G. G. Muir*, J. chlin. Path. *19*, 378 [1966].
37   *G. G. Muir & G. J. Valteris*, J. clin. Path. *21*, 24 [1968].
38   *G. G. Glock, P. McLean & J. K. Whitehead*, Biochem. J. *63*, 520 [1956].
39   *J. E. Horrocks, J. Ward & J. King*, J. clin. Path. *16*, 248 [1963].
40   *S. E. Kahana, O. H. Lowry, D. W. Schultz, J. V. Passonneau & E. J. Crawford*, J. biol. Chem. *235*, 2 178 [1960].
41   *P. H. Werners*, Clin. Chim. Acta *7*, 550 [1962].
42   *E. A. Noltmann*, J. biol. Chem. *239*, 1 545 [1964].
43   *C. W. Parr*, Nature *178*, 1 401 [1956].
43a *J. C. Detter, P. O. Ways, E. R. Giblett, M. A. Baughan, D. A. Hopkinson, S. Povey & H. Harris*, Ann. Hum. Genet, *31*, 329 [1968].
43b *L. I. Fitch, C. W. Parr & S. G. Welch*, Biochem. J. *110*, 56P [1968].
44   *N. D. Carter & C. W. Parr*, Nature *216*, 511 [1967].
45   *Y. Nakagawa & E. A. Noltmann*, J. biol. Chem. *242*, 4 782 [1967].
46   *F. Alvarado & A. Sols*, Biochem. Biophys. Acta *25*, 75 [1957].
47   *J. H. Roe, J. H. Epstein & N. P. Goldstein*, J. biol. Chem. *178*, 839 [1949].
48   *H. G. Hers, H. Beaufays & C. de Duve*, Biochem. Biophys. Acta *11*, 416 [1953].
49   *J. King:* Practical Clinical Enzymology, D. Van Nostrand Co., Ltd., London 1965, p. 305.
50   *G. G. Muir & A. N. Fawcett*, Brit. J. Cancer *19*, 274 [1965].

Tetrahydrofolate Formylase

Wolfgang Wilmanns

Tetrahydrofolate formylase, FH_4-formylase (Formate: tetrahydrofolate ligase (ADP-forming), EC 6.3.4.3) is also called the formate activating enzyme and formyltetrahydrofolate synthetase in the literature. The enzyme was discovered in 1955 by *Greenberg, Jaenicke* and *Silverman*[1] in pigeon liver and purified from this organ. Other purifications of the enzyme were described by *Whiteley, Osborn* and *Huennekens* from *Micrococcus aerogenes*[2] in 1959, from pigeon liver by *Jaenicke* and *Brode*[3], 1961, and from erythrocytes by *Bertino, Simmons* and *Donohue* in 1962[4]. *Clostridium cylindrosporum* is particularly rich in FH_4-formylase. The enzyme was obtained in crystalline form from this micro-organism by *Rabinowitz* and *Pricer*[5,6]. The enzyme has been detected in both mature and immature white and red cells of blood and bone marrow (*Bertino* et al.[7,8]; *Wilmanns*[9]; *Wilmanns* and *Jaenicke*[10]; *Grignani, Martelli* and *Colonna*[11]). The activity is higher in the immature cells. The highest activity has been shown in myeloid cells in acute and chronic leukaemia, the lowest in erythrocytes. In red blood cells the shorter the life time of the erythrocyte population the higher the activity (*Wilmanns, Sauer* and *Gelinski*[12]).

The method described here for the determination of FH_4-formylase activity is based on the fact that the enzymatically formed 10-formyltetrahydrofolic acid is quantitatively converted to 5,10-methenyltetrahydrofolic acid.

Application of Method: In biochemistry, in biochemical haematology and in experimental tumour research.

Principle

(1)
$$HCOOH + ATP + FH_4 \underset{FH_4-formylase}{\overset{Mg^{2+},\ NH_4^+}{\rightleftharpoons}} \text{10-Formyl-}FH_4 + ADP + P_i$$

(2)
$$\text{10-Formyl-}FH_4 \xrightarrow{H^+} \text{5,10-Methenyl-}FH_4$$

The amount of 5,10-methenyltetrahydrofolic acid formed per unit time, as measured by the increase in extinction at 355 nm, is a measure of the FH_4-formylase activity.

Under the usual assay conditions the equilibrium of the reaction lies far to the right. With excess of 10-formyl-FH_4 and ADP the reaction can also proceed in the opposite direction. *Clostridia* fermenting purine can in this way cleave 10-formyl-FH_4 to formic acid and tetrahydrofolic acid as a source of energy. With excess formic acid, tetrahydrofolic acid and ATP the reaction proceeds quantitatively to the right. It can therefore be used for the quantitative assay of the participating substrates (*Rabinowitz* and *Pricer*, Jr.[13]). ATPases present in cells can interfere with the assay, but this interference can be reduced if phosphoenolpyruvate and pyruvate kinase are added for regeneration of ATP.

Optimum Conditions for Measurements

The reaction has no clear pH optimum. *Scrimgeour* and *Huennekens*[14] determined the activity of the enzyme obtained from chicken liver at pH 7.5; *Rabinowitz* and *Pricer* Jr.[13] determined the activity of the crystalline enzyme from *Cl. cylindrosporum* at pH 8.0. The study of blood cell lysates is carried out under optimum conditions at pH 7.0[9,16]. The Michaelis constants for the substrates determined by various workers on enzyme preparations from bacteria and mammalian cells are given in Table 1.

Table 1. K_M Values for the substrates of tetrahydrofolate formylase.

Substrate:	Formate	ATP	FH_4
M. aerogenes	25 mM	0.11 mM	1.1 mM
Cl. cylindrosporum	6.7 mM	0.29 mM	0.52 mM
Pigeon liver	1.2 mM	0.11 mM	1.6 mM
Leucocytes	5 mM	0.52 mM	1 mM
Erythrocytes	2.5 mM	0.46 mM	0.3 mM

In addition to the substrates already mentioned the enzyme requires divalent cations, preferably Mg^{2+}, and monovalent cations, NH_4^+ or K^+. Mg^{2+} can be replaced by Mn^{2+} and Ca^{2+}.

As products of reaction (1) ADP and orthophosphate are inhibitors of formate activation, therefore the incubation should be carried out in tris buffer rather than phosphate buffer. The enzyme is also inhibited by p-chloromercuribenzoate, p-mercuribenzoate and $HgCl_2$[14].

To exclude interference in the assay due to reduced pyridine nucleotides, especially in the simultaneous assay of the enzyme methylene-tetrahydrofolate dehydrogenase, the measurements are carried out at 355 nm rather than at the absorption maximum of 350 nm.

The optimum temperature is 41 °C; at 33 °C and 46 °C the enzyme still has 75% of the activity at the optimum temperature.

Equipment

Constant temperature water bath (37 °C); stopwatch; spectrophotometer suitable for accurate measurements at 355 nm. Hydrogenation apparatus for the preparation of tetrahydrofolic acid.

Reagents

For reagents for preparation of sample, see chapter on Dihydrofolate Reductase, p. 666.

1. Tris-hydroxymethyl-aminomethane, tris
2. Magnesium chloride, A. R. $MgCl_2 \cdot 6 H_2O$
3. 2-Mercaptoethanol
4. Ethylenediaminetetra-acetate magnesium-dipotassium salt, $EDTA\text{-}MgK_2 \cdot 2 H_2O$
5. Ammonium chloride, A. R., anhydrous
6. Adenosine-5'-triphosphoric acid, ATP disodium salt, $ATP\text{-}Na_2H_2 \cdot 3 H_2O$; commercial preparation, see p. 527.
7. Pyruvate kinase
   from rabbit muscle, crystalline suspension in 3.2 M ammonium sulphate solution, $\geqq 150$ U/mg. (15 °C); commercial preparation, see p. 509.
8. Ammonium sulphate, A. R.
9. Phosphoenolpyruvate potassium salt, $PEP\text{-}K \cdot H_2O$; commercial preparation, see p. 548.
10. Sodium formate, A. R.
11. DL-Tetrahydrofolic acid
    Commercial preparation, see p. 552. Because of the ease with which it is oxidized it is recommended to prepare it by the method of[3, 15].
12. Hydrochloric acid, A. R., 2 N
13. Potassium hydroxide, A. R., 1 N and 4 N
14. Petroleum ether

Preparation of Solutions

Prepare all solutions with doubly distilled water. For solutions for preparation of samples, see chapter on "Dihydrofolate Reductase", p. 666.

  I. Tris buffer (1 M; pH 7.0):
     Dissolve 24.3 g. tris in 100 ml. distilled water. Mix 50 ml. of this solution with 45 ml. 2 N HCl and add more 2 N HCl to give pH 7.0. Dilute to 100 ml. with distilled water.
  II. 2-Mercaptoethanol (0.3 M):
     Dilute 1 ml. 2-mercaptoethanol with 45.5 ml. distilled water.
  III. $KHCO_3$/2-mercaptoethanol (50 mM/30 mM):
     Dissolve 50 mg. $KHCO_3$ and 1 ml. 0.3 M 2-mercaptoethanol in distilled water and make up to 10 ml.
  IV. Magnesium chloride (0.2 M):
     Dissolve 4.07 g. $MgCl_2 \cdot 6 H_2O$ in distilled water and make up to 100 ml.
  V. EDTA (0.1 M; pH 7.4):
     Dissolve 4.267 g. $EDTA\text{-}MgK_2 \cdot 2 H_2O$ in distilled water, adjust to pH 7.4 with 1 N KOH and dilute to 100 ml. with distilled water.
  VI. Ammonium chloride (0.2 M):
     Dissolve 1.07 g. NH_4Cl in distilled water and make up to 100 ml.
  VII. Adenosine-5'-triphosphate (50 mM):
     Suspend 121 mg. $ATP\text{-}Na_2H_2 \cdot 3 H_2O$ in distilled water, bring into solution by neutralization with 4 N KOH and dilute to 4 ml. with distilled water.
  VIII. Phosphoenolpyruvate (0.1 M):
     Dissolve 82.4 mg. $PEP\text{-}K \cdot H_2O$ in 4 ml. distilled water; store at 0 °C.
  IX. Pyruvate kinase (0.5 mg. protein/ml.):
     Dilute 0.01 ml. stock suspension (10 mg./ml.) with 3.2 M $(NH_4)SO_4$ solution to 0.2 ml.
  X. Formate (0.2 M):
     Dissolve 1.36 g. sodium formate in distilled water and make up to 100 ml.
  XI. DL-Tetrahydrofolic acid (13 mM):
     Dissolve 6 mg. tetrahydrofolic acid in 1 ml. 50 mM $KHCO_3$ solution (containing 30 mM 2-mercaptoethanol).

Stability of Solutions

Prepare the tetrahydrofolic acid solution immediately before use. All other solutions are stable for several months at 0–4 °C.

Procedure

The assay of FH_4-formylase activity in cytolysates of blood and bone marrow cells is described here.

Collection, Treatment and Stability of Sample

Isolation and cytolysis of leucocytes and bone marrow cells is described in the chapter "Dihydrofolate Reductase", p. 666.

Isolation of erythrocytes:

Suck of the upper erythrocyte layer together with the leucocyte pellet. Centrifuge the remaining erythrocytes for 10 min. at 480 g in a refrigerated centrifuge (Sorvall) and remove the supernatant fluid over the thick, packed erythrocyte sediment. Wash the erythrocytes 3 times in calcium-free Ringer phosphate-glucose solution. Count the erythrocytes in the final suspension in a counting chamber and determine the contamination with leucocytes. Suspend the final erythrocyte sediment in 1 mM potassium phosphate buffer (pH 7.5), corresponding to a concentration of 10^9 erythrocytes per ml. and haemolyse by standing for an hour at 0 °C. Finally, sediment the cell stroma by centrifugation for 30 min. at 38000 g in a refrigerated centrifuge. Use the supernatant fluid for the assay.

Stability of enzyme in cytolysates:

The determination of activity must be made within 4 hr. after the completion of cell isolation, otherwise there is large loss of activity. Stabilization of the enzyme in the cytolysate for 24 hr. can be achieved by addition of 100 mg. glucose per ml. cytolysate.

Assay System

Incubation volume: 1 ml.; incubation temperature: 37 °C; wavelength: 355 nm; light path: 1 cm.; final volume: 2 ml.; read against 0 min. value. Prepare a blank containing distilled water instead of sample for each series of measurements.

If several assays are to be carried out it is recommended to prepare a "reagent mixture" (sufficient for 10 assays). Just before use, pipette:

Tris buffer	(I)	1.0 ml.
Mercaptoethanol solution	(II)	1.0 ml.
MgCl₂ solution	(IV)	0.5 ml.
EDTA solution	(V)	1.0 ml.
NH₄Cl solution	(VI)	0.5 ml.
ATP solution	(VII)	0.5 ml.
Phosphoenolpyruvate solution	(VIII)	0.5 ml.
Formate solution	(X)	0.5 ml.
		5.5 ml.

Pipette into a test tube:			Concentration in assay mixture
Reagent mixture		0.55 ml.	0.1 M tris 30 mM mercaptoethanol 10 mM $MgCl_2$ 10 mM EDTA 10 mM NH_4Cl 2.5 mM ATP 5 mM PEP 10 mM formate
Pyruvate kinase	(IX)	0.01 ml.	2.5 μg./ml. $\cong$ 0.375 U/ml.
Tetrahydrofolic acid	(XI)	0.10 ml.	13 mM
Sample (cytolysate)		0.05 ml.	ca. 0.5×10^7 cells

Mix, layer with petroleum ether and incubate in dark. After 0 min. and 60 min. add 0.4 ml. from each tube to 1.6 ml. 1 N $HClO_4$, allow to stand for at least 15 min. and centrifuge. Pour the supernatant into cuvettes and read the extinction of the 60 min. tube against the 0 min. tube.

The $\Delta E/60$ min. value, read against the 0 min. value, should not exceed 0.800, otherwise after deproteinization dilute the supernatant fluid accordingly.

Calculations

From the increase in extinction $\Delta E/60$ min. (measured against the 0 min. value) subtract the $\Delta E/60$ min. of the blank (0.069 ± 0.037). The corrected $\Delta E/60$ min. value is used for the further calculations. The extinction coefficient for 355 nm is 25.0 cm.^{2}/μmole. With 0.5×10^7 cells and use of 0.4 ml. of the incubation mixture in 2.0 ml final volume for the FH_4 formylase assay, the activity is given by:

$$(\Delta E/60 \text{ min}) \frac{2 \times 10^{10}}{60 \times 25 \times 0.5 \times 10^7 \times 0.4} = 6.67 \times \Delta E/60 \text{ min. } [U/10^{10} \text{ cells}]$$

The enzyme activity can also be related to mg. protein, but for clinical and biochemical purposes the cell count is the more suitable system of reference. In the analysis of haemolysates the enzyme activity can also be related to the haemoglobin content.

Normal Values

The activities given in Table 2 were found in bone marrow cells and in peripheral leucocytes[16].
The younger the erythrocytes and the higher the reticulocyte[12] count the higher the activity of the enzyme in the erythrocytes. A strict correlation between the reticulocyte count and the activity of tetrahydrofolate

Table 2. Activities of tetrahydrofolate formylase in different blood and bone marrow cells.

Type of cells	N	U/10^{10} cells ($\bar{x} \pm s$)
Normal bone marrow cells	16	0.85 ± 0.43
Normal leucocytes (peripheral blood)	29	0.37 ± 0,25
Acute leukaemia (peripheral blood)	50	2.24 ± 0.85
Acute leukaemia, marrow cells	14	2.28 ± 0.96
Chronic myeloid leukaemia (peripheral blood)	19	1.58 ± 0.60
Acute myeloblastic crisis in chronic myeloid leukaemia (peripheral blood)	5	2,78 ± 0.95
Lymphadenosis (peripheral blood)	14	0.67 ± 0.33

N = number of cases; $\bar{x}$ = mean; s = standard deviation.

formylase, however, occurs only in those patients who receive no therapy specifically affecting the erythro-poesis.

Sources of Error

Effects of drugs and other therapeutic measures: On treatment of leukaemia with cytostatic drugs the activity of tetrahydrofolate formylase decreases with improvement of the differential blood picture. In patients treated with 6-mercaptopurine (Purinethol®) a decrease in enzyme activity can be demonstrated before any recognizable improvement in the blood picture. Therefore determination of tetrahydrofolate formylase activity is suitable for judging whether leukaemic cells are sensitive to 6-mercaptopurine[12].

Interference in the assay technique: Interference by ATPases in crude homogenates is compensated for by the addition of an ATP-regenerating system (phosphoenolpyruvate and pyruvate kinase) to the incubation mixture.
Interference can occur when other enzymes are present in the homogenates and cytolysates which react with 10-formyltetrahydrofolic acid. A most likely candidate is formyltetrahydrofolate deacylase[14]. This enzyme could not be detected in cytolysates of erythrocytes.
10-Formyltetrahydrofolic acid can be formed by enzyme reactions other than the formylase reaction, in which biologically bound formyl groups are liberated. Sources of such formyl groups are purines and the amino acids, serine and histidine. In cytolysates of human blood and bone marrow cells no interference in the tetrahydrofolate formylase reaction could be detected.

Other Methods of Determination of Activity

According to *Goldthwait* and *Greenberg*[18] and *Jaenicke* and *Brode*[3] the activity of tetrahydrofolate formylase can also be determined by fixation of formate-[^{14}C] in the anhydrocitrovorum factor (ACF; 5,10-methenyl-FH$_4$). A portion of the supernatant fluid after deproteinization is evaporated in open dishes. The free formic acid distills off, while the formate-[^{14}C] fixed into the ACF remains on the dish and can be counted directly. The measured counts together with the known specific radioactivity of the formate-[^{14}C] solution is a measure of the enzyme activity.

Appendix

Preparation of Tetrahydrofolic Acid

Method of *O'Dell*[15], modified by *Jaenicke* and *Brode*[3]

Reagents

Folic acid, for biochemical purposes

Acetic acid, 99–100%, A. R.

Platinum oxide, PtO$_2$ (about 81% Pt, hydrogenation catalyst)

Diethyl ether, A. R., peroxide-free

Potassium hydrogen carbonate, A. R.

Method

Suspend 30 mg. platinum oxide in a round-bottomed flask with 10 ml. acetic acid and 10 glass beads (diameter 3–4 mm). Reduce the platinum in a hydrogenation apparatus with shaking at 25 °C and atmospheric pressure until no further hydrogen is taken up and black flecks of platinum precipitate (about 20 min.). Add 100 mg. folic acid, and with continuous shaking reduce the folic acid (about 2 hr.). As it is reduced it goes into solution. Rapidly centrifuge off the platinum from the practically colourless solution and wash with peroxide-free diethyl ether. Wash the light cream-coloured tetrahydrofolic acid 3 times with ether and dry *in vacuo*. Because of the ease with which folic acid is oxidized, the washing and centrifugation must be carried out as rapidly as possible. The dry powder is stable at −15 °C in a desiccator in the dark for several months.

References

1 *G. R. Greenberg, L. Jaenicke & M. Silverman*, Biochim. biophys. Acta *17*, 589 [1955].
2 *H. R. Whiteley, M. J. Osborn & F. M. Huennekens*, J. biol. Chem. *234*, 1538 [1959].
3 *L. Jaenicke & E. Brode*, Biochem. Z. *334*, 108 [1961].
4 *J. R. Bertino, B. Simmons & D. M. Donohue*, J. biol. Chem. *237*, 1314 [1962].
5 *J. C. Rabinowitz & W. E. Pricer jr.*, Fed. Proc. *17*, 293 [1958].
6 *J. C. Robinowitz & W. E. Pricer fr.*, J. biol. Chem. *237*, 2898 [1962].
7 *J. R. Bertino, A. Alenty, B. W. Gabrio & F. M. Huennekens*, Clin. Res. Proc. *8*, 206 [1960].
8 *J. R. Bertino, R. Silber, M. Freeman, A. Alenty, M. Albrecht, B. W. Gabrio & F. M. Huennekens*, J. clin. Invest. *42*, 1899 [1963].
9 *W. Wilmanns*, Klin. Wschr. *39*, 884 [1961].
10 *W. Wilmanns & L. Jaenicke*, Klin. Wschr. *41*, 1077 [1963].
11 *F. Grignani, M. Martelli & A. Colonna*, Hämatologica *48*, 613 [1963].
12 *W. Wilmanns, H. J. Sauer & P. Gelinsky*, Blut, *19*, 457 [1969].
13 *J. C. Rabinowitz & W. E. Pricer jr.*, J. biol. Chem. *229*, 321 [1957].
14 *K. G. Scrimgeour & F. M. Huennekens* in Hoppe-Seyler/Thierfelder: Handb. der Physiol u. pathol.-chem. Analyse. 16th. edn., 6. Vol., Part B, p. 192, Springer-Verlag 1966.
15 *B. L. O'Dell, J. M. Vandenbelt, E. S. Bloom & J. J. Pfiffner*, J. Amer. Chem. Soc. *69*, 250 [1947].
16 *W. Wilmanns*, Zschr. ges. exp. Med. *147*, 154 1968].
17 *W. Wilmanns*, Dtsch. med. Wschr. *88*, 900 [1963].
18 *D. A. Goldthwait & G. R. Greenberg* in *S. P. Colowick & N. O. Kaplan:* Methods in Enzymology Vol. II, p. 504, Academic Press, New York 1955.

Index

Index

The key words are arranged alphabetically without regard to prefixes such as D, L, (+), (−), α, β. Where necessary reference to other synonyms is given.

A

Abbreviations
– biochemical reagents   417
– list of   XXXIV
Absorption coefficient
– Bunsen's   253
Absorption curve
– dinitrophenylhydrazones
– – of pyruvate and 2-oxoglutarate   184
– general   182
– NAD and NADH   104, 184
Absorption photometry   180
ABTS   1212, 1215
Acceptor activity of tRNA
– determination of   1894
Acetaldehyde
– determination with
– – alcohol dehydrogenase   1506
– – aldehyde dehydrogenase   1509
– normal values in blood   1508
Acetate
– concentration in animal tissues   2293
– determination with
– – acetate kinase and hydroxylamine   1528
– – acetate kinase, PTA, CS and MDH   1520
– – acetyl-CoA synthetase and sulphanilamide
  1532
– – preceding indicator reaction;
  principle and theory   113
– distillation according to *Bartley*   1525
– normal values   1527
Acetate kinase
– assay of activity   425
– characteristics and commercial preparations
  425
– relative rates of reaction with nucleoside
  triphosphates   2081
Acetoacetate
– concentration in animal tissues   2291
– determination   1840
– normal values   1843
– stability in sample   1842
Acetoacetyl-CoA

– determination
– – other methods   2004
– – with HOADH   2001
– preparation with diketene from CoASH   1970
N-Acetylaspartate
– concentration in animal tissues   2285
Acetylcarnitine
– concentration in animal tissues   2288
– determination   1764
Acetylcholine
– determination   1819
– electrophoretic separation from choline   1821
– hydrolysis   1822
– normal values   1823
Acetylcholinesterase, see cholinesterase
Acetyl-CoA
– characteristics and commercial preparations
  524
– concentration in animal tissues   2288
– determination
– – catalytic assay with PTA   1975
– – fluorimetric with CS and MDH   1993
– – fluorimetric with oxoglutarate dehydrogenase
  and PTA   1994
– – other methods   1992
– – radiochemical   1994
– – UV-assay   1988
– normal values   1991, 1994
N-Acetyl-D-glucosamine
– characteristics and commercial preparations
  524
Acetyl groups
– determination in proteins   1640
Acetylhydroxamic acid
– absorption curve of ferric complex   1529
Acetyl phosphate
– characteristics and commercial preparations
  524
– determination   1538
Acetylpyridine-adenine dinucleotide
– characteristics and commercial preparations
  525
– reduced, extinction coefficient   1595
S-Acetyl-N-succinyl-cysteamine

S-Acetyl-N-succinyl-cysteamine
– extinction coefficient　1972
Acid phosphatase
– see phosphatase, acid
Aconitase
– in progressive muscular dystrophy　38
Acrylyl-CoA
– determination　2005
Acylcarnitines
– concentration in animal tissues　2289
– determination
– – acetylcarnitine　1764
– – long-chain (C > 12)　1769
– – other methods　1770
– – short-chain ($C_3 - C_{10}$)　1767
Acyl-CoA
– determination
– – colorimetric assay　2010
– – fluorimetric　2015
Acyl-CoA dehydrogenase
– isolation　2014
Acylphosphate:D-glucose-6-phosphotransferase
– for determination of glucose　1222
– Michaelis constants　1223
Additional (side) activities
– definition　108
Additive models　343
Adenine
– determination　1909
– normal values　1915
Adenosine
– cleavage by nucleoside phosphorylase　1934
– determination　1919
– extinction coefficient　1921
Adenosine deaminase
– assay of activity
– – colorimetric　1092
– – UV-assay　426
– characteristics and commercial preparations
　426
– importance in clinical chemistry　1092
– in serum of patients with typhus　1097
– normal values　1098
Adenosine-5'-diphosphate
– characteristics and commercial preparations
　525
– content in
– – animal tissues　2295
– – rat heart　2295
– – rat liver　2295

– – skeletal muscle　2295
– determination
– – with MK, PGK and GAPDH　2078
– – with PK and LDH　2127
– normal values in blood　2131
– stability in blood　166
Adenosine-5'-diphosphoglucose
– determination　2204
– see also ADP-glucose
Adenosine-3':5'-monophosphate (cyclic)
– characteristics and commercial preparations
　526
– concentration in animal tissues　2296
– determination with
– – FDPase by AMP inhibition　2144
– – other methods　2136
– – protein binding test　2137
– normal values　2142
A-3:5-MP-binding protein
– isolation　2143
Adenosine-5'-monophosphate
– characteristics and commercial preparations
　526
– concentration in
– – animal tissues　2086, 2296
– – rat heart　2086
– – rat liver　2086, 2296
– – rat skeletal muscle　2086, 2296
– determination　2088, 2127
– normal values in blood　2131
– stability in blood　166
Adenosine-5'-nucleotides　2088
Adenosine phosphates
– determination　2132
Adenosine-5'-triphosphate
– characteristics and commercial preparations
　527
– concentration in
– – animal tissues　2293
– – liver in viral hepatitis　8
– – rat heart　2294
– – rat liver　2293
– – rat skeletal muscle　2294
– determination with
– – AK, AGT and G6P-DH　2080
– – formyltetrahydrofolate synthetase　2110
– – HK & G6P-DH　2101
– – luciferase　2112
– – other methods　2109
– – PGK & GAPDH　2097

The key words are arranged alphabetically without regard to prefixes such

Adenosine-5′-triphosphate
– normal values 2100
– stability in blood 166
Adenosine triphosphatase (ATPase)
– in blood diseases 52
– in muscular dystrophy
– – in muscle 38
Adenylate deaminase
– in progressive muscular dystrophy 38
Adenylate kinase
– assay of activity 486
– characteristics and commercial preparations 486
– see also myokinase
2′-Adenylic acid
– hydrolysis by myo-inositol-1-phosphatase 1340
ADP-glucose
– see adenosine-5′-diphosphoglucose
ADP-glucose pyrophosphorylase
– isolation 2207
Age dependence
– of normal range 388, 731, 756
– of experimental values 384, 731, 756
D-Alanine
– determination 1686
L-Alanine
– concentration in animal tissues 2284
– determination with
– – alanine dehydrogenase 1679
– – GPT and LDH 1682
– normal values 1681
Alanine dehydrogenase
– assay of activity 427
– characteristics and commercial preparation 427
Alcohol
– determination with
– – ADH and APAD 1502
– – ADH and NAD 1499
Alcohol dehydrogenase
– assay of activity 429
– characteristics and commercial preparations 428
– equilibrium constants 428
– in acute hepatitis 15
– specificity 429
Aldehyde dehydrogenase
– isolation from yeast 1513
Aldolase
– assay of activity 430
– characteristics and commercial preparations 430

– in blood diseases 54
– in muscular dystrophy
– – in muscle 38
– – in serum 38
– in serum of rats after exercise 8
– in various myopathies 43
– stability in serum 168
Aldolase, from liver
– for determination of F-1-P 1308
– isolation 1312
Allitol
– reaction with sorbitol dehydrogenase 572
Allowable limits of error, A. L. E. 378
Alkaline phosphatase
– see phosphatase, alkaline normal values
Altronate dehydrogenase
– isolation 1302
Altrose
– oxidation by GOD 1212
Amine oxidase
– isolation 1747
Amino acid arylamidase
– for the diagnosis of kidney diseases 62
– in diseases of kidney and urinary tract 62
– in human urine 67
– in structures of human kidneys 65
– stability in serum 169
Amino acid arylamidases
– assay of activity 958
– normal values 962
Amino acid decarboxylases
– preparation 1668
– reaction products 1663
D-Amino acid oxidase
– apoenzyme, preparation 2184
– assay of activity 431
– characteristics and commercial preparations 431
– isolation 1654
– rate of oxidation of D-amino acids 1648
Amino acids
– concentrations in animal tissues 2284
D-Amino acids
– determination
– – manometric 1648
– – micro methods 1653
L-Amino acids
– determination
– – manometric 1662
– – colorimetric with fluorodinitrobenzene 1669

as D, L, (+), (−), α, β. Where necessary reference to other synonyms is given.

L-Amino acids, determination
– – tRNA loading test, isotope dilution   1656
γ-Aminobutyric acid
– determination   1690
– normal values   1694
Aminopeptidases and amino acid arylamidases
– activity optima   952, 953
– classification   952, 953
– general information   950
– occurrence   952, 953
– purification   952, 953
– substrates   952, 953
Aminotransferase
– apoenzyme, isolation   2198
Ammonia
– concentration in animal tissues   2286
– determination   1802
Ampoule divers   243
Amylase
– in honey   74
– in milk   74
– in production of grain   84
α-Amylase
– assay of activity   432
– characteristics and commercial preparations
   432
– for the quality control of plant products   84
– general information   885
– measurements
– – after electrophoretic separation   909
– – by end-point determination on paper   903
– – of degradation products, maltose and glucose
   890
– – of iodine-starch-complex   898
– – of reducing groups   885
– – with coloured insoluble substrates   894
– normal values   888, 897, 902, 908
– stability in serum   168
β-Amylase
– assay of activity   433
– characteristics and commercial preparations
   433
Amylo-1,6-glucosidase
– assay of activity   434
– characteristics and commercial preparations
   434
– for determination of glycogen   1127
Amylose
– preparation   902
Analytical mixture

– transport in automatic analysers   207
Aneurin pyrophosphate
– see thiamine pyrophosphate
Angiotensinase
– assay of activity   964
– normal values in serum   966
Anti-oxidants
– enzymatic determination in foodstuff chemistry
   75
Apoaminotransferase
– preparation   2198
Apparatus
– for automation of analysis   205 et seq.
– for electrophoresis   262 et seq.
– for luminescence measurements   2114
– for microtechniques   230 et seq.
– for photometry   184 et seq.
– for radiometry   283 et seq.
L-Arabinose
– characteristics and commercial preparations
– determination with
– – L-arabinose isomerase   1350
– oxidation by Gal-DH   453
L-Arabinose isomerase
– isolation   1352
L-Arginine
– determination
– – colorimetric assay with fluorodinitrobenzene
   1669
– – manometric   1662
Arylesterases
– assay with
– – β-naphthylpropionate as substrate   810
– – phenylacetate as substrate   807
– general information   860
– normal values   809, 813
Arylsulphatase
– assay of activity   435
– characteristics and commercial preparations
   435
– in muscular dystrophy   38
– in serum in pregnancy   58
L-Asparagine
– determination   1696
– normal values   1700
L-Asparaginase
– assay of activity   435
– characteristics and commercial preparations   435
D-Aspartate
– determination, possible method of   1700

The key words are arranged alphabetically without regard to prefixes such

L-Aspartate
– concentration in animal tissues   2284
– determination
– – manometric   1662
– – UV-assay   1696
– electrophoretic separation from citrate   1998
– normal values   1700
L-Aspartate decarboxylase   1663
Assessment
– longitudinal   383
– transverse   391
Asymmetry (in statistics)   326
Automatic analysers
– commercial   221
– fast analysers   213
– technique   205
Automation
– continual flow working   203
– discontinuous working   203
– of analysis   202
– serial and parallel analysis   203
Auxiliary enzyme   109
Auxiliary reaction   109
Azocasein
– preparation   1005
– substrate for proteinases   1000

B

Bartley, distillation flask   1525
Benzoyl-CoA
– determination   2008
Bile acids
– determination   1886
– normal values   1889
Biochemical reagents
– control of   158 et seq.
– manufacturers and suppliers   559
– stability of   164 et seq.
– storage of   158 et seq.
Biological manometry   248
Biuret method for protein   174
Blood
– calculation of proportion in tissue   2107
– mailing of samples on paper   167
Brodie solution   253
Buffer capacity   257
Bunsen, absorption coefficient   253
Burettes
– for micro-analysis   232

Butyleneglycol
– reaction with sorbitol dehydrogenase   1323
Butyraldehyde
– oxidation by aldehyde dehydrogenase   1513
– reduction by ADH   1508
Butyryl-CoA
– determination
– – colorimetric   2010
– – fluorimetric   2015

C

Caeruloplasmin
– isoenzymes   11
Calculation of experimental results   308 et seq.
Capillary pipettes   232
Carbamates with insecticide activity
– determination   2249, 2257
Carbamoyl phosphate
– characteristics and commercial preparations
  528
– determination   1749
Carbonic anhydrase
– in nephron of human kidneys   64
Carboxypeptidase A
– assay of activity   437, 989, 993
– characteristics and commercial preparations
  436, 437
– normal values   992, 996
Carboxypeptidase B
– assay of activity   996
– normal values   998
Carboxypeptidases
– effectors   987, 988
– general information   986
– occurrence   987, 988
– pH-optima   987, 988
– purification   987, 988
– substrate optima   987, 988
Carnitine
– concentration in animal tissues   2290
– determination
– – DTNB method   1762
– – thiokinase method   1758
Carnitine acetyltransferase
– assay of activity   438
– characteristics and commercial preparations
  438
Cartesian diver   243

Catalase
– assay of activity
– – other methods   680
– – titrimetric   678
– – UV-assay   439, 674
– characteristics and commercial preparations
   438, 439
– general information   673
– in cereal products   74
– in milk   73
– kinetics   674
– normal values in blood   677
– units   681
Catalytic assays   132
CDP-glucose
– see cytidine-5′-diphosphoglucose
CDP-glucose dehydratase
– isolation   2212
Cell disintegration   396
Cell fractionation   407
Cell suspensions, heterogeneous   399
Cellular enzymes   7
Cellulase, crude enzyme
– preparation   1142
Cellulose
– determination by measurements of
– – of glucose formed   1139
– – of insoluble residue   1132
– – of soluble products   1137
– normal values   1136
Chitosamine,
– see D-glucosamine
Choice of probands
– for determination of normal range   386
β-Chlorolactate
– oxidation by LDH   1468
Chloroplasts
– fraction of total activity   412
– isolation   411
Cholesterol
– determination   1890
– esterified   1890
– normal values   1893
Cholesterol oxidase
– assay of activity   440
– characteristics and commercial preparations   440
Choline
– determination   1819
– electrophoretic separation from acetyl choline
   1821

– normal values   1823
Cholinesterase
– inhibition by insecticides   2249
– in liver diseases
– – acute hepatitis   15, 26
– – chronic hepatitis and cirrhosis   27
– – hepatic obstruction   26
– – in serum   26, 27
– – liver tumours   23, 27
– – obstructive jaundice   22
– – toxic liver damage   20
– isoenzymes   11
– stability in serum   169
Cholinesterases
– assay methods
– – colorimetric   840
– – electrometric   838
– – manometric   835
– assay of activity of AChE
– – in erythrocytes   844
– – in serum   845
– – in whole blood   843
– assay of activity of PChE
– – in serum   846
– determination of dibuccaine number and
   fluoride number in serum   846
– general information   831
– importance in clinical chemistry   833
– measurements with automatic analysers, in blood
   851
– nomenclature   83
– normal values
– – dibuccaine number and fluoride number   849
– – in erythrocytes   837, 840, 845
– – in serum   845
– – in whole blood   843
– substrates   832
– trivial names   831
Chondroitin sulphate
– absorption spectrum of dissacharide
– – after enzymatic degradation   1166
– determination   1165
– isolation from biological samples   1168
– occurrence   1165
Chymotrypsin
– assay of activity
– – with N-acetyl-L-tyrosine-ethylester as substrate
   441
– – with N-benzoyl-L-tyrosine-ethylester as
   substrate   1009

The key words are arranged alphabetically without regard to prefixes such

Chymotrypsin, assay of activity
– – with casein as substrate   1007
– different forms, formation   1006
– general   1006
– isoenzymes   11
Chymotrypsin A
– assay of activity   441, 442
– characteristics and commercial preparations
  440, 441
Chymotrypsin inhibitors
– determination of activity   1074
Citrate
– concentration in animal tissues   2280
– determination
– – fluorimetric   1565
– – UV-assay   1562
– electrophoretic separation from aspartate   1998
– normal values   1569
Citrate lyase
– assay of activity   442
– characteristics and commercial preparations
  442
Citrate synthase
– assay of activity   443
– characteristics and commercial preparations
  443
Cleavage of proteins
– to peptides with
– – chymotrypsin   1629
– – other proteases   1631
– – pepsin   1630
– – trypsin   1625
Clostridiopeptidase A
– assay of activity   1059
Cocarboxylase
– see thiamine pyrophosphate
Coefficient of variation   312, 314, 327
Coenzyme A
– characteristics and commercial preparations
  528
– concentration in animal tissues   2287
– determination
– – fluorimetric with oxoglutarate dehydrogenase
  1981
– – method of choice   1967
– – with HOADH   1968
– – with PTA, catalytic method   1975
– – with PTA, end-point method   1972
– normal values   1967
Coenzyme A derivatives

– higher saturated fatty acids
– – determination, colorimetric   2010
Coenzyme A thioesters
– determination   2008
Coenzyme B_{12}
– determination   2200
Coenzymes
– as biochemical reagents   523
Collagenases
– assay of activity   1059
– general information   1058
Colorimeter   190
Competitive inhibition   151, 153, 154, 155
Concentration
– calculation   312
– definition   310
– of blood constituents, diurnal variations   390
– of metabolites in animal tissues   2266 et seq.
Constriction pipettes   323
Contaminating activity, definition   108
Content, definition   310
Control
– of experimental results   374
– of quantitative chemical analysis   370
Control chart   371, 372, 376
Conway diffusion and disher   1535
Coupled reaction   109
Creatine
– concentration in animal tissues   2300
– determination   1772
– normal values   1776
Creatine kinase
– assay of activity with
– – automatic analysers   793
– – creatine as substrate   785
– – creatine phosphate as substrate   789
– characteristics and commercial preparations
  444
– general information   784
– in heart diseases
– – differential diagnosis   36
– – myocardial infarct   31
– in muscle, striated   38
– in muscular dystrophy   38
– in myopathies, various   43
– normal values   788, 791, 797
– relative rates of reaction with nucleoside
  diphosphates   2079
– stability in serum   169
– stabilization and reactivation   171

as D, L, (+), (−), α, β. Where necessary reference to other synonyms is given.

Creatine phosphate
– characteristics and commercial preparations 529
– concentration in animal tissues 2299
– determination
– – other methods 1785
– – with CK, HK and G6P-DH 1777
– – with CK, PGK and GAPDH 1781
– – with luciferase 2112
Creatininase
– assay of activity 446
– characteristics and commercial preparations 445
Creatinine
– determination 1786
– normal values 1790
"Creep" 308
Crotonase
– isolation 2021
Crotonyl-CoA
– determination
– – other methods 2020
– – UV-assay 2017
CTP effect 1899
Cuvettes 191
Cyclodeaminase
– isolation 1561
Cytidine
– determination 1923
– normal values 1926
Cytidine deaminase
– isolation 1927
Cytidine-5′-diphosphate
– determination 2149
Cytidine-5′-diphosphoglucose
– characteristics and commercial preparations 529
– determination 2209
Cytidine-5′-monophosphate
– determination 2153
Cytidine-5′-triphosphate
– determination
– – other methods 2148
– – with F-6-PK 2145
Cytochrome c
– in muscular dystrophy 38
Cytochrome c-reductases
– in muscular dystrophy
– – in muscle 38
Cytochrome oxidase
– in plant diseases 83
Cytolysis
– of blood elements 639, 640

Cytosine
– determination 1916
Cytosine deaminase
– isolation 1918

D

Data, theoretical treatment 332
Data processing 4
Day-to-day reproducibility 378
Decision 347
Decision method, statistical 347
Dehydrogenases
– assay after electrophoretic separation 273
Deoxy-CDP-glucose
– reaction with CDP-glucose dehydratase 2212
Deoxycytidine
– determination 1923
– normal values 1926
Deoxy-GDP-mannose
– reduction with GDP-mannose dehydrogenase
  2215
Deoxyribonuclease I
– assay of activity 447
– characteristics and commercial preparations 447
Deoxythymidine
– determination 1935
– extinction coefficient 1935
– normal values 1939
Deoxythymidine-5′-diphosphoglucose
– characteristics and commercial preparations 530
– determination 2217
Deoxythymidine phosphorylase
– isolation 1939
Deoxyuridine
– determination 1935
– extinction coefficient 1935
– normal values 1939
Deproteinization
– general 177
– volume displacement effect 177
– with barium-zinc 1253
– with perchloric acid 1448, 2104
– with uranyl acetate 1208
DeRitis quotient
– in liver diseases
– – acute hepatitis 14
– – chronic hepatitis and cirrhosis 16
– – liver obstruction 20
– – liver tumours 24

The key words are arranged alphabetically without regard to prefixes such

De Ritis quotient, in liver diseases
– – obstructive jaundice 21
– – toxic liver damage 19
– in myocardial infarct 31
Dermatan sulphate
– determination 1165
– occurrence 1165
– normal values 1170
Detergents
– effects on enzyme activities 168
Determination of normal range 385
Determination of substrates
– with radiobiochemicals 283
Diamine oxidase
– assay of activity 660
– normal values in human serum 664
Diaphorase
– assay of activity 448
– characteristics and commercial preparations 448
Diastase in honey 74
Dibuccaine number 846
Dihydrofolate reductase
– assay of activity, UV-assay 666
– normal values in various diseases of blood and
   bone marrow 669
– other methods 670
Dihydrofolic acid
– preparation 671
Dihydroorotic acid dehydrogenase
– isolation 1966
Dihydroxyacetone
– determination 1442
– values in serum 1445
Dihydroxyacetone phosphate
– characteristics and commercial preparations 531
– concentration in animal tissues 2273
– determination 1314
Diketene
– for conversion of CoA-SH to AcAc-CoA 1970
Diketo acid hydrolase
– isolation 1847
Di- and polypeptidases
– activity optima 979, 980
– classification 979, 980
– general information 978
– occurrence 979, 980
– optimum conditions for measurements 981
– purification 979, 980
– substrates 979, 980
2,3-Diphosphoglycerate

– see D-glycerate-2,3-diphosphate
Diphosphopyridine nucleotide
– see nicotinamide-adenine dinucleotide
Disaccharides
– assay of activity 916
– general information 916
– nomenclature 916
– normal values 921
– specificity 921
Disc electrophoresis 268
Disintegration
– general 396
– of cells and tissues 399, 401
– of plant tissues 410
– – biological-enzymatic 405
– – chemical 405
– – thermal 404
Dispensing
– of samples and reagents 206
Dispensing units
– for micro-analysis 232
Distillation vessel according to *Bartley* 1525
Distribution
– empirical 322
– frequency 322
– probability 336
Diurnal variations
– of normal range 390
– of the concentrations of blood constituents 384
Documentation
– in automation 209
dTDP-glucose
– see deoxythymidine-5'-diphosphoglucose
dTDP-glucose dehydrase
– isolation 2220
Duplicate analysis

E

Effect of treatment (t-test) 353
Elastase
– assay of activity with orceinelastin 1041
– general information 1041
Electrochemical methods
– in microtechniques 245
Electron-transferring flavoprotein (ETF)
– isolation 2014
Electrophoresis
– preparation of plates 265
Electrophoretic separation 262

as D, L, (+), (−), α, β. Where necessary reference to other synonyms is given.

Emission spectra
– usual sources of radiation   184
Empirical distribution
– function   322
End-point method
– schematic   105
End-point, non-constant   308
Enolase
– assay of activity   449
– characteristics and commercial preparations 449
– in muscular dystrophy
– – in muscle   38
– – in serum   38
Enzymatic cycling
– examples   133
– for determination of nicotinamide-adenine
    nucleotides   2059
– for determination of prostaglandins   1877
– kinetics   135
– sensitivity of the assays   134
Enzymatic analysis
– basis   94 et seq.
– definition   94
– for control of growth of micro-oroganisms   88
– for control of microbiological metabolism   90
– in beverages   76
– in biochemistry   3
– in botany and agricultural chemistry   82
– in foodstuff chemistry   71
– in medicine   6
– in microbiology   87
– of confectionery, chocolate, sugar and sugar
    products   76
– of sugars and sugar phosphates (schematic) 111
– with radiobiochemicals   283
Enzymatic browning of plant products   84
Enzymatic isotope dilution principle   296
Enzyme activities
– assay after electrophoresis   272
– determination with radiobiochemicals   301
– for diagnosis, control of progress and therapy
    14 et seq.
– for differential diagnosis   25, 36
– for evaluation of plant products   83
– in blood diseases   50
– in fruit and berries   84
– in gynaecology   56
– in heart diseases   31 et seq.
– – differential diagnosis   36
– – myocardial infarct   31

– in liver diseases
– – acute hepatitis   14
– – chronic hepatitis and cirrhosis   16
– – liver obstruction   20
– – liver tumours   23
– – obstructive jaundice   21
– in muscle diseases
– – in striated muscle   37, 45
– – neural myopathies   43
– – progressive muscular dystrophies   37
– – various myopathies   43
– in serum
– – in rats after exercise   8
– – over a decade   9
– in soil   85
– in urine
– – in diseases of kidney and urinary tract   68
– – normal values   67
– of kidney structures   65
Enzyme activity assays
– reproducibility from day to day   379
Enzyme distribution patterns
– in nephrons of human kidney   64
Enzyme elimination
– immediate effect   10
– in humans   10
Enzyme induction
– in micro-organisms   87
Enzyme inhibitors
– in urine   63
Enzyme level
– in serum of healthy subjects   9
Enzyme patterns
– distortion   13
– in human tissues   12
– in infectious mononucleosis   18
– in serum in liver diseases   26, 27
Enzyme reactions
– pH dependence   129
Enzyme repression
– in micro-organisms   88
Enzymes
– as biochemical reagents   425
– in blood plasma   7
– in liver damge, toxic   19
– in milk   71
– of glycolysis
– – in muscle   45
– of respiratory chain
– – in muscle   46

The key words are arranged alphabetically without regard to prefixes such

Enzymes
– of tissue metabolism   7
– organ-specific   7
– plasma-specific   7
– release from cells   7
– stability in sample   168
Enzyme units   121, 311, 421
Equilibrium constants
– of enzymatic reactions   107
Errors
– type I   371
– type II   372
– in collection and transport of biological samples
  369
– random   363, 366·
– systematic   363, 368
– theory   363 et seq.
D-Erythrose-4-phosphate
– characteristics and commercial preparations
  531
– determination   1391
L-Erythrulose
– determination with polyol dehydrogenase   1394
– reduction by NAD-xylitol dehydrogenase   1369
Esterases
– after electrophoretic separation   275
– in blood diseases   54
Ethanol, see alcohol
Evaluation of
– electropherograms   271 et seq.
– experimental results   308
Experimental data, evaluation   308
Experimental results
– calculation of   312
– diurnal rhythms   384, 390
– evaluation, control, calculations and interpretation   308
– racial differences   317
– relation to body weight   317, 756
– seasonal differences   317
– sex-specific differences   317, 756
Experimental techniques   158 et seq.
Extinction   181
Extinction coefficient
– for NADH (NADPH)   184, 546
Extrapolation
– with non-constant end-points   308

F

Fast analyser   213
Fatty acid synthetase
– determination of activity in isotopic assay   305
– isolation from baker's yeast   2037
Fatty acids, unsaturated
– determination   1807
FIGLU transferase
– isolation   1561
Filter photometer   190
Findings
– not in agreement with clinical picture   393
– transmission of   212
Fixing the normal range   385
Flavin-adenine dinucleotide
– characteristics and commercial preparations 532
– determination   2182
Flavin mononucleotide
– characteristics and commercial preparations 533
– determination   2179
Fluorescence, decrease of background
– of tissue extracts   1575
Fluorimeter
– for micro-analysis   231
Fluorimetry
– in microtechniques   239–242
– principle   240
– procedure   240
– sensitivity   241
Folic acid
– characteristics and commercial preparations 533
Formaldehyde
– reduction by ADH   1508
Formate
– determination with
– – FH_4-synthetase   1546
– – formate dehydrogenase   1551
– values in urine   1549
Formate dehydrogenase
– isolation   1554
Formate-nitrate reductase
– isolation   2264
Formiminoglutamate
– determination   1556
Formulae
– for calculation of experimental results   312, 313

Fractionation
– of tissues and cells   407
Freeze-stop method   400
β-Fructofuranosidase
– assay of activity   450
– characteristics and commercial preparations 450
D-Fructose
– determination   1304
Fructose-1,6-diphosphatase
– activities in rabbit tissues   710
– determination of activity   881
– normal values   884
D-Fructose-1,6-diphosphate
– characteristics and commercial preparations 534
– concentration in animal tissues   2272
– determination   1314
– example of a determination in liver   315
Fructose-1,6-diphosphate aldolase
– activity in rabbit tissues   710
– activity in rat tissues   1100
– activity in serum   1100
– assay of activity
– – in tissues 1105
– – UV-assay, manual method   1100
– – UV-assay, automated method   1106
– normal values in human serum   1104, 1108
D-Fructose-1-phosphate
– characteristics and commercial preparations 534
– concentration in animal tissues   2271
– determination with
– – liver aldolase   1308
– values in rat tissues   1311
Fructose-1-phosphate aldolase
– see phosphofructoaldolase
D-Fructose-6-phosphate
– characteristics and commercial preparations 535
– concentration in animal tissues   2271
– determination   1238
– reaction with mannitol-1-P dehydrogenase 1278
Fructose-6-phosphate kinase
– assay of activity   126, 451
– characteristics and commercial preparations 451
– relative rates with nucleoside triphosphates 2081
– see also phosphofructokinase
β-D-Fucose
– oxidation by Gal-DH   1281
Fumarase
– assay of activity   452
– characteristics and commercial preparations 452
– in muscular dystrophy

– – in muscle   38, 46
– – in serum   38
Fumarate
– content in animal tissues   2282
– determination
– – fluorimetric   1600
– normal values   1603
Fumarylacetoacetate
– determination   1844
Functional state of tissues   317, 397

G

Galactinol
– cleavage by α-galactosidase   1174
Galactocerebroside
– oxidation by Gal-OD   1286
D-Galactosamine
– determination
– – submicromethod with ATP-γ-[^{32}P]   1232
– oxidation by Gal-OD   1286
D-Galactose
– determination
– – colorimetric assay with galactose oxidase
    1282
– – submicromethod with ATP-γ-[^{32}P]   1232
– – UV-assay with Gal-DH   1279
– oxidation with GOD   1212
β-Galactose dehydrogenase
– assay of activity   453
– characteristics and commercial preparations 453
– in determination of lactose   1180
Galactose oxidase
– assay of activity   454
– characteristics and commercial preparations 454
D-Galactose-1-phosphate
– characteristics and commercial preparations 535
– determination
– – as galactose after cleavage of phosphate   1201
– – with uridyltransferase   1288
D-Galactose-6-phosphate
– determination   1296
α-Galactosidase
– assay of activity   455
– characteristics and commercial preparations 455
β-Galactosidase
– assay of activity   456
– characteristics and commercial preparations 456
– in determination of lactose   1180

The key words are arranged alphabetically without regard to prefixes such

β-D-Galactoside
– determination   1180
D-Galacturonate
– determination   1299
– normal values   1302
– oxidation by Gal-OD   1286
Galacturonate isomerase
– isolation   1302
Gastricsin
– characteristics   1055
GDP-mannose
– see guanosine-5′-diphosphate mannose
GDP-mannose dehydrogenase
– isolation   2216
Gentianose
– cleavage by saccharase   1178
Glass electrode
– methods with aid of   261
D-Gluconate
– determination   1243
– values in wine   1246
Gluconate kinase
– assay of activity   457
– characteristics and commercial preparations   457
– relative rates of reaction with nucleoside
   triphosphates   2081
D-Gluconate-6-phosphate
– characteristics and commercial preparations   535
– concentration in animal tissues   2286
– determination   1248
D-Glucosamine
– characteristics and commercial preparations   536
– determination
– – submicromethod with ATP-γ-[^{32}P]   1228
– – with hexokinase   1251
D-Glucosamine-6-phosphate
– characteristics and commercial preparations   536
– determination   1257
D-glucosamine-6-phosphate-N-acetylase
– isolation   1262
D-Glucose
– concentration in animal tissues   2268
– destruction in experimental material   1177
– determination
– – in haemolysed blood, UV-assay   1199
– – with AGT   1222
– – with ATP-γ-[^{32}P], submicromethod   1228
– – with automatic analysers, fluorimetric   1201
– – with automatic analysers, with GOD, POD,
   and ABTS   1215

– – with GOD and POD, rapid assay   1211
– – with GOD, POD and ABTS   1212
– – with GOD, POD and o-dianisidine   1206
– – with HK and G6P-DH   1196
– – with test paper, semiquantitative   1211
– normal values in blood, serum and plasma   1210
– stability in blood   166
D-Glucose-1,6-diphosphate
– characteristics and commercial preparations 537
– concentration in animal tissues   2271
Glucose oxidase
– assay of activity   457
– characteristics and commercial preparations 457
– rate of reaction with various sugars   458
D-Glucose-1-phosphate
– characteristics and commercial preparations 537
– concentration in animal tissues   2269
– determination   1233
– hydrolysis constant   1235
– normal values   1236
Glucose-6-phosphatase
– assay of activity   876
D-Glucose-6-phosphate
– characteristics and commercial preparations 538
– concentration in animal tissues   2269
– determination   1238
Glucose-6-phosphate dehydrogenase
– assay of activity
– – UV-assay   459, 636
– characteristics and commercial preparations 458
– in blood diseases   52
– in muscular dystrophy
– – in muscle   38, 45
– – in serum   38
– in nephrons of human kidneys   64
– Michaelis constants   458, 637
– normal values in
– – blood elements   643
– – liver tissue   643
Glucose phosphate isomerase
– assay of activity, colorimetric assay   1113
– characteristics and commercial preparations 501
– normal values   1115
α-Glucosidase
– assay of activity   459
– characteristics and commercial preparations 459
– for determination of maltose   1185
– specificity   459, 1188
2-O-α-D-Glucosido-D-erythrose
– cleavage by α-glucosidase   1188

as D, L, (+), (−), α, β. Where necessary reference to other synonyms is given.

Glucotest® 1198
β-Glucuronidase
– assay of activity   460, 929
– characteristics and commercial preparations 460
– general information   929
– in diagnosis of kidney diseases   62
– in muscular dystrophy   38
– measurements in
– – bile   940
– – cerebrospinal fluid   939
– – gastric juice   941
– – serum   930, 932
– – serum in pregnancy   58
– – tissues   934, 937
– – urine   938
– – vaginal fluid   941
– normal values in serum   932
L-Glutamate
– concentration in animal tissues   2285
– determination
– – manometric   1662
– – with a regenerating system   108
– – with GlDH and APAD   1713
– – with GlDH and NAD   1704
– – with GlDH and tetrazolium salt   1708
– normal values   1707, 1712
Glutamate decarboxylase
– assay of activity by radiochemical method   305
L-Glutamate decarboxylase   1663
L-Glutamate dehydrogenase
– assay conditions for liver from various species
  655
– assay of activity
– – colorimetric assay   656
– – UV-assay   650
– characteristics and commercial preparations 461
– equilibrium constants   461
– in liver diseases
– – acute hepatitis   15
– – chronic hepatitis and cirrhosis   16
– – in serum   26, 27
– – liver obstruction   20
– – liver tumours   23
– – obstructive jaundice   21
– – toxic liver damage   20
– in mononucleosis, infectious   18
– in muscular dystrophy
– – in muscle   38, 46
– – in serum   38
– in nephrons of human kidney   64

– in serum
– – normal values   654, 659
– – stability   169
– normal values in organ extracts of various
  species   654
Glutamate-oxaloacetate transaminase
– apoenzyme, isolation   2198
– assay of activity
– – colorimetric assay according to Reitman and
  Frankel   735
– – colorimetric assay according to Tonhazy   739
– – colorimetric assay with BMTD   742
– – UV-assay with MDH, automated   733
– – UV-assay with MDH, manual   727
– – with automatic analysers   733, 768, 771
– characteristics and commercial preparations 462
– dependence
– – on age and body weight   731
– – on sex   731
– determination after electrophoretic separation
  745
– in blood diseases   51
– in heart diseases
– – differential diagnosis   36
– – myocardial infarct   31
– in liver diseases
– – acute hepatitis   14
– – chronic hepatitis and cirrhosis   16
– – in serum   26, 27
– – liver tumours   23
– – obstructive jaundice   21
– in meat   75
– in mononucleosis, infectious   18
– in muscle diseases
– – muscular dystrophy   39
– – myopathies, various   44
– in nephrons of human kidneys   64
– in serum
– – healthy subjects   9
– – normal values   731
– – of rats after exercise   8
– – stability   169
– in urine   66
– isoenzymes   10
Glutamate-pyruvate transaminase
– assay of activity
– – colorimetric assay according to Reitman and
  Frankel   760
– – colorimetric assay according to Tonhazy   764
– – UV-assay LDH, automated   758

The key words are arranged alphabetically without regard to prefixes such

Glutamate-pyruvate transaminase
– assay of activity
– – UV-assay with LDH, manual   752
– – with automatic analysers   758, 768, 771
– characteristics and commercial preparations 463
– dependence
– – on age and weight   756
– – on sex   756
– DeRitis quotient   14, 16, 17, 20, 21, 24
– in heart diseases
– – differential diagnosis   36
– – myocardial infarct   31
– in human liver   12
– in liver diseases
– – acute hepatitis   14
– – chronic hepatitis and cirrhosis   16
– – in serum   26, 27
– – liver tumours   22
– – obstructive jaundice   21
– – toxic liver damage   20
– – viral hepatitis in mice   8
– in mononucleosis, infectious   18
– in muscle diseases
– – muscular dystrophy   39
– – myopathies, various   44
– in nephrons of human kidney   64
– in serum
– – healthy subjects   9
– – normal values   756
– – of rats after exercise   8
– – stability   169
Glutaminase
– assay of activity   465
– characteristics and commercial preparations 465
L-Glutamine
– concentration in animal tissues   2285
– determination with
– – glutaminase and GlDH   1719
– – glutamine synthetase   1716
– normal values   1718, 1722
Glutamine synthetase
– isolation   1719
γ-Glutamyl transpeptidase
– activity in blood elements and tissues of various
   species   718
– assay of activity, colorimetric assay   715
– in liver diseases
– – acute hepatitis   15
– – in serum   26, 27
– – liver tumours   23

– – obstructive jaundice   21
– – toxic liver damage   20
– normal values in serum   718
Glutathione (GSH + GSSG)
– characteristics and commercial preparations
   538, 539
– determination   1643
– normal values   1647
Glutathione reductase
– assay of activity   465
– characteristics and commercial preparations 465
Glutathione reductases
– in blood diseases   52
– in muscular dystrophy   39
Glutathione synthetase
– in blood diseases 52
Glyceraldehyde
– oxidation by aldehyde dehydrogenase   1508
D-Glyceraldehyde-3-phosphate
– concentration in animal tissues   2274
– determination   1314
DL-Glyceraldehyde-3-phosphate
– characteristics and commercial preparations 539
L-Glyceraldehyde-3-phosphate
– determination   1439
Glyceraldehyde-3-phosphate dehydrogenase
– assay of activity   466
– characteristics and commercial preparations 466
– in blood diseases   54
– in muscular dystrophy
– – in muscle   39, 45
– – in serum   39
D-Glycerate
– determination 1419
– normal values   1422
D-Glycerate dehydrogenase
– see glyoxylate reductase
D-Glycerate-1,3-diphosphate
– characteristics   1430
– determination   1429
D-Glycerate-2,3-diphosphate
– characteristics and commercial preparations   540
– determination   1433
– method of choice   1433
– normal values in erythrocytes   1438
D-Glycerate-2-phosphate
– concentration in animal tissues 2276
– determination   1446
D-Glycerate-3-phosphate
– characteristics and commercial preparations 540

as D, L, (+), (−), α, β. Where necessary reference to other synonyms is given.

D-Glycerate-3-phosphate
- concentration in animal tissues 2275
- determination 1424
Glycerokinase
- assay of activity 469
- characteristics and commercial preparations 468, 469
- relative rate of reaction with nucleoside triphosphates 2081
Glycerol
- determination
-- radiochemical 1409
-- UV-assay with GK and GDH 1404
-- UV-assay with GK, PK and LDH 1825
- normal values in serum 1408, 1830
- reaction with sorbitol dehydrogenase 1326
L-Glycerol-3-phosphate
- concentration in animal tissues 2274
- determination 1415
Glycerol-3-phosphate dehydrogenase
- assay of activity 468
- characteristics and commercial preparations 468
- in muscular dystrophy
-- in muscle 39, 45
-- in serum 39
Glycocyamine
- reaction with CK 1776
Glycogen
- characteristics and commercial preparations 540
- concentration in animal tissues 2267
- determination with
-- amyloglucosidase 1127
- hydrolysis 1127
- normal values 1131
Glycolaldehyde
- determination 1514
Glycollate-2-phosphate
- characteristics and commercial preparations 541
- in determination of glycerate-2,3-diphosphate 1433
Glycylglycine dipeptidase
- assay of activity 982
- normal values 984
Glyoxalase I
- assay of activity 469
- characteristics and commercial preparations 469
Glyoxylate
- determination 1517
- reduction by LDH 1451
Glyoxylic acid reductase

- assay of activity 470
- characteristics and commercial preparations 470
Guanase
- assay of activity, UV-assay 1086
- characteristics and commercial preparations 471
- importance in clinical chemistry 1086
- normal values 1090
Guanine
- characteristics and commercial preparations 541
- determination 1909
- extinction coefficient 1913
- normal values 1915
Guanosine
- characteristics and commercial preparations 542
- cleavage by nucleoside phosphorylase 1934
- determination 1928
Guanosine-5'-diphosphate
- determination 2149
Guanosine-5'-diphosphomannose
- determination 2213
- see also GDP-mannose
Guanosine-3':5'-monophosphate (cyclic)
- concentration in animal tissues 2297
- determination 2166
Guanosine-5'-monophosphate
- determination
-- other methods 2165
-- with G-5-MP-kinase 2162
Guanosine-5'-monophosphate kinase
- assay of activity 472
- characteristics and commercial preparations 472
Guanosine-5'-triphosphate
- characteristics and commercial preparations 542
- concentration in
-- rat heart 2081
-- rat liver 2081
-- rat skeletal muscle 2081
- determination
-- other methods 2161
-- together with ITP 2078
-- with PGK 2158

H

Hemicellulase
- preparation of crude product 1147
Hemicelluloses
- determination 1143
- normal values 1147

The key words are arranged alphabetically without regard to prefixes such

Heparin
– determination
– – spectrophotometric   1151
– – titrimetric   1154
Hexokinase
– assay of activity   473
– characteristics and commercial preparations   473
– in blood diseases   52
– in muscular dystrophy
– – in muscle   39, 45
– relative rates with nucleoside triphosphates 2081
Hg Lamp, lines   189
Hill coefficient
– in PK from yeast   781
Histaminase
– in serum in pregnancy   58
L-Histidine
– determination
– – colorimetric assay   1669
– – manometric assay   1662
L-Histidine decarboxylase   1663
Histogram   322
HMG-CoA lyase
– isolation   2029
HMG-CoA reductase
– assay of activity by a radiochemical assay   303, 304
Homogenates
– moist   401
– dry   407
Homogenizers   401–404
Hyaluronate lyase
– assay of activity   944
– isolation   1163
– *Michaelis* constants   1161
Hyaluronic acid
– absorption spectrum   1158
– characteristics and commercial preparations   543
– competitive inhibition of degradation   1158
– determination
– – colorimetric assay   1162
– – dependence of the UV-assay of the degree of polymerization   1161
– – UV-assay   1157
– normal values   1160
Hyaluronidase
– see hyaluronate lyase
Hydrazine
– reaction with NAD
– – light absorption of   107, 1706

Hydrogen peroxide
– determination with peroxidase   2246
3-Hydroxyacyl-CoA dehydrogenase
– assay of activity   474
– characteristics and commercial preparations 474
3-Hydroxyanthranilic acid
– determination   1736
– normal values in urine   1739
3-Hydroxyanthranilic acid oxidase
– isolation   1739
2-Hydroxybutyrate
– oxidation by LDH   1468
2-Hydroxybutyrate dehydrogenase
– determination in serum,
– – colorimetric assay   607
– – UV-assay, automated   611
– – UV-assay, manual   603
– in liver tumours   24
– in muscular dystrophy   39
– in myocardial infarct   33
– normal values in serum   606, 610
D-3-Hydroxybutyrate
– concentration in animal tissues   2292
– determination   1836
– normal values   1838
D-3-Hydroxybutyrate dehydrogenase
– assay of activity   475
– characteristics and commercial preparations 475
– specificity   1839
DL-3-Hydroxybutyric acid
– characteristics and commercial preparations 543
L-3-Hydroxybutyryl-CoA
– determination
– – other methods   2025
– – UV-assay   2022
– normal values   2024
3-Hydroxykynurenine
– determination   1731
– normal values   1734
3-Hydroxy-3-methylglutaryl-CoA
– concentration in animal tissues   2291
– determination
– – other methods   2029
– – UV-assay   2026
– normal values   2029
L-Hydroxyproline
– determination   1723
– normal values in urine   1725
3-Hydroxypropionyl-CoA
– determination   2031

as D, L, (+), (−), α, β. Where necessary reference to other synonyms is given.

3-Hydroxypropionyl-CoA dehydrogenase
– isolation 2033
Hydroxypyruvate
– determination with
– – D-glycerate dehydrogenase 1457
– – LDH 1451
– normal values in rat tissues 1459
3 α-Hydroxysteroid dehydrogenase
– assay of activity 476
– characteristics and commercial preparations 476
– isolation 1874
3 ., 20 β-Hydroxysteroid dehydrogenase
– assay of activity 477
– characteristics and commercial preparations 477
3 β, 17 β-Hydroxysteroid dehydrogenase
– assay of activity 477
– characteristics and commercial preparations 477
– isolation 1874
Hypoxanthine
– absorption curve 1941
– characteristics and commercial preparations 543
– determination
– – colorimetric assay 1945
– – UV-assay 1941
– normal values 1945, 1949

I

Ice bath 160
Identification of sample 205
Iditol
– reaction with sorbitol dehydrogenase 572, 1326
Immobilized enzymes
– for determination of glucose 119
– in enzymatic analysis 119, 120
Independent variables 328
Indicator enzyme 109
Indicator reaction
– definition 109
– examples 109 et seq.
– preceding 112
– succeeding 111
Individual steps
– in quantitative chemical analysis 205
Individual values
– for uric acid 383
Inhibitor constants
– determination
– – in one-substrate reactions 152

– – in two-substrate reactions 155
– – of type of inhibition 152
– theory 151
Inhibitors for
– chymotrypsin 1074
– kallikrein 1077
– plasmin 1066, 1077
– thrombin 1077
– trypsin 1066
Inhibitor unit
– definition 1064
Inosine
– characteristics and commercial preparations 544
– determination 1932
Inosine-5′-monophosphate
– determination 2168
Inosine-5′-triphosphate
– concentration (+ GTP) in
– – rat heart 2086
– – rat liver 2086
– – rat skeletal muscle 2086
– determination
– – with PGK, GAPDH 2158
– – together with GTP 2078
– – other methods 2161
Inositol dehydrogenase
– isolation 1336
(−)-Inositol-3-phosphate
– hydrolysis by myo-inositol-1-phosphatase 1340
myo-Inositol
– characteristics and commercial preparations 544
– determination 1333
myo-Inositol-1-phosphatase
– isolation 1340
myo-Inositol-1-phosphate
– determination 1337
Insecticides
– determination with
– – cholinesterase 2249
– – other methods 2257
International Units 121, 311, 421
Inulin
– cleavage by saccharase 1179
– determination 1149
Inulin clearance 1149
Invertase
– assay of activity 450, 923
– characteristics and commercial preparations 450
– normal values 927
– see also β-fructofuranosidase

The key words are arranged alphabetically without regard to prefixes such

Isobutyraldehyde
- oxidation by aldehyde dehydrogenase 1508
Isocitrate
- concentration in animal tissues 2281
- determination
- - fluorimetric 1573
- - UV-assay 1570
- normal values 1576
Isocitrate dehydrogenase
- assay of activity,
- - colorimetric assay 627
- - UV-assay 624
- characteristics and commercial preparations 479
- in blood diseases 54
- in hepatitis
- - acute 15
- - chronic and cirrhosis 16
- in mononucleosis, infectious 19
- in muscular dystrophy
- - in muscle 39, 46
- in nephrons of human kidney 64
- isoenzymes 11
- - in muscle 49
- normal values in human serum 626, 631
Isoenzymes
- characterization and measurement after
  separation 272
- definition 261
- electrophoretic separation 262
- importance 262
- in medicine 11
Isotope dilution principle 296
Isotope laboratories
- furnishing and operation 283-285

K

Kallikrein
- characteristics 1031
- determination
- - fluorimetric 1037
- - UV-assay, manual 1033
- - UV-assay with autoanalysers 1034
3-Ketoacid CoA-transferase
- see 3-oxoacid CoA-transferase
2-Ketobutyrate
- see 2-oxobutyrate
2-Ketoglutarate
- see 2-oxoglutarate

2-Ketoglutarate dehydrogenase
- see 2-oxoglutarate dehydrogenase
2-Keto-n-valerate
- see 2-oxo-n-valerate
20-Ketosteroids
- determination
- - fluorimetric 1864
- - UV-assay 1858
- normal values 1862, 1867
Kinases
- relative rates with nucleoside di- and triphosphates 2081
Kinetics
- chemical reactions 95-96
- enzyme reactions 96 et seq.
- of enzymatic cycling 135
Kynureninase
- isolation 1735

L

D-Lactate
- determination with D-LDH 1492
D-Lactate dehydrogenase
- assay of activity 480
- characteristics and commercial preparations 480
L-Lactate
- concentration in animal tissues 2278
- determination
- - fluorimetric 1468
- - with automatic analysers 1479
- - with LDH and NAD 1464
- - with LDH from yeast 1483
- - with LDH, GPT and NAD 1475
- normal values 1468, 1471, 1474, 1479, 1487
- stability in blood 166
L-Lactate dehydrogenase
- assay of activity
- - colorimetric assay with lactate, NAD and
    phenazinemethosulphate 579
- - UV-assay with pyruvate and NADH 574
- - with automatic analysers 582
- equilibrium constant 481
- in blood diseases 51
- in diseases of kidney and urinary tract
- - for diagnosis 62 et seq.
- in gynaecological diseases 57
- in heart diseases
- - differential diagnosis 36

as D, L, (+), (−), α, β. Where necessary reference to other synonyms is given.

L-Lactate dehydrogenase, in heart diseases
– – myocardial infarct   31
– in liver diseases
– – acute hepatitis   16
– – chronic hepatitis and cirrhosis   16
– – in serum   26, 27
– – liver obstruction   20
– – liver tumours   23
– – obstructive jaundice   21
– – toxic liver damage   19
– in mononucleosis, infectious   18
– in muscular dystrophy
– – in muscle   39, 45
– – in serum   39
– in myopathies, various   43
– in pig as a sign of meat quality   75
– in serum
– – healthy subjects   9
– – normal values   9
– – of rats after exercise   8
– – stability   169
– in urine   62
– isoenzymes
– – assay of activity in serum   590, 593, 603, 607, 611
– – in heart diseases   33
– – in nephrons of kidneys   65
– – in skeletal muscle   48
– – in human tissues   11
– – in urine   66
– – measurements after electrophoretic separation   593
– – myocardial infarct   31
– – separation on DEAE-Sephadex   590
– of kidney
– – in nephrons   65
– – in the structures   65
– total activity of human liver   14
L-Lactate dehydrogenase from beef heart
– characteristics and commercial preparations   482
L-Lactate dehydrogenase from rabbit muscle
– assay of activity   481
– characteristics and commercial preparations 481
L-Lactate dehydrogenase from yeast
– assay of activity   1490
– isolation   1489
Lactate oxidase
– apoenzyme   2181
– isolation   2181

Lactose
– determination   1180
– oxidation by Gal-OD   1286
Lambert-Beer's Law   183
LDH-1-isoenzyme
– after electrophoretic separation   593
– see also 2-hydroxybutyrate dehydrogenase
– stability in serum   170
LDH-5-isoenzyme
– after electrophoretic separation   593
Lecithin
– determination   1813
– values in foodstuffs   1817
Leucine aminopeptidase
– assay of activity   954
– characteristics and commercial preparations   482, 952
– general   950
– in diseases of kidney and urinary tract   66
– in liver diseases
– – acute hepatitis   15
– – chronic hepatitis and cirrhosis   16
– – in serum   26, 27
– – liver obstruction   21
– – liver tumours   24
– – obstructive jaundice   21
– in mononucleosis, infectious   18
– in serum in pregnancy   58
– isoenzymes
– – in obstructive jaundice   22
– normal values   957
Leucine nitroanilidase
– assay of activity   958
– normal values   962
Linear regression
– check of   359
Lineweaver-Burk plot   146, 147
Lipase
– assay of activity
– – photometric   819
– – titrimetric   814
– in milk   74
– in oil-containing seed   84
– normal values
– – in duodenal juice   822
– – in serum   818, 822
– see also post-heparin lipase
Lipoamide dehydrogenase
– assay of activity   448
– characteristics and commercial preparations 448

The key words are arranged alphabetically without regard to prefixes such

Lipoxidases
– in foodstuff chemistry   75
– in oil-containing seeds   84
Lipoxygenase
– assay of activity   483
– characteristics and commercial preparations 483
Liquid content of tissues
– calculations   314
Liver
– enzyme activity patterns in human liver   12
Liver aldolase
– isolation   1312
Logarithmic-normal distribution   350
Longitudinal assessment   383
Luciferase
– isolation   2125
L-Lysine
– determination
– – colorimetric assay   1669
– – manometric assay   1662
– – with automatic analysers   1701
L-Lysine decarboxylase
– assay of activity   484
– characteristics and commercial preparations 484

M

Maceration juice   411
Mailing
– of biological samples   167
L-Malate
– concentration in animal tissues   2282
– determination
– – fluorimetric with MDH and APAD   1600
– – with MDH and APAD   1593
– – with MDH and GOT   1589
– – with MDH and NAD   1585
– – with MDH in coupled assay   1596
– normal values   1592, 1599, 1603
L-Malate dehydrogenase
– assay of activity,
– – after electrophoretic separation   618
– – UV-assay   485, 613
– characteristics and commercial preparations 485
– equilibrium constants   485
– in blood diseases   51, 53, 54
– in hepatitis, acute   16
– in muscular dystrophy
– – in muscle   39, 46
– – in serum   39

– in nephrons of kidney   64
– in serum
– – normal values   616, 622
– – stability   170, 615
– in structures of kidney   65
– isoenzymes   48, 618
– measurements after electrophoretic separation
   618
Maleate
– determination   1622
Maleate isomerase
– isolation   1624
Malonyl-CoA
– determination   2034
– concentration in animal tissues   2293
Malonylsemialdehyde-CoA
– determination   2034
Maltase
– assay of activity   459
– characteristics and commercial preparations
   459
– see also α-glucosidase
Maltose, determination   1185
D-Mannitol
– content of in spores of *A. oryzae*   1273
– determination   1271
D-Mannitol dehydrogenase
– isolation   1274
– substrate specificity   1273
D-Mannitol-1-phosphate
– concentration in *E. coli*   1278
– determination   1275
D-Mannitol-1-phosphate dehydrogenase
– isolation   1278
– specificity   1278
D-Mannosamine
– reaction with HK   1232, 1255
D-Mannose
– determination   1263
– oxidation by GOD   1212
D-Mannose-1-phosphate
– determination   1268
D-Mannose-6-phosphate
– determination   1263
Manometer capillaries   252
Manometer fluids   253
Manometry
– calculations   249
– in microtechniques   248
– review   248

as D, L, (+), (−), α, β. Where necessary reference to other synonyms is given.

Manometry, technical details 252
– two-vessel method 249–251
Mean
– probability distribution 337
– arithmetic 330
Measurements
– against the reaction equilibrium 107
– continuous 122
– kinetic 131
– new techniques 117
– of concentrations by activation or inhibition of enzymes 134
– of enzyme activities (schematic) 122
– of metabolites on a kinetic basis 131
– of metabolites (schematic) 105
– of protein concentration 171–176
– two-point method 122
– with aid of coupled reactions 109
– with preceding indicator reaction
– – definition 112
– – details and calculations 112 et seq.
– with succeeding indicator reaction 109
– with unspecific enzymes 108
Measurements, presentation of photometric
– analogue 193
– digital 193
Measuring techniques
– automated 202 et seq.
– calorimetry 118
– conductivity 118
– immobilized enzymes 119
– manometry 248 et seq.
– microtechniques 228 et seq.
– photometry 180 et seq.
– radiometry 118
– review of new methods 117 et seq.
– with electrodes 118, 254 et seq.
3-Mercaptopyruvate
– determination 1460
Messenger RNA
– determination of the activity in peptidizing system 1901
Metabolites
– as biochemical reagents 523
– concentration in animal tissues 2266 et seq.
– distribution in intracellular compartments 398
– stability in blood 166
– stability to deproteinizing agents 165
6-O-Methyl-D-galactose
– oxidation by Gal-DH 453

Methyl glyoxal
– determination 1496
4-Methyl umbelliferone
– as aglycone 721
– as substrate for UDP-glucuronyl transferase 721
Michaelis constants
– determination
– – according to *Florini & Vestling*, two substrates 149
– – according to *Frieden*, two substrates 150
– – according to *Hofstee* 147
– – according to *Lineweaver v Burk* 146
– – according to *Wilkinson* 147
Michaelis-Menten equation 100, 145
Microanalyser for gases 248
Microanalysis, apparatus for 230
Microanalytical balances 235
Microanalytical systems 236
Microcentrifuges 235
Microcuvettes 238
Microdissection techniques 238
Microgasometry 242
Microgenerator for gases 248
Micromethods 237
Microphotometry 237
Microtechniques 228 et seq.
Microtest tubes 235
Mitochondria from yeast
– preparation 407
Mixers for microanalysis 235
Mixing of samples
– in automation 206
Model, additive 343
Monochromatic light 185
myo-Inositol, see under I
Myokinase
– assay of activity 486
– characteristics and commercial preparations 486
– in muscular dystrophy
– – in muscle 39
– – in serum 39
– relative rates of reaction with nucleoside diphosphates 2081

N

NAD-analogues
– use in metabolite assays 107

NAD-pyrophosphorylase
– assay of activity   487
– characteristics and commercial preparations
  487
Nicotinamide-adenine dinucleotide
– absorption curve   104, 184
– characteristics and commercial preparations
  545
– concentration in animal tissues   2298
– normal values in rat tissues   2072
Nicotinamide-adenine dinucleotide, reduced
– absorption curve   104, 184
– characteristics and commercial preparations 545
– concentration in animal tissues   2298
– concentration in rat tissues   2072
– determination
– – by enzymatic cycling   2066
– – fluorimetric   2058
– – other methods   2053
– – UV-assay   2052
– extinction coefficient   184, 546
– stability   158
Nicotinamide-adenine dinucleotide phosphate
– characteristics and commercial preparations 546
– concentration in animal tissues   2298
– determination
– – by enzymatic cycling   2060
– – fluorimetric   2058
– – UV-assay   2050
Nicotinamide-adenine dinucleotide phosphate,
  reduced
– concentration in animal tissues   2298
– determination
– – by enzymatic cycling   2066
– – fluorimetric   2058
– – other methods   2056
– – UV-assay   2054
Nicotinamide-adenine nucleotides
– determination
– – by enzymatic cycling   2059
– – fluorimetric   2057
– – UV-assay   2048
– extraction
– – methods   2045
Nicotinamide-mononucleotide
– determination   2073
Nitrate
– determination   2260
– normal values   2264
Nitrate reductase

– in foodstuff chemistry   75
p-Nitrophenyl-α-D-glucoside
– hydrolysis by α-glucosidase   1188
Normal distribution
– logarithmic   350
– probability density   336
– test of   350
Normal range
– comparison of data in literature   391
– definition   385
– dependence
– – on age   388
– – on sex   388
– determination   385
– diurnal variations   384
– selection of probands   386
Normal values
– determination methods   385
– – deductive   384
– – graphical   389
– – others   388
– – probit analysis   388
"Nothing" dehydrogenase   274
Nucleoside diphosphate kinase
– assay of activity   488
– characteristics and commercial preparations 488
Nucleoside monophosphate kinase
– assay of activity   489
– characteristics and commercial preparations 489
Nucleoside phosphorylase
– assay of activity   490
– characteristics and commercial preparations 490
5'-Nucleotidase
– in liver diseases
– – chronic hepatitis and cirrhosis   17
– – obstructive jaundice   22
– in muscular dystrophy
– – in muscle   39
5'-Nucleotidases
– assay of activity   871
– general information   871
– normal values   874
Nucleotides
– concentration in
– – animal tissues   2293
– – rat heart   2086
– – rat liver 2086
– – rat skeletal muscle   2086
Nuclides, physical properties   283
Null hypothesis (statistics)   348

as D, L, (+), (−), α, β. Where necessary reference to other synonyms is given.

O

Oestradiol dehydrogenase
- assay of activity *in vivo* with isotopes   306
Olive oil emulsion
- stabilized dry preparation   816
Operating characteristic curve   373
Operational isomers   396
Optimum conditions for method   379
Optimal system
- for quality control   374
L-Ornithine
- determination
- - colorimetric assay   1669
- - manometric assay   1662
Ornithine carbamoyltransferase
- assay of activity
- - manual   691
- - with automatic analysers   695
- in liver damage, toxic   20
- in muscular dystrophy   39
- normal values in serum   695
L-Ornithine decarboxylase   1663, 1670
Orotic acid (orotate)
- characteristics and commercial preparations   548
- determination
- - with dihydroorotate dehydrogenase   1963
- - with O-5-MP pyrophosphorylase   1959
- extinction coefficient   1961
- normal values   1962
Outliers (in statistics)   362
Overflow pipettes   233
Oxalate
- determination
- - manometric   1543
- - photometric   1544
Oxalate decarboxylase
- isolation   1544
Oxaloacetate
- concentration in animal tissues   2280
- determination
- - fluorimetric   1608
- - UV-assay   1604
- - with [^{14}C]-acetyl-CoA   1611
- normal values
- - in mouse brain   1611
- - in rat liver   1615
Oxidases
- assay after electrophoretic separation   274

3-Oxoacid CoA transferase
- isolation   2044
2-Oxobutyrate
- reduction by LDH   1451
2-Oxoglutarate
- characteristics and commercial preparations   548
- concentration in animal tissues   2281
- determination
- - fluorimetric   1580
- - UV-assay   1577
- normal values in blood   1579
- stability in blood   166
2-Oxoglutarate dehydrogenase
- isolation   1986
2-Oxo-n-valerate
- reduction by LDH   1451
- reductive amination by GlDH   1580
Oxytocinase
- assay of activity
- - with L-cystine-di-β-naphthylamide   967
- - with S-benzyl-L-cystine -p-nitroanilide   971
- general   951
- in serum
- - in pregnancy   58
- normal values   970, 973

P

Paired vessels
- in manometry   250
Palmitoyl-coenzyme A
- determination   1986
Papain
- assay of activity   491
- characteristics and commercial preparations   491
Pentose monophosphates
- in chloroplasts   1389
- radiochemical determination   1385
Pentose phosphates
- concentration in animal tissues   2286
Pepsin
- assay of activity
- - with haemoglobin as substrate   1046
- - with N-acetyl-L-phenylalanyl-1-3,5-di-iodotyrosine as substrate   1052
- characteristics and commercial preparations   493
- details for measurements
- - in serum   1052
- - in tissues   1052
- isoenzymes   77
- normal values in gastric juice   1051, 1055

The key words are arranged alphabetically without regard to prefixes such

Pepsinogen
– activation   1046
– characteristics   1046
Peptidases
– assay of activity   950–999
– after electrophoretic separation   275
– in serum in pregnancy   58
– review   949
Peptides
– characterization with enzyme   1625
– stepwise degradation   1632
Percentile   325
Peroxidases
– assay of activity   495
– – colorimetric assay   685
– characteristics and commercial preparations 494
– in blood diseases   54
– in milk   72
– in plant diseases   83
– in vegetables and fruit   74
– measurements in tissues   689
Peroxides, inorganic
– determination   2246
Phenol oxidase, in vegetables and fruit   75
Phenolphthalein glucuronide
– preparation   942
Phenyl-α-D-glucoside
– cleavage by α-glucosidase   1188
Phosphatase, acid
– assay of activity 496
– – in serum, two-point method   856
– characteristics and commercial preparations 495
– in muscular dystrophy   40
– in serum
– – in pregnancy   58
– – stability   170
– isoenzymes   11
Phosphatase, alkaline
– assay of activity   496
– – in milk   868
– – in serum, continuous method   860
– – in serum, two-point method   856
– – in serum with automatic analysers   864
– characteristics and commercial preparations 496
– in blood diseases   53
– in diseases of kidney and urinary tract   68
– in kidney
– – in human nephrons   64
– in liver diseases
– – acute hepatitis   14

– – chronic hepatitis and cirrhosis   16
– – in serum   26, 27
– – liver tumours   23
– – obstructive jaundice   21
– – toxic liver damage   19
– in milk   868
– in mononucleosis, infectious   18
– in muscular dystrophy   40
– in serum
– – assay with automatic analysers   864
– – continuous assay   860
– – in pregnancy   58
– – normal values   860, 863
– – stability   170
– in urine   67
– see also alkaline phosphatase
Phosphatases, general
– acid and alkaline phosphatase in serum, two-
   point method   856
– in meat and meat products   75
– in milk   72
– normal values   860, 863, 870
Phosphate, inorganic
– concentration in animal tissues   2300
– determination
– – chemical   2124
– – fluorimetric   2229
– – other methods   2238
– – UV-assay   2234
– normal values   2233
Phosphocreatine
– characteristics and commercial preparations
   529
– see also creatine phosphate
Phosphodiesterase
– assay of activity in isotope assay   304
– from beef heart
– – assay of activity   497
– – characteristics and commercial preparations
   497
– from Crotalus terr. terr.
– – assay of activity   498
– – characteristics and commercial preparations
   498
Phosphoenolpyruvate
– characteristics and commercial preparations 548
– concentration in animal tissues   2276
– determination   1446
1-Phosphofructoaldolase
– assay of activity

as D, L, (+), (−), α, β. Where necessary reference to other synonyms is given.

1-Phosphofructoaldolase, assay of activity
– – UV-assay   1109
– normal values   1111
Phosphofructokinase
– in muscular dystrophy   40
– relative rates with nucleoside triphosphates 2081
– see also fructose-6-phosphate kinase
Phosphoglucomutase
– assay of activity   499
– – UV-assay   798
– characteristics and commercial preparations 499
– in muscular dystrophy
– – in muscle   40
– – in serum   40
– normal values   801
6-Phosphogluconate
– characteristics and commercial preparations 535
– see gluconate-6-phosphate
6-Phosphogluconate dehydrogenase
– assay of activity   500
– – UV-assay   632
– characteristics and commercial preparations 500
– in blood diseases   53
– in muscular dystrophy
– – in muscle   40
– – in serum   40
– in plant diseases   83
– normal values in serum   634
Phosphoglucose isomerase
– assay of activity   501, 1113
– characteristics and commercial preparations 501
– in muscular dystrophy
– – in muscle   40
– – in serum   40
– see also
– – glucosephosphate isomerase
– – phosphohexose isomerase
3-Phosphoglycerate
– characteristics and commercial preparations 540
– see also glycerate-3-phosphate
3-Phosphoglycerate kinase
– assay of activity   502
– characteristics and commercial preparations 502
– in blood diseases   54
– in muscular dystrophy
– – in muscle   40
– relative rates of reaction with nucleoside
   triphosphates   2081
Phosphoglycerate mutase
– assay of activity   503

– characteristics and commercial preparations 503
– in blood diseases   52
– in muscular dystrophy
– – in muscle   40
2-Phosphoglycollate
– see glycollate-2-phosphate
Phosphohexose isomerase
– see phosphoglucose isomerase
Phospholipase D
– assay of activity   504
– characteristics and commercial preparations
   504
Phosphomannose isomerase
– assay of activity   505
– characteristics and commercial preparations 505
5'-Phospho-α-D-ribose-1-diphosphate
– determination   1346
Phosphoric acid esters, with insecticide activity
– determination   2249
Phosphorylase a
– assay of activity   505
– characteristics and commercial preparations 505
Phosphorylases
– in muscular dystrophy   40
Phosphotransacetylase
– assay of activity   507
– characteristics and commercial preparations 507
Photometers
– principles of   184
– review of available models   196–201
Photometric measurements
– errors   193
– in automation   209
Photometry
– in microtechniques   237
pH recording
– for enzymatic determination of metabolites   258
Pipettes
– according to Sanz   233
– for micro-analysis   232
– standardization   161
– tray   163
Plasma-specific enzymes   7
Plasmin inhibitors
– assay with azocasein as substrate   1071
– normal values   1074
Plastic equipment   161
Plastics
– chemical stability   162
– in analysis   161

The key words are arranged alphabetically without regard to prefixes such

Plastics
– properties and applications   162
Point estimation procedure (statistics)   349
Poisson distribution   364
Polarography   245
Polyol dehydrogenase
– see sorbitol dehydrogenase
Poly- and dipeptidases
– activity optima   979–980
– classification   979–980
– general information   978
– occurrence   979–980
– optimum conditions for measurements   981
– purification   979–980
– substrates   981
Polyphenoloxidase
– in plant diseases   83
– in serum in pregnancy   58
Polyribonucleotides
– determination of activities in peptidizing systems
   1901
– incorporation yield   1906
Polyunsaturated fatty acids
– determination   1807
Polyuridylic acid
– characteristics and commercial preparations 549
Postheparin lipase
– assay of activity
– – 1-mono-olein as substrate   828
– – triolein as substrate   825
– general   824
– nomenclature   824
– normal values   827, 830
Precision
– control   370 et seq.
– from day to day   367, 378
– in the same series   367
– of assay methods   314
– of measurements   314, 366
– of measurements of radioactivity   292
Prekallikrein
– determination with autoanalysers   1034
Preparation of control samples   373, 376
Preparation of samples
– for microtechniques   229
Primary standard   373
Probability   333
Probability density   336
Probability distribution
– mean   337

Probability distribution
– median   337
– dispersion   338
Producers' risk   371
n-Propanol
– oxidation by ADH   1502
Propionaldehyde
– reduction by aldehyde dehydrogenase   1508
Propionate
– phosphorylation by acetate kinase   425, 1527
Propyleneglycol
– reaction with sorbitol dehydrogenase   1326
Prostaglandin dehydrogenase
– isolation   1883
Prostaglandins
– determination   1887
Protease inhibitors
– definition of inhibitor unit   1064
– enzyme-inhibitor complex   1064
– general   1064
– substrates for enzymatic assays   1065
Proteinases
– assay of activity with autoanalysers   1000
Protein-binding assay
– determination of A-3:5-MP   2136
– principle   2137
Proteins
– characterization with enzymes   1625
– cleavage with
– – chymotrypsin   1629
– – other proteases   1631
– – pepsin   1630
– – trypsin   1625
– stepwise degradation   1632
Pteroylglutamic acid
– characteristics and commercial preparations 552
Purine nucleotides
– analytical differentiation   2078
Purity criteria
– for reagents   421–423
Purity definitions
– for coenzymes and substrates   422
– for enzymes   421
Pyridoxal-5-phosphate
– characteristics and commercial preparations 550
– determination   2194
– normal values   2198
– reduction to pyridoxamine-5-phosphate   2196
Pyridoxamine-5-phosphate
– determination   2194

as D, L, (+), (−), α, β. Where necessary reference to other synonyms is given.

Pyridoxamine-5-phosphate
– normal values 2198
Pyrimidine nucleotides
– analytical differentiation 2078
Pyrophosphatase, inorganic
– assay of activity 508
– characteristics and commercial preparations 508
Pyrophosphate, inorganic
– concentration in animal tissues 2300
– determination 2239
Pyruvate
– characteristics and commercial preparations
  550
– concentrations in animal tissues 2276
– determination
– – fluorimetric 1452
– – with LDH 1446
– – with pH-stat 258
– – UV-assay 1446
– formation of dimers in solution 1453
– normal values 1455
– reduction by glyoxylate reductase 1519
– stability in blood 166
Pyruvate decarboxylase
– apoenzyme, isolation 2192
– assay of activity 509
– characteristics and commercial preparations
  509
– isolation 2191
Pyruvate kinase (muscle)
– assay of activity 510, 774, 778
– characteristics and commercial preparations
  509–510
– in blood diseases 52
– in muscular dystrophy
– – in muscle 40, 45
– measurements in serum and erythrocytes
– – normal values 777
– relative rates of reaction with nucleoside
  diphosphates 2081
Pyruvate kinase from yeast
– assay of activity 778
– characteristics 778
– Hill coefficients 778
– measurements
– – kinetic constants 781
– – of cellular PK activity 780
– molecular weight 778

Q

Quality
– biochemical reagents 418–420
Quality control
– minimal system 374
– optimal system 374
– practical execution 374
– statistical 370
Quantile
– of a probability distribution 338
Quantum counter 2114
Quartz fibre balance 236
Quinolinate phosphoribosyltransferase
– isolation 1346
Quinone reductase
– in plant diseases 83

R

Radiation, instruments for measuring 285–291
Radiation, sources of
– for photometry 184–187
Radioactivity determination
– precision 292
Raffinose
– determination 1172
Range, normal 384–391
Ranked data 320
Raw data 320
Reaction curves, non-linear 309
Reaction kinetics 95
Reactions
– coupled 101
– simple 99
Reagents
– biochemical
– – description of 425–556
– – handling of 158
– – manufacturers and suppliers 424
– complete kits 557
– control of 158 et seq.
– for procedures with radiobiochemicals 301
Recording of photometric measurements 193
Reductases
– in milk 73
Reference diver 243

The key words are arranged alphabetically without regard to prefixes such

Reference units   310
Regenerating systems   133
Regression
– linear   328
Regression line
– test of slope   359
Reporting the normal range
– necessary information   389
Ribitol
– oxidation by
– – ribitol dehydrogenase   1354
– – sorbitol dehydrogenase   1326
Ribitol dehydrogenase
– isolation   1356
Ribonuclease
– assay of activity   511
– characteristics and commercial preparations 511
– in blood diseases   54
– inhibition by heparin   1151
– in muscular dystrophy   40
– isoenzymes   11
Ribonucleic acid
– characteristics and commercial preparations 551
– mRNA, determination of activity in peptidizing
  systems   1901
– tRNA, determination of acceptor activity for
  amino acids   1894
D-Ribose-5-phosphate
– characteristics and commercial preparations 551
– determination
– – radiochemical   1385
– – UV-assay   1342
Ribose-5-phosphate isomerase
– isolation   1344
Ribosomes
– preparation
– – animal   405
– – from E. coli   1907
D-Ribulose
– determination   1354
L-Ribulose
– determination   1350
D-Ribulose-1,5-diphosphate
– characteristics and commercial preparations 552
– determination
– – radiochemical   1385
– – UV-assay   1362
Ribulose-1,5-diphosphate carboxylase
– isolation   1389
D-Ribulose-5-phosphate

– concentration in animal tissues   2287
– determination
– – radiochemical   1385
– – UV-assay   1359
Ribulose-5-phosphate kinase
– isolation   1389
Rubber stoppers   159

S

S-134-fraction
– preparation   1907
Sample collection   164, 396, 400
Sample identification   205
Sample storage   165, 168
Sarcosomes
– preparation   406
Seasonal variation of results   389
Secondary standard   377
Secreted enzymes   7
Sedoheptitol
– oxidation by SDH   1384
D-Sedoheptulose-1,7-diphosphate
– determination   1193
D-Sedoheptulose-7-phosphate
– concentration in animal tissues   2287
– determination   1189
DL-Serine
– determination   1727
– normal values   1730
Sex dependence of normal range   388
Shewhart, statistical quality control   371
Side activities   108
Simple analysis of variants   353
Soluble ribonucleic acid
– characteristics and commercial preparations 553
Solutions
– of radiobiochemicals   292
D-Sorbitol
– determination
– – according to standard method   1323
– – in wine   1326
– normal values   1326, 1330
Sorbitol dehydrogenase
– assay of activity   512, 569
– characteristics and commercial preparations 512
– in heart diseases
– – differential diagnosis   36
– in liver   14

as D, L, (+), (−), α, β. Where necessary reference to other synonyms is given.

Sorbitol dehydrogenase
– in liver diseases, toxic   19
– in muscular dystrophy   40
– in organs   572
– in serum
– – normal values   572
– – stability   170
– myocardial infarction   31
D-Sorbitol-6-phosphate
– determination   1331
L-Sorbose-6-phosphate
– determination   1320
Specific activity
– of enzymes   311, 422
Specific radioactivity   294
Spectrophotometer
– review of models   198–200
Spectrum-line photometer
– review of models   197
Spermidine
– determination   1740
– normal values   1747
Spermidine oxidase
– isolation   1742
Spermine
– determination   1744
– normal values   1747
Stability
– of biochemical reagents   421
– of enzymes in serum   168–170
– of metabolites in blood and deproteinized
   solutions   166
Stachyose
– cleavage by α-galactosidase   1174
Standard
– primary   373
– secondary   377
Standard curves   310
Standard deviation   314, 338, 366
– empirical   325
Standardization of biochemical reagents   418
Statistical assessment of results   381 èt seq.
Statistical quality control   370
– basic principles   370
– practical execution   374
Statistical tests   332 et seq.
Statistical terms and methods   319 et seq.
Stepwise degradation
– of peptides and proteins with carboxypeptidase
   and LAP   1632

Steroid alcohols in urine
– determination   1868
– normal values   1872
Steroid conjugates
– hydrolysis   1848
Steroid sulphates
– hydrolysis   1854
Stirrers for micro-analysis   235
Stopper diver   243
Student distribution   353
Subcellular particles
– isolation   407
Substances
– handling of biochemicals   158
– storage, stability and control   158
Substrates
– as biochemical reagents   523–556
Succinate
– concentration in animal tissues   2282
– determination   1616
– normal values   1620
Succinate thiokinase
– in determination of succinate   1616
Succinyl-CoA
– determination   2041
Sucrose
– determination   1176
Sulphite inhibitions of enzymes   88
Systematic errors   363

T

t-Distribution   353
t-Test
– for paired differences   353
– to check for similarity of two expected values
   354
D-Tagaturonate
– determination   1299
L-Tartrate
– determination with L-tartrate dehydrase   1397
meso-Tartrate
– determination with L-tartrate dehydrogenase
   1400
L-Tartrate dehydrase
– isolation   1403
L-Tartrate dehydrogenase
– isolation   1403
– Michaelis-constants   1400

Temperature dependence
– of enzyme reactions 127
Test
– of equality between two variances (t-Test) 354
– of logarithmic-normal distribution 350
– of normal distribution 350
– of type of distribution 350
Tetrahydrofolate dehydrogenase
– see Dihydrofolate reductase
Tetrahydrofolate formylase
– assay of activity
– – other methods 1123
– – UV-assay 1118
– normal values 1123
Tetrahydrofolate synthetase
– isolation 1550
Tetrahydrofolic acid
– characteristics and commercial preparations 552
– preparation 1124, 1550
Tetrahydropteroylglutamic acid
– see tetrahydrofolic acid
Tetrazolium salts
– application in electrophoresis 274
– application in enzymatic reactions 139
– ditetrazolium salts 137
– monotetrazolium salts 137
– structural formulae 138
– reduction 137
– redox potentials 138
Thiamine pyrophosphate
– characteristics and commercial preparations 553
– determination with pyruvate decarboxylase 2186
– normal values 2190
– other methods 2190
Thiamine pyrophosphate deficiency
– transketolase activity 708
Thin-layer electrophoresis 264
DL-Threonine
– determination 1727
– normal values 1730
Thrombin inhibitors 1077
Thromboplastin time
– normal values 1029
– original method according to Quick 1027
– use of citrated blood 1029
– reaction mechanisms 1026
Thymidine
– see deoxythymidine
Tie (in statistics) 321
Tissue brei 399

Tissue disintegration
– chemical 305
– thermal 404
Tissue fixation 400
Tissue fractionation 407
Tissue, functional state 397
Tissue slices 399
Titrimetric methods
– in microtechniques 245
Total glycerol
– normal values in human serum 1830
Transaldolase
– assay of activity
– – UV-assay 514, 710
– characteristics and commercial preparation 513
– in rabbit tissues 710
Transamidinase
– assay of activity
– – colorimetric assay 699
Transfer ribonucleic acids
– characteristics and commercial preparations 551
– determination of acceptor activity for amino
  acids 1894
Transketolase
– assay of activity 703
– in muscular dystrophy 40
– in rabbit tissues 710
– in thiamine deficiency 708
– isolation and crystallization 1380
– normal values in blood 708
Transmission 181
Transsulphurase
– isolation 1463
Transverse assessment 391
Triacetate
– determination 1844
Triglycerides
– alkaline hydrolysis 1825
– average molecular weight 1829
– determination
– – after alkaline hydrolysis 1825
– – after enzymatic hydrolysis 1831
– enzymatic hydrolysis 1821
– normal values 1830
Triosephosphate isomerase
– assay of activity 515
– characteristics and commercial preparations 515
– in blood diseases 52
– in muscular dystrophy
– – in muscle 40

as D, L, (+), (−), α, β. Where necessary reference to other synonyms is given.

Triosephosphate isomerase in muscular dystrophy
– – in serum   40
Triphosphopyridine nucleotide
– see nicotinamide-adenine dinucleotide phosphate
Trypsin
– assay of activity with
– – casein as substrate   1018
– – haemoglobin as substrate   1013
– – N-benzoyl-L-arginine ethyl ester as substrate
    516
– – N α-p-toluenesulphonyl-L-argininemethyl
    ester as substrate   1021
– characteristics and commercial preparations   515
– general   1013
– normal values   1017, 1020, 1023
Trypsin inhibitor
– characteristics and commercial preparations   517
Trypsin inhibitors
– measurements with
– – azocasein as substrate   1071
– – N-benzoylarginine-p-nitroanilide as substrate
    1066
– normal values   1070, 1074
Turanose
– cleavage with α-glucosidase   1188
Two vessel method   249
L-Tyrosine
– determination
– – colorimetric assay   1669
– – manometric assay   1662
L-Tyrosine decarboxylase   1663

U

UDPG
– see uridine-5-diphosphoglucose
UDP-galactosamine
– reaction with uridyltransferase   802
UDP-galactose
– see uridine-5'-diphosphogalactose
UDP-glucuronyltransferase
– assay of activity
– – fluorimetric   721
– normal values in liver   724
– other assay methods   725
Ultramicromethods   228
Ultrasonic generator   404
Units
– of enzyme activity   121, 311, 313, 421

Unspecificity   108, 421
Urea
– determination with
– – automatic analysers   1798
– – GlDH as indicator enzyme   1794
– – phenol and hypochlorite as indicator reaction
    1791
Urease
– assay of activity
– – UV-assay   1081
– characteristics and commercial preparations   517
– normal values   1084
Uric acid
– characteristics and commercial preparations   554
– determination
– – colorimetric   1954
– – UV-assay   1951
– normal values   1054, 1057
Uricase
– assay of activity   518
– characteristics and commercial preparation   518
Uridine-5'-diphosphate
– determination   2172
Uridine-5'-diphosphogalactose
– determination   2221
– normal values   2224
Uridinediphosphogalactose pyrophosphorylase
– assay of activity in radiochemical assay   304
Uridine-5'-diphosphoglucose
– characteristics and commercial preparations   555
– concentration in animal tissues   2268
– determination   2225
– normal values   2227
Uridinediphosphoglucose dehydrogenase
– assay of activity   519
– characteristics and commercial preparations   519
Uridinediphosphoglucose pyrophosphorylase
– assay of activity   520
– characteristics and commercial preparations   519
Uridine-5'-diphosphoglucuronic acid
– characteristics and commercial preparations   555
Uridine-5'-monophosphate
– determination
– – with NMP-kinase, NDP-kinase, UDPG-pyro-
    phosphorylase and UDPG-dehydrogenase
    2172
– – with NMP-kinase, PK and LDH   2153
– – normal values   2178
Uridine-5'-triphosphate
– concentration in animal tissues   2297

The key words are arranged alphabetically without regard to prefixes such

Uridine-5'-triphosphate
– determination   2172
– normal values   2178
Uridyltransferase
– assay of activity
– – UV-assay   521, 802
– characteristics and commercial preparations 521
– normal values   805
Uropepsinogen
– characteristics   1046, 1056
– see also pepsin

V

Valeraldehyde
– reduction by ADH   1508
Values, true   363
Variability
– biological   389
Variables
– dependent   328
– independent   328
Variance
– analysis   327, 338
Variation coefficient   312, 314, 327
Visualization
– NAD(P)-dependent reactions
– – ethanol   142
– – glucose   142
– – glutamate   1708
– – glutamate dehydrogenase   142
– – lactate dehydrogenase   141
– – malate dehydrogenase   142
– – succinate dehydrogenase   141
Volume activity
– calculation   313
– definition   311

W

Water content of tissues   314, 315
Wavelengths, optimal   181

X

Xanthine
– characteristics and commercial preparations 556
– determination
– – colorimetric assay   1945
– – UV-assay   1941
– normal values   1945, 1949

Xanthine oxidase
– assay of activity
– – colorimetric assay   644
– – UV-assay   522
– characteristics and commercial preparations 521
– in milk   73
– isoenzymes   11
– normal values in blood, serum and organs   648
Xylitol
– determination with sorbitol dehydrogenase 1381
Xylitol dehydrogenase
– NAD-dependent
– – isolation   1369
– NADP-dependent
– – isolation   1369
D-Xylose
– characteristics and commercial preparations 556
– determination with D-xylose isomerase   1371
D-Xylose isomerase
– isolation   1375
D-Xylulose
– determination with
– – NAD-xylitol dehydrogenase   1368
– – D-xylulose isomerase   1371
L-Xylulose
– determination 1365
D-Xylulose dehydrogenase
– isolation   1369
L-Xylulose dehydrogenase
– isolation   1369
D-Xylulose-5-phosphate
– concentration in animal tissues   2287
– determination
– – radiochemical   1385
– – UV-assay   1377
Xylulose-5-phosphate epimerase
– isolation   1345

Y

Yeast LDH
– solation   1489

Z

Zwischenferment
– see glucose-6-phosphate dehydrogenase
Zymogram   263

as D, L, (+), (−), α, β. Where necessary reference to other synonyms is given.

Atomic Weights*

International atomic weights based** on the value 12 for the relative atomic mass of the carbon isotope ^{12}C (according to***).

Element	Symbol	Atomic number	Atomic weight	Element	Symbol	Atomic number	Atomic weight
Aluminium	Al	13	26.9815	Molybdenum	Mo	42	95.94
Antimony	Sb	51	121.75	Neodymium	Nd	60	144.24
Argon	Ar	18	39.948	Neon	Ne	10	20.183
Arsenic	As	33	74.9216	Nickel	Ni	28	58.71
Barium	Ba	56	137.34	Niobium	Nb	41	92.906
Beryllium	Be	4	9.0122	Nitrogen	N	7	14.0067
Bismuth	Bi	83	208.980	Osmium	Os	76	190.2
Boron	B	5	10.811	Oxygen	O	8	15.9994
Bromine	Br	35	79.909	Palladium	Pd	46	106.4
Cadmium	Cd	48	112.40	Phosphorus	P	15	30.9738
Caesium	Cs	55	132.905	Platinum	Pt	78	195.09
Calcium	Ca	20	40.08	Potassium	K	19	39.102
Carbon	C	6	12.01115	Praseodymium	Pr	59	140.907
Cerium	Ce	58	140.12	Rhenium	Re	75	186.2
Chlorine	Cl	17	35.453	Rhodium	Rh	45	102.905
Chromium	Cr	24	51.996	Rubidium	Rb	37	85.47
Cobalt	Co	27	58.9332	Ruthenium	Ru	44	101.07
Copper	Cu	29	63.54	Samarium	Sm	62	150.35
Dysprosium	Dy	66	162.50	Scandium	Sc	21	44.956
Erbium	Er	68	167.26	Selenium	Se	34	78.96
Europium	Eu	63	151.96	Silicon	Si	14	28.086
Fluorine	F	9	18.9984	Silver	Ag	47	107.870
Gadolinium	Gd	64	157.25	Sodium	Na	11	22.9898
Gallium	Ga	31	69.72	Strontium	Sr	38	87.62
Germanium	Ge	32	72.59	Sulphur	S	16	32.06
Gold	Au	79	196.967	Tantalum	Ta	73	180.948
Hafnium	Hf	72	178.49	Tellurium	Te	52	127.60
Helium	He	2	4.0026	Terbium	Tb	65	158.924
Holmium	Ho	67	164.930	Thallium	Tl	81	204.37
Hydrogen	H	1	1.00797	Thorium	Th	90	232.038
Indium	In	49	114.82	Thulium	Tm	69	168.934
Iodine	I	53	126.9044	Tin	Sn	50	118.69
Iridium	Ir	77	192.2	Titanium	Ti	22	47.90
Iron	Fe	26	55.847	Tungsten	W	74	183.85
Krypton	Kr	36	83.80	Uranium	U	92	238.03
Lanthanum	La	57	138.91	Vanadium	V	23	50.942
Lead	Pb	82	207.19	Xenon	Xe	54	131.30
Lithium	Li	3	6.939	Ytterbium	Yb	70	173.04
Lutetium	Lu	73	174.97	Yttrium	Y	39	88.905
Magnesium	Mg	12	24.312	Zinc	Zn	30	65.37
Manganese	Mn	25	54.9381	Zirconium	Zr	40	91.22
Mercury	Hg	80	200.59				

* Lanthanides and actinides are incomplete.

** International Union of Pure and Applied Chemistry, Report of the 10th General Assembly, Ottawa 1960, p. 24.

*** International Union of Pure and Applied Chemistry, Compt. rend. de la 24e Conférence 1967, Butterworth, London 1967, p. 130.

Numbering and Classification of Enzymes

Extract* of the official Recommendations (1972) of the Commission on Biochemical Nomenclature on the Nomenclature and Classification of Enzymes, together with their Units and the Symbols of Enzyme Kinetics.

1. Oxidoreductases

1.1 Acting on the CH-OH group of donors

1.1.1	With NAD$^+$ or NADP$^+$ as acceptor
1.1.2	With a cytochrome as acceptor
1.1.3	With oxygen as acceptor
1.1.99	With other acceptors

1.2 Acting on the aldehyde or keto group of donors

1.2.1	With NAD$^+$ or NADP$^+$ as acceptor
1.2.2	With a cytochrome as acceptor
1.2.3	With oxygen as acceptor
1.2.4	With a disulphide compound as acceptor
1.2.7	With an iron-sulphur protein as acceptor
1.2.99	With other acceptors

1.3 Acting on the CH-CH group of donors

1.3.1	With NAD$^+$ or NADP$^+$ as acceptor
1.3.2	With a cytochrome as acceptor
1.3.3	With oxygen as acceptor
1.3.7	With an iron-sulphur protein as acceptor
1.3.99	With other acceptors

1.4 Acting on the CH-NH$_2$ group of donors

1.4.1	With NAD$^+$ or NADP$^+$ as acceptor
1.4.3	With oxygen as acceptor
1.4.4	With a disulphide compound as acceptor
1.4.99	With other acceptors

1.5 Acting on the CH-NH group of donors

1.5.1	With NAD$^+$ or NADP$^+$ as acceptor
1.5.3	With oxygen as acceptor
1.5.99	With other acceptors

1.6 Acting on NADH or NADPH

1.6.1	With NAD$^+$ or NADP$^+$ as acceptor
1.6.2	With a cytochrome as acceptor
1.6.4	With a disulphide compound as acceptor
1.6.5	With a quinone or related compound as acceptor
1.6.6	With a nitrogenous group as acceptor
1.6.7	With an iron-sulphur protein as acceptor
1.6.99	With other acceptors

1.7 Acting on other nitrogenous compounds as donors

1.7.2	With a cytochrome as acceptor
1.7.3	With oxygen as acceptor
1.7.7	With an iron-sulphur protein as acceptor
1.7.99	With other acceptors

1.8 Acting on a sulphur group of donors

1.8.1	With NAD$^+$ or NADP$^+$ as acceptor
1.8.2	With a cytochrome as acceptor
1.8.3	With oxygen as acceptor
1.8.4	With a disulphide compound as acceptor
1.8.5	With a quinone or related compound as acceptor
1.8.6	With a nitrogenous group as acceptor
1.8.7	With an iron-sulphur protein as acceptor
1.8.99	With other acceptors

1.9 Acting on a haem group of donors

1.9.3	With oxygen as acceptor
1.9.6	With a nitrogenous group as acceptor
1.9.99	With other acceptors

1.10 *Acting on diphenols and related substances as donors*
  1.10.2 With a cytochrome as acceptor
  1.10.3 With oxygen as acceptor

1.11 *Acting on hydrogen peroxide as acceptor*

1.12 *Acting on hydrogen as donor*
  1.12.1 With NAD^+ or $NADP^+$ as acceptor
  1.12.2 With a cytochrome as acceptor
  1.12.7 With an iron-sulphur protein as acceptor

1.13 *Acting on single donors with incorporation of molecular oxygen (oxygenases)*
  1.13.11 With incorporation of two atoms of oxygen
  1.13.12 With incorporation of one atom of oxygen (internal monooxygenases or internal mixed function oxidases)
  1.13.99 Miscellaneous (requires further characterization)

1.14 *Acting on paired donors with incorporation of molecular oxygen*
  1.14.11 With 2-oxoglutarate as one donor, and incorporation of one atom each of oxygen into both donors
  1.14.12 With NADH or NADPH as one donor, and incorporation of two atoms of oxygen into one donor
  1.14.13 With NADH or NADPH as one donor, and incorporation of one atom of oxygen
  1.14.14 With reduced flavin or flavoprotein as one donor, and incorporation of one atom of oxygen
  1.14.15 With a reduced iron-sulphur protein as one donor, and incorporation of one atom of oxygen
  1.14.16 With reduced pteridine as one donor, and incorporation of one atom of oxygen
  1.14.17 With ascorbate as one donor, and incorporation of one atom of oxygen
  1.14.18 With another compound as one donor, and incorporation of one atom of oxygen
  1.14.99 Miscellaneous (requires further characterization)

1.15 *Acting on superoxide radicals as acceptor*

1.16 *Oxidizing metal ions*
  1.16.3 With oxygen as acceptor

1.17 *Acting on-CH_2-groups*
  1.17.1 With NAD^+ or $NADP^+$ as acceptor
  1.17.4 With a disulphide compound as acceptor

2. Transferases

2.1 *Transferring one-carbon groups*
  2.1.1 Methyltransferases
  2.1.2 Hydroxymethyl-, formyl- and related transferases
  2.1.3 Carboxyl- and carbamoyltransferases
  2.1.4 Amidinotransferases

2.2 *Transferring aldehyde or ketonic residues*

2.3 *Acyltransferases*
  2.3.1 Acyltransferases
  2.3.2 Aminoacyltransferases

2.4 *Glycosyltransferases*
  2.4.1 Hexosyltransferases
  2.4.2 Pentosyltransferases
  2.4.99 Transferring other glycosyl groups

2.5 *Transferring alkyl or aryl groups, other than methyl groups*

* Enzyme Nomenclature, Recommendations (1972) of the International Union of Pure and Applied Chemistry and the International Union of Biochemistry, Elsevier Scientific Publishing Company, Amsterdam 1973, p. 17–22.

Numbering and Classification of Enzymes (Continuation)

2.6 *Transferring nitrogenous groups*
  2.6.1 Aminotransferases
  2.6.3 Oximinotransferases

2.7 *Transferring phosphorus-containing groups*
  2.7.1 Phosphotransferases with an alcohol group as acceptor
  2.7.2 Phosphotransferases with a carboxyl group as acceptor
  2.7.3 Phosphotransferases with a nitrogenous group as acceptor
  2.7.4 Phosphotransferases with a phospho-group as acceptor
  2.7.5 Phosphotransferases with regeneration of donors (apparently catalysing intramolecular transfers)
  2.7.6 Diphosphotransferases
  2.7.7 Nucleotidyltransferases
  2.7.8 Transferases for other substituted phospho-groups
  2.7.9 Phosphotransferases with paired acceptors

2.8 *Transferring sulphur-containing groups*
  2.8.1 Sulphurtransferases
  2.8.2 Sulphotransferases
  2.8.3 CoA-transferases

3. Hydrolases

3.1 *Acting on ester bonds*
  3.1.1 Carboxylic ester hydrolases
  3.1.2 Thiolester hydrolases
  3.1.3 Phosphoric monoester hydrolases
  3.1.4 Phosphoric diester hydrolases
  3.1.5 Triphosphoric monoester hydrolases
  3.1.6 Sulphuric ester hydrolases
  3.1.7 Diphosphoric monoester hydrolases

3.2 *Acting on glycosyl compounds*
  3.2.1 Hydrolysing *O*-glycosyl compounds
  3.2.2 Hydrolysing *N*-glycosyl compounds
  3.2.3 Hydrolysing *S*-glycosyl compounds

3.3 *Acting on ether bonds*
  3.3.1 Thioether hydrolases
  3.3.2 Ether hydrolases

3.4 *Acting on peptide bonds (peptide hydrolases)*
  3.4.11 α-Aminoacylpeptide hydrolases
  3.4.12 Peptidylamino-acid or acylamino-acid hydrolases
  3.4.13 Dipeptide hydrolases
  3.4.14 Dipeptidylpeptide hydrolases
  3.4.15 Peptidyldipeptide hydrolases
  3.4.21 Serine proteinases
  3.4.22 SH-proteinases
  3.4.23 Acid proteinases
  3.4.24 Metalloproteinases
  3.4.99 Proteinases of unknown catalytic mechanism

3.5 *Acting on carbon-nitrogen bonds, other than peptide bonds*
  3.5.1 In linear amides
  3.5.2 In cyclic amides
  3.5.3 In linear amidines
  3.5.4 In cyclic amidines
  3.5.5 In nitriles
  3.5.99 In other compounds

3.6 *Acting on acid anhydrides*
  3.6.1 In phosphoryl-containing anhydrides
  3.6.2 In sulphonyl-containing anhydrides

3.7 *Acting on carbon-carbon bonds*
  3.7.1 In ketonic substances

3.8 *Acting on halide bonds*
  3.8.1 In C-halide compounds
  3.8.2 In P-halide compounds

3.9 *Acting on phosphorus-nitrogen bonds*
3.10 *Acting on sulphur-nitrogen bonds*
3.11 *Acting on carbon-phosphorus bonds*

4. Lyases

4.1 *Carbon-carbon lyases*
    4.1.1   Carboxy-lyases
    4.1.2   Aldehyde-lyases
    4.1.3   Oxo-acid-lyases
    4.1.99   Other carbon-carbon lyases
4.2 *Carbon-oxygen lyases*
    4.2.1   Hydro-lyases
    4.2.2   Acting on polysaccharides
    4.2.99   Other carbon-oxygen lyases
4.3 *Carbon-nitrogen lyases*
    4.3.1   Ammonia-lyases
    4.3.2   Amidine-lyases
4.4 *Carbon-sulphur lyases*
4.5 *Carbon-halide lyases*
4.6 *Phosphorus-oxygen lyases*
4.99 *Other lyases*

5. Isomerases

5.1 *Racemases and epimerases*
    5.1.1   Acting on amino acids and derivatives
    5.1.2   Acting on hydroxy acids and derivatives
    5.1.3   Acting on carbohydrates and derivatives
    5.1.99   Acting on other compounds

5.2 *Cis-trans isomerases*
5.3 *Intramolecular oxidoreductases*
    5.3.1   Interconverting aldoses and ketoses
    5.3.2   Interconverting keto- and enol-groups
    5.3.3   Transposing $C=C$ bonds
    5.3.4   Transposing S-S bonds
    5.3.99   Other intramolecular oxidoreductases
5.4 *Intramolecular transferases*
    5.4.1   Transferring acyl groups
    5.4.2   Transferring phosphoryl groups
    5.4.3   Transferring amino groups
    5.4.99   Transferring other groups
5.5 *Intramolecular lyases*
5.99 *Other isomerases*

6. Ligases (Synthetases)

6.1 *Forming carbon-oxygen bonds*
    6.1.1   Ligases forming aminoacyl-tRNA and related compounds
6.2 *Forming carbon-sulphur bonds*
    6.2.1   Acid-thiol ligases
6.3 *Forming carbon-nitrogen bonds*
    6.3.1   Acid-ammonia ligases (amide synthetases)
    6.3.2   Acid-amino-acid ligases (peptide synthetases)
    6.3.3   Cyclo-ligases
    6.3.4   Other carbon-nitrogen ligases
    6.3.5   Carbon-nitrogen ligases with glutamine as amido-N-donor
6.4 *Forming carbon-carbon bonds*
6.5 *Forming phosphate ester bonds*

5
6
B 7
C 8
D 9
E 0
F 1
G 2
H 3
I J 4